ORGANIC CHEMISTRY
VOLUME 1

Custom Edition for York University

CHEM 2020

L.G. Wade, Jr.

Taken from:
Organic Chemistry, Seventh Edition
by L.G. Wade, Jr.

Learning Solutions

New York Boston San Francisco
London Toronto Sydney Tokyo Singapore Madrid
Mexico City Munich Paris Cape Town Hong Kong Montreal

Cover photo courtesy of Alberto Donzelli

Taken from:

Organic Chemistry, Seventh Edition
by L.G. Wade, Jr.

Published by Prentice Hall
Upper Saddle River, New Jersey 07458

This special edition published in cooperation with Pearson Learning Solutions.

Pearson Learning Solutions, 501 Boylston Street, Suite 900, Boston, MA 02116
A Pearson Education Company
www.pearsoned.com

Printed in the United States of America

1 2 3 4 5 6 7 8 9 10 V0CR 15 14 13 12 11 10

000200010270582100

LL

ISBN 10: 0-558-76216-6
ISBN 13: 978-0-558-76216-2

ABOUT THE AUTHOR

L. G. "Skip" Wade decided to become a chemistry major during his sophomore year at Rice University, while taking organic chemistry from Professor Ronald M. Magid. After receiving his B.A. from Rice in 1969, Wade went on to Harvard University, where he did research with Professor James D. White. While at Harvard, he served as the Head Teaching Fellow for the organic laboratories and was strongly influenced by the teaching methods of two master educators, Professors Leonard K. Nash and Frank H. Westheimer.

After completing his Ph.D. at Harvard in 1974, Dr. Wade joined the chemistry faculty at Colorado State University. Over the course of fifteen years at Colorado State, Dr. Wade taught organic chemistry to thousands of students working toward careers in all areas of biology, chemistry, human medicine, veterinary medicine, and environmental studies. He also authored research papers in organic synthesis and in chemical education, as well as eleven books reviewing current research in organic synthesis. Since 1989, Dr. Wade has been a chemistry professor at Whitman College, where he teaches organic chemistry and pursues research interests in organic synthesis and forensic chemistry. Dr. Wade received the A. E. Lange Award for Distinguished Science Teaching at Whitman in 1993.

Dr. Wade's interest in forensic science has led him to testify as an expert witness in court cases involving drugs and firearms, and he has worked as a police firearms instructor, drug consultant, and boating safety officer. He also enjoys repairing and restoring old violins and bows, which he has done professionally for many years.

To my students and colleagues
at Whitman College

BRIEF CONTENTS

CONTENTS

3 STRUCTURE AND STEREOCHEMISTRY OF ALKANES 83

4 THE STUDY OF CHEMICAL REACTIONS 127

5 STEREOCHEMISTRY 169

6 ALKYL HALIDES: NUCLEOPHILIC SUBSTITUTION AND ELIMINATION 215

KEY MECHANISM BOXES

MECHANISM BOXES

PREFACE

To the Student

As you begin your study of organic chemistry, you might feel overwhelmed by the number of compounds, names, reactions, and mechanisms that confront you. You might even wonder whether you can learn all this material in a single year. The most important function of a textbook is to organize the material to show that most of organic chemistry consists of a few basic principles and many extensions and applications of these principles. Relatively little memorization is required if you grasp the major concepts and develop flexibility in applying those concepts. Frankly, I have a poor memory, and I hate memorizing lists of information. I don't remember the specifics of most of the reactions and mechanisms in this book, but I can work them out by remembering a few basic principles, such as "alcohol dehydrations usually go by E1 mechanisms."

Still, you'll have to learn some facts and fundamental principles to serve as the working "vocabulary" of each chapter. As a student, I learned this the hard way when I made a D on my second organic chemistry exam. I thought organic would be like general chemistry, where I could memorize a couple of equations and fake my way through the exams. For example, in the ideal gas chapter, I would memorize $PV = nRT$, and I was good to go. When I tried the same approach in organic, I got a D. We learn by making mistakes, and I learned a lot in organic chemistry.

In writing this book, I've tried to point out a small number of important facts and principles that should be learned to prepare for solving problems. For example, of the hundreds of reaction mechanisms shown in this book, about 20 are the fundamental mechanistic steps that combine into the longer, more complicated mechanisms. I've highlighted these fundamental mechanisms in *Key Mechanism* boxes to alert you to their importance. Spectroscopy is another area where a student might feel pressured to memorize hundreds of facts, such as NMR chemical shifts and infrared vibration frequencies. I couldn't do that, so I've always gotten by with knowing about a dozen NMR chemical shifts and about a dozen IR vibration frequencies, and knowing how they are affected by other influences. I've listed those important infrared frequencies in Table 12-2 and the important NMR chemical shifts in Table 13-3.

Don't try to memorize your way through this course. It doesn't work; you have to know what's going on so you can apply the material. Also, don't think (like I did) that you can get by without memorizing *anything*. Read the chapter, listen carefully to the lectures, and *work the problems*. The problems will tell you whether or not you know the material. If you can do the problems, you should do well on the exams. If you can't do the problems, you probably won't be able to do the exams, either. If you keep having to look up an item to do the problems, that item is a good one to learn.

Here are some hints I give my students at the beginning of the course:

1. Read the material in the book before the lecture (expect 13–15 pages per lecture). Knowing what to expect and what is in the book, you can take fewer notes and spend more time listening and understanding the lecture.
2. After the lecture, review your notes and the book, and do the in-chapter problems. Also, read the material for the next lecture.
3. If you are confused about something, visit your instructor during office hours immediately, before you fall behind. Bring your attempted solutions to problems with you to show the instructor where you are having trouble.
4. To study for an exam, begin by reviewing each chapter and your notes, then concentrate on the end-of-chapter problems. Also use old exams for practice, if available.

Remember the two "golden rules" of organic chemistry.

1. ***Don't Get Behind!*** The course moves too fast, and it's hard to catch up.
2. ***Work Lots of Problems.*** Everyone needs the practice, and the problems show where you need more work.

I am always interested to hear from students using this book. If you have any suggestions about how the book might be made better, or if you've found an error, please let me know (L. G. Wade, Whitman College, Walla Walla, WA 99362: E-mail wadelg@whitman.edu). I take students' suggestions seriously, and hundreds of them now appear in this book. For example, Whitman student Brian Lian suggested Figure 21-9, and University of Minnesota student (and race-car driver) Jim Coleman gave me the facts on the use of methanol at Indianapolis.

Good luck with your study of organic chemistry. I'm certain you will enjoy this course, especially if you let yourself relax and develop an interest in how organic compounds influence our lives. My goal in writing this book has been to make the process a little easier: to build the concepts logically on top of each other, so they flow naturally from one to the next. The hints and suggestions for problem solving have helped my students in the past, and I hope some of them will help you to learn and use the material. Even if your memory is worse than mine (highly unlikely), you should be able to do well in organic chemistry. I hope this will be a good learning experience for all of us.

L. G. Wade, Jr.
Walla Walla, Washington
wadelg@whitman.edu

To the Instructor

In writing the first edition of this text, my goal was to produce a modern, readable text that uses the most effective techniques of presentation and review. Subsequent editions extended and refined that goal, with substantial rewriting and reorganization and with the addition of several new features. This seventh edition incorporates even more refinements than the sixth, with revisions in the organization, writing, and graphics. Some of the modifications made in the most recent editions are:

1. ***Mechanism Boxes.*** About 100 of the most important mechanisms have been organized into mechanism boxes, with large blue headings for easy review. In this seventh edition, these boxes have been refined to make the individual steps clearer to students. I've tried to choose most of the standard mechanisms that nearly everyone teaches; yet, in some cases, it seems that other mechanisms would be good candidates. If there are additional mechanisms that should be boxed, or some that should not be boxed, please let me know what you think.

   In choosing the Key Mechanisms, I've used two major criteria. If the mechanism is one of the fundamental mechanisms that make up the longer, more complex mechanisms, then it must be a Key Mechanism. Examples are S_N1, S_N2, E1, E2, nucleophilic acyl substitution, electrophilic aromatic substitution, nucleophilic addition to carbonyls, and so on. The other criterion is more subjective. If the mechanism is one of the ones I routinely expect students to do on exams, then it is a Key Mechanism. Examples are formation of imines and acetals, aldol and Claisen condensations, and so on. If you feel I have left one out or included one that should not be a Key Mechanism, please let me know.
2. ***Updated Coverage.*** In the sixth and seventh editions, I've updated several terms to those that have gradually received acceptance among organic chemists. Examples are *bond-dissociation enthalpy* to replace the more ambiguous *bond-dissociation energy* and the newer transliteration *Zaitsev* to replace the older *Saytzeff.*

I've continued the gradual transition to the newer IUPAC names with the revised locations of numbers, such as in hexa-1,3-diene instead of 1,3-hexadiene. I've also completed the transition from kcal to kJ as the primary energy units, since kJ units are used in all general chemistry texts at this time.

I've added several sections to recent editions to cover new material or material of current interest.

Chapter 4: A section on free-radical inhibitors was added to show students how some of the common inhibitors break the free-radical chain reaction, and their importance in chemistry and biochemistry.

Chapter 5: Using the Mislow and Siegel definition (*J. Am. Chem. Soc.* **1984**, *106*, 3319), I introduce the popular (but often incorrectly defined) term *stereocenter* and explain the differences between this term and the IUPAC terms *chirality center* and *asymmetric carbon atom* (or *chiral carbon atom*). The term *stereocenter* is much broader than the more precise term *asymmetric carbon atom*, and it assumes that one already knows the stereochemical properties of the molecule (to know which bonds will give rise to stereoisomers upon their interchange). The casual use of the broad term *stereocenter* where a more precise term is required often results in logical fallacies (*J. Chem. Educ.* **2006**, *83*, 1793). Therefore, I have continued to encourage students to identify the (immediately apparent) asymmetric carbon atoms to use as tools in examining a molecule to determine its stereochemistry.

Chapter 8: The Nobel Prize–winning asymmetric reduction work by Noyori and Knowles is discussed, together with its implications for enantioselective drug synthesis. Another new section has been added covering the mechanism and synthetic uses of olefin metathesis, highlighting the work by Chauvin, Grubbs, and Schrock that recently won the Nobel Prize.

Chapter 12: Fourier-transform IR spectroscopy is discussed, together with the reasons why this technique gives improved sensitivity and resolution over the dispersive method.

Chapter 13: The NMR spectra have been converted to high-field (300 MHz) spectra from the excellent Aldrich collection. The expansion boxes have been refined and clarified to make sure that the individual splittings are visible. The DEPT technique has been expanded and used in more of the problems.

Chapter 14: The Nobel Prize–winning Sharpless asymmetric epoxidation is discussed, together with the factors that selectively enhance the formation of one enantiomer of the product.

Chapter 16: A section has been added that discusses the aromaticity of Fullerenes and their relationship to other allotropes of carbon.

Chapter 24: A section has been added that discusses *prions*: proteins which are thought to be infectious because of misfolding, resulting in clumping and formation of plaques. This topic relates the topic at hand (protein conformations) directly to the ongoing concern about mad cow disease.

3. ***Electrostatic Potential Maps.*** Electrostatic potential maps are used in cases where they might help students to visualize the charge distribution of a species in a way that helps to explain the electrophilic or nucleophilic nature of a compound. In introducing EPMs, I've emphasized their qualitative nature without stressing their mathematical derivation. As a result, I've explained and used EPMs much like they are introduced in the general chemistry textbooks. Several new EPMs have been added in the seventh edition.

The entire book has been edited, with many sections reorganized and rewritten to enhance clarity. As in the first edition, each new topic is introduced carefully and explained thoroughly. Many introductory sections have been rewritten to update them and make them more approachable for students. Whenever possible, illustrations have been added or modified to help students visualize the physical concepts.

The emphasis continues to be on *chemical reactivity*. Chemical reactions are introduced as soon as possible, and each functional group is considered in view of its reactivity toward electrophiles, nucleophiles, oxidants, reductants, and other reagents. "Electron-pushing" mechanisms are stressed throughout as a means of explaining and predicting this reactivity. Structural concepts such as stereochemistry and spectroscopy are thoroughly treated as useful techniques that enhance the fundamental study of chemical reactivity.

Organization

This book maintains the traditional organization that concentrates on one functional group at a time while comparing and contrasting the reactivity of different functional groups. Reactions are emphasized, beginning with Lewis acid–base reactions in Chapter 1, continuing with thermodynamics and kinetics in Chapter 4, and covering most of the important substitution, addition, and elimination reactions in the three chapters following stereochemistry.

Spectroscopic techniques (IR, MS, and NMR) are covered in Chapters 12 and 13, so that they can be included in the first semester if desired. This early coverage is needed to allow effective use of spectroscopy in the laboratory. Still, a large amount of organic chemistry has been covered before this digression into structure determination. The principles of spectroscopy are practiced and reinforced in later chapters, where the characteristic spectral features of each functional group are summarized and reinforced by practice problems.

Key Features

FLEXIBILITY OF COVERAGE

No two instructors teach organic chemistry exactly the same way. This book covers all the fundamental topics in detail, building each new concept on those that come before. Many topics may be given more or less emphasis at the discretion of the instructor. Examples of these topics are ^{13}C NMR spectroscopy, ultraviolet spectroscopy, conservation of orbital symmetry, amino acids and proteins, nucleic acids, and the special topics chapters, lipids and synthetic polymers.

Another area of flexibility is in the problems. The wide-ranging problem sets review the material from several viewpoints, and more study problems are provided than most students are able to complete. This large variety allows the instructor to select the most appropriate problems for the individual course.

UP-TO-DATE TREATMENT

In addition to the classical reactions, this book covers many techniques and reactions that have more recently gained wide use among practicing chemists. Molecular-orbital theory is introduced early and used to explain electronic effects in conjugated and aromatic systems, pericyclic reactions, and ultraviolet spectroscopy. Carbon-13 NMR spectroscopy is treated as the routine tool it has become in most research laboratories, and the DEPT technique is introduced in this edition. Many of the newer synthetic techniques are also included, such as asymmetric hydrogenation and epoxidation, use of sodium triacetoxyborohydride, Birch reduction, Swern oxidations, alkylation of 1,3-dithianes, olefin metathesis, and oxidations using pyridinium chlorochromate.

REACTION MECHANISMS

Reaction mechanisms are important in all areas of organic chemistry, but they are difficult for many students. Students fall into the trap of memorizing a mechanism while not understanding why it proceeds as it does. This book stresses the principles used to predict mechanisms. Problem-solving sections develop basic techniques for approaching mechanism problems, and they work to minimize rote memorization. These techniques emphasize deciding whether the reaction is acidic, basic, or free radical in nature, then breaking it down into Lewis acid–base interactions and using "electron pushing arrows" to illustrate these individual steps. Important mechanisms are highlighted by placing them in the *Mechanism* and *Key Mechanism* boxes.

INTRODUCTION TO MECHANISMS USING FREE-RADICAL HALOGENATION

The advantages and disadvantages of using free-radical halogenation to introduce reaction mechanisms have been debated for many years. The principal objection to free-radical halogenation is that it is not a useful synthetic reaction. But useful reactions such as nucleophilic substitution and additions to alkenes are complicated by participation of the solvent and other effects. Gas-phase free-radical halogenation allows a clearer treatment of kinetics and thermodynamics, as long as its disadvantages as a synthetic reaction are discussed and students are aware of the limitations.

ORGANIC SYNTHESIS

Organic synthesis is stressed throughout this book, with progressive discussions of the process involved in developing a synthesis. *Retrosynthetic analysis* is emphasized, and the student learns to work backward from the target compound and forward from the starting materials to find a common intermediate.

Typical yields have been provided for many synthetic reactions, although I hope students will not misuse these numbers. Too often students consider the yield of a reaction to be a fixed characteristic just as the melting point of a compound is fixed. In practice, many factors affect product yields, and literature values for apparently similar reactions often differ by a factor of 2 or more. The yields given in this book are *typical* yields that a good student with excellent technique might obtain.

SPECTROSCOPY

Spectroscopy is one of the most important tools of the organic chemist. This book develops the theory for each type of spectroscopy and then discusses the characteristic spectral features. The most useful and dependable characteristics are summarized into a small number of rules of thumb that allow the student to interpret most spectra without looking up or memorizing large tables of data. For reference use, extensive tables of NMR and IR data and a more complete version of the Woodward–Fieser rules for UV are provided as appendices.

This approach is particularly effective with IR and NMR spectroscopy, and with mass spectrometry. Practical rules are given to help students see what information is available in the spectrum and what spectral characteristics usually correspond to what structural features. Sample problems show how the information from various spectra is combined to propose a structure. The emphasis is on helping students develop an intuitive feel for using spectroscopy to solve structural problems.

NOMENCLATURE

IUPAC nomenclature is stressed throughout the book, but common nomenclature is also discussed and used to develop students' familiarity. Teaching only the IUPAC nomenclature might be justifiable in theory, but such an approach would handicap students in their further study and use of the literature. Much of the literature of chemistry, biology, and medicine uses common names such as methyl ethyl ketone, isovaleric acid, methyl *tert*-butyl ether, γ-aminobutyric acid, and ε-caprolactam. This book emphasizes why systematic nomenclature is often preferred, yet it encourages familiarity with common names as well.

I've enjoyed working on this new edition, and I hope that it is an improved fine-tuning of the sixth edition. I've tried to make this book as error-free as possible, but I'm sure some errors have slipped by. If you find errors, or have suggestions about how the book might be made better, please let me know (L. G. Wade, Whitman College,

Walla Walla, WA 99362; e-mail: wadelg@whitman.edu). Errors can be fixed quickly in the next printing. I've already started a file of possible changes and improvements for the eighth edition, and I hope many of the current users will contribute suggestions to this file. I hope this book makes your job easier and helps more of your students to succeed. That's the most important reason why I wrote it.

INSTRUCTOR RESOURCES

Instructor Resource on CD/DVD (0-32-159872-5) This lecture resource is prepared by Rizalia Klausmeyer of Baylor University and Christine Hermann of Radford University. This resource provides an integrated collection of resources to help you make efficient and effective use of your time. This CD/DVD features most art from the text including figures and tables in PDF format for high-resolution printing, as well as four pre-built PowerPoint presentations. The first contains images embedded within the slides, the second contains worked examples in progressive reveal format, the third contains Clicker "CRS" questions and the final PowerPoint presentation is a Lecture outline. This CD/DVD also contains the TestGen, a computerized version of the Test Item File that enables professors to create and tailor exams to their needs.

ACE Organic Chemistry On-Line Homework System Pearson Prentice Hall, in conjunction with Robert B. Grossman and Raphael A. Finkel and a team of programmers at the University of Kentucky, has developed a homework system for organic chemistry that can finally support the types of problems assigned in organic chemistry. The homework system contains hundreds of organic chemistry structure-drawing problems, allows students to draw structures, recognizes correct and incorrect answers, and provides structure-specific feedback. This drawing activity with immediate feedback results in a better learning experience for students. The homework system also grades student responses automatically and stores their activity in a gradebook, providing you a better way to track student learning while saving you time. Please contact your local Prentice Hall representative for more information.

Transparency Set (0-32-159869-5) This package comprises 275 four-color acetates of the most useful images, computer art, and line drawings from the text. The Transparency Pack is available at no charge to adopters of *Organic Chemistry,* Seventh Edition.

Test Item File (0-32-159868-7) by Gary Hollis of *Roanoke College*; Don Davies of *Weber State University*; and Todd Johnson of *Weber State University*. This is a printed version of all questions in the TestGen software found on the Instructor Resource on CD/DVD. The new Seventh Edition contains over 2600 questions.

BlackBoard and WebCT: Practice and assessment materials are available upon request in these course management platforms.

Acknowledgments

I am pleased to thank the many talented people who helped with this revision. More than anyone else, Jan Simek, author of the *Solutions Manual*, has consistently provided me with excellent advice and sound judgment through several editions of this book. In this edition, Jan provided input on all of the chapter revisions, and helped with the writing of the new section on olefin metathesis. He also co-authored most of the new problems and all of the Answers to Selected Problems. Particular thanks are also due to John Murdzek and Ray Mullaney, who both made thousands of useful suggestions throughout the writing and revision process, and who helped to shape this new edition.

I would like to thank the reviewers for their valuable insight and commentary. Although I did not adopt all their suggestions, most of them were helpful and contributed to the quality of the final product.

Seventh Edition Prescriptive Reviewers

Jung-Mo Ahn	University of Texas at Dallas
Arthur J. Ashe	University of Michigan
Merritt B. Andrus	Brigham Young University
David Brown	St. John's University
Kristen Meisenheimer	Cal Polytechnic at San Luis Obispo
Stephen A. Miller	University of Florida
Guillermo Moyna	University of the Sciences in Philadelphia
Anthony J. Pearson	Case Western Reserve University
Stanley Raucher	University of Washington
David Son	Southern Methodist University
Joseph B. Wachter	Michigan State University

Sixth Edition Prescriptive Reviewers

Bill Baker	University of South Florida
Barry Coddens	Northwestern University
Barbara Colonna	University of Miami
Chris Gorman	North Carolina State University
Geneive Henry	Susquehanna University
William Jenks	Iowa State University
Przemyslaw Maslak	Pennsylvania State University
Rabi Musah	University at Albany
Allan Pinhas	University of Cincinnati
Suzanne Ruder	Virginia Commonwealth University
Maria de Graca Vicente	Louisiana State University

Sixth Edition Manuscript Reviewers

David Alonso	Andrews University
Dan Becker	Loyola University
John Berger	Montclair State University
Bob Bly	University of South Carolina
Mary Boyd	Loyola University, Chicago
Hindy Bronstein	Fordham College at Lincoln Center
Philip Brown	North Carolina State University
Christine Brzezowski	University of Alberta
Patrick Buick	Florida Atlantic University
David Cantillo	Hillsborough Community College
Dee Ann Casteel	Bucknell University
Amber Charlebois	William Paterson University
Cai Chengzhi	University of Houston
Jamie Lee Cohen	Pace University
Richard Conley	Middlesex County College
Robert Crow	St. Louis College of Pharmacy
William Donaldson	Marquette University
Aouad Emmanuel	Rutgers University, Newark Campus
Malcolm Forbes	University of North Carolina, Chapel Hill
Anne Gaquere	State University of West Georgia
Rainer Glaser	University of Missouri, Columbia
Steven Graham	St. John's University, Jamaica
Fathi Halaweish	South Dakota State University
Julius Harp	North Carolina A&T University
Christine Hermann	Radford University
Kathy Hess	Cypress College
Steve Holmgren	Montana State University
Angela King	Wake Forest University
Vera Kolb	University of Wisconsin, Parkside
Paul Kropp	University of North Carolina, Chapel Hill
Scott Lewis	James Madison University
Guigen Li	Texas Tech University
Helena Malinakova	University of Kansas
Mark Mascal	University of California, Davis
John Masnovi	Cleveland State University
John McBride	Northwest Vista College
Martin McClinton	Brevard Community College
James R. McKee	University of the Sciences in Philadelphia
Gary Miracle	Texas Tech University
Gholam Mirafzal	Drake University
Tom Mitzel	Trinity College
David Modarelli	University of Akron
Andrew Morehead	East Carolina University
Richard Morrison	University of Georgia
Thomas Nalli	Winona State University
Michael Nee	University of California, Berkeley
Mark Niemczyk	Wheaton College
Glenn Nomura	Georgia Perimeter College
Patrick O'Connor	Rutgers University
Cyril Parkanyi	Florida Atlantic University
Anthony Pearson	Case Western Reserve University
John Penn	West Virginia University
James Poole	Ball State University
Owen Priest	Northwestern University
John Rainier	University of Utah
Kirk Schanze	University of Florida
David Shultz	North Carolina State University
Joseph Sloop	United States Military Academy
Luise Strange	Georgia Perimeter College
John Struss	University of Tampa
Joseph Tufariello	University at Buffalo
Kent Voelkner	Lake Superior State College
Dan Von Riesen	Roger Williams University
Sheild Wallace	Albuquerque Technical Vocational Institute
Lisa Whalen	University of New Mexico

Sixth Edition Accuracy Reviewers

Thomas Nalli	Winona State University
Susan Schelble	University of Colorado at Denver

Finally, I want to thank the people at Prentice Hall, whose dedication and flexibility contributed to the completion of this project. Assistant Editor Carol DuPont and Editor in Chief Nicole Folchetti kept the project moving, ensured the needed resources were available, and made many useful comments and suggestions. Production Editor Rebecca Dunn kept the production process organized, on track, and on schedule. It has been a pleasure working with all these thoroughly professional and competent people.

L. G. Wade, Jr.
Walla Walla, Washington

How your text will help you think differently about organic chemistry

In the next few pages, you will find a brief summary of some of the features used to help you through this course. Several kinds of study aids are provided to emphasize and review the most important points, and the text uses a color scheme that should help you identify each study aid and its purpose. A support package is also available to enhance your understanding of the material.

Think 24/7 Help

See how your text's media program is designed to build understanding and bring organic chemistry to life.

Think Blue

Check out features in blue that help you organize and review the material.

Think Green

Check out features in green that help you solve problems.

Think in Multiple Dimensions

Crafted especially for you, these support materials will help you grasp the major concepts and learn organic chemistry.

THINK Help Whenever You Need It.

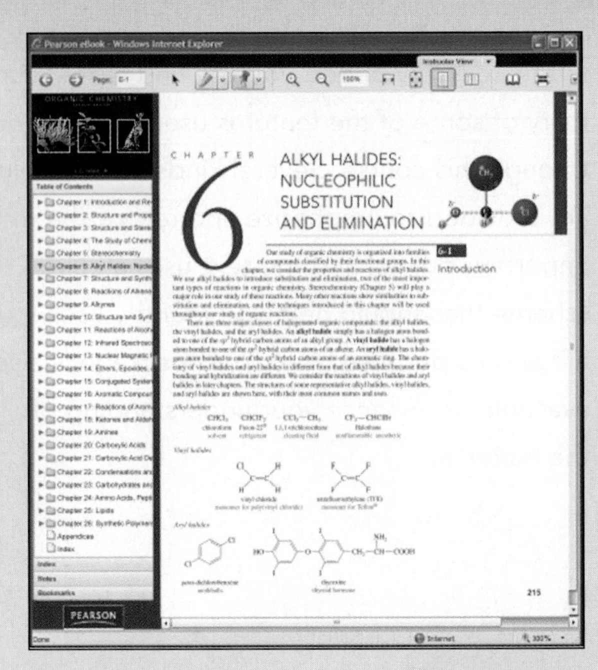

myeBook

myeBook enables you to make virtual notes within the text, as well as enlarge images, charts, and figures for better viewing 24/7. Within **myeBook** you can access Whiteboard videos (see below), where you can see and hear a professor working out the mechanisms and solved problems in the text.

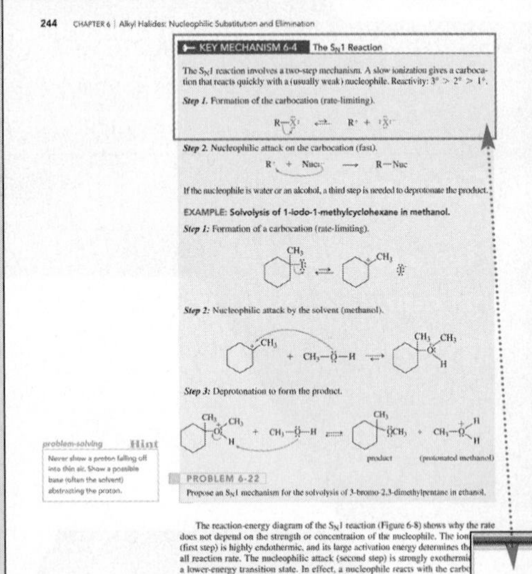
244 CHAPTER 6 | Alkyl Halides: Nucleophilic Substitution and Elimination

KEY MECHANISM 6-4 The S_N1 Reaction

The S_N1 reaction involves a two-step mechanism. A slow ionization gives a carbocation that reacts quickly with a (usually weak) nucleophile. Reactivity: 3° > 2° > 1°.

Step 1. Formation of the carbocation (rate-limiting).

Step 2. Nucleophilic attack on the carbocation (fast).

If the nucleophile is water or an alcohol, a third step is needed to deprotonate the product.

EXAMPLE: Solvolysis of 1-iodo-1-methylcyclohexane in methanol.

Step 1: Formation of a carbocation (rate-limiting).

Step 2: Nucleophilic attack by the solvent (methanol).

Step 3: Deprotonation to form the product.

PROBLEM 6-22

Propose an S_N1 mechanism for the solvolysis of 3-bromo-2,3-dimethylpentane in ethanol.

Virtual Lectures

Directly linked in **myeBook,** these professor-narrated videos provide step-by-step commentary on a virtual whiteboard for all of the mechanisms, key mechanisms, and solved problems throughout the text. These prerecorded videos enable you to pause, rewind, and fast-forward, to individualize your learning using on-demand tutoring.

KEY MECHANISM 6-4 The S_N1 Reaction

The S_N1 reaction involves a two-step mechanism. A slow ionization gives a carbocation that reacts quickly with a (usually weak) nucleophile. Reactivity: 3° > 2° > 1°.

Step 1. Formation of the carbocation (rate-limiting).

Increase your understanding and bring organic chemistry to life through the interactive **myeBook**, problem-solving videos, and **ACE Organic.**

ACE Organic—Online Tutorial and Assessment for Organic Chemistry

You answer organic chemistry problems by drawing structures. When you draw organic structures, **ACE Organic** evaluates your responses and provides feedback to help guide you to the correct answer without giving it away. The system grades your responses automatically and stores your activity in a gradebook, providing a better way to track your learning while saving time.

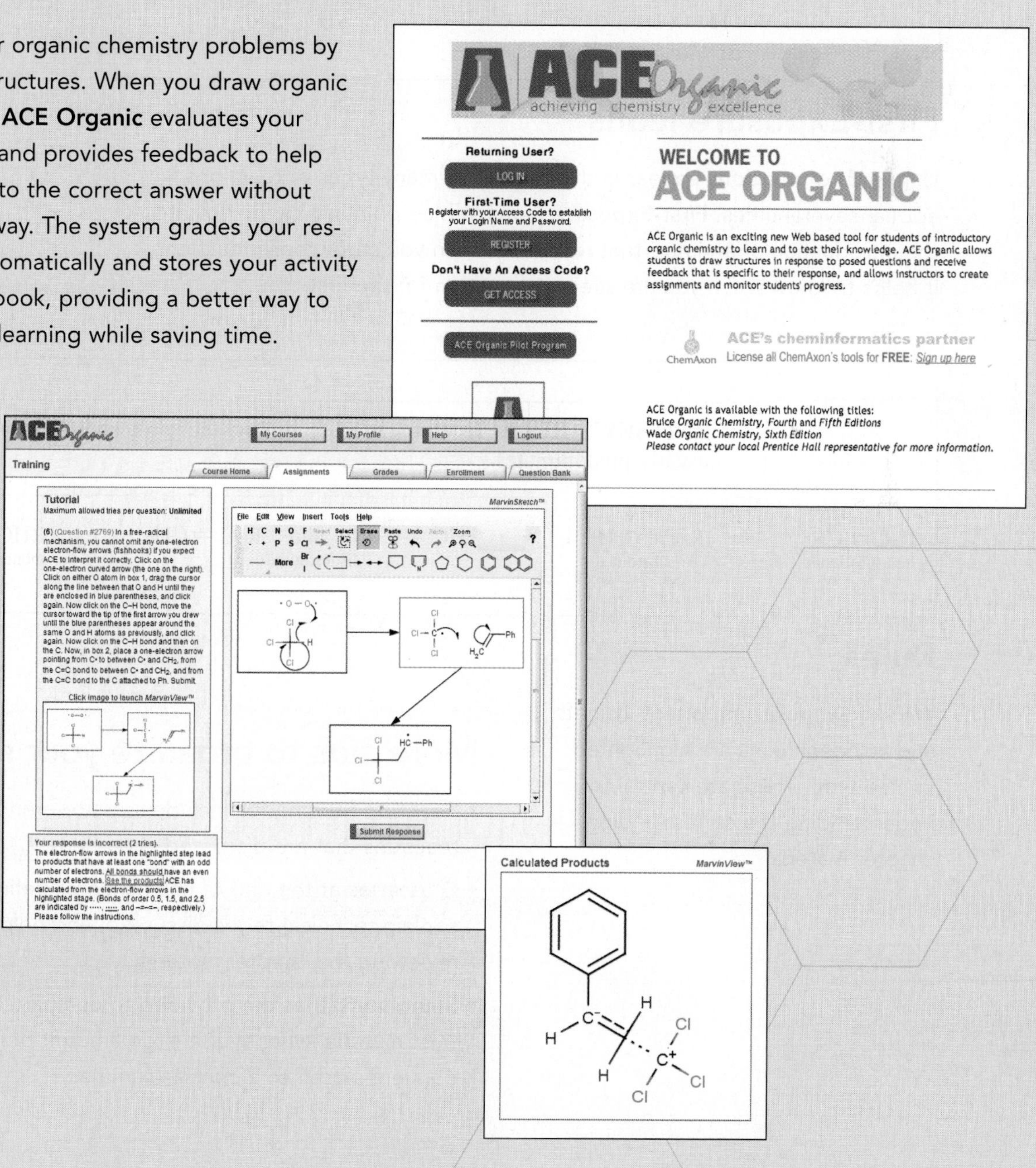

THINK Blue.

Nucleophilic substitution

$$-\overset{|}{\underset{|}{C}}-\overset{|}{\underset{|}{C}}- \;(\text{H},\ :\ddot{X}:) + \text{Nuc}:^- \longrightarrow -\overset{|}{\underset{|}{C}}-\overset{|}{\underset{|}{C}}- \;(\text{H},\ \text{Nuc}) + :\ddot{X}:^-$$

First-Exposure Icons

Hundreds of reactions appear in this text—and many types of reactions appear several times. **First-Exposure Icons,** a blue pointing hand, indicate the introduction of an important reaction. When you study these reactions, it helps to know when you are seeing a reaction for the first time.

ZAITSEV'S RULE: In elimination reactions, the most substituted alkene usually predominates.

$$\underset{\text{tetrasubstituted}}{R_2C{=}CR_2} > \underset{\text{trisubstituted}}{R_2C{=}CHR} > \underset{\text{disubstituted}}{RHC{=}CHR \text{ and } R_2C{=}CH_2} > \underset{\text{monosubstituted}}{RHC{=}CH_2}$$

Rules

Well-known rules, important insights, and key definitions are highlighted in blue type. These are central to understanding the corresponding chapter material.

More aids to organize your study:

- **Reaction Summaries** include cross-references to reactions that are discussed elsewhere.
- **Glossaries** at the end of each chapter define and explain technical terms discussed, and help you in reviewing the chapter material.
- **Summary tables** are provided to compare and contrast material whenever a large amount of information lends itself to a concise summary.

This book uses a color scheme to help you identify each study aid and its purpose. Features in **BLUE** help you organize and review the material.

MECHANISM 6-5 Racemization in the S_N1 Reaction

The S_N1 reaction involves ionization to a flat carbocation, which can be attacked from either side.

Step 1: Ionization of a tetrahedral carbon gives a flat carbocation.

$$C{-}X \rightleftarrows C^{+} \quad :X^{-}$$

Step 2: A nucleophile may attack either side of the carbocation.

Nuc:⁻ from the top / from the bottom Nuc:⁻ → retention or inversion

These two products may be different if the carbon atom is stereogenic.

Mechanism Boxes

Mechanism Boxes help you understand how reactions occur by focusing on the individual steps of each reaction. They have large blue headings so you can locate them easily as you thumb through the chapter.

Key Mechanism Boxes

Marked by a key icon, **Key Mechanisms** are the fundamental mechanistic principles that recur throughout the course. They are the pieces that compose most of the other, longer mechanisms.

You can find a full list of Key Mechanisms in the detailed Table of Contents.

KEY MECHANISM 6-8 The E1 Reaction

The E1 reaction requires ionization to a carbocation intermediate like the S_N1, so it follows the same order of reactivity: $3° > 2° >> 1°$.

A base (usually weak) deprotonates the carbocation to give an alkene.

Step 1: Unimolecular ionization to give a carbocation (rate-limiting).

$$H{-}C{-}C{-}X: \rightleftarrows H{-}C{-}C^{+} + {}^{-}:X:$$

Step 2: Deprotonation by a weak base (often the solvent) gives the alkene (fast).

$$B:^{-} \quad H{-}C{-}C^{+} \rightleftarrows B{-}H + C{=}C$$

THINK Green.

Problem-Solving Strategies

Approaching problem solving can be challenging for many students, and these strategies help you break down problems into simpler pieces. Methods for approaching complicated problems—like those that require proposing mechanisms and developing multistep synthesis—are provided. They serve as a starting point, not a guaranteed route to the answers.

PROBLEM-SOLVING STRATEGY

PREDICTING SUBSTITUTIONS AND ELIMINATIONS

S_N1

$$R{-}\ddot{X}: \rightleftarrows R^+ + :\ddot{X}:^- \quad \text{(slow)}$$

$$R^+ + Nuc:^- \longrightarrow R{-}Nuc \quad \text{(fast)}$$

S_N2

$$Nuc:^- + {>}C{-}\ddot{X}: \longrightarrow Nuc{-}C{<} + :\ddot{X}:^-$$

E1

$$-\underset{H}{\underset{|}{\overset{|}{C}}}-\underset{:X:}{\underset{|}{\overset{|}{C}}}- \rightleftarrows -\underset{H}{\underset{|}{\overset{|}{C}}}-\overset{+}{C}{<} + {}^-:\ddot{X}: \quad \text{(slow)}$$

$$B:^- \; -\underset{H}{\underset{|}{\overset{|}{C}}}-\overset{+}{C}{<} \rightleftarrows B{-}H + {>}C{=}C{<} \quad \text{(fast)}$$

E2

$$B:^- \; -\underset{|}{\overset{H}{\overset{|}{C}}}-\underset{:X:}{\underset{|}{\overset{|}{C}}}- \longrightarrow {>}C{=}C{<} + B{-}H + :\ddot{X}:^-$$

Given a set of reagents and solvents, how can we predict what products will result and which mechanisms will be involved? Should you memorize all this theory about substitutions and eliminations? Students sometimes feel overwhelmed at this point.

Memorizing is not the best way to approach this material because the answers are not absolute and too many factors are involved. Besides, the real world with its real reagents and solvents is not as clean as our equations on paper. Most nucleophiles are also basic, and most bases are also nucleophilic. Many solvents can solvate ions or react as nucleophiles, or both. We will review the most important factors that determine the reaction pathway and organize them in a sequence that allows you to predict as much as can be predicted.

The first principle you must understand is that *we cannot always predict one unique product or one unique mechanism.* Often, the best we can do is to eliminate some of the possibilities and make some good predictions. Remembering this limitation, here are some general guidelines:

When you need help solving problems, look for the features in **GREEN**—like Problem-Solving Strategies, Problem-Solving Hints, and Essential Problem-Solving Skills.

Problem-Solving Hints

These hints appear in the margins and remind you of facts or principles that may be useful for solving common types of problems. They are the tips the author gives his own students to help them work problems and review for exams.

problem-solving **Hint**

Don't try to memorize your way through this chapter. Try to understand what happens in the different reactions. Some memorizing is necessary, but simply memorizing everything won't allow you to predict new reactions.

Essential Problem-Solving Skills in Chapter 6

1. Correctly name alkyl halides, and identify them as 1°, 2°, or 3°.
2. Predict the products of S_N1, S_N2, E1, and E2 reactions, including stereochemistry.
3. Draw the mechanisms and energy profiles of S_N1, S_N2, E1, and E2 reactions.
4. Predict and explain the rearrangement of cations in first-order reactions.
5. Predict which substitutions or eliminations will be faster, based on differences in substrate, base/nucleophile, leaving group, or solvent.
6. Predict whether a reaction will be first-order or second-order.
7. When possible, predict predominance of substitution or elimination.
8. Use Zaitsev's rule to predict major and minor elimination products.

Essential Problem-Solving Skills

Found at the end of each chapter, this list reminds you of the skills needed to solve typical problems associated with that chapter's material. The list can point out concepts you might need to review, or suggest types of problems and solutions you have not considered. This review of problem-solving skills is often a good prelude to doing the end-of-chapter problems.

THINK In Multiple Dimensions.

Crafted especially for you, these support materials will help you grasp the major concepts and learn organic chemistry.

Student Solutions Manual
by Jan William Simek

ISBN-13: 978-0-321-59871-4
ISBN-10: 0-321-59871-7

The Solutions Manual contains complete solutions to all the problems, with helpful hints on how to approach each kind of problem. Appendix 1 of the Solutions Manual summarizes the IUPAC system of nomenclature. Appendix 2 reviews and demonstrates how acidity varies with structure in organic molecules, and how one can predict the direction of an acid–base equilibrium. Appendix 3 provides a sample of a reaction summary map.

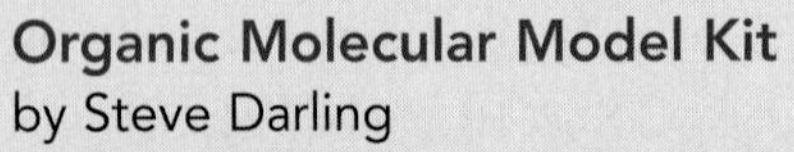

Organic Molecular Model Kit
by Steve Darling

ISBN-13: 978-0-13-233471-6
ISBN-10: 0-13-233471-2

Darling Models™ contain various pieces used to build atoms, bonds, and molecules. This model kit allows you to build molecules and see the three-dimensional aspects of organic chemistry that can only be imagined on a two-dimensional drawing.

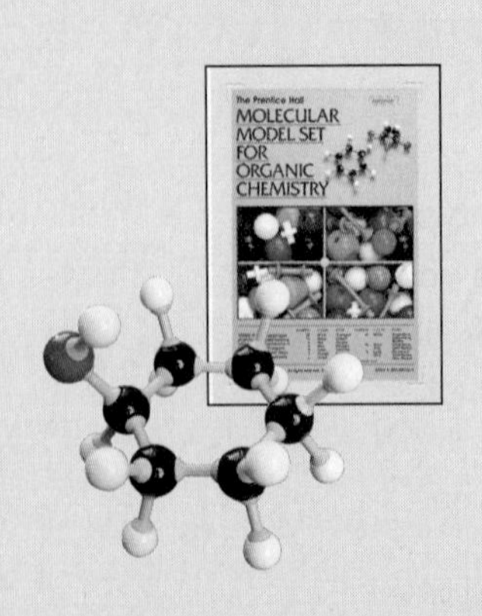

Prentice Hall Molecular Model Kit for Organic Chemistry

ISBN-13: 978-0-205-08136-3
ISBN-10: 0-205-08136-3

The Prentice Hall molecular model set allows you to build space-filling and ball-and-stick models of organic molecules. The components in this kit are precision-tooled from quality plastics, are virtually indestructible, and come in a sturdy plastic case for easy storage.

SpartanModel: An Electronic Model Kit (CD, Guide, and 3-D glasses)
by Warren J. Hehre

ISBN-13: 978-0-13-222044-6
ISBN-10: 0-13-222044-X

SpartanModel™ puts chemistry at your fingertips. The workbook includes a software tutorial and numerous challenging exercises that help you solve problems involving structure building and analysis, using the tools included in the two pieces of Spartan software. SpartanModel Software supports teaching and learning organic chemistry at the molecular level. Extending the use of models in your chemistry course, SpartanModel provides 3-D construction and visualization of almost any chemical system.

Framework Molecular Model Kit
by George Brumlik

ISBN-13: 978-0-13-330076-5
ISBN-10: 0-13-330076-5

This accurate, reasonably priced molecular model set enables users to represent all atoms having up to 12 electrons in their valence shells—including those which cannot be built with the most expensive sets (i.e., cyclopropane, cubane, etc.).

CHAPTER

INTRODUCTION AND REVIEW

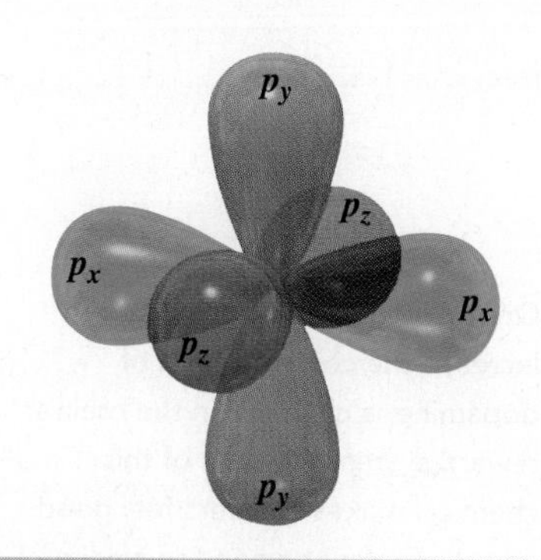

1-1 The Origins of Organic Chemistry

The modern definition of organic chemistry is *the chemistry of carbon compounds*. What is so special about carbon that a whole branch of chemistry is devoted to its compounds? Unlike most other elements, carbon forms strong bonds to other carbon atoms and to a wide variety of other elements. Chains and rings of carbon atoms can be built up to form an endless variety of molecules. It is this diversity of carbon compounds that provides the basis for life on Earth. Living creatures are composed largely of complex organic compounds that serve structural, chemical, or genetic functions.

The term **organic** literally means "derived from living organisms." Originally, the science of organic chemistry was the study of compounds extracted from living organisms and their natural products. Compounds such as sugar, urea, starch, waxes, and plant oils were considered "organic," and people accepted **Vitalism**, the belief that natural products needed a "vital force" to create them. Organic chemistry, then, was the study of compounds having the vital force. Inorganic chemistry was the study of gases, rocks, and minerals, and the compounds that could be made from them.

In the nineteenth century, experiments showed that organic compounds could be synthesized from inorganic compounds. In 1828, the German chemist Friedrich Wöhler converted ammonium cyanate, made from ammonia and cyanic acid, to urea simply by heating it in the absence of oxygen.

$$\underset{\substack{\text{ammonium cyanate} \\ \text{(inorganic)}}}{NH_4^+ \ ^-OCN} \xrightarrow{\text{heat}} \underset{\substack{\text{urea} \\ \text{(organic)}}}{H_2N{-}\overset{\overset{\displaystyle O}{\|}}{C}{-}NH_2}$$

Urea had always come from living organisms and was presumed to contain the vital force, yet ammonium cyanate is inorganic and thus lacks the vital force. Some chemists claimed that a trace of vital force from Wöhler's hands must have contaminated the reaction, but most recognized the possibility of synthesizing organic compounds from inorganics. Many other syntheses were carried out, and the vital force theory was eventually discarded.

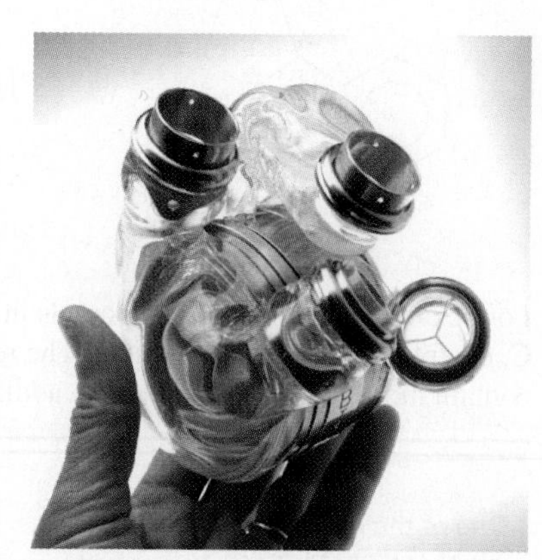

The Abiomed self-contained artificial heart, which was first implanted into a patient on July 2, 2001. The outer shell is polycarbonate, and the valves and inner bladder are polyurethane.

Since Vitalism was disproved in the early nineteenth century, you'd think it would be extinct by now. And you'd be wrong! Vitalism lives on today in the minds of those who believe that "natural" (plant-derived) vitamins, flavor compounds, etc. are somehow different and more healthful than the identical "artificial" (synthesized) compounds.

As chemists, we know that plant-derived compounds and the synthesized compounds are identical. Assuming they are pure, the only way to tell them apart is through ^{14}C dating: Compounds synthesized from petrochemicals have a lower content of radioactive ^{14}C and appear old because their ^{14}C has decayed over time. Plant-derived compounds are recently synthesized from CO_2 in the air. They have a higher content of radioactive ^{14}C. Some large chemical suppliers provide isotope-ratio analyses to show that their "naturals" have high ^{14}C content and are plant-derived. Such a sophisticated analysis lends a high-tech flavor to this twenty-first-century form of Vitalism.

Even though organic compounds do not need a vital force, they are still distinguished from inorganic compounds. The distinctive feature of organic compounds is that they *all* contain one or more carbon atoms. Still, not all carbon compounds are organic; substances such as diamond, graphite, carbon dioxide, ammonium cyanate, and sodium carbonate are derived from minerals and have typical inorganic properties. Most of the millions of carbon compounds are classified as organic, however.

One of nicotine's effects is to increase the concentration of dopamine, a chemical in the brain's reward system. Release of this chemical makes smokers feel good and reinforces the need to smoke.

We humans are composed largely of organic molecules, and we are nourished by the organic compounds in our food. The proteins in our skin, the lipids in our cell membranes, the glycogen in our livers, and the DNA in the nuclei of our cells are all organic compounds. Our bodies are also regulated and defended by complex organic compounds.

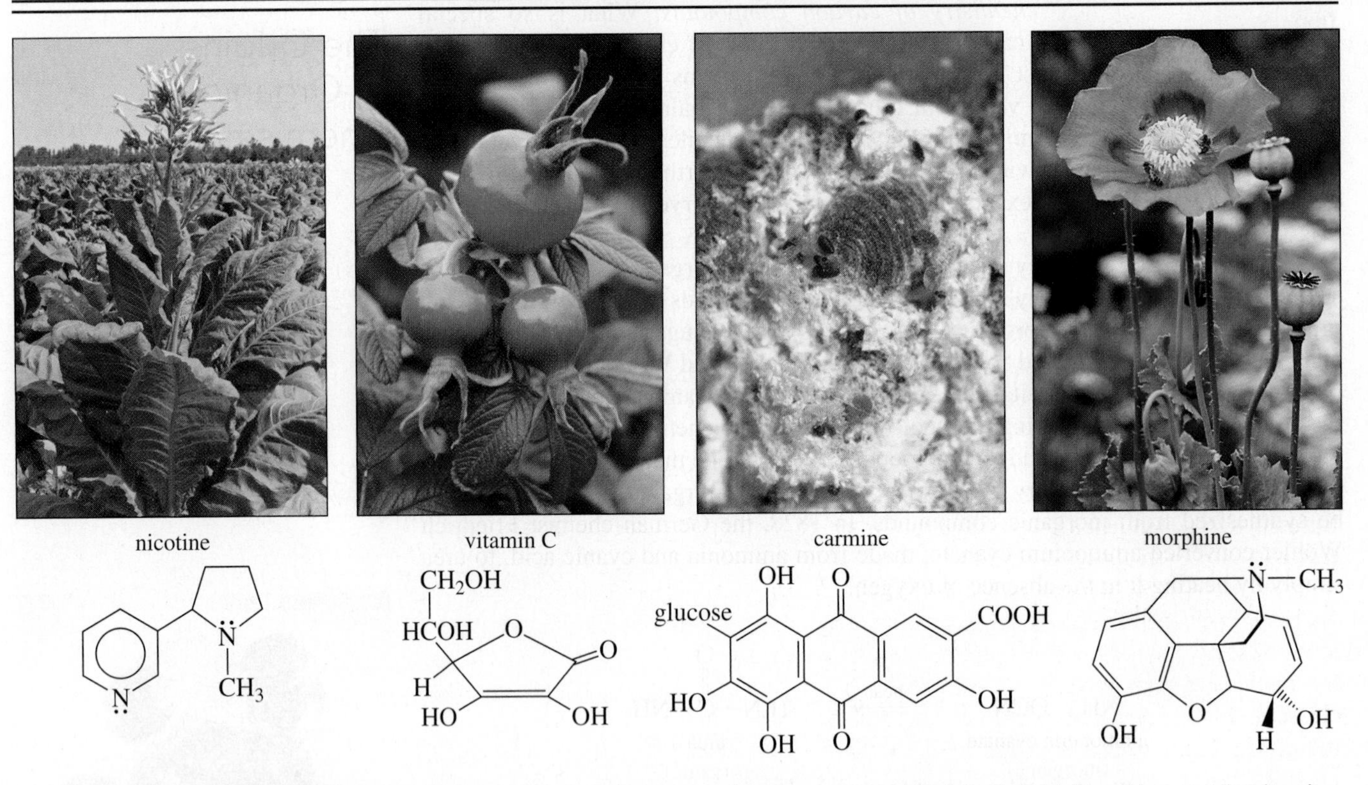

Four examples of organic compounds in living organisms. Tobacco contains nicotine, an addictive alkaloid. Rose hips contain vitamin C, essential for preventing scurvy. The red dye carmine comes from cochineal insects, shown on prickly pear cactus. Opium poppies contain morphine, a pain-relieving, addictive alkaloid.

One of the reasons chemists synthesize derivatives of complex organic compounds like morphine is to discover new drugs that retain the good properties (potent pain-relieving) but not the bad properties (highly addictive).

Chemists have learned to synthesize or simulate many of these complex molecules. The synthetic products serve as drugs, medicines, plastics, pesticides, paints, and fibers. Many of the most important advances in medicine are actually advances in organic chemistry. New synthetic drugs are developed to combat disease, and new polymers are molded to replace failing organs. Organic chemistry has gone full circle. It began as the study of compounds derived from "organs," and now it gives us the drugs and materials we need to save or replace those organs.

1-2 Principles of Atomic Structure

Before we begin our study of organic chemistry, we must review some basic principles. These concepts of atomic and molecular structure are crucial to your understanding of the structure and bonding of organic compounds.

1-2A Structure of the Atom

Atoms are made up of protons, neutrons, and electrons. Protons are positively charged and are found together with (uncharged) neutrons in the nucleus. Electrons, which have a negative charge that is equal in magnitude to the positive charge on the proton, occupy the space surrounding the nucleus (Figure 1-1). Protons and neutrons have similar masses, about 1800 times the mass of an electron. Almost all the atom's mass is in the nucleus, but it is the electrons that take part in chemical bonding and reactions.

Each element is distinguished by the number of protons in the nucleus (the atomic number). The number of neutrons is usually similar to the number of protons, although the number of neutrons may vary. Atoms with the same number of protons but different numbers of neutrons are called **isotopes**. For example, the most common kind of carbon atom has six protons and six neutrons in its nucleus. Its mass number (the sum of the protons and neutrons) is 12, and we write its symbol as ^{12}C. About 1% of carbon atoms have seven neutrons; the mass number is 13, written ^{13}C. A very small fraction of carbon atoms have eight neutrons and a mass number of 14. The ^{14}C isotope is radioactive, with a half-life (the time it takes for half of the nuclei to decay) of 5730 years. The predictable decay of ^{14}C is used to determine the age of organic materials up to about 50,000 years old.

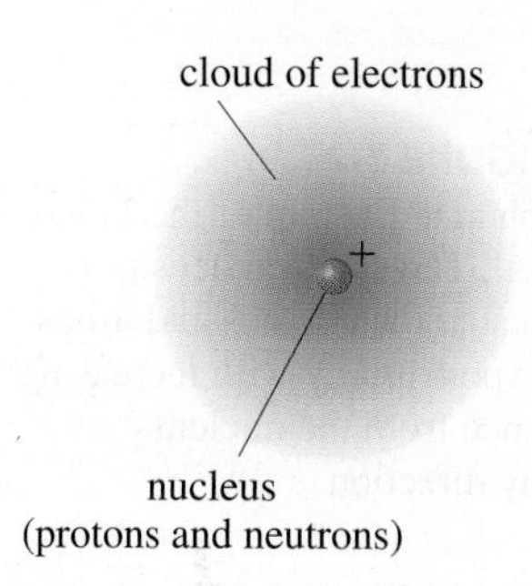

FIGURE 1-1
Basic atomic structure. An atom has a dense, positively charged nucleus surrounded by a cloud of electrons.

1-2B Electronic Structure of the Atom

An element's chemical properties are determined by the number of protons in the nucleus and the corresponding number of electrons around the nucleus. The electrons form bonds and determine the structure of the resulting molecules. Because they are small and light, electrons show properties of both particles and waves; in many ways, the electrons in atoms and molecules behave more like waves than like particles.

Electrons that are bound to nuclei are found in **orbitals**. The *Heisenberg uncertainty principle* states that we can never determine exactly where the electron is; nevertheless, we can determine the **electron density**, the probability of finding the electron in a particular part of the orbital. An orbital, then, is an allowed energy state for an electron, with an associated probability function that defines the distribution of electron density in space.

Atomic orbitals are grouped into different "shells" at different distances from the nucleus. Each shell is identified by a principal quantum number n, with $n = 1$ for the lowest-energy shell closest to the nucleus. As n increases, the shells are farther from the nucleus, higher in energy, and can hold more electrons. Most of the common elements in organic compounds are found in the first two rows of the periodic table, indicating that their electrons are found in the first two electron shells. The first shell ($n = 1$) can hold two electrons, and the second shell ($n = 2$) can hold eight.

The first electron shell contains just the 1*s* orbital. All *s* orbitals are spherically symmetrical, meaning that they are nondirectional. The electron density is only a function of the distance from the nucleus. The electron density of the 1*s* orbital is graphed in Figure 1-2. Notice how the electron density is highest *at* the nucleus and falls off exponentially with increasing distance from the nucleus. The 1*s* orbital might be imagined as a cotton boll, with the cottonseed at the middle representing the nucleus. The density of the cotton is highest nearest the seed, and it becomes less dense at greater distances from this "nucleus."

The second electron shell consists of the 2*s* and 2*p* orbitals. The 2*s* orbital is spherically symmetrical like the 1*s* orbital, but its electron density is not a simple exponential function. The 2*s* orbital has a smaller amount of electron density close to the nucleus. Most of the electron density is farther away, beyond a region of zero electron density

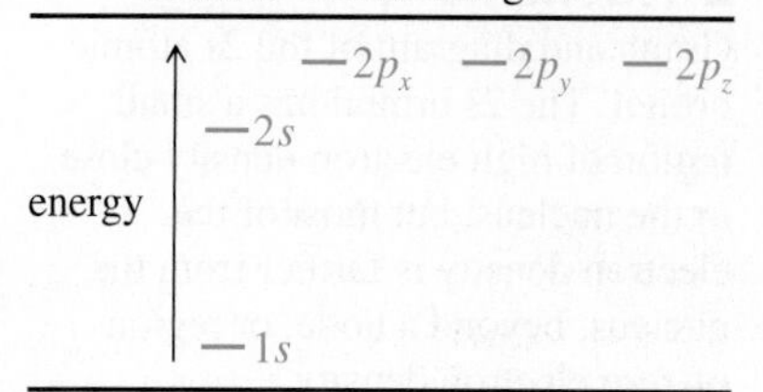

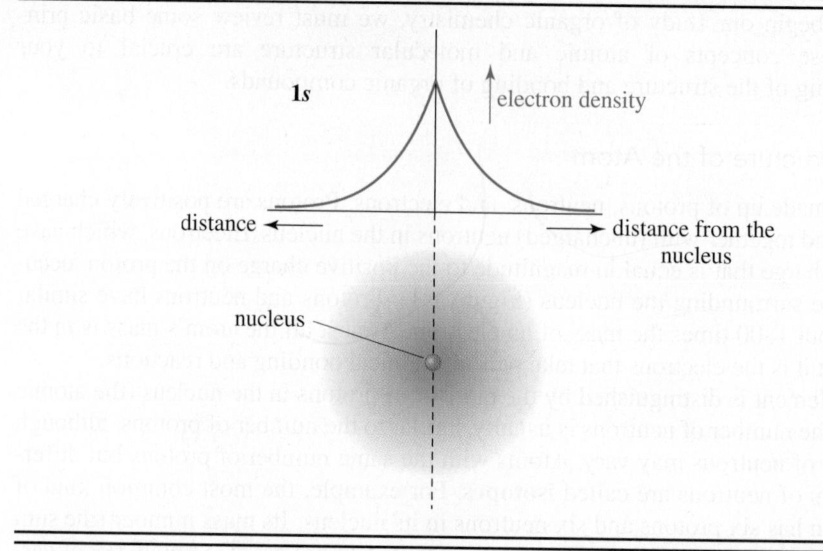

■ **FIGURE 1-2**
Graph and diagram of the 1*s* atomic orbital. The electron density is highest at the nucleus and drops off exponentially with increasing distance from the nucleus in any direction.

called a **node**. Because most of the 2*s* electron density is farther from the nucleus than that of the 1*s*, the 2*s* orbital is higher in energy. Figure 1-3 shows a graph of the 2*s* orbital.

In addition to the 2*s* orbital, the second shell also contains three 2*p* atomic orbitals, one oriented in each of the three spatial directions. These orbitals are called the $2p_x$, the $2p_y$, and the $2p_z$, according to their direction along the *x*, *y*, or *z* axis. The 2*p* orbitals are slightly higher in energy than the 2*s*, because the average location of the electron in a 2*p* orbital is farther from the nucleus. Each *p* orbital consists of two lobes, one on either side of the nucleus, with a **nodal plane** at the nucleus. The nodal plane is a flat (planar) region of space, including the nucleus, with zero electron density. The three 2*p* orbitals differ only in their spatial orientation, so they have identical energies. Orbitals with identical energies are called **degenerate orbitals**. Figure 1-4 shows the shapes of the three degenerate 2*p* atomic orbitals.

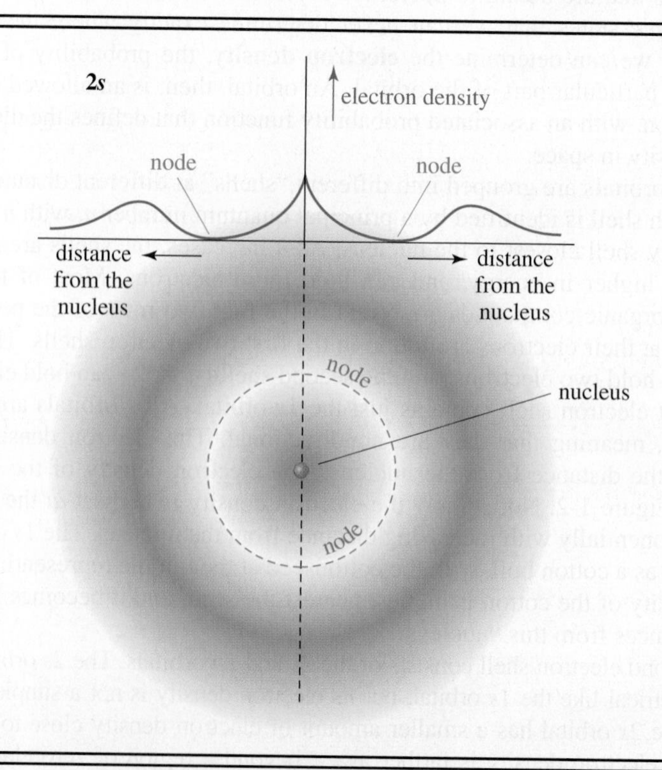

■ **FIGURE 1-3**
Graph and diagram of the 2*s* atomic orbital. The 2*s* orbital has a small region of high electron density close to the nucleus, but most of the electron density is farther from the nucleus, beyond a node, or region of zero electron density.

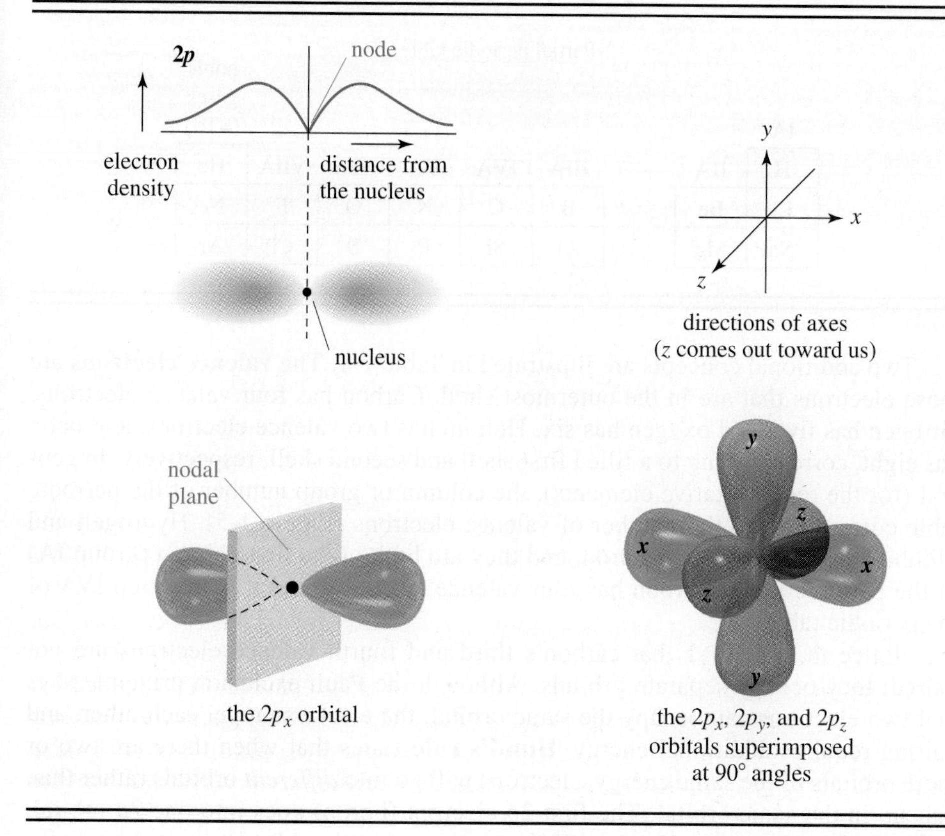

■ **FIGURE 1-4**
The 2*p* orbitals. Three 2*p* orbitals are oriented at right angles to each other. Each is labeled according to its orientation along the *x*, *y*, or *z* axis.

The *Pauli exclusion principle* tells us that each orbital can hold a maximum of two electrons, provided that their spins are paired. The first shell (one 1*s* orbital) can accommodate two electrons. The second shell (one 2*s* orbital and three 2*p* orbitals) can accommodate eight electrons, and the third shell (one 3*s* orbital, three 3*p* orbitals, and five 3*d* orbitals) can accommodate 18 electrons.

1-2C Electronic Configurations of Atoms

Aufbau means "building up" in German, and the *aufbau principle* tells us how to build up the electronic configuration of an atom's ground (most stable) state. Starting with the lowest-energy orbital, we fill the orbitals in order until we have added the proper number of electrons. Table 1-1 shows the ground-state electronic configurations of the elements in the first two rows of the periodic table.

TABLE 1-1
Electronic Configurations of the Elements of the First and Second Rows

Element	Configuration	Valence Electrons
H	$1s^1$	1
He	$1s^2$	2
Li	$1s^2 2s^1$	1
Be	$1s^2 2s^2$	2
B	$1s^2 2s^2 2p_x^1$	3
C	$1s^2 2s^2 2p_x^1 2p_y^1$	4
N	$1s^2 2s^2 2p_x^1 2p_y^1 2p_z^1$	5
O	$1s^2 2s^2 2p_x^2 2p_y^1 2p_z^1$	6
F	$1s^2 2s^2 2p_x^2 2p_y^2 2p_z^1$	7
Ne	$1s^2 2s^2 2p_x^2 2p_y^2 2p_z^2$	8

FIGURE 1-5
First three rows of the periodic table. The organization of the periodic table results from the filling of atomic orbitals in order of increasing energy. For these representative elements, the number of the column corresponds to the number of valence electrons.

Partial periodic table

IA							noble gases (VIII)
H	IIA	IIIA	IVA	VA	VIA	VIIA	He
Li	Be	B	C	N	O	F	Ne
Na	Mg	Al	Si	P	S	Cl	Ar

Lithium carbonate, a salt of lithium, is a mood-stabilizing agent used to treat the psychiatric disorder known as mania. Mania is characterized by behaviors such as elated mood, feelings of greatness, racing thoughts, and an inability to sleep. We don't know how lithium carbonate helps to stabilize these patients' moods.

Two additional concepts are illustrated in Table 1-1. The **valence electrons** are those electrons that are in the outermost shell. Carbon has four valence electrons, nitrogen has five, and oxygen has six. Helium has two valence electrons, and neon has eight, corresponding to a filled first shell and second shell, respectively. In general (for the representative elements), the column or group number of the periodic table corresponds to the number of valence electrons (Figure 1-5). Hydrogen and lithium have one valence electron, and they are both in the first column (group IA) of the periodic table. Carbon has four valence electrons, and it is in group IVA of the periodic table.

Notice in Table 1-1 that carbon's third and fourth valence electrons are not paired; they occupy separate orbitals. Although the Pauli exclusion principle says that two electrons can occupy the same orbital, the electrons repel each other, and pairing requires additional energy. **Hund's rule** states that when there are two or more orbitals of the same energy, electrons will go into *different* orbitals rather than pair up in the same orbital. The first $2p$ electron (boron) goes into one $2p$ orbital, the second (carbon) goes into a different orbital, and the third (nitrogen) occupies the last $2p$ orbital. The fourth, fifth, and sixth $2p$ electrons must pair up with the first three electrons.

PROBLEM 1-1

(a) Nitrogen has relatively stable isotopes (half-life greater than 1 second) of mass numbers 13, 14, 15, 16, and 17. (All except ^{14}N and ^{15}N are radioactive.) Calculate how many protons and neutrons are in each of these isotopes of nitrogen.
(b) Write the electronic configurations of the third-row elements shown in the partial periodic table in Figure 1-5.

1-3 Bond Formation: The Octet Rule

In 1915, G. N. Lewis proposed several new theories describing how atoms bond together to form molecules. One of these theories states that a filled shell of electrons is especially stable, and *atoms transfer or share electrons in such a way as to attain a filled shell of electrons.* A filled shell of electrons is simply the electron configuration of a noble gas, such as He, Ne, or Ar. This principle has come to be called the **octet rule** because a filled shell implies eight valence electrons for the elements in the second row of the periodic table.

1-3A Ionic Bonding

There are two ways that atoms can interact to attain noble-gas configurations. Sometimes atoms attain noble-gas configurations by transferring electrons from one atom to another. For example, lithium has one electron more than the helium configuration, and fluorine has one electron less than the neon configuration. Lithium easily loses its valence electron, and fluorine easily gains one:

$$Li\cdot \curvearrowright \cdot\ddot{\underset{..}{F}}: \longrightarrow Li^+ \quad + \quad :\ddot{\underset{..}{F}}:^- \longrightarrow Li^+ :\ddot{\underset{..}{F}}:^-$$

electron transfer — He configuration — Ne configuration — ionic bond

A transfer of one electron gives each of these two elements a noble-gas configuration. The resulting ions have opposite charges, and they attract each other to form an **ionic bond**. Ionic bonding usually results in the formation of a large crystal lattice rather than individual molecules. Ionic bonding is common in inorganic compounds but relatively uncommon in organic compounds.

1-3B Covalent Bonding

Covalent bonding, in which electrons are shared rather than transferred, is the most common type of bonding in organic compounds. Hydrogen, for example, needs a second electron to achieve the noble-gas configuration of helium. If two hydrogen atoms come together and form a bond, they "share" their two electrons, and each atom has two electrons in its valence shell.

$$H\cdot \; + \; H\cdot \longrightarrow H:H$$

each H shares two electrons (He configuration)

We will study covalent bonding in more detail in Chapter 2.

1-4 Lewis Structures

One way to symbolize the bonding in a covalent molecule is to use **Lewis structures.** In a Lewis structure, each valence electron is symbolized by a dot. A bonding pair of electrons is symbolized by a pair of dots or by a dash (—). We try to arrange all the atoms so they have their appropriate noble-gas configurations: two electrons for hydrogen, and octets for the second-row elements.

Consider the Lewis structure of methane (CH_4).

$$\begin{array}{c} H \\ H:\ddot{\underset{..}{C}}:H \\ H \end{array} \quad \text{or} \quad \begin{array}{c} H \\ | \\ H-C-H \\ | \\ H \end{array}$$

methane

Carbon contributes four valence electrons, and each hydrogen contributes one, to give a total of eight electrons. All eight electrons surround carbon to give it an octet, and each hydrogen atom shares two of the electrons.

The Lewis structure for ethane (C_2H_6) is more complex.

$$\begin{array}{c} H\;H \\ H:\ddot{\underset{..}{C}}:\ddot{\underset{..}{C}}:H \\ H\;H \end{array} \quad \text{or} \quad \begin{array}{c} H\quad H \\ |\quad\; | \\ H-C-C-H \\ |\quad\; | \\ H\quad H \end{array}$$

ethane

Once again, we have computed the total number of valence electrons (14) and distributed them so that each carbon atom is surrounded by 8 and each hydrogen by 2. The only possible structure for ethane is the one shown, with the two carbon atoms sharing a pair of electrons and each hydrogen atom sharing a pair with one of the carbons. The ethane structure shows the most important characteristic of carbon—its ability to form strong carbon–carbon bonds.

Nonbonding electrons are valence-shell electrons that are *not* shared between two atoms. A pair of nonbonding electrons is often called a **lone pair**. Oxygen atoms, nitrogen atoms, and the halogens (F, Cl, Br, I) usually have nonbonding electrons in their stable compounds. These lone pairs of nonbonding electrons help to determine the reactivity of their parent compounds. The following Lewis structures show one lone pair of electrons on the nitrogen atom of methylamine and two lone pairs on the oxygen atom of ethanol. Halogen atoms usually have three lone pairs, as shown in the structure of chloromethane.

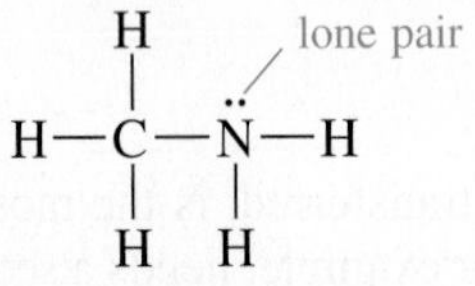

```
   H      lone pair        H  H      lone pairs            H
   |     /                 |  |   ..  /                    |   ..
H—C—N—H                 H—C—C—O:                        H—C—Cl:— lone pairs
   |  |                    |  |  |                         |   ..
   H  H                    H  H  H                         H
 methylamine              ethanol                     chloromethane
```

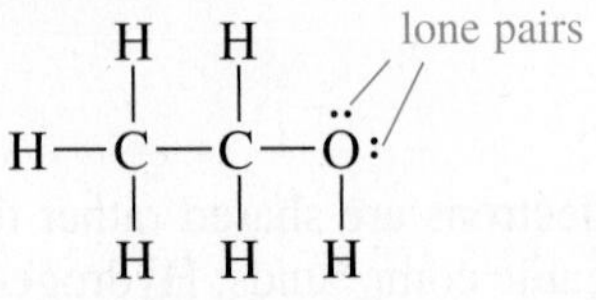

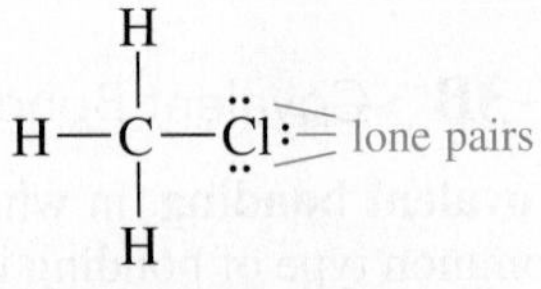

A correct Lewis structure should show any lone pairs. Organic chemists often draw structures that omit most or all of the lone pairs. These are not true Lewis structures because you must imagine the correct number of nonbonding electrons.

problem-solving **Hint**

Lewis structures are the way we write organic chemistry. Learning now to draw them quickly and correctly will help you throughout this course.

PROBLEM 1-2

Draw Lewis structures for the following compounds.

(a) ammonia, NH_3
(b) water, H_2O
(c) hydronium ion, H_3O^+
(d) propane, C_3H_8
(e) dimethylamine, CH_3NHCH_3
(f) diethyl ether, $CH_3CH_2OCH_2CH_3$
(g) 1-chloropropane, $CH_3CH_2CH_2Cl$
(h) 2-propanol, $CH_3CH(OH)CH_3$
(i) borane, BH_3
(j) boron trifluoride, BF_3

Explain what is unusual about the bonding in the compounds in parts (i) and (j).

1-5 Multiple Bonding

In drawing Lewis structures in Section 1-4, we placed just one pair of electrons between any two atoms. The sharing of one pair between two atoms is called a **single bond**. Many molecules have adjacent atoms sharing two or even three electron pairs. The sharing of two pairs is called a **double bond**, and the sharing of three pairs is called a **triple bond**.

Ethylene (C_2H_4) is an organic compound with a double bond. When we draw a Lewis structure for ethylene, the only way to show both carbon atoms with octets is to draw them sharing two pairs of electrons. The following examples show organic compounds with double bonds. In each case, two atoms share four electrons (two pairs) to give them octets. A double dash (=) symbolizes a double bond.

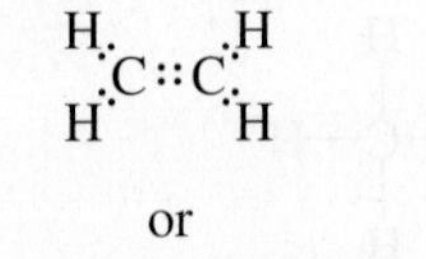

```
H.   .H          H.    ..          H.     .
 :C::C:           :C::O:            :C::N:
H'   'H          H'    ''          H'     'H

   or               or                or

H     H          H                 H      ..
 >C=C<            >C=O:             >C=N
H     H          H     ''          H      \H
ethylene         formaldehyde      formaldimine
```

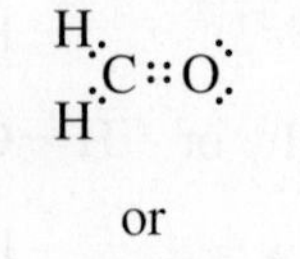

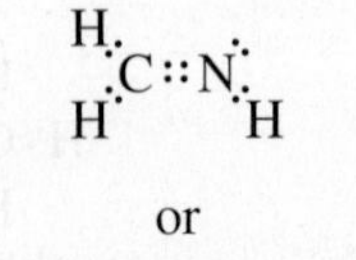

Acetylene (C_2H_2) has a triple bond. Its Lewis structure shows three pairs of electrons between the carbon atoms to give them octets. The following examples show organic compounds with triple bonds. A triple dash (≡) symbolizes a triple bond.

H:C:::C:H or H—C≡C—H
acetylene

$H{:}\ddot{C}{:}C{:::}C{:}\ddot{C}{:}H$ (with H above and below each terminal C) or H_3C—C≡C—CH_3 (each H drawn as a bond)
dimethylacetylene

$H{:}\ddot{C}{:}C{:::}N{:}$ (with H above and below C) or H—C(H)(H)—C≡N:
acetonitrile

Acetylene is a high-energy gaseous hydrocarbon that is explosive at high pressures. Combined with oxygen, acetylene burns with such a hot flame that it melts steel. Acetylene is commonly used in welding and cutting torches that work anywhere, even underwater. In gas cylinders, acetylene is dissolved in acetone to keep it from getting too concentrated and exploding.

All these Lewis structures show that carbon normally forms four bonds in neutral organic compounds. Nitrogen generally forms three bonds, and oxygen usually forms two. Hydrogen and the halogens usually form only one bond. The number of bonds an atom usually forms is called its **valence.** Carbon is tetravalent, nitrogen is trivalent, oxygen is divalent, and hydrogen and the halogens are monovalent. By remembering the usual number of bonds for these common elements, we can write organic structures more easily. If we draw a structure with each atom having its usual number of bonds, a correct Lewis structure usually results.

SUMMARY Common Bonding Patterns (Uncharged)

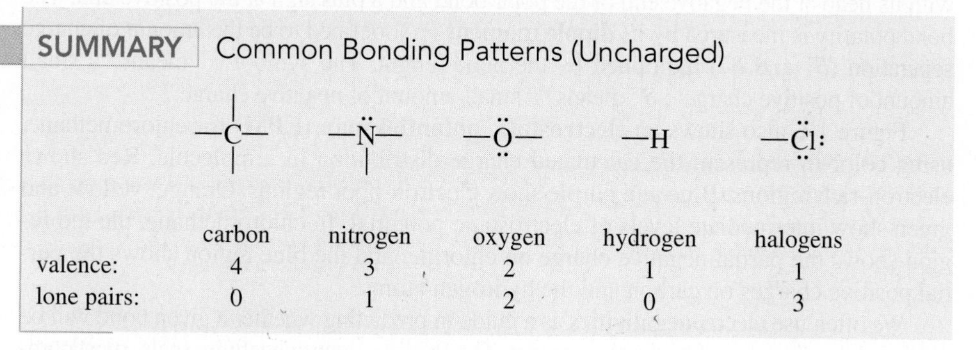

	carbon	nitrogen	oxygen	hydrogen	halogens
valence:	4	3	2	1	1
lone pairs:	0	1	2	0	3

problem-solving Hint

These "usual numbers of bonds" might be single bonds, or they might be combined into double and triple bonds. For example, three bonds to nitrogen might be three single bonds, one single bond and one double bond, or one triple bond (:N≡N:). In working problems, consider all possibilities.

PROBLEM 1-3

Write Lewis structures for the following molecular formulas.

(a) N_2 (b) HCN (c) HONO
(d) CO_2 (e) CH_3CHNH (f) HCO_2H
(g) C_2H_3Cl (h) HNNH (i) C_3H_6 (one double bond)
(j) C_3H_4 (two double bonds) (k) C_3H_4 (one triple bond)

PROBLEM 1-4

Circle any lone pairs (pairs of nonbonding electrons) in the structures you drew for Problem 1-3.

1-6 Electronegativity and Bond Polarity

A bond with the electrons shared equally between the two atoms is called a **nonpolar covalent bond**. The bond in H_2 and the C—C bond in ethane are nonpolar covalent bonds. In most bonds between two different elements, the bonding electrons are attracted more strongly to one of the two nuclei. An unequally shared pair of bonding electrons is called a **polar covalent bond**.

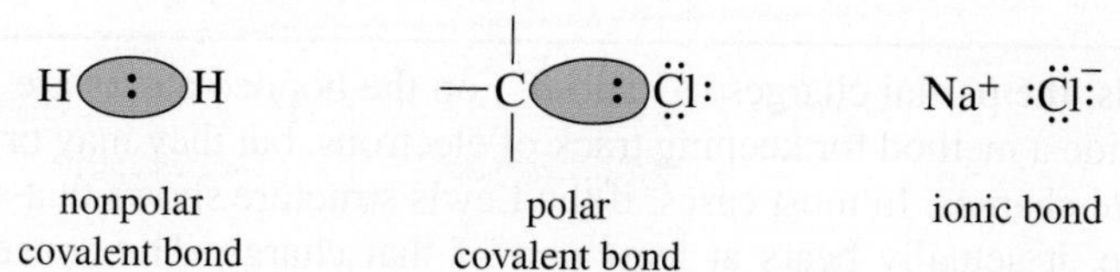

When carbon is bonded to chlorine, for example, the bonding electrons are attracted more strongly to the chlorine atom. The carbon atom bears a small partial positive charge,

$\overset{\mu}{\longrightarrow}$

H, H, H — $\overset{\delta^+}{C}$—$\overset{\delta^-}{Cl}$

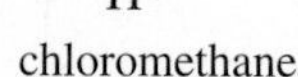

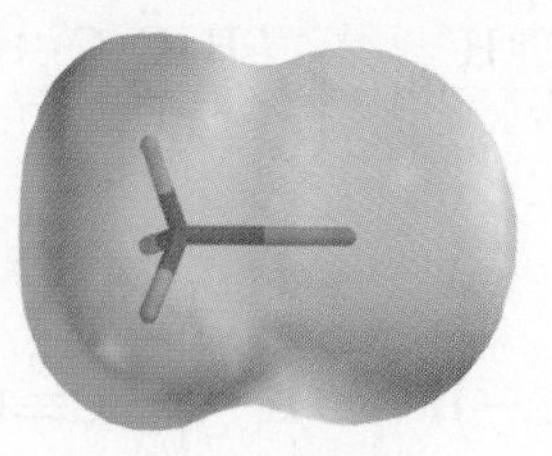

chloromethane

■ **FIGURE 1-6**
Bond polarity. Chloromethane contains a polar carbon–chlorine bond with a partial negative charge on chlorine and a partial positive charge on carbon. The electrostatic potential map shows a red region (electron-rich) around the partial negative charge and a blue region (electron-poor) around the partial positive charge. Other colors show intermediate values of electrostatic potential.

and the chlorine atom bears a partial negative charge. Figure 1-6 shows the polar carbon–chlorine bond in chloromethane. We symbolize the bond polarity by an arrow with its head at the negative end of the polar bond and a plus sign at the positive end. The bond polarity is measured by its **dipole moment** (μ), defined to be the amount of charge separation (δ^+ and δ^-) multiplied by the bond length. The symbol δ^+ means "a small amount of positive charge"; δ^- means "a small amount of negative charge."

Figure 1-6 also shows an **electrostatic potential map (EPM)** for chloromethane, using color to represent the calculated charge distribution in a molecule. Red shows electron-rich regions. Blue and purple show electron-poor regions. Orange, yellow, and green show intermediate levels of electrostatic potential. In chloromethane, the red region shows the partial negative charge on chlorine, and the blue region shows the partial positive charges on carbon and the hydrogen atoms.

H 2.2						
Li 1.0	Be 1.6	B 2.0	C 2.5	N 3.0	O 3.4	F 4.0
Na 0.9	Mg 1.3	Al 1.6	Si 1.9	P 2.2	S 2.6	Cl 3.2
K 0.8						Br 3.0
						I 2.7

■ **FIGURE 1-7**
The Pauling electronegativities of some of the elements found in organic compounds.

We often use **electronegativities** as a guide in predicting whether a given bond will be polar and the direction of its dipole moment. The Pauling electronegativity scale, most commonly used by organic chemists, is based on bonding properties, and it is useful for predicting the polarity of covalent bonds. Elements with higher electronegativities generally have more attraction for the bonding electrons. Therefore, in a bond between two different atoms, the atom with the higher electronegativity is the negative end of the dipole. Figure 1-7 shows Pauling electronegativities for some of the important elements in organic compounds.

Notice that the electronegativities increase from left to right across the periodic table. Nitrogen, oxygen, and the halogens are all more electronegative than carbon; sodium, lithium, and magnesium are less electronegative. Hydrogen's electronegativity is similar to that of carbon, so we usually consider C—H bonds to be nonpolar. We will consider the polarity of bonds and molecules in more detail in Section 2-9.

PROBLEM 1-5

Use electronegativities to predict the direction of the dipole moments of the following bonds.

(a) C—Cl **(b)** C—O **(c)** C—N **(d)** C—S **(e)** C—B
(f) N—Cl **(g)** N—O **(h)** N—S **(i)** N—B **(j)** B—Cl

1-7 Formal Charges

In polar bonds, the partial charges (δ^+ and δ^-) on the bonded atoms are *real*. **Formal charges** provide a method for keeping track of electrons, but they may or may not correspond to real charges. In most cases, if the Lewis structure shows that an atom has a formal charge, it actually bears at least part of that charge. The concept of formal charge helps us determine which atoms bear most of the charge in a charged molecule, and it also helps us to see charged atoms in molecules that are neutral overall.

To calculate formal charges, count how many electrons contribute to the charge of each atom and compare that number with the number of valence electrons in the free, neutral atom (given by the group number in the periodic table). The electrons that contribute to an atom's charge are

1. *all* its unshared (nonbonding) electrons; plus
2. *half* the (bonding) electrons it shares with other atoms, or one electron of each bonding pair.

The formal charge of a given atom can be calculated by the formula

$$\text{formal charge (FC)} = [\text{group number}] - [\text{nonbonding electrons}] - \tfrac{1}{2}[\text{shared electrons}]$$

SOLVED PROBLEM 1-1

Compute the formal charge (FC) on each atom in the following structures.

(a) Methane (CH_4)

H
H:C:H
H

SOLUTION

Each of the hydrogen atoms in methane has one bonding pair of electrons (two shared electrons). Half of two shared electrons is one electron, and one valence electron is what hydrogen needs to be neutral. Hydrogen atoms with one bond are formally neutral: $FC = 1 - 0 - 1 = 0$.

The carbon atom has four bonding pairs of electrons (eight electrons). Half of eight shared electrons is four electrons, and four electrons are what carbon (group IVA) needs to be neutral. Carbon is formally neutral whenever it has four bonds: $FC = 4 - 0 - \frac{1}{2}(8) = 0$.

(b) The hydronium ion, H_3O^+

two nonbonding electrons

H:O:H (with + charge on O)
H

three bonds, six bonding electrons

SOLUTION

In drawing the Lewis structure for this ion, we use eight electrons: six from oxygen plus three from the hydrogens, minus one because the ion has a positive charge. Each hydrogen has one bond and is formally neutral. Oxygen is surrounded by an octet, with six bonding electrons and two nonbonding electrons. Half the bonding electrons plus all the nonbonding electrons contribute to its charge: $\frac{6}{2} + 2 = 5$; but oxygen (group VIA) needs six valence electrons to be neutral. Consequently, the oxygen atom has a formal charge of +1: $FC = 6 - 2 - \frac{1}{2}(6) = +1$.

(c) $H_3N—BH_3$

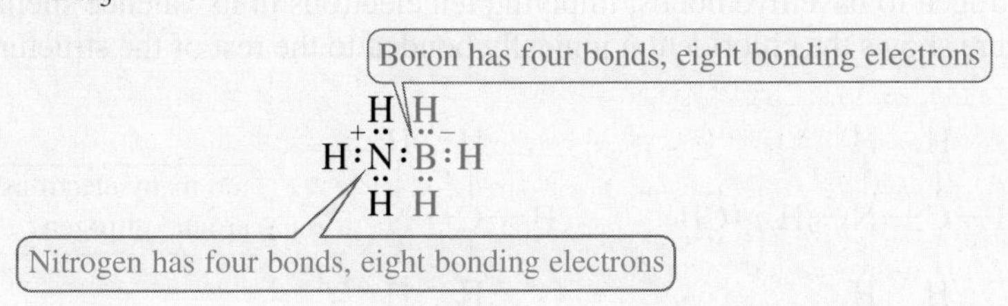
Boron has four bonds, eight bonding electrons
H H
H:N:B:H
H H
Nitrogen has four bonds, eight bonding electrons

SOLUTION

This is a neutral compound where the individual atoms are formally charged. The Lewis structure shows that both nitrogen and boron have four shared bonding pairs of electrons. Both boron and nitrogen have $\frac{8}{2} = 4$ electrons contributing to their charges. Nitrogen (group VA) needs five valence electrons to be neutral, so it bears a formal charge of +1. Boron (group IIIA) needs only three valence electrons to be neutral, so it bears a formal charge of −1.

$$\text{Nitrogen:} \quad FC = 5 - 0 - \tfrac{1}{2}(8) = +1$$
$$\text{Boron:} \quad FC = 3 - 0 - \tfrac{1}{2}(8) = -1$$

(d) $[H_2CNH_2]^+$

$$H_2C{=}\overset{+}{N}H_2$$

SOLUTION

In this structure, both carbon and nitrogen have four shared pairs of bonding electrons. With four bonds, carbon is formally neutral; however, nitrogen is in group VA, and it bears a formal positive charge: $FC = 5 - 0 - 4 = +1$.

This compound might also be drawn with the following Lewis structure:

$$H_2\overset{+}{C}{-}\ddot{N}H_2$$

In this structure, the carbon atom has three bonds with six bonding electrons. We calculate that $\frac{6}{2} = 3$ electrons, so carbon is one short of the four needed to be formally neutral: $FC = 4 - 0 - \frac{1}{2}(6) = +1$.

Nitrogen has six bonding electrons and two nonbonding electrons. We calculate that $\frac{6}{2} + 2 = 5$, so the nitrogen is uncharged in this second structure:

$$FC = 5 - 2 - \tfrac{1}{2}(6) = 0$$

The significance of these two Lewis structures is discussed in Section 1-9.

Most organic compounds contain only a few common elements, usually with complete octets of electrons. The summary table on the facing page shows the most commonly occurring bonding structures, using dashes to represent bonding pairs of electrons. Use the rules for calculating formal charges to verify the charges shown on these structures. A good understanding of the structures shown here will help you to draw organic compounds and their ions quickly and correctly.

1-8 Ionic Structures

Some organic compounds contain ionic bonds. For example, the structure of methylammonium chloride (CH_3NH_3Cl) cannot be drawn using just covalent bonds. That would require nitrogen to have five bonds, implying ten electrons in its valence shell. The correct structure shows the chloride ion ionically bonded to the rest of the structure.

$$H_3C{-}\overset{+}{N}H_3 \quad :\ddot{\underset{..}{Cl}}:^-$$

methylammonium chloride

$$H_3C{-}NH_2{-}\ddot{\underset{..}{Cl}}:$$

too many electrons around nitrogen

cannot be drawn covalently

SUMMARY Common Bonding Patterns in Organic Compounds and Ions

Atom	Valence Electrons	Positively Charged	Neutral	Negatively Charged
B	3		—B— (no octet)	—B⁻—
C	4	—C⁺— (no octet)	—C—	—C̈⁻—
N	5	—N⁺—	—N̈—	—N̈⁻—
O	6	—Ö⁺—	—Ö—	—Ö:⁻
halogen	7	—C̈l⁺—	—C̈l:	:C̈l:⁻

problem-solving Hint

This is a very important table. Work enough problems to become familiar with these bonding patterns so you can recognize other patterns as being either unusual or wrong.

Some molecules can be drawn either covalently or ionically. For example, sodium acetate ($NaOCOCH_3$) may be drawn with either a covalent bond or an ionic bond between sodium and oxygen. Because sodium generally forms ionic bonds with oxygen (as in NaOH), the ionically bonded structure is usually preferred. In general, bonds between atoms with very large electronegativity differences (about 2 or more) are usually drawn as ionic.

Na^+ $^-$:Ö—C(=O)—CH$_2$—H   Na—Ö—C(=O)—CH$_2$—H

drawn as ionic (more common)   drawn as covalent (less common)

PROBLEM 1-6

Draw Lewis structures for the following compounds and ions, showing appropriate formal charges.

(a) $[CH_3OH_2]^+$ (b) NH_4Cl (c) $(CH_3)_4NCl$
(d) $NaOCH_3$ (e) $^+CH_3$ (f) $^-CH_3$
(g) $NaBH_4$ (h) $NaBH_3CN$ (i) $(CH_3)_2O—BF_3$
(j) $[HONH_3]^+$ (k) $KOC(CH_3)_3$ (l) $[H_2C{=}OH]^+$

1-9 Resonance

1-9A Resonance Hybrids

Some compounds' structures are not adequately represented by a single Lewis structure. When two or more valence-bond structures are possible, differing only in the placement of electrons, the molecule will usually show characteristics of both structures. The different structures are called **resonance structures** or **resonance forms** because they are not different compounds, just different ways of drawing the same compound. The actual molecule is said to be a **resonance hybrid** of its resonance forms. In Solved Problem 1-1(d) we saw that the ion $[H_2CNH_2]^+$ might be represented by either of the following resonance forms:

$[H_2\overset{+}{C}—\ddot{N}H_2 \longleftrightarrow H_2C{=}\overset{+}{N}H_2] = H_2\overset{\delta+}{C}{=\!=}\overset{\delta+}{N}H_2$

resonance forms of a resonance hybrid   combined representation

The actual structure of this ion is a resonance hybrid of the two structures. In the actual molecule, the positive charge is **delocalized** (spread out) over both the carbon atom and the nitrogen atom. In the left resonance form, the positive charge is on carbon, but carbon does not have an octet. Nitrogen's nonbonding electrons can move into the bond (as indicated by the red arrow) to give the second structure (the one with a carbon–nitrogen double bond) a positive charge on nitrogen and an octet on carbon. The combined representation attempts to combine the two resonance forms into a single picture with the charge shared by carbon and nitrogen.

Spreading the positive charge over two atoms makes the ion more stable than it would be if the entire charge were localized only on the carbon or only on the nitrogen. We call this a **resonance-stabilized** cation. Resonance is most important when it allows a charge to be delocalized over two or more atoms, as in this example.

Resonance stabilization plays a crucial role in organic chemistry, especially in the chemistry of compounds having double bonds. We will use the concept of resonance frequently throughout this course. For example, the acidity of acetic acid (following) is enhanced by resonance effects. When acetic acid loses a proton, the resulting acetate ion has a negative charge delocalized over both of the oxygen atoms. Each oxygen atom bears half of the negative charge, and this delocalization stabilizes the ion. Each of the carbon–oxygen bonds is halfway between a single bond and a double bond, and they are said to have a *bond order* of $1\frac{1}{2}$.

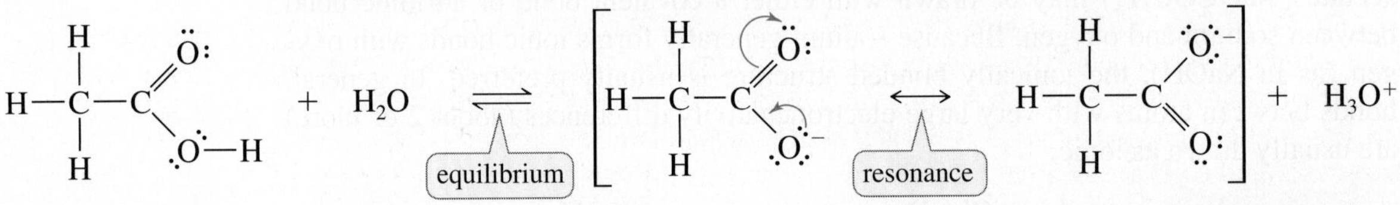

$$CH_3COOH + H_2O \rightleftharpoons \left[CH_3-C(=O)-O^- \longleftrightarrow CH_3-C(-O^-)=O \right] + H_3O^+$$

acetic acid — equilibrium — resonance — acetate ion

We use a single double-headed arrow between resonance forms (and often enclose them in brackets) to indicate that the actual structure is a hybrid of the Lewis structures we have drawn. By contrast, an equilibrium is represented by two arrows in opposite directions. Occasionally we use curved arrows (shown in red above) to help us see how we mentally move the electrons between one resonance form and another. The electrons do not actually "resonate" back and forth; they are delocalized over all the resonance forms at the same time.

problem-solving Hint

Second-row elements (B, C, N, O, F) cannot have more than eight electrons in their valence shells. The following is NOT a valid Lewis structure:

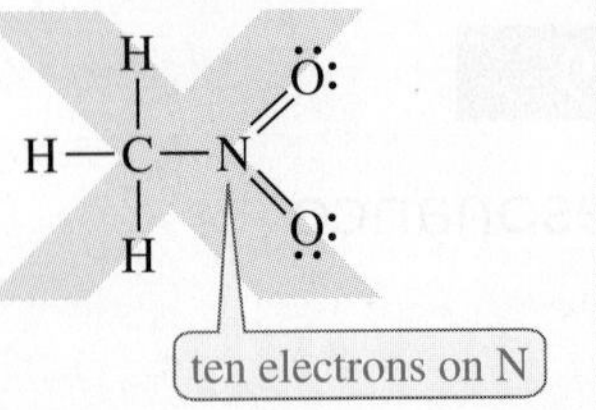

$$H_3C-N(=O)=O$$

ten electrons on N

Some uncharged molecules actually have resonance-stabilized structures with equal positive and negative formal charges. For example, we can draw two Lewis structures for nitromethane (CH_3NO_2), but both of them have a formal positive charge on nitrogen and a negative charge on one of the oxygens. Thus, nitromethane has a positive charge on the nitrogen atom and a negative charge spread equally over the two oxygen atoms. The N—O bonds are midway between single and double bonds, as indicated in the combined representation:

$$\left[H_3C-N^+(=O)-O^- \longleftrightarrow H_3C-N^+(-O^-)=O \right] = H_3C-N^+(O^{-\frac{1}{2}})(O^{-\frac{1}{2}})$$

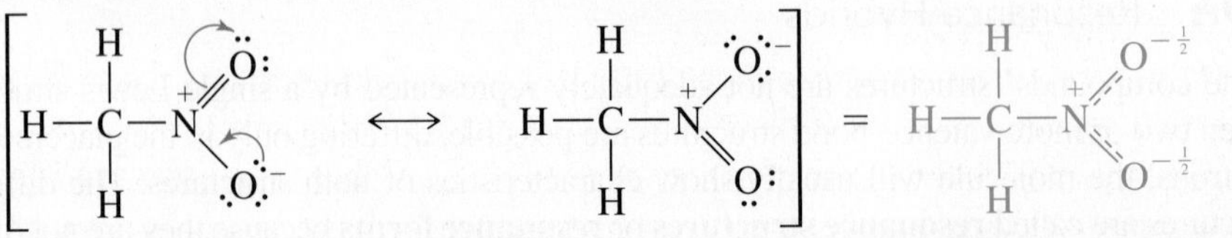

resonance forms — combined representation

Remember that individual resonance forms do not exist. The molecule does not "resonate" between these structures. It is a hybrid with some characteristics of both. An analogy is a mule, which is a hybrid of a horse and a donkey. The mule does not "resonate" between looking like a horse and looking like a donkey; it looks like a mule all the time, with the broad back of the horse and the long ears of the donkey.

1-9B Major and Minor Resonance Contributors

Two or more correct Lewis structures for the same compound may or may not represent electron distributions of equal energy. Although separate resonance forms do not exist, we can estimate their relative energies as if they did exist. More stable resonance forms are closer representations of the real molecule than less stable ones. The two resonance forms shown earlier for the acetate ion have similar bonding, and they are of identical energy. The same is true for the two resonance forms of nitromethane. The following resonance forms are bonded differently, however.

all octets
(major contributor)

no octet on C
(minor contributor)

These structures are not equal in estimated energy. The first structure has the positive charge on nitrogen. The second has the positive charge on carbon, and the carbon atom does not have an octet. The first structure is more stable because it has an additional bond and all the atoms have octets. Many stable ions have a positive charge on a nitrogen atom with four bonds (see the Summary Table, page 13). We call the more stable resonance form the **major contributor**, and the less stable form is the **minor contributor**. The structure of the actual compound resembles the major contributor more than it does the minor contributor.

Many organic molecules have major and minor resonance contributors. Formaldehyde ($H_2C{=}O$) can be written with a negative charge on oxygen, balanced by a positive charge on carbon. This polar resonance form is higher in estimated energy than the double-bonded structure because it has charge separation, fewer bonds, and a positively charged carbon atom without an octet. The charge-separated structure is only a minor contributor, but it helps to explain why the formaldehyde C=O bond is very polar, with a partial positive charge on carbon and a partial negative charge on oxygen. The electrostatic potential map (EPM) also shows an electron-rich region (red) around oxygen and an electron-poor region (blue) around carbon in formaldehyde.

all octets
no charge separation
(major contributor)

no octet on C
charge separation
(minor contributor)

dipole moment

EPM of formaldehyde

In drawing resonance forms, we try to draw structures that are as low in energy as possible. The best candidates are those that have the maximum number of octets and the maximum number of bonds. Also, we look for structures with the minimum amount of charge separation.

Only electrons can be delocalized. Unlike electrons, nuclei cannot be delocalized. They must remain in the same places, with the same bond distances and angles, in all the resonance contributors. The following general rules will help us to draw realistic resonance structures:

1. All the resonance structures must be valid Lewis structures for the compound.
2. Only the placement of the electrons may be shifted from one structure to another. (Electrons in double bonds and lone pairs are the ones that are most commonly shifted.) Nuclei cannot be moved, and the bond angles must remain the same.

resonance forms

NOT resonance

problem-solving Hint

Resonance forms can be compared using the following criteria, beginning with the most important:

1. As many octets as possible
2. As many bonds as possible
3. Any negative charges on electronegative atoms
4. As little charge separation as possible

3. The number of unpaired electrons (if any) must remain the same. Most stable compounds have no unpaired electrons, and all the electrons must remain paired in all the resonance forms.
4. The major resonance contributor is the one with the lowest energy. Good contributors generally have all octets satisfied, as many bonds as possible, and as little charge separation as possible. Negative charges are more stable on more electronegative atoms, such as O, N, and S.
5. Resonance stabilization is most important when it serves to delocalize a charge over two or more atoms.

SOLVED PROBLEM 1-2

For each of the following compounds, draw the important resonance forms. Indicate which structures are major and minor contributors or whether they would have the same energy.

(a) $[CH_3OCH_2]^+$

SOLUTION

$$\left[H_3C{-}\ddot{O}{-}CH_2^{+} \longleftrightarrow H_3C{-}\overset{+}{O}{=}CH_2 \right]$$

minor contributor | major contributor

The first (minor) structure has a carbon atom with only six electrons around it. The second (major) structure has octets on all atoms and an additional bond.

(b) $H_2\bar{\ddot{C}}{-}CH{=}O$

SOLUTION

$$\left[H_2\bar{\ddot{C}}{-}CH{=}\ddot{O}{:} \longleftrightarrow H_2C{=}CH{-}\ddot{O}{:}^{-} \right]$$

minor contributor | major contributor

Both of these structures have octets on oxygen and both carbon atoms, and they have the same number of bonds. The first structure has the negative charge on carbon; the second has it on oxygen. Oxygen is the more electronegative element, so the second structure is the major contributor.

(c) H_2SO_4

SOLUTION

$$\left[H{-}\ddot{O}{-}S({=}O)_2{-}\ddot{O}{-}H \longleftrightarrow H{-}\ddot{O}{-}\overset{+}{S}(O^{-})({=}O){-}\ddot{O}{-}H \longleftrightarrow H{-}\ddot{O}{-}\overset{+}{S}({=}O)(O^{-}){-}\ddot{O}{-}H \longleftrightarrow H{-}\ddot{O}{-}\overset{+2}{S}(O^{-})_2{-}\ddot{O}{-}H \right]$$

The first structure, with more bonds and less charge separation, is possible because sulfur is a third-row element with accessible *d* orbitals, giving it an expandable valence. For example, SF_6 is a stable compound with 12 electrons around sulfur. Theoretical calculations suggest that the last structure, with octets on all atoms, may be the major resonance contributor, however. We cannot always predict the major contributor of a resonance hybrid.

PROBLEM 1-7

Draw the important resonance forms for the following molecules and ions.

(a) CO_3^{2-} **(b)** NO_3^- **(c)** NO_2^- **(d)** $H_2C{=}CH{-}CH_2^+$
(e) $H_2C{=}CH{-}CH_2^-$ **(f)** SO_4^{2-} **(g)** $[CH_3C(OCH_3)_2]^+$ **(h)** $B(OH)_3$

PROBLEM 1-8

For each of the following compounds, draw the important resonance forms. Indicate which structures are major and minor contributors or whether they have the same energy.

(a) $[H_2CNO_2]^-$ **(b)** $H_2C{=}CH{-}NO_2$ **(c)** $[H_2COH]^+$
(d) H_2CNN **(e)** $[H_2CCN]^-$ **(f)** $H_2N{-}\overset{+}{C}H{-}CH{=}CH{-}NH_2$
(g) $H{-}\overset{O}{\overset{\|}{C}}{-}NH_2$ **(h)** $H{-}\overset{O}{\overset{\|}{C}}{-}\overset{-}{C}H{-}\overset{O}{\overset{\|}{C}}{-}H$ **(i)** $[CH_3C(OH)_2]^+$

problem-solving **Hint**

In drawing resonance forms for ions, see how you can delocalize the charge over several atoms. Try to spread a negative charge over electronegative elements like oxygen and nitrogen. Try to spread a positive charge over as many carbons as possible, but especially over any atoms that can bear the positive charge and still have an octet, such as oxygen (with three bonds) or nitrogen (with four bonds).

1-10 Structural Formulas

Several kinds of formulas are used by organic chemists to represent organic compounds. Some of these formulas involve a shorthand notation that requires some explanation. **Structural formulas** actually show which atoms are bonded to which. There are two types of structural formulas, complete Lewis structures and condensed structural formulas. In addition, there are several ways of drawing condensed structural formulas. As we have seen, a Lewis structure symbolizes a bonding pair of electrons as a pair of dots or as a dash (—). Lone pairs of electrons are shown as pairs of dots.

1-10A Condensed Structural Formulas

Condensed structural formulas (Table 1-2) are written without showing all the individual bonds. In a condensed structure, each central atom is shown together with the atoms that are bonded to it. The atoms bonded to a central atom are often listed after the central atom (as in CH_3CH_3 rather than $H_3C{-}CH_3$) even if that is not their actual bonding order. In many cases, if there are two or more identical groups, parentheses and a subscript may be used to represent all the identical groups. Nonbonding electrons are rarely shown in condensed structural formulas.

TABLE 1-2
Examples of Condensed Structural Formulas

Compound	Lewis Structure	Condensed Structural Formula
ethane	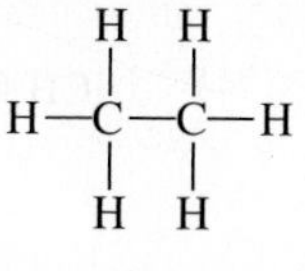 H H H—C—C—H H H	CH_3CH_3
isobutane	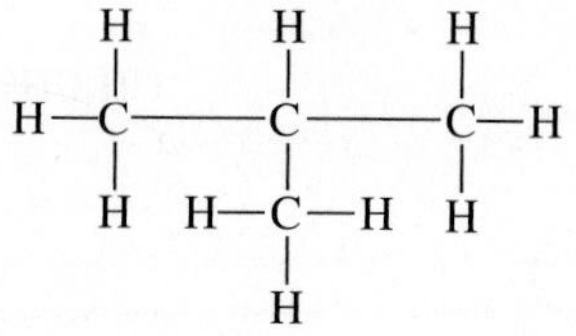 H H H H—C——C——C—H H H—C—H H H	$(CH_3)_3CH$
n-hexane	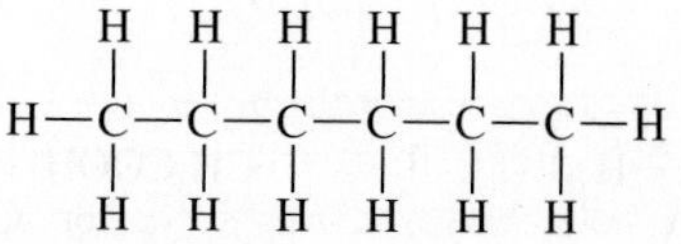 H H H H H H H—C—C—C—C—C—C—H H H H H H H	$CH_3(CH_2)_4CH_3$

(Continued)

TABLE 1-2

Continued

Compound	Lewis Structure	Condensed Structural Formula
diethyl ether	H H H H H—C—C—Ö—C—C—H H H H H	$CH_3CH_2OCH_2CH_3$ or $CH_3CH_2—O—CH_2CH_3$ or $(CH_3CH_2)_2O$
ethanol	H H H—C—C—Ö—H H H	CH_3CH_2OH
isopropyl alcohol	H :Ö—H H H—C—C——C—H H H H	$(CH_3)_2CHOH$
dimethylamine	H H H—C—N̈—C—H H H H	$(CH_3)_2NH$

When a condensed structural formula is written for a compound containing double or triple bonds, the multiple bonds are often drawn as they would be in a Lewis structure. Table 1-3 shows examples of condensed structural formulas containing multiple bonds. Notice that the —CHO group of an aldehyde and the —COOH group of a carboxylic acid are actually bonded differently from what the condensed notation suggests.

TABLE 1-3

Condensed Structural Formulas for Double and Triple Bonds

Compound	Lewis Structure	Condensed Structural Formula
2-butene	H H H H—C—C=C—C—H H H H	$CH_3CHCHCH_3$ or $CH_3CH=CHCH_3$
acetonitrile	H H—C—C≡N: H	CH_3CN or $CH_3C \equiv N$
acetaldehyde	H :Ö: H—C—C—H H	CH_3CHO or CH_3CH (with =O on C)
acetone	H :Ö: H H—C—C—C—H H H	CH_3COCH_3 or CH_3CCH_3 (with =O on central C)
acetic acid	H :Ö: H—C—C—Ö—H H	CH_3COOH or $CH_3C—OH$ (with =O on C) or CH_3CO_2H

As you can see from Tables 1-2 and 1-3, the distinction between a complete Lewis structural formula and a condensed structural formula can be blurry. Chemists often draw formulas with some parts condensed and other parts completely drawn out. You should work with these different types of formulas so that you understand what all of them mean.

PROBLEM 1-9

Draw complete Lewis structures for the following condensed structural formulas.

(a) $CH_3(CH_2)_3CH(CH_3)_2$
(b) $(CH_3)_2CHCH_2Cl$
(c) CH_3CH_2COCN
(d) CH_2CHCHO
(e) $(CH_3)_3CCOCHCH_2$
(f) $CH_3COCOOH$
(g) $(CH_3CH_2)_2CO$
(h) $(CH_3)_3COH$

1-10B Line–Angle Formulas

Another kind of shorthand used for organic structures is the **line–angle formula**, sometimes called a **skeletal structure** or a **stick figure**. Line–angle formulas are often used for cyclic compounds and occasionally for noncyclic ones. In a stick figure, bonds are represented by lines, and carbon atoms are assumed to be present wherever two lines meet or a line begins or ends. Nitrogen, oxygen, and halogen atoms are shown, but hydrogen atoms are not usually drawn unless they are bonded to an atom that is drawn. Each carbon atom is assumed to have enough hydrogen atoms to give it a total of four bonds. Nonbonding electrons are rarely shown. Table 1-4 shows some examples of line–angle drawings.

TABLE 1-4
Examples of Line–Angle Drawings

Compound	Condensed Structure	Line–Angle Formula
hexane	$CH_3(CH_2)_4CH_3$	
2-hexene	$CH_3CH{=}CHCH_2CH_2CH_3$	
3-hexanol	$CH_3CH_2CH(OH)CH_2CH_2CH_3$	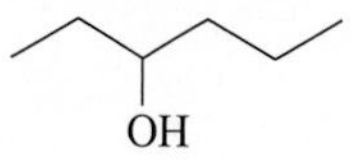 OH
2-cyclohexenone	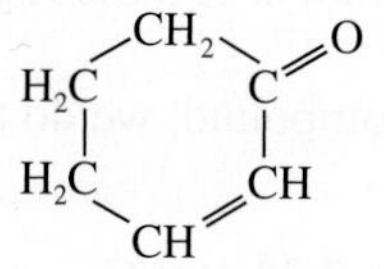 CH_2, H_2C, C=O, H_2C, CH, CH (ring)	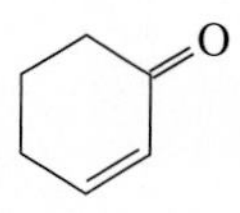 O
2-methylcyclohexanol	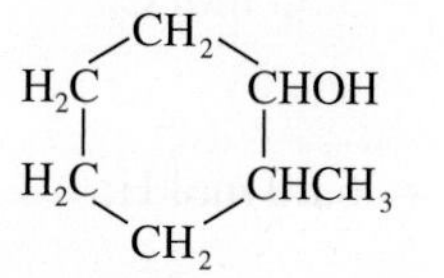 CH_2, H_2C, CHOH, H_2C, $CHCH_3$, CH_2 (ring)	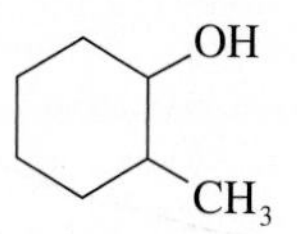 OH, CH_3 or OH 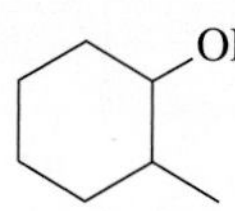
nicotinic acid (a vitamin, also called niacin)	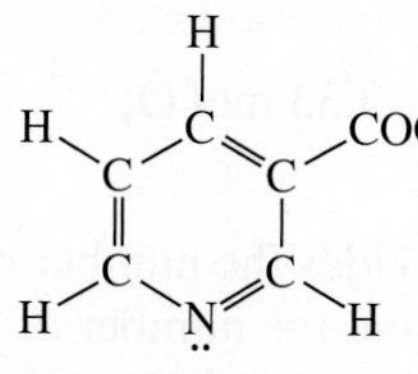 H, C, H, C, C, COOH, C, C, H, N, H (ring)	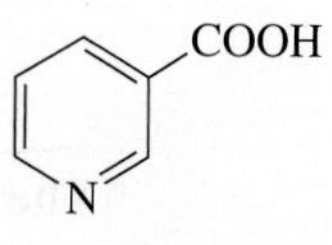 COOH, N or O, OH, N 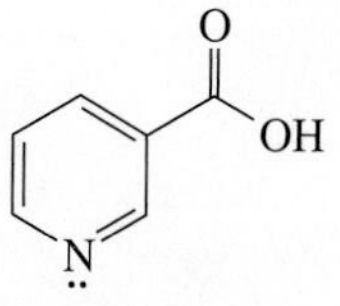

PROBLEM 1-10

Give Lewis structures corresponding to the following line–angle structures.

(a) N H (b) O (c) N H (d) OH

(e) CHO (f) O (g) O (h) O

PROBLEM 1-11

Repeat Problem 1-9, this time drawing line–angle structures for compounds (a) through (h).

1-11 Molecular Formulas and Empirical Formulas

Before we can write possible structural formulas for a compound, we need to know its molecular formula. The **molecular formula** simply gives the number of atoms of each element in one molecule of the compound. For example, the molecular formula for 1-butanol is $C_4H_{10}O$.

$$CH_3CH_2CH_2CH_2OH$$

1-butanol, molecular formula $C_4H_{10}O$

Calculation of the Empirical Formula Molecular formulas can be determined by a two-step process. The first step is the determination of an **empirical formula**, simply the relative ratios of the elements present. Suppose, for example, that an unknown compound was found by quantitative elemental analysis to contain 40.0% carbon and 6.67% hydrogen. The remainder of the weight (53.3%) is assumed to be oxygen. To convert these numbers to an empirical formula, we can follow a simple procedure.

1. Assume the sample contains 100 g, so the percent value gives the number of grams of each element. Divide the number of grams of each element by the atomic weight to get the number of moles of that atom in the 100-g sample.
2. Divide each of these numbers of moles by the smallest one. This step should give recognizable ratios.

For the unknown compound, we do the following computations:

$$\frac{40.0 \text{ g C}}{12.0 \text{ g/mol}} = 3.33 \text{ mol C}; \qquad \frac{3.33 \text{ mol}}{3.33 \text{ mol}} = 1$$

$$\frac{6.67 \text{ g H}}{1.01 \text{ g/mol}} = 6.60 \text{ mol H}; \qquad \frac{6.60 \text{ mol}}{3.33 \text{ mol}} = 1.98 \cong 2$$

$$\frac{53.3 \text{ g O}}{16.0 \text{ g/mol}} = 3.33 \text{ mol O}; \qquad \frac{3.33 \text{ mol}}{3.33 \text{ mol}} = 1$$

The first computation divides the number of grams of carbon by 12, the number of grams of hydrogen by 1, and the number of grams of oxygen by 16. We compare these numbers by dividing them by the smallest number, 3.33. The final result is a ratio of one carbon to two hydrogens to one oxygen. This result gives the empirical formula $C_1H_2O_1$ or CH_2O, which simply shows the ratios of the elements. The molecular formula can be any multiple of this empirical formula, because any multiple also has the same ratio of elements. Possible molecular formulas are CH_2O, $C_2H_4O_2$, $C_3H_6O_3$, $C_4H_8O_4$, etc.

Calculation of the Molecular Formula How do we know the correct molecular formula? We can choose the right multiple of the empirical formula if we know the molecular weight. Molecular weights can be determined by methods that relate the freezing-point depression or boiling-point elevation of a solvent to the molal concentration of the unknown. If the compound is volatile, we can convert it to a gas and use its volume to determine the number of moles according to the gas law. Newer methods include *mass spectrometry*, which we will cover in Chapter 11.

For our example (empirical formula CH_2O), let's assume that the molecular weight is determined to be about 60. The weight of one CH_2O unit is 30, so our unknown compound must contain twice this many atoms. The molecular formula must be $C_2H_4O_2$. The compound might be acetic acid.

In Chapters 12, 13, and 15 we will use spectroscopic techniques to determine the complete structure for a compound once we know its molecular formula.

$$CH_3-\overset{\overset{\displaystyle O}{\|}}{C}-OH$$

acetic acid, $C_2H_4O_2$

PROBLEM 1-12

Compute the empirical and molecular formulas for each of the following elemental analyses. In each case, propose at least one structure that fits the molecular formula.

	C	H	N	Cl	MW
(a)	40.0%	6.67%	0	0	90
(b)	32.0%	6.67%	18.7%	0	75
(c)	25.6%	4.32%	15.0%	37.9%	93
(d)	38.4%	4.80%	0	56.8%	125

problem-solving **Hint**

If an elemental analysis does not add up to 100%, the missing percentage is assumed to be oxygen.

1-12 Arrhenius Acids and Bases

The properties and reactions of acids and bases are central to our study of organic chemistry. We need to consider exactly what is meant by the terms **acid** and **base**. Most people would agree that H_2SO_4 is an acid and NaOH is a base. Is BF_3 an acid or a base? Is ethylene ($H_2C{=}CH_2$) an acid or a base? To answer these questions, we need to understand the three different definitions of acids and bases: the Arrhenius definition, the Brønsted–Lowry definition, and the Lewis definition.

Acidic compounds were first classified on the basis of their sour taste. The Latin terms *acidus* (sour) and *acetum* (vinegar) gave rise to our modern terms *acid* and *acetic acid*. Alkaline compounds (bases) were substances that neutralize acids, such as limestone and plant ashes (*al kalai* in Arabic).

The **Arrhenius** theory, developed at the end of the nineteenth century, defined acids as *substances that dissociate in water to give* H_3O^+ *ions*. The stronger acids, such as sulfuric acid (H_2SO_4), were assumed to dissociate to a greater degree than weaker acids, such as acetic acid (CH_3COOH).

$$\underset{\text{sulfuric acid}}{H_2SO_4} + H_2O \rightleftarrows H_3O^+ + HSO_4^-$$

$$\underset{\text{acetic acid}}{CH_3-\overset{\overset{\displaystyle O}{\|}}{C}-OH} + H_2O \rightleftarrows H_3O^+ + CH_3-\overset{\overset{\displaystyle O}{\|}}{C}-O^-$$

According to the Arrhenius definition, bases are *substances that dissociate in water to give hydroxide ions*. Strong bases, such as NaOH, were assumed to dissociate more completely than weaker, sparingly soluble bases such as $Mg(OH)_2$.

$$NaOH \rightleftarrows Na^+ + {}^-OH$$

$$Mg(OH)_2 \rightleftarrows Mg^{2+} + 2\ {}^-OH$$

The acidity or basicity of an aqueous (water) solution is measured by the concentration of H_3O^+. This value also implies the concentration of ^-OH because these two concentrations are related by the water ion-product constant:

$$K_w = [H_3O^+][^-OH] = 1.00 \times 10^{-14}\ M^2 \text{ (at 25 °C)}$$

In a neutral solution, the concentrations of H_3O^+ and ^-OH are equal.

$$[H_3O^+] = [^-OH] = 1.00 \times 10^{-7}\ M \text{ in a neutral solution}$$

Acidic and basic solutions are defined by an excess of H_3O^+ or ^-OH.

$$\text{acidic: } [H_3O^+] > 10^{-7}\ M \text{ and } [^-OH] < 10^{-7}\ M$$

$$\text{basic: } [H_3O^+] < 10^{-7}\ M \text{ and } [^-OH] > 10^{-7}\ M$$

Because these concentrations can span a wide range of values, the acidity or basicity of a solution is usually measured on a logarithmic scale. The **pH** is defined as the negative logarithm (base 10) of the H_3O^+ concentration.

$$pH = -\log_{10}[H_3O^+]$$

A neutral solution has a pH of 7, an acidic solution has a pH less than 7, and a basic solution has a pH greater than 7.

PROBLEM 1-13

Calculate the pH of the following solutions.
(a) 5.00 g of HBr in 100 mL of aqueous solution
(b) 1.50 g of NaOH in 50 mL of aqueous solution

The Arrhenius definition was an important contribution to understanding many acids and bases, but it does not explain why a compound such as ammonia (NH_3) neutralizes acids, even though it has no hydroxide ion in its molecular formula. In Section 1-13 we discuss a more versatile theory of acids and bases that will include ammonia and a wider variety of organic acids and bases.

1-13 Brønsted–Lowry Acids and Bases

In 1923, Brønsted and Lowry defined acids and bases on the basis of the transfer of protons. A **Brønsted–Lowry acid** is *any species that can donate a proton*, and a **Brønsted–Lowry base** is *any species that can accept a proton*. These definitions also include all the Arrhenius acids and bases because compounds that dissociate to give H_3O^+ are proton donors, and compounds that dissociate to give ^-OH are proton acceptors. (Hydroxide ion accepts a proton to form H_2O.)

In addition to Arrhenius acids and bases, the Brønsted–Lowry definition includes bases that have no hydroxide ions, yet can accept protons. Consider the following examples of acids donating protons to bases. NaOH is a base under either the Arrhenius or Brønsted–Lowry definition. The other three are Brønsted–Lowry bases but not Arrhenius bases, because they have no hydroxide ions.

$$\underset{\text{proton donor}}{HCl} + \underset{\text{proton acceptor}}{NaOH} \rightleftharpoons NaCl + H{-}OH$$

$$\underset{\text{proton donor}}{H_2SO_4} + \underset{\text{proton acceptor}}{:NH_3} \rightleftharpoons HSO_4^- + H{-}\overset{+}{N}H_3$$

$$\underset{\text{proton donor}}{HCl} + \underset{\text{proton acceptor}}{H_2C{=}CH(CH_3)} \rightleftharpoons Cl^- + H_3C{-}\overset{+}{C}H(CH_3)$$

$$\underset{\text{proton donor}}{HNO_3} + \underset{\text{proton acceptor}}{H_2C{=}\ddot{N}H} \rightleftharpoons NO_3^- + H_2C{=}\overset{+}{N}H_2$$

When a base accepts a proton, it becomes an acid capable of returning that proton. When an acid donates its proton, it becomes a base capable of accepting that proton back. One of the most important principles of the Brønsted–Lowry definition is this concept of **conjugate acids and bases**. For example, NH_4^+ and NH_3 are a conjugate acid–base pair. NH_3 is the base; when it accepts a proton, it is transformed into its conjugate acid, NH_4^+. Many compounds (water, for instance) can react either as an acid or as a base. Here are some additional examples of conjugate acid–base pairs.

$$\underset{\text{acid}}{H_2SO_4} + \underset{\text{base}}{H_2O} \rightleftharpoons \underset{\text{conjugate base}}{HSO_4^-} + \underset{\text{conjugate acid}}{H_3O^+}$$

$$\underset{\text{acid}}{H_2O} + \underset{\text{base}}{:NH_3} \rightleftharpoons \underset{\text{conjugate base}}{^-OH} + \underset{\text{conjugate acid}}{NH_4^+}$$

$$\underset{\text{acid}}{H{-}\overset{O}{\overset{\|}{C}}{-}OH} + \underset{\text{base}}{CH_3{-}\ddot{\underset{..}{O}}{:}^-} \rightleftharpoons \underset{\text{conjugate base}}{H{-}\overset{O}{\overset{\|}{C}}{-}\ddot{\underset{..}{O}}{:}^-} + \underset{\text{conjugate acid}}{CH_3{-}\ddot{\underset{..}{O}}{-}H}$$

1-13A Acid Strength

The strength of a Brønsted–Lowry acid is expressed as it is in the Arrhenius definition, by the extent of its ionization in water. The general reaction of an acid (HA) with water is the following:

$$\underset{\text{acid}}{HA} + H_2O \overset{K_a}{\rightleftharpoons} H_3O^+ + \underset{\text{base}}{A^-} \qquad K_a = \frac{[H_3O^+][A^-]}{[HA]}$$

(HA and A⁻: conjugate acid–base pair)

K_a is called the **acid-dissociation constant**, and its value indicates the relative strength of the acid. The stronger the acid, the more it dissociates, giving a larger value of K_a.

Acid-dissociation constants vary over a wide range. Strong acids are almost completely ionized in water, and their dissociation constants are greater than 1. Most organic acids are weak acids, with K_a values less than 10^{-4}. Many organic compounds are extremely weak acids; for example, methane and ethane are essentially nonacidic, with K_a values less than 10^{-40}.

Because they span such a wide range, acid-dissociation constants are often expressed on a logarithmic scale. The pK_a of an acid is defined just like the pH of a solution: as the negative logarithm (base 10) of K_a.

$$pK_a = -\log_{10} K_a$$

SOLVED PROBLEM 1-3

Calculate K_a and pK_a for water.

SOLUTION

The equilibrium that defines K_a for water is

$$\underset{\text{acid (HA)}}{H_2O} + \underset{\text{solvent}}{H_2O} \overset{K_a}{\rightleftharpoons} H_3O^+ + \underset{\text{conjugate base } (A^-)}{^-OH}$$

Water serves as both the acid and the solvent in this dissociation. The equilibrium expression is

$$K_a = \frac{[H_3O^+][A^-]}{[HA]} = \frac{[H_3O^+][^-OH]}{[H_2O]}$$

We already know that $[H_3O^+][^-OH] = 1.00 \times 10^{-14}\ M^2$, the ion-product constant for water.

The concentration of H_2O in water is simply the number of moles of water in 1 L (about 1 kg).

$$\frac{1000 \text{ g/L}}{18 \text{ g/mol}} = 55.6 \text{ mol/L}$$

Substitution gives

$$K_a = \frac{[H_3O^+][^-OH]}{[H_2O]} = \frac{1.00 \times 10^{-14}}{55.6} = 1.8 \times 10^{-16}\ M$$

The logarithm of 1.8×10^{-16} is -15.7, so the pK_a of water is 15.7.

Strong acids generally have pK_a values around 0 (or even negative), and weak acids, such as most organic acids, have pK_a values that are greater than 4. *Weaker acids have larger* pK_a *values.* Table 1-5 lists K_a and pK_a values for some common inorganic and organic compounds. Notice that the pK_a values increase as the K_a values decrease.

problem-solving Hint

In most cases, the pK_a of an acid corresponds to the pH where the acid is about half dissociated. At a lower (more acidic) pH, the acid is mostly undissociated; at a higher (more basic) pH, the acid is mostly dissociated.

PROBLEM 1-14

Ammonia appears in Table 1-5 both as an acid and as a conjugate base.

(a) Explain how ammonia can act as both an acid and a base. Which of these roles does it commonly fill in aqueous solutions?
(b) Show how water can serve as both an acid and a base.
(c) Calculate K_a and pK_a for the hydronium ion, H_3O^+.
(d) Show how methanol (CH_3OH) can serve as both an acid and a base. Write an equation for the reaction of methanol with sulfuric acid.

1-13B Base Strength

The strength of an acid is inversely related to the strength of its conjugate base. For an acid (HA) to be strong, its conjugate base (A^-) must be stable in its anionic form; otherwise,

TABLE 1-5

Relative Strength of Some Common Organic and Inorganic Acids and Their Conjugate Bases

Acid strength	Acid			Conjugate Base		Base strength	K_a	pK_a
stronger; strong acids	HCl hydrochloric acid	$+ H_2O$	$\rightleftharpoons$	$H_3O^+ +$	Cl^- chloride ion	weaker bases	1×10^7	-7
	H_3O^+ hydronium ion	$+ H_2O$	$\rightleftharpoons$	$H_3O^+ +$	H_2O water		55.6	-1.7
	HF hydrofluoric acid	$+ H_2O$	$\rightleftharpoons$	$H_3O^+ +$	F^- fluoride ion		6.8×10^{-4}	3.17
	$H{-}C({=}O){-}OH$ formic acid	$+ H_2O$	$\rightleftharpoons$	$H_3O^+ +$	$H{-}C({=}O){-}O^-$ formate ion		1.7×10^{-4}	3.76
	$CH_3{-}C({=}O){-}OH$ acetic acid	$+ H_2O$	$\rightleftharpoons$	$H_3O^+ +$	$CH_3{-}C({=}O){-}O^-$ acetate ion		1.8×10^{-5}	4.74
weak acids	$H{-}C{\equiv}N{:}$ hydrocyanic acid	$+ H_2O$	$\rightleftharpoons$	$H_3O^+ +$	$^-{:}C{\equiv}N{:}$ cyanide ion		6.0×10^{-10}	9.22
	$^+NH_4$ ammonium ion	$+ H_2O$	$\rightleftharpoons$	$H_3O^+ +$	$:NH_3$ ammonia		5.8×10^{-10}	9.24
	$CH_3{-}OH$ methyl alcohol	$+ H_2O$	$\rightleftharpoons$	$H_3O^+ +$	CH_3O^- methoxide ion		3.2×10^{-16}	15.5
	H_2O water	$+ H_2O$	$\rightleftharpoons$	$H_3O^+ +$	HO^- hydroxide ion		1.8×10^{-16}	15.7
very weak	NH_3 ammonia	$+ H_2O$	$\rightleftharpoons$	$H_3O^+ +$	$^-{:}\ddot{N}H_2$ amide ion		10^{-33}	33
not acidic; weaker	CH_4 methane	$+ H_2O$	$\rightleftharpoons$	$H_3O^+ +$	$^-{:}CH_3$ methyl anion	stronger bases	$<10^{-40}$	>40

HA would not easily lose its proton. Therefore, the conjugate base of a strong acid must be a weak base. On the other hand, if an acid is weak, its conjugate base is a strong base.

$$\underset{\text{strong acid}}{HCl} + H_2O \rightleftharpoons H_3O^+ + \underset{\text{weak base}}{Cl^-}$$

$$\underset{\text{weak acid}}{CH_3{-}\ddot{O}H} + H_2O \rightleftharpoons H_3O^+ + \underset{\text{strong base}}{CH_3\ddot{O}{:}^-}$$

In the reaction of an acid with a base, the equilibrium generally favors the *weaker* acid and base. For example, in the preceding reactions, H_3O^+ is a weaker acid than HCl but a stronger acid than CH_3OH. It also follows that H_2O is a stronger base than Cl^- but a weaker base than CH_3O^-.

The strength of a base is measured much like the strength of an acid, by using the equilibrium constant of the hydrolysis reaction.

$$\underset{\text{conjugate base}}{A^-} + H_2O \underset{}{\overset{K_b}{\rightleftharpoons}} \underset{\text{conjugate acid}}{HA} + {}^-OH$$

The equilibrium constant (K_b) for this reaction is called the *base-dissociation constant* for the base A^-. Because this constant spans a wide range of values, it is often given in logarithmic form. The negative logarithm (base 10) of K_b is defined as pK_b.

$$K_b = \frac{[HA][^-OH]}{[A^-]} \qquad pK_b = -\log_{10} K_b$$

The acid–base properties of many natural products are important for their isolation, distribution in the body, and therapeutic effects. For example, morphine (page 2) is isolated from the opium poppy and crosses into the brain as the free base, where the nitrogen is not charged. However, it exerts its pain-relieving effects as the protonated, charged species.

When we multiply K_a by K_b, we can see how the acidity of an acid is related to the basicity of its conjugate base.

$$(K_a)(K_b) = \frac{[H_3O^+][A^-]}{[HA]}\frac{[HA][^-OH]}{[A^-]} = \underset{\text{water ion-product constant}}{[H_3O^+][^-OH]} = 1.0 \times 10^{-14}$$

$$(K_a)(K_b) = 10^{-14}$$

Logarithmically,

$$pK_a + pK_b = -\log 10^{-14} = 14$$

The product of K_a and K_b must always equal the ion-product constant of water, 10^{-14}. If the value of K_a is large, the value of K_b must be small; that is, the stronger an acid, the weaker its conjugate base. Similarly, a small value of K_a (weak acid) implies a large value of K_b (strong base).

> The stronger an acid, the weaker its conjugate base.
> The weaker an acid, the stronger its conjugate base.
> Acid–base reactions favor the weaker acid and the weaker base.

problem-solving Hint

An acid will donate a proton to the conjugate base of any weaker acid (smaller K_a or higher pK_a).

PROBLEM 1-15 (PARTIALLY SOLVED)

Write equations for the following acid–base reactions. Use the information in Table 1-5 to predict whether the equilibrium will favor the reactants or the products.

(a) $HCOOH + {}^-CN$
(b) $CH_3COO^- + CH_3OH$
(c) $CH_3OH + NaNH_2$
(d) $NaOCH_3 + HCN$
(e) $HCl + H_2O$
(f) $H_3O^+ + CH_3O^-$

Solution to **(a)**: Cyanide is the conjugate base of HCN. It can accept a proton from formic acid:

$$\underset{\substack{\text{formic acid}\\\text{stronger acid}}}{H-\overset{\overset{\displaystyle :\ddot{O}}{\|}}{C}-\ddot{O}-H} + \underset{\substack{\text{cyanide}\\\text{stronger base}}}{{}^-:C\equiv N:} \rightleftharpoons \underset{\substack{\text{formate}\\\text{weaker base}}}{H-\overset{\overset{\displaystyle :\ddot{O}}{\|}}{C}-\ddot{O}:^-} + \underset{\text{weaker acid}}{H-C\equiv N:}$$

Reading from Table 1-5, formic acid (pK_a = 3.76) is a stronger acid than HCN (pK_a = 9.22), and cyanide is a stronger base than formate. The products (weaker acid and base) are favored.

SOLVED PROBLEM 1-4

Each of the following compounds can act as an acid. Show the reaction of each compound with a general base (A^-), and show the Lewis structure of the conjugate base that results.

(a) CH_3CH_2OH (b) CH_3NH_2 (c) CH_3COOH

SOLUTION

(a) Ethanol (CH_3CH_2OH) can lose the O—H proton to give a conjugate base that is an organic analogue of hydroxide ion.

$$CH_3CH_2-\ddot{O}-H + A:^- \rightleftharpoons CH_3CH_2-\ddot{O}:^- + HA$$

ethanol (weak acid); base; ethoxide (strong base)

(C—H protons are much less acidic than O—H protons because carbon is less electronegative than oxygen, and the negative charge is therefore less stable on carbon.)

(b) Methylamine (CH_3NH_2) is a very weak acid. A very strong base can abstract a proton to give a powerful conjugate base.

$$CH_3-\ddot{N}(H)-H + A:^- \rightleftharpoons CH_3-\ddot{N}^--H + HA$$

methylamine (very weak acid); very strong base; (powerful base)

(c) Acetic acid (CH_3COOH) is a moderately strong acid, giving the resonance-stabilized acetate ion as its conjugate base.

$$CH_3-C(=\ddot{O})-\ddot{O}-H + A:^- \rightleftharpoons \left[CH_3-C(=\ddot{O})-\ddot{O}:^- \longleftrightarrow CH_3-C(-\ddot{O}:^-)=\ddot{O}\right] + HA$$

acetic acid (moderate acid); acetate ion (moderate base)

SOLVED PROBLEM 1-5

Each of the compounds in Solved Problem 1-4 can also react as a base. Show the reaction of each compound with a general acid (HA), and show the Lewis structure of the conjugate acid that results.

SOLUTION

(a) Ethanol can undergo protonation on its oxygen atom. Notice that one of the lone pairs of the oxygen forms the new O—H bond.

$$CH_3CH_2-\ddot{O}-H + HA \rightleftharpoons CH_3CH_2-\dot{O}^+(H)-H + A:^-$$

ethanol (weak base); acid; (strong acid)

(b) The nitrogen atom of methylamine has a pair of electrons that can bond to a proton.

$$CH_3-\ddot{N}H_2 + HA \rightleftharpoons CH_3-\overset{+}{N}H_2(H) + A:^-$$

methylamine (moderate base); acid; (moderate acid)

(c) Acetic acid has nonbonding electrons on both of its oxygen atoms. Either of these oxygen atoms might become protonated, but protonation of the double-bonded oxygen is favored because protonation of this oxygen gives a symmetrical, resonance-stabilized conjugate acid.

$$CH_3-C(=\ddot{O})-\ddot{O}-H + HA \rightleftharpoons \left[CH_3-C(=\overset{+}{O}-H)-\ddot{O}-H \longleftrightarrow CH_3-\overset{+}{C}(-\ddot{O}-H)-\ddot{O}-H \longleftrightarrow CH_3-C(-\ddot{O}-H)=\overset{+}{O}-H\right] + A:^-$$

acetic acid (very weak base); conjugate acid of acetic acid (very strong acid)

PROBLEM 1-16

Solved Problem 1-5(c) showed protonation of the double-bonded oxygen in acetic acid. Show the product of protonation on the other ($-OH$) oxygen. Explain why protonation of the double-bonded oxygen is favored.

PROBLEM 1-17

(a) Rank ethanol, methylamine, and acetic acid in decreasing order of acidity.
(b) Rank ethanol, methylamine (pK_b 3.36), and ethoxide ion ($CH_3CH_2O^-$) in decreasing order of basicity. In each case, explain your ranking.

1-13C Structural Effects on Acidity

How can we look at a structure and predict whether a compound will be a strong acid, a weak acid, or not an acid at all? To be a Brønsted–Lowry acid (HA), a compound must contain a hydrogen atom that can be lost as a proton. A strong acid must have a stable conjugate base ($A:^-$) after losing the proton.

The stability of the conjugate base is a good guide to acidity. More stable anions tend to be weaker bases, and their conjugate acids tend to be stronger acids. Some of the factors that affect the stability of conjugate bases are electronegativity, size, and resonance.

Electronegativity A more electronegative element bears a negative charge more easily, giving a more stable conjugate base and a stronger acid. Electronegativities increase from left to right in the periodic table:

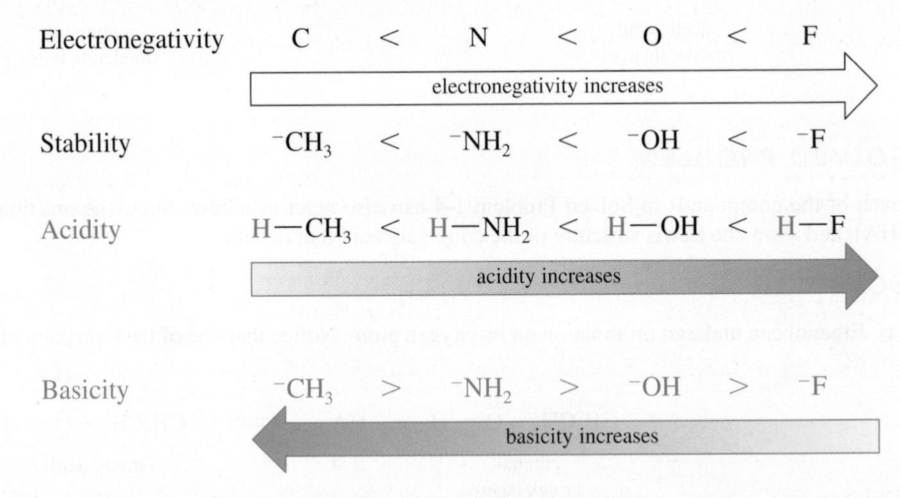

problem-solving Hint

To evaluate or compare the acidity of acids, consider the stability of their conjugate bases. To compare the basicity of bases, consider the stability of their conjugate acids.

Size The negative charge of an anion is more stable if it is spread over a larger region of space. Within a column of the periodic table, acidity increases down the column, as the size of the element increases.

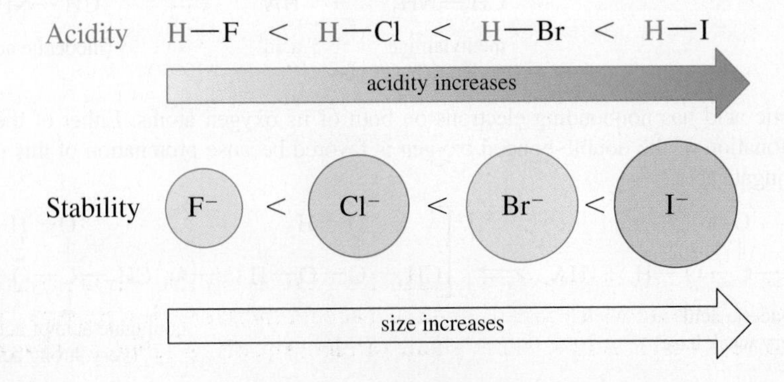

Resonance Stabilization The negative charge of a conjugate base may be delocalized over two or more atoms by resonance. Depending on how electronegative those atoms are, and how many share the charge, resonance delocalization is often the dominant effect helping to stabilize an anion. Consider the following conjugate bases.

Conjugate Base	Acid	pK_a
$CH_3CH_2-\ddot{O}:^-$ ethoxide ion	CH_3CH_2-OH ethanol	15.9 (weak acid)
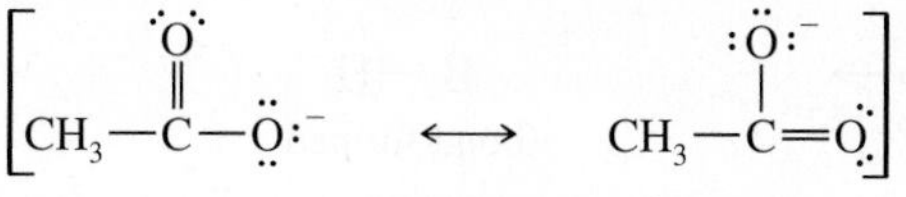 $[CH_3-C(=O)-\ddot{O}:^- \longleftrightarrow CH_3-C(-O^-)=O]$ acetate ion	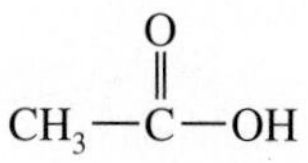 $CH_3-C(=O)-OH$ acetic acid	4.74 (moderate acid)
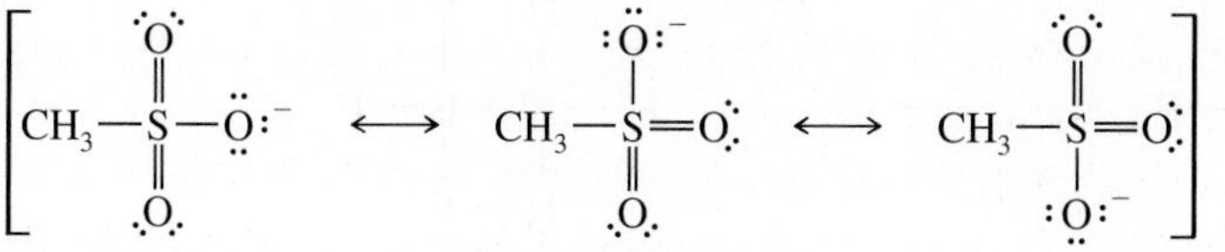 $[CH_3-S(=O)_2-\ddot{O}:^- \longleftrightarrow CH_3-S(=O)(-O^-)=O \longleftrightarrow CH_3-S(=O)(=O)-O^-]$ methanesulfonate ion	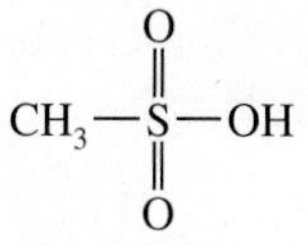 $CH_3-S(=O)_2-OH$ methanesulfonic acid	−1.2 (strong acid)

Ethoxide ion is the strongest of these three bases. Ethoxide has a negative charge localized on one oxygen atom; acetate ion has the negative charge shared by two oxygen atoms; and the methanesulfonate ion has the negative charge spread over three oxygen atoms. The pK_a values of the conjugate acids of these anions show that acids are stronger if they deprotonate to give resonance-stabilized conjugate bases.

PROBLEM 1-18

Write equations for the following acid–base reactions. Label the conjugate acids and bases, and show any resonance stabilization. Predict whether the equilibrium favors the reactants or products.

(a) $CH_3CH_2OH + CH_3NH^-$
(b) $CH_3CH_2COOH + CH_3NHCH_3$
(c) $CH_3OH + H_2SO_4$
(d) $NaOH + H_2S$
(e) $CH_3NH_3^+ + CH_3O^-$
(f) $CH_3O^- + CH_3COOH$
(g) $CH_3SO_3^- + CH_3COOH$
(h) $CF_3COOH + CH_3COO^-$

1-14 Lewis Acids and Bases

The Brønsted–Lowry definition of acids and bases depends on the transfer of a proton from the acid to the base. The base uses a pair of nonbonding electrons to form a bond to the proton. G. N. Lewis reasoned that this kind of reaction does not need a proton. Instead, a base could use its lone pair of electrons to bond to some other electron-deficient atom. In effect, we can look at an acid–base reaction from the viewpoint of the *bonds* that are formed and broken rather than a proton that is transferred. The following reaction shows the proton transfer, with emphasis on the bonds being broken and formed. Organic chemists routinely use curved arrows to show the movement of the participating electrons.

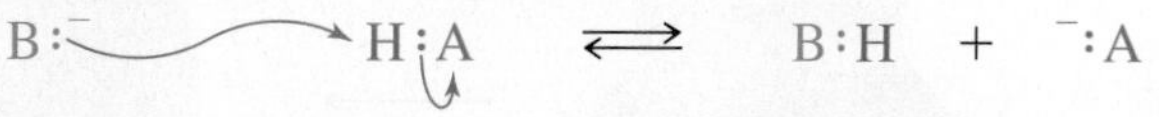

$$B: + H:A \rightleftharpoons B:H + {}^-:A$$

Lewis bases are species with available electrons that can be donated to form new bonds. **Lewis acids** are species that can accept these electron pairs to form new bonds. Since a Lewis acid *accepts* a pair of electrons, it is called an **electrophile**, from the Greek words meaning "lover of electrons." A Lewis base is called a **nucleophile**, or "lover of nuclei," because it donates electrons to a nucleus with an empty (or easily vacated) orbital. In this book, we sometimes use colored type for emphasis: blue for nucleophiles, green for electrophiles, and occasionally red for acidic protons.

problem-solving Hint

A nucleophile donates electrons. An electrophile accepts electrons. Acidic protons may serve as electron acceptors.

The Lewis acid–base definitions include reactions having nothing to do with protons. Following are some examples of Lewis acid–base reactions. Notice that the common Brønsted–Lowry acids and bases also fall under the Lewis definition, with a proton serving as the electrophile. Curved arrows (red) are used to show the movement of electrons, generally from the nucleophile to the electrophile.

$$B{:}^- \;+\; H^+ \longrightarrow B\text{—}H$$

nucleophile (Lewis base) · electrophile (Lewis acid) · bond formed

$$H_3N{:} \;+\; BF_3 \longrightarrow H_3\overset{+}{N}\text{—}\overset{-}{B}F_3$$

nucleophile · electrophile · bond formed

$$CH_3\text{—}\ddot{O}{:}^- \;+\; H\text{—}CH_2\text{—}\ddot{Cl}{:} \longrightarrow CH_3\text{—}\ddot{O}\text{—}CH_2\text{—}H \;+\; {:}\ddot{Cl}{:}^-$$

nucleophile · electrophile · bond formed

$$H_3N{:} \;+\; H\text{—}\ddot{O}\text{—}C(=O)\text{—}CH_3 \longrightarrow H_3\overset{+}{N}\text{—}H \;+\; {:}\ddot{O}^-\text{—}C(=O)\text{—}CH_3$$

nucleophile base · electrophile acid · bond formed (conjugate acid) · (conjugate base)

Some of the terms associated with acids and bases have evolved specific meanings in organic chemistry. When organic chemists use the term *base*, they usually mean a proton acceptor (a Brønsted–Lowry base). Similarly, the term *acid* usually means a proton donor (a Brønsted–Lowry acid). When the acid–base reaction involves formation of a bond to some other element (especially carbon), organic chemists refer to the electron donor as a *nucleophile* (Lewis base) and the electron acceptor as an *electrophile* (Lewis acid).

The following illustration shows electrostatic potential maps for the reaction of NH_3 (the nucleophile/electron donor) with BF_3 (the electrophile/electron acceptor). The electron-rich (red) region of NH_3 attacks the electron-poor (blue) region of BF_3. The product shows high electron density on the boron atom and its three fluorine atoms and low electron density on nitrogen and its three hydrogen atoms.

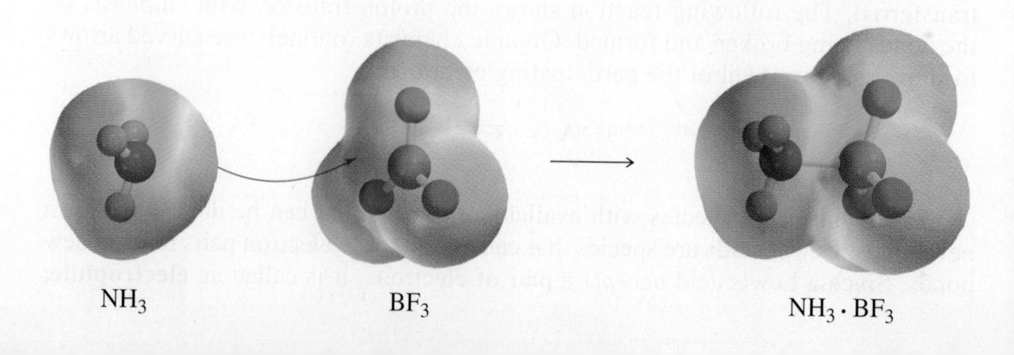

The **curved-arrow formalism** is used to show the flow of an electron pair *from the electron donor to the electron acceptor*. The movement of each pair of electrons involved in making or breaking bonds is indicated by its own separate arrow, as shown in the preceding set of reactions. In this book, these curved arrows are always printed in red. In the preceding reaction of CH_3O^- with CH_3Cl, one curved arrow shows the lone pair on oxygen forming a bond to carbon. Another curved arrow shows that the C—Cl bonding pair detaches from carbon and becomes a lone pair on the Cl^- product.

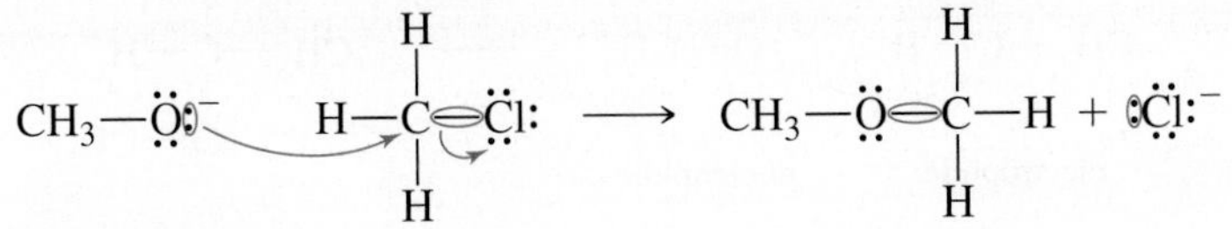

$$CH_3{-}\ddot{\underset{..}{O}}{:}^- + H{-}\underset{H}{\overset{H}{C}}{-}\ddot{\underset{..}{Cl}}{:} \longrightarrow CH_3{-}\ddot{\underset{..}{O}}{-}\underset{H}{\overset{H}{C}}{-}H + {:}\ddot{\underset{..}{Cl}}{:}^-$$

nucleophile (electron donor) — electrophile (electron acceptor)

The curved-arrow formalism is universally used for keeping track of the flow of electrons in reactions. We have also used this device (in Section 1-9, for example) to keep track of electrons in resonance structures as we imagined their "flow" in going from one resonance structure to another. Remember that electrons do not "flow" in resonance structures; they are simply delocalized. Still, the curved-arrow formalism helps our *minds* flow from one resonance structure to another. We will find ourselves constantly using these (red) curved arrows to keep track of electrons, both as reactants change to products and as we imagine additional resonance structures of a hybrid.

problem-solving **Hint**

Use one curved arrow for each pair of electrons participating in the reaction.

PROBLEM 1-19 (PARTIALLY SOLVED)

In the following acid–base reactions,

1. determine which species are acting as electrophiles (acids) and which are acting as nucleophiles (bases).
2. use the curved-arrow formalism to show the movement of electron pairs in these reactions, as well as the imaginary movement in the resonance hybrids of the products.
3. indicate which reactions are best termed Brønsted–Lowry acid–base reactions.

(a)

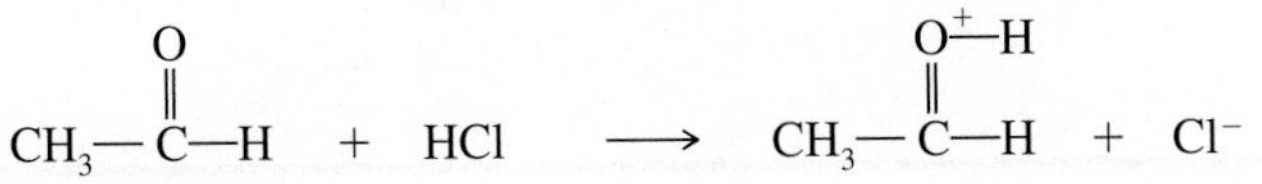

$$CH_3{-}\overset{\overset{O}{\|}}{C}{-}H + HCl \longrightarrow CH_3{-}\overset{\overset{O^+{-}H}{\|}}{C}{-}H + Cl^-$$

acetaldehyde

This reaction is a proton transfer from HCl to the C=O group of acetaldehyde. Therefore, it is a Brønsted–Lowry acid–base reaction, with HCl acting as the acid (proton donor) and acetaldehyde acting as the base (proton acceptor). Before drawing any curved arrows, remember that arrows must show the movement of electrons *from* the electron-pair donor (the base) *to* the electron-pair acceptor (the acid). An arrow must go *from* the electrons on acetaldehyde that form the bond *to* the hydrogen atom, and the bond to chlorine must break, with the chloride ion taking these electrons. Drawing these arrows is easier once we draw valid Lewis structures for all the reactants and products.

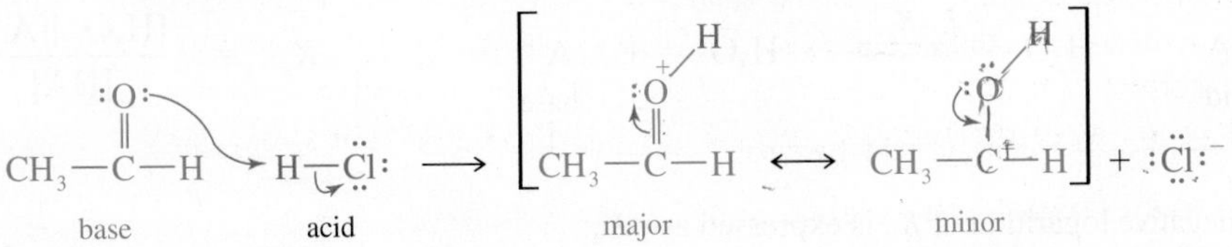

$$CH_3{-}\overset{\overset{:O:}{\|}}{C}{-}H + H{-}\ddot{\underset{..}{Cl}}{:} \longrightarrow \left[CH_3{-}\overset{\overset{:O^+{-}H}{\|}}{C}{-}H \longleftrightarrow CH_3{-}\overset{\overset{:\ddot{O}{-}H}{|}}{C^+}{-}H\right] + {:}\ddot{\underset{..}{Cl}}{:}^-$$

base — acid — major — minor

The resonance forms of the product show that a pair of electrons can be moved between the oxygen atom and the C=O pi bond. The positive charge is delocalized over the carbon and oxygen atoms, with most of the positive charge on oxygen because all octets are satisfied in that resonance structure.

problem-solving **Hint**

The curved arrows we use in mechanisms show the *flow of electrons* and not the movement of atoms. We will use these curved arrows consistently throughout this course.

(b)

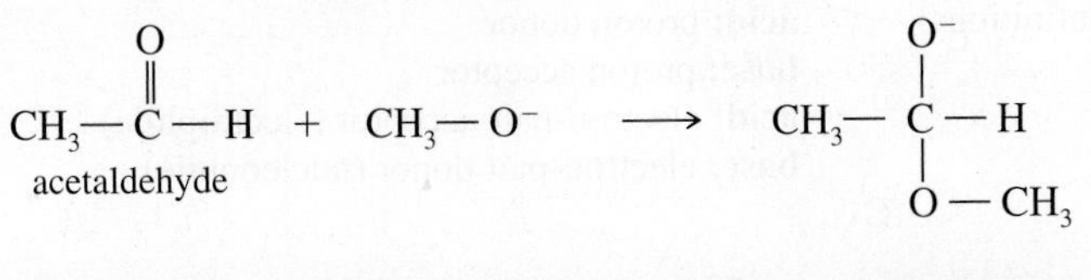

$$CH_3{-}\overset{\overset{O}{\|}}{C}{-}H + CH_3{-}O^- \longrightarrow CH_3{-}\underset{\underset{O-CH_3}{|}}{\overset{\overset{O^-}{|}}{C}}{-}H$$

acetaldehyde

In this case, no proton has been transferred, so this is not a Brønsted–Lowry acid–base reaction. Instead, a bond has formed between the C=O carbon atom and the oxygen of the $CH_3—O^-$ group. Drawing the Lewis structures helps to show that the $CH_3—O^-$ group (the nucleophile in this reaction) donates the electrons to form the new bond to acetaldehyde (the electrophile). This result agrees with our intuition that a negatively charged ion is likely to be electron-rich and therefore an electron donor.

$$CH_3—C(=O)—H + {}^-:\ddot{O}—CH_3 \longrightarrow CH_3—C(—O^-)(—OCH_3)—H$$

electrophile nucleophile

Notice that acetaldehyde acts as the nucleophile (Lewis base) in part (a) and as the electrophile (Lewis acid) in part (b). Like most organic compounds, acetaldehyde is both acidic and basic. It acts as a base if we add a strong enough acid to make it donate electrons or accept a proton. It acts as an acid if the base we add is strong enough to donate an electron pair or abstract a proton.

(c) $BH_3 + CH_3—O—CH_3 \longrightarrow CH_3—\overset{+}{O}(—{}^-BH_3)—CH_3$

(d) $CH_3—C(=O)—H + {}^-OH \longrightarrow CH_3—C(—O^-)(—OH)—H$

(e) $CH_3—C(=O)—H + {}^-OH \longrightarrow [H—CH_2—C(=O)—H \longleftrightarrow H—CH=C(—O^-)—H] + H_2O$

(f) $CH_3—NH_2 + CH_3—Cl \longrightarrow CH_3—\overset{+}{N}H_2—CH_3 + Cl^-$

1 Glossary

Each chapter ends with a glossary that summarizes the most important new terms in the chapter. These glossaries are more than just a dictionary to look up unfamiliar terms as you encounter them (the index serves that purpose). The glossary is one of the tools for reviewing the chapter. You can read carefully through the glossary to see if you understand and remember all the terms and associated chemistry mentioned there. Anything that seems unfamiliar should be reviewed by turning to the page number given in the glossary listing.

acid-dissociation constant (K_a) The equilibrium constant for the reaction of the acid with water to generate H_3O^+. (p. 23)

$$\underset{\text{acid}}{HA} + H_2O \underset{}{\overset{K_a}{\rightleftharpoons}} H_3O^+ + \underset{\text{base}}{A^-} \qquad K_a = \frac{[H_3O^+][A^-]}{[HA]}$$

conjugate acid–base pair (HA and A^-)

The negative logarithm of K_a is expressed as **pK_a**:

$$pK_a = -\log_{10} K_a$$

acids and **bases** (pp. 21–32)

(**Arrhenius** definitions)	**acid:** dissociates in water to give H_3O^+ **base:** dissociates in water to give ^-OH
(**Brønsted–Lowry** definitions)	**acid:** proton donor **base:** proton acceptor
(**Lewis** definitions)	**acid:** electron-pair acceptor (electrophile) **base:** electron-pair donor (nucleophile)

conjugate acid The acid that results from protonation of a base. (p. 23)
conjugate base The base that results from loss of a proton from an acid. (p. 23)
covalent bonding Bonding that occurs by the sharing of electrons in the region between two nuclei. (pp. 7, 9)
single bond A covalent bond that involves the sharing of one pair of electrons. (p. 8)
double bond A covalent bond that involves the sharing of two pairs of electrons. (p. 8)
triple bond A covalent bond that involves the sharing of three pairs of electrons. (p. 8)
curved-arrow formalism A method of drawing curved arrows to keep track of electron movement from nucleophile to electrophile (or within a molecule) during the course of a reaction. (p. 31)
degenerate orbitals Orbitals with identical energies. (p. 4)
dipole moment (μ) A measure of the polarity of a bond (or a molecule), proportional to the product of the charge separation times the bond length. (p. 10)
electron density The relative probability of finding an electron in a certain region of space. (p. 3)
electronegativity A measure of an element's ability to attract electrons. Elements with higher electronegativities attract electrons more strongly. (p. 10)
electrophile An electron-pair acceptor (Lewis acid). (p. 29)
electrostatic potential map (EPM) A computer-calculated molecular representation that uses colors to show the charge distribution in a molecule. In most cases, the EPM uses red to show electron-rich regions (most negative electrostatic potential) and blue or purple to show electron-poor regions (most positive electrostatic potential). The intermediate colors orange, yellow, and green show regions with intermediate electrostatic potentials. (p. 10)
empirical formula The ratios of atoms in a compound. (p. 20) See also **molecular formula**.
formal charges A method for keeping track of charges, showing what charge would be on an atom in a particular Lewis structure. (p. 10)
Hund's rule When there are two or more unfilled orbitals of the same energy (degenerate orbitals), the lowest-energy configuration places the electrons in different orbitals (with parallel spins) rather than paired in the same orbital. (p. 6)
ionic bonding Bonding that occurs by the attraction of oppositely charged ions. Ionic bonding usually results in the formation of a large, three-dimensional crystal lattice. (p. 7)
isotopes Atoms with the same number of protons but different numbers of neutrons; atoms of the same element but with different atomic masses. (p. 3)
Lewis acid, Lewis base See **acids** and **bases**.
Lewis structure A structural formula that shows all valence electrons, with the bonds symbolized by dashes (—) or by pairs of dots, and nonbonding electrons symbolized by dots. (p. 7)
line–angle formula (skeletal structure, stick figure) A shorthand structural formula with bonds represented by lines. Carbon atoms are implied wherever two lines meet or a line begins or bends. Atoms other than C and H are drawn in, but hydrogen atoms are not shown unless they are on an atom that is drawn. Each carbon atom is assumed to have enough hydrogens to give it four bonds. (p. 19)

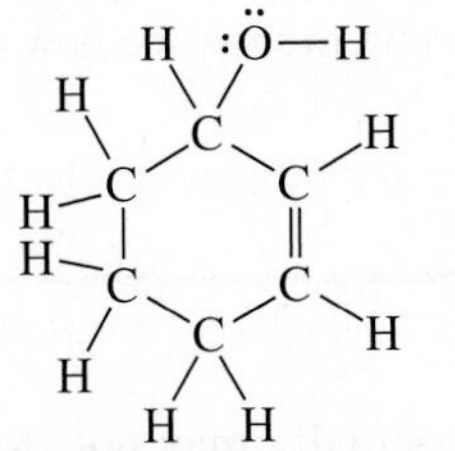

Lewis structure of 2-cyclohexenol

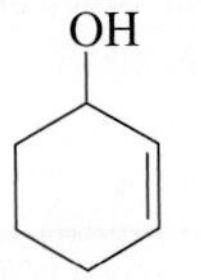

2-cyclohexenol
equivalent line–angle formula

lone pair A pair of nonbonding electrons. (p. 8)
molecular formula The number of atoms of each element in one molecule of a compound. The **empirical formula** simply gives the ratios of atoms of the different elements. For example, the molecular formula of glucose is $C_6H_{12}O_6$. Its empirical formula is CH_2O. Neither the molecular formula nor the empirical formula gives structural information. (p. 20)
node A region in an orbital with zero electron density. (p. 4)
nodal plane A flat (planar) region of space with zero electron density. (p. 4)
nonbonding electrons Valence electrons that are not used for bonding. A pair of nonbonding electrons is often called a **lone pair**. (p. 8)
nucleophile An electron-pair donor (Lewis base). (p. 30)
octet rule Atoms generally form bonding arrangements that give them filled shells of electrons (noble-gas configurations). For the second-row elements, this configuration has eight valence electrons. (p. 6)

orbital An allowed energy state for an electron bound to a nucleus; the probability function that defines the distribution of electron density in space. The *Pauli exclusion principle* states that up to two electrons can occupy each orbital if their spins are paired. (p. 3)
organic chemistry New definition: The chemistry of carbon compounds. Old definition: The study of compounds derived from living organisms and their natural products. (p. 1)
pH A measure of the acidity of a solution, defined as the negative logarithm (base 10) of the H_3O^+ concentration: $pH = -\log_{10}[H_3O^+]$ (p. 22)
polar covalent bond A covalent bond in which electrons are shared unequally. A bond with equal sharing of electrons is called a **nonpolar covalent bond**. (p. 9)
resonance hybrid A molecule or ion for which two or more valid Lewis structures can be drawn, differing only in the placement of the valence electrons. These Lewis structures are called **resonance forms** or **resonance structures**. Individual resonance forms do not exist, but we can estimate their relative energies. The more important (lower-energy) structures are called **major contributors**, and the less important (higher-energy) structures are called **minor contributors**. When a charge is spread over two or more atoms by resonance, it is said to be **delocalized** and the molecule is said to be **resonance stabilized.** (pp. 13–16)
structural formulas A **complete structural formula** (such as a Lewis structure) shows all the atoms and bonds in the molecule. A **condensed structural formula** shows each central atom along with the atoms bonded to it. A **line–angle formula** (sometimes called a **skeletal structure** or **stick figure**) assumes that there is a carbon atom wherever two lines meet or a line begins or ends. See Section 1-10 for examples. (p. 17)
valence The number of bonds an atom usually forms. (p. 9)
valence electrons Those electrons that are in the outermost shell. (p. 6)
Vitalism The belief that syntheses of organic compounds require the presence of a "vital force." (p. 1)

Essential Problem-Solving Skills in Chapter I

1. Draw and interpret Lewis, condensed, and line–angle structural formulas. Show which atoms bear formal charges.
2. Draw resonance forms, and use them to predict stabilities.
3. Calculate empirical and molecular formulas from elemental compositions.
4. Predict relative acidities and basicities based on structure, bonding, and resonance of conjugate acid–base pairs.
5. Calculate, use, and interpret values of K_a and pK_a.
6. Identify nucleophiles (Lewis bases) and electrophiles (Lewis acids), and write equations for Lewis acid–base reactions using curved arrows to show the flow of electrons.

Study Problems

It's easy to fool yourself into thinking you understand organic chemistry when you actually may not. As you read through this book, all the facts and ideas may make sense, yet you have not learned to combine and use those facts and ideas. An examination is a painful time to learn that you do not really understand the material.

The best way to learn organic chemistry is to use it. You will certainly need to read and reread all the material in the chapter, but this level of understanding is just the beginning. Problems are provided so you can work with the ideas, applying them to new compounds and new reactions that you have never seen before. By working problems, you force yourself to use the material and fill in the gaps in your understanding. You also increase your level of self-confidence and your ability to do well on exams.

Several kinds of problems are included in each chapter. There are problems within the chapters, providing examples and drill for the material as it is covered. Work these problems as you read through the chapter to ensure your understanding as you go along. Answers to many of these in-chapter problems are found at the back of this book. Study Problems at the end of each chapter give you additional experience using the material, and they force you to think in depth about the ideas. Problems with red stars (*) are more difficult problems that require extra thought and perhaps some extension of the material presented in the chapter. Some of the Study Problems have short answers in the back of this book, and all of them have detailed answers in the accompanying Solutions Manual.

Taking organic chemistry without working the problems is like skydiving without a parachute. Initially there is a breezy sense of freedom and daring. But then, there is the inevitable jolt that comes at the end for those who went unprepared.

1-20 Define and give an example for each term.
(a) isotopes **(b)** orbital **(c)** node
(d) degenerate orbitals **(e)** valence electrons **(f)** ionic bonding
(g) covalent bonding **(h)** Lewis structure **(i)** nonbonding electrons
(j) single bond **(k)** double bond **(l)** triple bond
(m) polar bond **(n)** formal charges **(o)** resonance forms
(p) molecular formula **(q)** empirical formula **(r)** Arrhenius acid and base
(s) Brønsted–Lowry acid and base **(t)** Lewis acid and base **(u)** electrophile
(v) nucleophile

1-21 Name the element that corresponds to each electronic configuration.
(a) $1s^2 2s^2 2p^2$ **(b)** $1s^2 2s^2 2p^4$ **(c)** $1s^2 2s^2 2p^6 3s^2 3p^3$ **(d)** $1s^2 2s^2 2p^6 3s^2 3p^5$

1-22 There is a small portion of the periodic table that you must know to do organic chemistry. Construct this part from memory, using the following steps.
(a) From memory, make a list of the elements in the first two rows of the periodic table, together with their numbers of valence electrons.
(b) Use this list to construct the first two rows of the periodic table.
(c) Organic compounds often contain sulfur, phosphorus, chlorine, bromine, and iodine. Add these elements to your periodic table.

1-23 For each compound, state whether its bonding is covalent, ionic, or a mixture of covalent and ionic.
(a) NaCl **(b)** NaOH **(c)** CH_3Li **(d)** CH_2Cl_2
(e) $NaOCH_3$ **(f)** HCO_2Na **(g)** CF_4

1-24 **(a)** Both PCl_3 and PCl_5 are stable compounds. Draw Lewis structures for these two compounds.
(b) NCl_3 is a known compound, but all attempts to synthesize NCl_5 have failed. Draw Lewis structures for NCl_3 and a hypothetical NCl_5, and explain why NCl_5 is an unlikely structure.

1-25 Draw a Lewis structure for each species.
(a) N_2H_4 **(b)** N_2H_2 **(c)** $(CH_3)_2NH_2Cl$ **(d)** CH_3CN
(e) CH_3CHO **(f)** $CH_3S(O)CH_3$ **(g)** H_2SO_4 **(h)** CH_3NCO
(i) $CH_3OSO_2OCH_3$ **(j)** $CH_3C(NH)CH_3$ **(k)** $(CH_3)_3CNO$

1-26 Draw a Lewis structure for each compound. Include all nonbonding pairs of electrons.
(a) $CH_3COCH_2CHCHCOOH$ **(b)** $NCCH_2COCH_2CHO$
(c) $CH_2CHCH(OH)CH_2CO_2H$ **(d)** $CH_2CHC(CH_3)CHCOOCH_3$

1-27 Draw a line–angle formula for each compound in Problem 1-26.

1-28 Draw Lewis structures for
(a) two compounds of formula C_4H_{10} **(b)** two compounds of formula C_2H_6O
(c) two compounds of formula C_2H_7N **(d)** three compounds of formula C_2H_7NO
(e) three compounds of formula $C_3H_8O_2$ **(f)** three compounds of formula C_2H_4O

1-29 Draw a complete structural formula and a condensed structural formula for
(a) three compounds of formula C_3H_8O **(b)** five compounds of formula C_3H_6O

1-30 Some of the following molecular formulas correspond to stable compounds. When possible, draw a stable structure for each formula.

CH_2 CH_3 CH_4 CH_5
C_2H_2 C_2H_3 C_2H_4 C_2H_5 C_2H_6 C_2H_7
C_3H_3 C_3H_4 C_3H_5 C_3H_6 C_3H_7 C_3H_8 C_3H_9

Can you propose a general rule for the numbers of hydrogen atoms in stable hydrocarbons?

1-31 Draw complete Lewis structures, including lone pairs, for the following compounds.

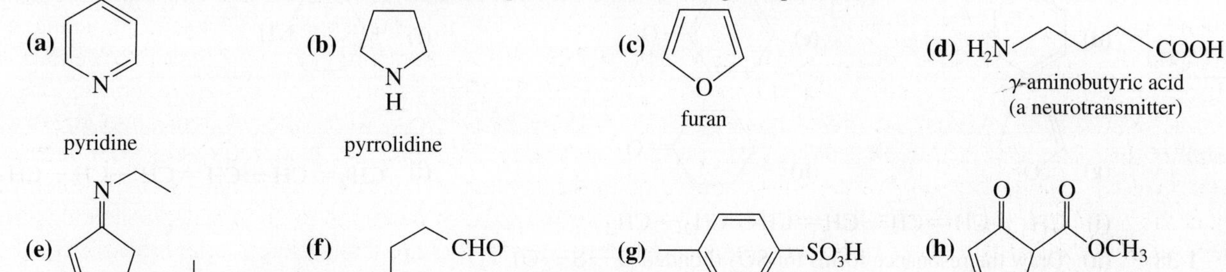

1-32 Give the molecular formula of each compound shown in Problem 1-31.

1-33 Compound X, isolated from lanolin (sheep's wool fat), has the pungent aroma of dirty sweatsocks. A careful analysis showed that compound X contains 62.0% carbon and 10.4% hydrogen. No nitrogen or halogen was found.

(a) Compute an empirical formula for compound X.
(b) A molecular weight determination showed that compound X has a molecular weight of approximately 117. Find the molecular formula of compound X.
(c) Many possible structures have this molecular formula. Draw complete structural formulas for four of them.

1-34 For each of the following structures,

1. Draw a Lewis structure; fill in any nonbonding electrons.
2. Calculate the formal charge on each atom other than hydrogen. All are electrically neutral except as noted.

(a) $[H_2C{=}N{=}N \longleftrightarrow H_2C{-}N{\equiv}N]$ **(b)** $(CH_3)_3NO$ (trimethylamine oxide)

(c) $[CH_2{=}CH{-}CH_2]^+$ **(d)** CH_3NO_2 **(e)** $[(CH_3)_3O]^+$

1-35
1. From what you remember of electronegativities, show the direction of the dipole moments of the following bonds.
2. In each case, predict whether the dipole moment is relatively large (electronegativity difference >0.5) or small.

(a) C—Cl **(b)** C—H **(c)** C—Li **(d)** C—N **(e)** C—O
(f) C—B **(g)** C—Mg **(h)** N—H **(i)** O—H **(j)** C—Br

1-36 Determine whether the following pairs of structures are actually different compounds or simply resonance forms of the same compounds.

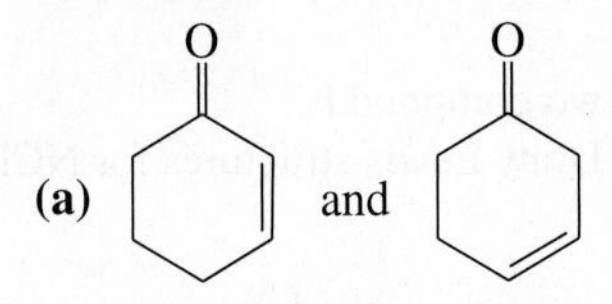

(a) and **(b)** and

(c) and **(d)** $CH_2{=}C(O^-){-}H$ and $\overset{-}{C}H_2{-}C({=}O){-}H$

(e) $H{-}C({=}O){-}CH_2{-}H$ and $H{-}C(OH){=}CH{-}H$ **(f)** $H{-}\overset{+}{C}H{-}OH$ and $H{-}CH{=}\overset{+}{O}{-}H$

(g) $H{-}C({=}O){-}NH_2$ and $H{-}C(O^-){=}\overset{+}{N}H_2$ **(h)** $CH_2{=}C{=}O$ and $H{-}C{\equiv}C{-}OH$

(i) $CH_2{=}CH{-}\overset{+}{C}H_2$ and $\overset{+}{C}H_2{-}CH{=}CH_2$ **(j)** $CH_3{-}C({=}O){-}CH{=}CH_2$ and $CH_3{-}C(O^-){=}CH{-}\overset{+}{C}H_2$

1-37 Draw the important resonance forms to show the delocalization of charges in the following ions.

(a) $CH_3{-}C({=}O){-}\overset{-}{C}H_2$ **(b)** $H{-}C({=}O){-}CH{=}CH{-}\overset{-}{C}H_2$ **(c)** $C_6H_5{-}\overset{+}{C}H_2$

(d) **(e)** $C_6H_5{-}O^-$ **(f)**

(g) **(h)** **(i)** $CH_2{=}CH{-}CH{=}CH{-}\overset{+}{C}H{-}CH_3$

(j) $CH_3{-}CH{=}CH{-}CH{=}CH{-}CH_2{-}\overset{+}{C}H_2$

1-38 **(a)** Draw the resonance forms for SO_2 (bonded O—S—O).
(b) Draw the resonance forms for ozone (bonded O—O—O).
(c) Sulfur dioxide has one more resonance form than ozone. Explain why this structure is not possible for ozone.

***1-39** The following compound can become protonated on any of the three nitrogen atoms. One of these nitrogens is much more basic than the others, however.

(a) Draw the important resonance forms of the products of protonation on each of the three nitrogen atoms.

(b) Determine which nitrogen atom is the most basic.

$$CH_3-NH-C(=NH)-NH_2$$

1-40 In the following sets of resonance forms, label the major and minor contributors and state which structures would be of equal energy. Add any missing resonance forms.

(a) $\left[CH_3-\ddot{C}H^{-}-C\equiv N: \longleftrightarrow CH_3-CH=C=\ddot{N}:^{-}\right]$

(b) $\left[CH_3-C(O^-)=CH-\overset{+}{C}H-CH_3 \longleftrightarrow CH_3-\overset{+}{C}(O^-)-CH=CH-CH_3\right]$

(c) $\left[CH_3-C(=O)-\overset{-}{C}H-C(=O)-CH_3 \longleftrightarrow CH_3-C(O^-)=CH-C(=O)-CH_3\right]$

(d) $\left[CH_3-\overset{-}{C}H-CH=CH-NO_2 \longleftrightarrow CH_3-CH=CH-\overset{-}{C}H-NO_2\right]$

(e) $\left[CH_3-CH_2-\overset{+}{C}(NH_2)-NH_2 \longleftrightarrow CH_3-CH_2-C(NH_2)=\overset{+}{N}H_2\right]$

1-41 For each pair of ions, determine which ion is more stable. Use resonance forms to explain your answers.

(a) $CH_3-\overset{+}{C}H-CH_3$ or $CH_3-\overset{+}{C}H-OCH_3$

(b) $CH_2=CH-\overset{+}{C}H-CH_3$ or $CH_2=CH-CH_2-\overset{+}{C}H_2$

(c) $\overset{-}{C}H_2-CH_3$ or $\overset{-}{C}H_2-C\equiv N:$

(d) (cyclohexene with $\overset{+}{C}H_2$ on the alkene carbon) or (cyclohexene with $\overset{+}{C}H_2$ on the carbon allylic to the double bond)

(e) $CH_3-\overset{+}{C}(CH_3)-N(CH_3)-CH_3$ or $CH_3-\overset{+}{C}(CH_3)-CH(CH_3)-CH_3$

1-42 Rank the following species in order of increasing acidity. Explain your reasons for ordering them as you do.

$HF \quad NH_3 \quad H_2SO_4 \quad CH_3OH \quad CH_3COOH \quad H_3O^+ \quad H_2O$

1-43 Rank the following species in order of increasing basicity. Explain your reasons for ordering them as you do.

$NH_3 \quad CH_3O^- \quad H_2O \quad CH_3COO^- \quad NaOH \quad NH_2^- \quad HSO_4^-$

1-44 The K_a of phenylacetic acid is 5.2×10^{-5}, and the pK_a of propionic acid is 4.87.

$$C_6H_5-CH_2-C(=O)-OH \qquad CH_3-CH_2-C(=O)-OH$$

phenylacetic acid, $K_a = 5.2 \times 10^{-5}$ propionic acid, p$K_a = 4.87$

(a) Calculate the pK_a of phenylacetic acid and the K_a of propionic acid.

(b) Which of these is the stronger acid? Calculate how much stronger an acid it is.

(c) Predict whether the following equilibrium will favor the reactants or the products.

$$C_6H_5-CH_2COO^- + CH_3CH_2COOH \rightleftarrows C_6H_5-CH_2COOH + CH_3CH_2COO^-$$

1-45 Label the reactants in these acid–base reactions as Lewis acids (electrophiles) or Lewis bases (nucleophiles). Use curved arrows to show the movement of electron pairs in the reactions.

(a) $CH_3\ddot{O}{:}^- + CH_3{-}\ddot{Cl}{:} \longrightarrow CH_3{-}\ddot{O}{-}CH_3 + {:}\ddot{Cl}{:}^-$

(b) $CH_3{-}\ddot{O}^+(CH_3){-}CH_3 + {:}\ddot{O}(H){-}H \longrightarrow CH_3{-}\ddot{O}{:}(CH_3) + CH_3{-}\ddot{O}^+(H){-}H$

(c) $H{-}C({=}O){-}H + {:}NH_3 \longrightarrow H{-}C({:}\ddot{O}{:}^-)({}^+NH_3){-}H$

(d) $CH_3{-}\ddot{N}H_2 + CH_3{-}CH_2{-}\ddot{Cl}{:} \longrightarrow CH_3{-}\overset{+}{N}H_2{-}CH_2CH_3 + {:}\ddot{Cl}{:}^-$

(e) $CH_3{-}C({=}\ddot{O}){-}CH_3 + H_2SO_4 \longrightarrow CH_3{-}C({=}\overset{+}{\ddot{O}}{-}H){-}CH_3 + HSO_4^-$

(f) $(CH_3)_3CCl + AlCl_3 \longrightarrow (CH_3)_3C^+ + {}^-AlCl_4$

(g) $CH_3{-}C({=}\ddot{O}){-}CH_3 + {}^-{:}\ddot{O}{-}H \longrightarrow CH_3{-}C({:}\ddot{O}{:}^-){=}CH_2 + H{-}\ddot{O}{-}H$

(h) $CH_2{=}CH_2 + BF_3 \longrightarrow \overset{-}{B}F_3{-}CH_2{-}\overset{+}{C}H_2$

(i) $\overset{-}{B}F_3{-}CH_2{-}\overset{+}{C}H_2 + CH_2{=}CH_2 \longrightarrow \overset{-}{B}F_3{-}CH_2{-}CH_2{-}CH_2{-}\overset{+}{C}H_2$

1-46 Predict the products of the following acid–base reactions.

(a) $H_2SO_4 + CH_3COO^- \rightleftharpoons$

(b) $CH_3COOH + (CH_3)_3N{:} \rightleftharpoons$

(c) $C_6H_5{-}C({=}O){-}OH + {}^-OH \rightleftharpoons$

(d) $(CH_3)_3\overset{+}{N}H + {}^-OH \rightleftharpoons$

(e) $HO{-}C({=}O){-}OH + 2\ {}^-OH \rightleftharpoons$

(f) $H_2O + NH_3 \rightleftharpoons$

(g) $HCOOH + CH_3O^- \rightleftharpoons$

1-47 The following compounds are listed in increasing order of acidity. In each case, the most acidic proton is shown in red.

$C_6H_5{-}C({=}O){-}CH_2{-}H$ — **W**, pKa = 25

$C_6H_5{-}C({=}O){-}NH{-}H$ — **X**, pKa = 23

$C_6H_5{-}C({=}O){-}N(OH){-}H$ — **Y**, pKa = 8.8

$C_6H_5{-}C({=}O){-}O{-}H$ — **Z**, pKa = 4.2

(a) Show the structure of the conjugate base of each acid, including any resonance forms.
(b) Explain why **X** is a stronger acid than **W**.
(c) Explain why **Y** is a stronger acid than **X**.
(d) Explain why **Z** is a stronger acid than **Y**.

1-48 Amides such as acetamide ($CH_3{-}C({=}O){-}NH_2$) are much weaker bases than amines, such as ethylamine ($CH_3CH_2NH_2$).
(a) Use resonance forms to show why the nonbonding electrons on the nitrogen atom of the amide are very weakly basic.
(b) Strong acid is required to protonate the amide. Predict where acetamide will undergo protonation, and use resonance forms to show why the site you have chosen is more basic. (*Hint:* To compare basicities, compare the stabilities of the conjugate acids.)

***1-49** Methyllithium (CH_3Li) is often used as a base in organic reactions.
(a) Predict the products of the following acid–base reaction.

$$CH_3CH_2-OH \ + \ CH_3-Li \ \rightarrow$$

(b) What is the conjugate acid of CH_3Li? Would you expect CH_3Li to be a strong base or a weak base?

1-50 The following four compounds can all react as acids.

$$CH_3-\overset{O}{\overset{\|}{C}}-OH \qquad CF_3-\overset{O}{\overset{\|}{C}}-OH \qquad CH_3-\overset{O}{\overset{\|}{C}}-OOH \qquad CF_3CH_2-\overset{O}{\overset{\|}{C}}-OH$$

(a) For each compound, show its conjugate base. Show any resonance forms if applicable.
(b) Rank the conjugate bases in the order you would predict, from most stable to least stable.
(c) Rank the original compounds in order, from strongest acid to weakest acid.

1-51 The following compounds can all react as bases.

$$CH_3CH_2-NH_2 \qquad CH_3-\overset{O}{\overset{\|}{C}}-NH_2 \qquad NaOH \qquad CH_3CH_2-OH$$

(a) For each compound, show its conjugate acid. Show any resonance forms if applicable.
(b) Rank the conjugate acids in the order you would predict, from most stable to least stable.
(c) Rank the original compounds in order, from strongest base to weakest base.

1-52 The following compounds can all react as acids.

$$CH_3-\overset{O}{\overset{\|}{C}}-OH \qquad CH_3-\overset{O}{\overset{\|}{C}}-NH_2 \qquad CH_3-\overset{O}{\overset{\|}{S}}-OH \qquad CH_3-\underset{\underset{O}{\|}}{\overset{O}{\overset{\|}{S}}}-OH$$

(a) For each compound, show its conjugate base. Show any resonance forms if applicable.
(b) Rank the conjugate bases in the order you would predict, from most stable to least stable.
(c) Rank the original compounds in order, from strongest acid to weakest acid.

***1-53** In 1934, Edward A. Doisy of Washington University extracted 3000 lb of hog ovaries to isolate a few milligrams of pure estradiol, a potent female hormone. Doisy burned 5.00 mg of this precious sample in oxygen and found that 14.54 mg of CO_2 and 3.97 mg of H_2O were generated.
(a) Determine the empirical formula of estradiol.
(b) The molecular weight of estradiol was later determined to be 272. Determine the molecular formula of estradiol.

***1-54** The pK_a of ascorbic acid (vitamin C, page 2) is 4.17, showing that it is slightly more acidic than acetic acid (CH_3COOH, pK_a 4.74).
(a) Show the four different conjugate bases that would be formed by deprotonation of the four different OH groups in ascorbic acid.
(b) Compare the stabilities of these four conjugate bases, and predict which OH group of ascorbic acid is the most acidic.
(c) Compare the most stable conjugate base of ascorbic acid with the conjugate base of acetic acid, and suggest why these two compounds have similar acidities, even though ascorbic acid lacks the carboxylic acid (COOH) group.

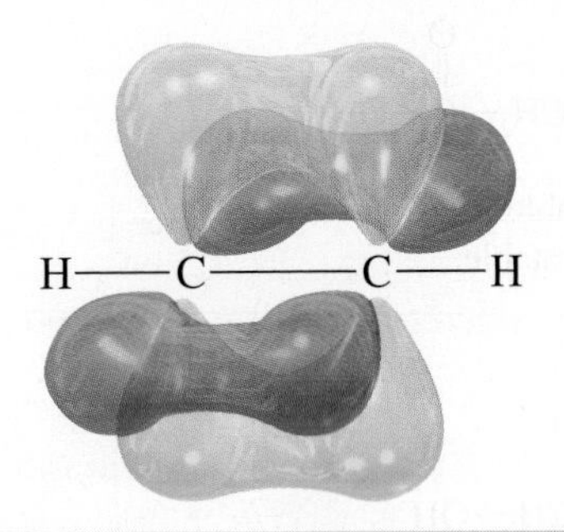

STRUCTURE AND PROPERTIES OF ORGANIC MOLECULES

CHAPTER

2

In Chapter 1, we considered how atoms bond together to gain noble-gas configurations, forming molecules in the process. Using the octet rule, we drew Lewis structures for organic molecules and used these diagrams to determine which bonds are single bonds, double bonds, and triple bonds. We discussed various ways of drawing organic structures, and we saw how resonance structures represent molecules whose actual bonding cannot be described by a single Lewis structure.

Chapter 1 did not explain the actual shapes and properties of organic molecules. To understand these aspects of molecular structure we need to consider how the atomic orbitals on an atom mix to form *hybrid atomic orbitals* and how orbitals on different atoms combine to form *molecular orbitals*. In this chapter, we look more closely at how combinations of orbitals account for the shapes and properties we observe in organic molecules.

2-1 Wave Properties of Electrons in Orbitals

We like to picture the atom as a miniature solar system, with the electrons orbiting around the nucleus. This solar system picture satisfies our intuition, but it does not accurately reflect today's understanding of the atom. About 1923, Louis de Broglie suggested that the properties of electrons in atoms are better explained by treating the electrons as waves rather than as particles.

There are two general kinds of waves, *traveling waves* and *standing waves*. Examples of traveling waves are the sound waves that carry a thunderclap and the water waves that form the wake of a boat. Standing waves vibrate in a fixed location. Standing waves are found inside an organ pipe, where the rush of air creates a vibrating air column, and in the wave pattern of a guitar string when it is plucked. An electron in an atomic orbital is like a stationary, bound vibration: a standing wave.

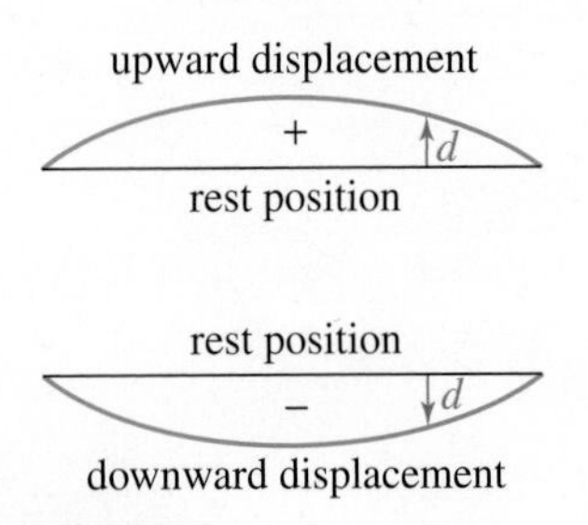

FIGURE 2-1
A standing wave. The fundamental frequency of a guitar string is a standing wave with the string alternately displaced upward and downward.

To understand the features of an orbital (a three-dimensional standing wave) more easily, let's consider the vibration of a guitar string as a one-dimensional analogy (see Figure 2-1). If you pluck a guitar string at its middle, a standing wave results. In this mode of vibration, all of the string is displaced upward for a fraction of a second, then downward for an equal time. An instantaneous picture of the waveform shows the string displaced in a smooth curve either upward or downward, depending on the exact instant of the picture.

The waveform of a 1*s* orbital is like this guitar string, except that it is three-dimensional. The orbital can be described by its **wave function**, ψ, which is the mathematical description of the shape of the wave as it vibrates. All of the wave is positive in sign for a brief instant; then it is negative in sign. The electron density

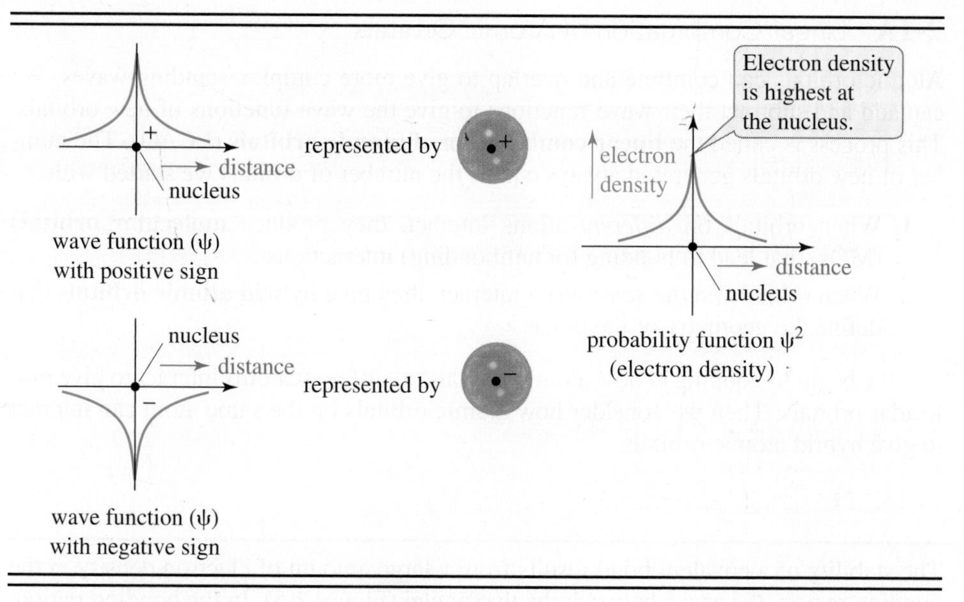

■ **FIGURE 2-2**
The 1*s* orbital. The 1*s* orbital is similar to the fundamental vibration of a guitar string. The wave function is instantaneously all positive or all negative. The square of the wave function gives the electron density. A circle with a nucleus is used to represent the spherically symmetrical *s* orbital.

at any point is given by ψ^2, the square of the wave function at that point. *Notice that the plus sign and the minus sign of these wave functions are not charges. The plus or minus sign is the instantaneous phase of the constantly changing wave function.* The 1*s* orbital is spherically symmetrical, and it is often represented by a circle (representing a sphere) with a nucleus in the center and with a plus or minus sign to indicate the instantaneous sign of the wave function (Figure 2-2).

If you gently place a finger at the center of a guitar string while plucking the string, your finger keeps the midpoint of the string from moving. The displacement (movement + or −) at the midpoint is always zero; this point is a **node**. The string now vibrates in two parts, with the two halves vibrating in opposite directions. We say that the two halves of the string are *out of phase*: When one is displaced upward, the other is displaced downward. Figure 2-3 shows this first *harmonic* of the guitar string.

The first harmonic of the guitar string resembles the 2*p* orbital (Figure 2-4). We have drawn the 2*p* orbital as two "lobes," separated by a node (a nodal plane). The two lobes of the *p* orbital are out of phase with each other. Whenever the wave function has a plus sign in one lobe, it has a minus sign in the other lobe. When phase relationships are important, organic chemists often represent the phases with colors. Figures 2-1 and 2-2 use blue for regions with a positive phase, and green for a negative phase.

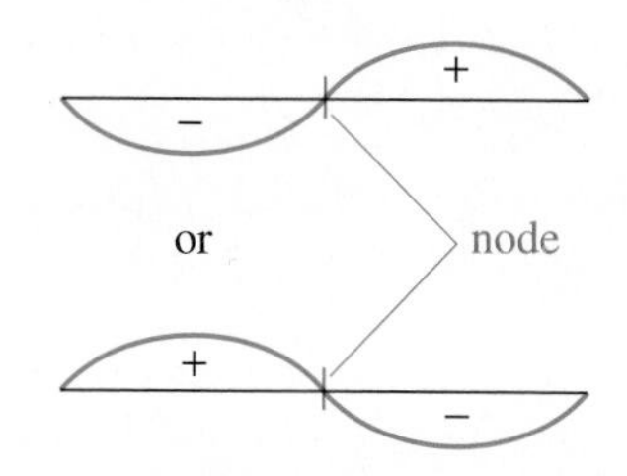

■ **FIGURE 2-3**
First harmonic of a guitar string. The two halves of the string are separated by a node, a point with zero displacement. The two halves vibrate out of phase with each other.

nodal plane
nucleus
represented by
nucleus
wave function (instantaneous picture)
nodal plane
nodal plane
nucleus
represented by
nucleus
equivalent wave function (instantaneous picture)
nodal plane

■ **FIGURE 2-4**
The 2*p* orbital. The 2*p* orbital has two lobes, separated by a nodal plane. The two lobes are out of phase with each other. When one has a plus sign, the other has a minus sign.

2-1A Linear Combination of Atomic Orbitals

Atomic orbitals can combine and overlap to give more complex standing waves. We can add and subtract their wave functions to give the wave functions of new orbitals. This process is called the **linear combination of atomic orbitals** (LCAO). The number of new orbitals generated always equals the number of orbitals we started with.

problem-solving **Hint**

When orbitals combine to form hybrid atomic orbitals or molecular orbitals, the number of orbitals formed always equals the number of orbitals that combine to form them.

1. When orbitals on *different* atoms interact, they produce **molecular orbitals** (MOs) that lead to bonding (or antibonding) interactions.
2. When orbitals on the *same* atom interact, they give **hybrid atomic orbitals** that define the geometry of the bonds.

We begin by looking at how atomic orbitals on different atoms interact to give molecular orbitals. Then we consider how atomic orbitals on the same atom can interact to give hybrid atomic orbitals.

2-2 Molecular Orbitals

The stability of a covalent bond results from a large amount of electron density in the bonding region, the space between the two nuclei (Figure 2-5). In the bonding region, the electrons are close to both nuclei, lowering the overall energy. The bonding electrons also mask the positive charges of the nuclei, so the nuclei do not repel each other as much as they would otherwise.

There is always an optimum distance for the two bonded nuclei. If they are too far apart, their attraction for the bonding electrons is diminished. If they are too close together, their electrostatic repulsion pushes them apart. The internuclear distance where attraction and repulsion are balanced, which also gives the minimum energy (the strongest bond), is the *bond length.*

bonding region

nucleus 1

electrons in this region attract both nuclei and mask the positive charges from repelling each other

nucleus 2

■ **FIGURE 2-5**
The bonding region. Electrons in the space between the two nuclei attract both nuclei and mask their positive charges. A bonding molecular orbital places a large amount of electron density in the bonding region.

2-2A The Hydrogen Molecule; Sigma Bonding

The hydrogen molecule is the simplest example of covalent bonding. As two hydrogen atoms approach each other, their 1*s* wave functions can add *constructively* so that they reinforce each other, or *destructively* so that they cancel out where they overlap. Figure 2-6 shows how the wave functions interact constructively when they are in phase and have the same sign in the region between the nuclei. The wave functions reinforce each other and increase the electron density in this bonding region. The result is a **bonding molecular orbital** (bonding MO).

The bonding MO depicted in Figure 2-6 has most of its electron density centered *along the line connecting the nuclei.* This type of bond is called a *cylindrically symmetrical bond* or a **sigma bond (σ bond)**. Sigma bonds are the most common bonds in organic compounds. All single bonds in organic compounds are sigma bonds, and every double or triple bond contains one sigma bond. The electrostatic potential map of H_2 shows its cylindrically symmetrical sigma bond, with the highest electron density (red) in the bonding region between the two protons.

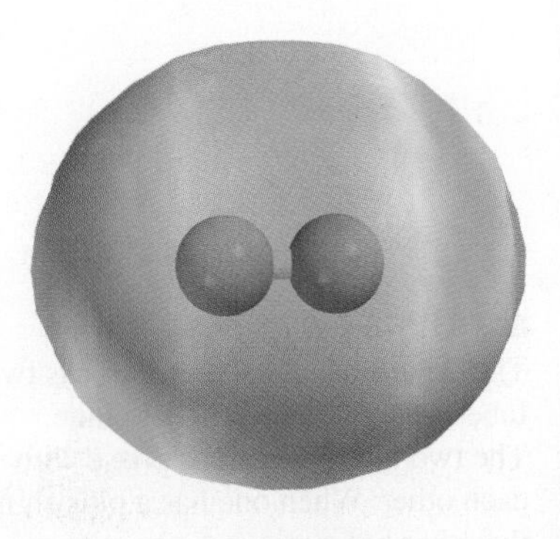

EPM of H_2

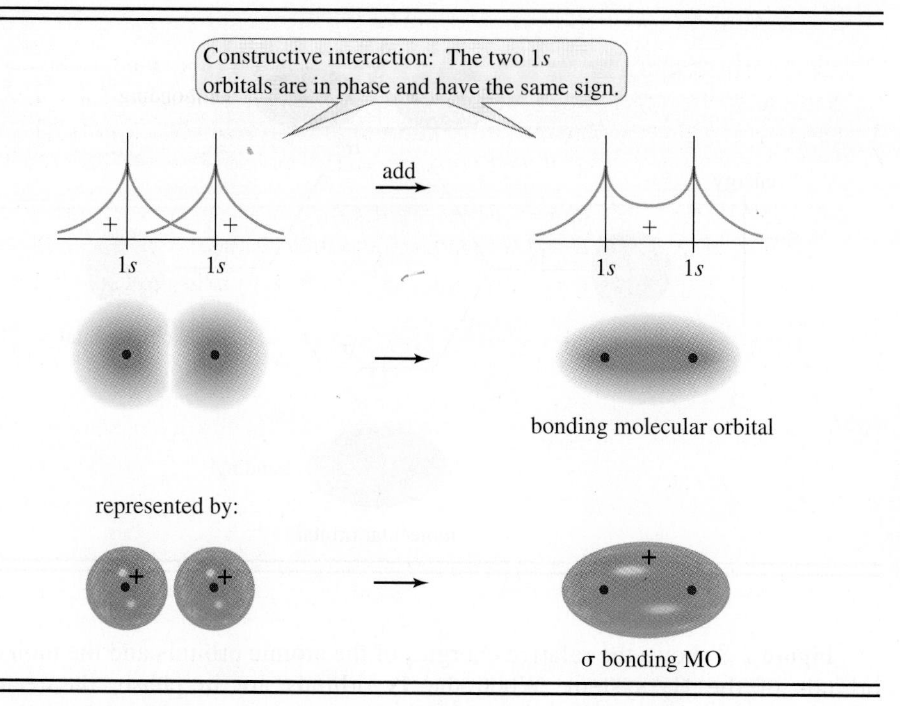

■ **FIGURE 2-6**
Formation of a σ bonding MO. When the $1s$ orbitals of two hydrogen atoms overlap in phase, they interact constructively to form a bonding MO. The electron density in the bonding region (between the nuclei) is increased. The result is a cylindrically symmetrical bond, or sigma (σ) bond.

When two hydrogen $1s$ orbitals overlap *out of phase* with each other, an **antibonding molecular orbital** results (Figure 2-7). The two $1s$ wave functions have opposite signs, so they tend to cancel out where they overlap. The result is a node (actually a nodal plane) separating the two atoms. The presence of a node separating the two nuclei usually indicates that the orbital is antibonding. The antibonding MO is designated σ^* to indicate an antibonding (*), cylindrically symmetrical (σ) molecular orbital.

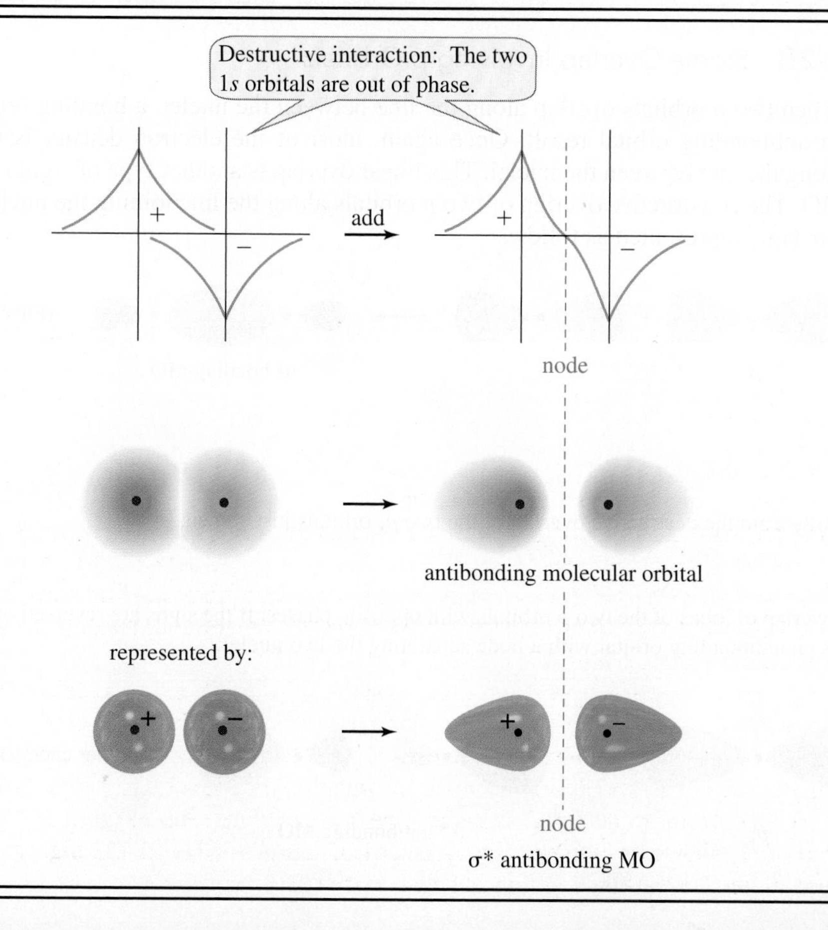

■ **FIGURE 2-7**
Formation of a σ^* antibonding MO. When two $1s$ orbitals overlap out of phase, they interact destructively to form an antibonding MO. The positive and negative values of the wave functions tend to cancel out in the region between the nuclei, and a node separates the nuclei. We use an asterisk (*) to designate antibonding orbitals such as this sigma antibonding orbital, σ^*.

■ **FIGURE 2-8**
Relative energies of atomic and molecular orbitals. When the two hydrogen 1*s* orbitals overlap, a sigma bonding MO and a sigma antibonding MO result. The bonding MO is lower in energy than the atomic 1*s* orbital, and the antibonding orbital is higher in energy. Two electrons (represented by arrows) go into the bonding MO with opposite spins, forming a stable H_2 molecule. The antibonding orbital is vacant.

***problem-solving* Hint**

In stable compounds, most or all of the bonding orbitals will be filled, and most or all of the antibonding orbitals will be empty.

Figure 2-8 shows the relative energies of the atomic orbitals and the molecular orbitals of the H_2 system. When the 1*s* orbitals are in phase, the resulting molecular orbital is a σ bonding MO, with lower energy than that of a 1*s* atomic orbital. When two 1*s* orbitals overlap out of phase, they form an antibonding (σ^*) orbital with higher energy than that of a 1*s* atomic orbital. The two electrons in the H_2 system are found with paired spins in the sigma bonding MO, giving a stable H_2 molecule. Both bonding and antibonding orbitals exist in all molecules, but the antibonding orbitals (such as σ^*) are usually vacant in stable molecules.

2-2B Sigma Overlap Involving *p* Orbitals

When two *p* orbitals overlap along the line between the nuclei, a bonding orbital and an antibonding orbital result. Once again, most of the electron density is centered along the line between the nuclei. This linear overlap is another type of sigma bonding MO. The constructive overlap of two *p* orbitals along the line joining the nuclei forms a σ bond represented as follows:

p_x + p_x → σ bonding MO (lower energy)

SOLVED PROBLEM 2-1

Draw the σ^* antibonding orbital that results from the destructive overlap of the two p_x orbitals just shown.

SOLUTION

This orbital results from the destructive overlap of lobes of the two *p* orbitals with opposite phases. If the signs are reversed on one of the orbitals, adding the two orbitals gives an antibonding orbital with a node separating the two nuclei:

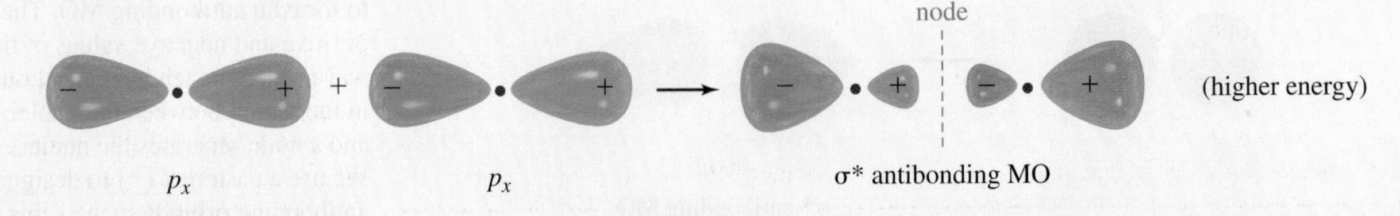

Overlap of an *s* orbital with a *p* orbital also gives a bonding MO and an antibonding MO, as shown in the following illustration. Constructive overlap of the *s* orbital with the p_x orbital gives a sigma bonding MO with its electron density centered along the line between the nuclei. Destructive overlap gives a antibonding orbital with a node separating the nuclei.

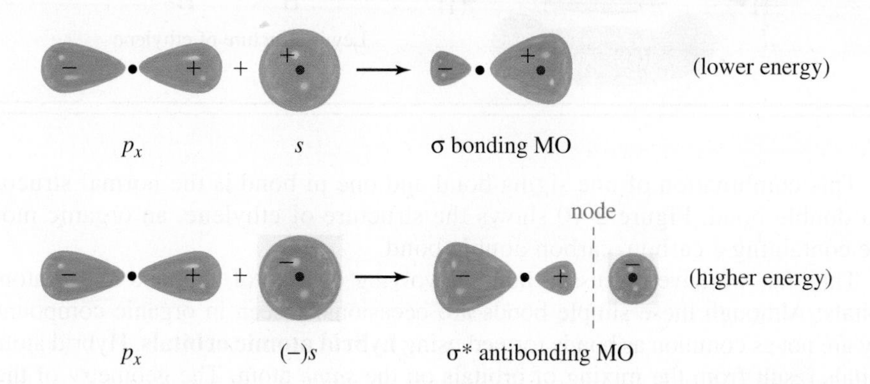

2-3 Pi Bonding

A **pi bond (π bond)** results from overlap between two *p* orbitals oriented perpendicular to the line connecting the nuclei (Figure 2-9). These parallel orbitals overlap sideways, with most of the electron density centered *above and below* the line connecting the nuclei. This overlap is parallel, not linear (a sigma bond is linear), so a pi molecular orbital is *not* cylindrically symmetrical. Figure 2-9 shows a π bonding MO and the corresponding π* antibonding MO.

2-3A Single and Double Bonds

A **double bond** requires the presence of four electrons in the bonding region between the nuclei. The first pair of electrons goes into the sigma bonding MO, forming a strong sigma bond. The second pair of electrons cannot go into the same orbital or the same space. It goes into a pi bonding MO, with its electron density centered above and below the sigma bond.

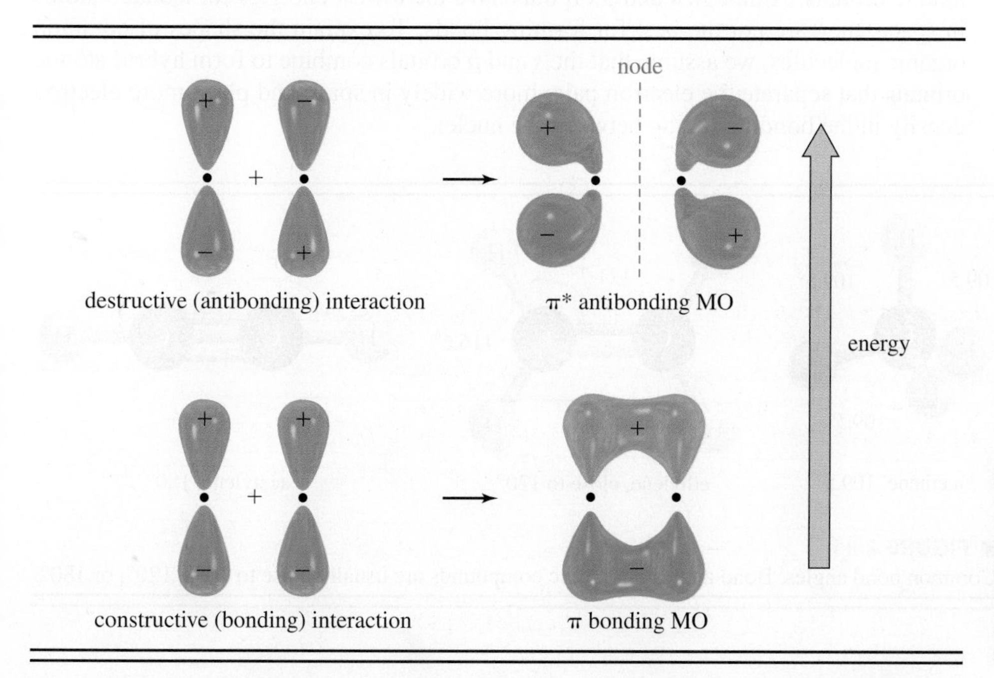

■ FIGURE 2-9
Pi bonding and antibonding molecular orbitals. The sideways overlap of two *p* orbitals leads to a π bonding MO and a π* antibonding MO. A pi bond is not as strong as most sigma bonds.

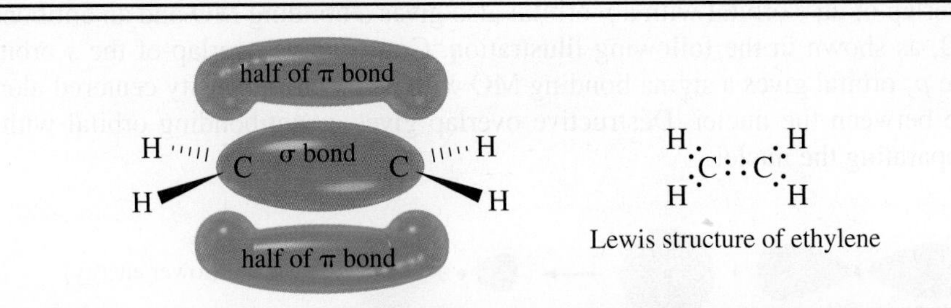

■ **FIGURE 2-10**
Structure of the double bond in ethylene. The first pair of electrons forms a σ bond. The second pair forms a π bond. The π bond has its electron density centered in two lobes, above and below the σ bond. Together, the two lobes of the π bonding molecular orbital constitute one bond.

This combination of one sigma bond and one pi bond is the normal structure of a double bond. Figure 2-10 shows the structure of ethylene, an organic molecule containing a carbon–carbon double bond.

Thus far, we have discussed bonds involving overlap of simple *s* and *p* atomic orbitals. Although these simple bonds are occasionally seen in organic compounds, they are not as common as bonds formed using **hybrid atomic orbitals**. Hybrid atomic orbitals result from the mixing of orbitals on the *same* atom. The geometry of these hybrid orbitals helps us to account for the actual structures and bond angles observed in organic compounds.

2-4 Hybridization and Molecular Shapes

If we predict the bond angles of organic molecules using just the simple *s* and *p* orbitals, we expect bond angles of about 90°. The *s* orbitals are nondirectional, and the *p* orbitals are oriented at 90° to one another (see Figure 1-3). Experimental evidence shows, however, that bond angles in organic compounds are usually close to 109°, 120°, or 180° (Figure 2-11). A common way of accounting for these bond angles is the **valence-shell electron-pair repulsion theory (VSEPR theory)**: Electron pairs repel each other, and the bonds and lone pairs around a central atom generally are separated by the largest possible angles. An angle of 109.5° is the largest possible separation for four pairs of electrons; 120° is the largest separation for three pairs; and 180° is the largest separation for two pairs. All the structures in Figure 2-11 have bond angles that separate their bonds about as far apart as possible.

The shapes of these molecules cannot result from bonding between simple *s* and *p* atomic orbitals. Although *s* and *p* orbitals have the lowest energies for isolated atoms in space, they are not the best for forming bonds. To explain the shapes of common organic molecules, we assume that the *s* and *p* orbitals combine to form hybrid atomic orbitals that separate the electron pairs more widely in space and place more electron density in the bonding region between the nuclei.

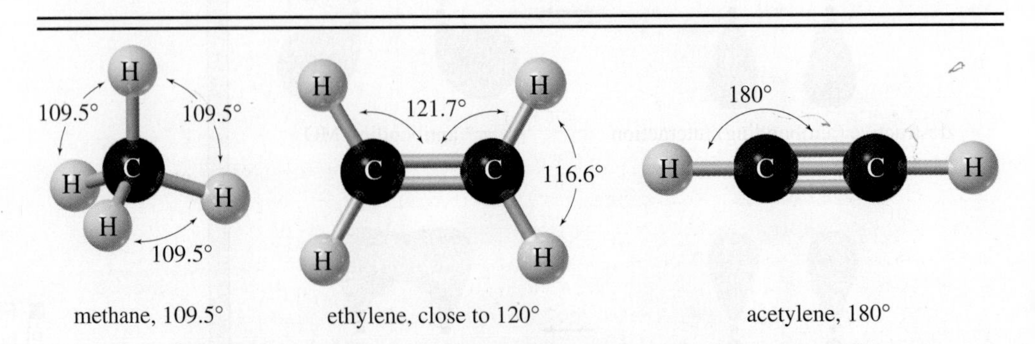

■ **FIGURE 2-11**
Common bond angles. Bond angles in organic compounds are usually close to 109°, 120°, or 180°.

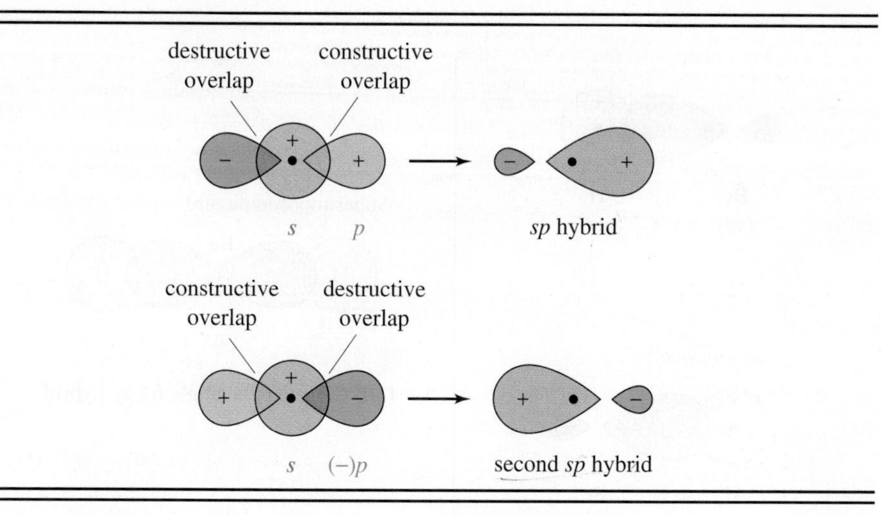

■ **FIGURE 2-12**
Formation of a pair of *sp* hybrid atomic orbitals. Addition of an *s* orbital to a *p* orbital gives an *sp* hybrid atomic orbital, with most of its electron density on one side of the nucleus. Adding the *p* orbital with opposite phase gives the other *sp* hybrid orbital, with most of its electron density on the opposite side of the nucleus from the first hybrid.

2-4A *sp* Hybrid Orbitals

Orbitals can interact to form new orbitals. We have used this principle to form molecular orbitals by adding and subtracting atomic orbitals on *different* atoms. We can also add and subtract orbitals on the *same* atom. Consider the result, shown in Figure 2-12, when we combine a *p* orbital and an *s* orbital on the same atom.

The resulting orbital is called an ***sp* hybrid orbital**. Its electron density is concentrated toward one side of the atom. We started with two orbitals (*s* and *p*), so we must finish with two *sp* hybrid orbitals. The second *sp* hybrid orbital results if we add the *p* orbital with the opposite phase (Figure 2-12).

The result of this hybridization is a pair of directional *sp* hybrid orbitals pointed in opposite directions. These hybridized orbitals provide enhanced electron density in the bonding region for a sigma bond toward the left of the atom and for another sigma bond toward the right. They give a bond angle of 180°, separating the bonding electrons as much as possible. In general, *sp* hybridization results in this **linear** bonding arrangement.

SOLVED PROBLEM 2-2

Draw the Lewis structure for beryllium hydride, BeH_2. Draw the orbitals that overlap in the bonding of BeH_2, and label the hybridization of each orbital. Predict the H—Be—H bond angle.

SOLUTION

First, draw a Lewis structure for BeH_2.

H:Be:H

There are only four valence electrons in BeH_2 (two from Be and one from each H), so the Be atom cannot have an octet. The bonding must involve orbitals on Be that give the strongest bonds (the most electron density in the bonding region) and also allow the two pairs of electrons to be separated as far as possible.

Hybrid orbitals concentrate the electron density in the bonding region, and *sp* hybrids give 180° separation for two pairs of electrons. Hydrogen cannot use hybridized orbitals, since the closest available *p* orbitals are the 2*p*'s, and they are much higher in energy than the 1*s*. The bonding in BeH_2 results from overlap of *sp* hybrid orbitals on Be with the 1*s* orbitals on hydrogen. Figure 2-13 shows how this occurs.

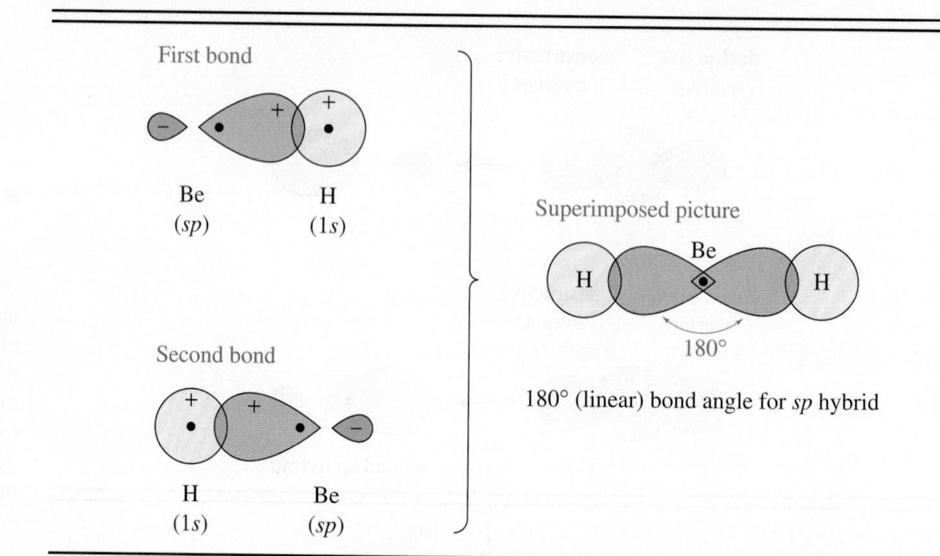

■ **FIGURE 2-13**
Linear geometry in the bonding of BeH_2. To form two sigma bonds, the two *sp* hybrid atomic orbitals on Be overlap with the 1*s* orbitals of hydrogen. The bond angle is 180° (linear).

2-4B sp^2 Hybrid Orbitals

To orient three bonds as far apart as possible, bond angles of 120° are required. When an *s* orbital combines with two *p* orbitals, the resulting three hybrid orbitals are oriented at 120° angles to each other (Figure 2-14). These orbitals are called **sp^2 hybrid orbitals** because they are composed of one *s* and two *p* orbitals. The 120° arrangement is called **trigonal** geometry, in contrast to the linear geometry associated with *sp* hybrid orbitals. There remains an unhybridized *p* orbital (p_z) perpendicular to the plane of the three sp^2 hybrid orbitals.

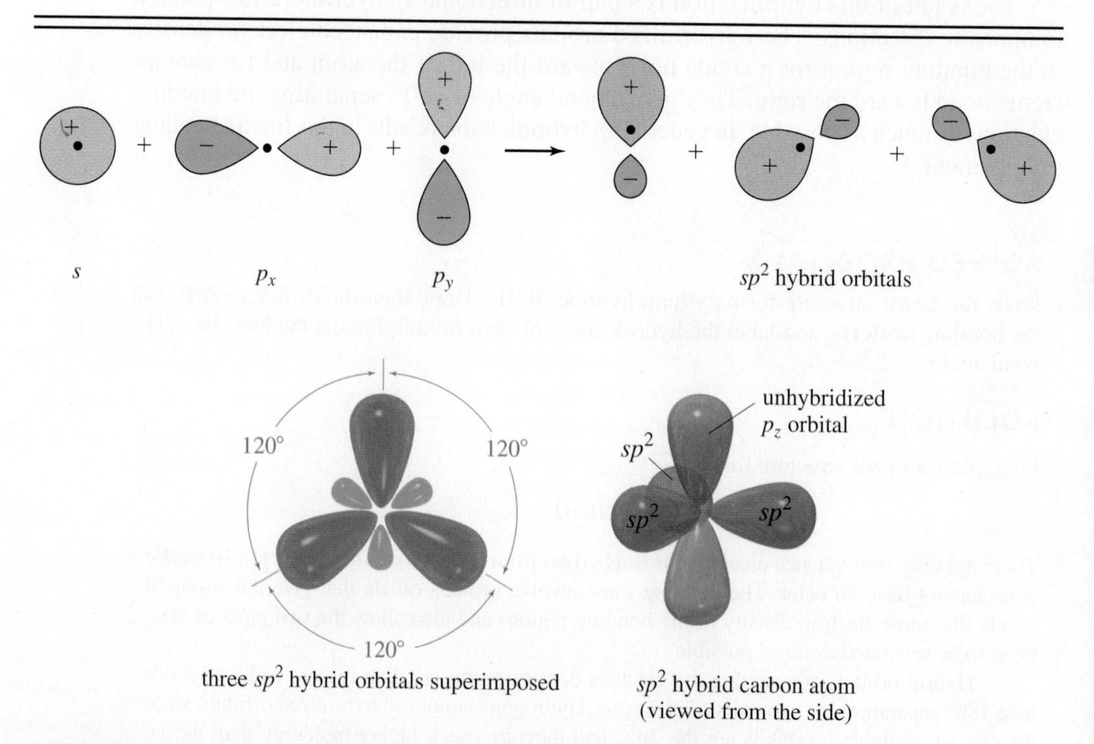

■ **FIGURE 2-14**
Trigonal geometry with sp^2 hybrid orbitals. Hybridization of an *s* orbital with two *p* orbitals gives a set of three sp^2 hybrid orbitals. This trigonal structure has bond angles of about 120°. The remaining *p* orbital is perpendicular to the plane of the three hybrid orbitals.

SOLVED PROBLEM 2-3

Borane (BH_3) is unstable under normal conditions, but it has been detected at low pressure.
(a) Draw the Lewis structure for borane.
(b) Draw a diagram of the bonding in BH_3, and label the hybridization of each orbital.
(c) Predict the H—B—H bond angle.

SOLUTION

There are only six valence electrons in borane, so the boron atom cannot have an octet. Boron has a single bond to each of the three hydrogen atoms.

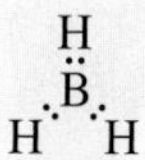

The best bonding orbitals are those that provide the greatest electron density in the bonding region while keeping the three pairs of bonding electrons as far apart as possible. Hybridization of an *s* orbital with two *p* orbitals gives three sp^2 hybrid orbitals directed 120° apart. Overlap of these orbitals with the hydrogen 1*s* orbitals gives a planar, trigonal molecule. (Note that the small back lobes of the hybrid orbitals have been omitted.)

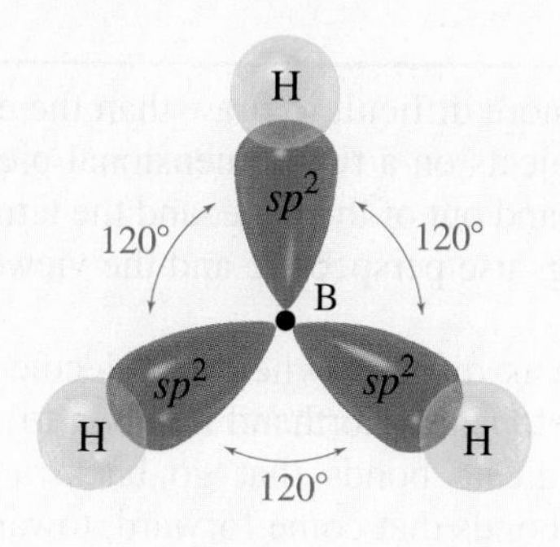

problem-solving Hint

The number of hybrid orbitals formed is always the same as the total number of *s* and *p* orbitals hybridized.

Number of Orbitals	Hybrid	Angle
2	*sp*	180°
3	sp^2	120°
4	sp^3	109.5°

2-4C sp^3 Hybrid Orbitals

Many organic compounds contain carbon atoms that are bonded to four other atoms. When four bonds are oriented as far apart as possible, they form a regular tetrahedron (109.5° bond angles), as pictured in Figure 2-15. This **tetrahedral** arrangement can be explained by combining the *s* orbital with all three *p* orbitals. The resulting four orbitals are called sp^3 **hybrid orbitals** because they are composed of one *s* and three *p* orbitals.

Methane (CH_4) is the simplest example of sp^3 hybridization (Figure 2-16). The Lewis structure for methane has eight valence electrons (four from carbon and one from each hydrogen), corresponding to four C—H single bonds. Tetrahedral geometry separates these bonds by the largest possible angle, 109.5°.

Methanotrophs are bacteria or archaea that use methane as their source of carbon and energy. Those that live in the air use oxygen to oxidize methane to formaldehyde ($H_2C{=}O$) and CO_2. Those that live in anoxic marine sediments use sulfate (SO_4^{2-}) to oxidize methane to formaldehyde and CO_2, also reducing sulfate to H_2S.

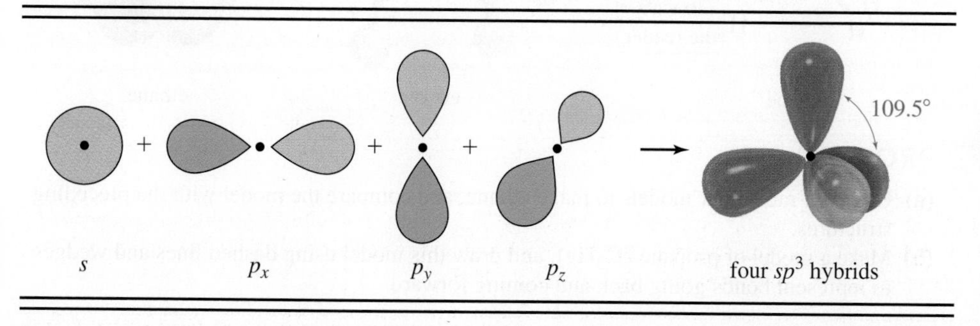

FIGURE 2-15
Tetrahedral geometry with sp^3 hybrid orbitals. Hybridization of an *s* orbital with all three *p* orbitals gives four sp^3 hybrid orbitals with tetrahedral geometry corresponding to 109.5° bond angles.

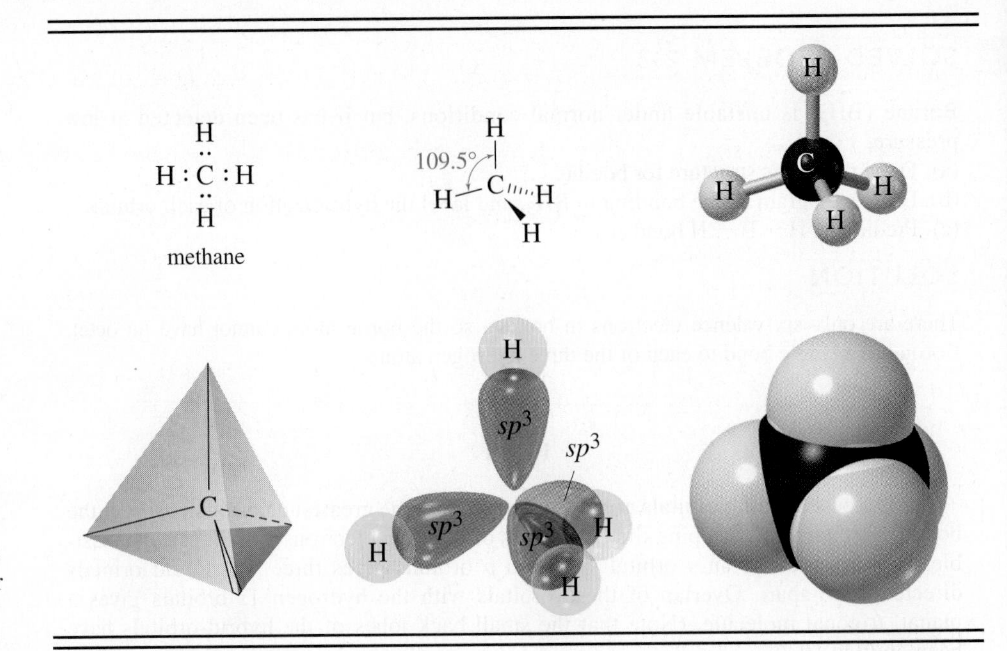

■ **FIGURE 2-16**
Several views of methane. Methane has tetrahedral geometry, using four sp^3 hybrid orbitals to form sigma bonds to the four hydrogen atoms.

2-5 Drawing Three-Dimensional Molecules

Figures 2-15 and 2-16 are more difficult to draw than the earlier figures because they depict three-dimensional objects on a two-dimensional piece of paper. The p_z orbital should look like it points in and out of the page, and the tetrahedron should look three-dimensional. These drawings use perspective and the viewer's imagination to add the third dimension.

The use of perspective is difficult when a molecule is large and complicated. Organic chemists have developed a shorthand notation to simplify three-dimensional drawings. Dashed lines indicate bonds that go backward, away from the reader. Wedge-shaped lines depict bonds that come forward, toward the reader. Straight lines are bonds in the plane of the page. Dashed lines and wedges show perspective in the second drawing of methane in Figure 2-16.

The three-dimensional structure of ethane, C_2H_6, has the shape of two tetrahedra joined together. Each carbon atom is sp^3 hybridized, with four sigma bonds formed by the four sp^3 hybrid orbitals. Dashed lines represent bonds that go away from the viewer, wedges represent bonds that come out toward the viewer, and other bond lines are in the plane of the page. All the bond angles are close to 109.5°.

problem-solving **Hint**

When showing perspective, do not draw another bond between the two bonds in the plane of the paper. Such a drawing shows an incorrect shape.

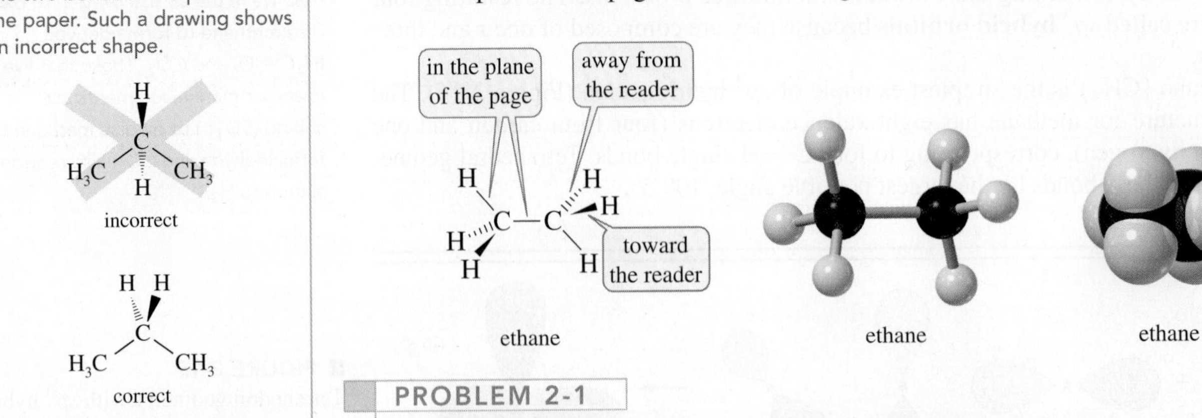

PROBLEM 2-1

(a) Use your molecular models to make ethane, and compare the model with the preceding structures.

(b) Make a model of propane (C_3H_8), and draw this model using dashed lines and wedges to represent bonds going back and coming forward.

2-6 General Rules of Hybridization and Geometry

At this point, we can consider some general rules for determining the hybridization of orbitals and the bond angles of atoms in organic molecules. After stating these rules, we solve some problems to show how the rules are used.

Rule 1: Both sigma bonding electrons and lone pairs can occupy hybrid orbitals. The number of hybrid orbitals on an atom is computed by adding the number of sigma bonds and the number of lone pairs of electrons on that atom.

Because the first bond to another atom is always a sigma bond, the number of hybrid orbitals may be computed by adding the number of lone pairs to the number of atoms bonded to the central atom.

Rule 2: Use the hybridization and geometry that give the widest possible separation of the calculated number of bonds and lone pairs.

Summary of Hybridization and Geometry

Hybrid Orbitals	Hybridization	Geometry	Approximate Bond Angles
2	$s + p = sp$	linear	180°
3	$s + p + p = sp^2$	trigonal	120°
4	$s + p + p + p = sp^3$	tetrahedral	109.5°

The number of hybrid orbitals obtained equals the number of atomic orbitals combined. Lone pairs of electrons take up more space than bonding pairs of electrons; thus they compress the bond angles.

Rule 3: If two or three pairs of electrons form a multiple bond between two atoms, the first bond is a sigma bond formed by a hybrid orbital. The second bond is a pi bond, consisting of two lobes above and below the sigma bond, formed by two unhybridized *p* orbitals (see the structure of ethylene in Figure 2-17). The third bond of a triple bond is another pi bond, perpendicular to the first pi bond (shown in Figure 2-18).

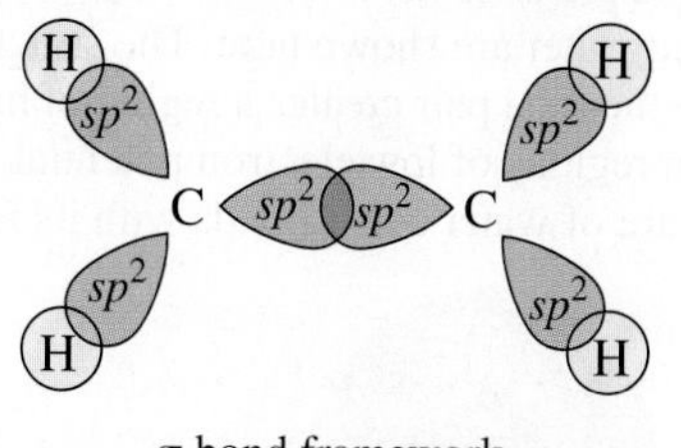

σ bond framework
(viewed from above the plane)

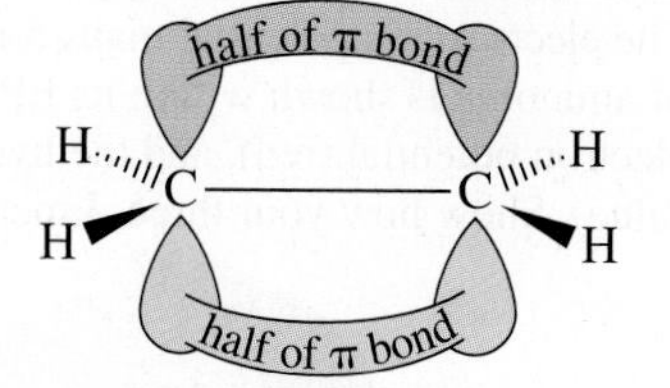

π bond
(viewed from alongside the plane)

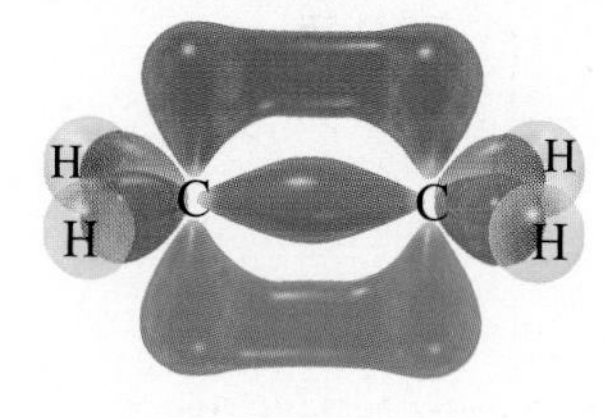

ethylene

■ **FIGURE 2-17**
Planar geometry of ethylene. The carbon atoms in ethylene are sp^2 hybridized, with trigonal bond angles of about 120°. All the carbon and hydrogen atoms lie in the same plane.

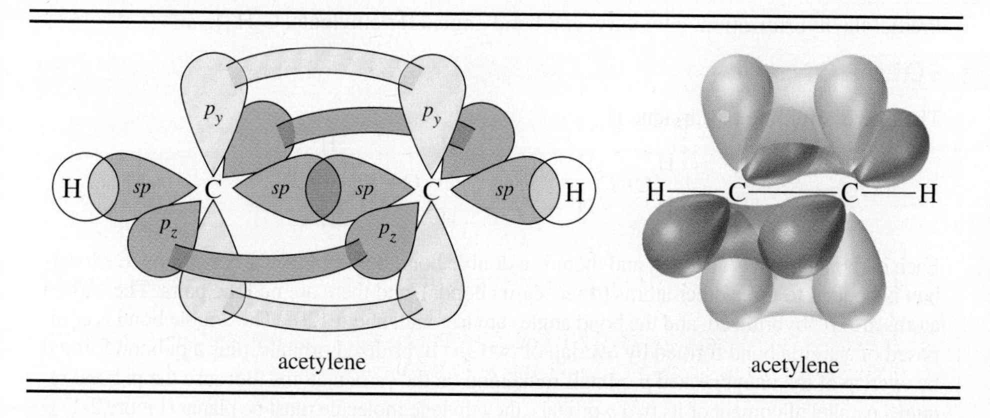

acetylene

acetylene

■ **FIGURE 2-18**
Linear geometry of acetylene. The carbon atoms in acetylene are *sp* hybridized, with linear (180°) bond angles. The triple bond contains one sigma bond and two perpendicular pi bonds.

Solved Problems 2-4 through 2-8 show how to use these rules to predict the hybridization and bond angles in organic compounds.

SOLVED PROBLEM 2-4

Predict the hybridization of the nitrogen atom in ammonia, NH_3. Draw a picture of the three-dimensional structure of ammonia, and predict the bond angles.

SOLUTION

The hybridization depends on the number of sigma bonds plus lone pairs. A Lewis structure provides this information.

H:N̈:H (with H above) or H—N: (with H above and below) — lone pair

In this structure, there are three sigma bonds and one pair of nonbonding electrons. Four hybrid orbitals are required, implying sp^3 hybridization and tetrahedral geometry around the nitrogen atom, with bond angles of about 109.5°. The resulting structure is much like that of methane, except that one of the sp^3 hybrid orbitals is occupied by a lone pair of electrons.

107.3°

The bond angles in ammonia (107.3°) are slightly smaller than the ideal tetrahedral angle, 109.5°. The nonbonding electrons are more diffuse than a bonding pair of electrons, and they take up more space. The lone pair repels the electrons in the N—H bonds, compressing the bond angle.

PROBLEM 2-2

(a) Predict the hybridization of the oxygen atom in water, H_2O. Draw a picture of its three-dimensional structure, and explain why its bond angle is 104.5°.

(b) The electrostatic potential maps for ammonia and water are shown here. The structure of ammonia is shown within its EPM. Note how the lone pair creates a region of high electron potential (red), and the hydrogens are in regions of low electron potential (blue). Show how your three-dimensional structure of water corresponds with its EPM.

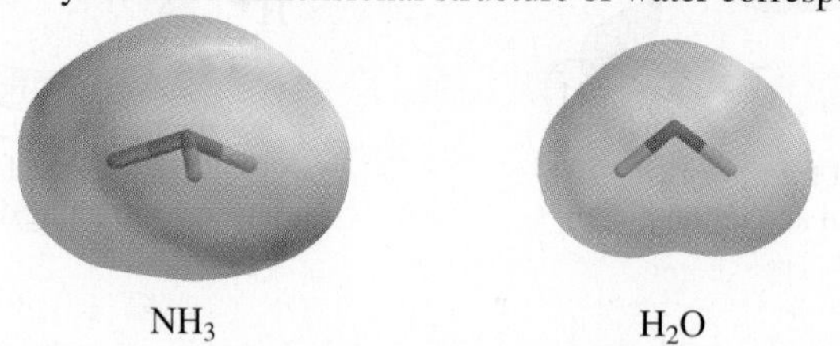

NH_3 H_2O

SOLVED PROBLEM 2-5

Predict the hybridization, geometry, and bond angles for ethylene (C_2H_4).

SOLUTION

The Lewis structure of ethylene is

H₂C::CH₂ or H₂C=CH₂

Each carbon atom has an octet, and there is a double bond between the carbon atoms. Each carbon is bonded to three other atoms (three sigma bonds), and there are no lone pairs. The carbon atoms are sp^2 hybridized, and the bond angles are trigonal: about 120°. The double bond is composed of a sigma bond formed by overlap of two sp^2 hybridized orbitals, plus a pi bond formed by overlap of the unhybridized p orbitals remaining on the carbon atoms. Because the pi bond requires parallel alignment of its two p orbitals, the ethylene molecule must be planar (Figure 2-17).

PROBLEM 2-3

Predict the hybridization, geometry, and bond angles for the central atoms in
(a) 2-butene, $CH_3CH{=}CHCH_3$ **(b)** $CH_3CH{=}NH$

SOLVED PROBLEM 2-6

Predict the hybridization, geometry, and bond angles for the carbon atoms in acetylene, C_2H_2.

SOLUTION

The Lewis structure of acetylene is

$$H{:}C{:::}C{:}H \quad \text{or} \quad H{-}C{\equiv}C{-}H$$

Both carbon atoms have octets, but each carbon is bonded to just two other atoms, requiring two sigma bonds. There are no lone pairs. Each carbon atom is *sp* hybridized and linear (180° bond angles). The *sp* hybrid orbitals are generated from the *s* orbital and the p_x orbital (the *p* orbital directed along the line joining the nuclei). The p_y orbitals and the p_z orbitals are unhybridized.

The **triple bond** is composed of one sigma bond, formed by overlap of *sp* hybrid orbitals, plus two pi bonds. One pi bond results from overlap of the two p_y orbitals and another from overlap of the two p_z orbitals (Figure 2-18).

problem-solving **Hint**

Begin with a valid Lewis structure, and use hybrid orbitals for the sigma bonds and lone pairs. Use pi bonds between unhybridized *p* orbitals for the second and third bonds of double and triple bonds.

PROBLEM 2-4

Predict the hybridization, geometry, and bond angles for the carbon and nitrogen atoms in acetonitrile ($CH_3{-}C{\equiv}N{:}$).

SOLVED PROBLEM 2-7

Predict the hybridization, geometry, and bond angles for the carbon and oxygen atoms in acetaldehyde (CH_3CHO).

SOLUTION

The Lewis structure for acetaldehyde is

H:C(H)(H):C(:Ö:)H or H—C(H)(H)—C(=Ö:)—H

The oxygen atom and both carbon atoms have octets. The CH_3 carbon atom is sigma bonded to four atoms, so it is sp^3 hybridized (and tetrahedral). The C=O carbon is bonded to three atoms (no lone pairs), so it is sp^2 hybridized and its bond angles are about 120°.

The oxygen atom is probably sp^2 hybridized because it is bonded to one atom (carbon) and has two lone pairs, requiring a total of three hybrid orbitals. We cannot experimentally measure the angles of the lone pairs on oxygen, however, so it is impossible to confirm whether the oxygen atom is really sp^2 hybridized.

The double bond between carbon and oxygen looks just like the double bond in ethylene. There is a sigma bond formed by overlap of sp^2 hybrid orbitals and a pi bond formed by overlap of the unhybridized *p* orbitals on carbon and oxygen (Figure 2-19).

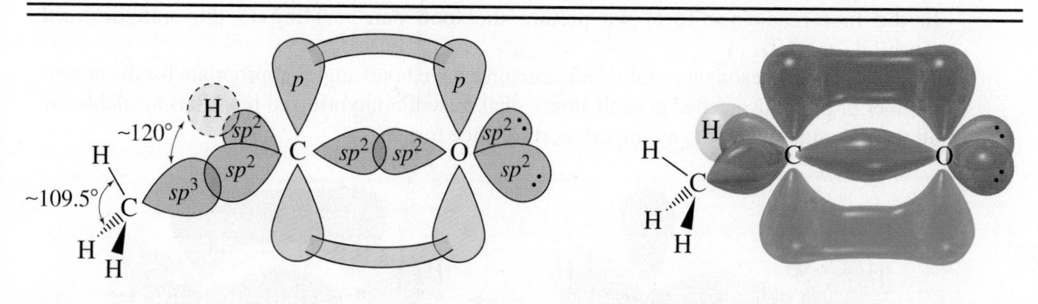

■ **FIGURE 2-19**
Structure of acetaldehyde. The CH_3 carbon in acetaldehyde is sp^3 hybridized, with tetrahedral bond angles of about 109.5°. The carbonyl (C=O) carbon is sp^2 hybridized, with bond angles of about 120°. The oxygen atom is probably sp^2 hybridized, but we cannot measure any bond angles to verify this prediction.

PROBLEM 2-5

1. Draw a Lewis structure for each compound.
2. Label the hybridization, geometry, and bond angles around each atom other than hydrogen.
3. Draw a three-dimensional representation (using wedges and dashed lines) of the structure.

(a) CO_2 **(b)** CH_3OCH_3 **(c)** $(CH_3)_3O^+$
(d) CH_3COOH **(e)** CH_3CCH **(f)** CH_3CHNCH_3
(g) H_2CCO

PROBLEM 2-6

Allene, $CH_2{=}C{=}CH_2$, has the structure shown below. Explain how the bonding in allene requires the two $=CH_2$ groups at its ends to be at right angles to each other.

$$H_2C{=}C{=}CH_2$$

allene

SOLVED PROBLEM 2-8

In Sections 1–7 and 1–9, we considered the electronic structure of $[CH_2NH_2]^+$. Predict its hybridization, geometry, and bond angles.

SOLUTION

This is a tricky question. This ion has two important resonance forms:

$$\left[H_2\overset{+}{C}{-}\ddot{N}H_2 \longleftrightarrow H_2C{=}\overset{+}{N}H_2\right] = H_2\overset{\delta^+}{C}{=\!=}\overset{\delta^+}{N}H_2$$

resonance forms combined representation

When resonance is involved, different resonance forms may suggest different hybridization and bond angles. Only electrons can be delocalized, however. The molecule can have only one set of bond angles, which must be compatible with all the important resonance forms.

Looking at either resonance form for $[CH_2NH_2]^+$, we would predict sp^2 hybridization (120° bond angles) for the carbon atom; however, the first resonance form suggests sp^3 hybridization for nitrogen (109° bond angles), and the second suggests sp^2 hybridization (120° bond angles). Which is correct?

Experiments show that the bond angles on both carbon and nitrogen are about 120°, implying sp^2 hybridization. Nitrogen cannot be sp^3 hybridized because there must be an unhybridized p orbital available to form the pi bond in the second resonance form. In the first resonance form we picture the lone pair residing in this unhybridized p orbital.

In general, resonance-stabilized structures have bond angles appropriate for the largest number of pi bonds needed at each atom—that is, with unhybridized p orbitals available for all the pi bonds shown in any important resonance form.

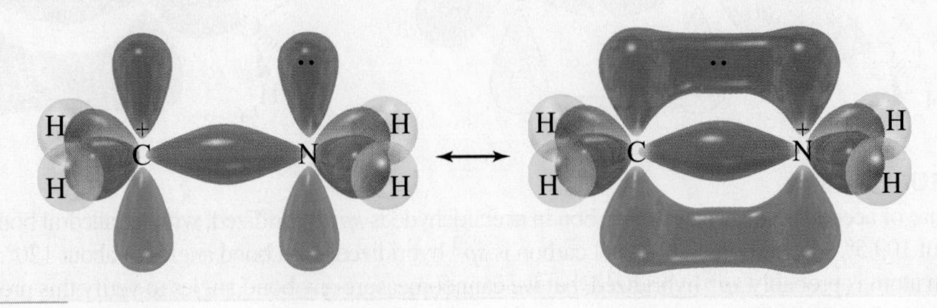

PROBLEM 2-7

1. Draw the important resonance forms for each compound.
2. Label the hybridization and bond angles around each atom other than hydrogen.
3. Use a three-dimensional drawing to show where the electrons are pictured to be in each resonance form.

(a) $[H_2COH]^+$ (b) 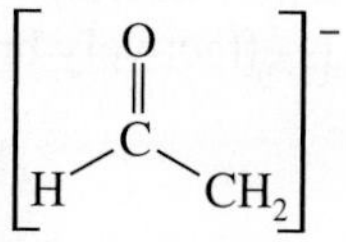 $[H{-}C({=}O){-}CH_2]^-$ (c) $H{-}C({=}O){-}NH_2$ (d) $[H_2CCN]^-$

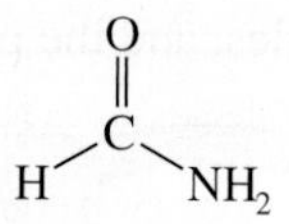

(e) $B(OH)_3$ (f) ozone (O_3), bonded OOO

problem-solving Hint

To predict the hybridization and geometry of an atom in a resonance hybrid, consider the resonance form with the most pi bonds to that atom. An atom involved in resonance generally will not be sp^3 hybridized because it needs at least one unhybridized *p* orbital for pi-bonding overlap.

2-7 Bond Rotation

Some bonds rotate easily, but others do not. When we look at a structure, we must recognize which bonds rotate and which do not. If a bond rotates easily, each molecule can rotate through the different angular arrangements of atoms. If a bond cannot rotate, however, different angular arrangements may be distinct compounds (isomers) with different properties.

2-7A Rotation of Single Bonds

In ethane ($CH_3{-}CH_3$), both carbon atoms are sp^3 hybridized and tetrahedral. Ethane looks like two methane molecules that have each had a hydrogen plucked off (to form a methyl group) and are joined by overlap of their sp^3 orbitals (Figure 2-20).

We can draw many structures for ethane, differing only in how one methyl group is twisted in relation to the other one. Such structures, differing only in rotations about a single bond, are called *conformations*. Two of the infinite number of conformations of ethane are shown in Figure 2-20. Construct a molecular model of ethane, and twist the model into these two conformations.

Which of these structures for ethane is the "right" one? Are the two methyl groups lined up so that their C—H bonds are parallel (*eclipsed*), or are they *staggered*, as in the drawing on the right? The answer is that both structures, and all the possible structures in between, are correct structures for ethane, and a real ethane molecule rotates through all these conformations. The two carbon atoms are bonded by overlap of their sp^3 orbitals to form a sigma bond along the line between the carbons. The magnitude of this sp^3–sp^3 overlap remains nearly the same during rotation because the sigma bond is cylindrically symmetrical about the line joining the carbon nuclei. No matter how you turn one of the methyl groups, its sp^3 orbital still overlaps with the sp^3 orbital of the other carbon atom.

problem-solving Hint

Drawings that differ only by rotations of single bonds usually represent the same compound. For example, the following drawings all represent *n*-butane:

$CH_3CH_2CH_2CH_3$ $H_3C{-}CH(CH_3){-}CH_2{-}H$ (H, CH_3 above; H, H below)

$H{-}C(CH_3)H{-}C(CH_3)H{-}H$ (CH₃ CH₃ above; H H below) $H{-}CH(H){-}CH(CH_3){-}H$ (H CH₃ above; CH₃ H below)

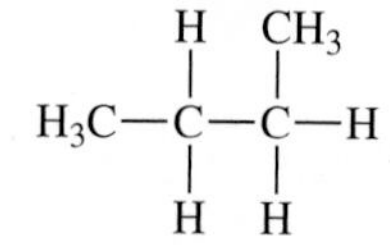

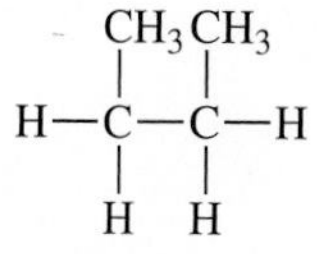

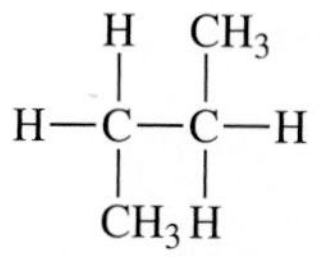

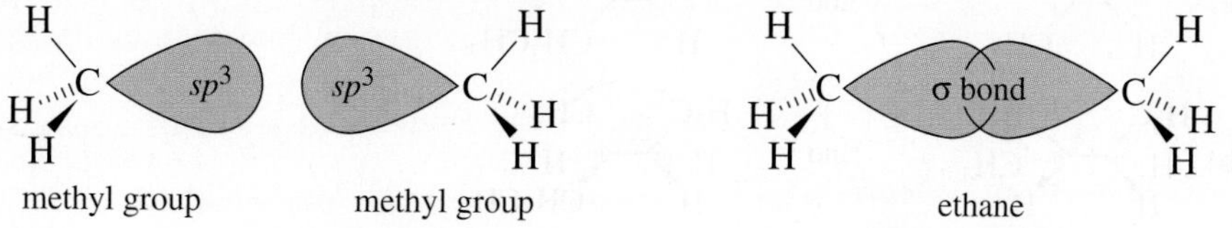

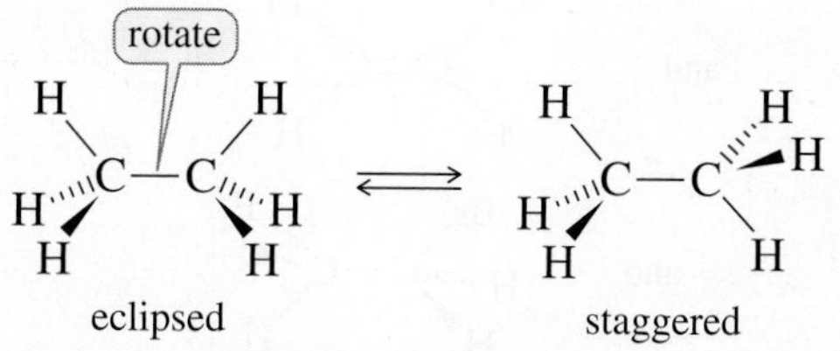

■ FIGURE 2-20
Rotation of single bonds. Ethane is composed of two methyl groups bonded by overlap of their sp^3 hybrid orbitals. These methyl groups may rotate with respect to each other.

2-7B Rigidity of Double Bonds

Not all bonds allow free rotation; ethylene, for example, is quite rigid. In ethylene, the double bond between the two CH_2 groups consists of a sigma bond and a pi bond. When we twist one of the two CH_2 groups, the sigma bond is unaffected but the pi bond loses its overlap. The two *p* orbitals cannot overlap when the two ends of the molecule are at right angles, and the pi bond is effectively broken in this geometry.

hold in position

try to twist

overlap destroyed

We can make the following generalization:

> Rotation about single bonds is allowed, but double bonds are rigid and cannot be twisted.

Because double bonds are rigid, we can separate and isolate compounds that differ only in how their substituents are arranged on a double bond. For example, the double bond in 2-butene ($CH_3—CH{=}CH—CH_3$) prevents the two ends of the molecule from rotating. Two different compounds are possible, and they have different physical properties:

cis-2-butene
bp = 3.7 °C

trans-2-butene
bp = 0.9 °C

The molecule with the methyl groups on the same side of the double bond is called *cis*-2-butene, and the one with the methyl groups on opposite sides is called *trans*-2-butene. These kinds of molecules are discussed further in Section 2-8B.

PROBLEM 2-8

For each pair of structures, determine whether they represent different compounds or a single compound.

(a) and

(b) and

(c) and

(d) and

PROBLEM 2-9

Two compounds with the formula $CH_3—CH=N—CH_3$ are known.
(a) Draw a Lewis structure for this molecule, and label the hybridization of each carbon and nitrogen atom.
(b) What two compounds have this formula?
(c) Explain why only one compound with the formula $(CH_3)_2CNCH_3$ is known.

2-8 Isomerism

Isomers are different compounds with the same molecular formula. There are several types of isomerism in organic compounds, and we will cover them in detail in Chapter 5 (Stereochemistry). For now, we need to recognize the two large classes of isomers: constitutional isomers and stereoisomers.

2-8A Constitutional Isomerism

Constitutional isomers (or structural isomers) are isomers that differ in their bonding sequence; that is, their atoms are connected differently. Let's use butane as an example. If you were asked to draw a structural formula for C_4H_{10}, either of the following structures would be correct:

$CH_3—CH_2—CH_2—CH_3$ (*n*-butane) $CH_3—CH(CH_3)—CH_3$ (isobutane)

These two compounds are isomers because they have the same molecular formula. They are constitutional isomers because their atoms are connected differently. The first compound (*n*-butane for "normal" butane) has its carbon atoms in a straight chain four carbons long. The second compound ("isobutane" for "an isomer of butane") has a branched structure with a longest chain of three carbon atoms and a methyl side chain.

There are three constitutional isomers of pentane (C_5H_{12}), whose common names are *n*-pentane, isopentane, and neopentane. The number of isomers increases rapidly as the number of carbon atoms increases.

$CH_3—CH_2—CH_2—CH_2—CH_3$ (*n*-pentane) $CH_3—CH(CH_3)—CH_2—CH_3$ (isopentane) $CH_3—C(CH_3)_2—CH_3$ (neopentane)

Constitutional isomers may differ in ways other than the branching of their carbon chain. They may differ in the position of a double bond or other group or by having a ring or some other feature. Notice how the following constitutional isomers all differ by the ways in which atoms are bonded to other atoms. (Check the number of hydrogens bonded to each carbon.) These compounds are not isomers of the pentanes just shown, however, because these have a different molecular formula (C_5H_{10}).

problem-solving Hint

Constitutional isomers (structural isomers) differ in the order in which their atoms are bonded.

$H_2C=CH—CH_2CH_2CH_3$ (1-pentene) $CH_3—CH=CH—CH_2CH_3$ (2-pentene)   cyclopentane   methylcyclobutane (CH_3)

2-8B Stereoisomers

problem-solving Hint

Stereoisomers are different compounds that differ only in how their atoms are oriented in space.

Stereoisomers are isomers that differ only in how their atoms are oriented in space. Their atoms are bonded in the same order, however. For example, *cis*- and *trans*-2-butene have the same connections of bonds, so they are not constitutional isomers. They are stereoisomers because they differ only in the spatial orientation of the groups attached to the double bond. The cis isomer has the two methyl groups on the same side of the double bond, and the trans isomer has them on opposite sides. In contrast, 1-butene is a constitutional isomer of *cis*- and *trans*-2-butene.

problem-solving Hint

Similar groups on the same side of the double bond: *cis*.
Similar groups on opposite sides of the double bond: *trans*.

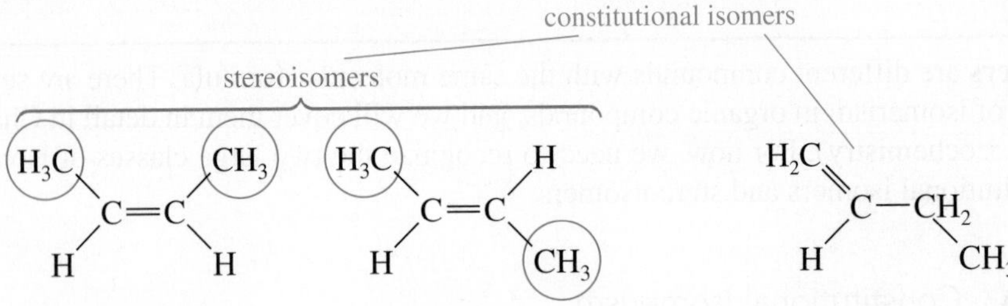

constitutional isomers

stereoisomers

$H_3C(H)C{=}C(H)CH_3$ — *cis*-2-butene

$H_3C(H)C{=}C(H)CH_3$ — *trans*-2-butene

$H_2C{=}C(H)-CH_2CH_3$ — 1-butene

Cis and trans isomers are only one type of stereoisomerism. The study of the structure and chemistry of stereoisomers is called **stereochemistry**. We will encounter stereochemistry throughout our study of organic chemistry, and Chapter 5 is devoted entirely to this field.

Cis-trans isomers are also called **geometric isomers** because they differ in the geometry of the groups on a double bond. The cis isomer is always the one with similar groups on the same side of the double bond, and the trans isomer has similar groups on opposite sides of the double bond.

Stereoisomers can have different therapeutic effects. Quinine, a natural product isolated from the bark of the cinchona tree, was the first compound effective against malaria. Quinidine, a stereoisomer of quinine, is used to treat irregular heartbeat.

To have cis-trans isomerism, there must be two *different* groups on each end of the double bond. For example, 1-butene has two identical hydrogens on one end of the double bond. Reversing their positions does not give a different compound. Similarly, 2-methyl-2-butene has two identical methyl groups on one end of the double bond. Reversing the methyl groups does not give a different compound. These compounds cannot show cis-trans isomerism.

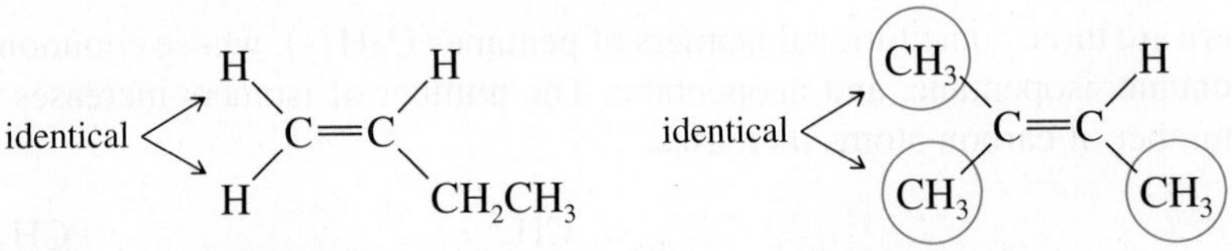

identical: $H_2C{=}C(H)CH_2CH_3$ — 1-butene, no cis or trans

identical: $(CH_3)_2C{=}C(H)CH_3$ — 2-methyl-2-butene, no cis or trans

PROBLEM 2-10

problem-solving Hint

Identical groups on one of the double-bonded carbons implies no cis-trans isomerism.

Which of the following compounds show cis-trans isomerism? Draw the cis and trans isomers of those that do.

(a) $CHF{=}CHF$ (b) $F_2C{=}CH_2$ (c) $CH_2{=}CH{-}CH_2{-}CH_3$

(d) 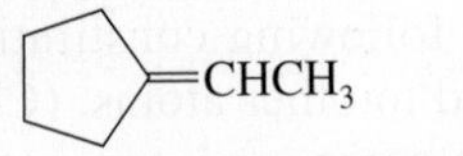 cyclopentylidene$=CHCH_3$ (e) 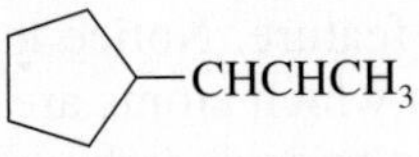 cyclopentyl$-CHCHCH_3$ (f) 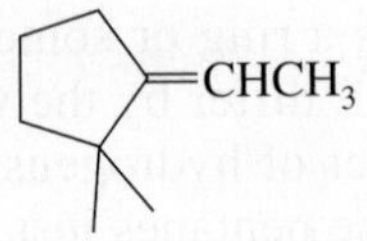 2,2-dimethylcyclopentylidene$=CHCH_3$

PROBLEM 2-11

Give the relationship between the following pairs of structures. The possible relationships are

same compound — *constitutional isomers (structural isomers)*
cis-trans isomers — *not isomers (different molecular formula)*

(a) $CH_3CH_2CHCH_2CH_3$ (with CH_2CH_3 on C3) and $CH_3CH_2CHCH_2CH_2CH_3$ (with CH_3 on C3)

(b) (Br)(H)C=C(H)(Br) and (Br)(H)C=C(Br)(H) (c) (Br)(H)C=C(H)(Br) and (Br)(Br)C=C(H)(H)

(d) (Br)(H)C=C(H)(Br) and (H)(Br)C=C(Br)(H) (e) H—C(H)(Cl)—C(Cl)(H)—H and H—C(Cl)(H)—C(Cl)(H)—H

(f) H—C(H)(CH_3)—C(CH_3)(H)—H and H—C(CH_3)(H)—C(H)(H)—CH_3

(g) $CH_3-CH_2-CH_2-CH_3$ and $CH_3-CH{=}CH-CH_3$

(h) $CH_2{=}CH-CH_2CH_2CH_3$ and $CH_3-CH{=}CH-CH_2CH_3$

(i) $CH_2{=}CHCH_2CH_2CH_3$ and $CH_3CH_2CH_2CH{=}CH_2$

(j) 1,2-dimethylcyclohexane (CH_3, CH_3) and 1,4-dimethylcyclohexane (CH_3, CH_3) (k) 1-methylcyclohexene (CH_3) and 3-methylcyclohexene (CH_3)

2-9 Polarity of Bonds and Molecules

In Section 1-6, we reviewed the concept of polar covalent bonds between atoms with different electronegativities. Now we are ready to combine this concept with molecular geometry to study the polarity of entire molecules.

2-9A Bond Dipole Moments

Bond polarities can range from nonpolar covalent, through polar covalent, to totally ionic. In the following examples, ethane has a nonpolar covalent C—C bond. Methyl-amine, methanol, and chloromethane have increasingly polar (C—N, C—O, and C—Cl) covalent bonds. Methylammonium chloride ($CH_3NH_3^+\ Cl^-$) has an ionic bond between the methylammonium ion and the chloride ion.

H_3C-CH_3	H_3C-NH_2	H_3C-OH	H_3C-Cl	$H_3C\overset{+}{N}H_3\ Cl^-$
ethane	methylamine	methanol	chloromethane	methylammonium chloride
nonpolar	increasing polarity →			ionic

The polarity of an individual bond is measured as its **bond dipole moment**, μ, defined as

$$\mu = \delta \times d$$

where δ is the amount of charge at either end of the dipole and d is the distance between the charges.

Dipole moments are expressed in units of the **debye** (D), where 1 debye $= 3.34 \times 10^{-30}$ coulomb meters. If a proton and an electron (charge 1.60×10^{-19} coulomb) were 1 Å apart (distance 10^{-10} meter), the dipole moment would be

$$\mu = (1.60 \times 10^{-19}\ \text{coulomb}) \times (10^{-10}\ \text{meter}) = 1.60 \times 10^{-29}\ \text{coulomb meter}$$

Expressed in debyes,

$$\mu = \frac{1.60 \times 10^{-29}\ \text{C}\cdot\text{m}}{3.34 \times 10^{-30}\ \text{C}\cdot\text{m/D}} = 4.8\ \text{D}$$

A simple rule of thumb, using common units, is that

$$\mu\ (\text{in debyes}) = 4.8 \times \delta\ (\text{electron charge}) \times d\ (\text{in angstroms})$$

Dipole moments are measured experimentally, and they can be used to calculate other information such as bond lengths and charge separations.

Bond dipole moments in organic compounds range from zero in symmetrical bonds to about 3.6 D for the strongly polar C≡N: triple bond. Table 2-1 shows typical dipole moments for some of the bonds common in organic molecules. Recall that the positive end of the crossed arrow corresponds to the less electronegative (partial positive charge) end of the dipole.

TABLE 2-1

Bond Dipole Moments (Debye) for Some Common Covalent Bonds

Bond	Dipole Moment, μ	Bond	Dipole Moment, μ
C—N	0.22 D	H—C	0.3 D
C—O	0.86 D	H—N	1.31 D
C—F	1.51 D	H—O	1.53 D
C—Cl	1.56 D	C=O	2.4 D
C—Br	1.48 D	C≡N	3.6 D
C—I	1.29 D		

SOLVED PROBLEM 2-9

Calculate the amount of charge separation for a typical C—O single bond, with a bond length of 1.43 Å and a dipole moment of 0.86 D.

SOLUTION

$\mu = 0.86$ D, δ^+ C—O δ^-, 1.43 Å

Using the formula for the dipole moment, we have

$$0.86\ \text{D} = 4.8 \times \delta \times 1.43\ \text{Å}$$

$$\delta = 0.125\ e$$

The amount δ of charge separation is about 0.125 electronic charge, so the carbon atom has about an eighth of a positive charge, and the oxygen atom has about an eighth of a negative charge.

PROBLEM 2-12

The C=O double bond has a dipole moment of about 2.4 D and a bond length of about 1.23 Å.

(a) Calculate the amount of charge separation in this bond.

(b) Use this information to evaluate the relative importance of the following two resonance contributors:

[$R_2C=\ddot{O}$: ⟷ $R_2C^+—:\ddot{O}:^-$]

2-9B Molecular Dipole Moments

A **molecular dipole moment** is the dipole moment of the molecule taken as a whole. It is a good indicator of a molecule's overall polarity. Molecular dipole moments can be measured directly, in contrast to bond dipole moments, which must be estimated by comparing various compounds. The value of the molecular dipole moment is equal to the *vector* sum of the individual bond dipole moments. This vector sum reflects both the magnitude and the direction of each individual bond dipole moment.

For example, formaldehyde has one strongly polar C=O bond, and carbon dioxide has two. We might expect CO_2 to have the larger dipole moment, but its dipole moment is actually zero. The symmetry of the carbon dioxide molecule explains this surprising result. The structures of formaldehyde and carbon dioxide are shown here, together with their electrostatic potential maps. These electrostatic potential maps show the bond dipole moments, with red at the negative ends and blue at the positive ends of the dipoles. In carbon dioxide, the bond dipole moments are oriented in opposite directions, so they cancel each other.

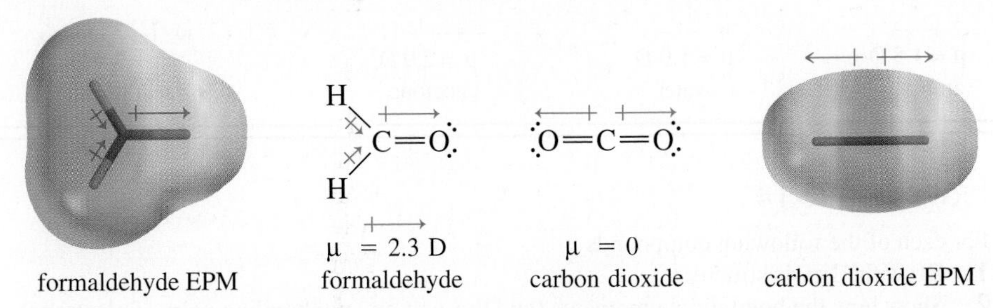

Figure 2-21 shows some examples of molecular dipole moments. Notice that the dipole moment of C—H bonds is small, so we often treat C—H bonds as nearly nonpolar. Also note that the tetrahedral symmetry of CCl_4 positions the four C—Cl dipole moments in directions so that they cancel. A partial canceling of the bond dipole moments explains why $CHCl_3$, with three C—Cl bonds, has a smaller molecular dipole moment than CH_3Cl, with only one.

Lone pairs of electrons contribute to the dipole moments of bonds and molecules. Each lone pair corresponds to a charge separation, with the nucleus having a partial positive charge balanced by the negative charge of the lone pair. Figure 2-22 shows four molecules with lone pairs and large dipole moments. Notice how the lone pairs contribute to the large dipole moments, especially in the C=O and C≡N bonds. Also notice the red areas in the electrostatic potential maps, indicating high negative potential in the electron-rich regions of the lone pairs.

PROBLEM 2-13

The N—F bond is more polar than the N—H bond, but NF_3 has a *smaller* dipole moment than NH_3. Explain this curious result.

NH_3 $\mu = 1.5$ D

NF_3 $\mu = 0.2$ D

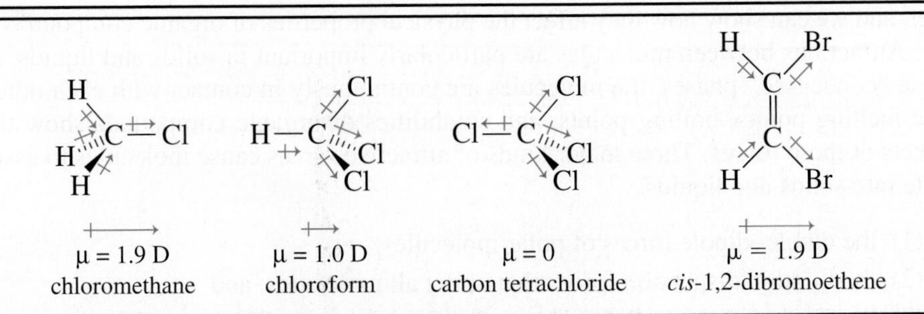

FIGURE 2-21 Molecular dipole moments. A molecular dipole moment is the vector sum of the individual bond dipole moments.

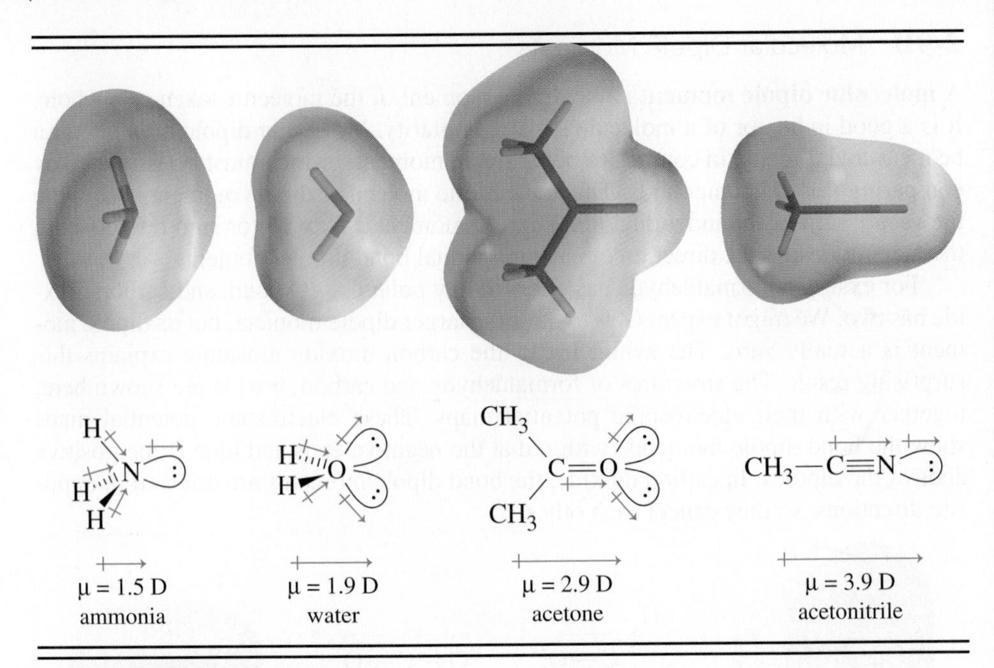

■ **FIGURE 2-22**
Effects of lone pairs on dipole moments. Lone pairs can make large contributions to molecular dipole moments.

PROBLEM 2-14

For each of the following compounds

1. Draw the Lewis structure.
2. Show how the bond dipole moments (and those of any nonbonding pairs of electrons) contribute to the molecular dipole moment.
3. Predict whether the compound has a large (>1 D), small, or zero dipole moment.

(a) CH_2Cl_2 **(b)** CH_3F **(c)** CF_4 **(d)** CH_3OH
(e) O_3 **(f)** HCN **(g)** CH_3CHO **(h)** $H_2C{=}NH$
(i) $(CH_3)_3N$ **(j)** $CH_2{=}CHCl$ **(k)** BF_3 **(l)** $BeCl_2$
(m) NH_4^+

PROBLEM 2-15

Two isomers of 1,2-dichloroethene are known. One has a dipole moment of 2.4 D; the other has zero dipole moment. Draw the two isomers and explain why one has zero dipole moment.

$$CHCl{=}CHCl$$
1,2-dichloroethene

2-10 Intermolecular Forces

When two molecules approach, they attract or repel each other. This interaction can be described fairly simply in the case of atoms (like the noble gases) or simple molecules such as H_2 or Cl_2. In general, the forces are attractive until the molecules come so close that they infringe on each other's van der Waals radius. When this happens, the small attractive force quickly becomes a large repulsive force, and the molecules "bounce" off each other. With complicated organic molecules, these attractive and repulsive forces are more difficult to predict. We can still describe the nature of the forces, however, and we can show how they affect the physical properties of organic compounds.

Attractions between molecules are particularly important in solids and liquids. In these "condensed" phases, the molecules are continuously in contact with each other. The melting points, boiling points, and solubilities of organic compounds show the effects of these forces. Three major kinds of attractive forces cause molecules to associate into solids and liquids:

(1) the dipole–dipole forces of polar molecules;
(2) the London dispersion forces that affect all molecules; and
(3) the "hydrogen bonds" that link molecules having —OH or —NH groups.

2-10A Dipole–Dipole Forces

Most molecules have permanent dipole moments as a result of their polar bonds. Each molecular dipole moment has a positive end and a negative end. The most stable arrangement has the positive end of one dipole close to the negative end of another. When two negative ends or two positive ends approach each other, they repel, but they may turn and orient themselves in the more stable positive-to-negative arrangement. **Dipole–dipole forces**, therefore, are generally attractive intermolecular forces resulting from the attraction of the positive and negative ends of the dipole moments of polar molecules. Figure 2-23 shows the attractive and repulsive orientations of polar molecules, using chloromethane as the example.

Polar molecules are mostly oriented in the lower-energy positive-to-negative arrangement, and the net force is attractive. This attraction must be overcome when the liquid vaporizes, resulting in larger heats of vaporization and higher boiling points for strongly polar compounds.

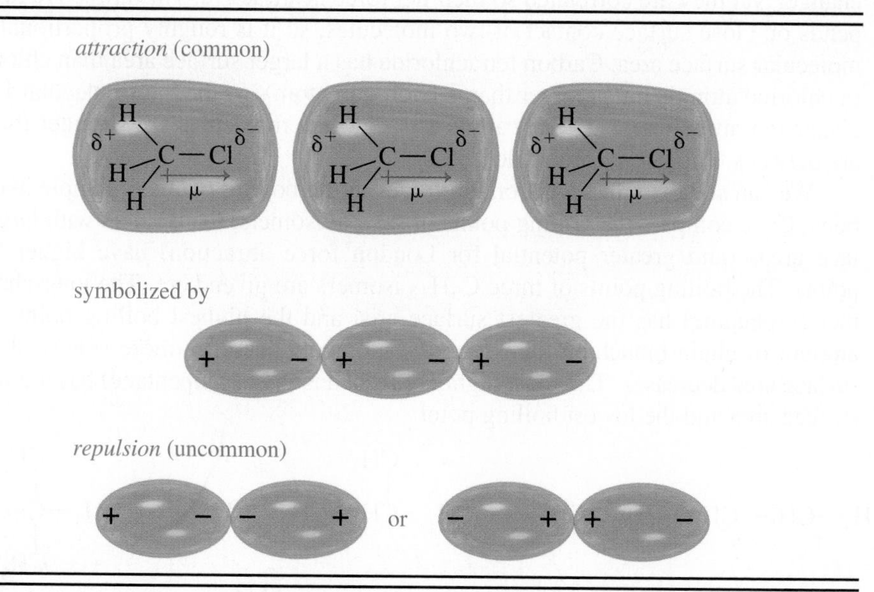

■ **FIGURE 2-23**
Dipole–dipole interactions. Dipole–dipole interactions result from the approach of two polar molecules. If their positive and negative ends approach, the interaction is attractive. If two negative ends or two positive ends approach, the interaction is repulsive. In a liquid or a solid, the molecules mostly orient with their positive and negative ends together, and the net force is attractive.

2-10B The London Dispersion Force

Carbon tetrachloride (CCl_4) has zero dipole moment, yet its boiling point is higher than that of chloroform ($\mu = 1.0$ D). Clearly, there must be some kind of force other than dipole–dipole forces holding the molecules of carbon tetrachloride together.

$\mu = 0$	$\mu = 1.0$ D
carbon tetrachloride, bp = 77 °C	chloroform, bp = 62 °C

In nonpolar molecules such as carbon tetrachloride, the principal attractive force is the **London dispersion force**, one of the **van der Waals forces** (Figure 2-24). The London force arises from temporary dipole moments that are induced in a molecule by other nearby molecules. Even though carbon tetrachloride has no permanent dipole moment, the electrons are not always evenly distributed. A small temporary dipole moment is induced when one molecule approaches another molecule in which the electrons are slightly displaced from a symmetrical arrangement. The electrons in the approaching molecule are displaced slightly so that an attractive dipole–dipole interaction results.

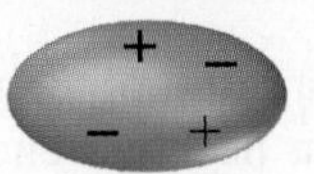
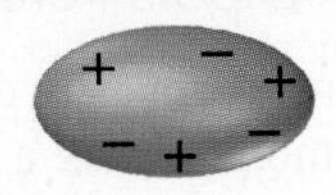

random temporary dipoles when separated

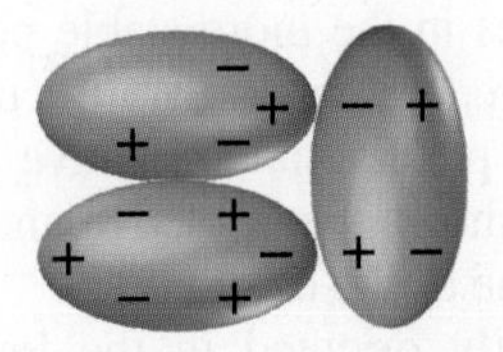

correlated temporary dipoles when in contact

■ **FIGURE 2-24**
London dispersion forces. London dispersion forces result from the attraction of correlated temporary dipoles.

These temporary dipoles last only a fraction of a second, and they constantly change; yet they are correlated so their net force is attractive. This attractive force depends on close surface contact of two molecules, so it is roughly proportional to the molecular surface area. Carbon tetrachloride has a larger surface area than chloroform (a chlorine atom is much larger than a hydrogen atom), so the intermolecular London dispersion attractions between carbon tetrachloride molecules are stronger than they are between chloroform molecules.

We can see the effects of London forces in the boiling points of simple hydrocarbons. If we compare the boiling points of several isomers, the isomers with larger surface areas (and greater potential for London force attraction) have higher boiling points. The boiling points of three C_5H_{12} isomers are given here. The long-chain isomer (*n*-pentane) has the greatest surface area and the highest boiling point. As the amount of chain branching increases, the molecule becomes more spherical and its surface area decreases. The most highly branched isomer (neopentane) has the smallest surface area and the lowest boiling point.

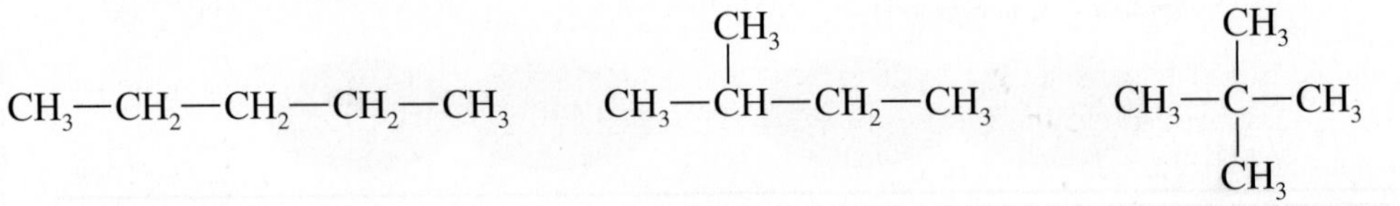

$CH_3-CH_2-CH_2-CH_2-CH_3$
n-pentane, bp = 36 °C

$CH_3-CH(CH_3)-CH_2-CH_3$
isopentane, bp = 28 °C

$CH_3-C(CH_3)_2-CH_3$
neopentane, bp = 10 °C

2-10C Hydrogen Bonding

A **hydrogen bond** is not a true bond but a particularly strong dipole–dipole attraction. A hydrogen atom can participate in hydrogen bonding if it is bonded to oxygen, nitrogen, or fluorine. Organic compounds do not contain H—F bonds, so we consider only N—H and O—H hydrogens to be hydrogen bonded (Figure 2-25).

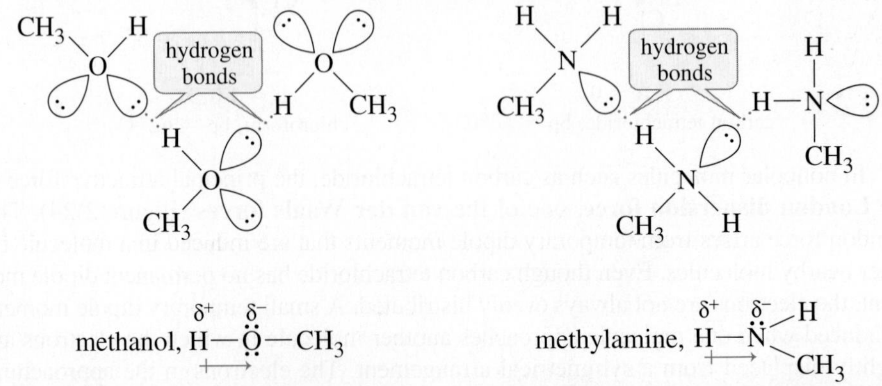

hydrogen bonds

hydrogen bonds

methanol, $\overset{\delta+}{H}-\overset{\delta-}{\ddot{O}}-CH_3$

methylamine, $\overset{\delta+}{H}-\overset{\delta-}{\ddot{N}}(H)-CH_3$

■ **FIGURE 2-25**
Hydrogen bonding. Hydrogen bonding is a strong attraction between an electrophilic O—H or N—H hydrogen atom and a pair of nonbonding electrons.

The O—H and N—H bonds are strongly polarized, leaving the hydrogen atom with a partial positive charge. This electrophilic hydrogen has a strong affinity for nonbonding electrons, and it forms intermolecular attachments with the nonbonding electrons on oxygen or nitrogen atoms.

Although hydrogen bonding is a strong form of intermolecular attraction, it is much weaker than a normal C—H, N—H, or O—H covalent bond. Breaking a hydrogen bond requires about 20 kJ/mol (5 kcal/mol), compared with about 400 kJ/mol (about 100 kcal/mol) required to break a C—H, N—H, or O—H bond.

Hydrogen bonding has a large effect on the physical properties of organic compounds, as shown by the boiling points of ethanol (ethyl alcohol) and dimethyl ether, two isomers of molecular formula C_2H_6O:

$CH_3—CH_2—OH$ — ethanol, bp 78 °C

$CH_3—O—CH_3$ — dimethyl ether, bp −25 °C

These two isomers have the same size and the same molecular weight. Alcohols like ethanol have O—H hydrogens, however, so they are extensively hydrogen bonded. Dimethyl ether has no O—H hydrogen, so it cannot form hydrogen bonds. As a result of its hydrogen bonding, ethanol has a boiling point more than 100 °C higher than that of dimethyl ether.

The effect of N—H hydrogen bonding on boiling points can be seen in the isomers of formula C_3H_9N shown below. Trimethylamine has no N—H hydrogens, so it is not hydrogen bonded. Ethylmethylamine has one N—H hydrogen atom, and the resulting hydrogen bonding raises its boiling point about 34 °C above that of trimethylamine. Propylamine, with two N—H hydrogens, is more extensively hydrogen bonded and has the highest boiling point of these three isomers.

$CH_3—\ddot{N}(CH_3)—CH_3$ — trimethylamine, bp 3.5 °C

$CH_3CH_2—\ddot{N}(H)—CH_3$ — ethylmethylamine, bp 37 °C

$CH_3CH_2CH_2—\ddot{N}(H)—H$ — propylamine, bp 49 °C

Alcohols form stronger hydrogen bonds than amines, probably because oxygen is more electronegative than nitrogen. Thus, the O—H bond is more strongly polarized than the N—H bond. This effect is seen in the boiling points of the preceding isomers, with more than 100 °C difference in the boiling points of ethanol and dimethyl ether, compared with a 34 °C difference for ethylmethylamine and trimethylamine.

The Joule is the SI unit for energy, corresponding to the energy of a mass of 2 kg moving at 1 meter per second. The calorie is the cgs unit for energy, corresponding to the energy required to raise the temperature of 1 gram of water from 14.5 °C to 15.5 °C.

Both units are widely used. They are related by

1 cal = 4.184 J, or

1 kcal = 4.184 kJ.

Hydrogen bonding is essential for the structural integrity of many biological molecules. For example, the double helix structure of DNA is maintained, in part, by hydrogen bonds between the bases: adenine pairs with thymine and guanine pairs with cytosine. Figure 23-25 shows this base-pairing.

PROBLEM 2-16

Draw the hydrogen bonding that takes place between
(a) two molecules of ethanol.
(b) two molecules of propylamine.

SOLVED PROBLEM 2-10

Rank the following compounds in order of increasing boiling points. Explain the reasons for your chosen order.

$CH_3—C(CH_3)_2—CH_3$ — neopentane

2-methylbutan-2-ol (OH)

2,3-dimethylbutane

pentan-1-ol (OH)

hexane

SOLUTION

To predict relative boiling points, we should look for differences in (1) hydrogen bonding, (2) molecular weight and surface area, and (3) dipole moments. Except for neopentane, these compounds have similar molecular weights. Neopentane is the lightest, and it is a compact spherical structure that minimizes van der Waals attractions. Neopentane is the lowest-boiling compound.

Neither *n*-hexane nor 2,3-dimethylbutane is hydrogen bonded, so they will be next higher in boiling points. Because 2,3-dimethylbutane is more highly branched (and has a smaller surface area) than *n*-hexane, 2,3-dimethylbutane will have a lower boiling point than *n*-hexane. So far, we have

neopentane $<$ 2,3-dimethylbutane $<$ hexane $<$ the others

The two remaining compounds are both hydrogen-bonded, and pentan-1-ol has more area for van der Waals forces. Therefore, pentan-1-ol should be the highest-boiling compound. We predict the following order:

neopentane	$<$	2,3-dimethylbutane	$<$	*n*-hexane	$<$	2-methylbutan-2-ol	$<$	pentan-1-ol
10 °C		58 °C		69 °C		102 °C		138 °C

The actual boiling points are given here to show that our prediction is correct.

PROBLEM 2-17

For each pair of compounds, circle the compound you expect to have the higher boiling point. Explain your reasoning.

(a) $(CH_3)_3C{-}C(CH_3)_3$ and $(CH_3)_2CH{-}CH_2CH_2{-}CH(CH_3)_2$
(b) $CH_3(CH_2)_6CH_3$ and $CH_3(CH_2)_5CH_2OH$
(c) $CH_3CH_2OCH_2CH_3$ or $CH_3CH_2CH_2CH_2OH$
(d) $HOCH_2{-}(CH_2)_4{-}CH_2OH$ and $(CH_3)_3CCH(OH)CH_3$
(e) $(CH_3CH_2CH_2)_2NH$ and $(CH_3CH_2)_3N$
(f) (cyclohexane ring)NH and (cyclohexane ring)$-NH_2$

problem-solving **Hint**

To predict relative boiling points, look for differences in
1. hydrogen bonding,
2. molecular weight and surface area, and
3. dipole moments.

2-11 Polarity Effects on Solubilities

In addition to affecting boiling points and melting points, intermolecular forces determine the solubility properties of organic compounds. The general rule is that "*like dissolves like*." Polar substances dissolve in polar solvents, and nonpolar substances dissolve in nonpolar solvents. We discuss the reasons for this rule now, then apply the rule in later chapters when we discuss the solubility properties of organic compounds.

We should consider four different cases: (1) a polar solute with a polar solvent, (2) a polar solute with a nonpolar solvent, (3) a nonpolar solute with a nonpolar solvent, and (4) a nonpolar solute with a polar solvent. We will use sodium chloride and water as examples of polar solutes and solvents, and paraffin "wax" and gasoline as examples of nonpolar solutes and solvents.

Polar Solute in a Polar Solvent (Dissolves) When you think about sodium chloride dissolving in water, it seems remarkable that the oppositely charged ions can be separated from each other. A great deal of energy is required to separate these ions. A polar solvent (such as water) can separate the ions because it *solvates* them (Figure 2-26). If water is the solvent, the solvation process is called *hydration*. As the salt dissolves, water molecules surround each ion, with the appropriate end of the water dipole moment next to the ion. The oxygen atoms of the water molecules approach the positively charged sodium ions. Water's hydrogen atoms approach the negatively charged chloride ions.

Because water molecules are strongly polar, a large amount of energy is released when the sodium and chloride ions are hydrated. This energy is nearly sufficient to overcome the lattice energy of the crystal. The salt dissolves, partly because of strong

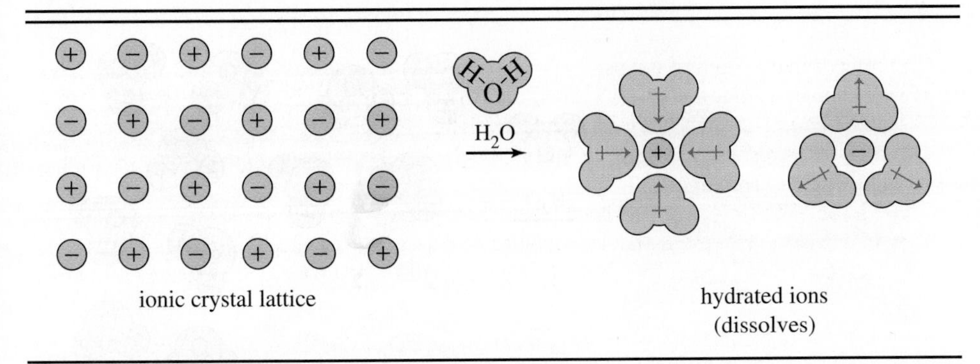

■ **FIGURE 2-26**
Polar solute in water (a polar solvent). The hydration of sodium and chloride ions by water molecules overcomes the lattice energy of sodium chloride. The salt dissolves.

solvation by water molecules and partly because of the increase in entropy (randomness or freedom of movement) when it dissolves.

Polar Solute in a Nonpolar Solvent (Does Not Dissolve) If you stir sodium chloride with a nonpolar solvent such as turpentine or gasoline, you will find that the salt does not dissolve (Figure 2-27). The nonpolar molecules of these solvents do not solvate ions very strongly, and they cannot overcome the large lattice energy of the salt crystal. This is a case where the attractions of the ions in the solid for each other are much greater than their attractions for the solvent.

Nonpolar Solute in a Nonpolar Solvent (Dissolves) Paraffin "wax" dissolves in gasoline. Both paraffin and gasoline are mixtures of nonpolar hydrocarbons (Figure 2-28). The molecules of a nonpolar substance (paraffin) are weakly attracted to each other, and these van der Waals attractions are easily overcome by van der Waals attractions with the solvent. Although there is little change in energy when the nonpolar substance dissolves in a nonpolar solvent, there is a large increase in entropy.

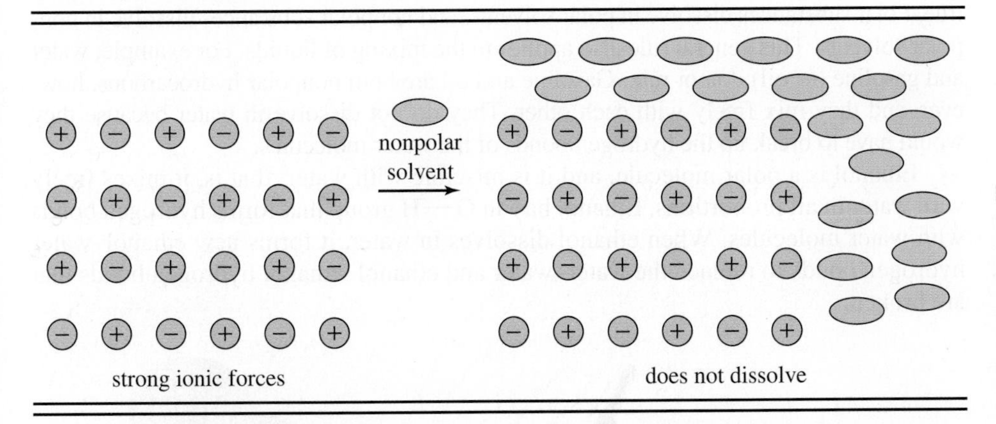

■ **FIGURE 2-27**
Polar solute in a nonpolar solvent. The intermolecular attractions of polar substances are stronger than their attractions for nonpolar solvent molecules. Thus, a polar substance does not dissolve in a nonpolar solvent.

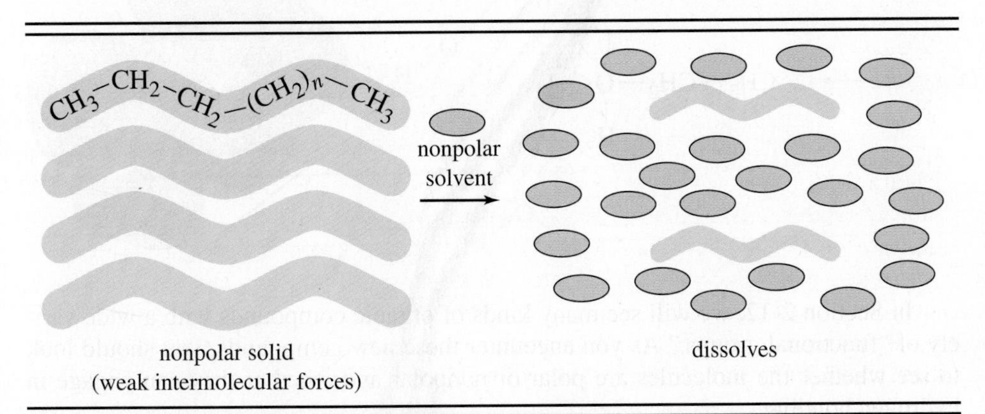

■ **FIGURE 2-28**
Nonpolar solute in a nonpolar solvent. The weak intermolecular attractions of a nonpolar substance are overcome by the weak attractions for a nonpolar solvent. The nonpolar substance dissolves.

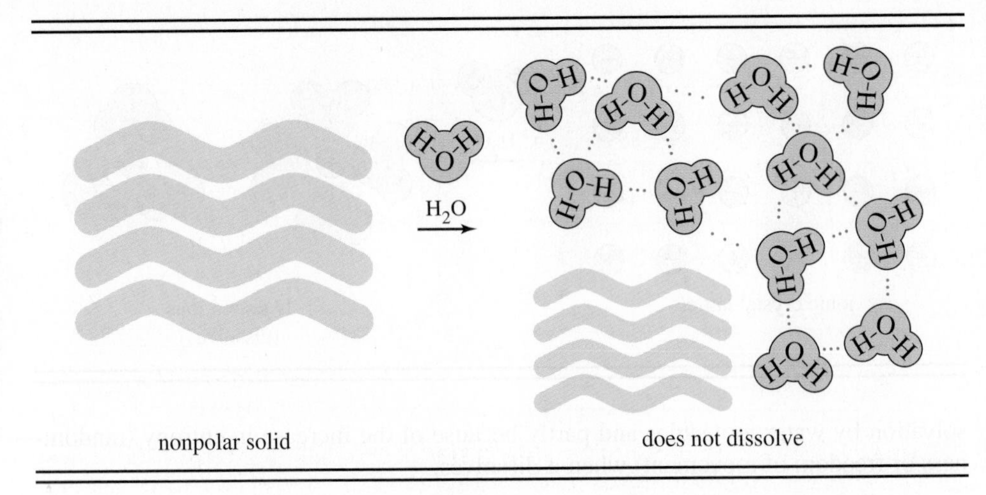

■ **FIGURE 2-29**
Nonpolar solute in a polar solvent (water). Nonpolar substances do not dissolve in water because of the unfavorable entropy effects associated with forming a hydrogen-bonded shell of water molecules around a nonpolar molecule.

Nonpolar Solute in a Polar Solvent (Does Not Dissolve) Anyone who does home canning knows that a nonpolar solid such as paraffin does not dissolve in a polar solvent such as water. Why not? The nonpolar molecules are only weakly attracted to each other, and little energy is required to separate them. The problem is that the water molecules are strongly attracted to each other by their hydrogen bonding. If a nonpolar paraffin molecule were to dissolve, the water molecules around it would have to form a cavity. Water molecules at the edge of the cavity have fewer available neighbors for hydrogen bonding, resulting in a tighter, more rigid, ice-like structure around the cavity. This tighter structure results in an unfavorable decrease in the entropy of the system: $\Delta G = \Delta H - T\Delta S$, and ΔH is small in most cases. Therefore, the negative value of ΔS makes ΔG positive (unfavorable), and the nonpolar substance does not dissolve (Figure 2-29).

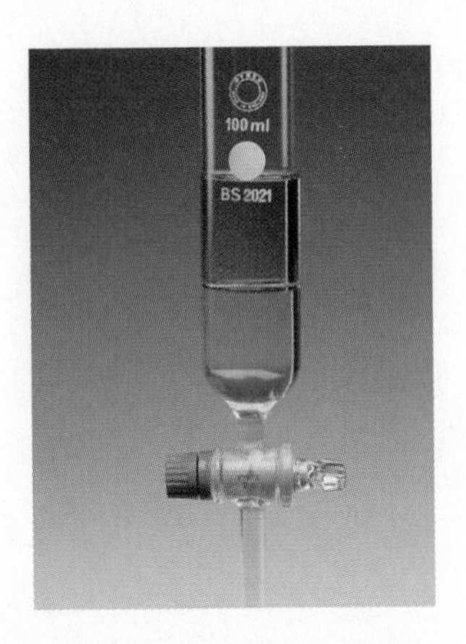

Motor oil and water do not mix because the nonpolar oil molecules cannot displace the strong intermolecular attractions between water molecules.

Figures 2-26 through 2-29 show why the saying "like dissolves like" is generally true. Polar substances dissolve in polar solvents, and nonpolar substances dissolve in nonpolar solvents. This general rule also applies to the mixing of liquids. For example, water and gasoline (or oil) do not mix. Gasoline and oil are both nonpolar hydrocarbons, however, and they mix freely with each other. They do not dissolve in water because they would have to break up the hydrogen bonds of the water molecules.

Ethanol is a polar molecule, and it is miscible with water; that is, it mixes freely with water in all proportions. Ethanol has an O—H group that forms hydrogen bonds with water molecules. When ethanol dissolves in water, it forms new ethanol–water hydrogen bonds to replace the water–water and ethanol–ethanol hydrogen bonds that are broken:

$$CH_3-CH_2-\ddot{O}-H \;+\; H-\ddot{O}-H \longrightarrow CH_3-CH_2-\underset{\substack{|\\ H\cdots \ddot{O}H_2}}{\ddot{O}}\cdots H-\ddot{O}-H \;(\text{and } \cdots H-\ddot{O}-H)$$

In Section 2-12, we will see many kinds of organic compounds with a wide variety of "functional groups." As you encounter these new compounds, you should look to see whether the molecules are polar or nonpolar and whether they can engage in hydrogen bonding.

PROBLEM 2-18

Circle the member of each pair that is more soluble in water.
(a) $CH_3CH_2OCH_2CH_3$ or $CH_3CH_2CH_2CH_2CH_3$
(b) $CH_3CH_2OCH_2CH_3$ or $CH_3CH_2CH_2OH$
(c) $CH_3CH_2NHCH_3$ or $CH_3CH_2CH_2CH_3$
(d) CH_3CH_2OH or $CH_3CH_2CH_2CH_2OH$
(e)

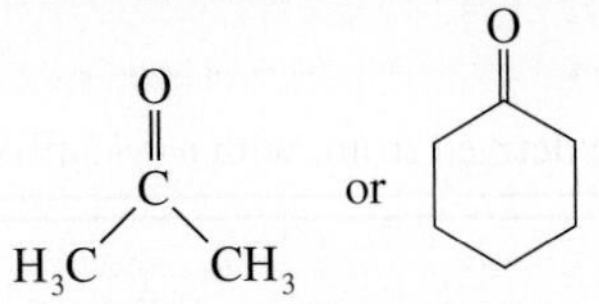

Most vitamins contain charged groups, making them water-soluble. As a result, they are rapidly eliminated and generally nontoxic. Vitamins A and D, however, are nonpolar and are stored in the fat tissue of the body, which is also nonpolar. Hence, these two vitamins are potentially toxic in large doses.

2-12 Hydrocarbons

In future chapters, we will study many different types of organic compounds. The various kinds of compounds are briefly described here so that you can recognize them as you encounter them. For the purpose of this brief survey, we divide organic compounds into three classes: (1) hydrocarbons, (2) compounds containing oxygen, and (3) compounds containing nitrogen.

The **hydrocarbons** are compounds composed entirely of carbon and hydrogen. The major classes of hydrocarbons are alkanes, alkenes, alkynes, and aromatic hydrocarbons.

2-12A Alkanes

Alkanes are hydrocarbons that contain only single bonds. Alkane names generally have the *-ane* suffix, and the first part of the name indicates the number of carbon atoms. Table 2-2 shows how the prefixes in the names correspond with the number of carbon atoms.

The **cycloalkanes** are a special class of alkanes in the form of a ring. Figure 2-30 shows the Lewis structures and line–angle formulas of cyclopentane and cyclohexane, the cycloalkanes containing five and six carbons, respectively.

TABLE 2-2

Correspondence of Prefixes and Numbers of Carbon Atoms

Alkane Name	Number of Carbons	Alkane Name	Number of Carbons
*meth*ane	1	*hex*ane	6
*eth*ane	2	*hept*ane	7
*prop*ane	3	*oct*ane	8
*but*ane	4	*non*ane	9
*pent*ane	5	*dec*ane	10

CH_4 (methane) $CH_3{-}CH_3$ (ethane) $CH_3{-}CH_2{-}CH_3$ (propane) $CH_3{-}CH_2{-}CH_2{-}CH_3$ (butane) $CH_3{-}CH(CH_3){-}CH_3$ (isobutane)

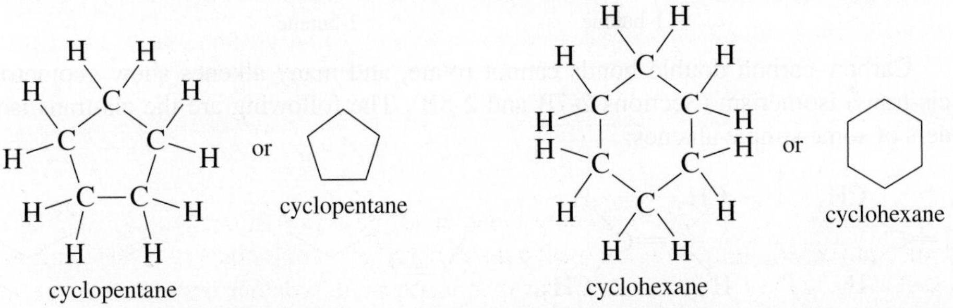

■ **FIGURE 2-30** Cycloalkanes. Cycloalkanes are alkanes in the form of a ring.

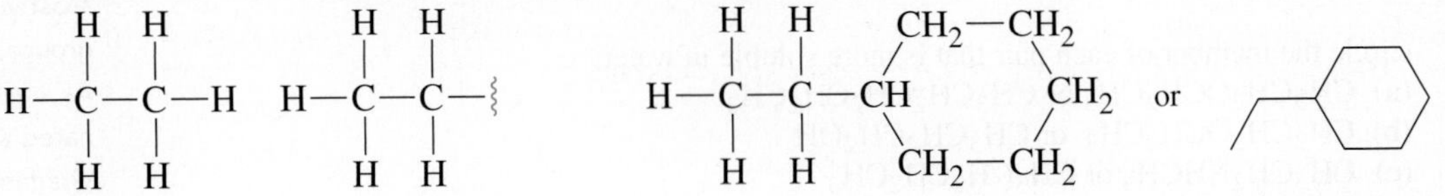

ethane — ethyl group — ethylcyclohexane — or — ethylcyclohexane

■ **FIGURE 2-31**
Naming alkyl groups. Alkyl groups are named like the alkanes they are derived from, with a *-yl* suffix.

Alkanes are the major components of heating gases (natural gas and liquefied petroleum gas), gasoline, jet fuel, diesel fuel, motor oil, fuel oil, and paraffin "wax." Other than combustion, alkanes undergo few reactions. In fact, when a molecule contains an alkane portion and a nonalkane portion, we often ignore the presence of the alkane portion because it is relatively unreactive. Alkanes undergo few reactions because they have no **functional group**, the part of the molecule where reactions usually occur. Functional groups are distinct chemical units, such as double bonds, hydroxyl groups, or halogen atoms, that are reactive. Most organic compounds are characterized and classified by their functional groups.

An **alkyl group** is an alkane portion of a molecule, with one hydrogen atom removed to allow bonding to the functional group. Figure 2-31 shows an ethyl group (C_2H_5) attached to cyclohexane to give ethylcyclohexane. We might try to name this compound as "cyclohexylethane," but we should treat the larger fragment as the parent compound (cyclohexane), and the smaller group as the alkyl group (ethyl).

We are often concerned primarily with the structure of the most important part of a molecule. In these cases, we can use the symbol R as a substituent to represent an alkyl group. We presume that the exact nature of the R group is unimportant.

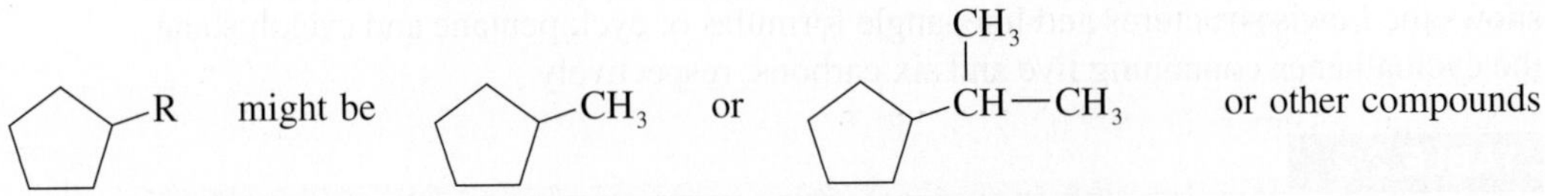

an alkylcyclopentane (—R) might be methylcyclopentane ($-CH_3$) or isopropylcyclopentane ($-CH(CH_3)-CH_3$) or other compounds

2-12B Alkenes

Alkenes are hydrocarbons that contain carbon–carbon double bonds. A carbon–carbon double bond is the most reactive part of an alkene, so we say that the double bond is the *functional group* of the alkene. Alkene names end in the *-ene* suffix. If the double bond might be in more than one position, then the chain is numbered and the lower number of the two double-bonded carbons is added to the name to indicate the position of the double bond.

$CH_2{=}CH_2$ ethene (ethylene)

$CH_2{=}CH{-}CH_3$ propene (propylene)

$\overset{1}{C}H_2{=}\overset{2}{C}H{-}\overset{3}{C}H_2{-}\overset{4}{C}H_3$ 1-butene

$\overset{1}{C}H_3{-}\overset{2}{C}H{=}\overset{3}{C}H{-}\overset{4}{C}H_3$ 2-butene

Carbon–carbon double bonds cannot rotate, and many alkenes show geometric (cis-trans) isomerism (Sections 2-7B and 2-8B). The following are the cis-trans isomers of some simple alkenes:

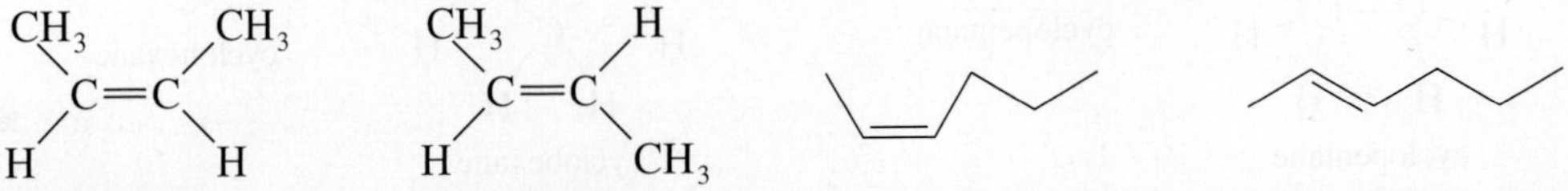

cis-2-butene — *trans*-2-butene — *cis*-2-hexene — *trans*-2-hexene

Cycloalkenes are also common. Unless the rings are very large, cycloalkenes are always the cis isomers, and the term *cis* is omitted from the names. In a large ring, a trans double bond may occur, giving a *trans*-cycloalkene.

cyclopentene cyclohexene *trans*-cyclodecene

2-12C Alkynes

Alkynes are hydrocarbons with carbon–carbon triple bonds as their functional group. Alkyne names generally have the *-yne* suffix, although some of their common names (*acetylene*, for example) do not conform to this rule. The triple bond is linear, so there is no possibility of geometric (cis-trans) isomerism in alkynes.

$H-C\equiv C-H$ ethyne (acetylene)

$H-C\equiv C-CH_3$ propyne (methylacetylene)

$\overset{1}{H}-\overset{2}{C}\equiv \overset{3}{C}-\overset{4}{CH_2}-CH_3$ 1-butyne

$\overset{1}{CH_3}-\overset{2}{C}\equiv \overset{3}{C}-\overset{4}{CH_3}$ 2-butyne

In an alkyne, four atoms must be in a straight line. These four collinear atoms are not easily bent into a ring, so cycloalkynes are rare. Cycloalkynes are stable only if the ring is large, containing eight or more carbon atoms.

H_2C-CH_2, C, CH_2, C, CH_2, H_2C-CH_2

cyclooctyne

2-12D Aromatic Hydrocarbons

The following compounds may look like cycloalkenes, but their properties are different from those of simple alkenes. These **aromatic hydrocarbons** (also called **arenes**) are all derivatives of *benzene*, represented by a six-membered ring with three double bonds. This bonding arrangement is particularly stable, for reasons that are explained in Chapter 16.

or benzene

CH_2CH_3 or ethylbenzene

R or an alkylbenzene

The presence of a methyl or ethyl group can make a big difference in biological systems. For example, benzene is quite toxic and causes leukemia, while methyl benzene (and ethyl benzene) are less toxic because enzymes can oxidize the methyl or ethyl group.

Just as a generic alkyl group substituent is represented by R, a generic aryl group is represented by Ar. When a benzene ring serves as a substituent, it is called a phenyl group, abbreviated Ph.

Ar might be Ph = or other compounds

an arylcyclopentane phenylcyclopentane

PROBLEM 2-19

Classify the following hydrocarbons, and draw a Lewis structure for each one. A compound may fit into more than one of the following classifications:

alkane	cycloalkane	aromatic hydrocarbon
alkene	cycloalkene	
alkyne	cycloalkyne	

(a) $(CH_3CH_2)_2CHCH(CH_3)_2$ **(b)** $CH_3CHCHCH_2CH_3$ **(c)** $CH_3CCCH_2CH_2CH_3$

(d) $CH_2-C\equiv C-CH_2$ / $CH_2-CH_2-CH_2-CH_2$ **(e)** (cyclobutane ring)$-CHCH_2$ **(f)** (benzene ring)$-CCH$

(g) (cyclohexadiene ring)$-CHC(CH_3)_2$ **(h)** (cyclopentane ring)$-CH_2CH_3$ **(i)** (dihydronaphthalene)

2-13 Organic Compounds Containing Oxygen

Many organic compounds contain oxygen atoms bonded to alkyl groups. The major classes of oxygen-containing compounds are alcohols, ethers, ketones, aldehydes, carboxylic acids, and acid derivatives.

2-13A Alcohols

Alcohols are organic compounds that contain the **hydroxyl group** ($-OH$) as their functional group. The general formula for an alcohol is $R-OH$. Alcohols are among the most polar organic compounds because the hydroxyl group is strongly polar and can participate in hydrogen bonding. Some of the simple alcohols like ethanol and methanol are miscible (soluble in all proportions) with water. Names of alcohols end in the *-ol* suffix from the word "alcohol," as shown for the following common alcohols:

$R-OH$	CH_3-OH	CH_3CH_2-OH	$CH_3-CH_2-CH_2-OH$	$CH_3-CH(OH)-CH_3$
an alcohol	methanol (methyl alcohol)	ethanol (ethyl alcohol)	1-propanol (*n*-propyl alcohol)	2-propanol (isopropyl alcohol)

Alcohols are some of the most common organic compounds. Methyl alcohol (methanol), also known as "wood alcohol," is used as an industrial solvent and as an automotive racing fuel. Ethyl alcohol (ethanol) is sometimes called "grain alcohol" because it is produced by the fermentation of grain or almost any other organic material. "Isopropyl alcohol" is the common name for 2-propanol, used as "rubbing alcohol."

Ethanol is widely used as an additive to gasoline. "Gasohol" is an "oxygenated" fuel that contains about 10% ethanol, which causes the fuel to burn at a slightly lower temperature, producing lower concentrations of pollutants such as nitrogen oxides. Ethanol has largely replaced MTBE (methyl *tert*-butyl ether) as an oxygenated fuel additive because of safety concerns about MTBE contaminating groundwater when it leaks from storage tanks.

2-13B Ethers

Ethers are composed of two alkyl groups bonded to an oxygen atom. The general formula for an ether is $R-O-R'$. (The symbol R' represents another alkyl group, either the same as or different from the first.) Like alcohols, ethers are much more polar than hydrocarbons. Ethers have no $O-H$ hydrogens, however, so they cannot hydrogen bond with themselves. Ether names are often formed from the names of the alkyl groups and the word "ether." Diethyl ether is the common "ether" used for starting engines in cold weather and once used for surgical anesthesia.

$R-O-R'$ — ROR′, an ether

CH_3-O-CH_3 — dimethyl ether

$CH_3CH_2-O-CH_2CH_3$ — diethyl ether

furan

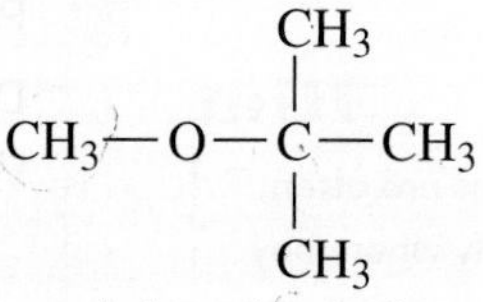

$CH_3-O-C(CH_3)_3$ — methyl *tert*-butyl ether

2-13C Aldehydes and Ketones

The **carbonyl group**, C=O, is the functional group for both aldehydes and ketones. A **ketone** has two alkyl groups bonded to the carbonyl group; an **aldehyde** has one alkyl group and a hydrogen atom bonded to the carbonyl group. Ketone names generally have the *-one* suffix; aldehyde names use either the *-al* suffix or the *-aldehyde* suffix.

The carbonyl group is strongly polar, and most ketones and aldehydes are somewhat soluble in water. Both acetone and acetaldehyde are miscible with water. Acetone, often used as nail polish remover, is a common solvent with low toxicity.

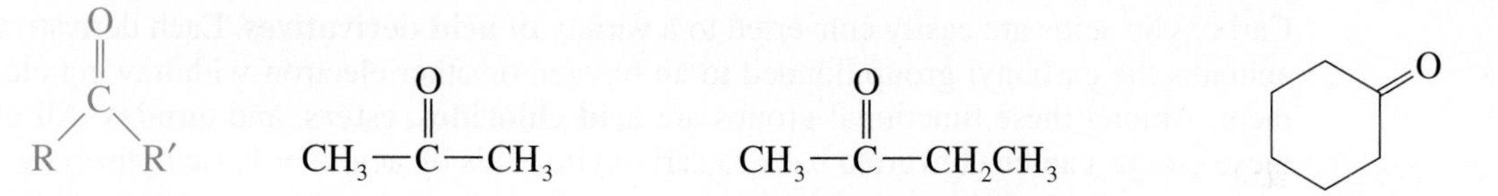

$R-C(=O)-R'$ — RCOR′, a ketone

$CH_3-C(=O)-CH_3$ — 2-propanone (acetone)

$CH_3-C(=O)-CH_2CH_3$ — 2-butanone (methyl ethyl ketone)

cyclohexanone

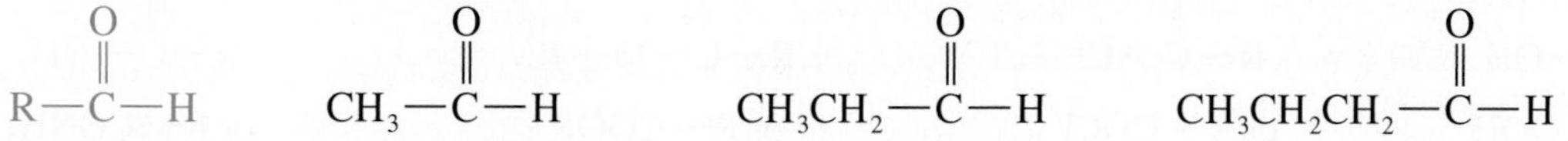

$R-C(=O)-H$ or RCHO — an aldehyde

$CH_3-C(=O)-H$ or CH_3CHO — ethanal (acetaldehyde)

$CH_3CH_2-C(=O)-H$ or CH_3CH_2CHO — propanal (propionaldehyde)

$CH_3CH_2CH_2-C(=O)-H$ or $CH_3CH_2CH_2CHO$ — butanal (butyraldehyde)

2-13D Carboxylic Acids

Carboxylic acids contain the **carboxyl group**, —COOH, as their functional group. The general formula for a carboxylic acid is R—COOH (*or* RCO_2H). The carboxyl group is a combination of a carbonyl group and a hydroxyl group, but this combination has different properties from those of ketones and alcohols. Carboxylic acids owe their acidity (pK_a of about 5) to the resonance-stabilized *carboxylate anions* formed by deprotonation. The following reaction shows the dissociation of a carboxylic acid:

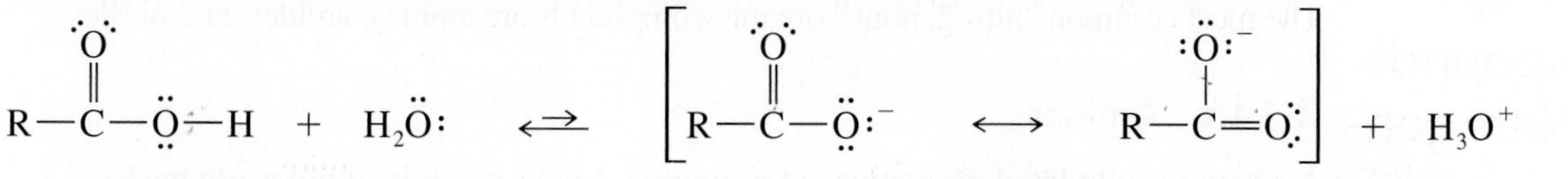

$$R-C(=O)-O-H + H_2O \rightleftharpoons \left[R-C(=O)-O^- \longleftrightarrow R-C(-O^-)=O \right] + H_3O^+$$

carboxylic acid — carboxylate anion

Systematic names for carboxylic acids use the *-oic acid* suffix, but historical names are commonly used. Formic acid was first isolated from ants, genus *Formica*. Acetic acid, found in vinegar, gets its name from the Latin word for "sour" *(acetum)*. Propionic acid gives the tangy flavor to sharp cheeses, and butyric acid provides the pungent aroma of rancid butter.

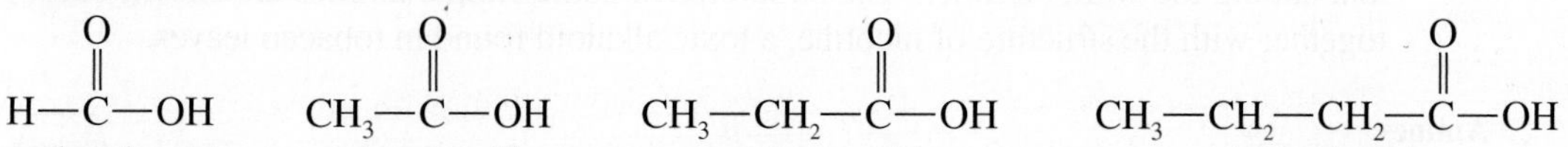

$H-C(=O)-OH$ — methanoic acid (formic acid)

$CH_3-C(=O)-OH$ — ethanoic acid (acetic acid)

$CH_3-CH_2-C(=O)-OH$ — propanoic acid (propionic acid)

$CH_3-CH_2-CH_2-C(=O)-OH$ — butanoic acid (butyric acid)

Carboxylic acids are strongly polar, like ketones, aldehydes, and alcohols. They are relatively soluble in water; in fact, all four of the carboxylic acids shown here are miscible (soluble in all proportions) with water.

PROBLEM 2-20

problem-solving Hint

Condensed formulas are often confusing, especially when they involve carbonyl groups. Whenever you see a complicated condensed formula, convert it to a Lewis structure first for clarity.

Draw a Lewis structure, and classify each of the following compounds. The possible classifications are as follows:

alcohol	ketone	carboxylic acid
ether	aldehyde	alkene

(a) CH_2CHCHO **(b)** $CH_3CH_2CH(OH)CH_3$ **(c)** $CH_3COCH_2CH_3$

(d) $CH_3CH_2OCHCH_2$ **(e)** (cyclohexane ring bearing COOH) **(f)** (six-membered ring containing O)

(g) (cyclopentenone ring, =O) **(h)** (cyclopentane ring bearing CHO) **(i)** (cyclopentane ring bearing CH_2OH)

2-13E Carboxylic Acid Derivatives

Carboxylic acids are easily converted to a variety of **acid derivatives**. Each derivative contains the carbonyl group bonded to an oxygen or other electron-withdrawing element. Among these functional groups are **acid chlorides, esters,** and **amides**. All of these groups can be converted back to carboxylic acids by acidic or basic hydrolysis.

R—C(=O)—OH	R—C(=O)—Cl	R—C(=O)—O—R′	R—C(=O)—NH_2
or R—COOH	or R—COCl	or R—COOR′	or R—$CONH_2$
carboxylic acid	acid chloride	ester	amide
CH_3—C(=O)—OH	CH_3—C(=O)—Cl	CH_3—C(=O)—O—CH_2CH_3	CH_3—C(=O)—NH_2
or CH_3COOH	or CH_3COCl	or $CH_3COOCH_2CH_3$	or CH_3CONH_2
acetic acid	acetyl chloride	ethyl acetate	acetamide

2-14 Organic Compounds Containing Nitrogen

Nitrogen is another element often found in the functional groups of organic compounds. The most common "nitrogenous" organic compounds are amines, amides, and nitriles.

2-14A Amines

Amines are alkylated derivatives of ammonia. Like ammonia, amines are basic.

$$R-\ddot{N}H_2 + H_2O \rightleftharpoons R-\overset{+}{N}H_3 \ {}^{-}OH \qquad K_b \cong 10^{-4}$$

Because of their basicity ("alkalinity"), naturally occurring amines are often called *alkaloids*. Simple amines are named by naming the alkyl groups bonded to nitrogen and adding the word "amine." The structures of some simple amines are shown below, together with the structure of nicotine, a toxic alkaloid found in tobacco leaves.

Amines:

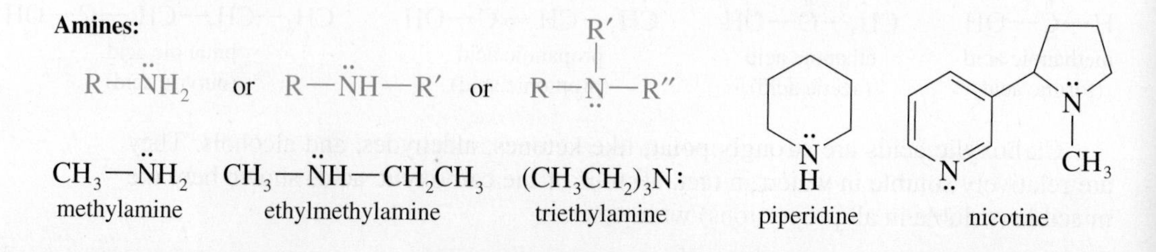

2-14B Amides

Amides are acid derivatives that result from a combination of an acid with ammonia or an amine. Proteins have the structure of long-chain, complex amides.

$$\mathrm{R{-}C({=}O){-}NH_2} \quad \text{or} \quad \mathrm{R{-}C({=}O){-}NHR'} \quad \text{or} \quad \mathrm{R{-}C({=}O){-}NR'_2}$$

amides

$$\mathrm{CH_3{-}C({=}O){-}NH_2} \qquad \mathrm{CH_3{-}C({=}O){-}NH{-}CH_3} \qquad \mathrm{C_6H_5{-}C({=}O){-}N(CH_3)_2}$$

acetamide — *N*-methylacetamide — *N*,*N*-dimethylbenzamide

Amides are among the most stable acid derivatives. The nitrogen atom of an amide is not as basic as the nitrogen of an amine because of the electron-withdrawing effect of the carbonyl group. The following resonance forms help to show why amides are very weak bases:

$$\left[\mathrm{R{-}C({=}\ddot{O}){-}\ddot{N}H_2} \longleftrightarrow \mathrm{R{-}C(\ddot{O}{:}^{-}){=}\overset{+}{N}H_2}\right]$$

very weak base

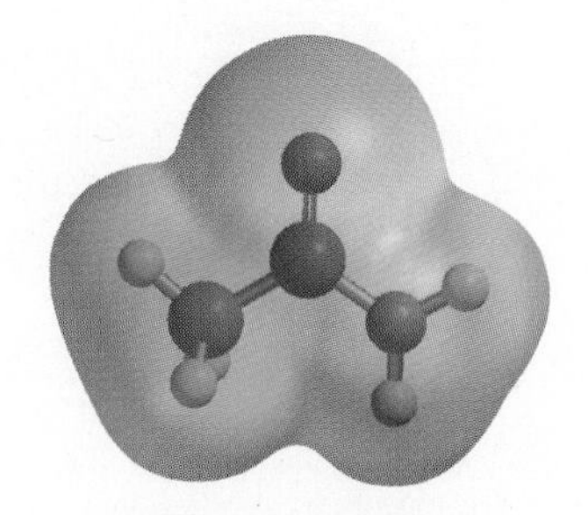
EPM of acetamide

Amides form particularly strong hydrogen bonds, giving them high melting points and high boiling points. The strongly polarized amide N—H hydrogen forms unusually strong hydrogen bonds with the carbonyl oxygen that carries a partial negative charge in the polarized resonance form shown above. The following illustration shows this strong intermolecular hydrogen bonding.

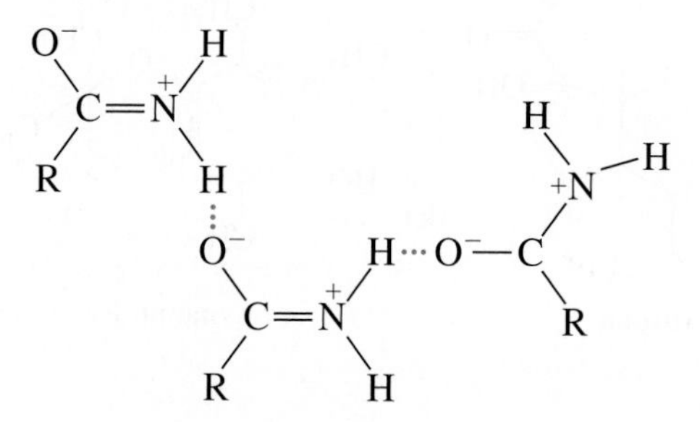
hydrogen bonding in amides

Proteins are specialized polymers of amides (covered in Chapter 24). Their three-dimensional structures are defined and stabilized by the strong hydrogen bonding found in amides.

2-14C Nitriles

A **nitrile** is a compound containing the **cyano group**, —C≡N. The cyano group was introduced in Section 2-6 as an example of *sp* hybridized bonding. The cyano group is strongly polar by virtue of the C≡N triple bond, and most small nitriles are somewhat soluble in water. Acetonitrile is miscible with water.

$$\mathrm{R{-}C{\equiv}N{:}} \qquad \mathrm{CH_3{-}C{\equiv}N{:}} \qquad \mathrm{CH_3CH_2{-}C{\equiv}N{:}} \qquad \mathrm{C_6H_5{-}C{\equiv}N{:}}$$

a nitrile — acetonitrile — propionitrile — benzonitrile

All of these classes of compounds are summarized in the table of Common Organic Compounds and Functional Groups, given on the front inside cover for convenient reference.

PROBLEM 2-21

Draw a Lewis structure, and classify each of the following compounds:

(a) $CH_3CH_2CONHCH_3$ **(b)** $(CH_3CH_2)_2NH$ **(c)** $(CH_3)_2CHCOOCH_3$
(d) $CH_3CHCHCOCl$ **(e)** $(CH_3CH_2)_2O$ **(f)** $CH_3CH_2CH_2CN$
(g) $(CH_3)_3CCH_2CH_2COOH$ **(h)** 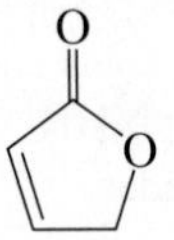 **(i)**

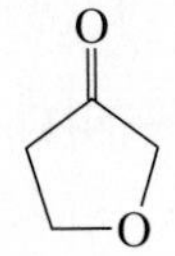

(j) 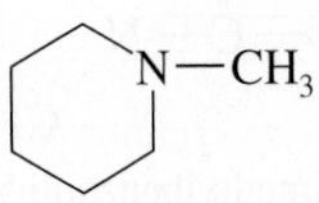 N—CH_3 **(k)** O, N—CH_3 **(l)** N—C(=O)—CH_3

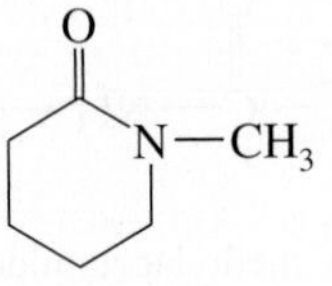

(m) O, O **(n)** CH_3 O, N, C—H **(o)** $COCH_3$

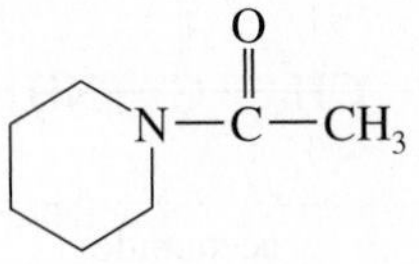

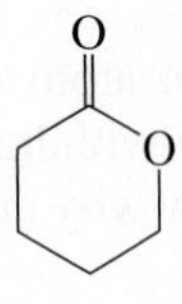

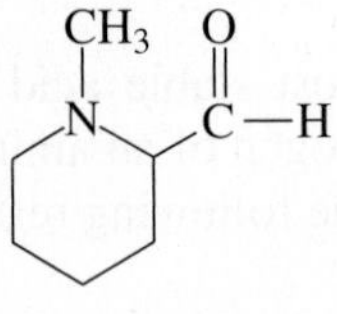

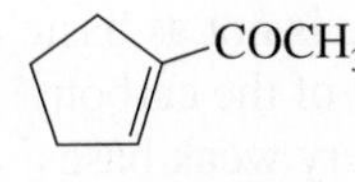

PROBLEM 2-22

Circle the functional groups in the following structures. State to which class (or classes) of compounds the structure belongs.

(a) $CH_2{=}CHCH_2COOCH_3$ **(b)** CH_3OCH_3 **(c)** CH_3CHO
(d) CH_3CONH_2 **(e)** CH_3NHCH_3 **(f)** RCOOH
(g) 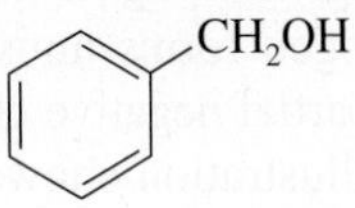 CH_2OH **(h)** 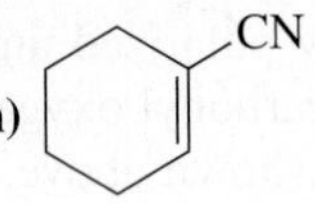 CN **(i)** 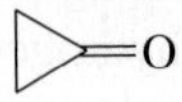 =O

(j) 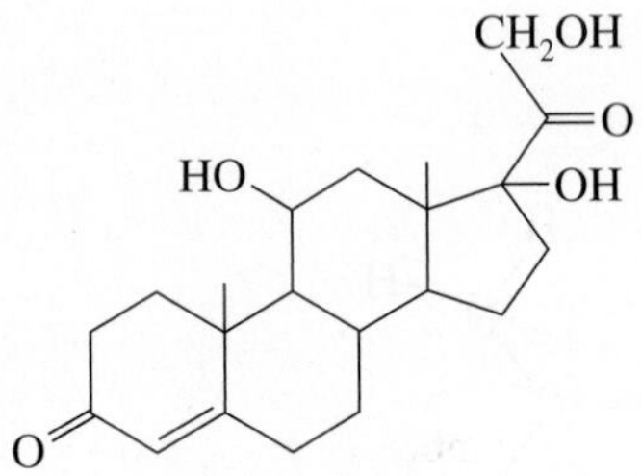 CH_2OH, =O, HO, OH, O
hydrocortisone

(k) 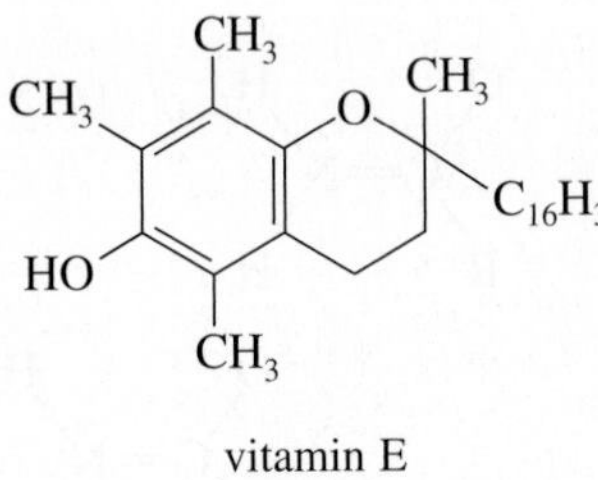 CH_3, CH_3, O, CH_3, $C_{16}H_{33}$, HO, CH_3
vitamin E

2 Glossary

acid chloride An acid derivative with a chlorine atom in place of the hydroxyl group. (p. 74)

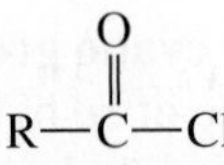

$$R{-}\overset{O}{\overset{\|}{C}}{-}Cl$$

alcohol A compound that contains a hydroxyl group bonded to a carbon atom; R—OH. (p. 72)

aldehyde A carbonyl group with one alkyl group and one hydrogen. (p. 73)

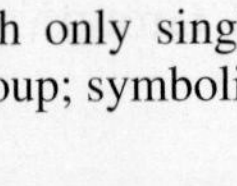

$$R{-}\overset{O}{\overset{\|}{C}}{-}H$$

alkanes Hydrocarbons containing only single bonds. (p. 69)

alkenes Hydrocarbons containing one or more C=C double bonds. (p. 70)

alkyl group A hydrocarbon group with only single bonds; an alkane with one hydrogen removed, to allow bonding to another group; symbolized by R. (p. 70)

alkynes Hydrocarbons containing one or more C≡C triple bonds. (p. 71)
amide An acid derivative that contains a nitrogen atom instead of the hydroxyl group of the acid. (p. 75)

$$R-\overset{\overset{\displaystyle O}{\|}}{C}-NH_2 \quad R-\overset{\overset{\displaystyle O}{\|}}{C}-NHR' \quad R-\overset{\overset{\displaystyle O}{\|}}{C}-NR'_2$$

amine An alkylated analogue of ammonia; $R-NH_2$, R_2NH, or R_3N. (p. 74)
aromatic hydrocarbons (arenes) Hydrocarbons containing a *benzene ring*, a six-membered ring with three double bonds. (p. 71)
bond dipole moment A measure of the polarity of an individual bond in a molecule, defined as $\mu = (4.8 \times d \times \delta)$, where μ is the dipole moment in **debyes** (10^{-10} esu - Å), d is the bond length in angstroms, and δ is the effective amount of charge separated, in units of the electronic charge. (p. 59)
carbonyl group The >C=O functional group, as in a ketone or aldehyde. (p. 73)
carboxyl group The —COOH functional group, as in a carboxylic acid. (p. 73)
carboxylic acid A compound that contains the carboxyl group, —COOH. (p. 73)

$$R-\overset{\overset{\displaystyle O}{\|}}{C}-OH$$

cis-trans isomers (geometric isomers) Stereoisomers that differ in their cis-trans arrangement on a double bond or on a ring. The cis isomer has similar groups on the same side, and the trans isomer has similar groups on opposite sides. (p. 58)
constitutional isomers (structural isomers) Isomers whose atoms are connected differently; they differ in their bonding sequence. (p. 57)
cyano group The —C≡N functional group, as in a nitrile. (p. 75)
dipole–dipole forces Attractive intermolecular forces resulting from the attraction of the positive and negative ends of the permanent dipole moments of polar molecules. (p. 63)
dipole moment See **bond dipole moment** and **molecular dipole moment**. (p. 59)
double bond A bond containing four electrons between two nuclei. One pair of electrons forms a sigma bond, and the other pair forms a pi bond. (p. 45)
ester An acid derivative with an alkyl group replacing the acid proton. (p. 75)

$$R-\overset{\overset{\displaystyle O}{\|}}{C}-OR'$$

ether A compound with an oxygen bonded between two alkyl (or aromatic) groups; R—O—R′. (p. 72)
functional group The reactive, nonalkane part of an organic molecule. (p. 70)
geometric isomers See **cis-trans isomers**. (p. 58)
hybrid atomic orbital A directional orbital formed from a combination of s and p orbitals on the same atom. (pp. 42, 46)

***sp* hybrid orbitals** give two orbitals with a bond angle of 180° (**linear** geometry).
sp^2 hybrid orbitals give three orbitals with bond angles of 120° (**trigonal** geometry).
sp^3 hybrid orbitals give four orbitals with bond angles of 109.5° (**tetrahedral** geometry).

hydrocarbons Compounds composed exclusively of carbon and hydrogen.

alkanes: Hydrocarbons containing only single bonds. (p. 69)
alkenes: Hydrocarbons containing one or more C=C double bonds. (p. 70)
alkynes: Hydrocarbons containing one or more C≡C triple bonds. (p. 71)
cycloalkanes, cycloalkenes, cycloalkynes: Alkanes, alkenes, and alkynes in the form of a ring. (p. 69)
aromatic hydrocarbons: Hydrocarbons containing a *benzene ring*, a six-membered ring with three double bonds. (p. 71)

benzene

hydrogen bond A particularly strong attraction between a nonbonding pair of electrons and an electrophilic O—H or N—H hydrogen. Hydrogen bonds have bond energies of about 20 kJ/mol (5 kcal/mol), compared with about 400 kJ/mol (about 100 kcal/mol) for typical C—H bonds. (p. 64)

hydroxyl group The —OH functional group, as in an alcohol. (p. 72)
isomers Different compounds with the same molecular formula. (p. 57)
 constitutional isomers (structural isomers) are connected differently; they differ in their bonding sequence.
 stereoisomers differ only in how their atoms are oriented in space.
 cis-trans isomers (geometric isomers) are stereoisomers that differ in their cis-trans arrangement on a double bond or on a ring.
 stereochemistry is the study of the structure and chemistry of stereoisomers.
ketone A carbonyl group with two alkyl groups attached. (p. 73)

$$\mathrm{R-\overset{\overset{\displaystyle O}{\|}}{C}-R'}$$

linear combination of atomic orbitals (LCAO) Wave functions can add to each other to produce the wave functions of new orbitals. The number of new orbitals generated equals the original number of orbitals. (p. 42)
London dispersion forces Intermolecular forces resulting from the attraction of correlated temporary dipole moments induced in adjacent molecules. (p. 63)
molecular dipole moment The vector sum of the bond dipole moments (and any nonbonding pairs of electrons) in a molecule; a measure of the polarity of a molecule. (p. 61)
molecular orbital (MO) An orbital formed by the overlap of atomic orbitals on different atoms. MOs can be either bonding or antibonding, but only the bonding MOs are filled in most stable molecules. (p. 42)
 A **bonding molecular orbital** places a large amount of electron density in the bonding region between the nuclei. The energy of an electron in a bonding MO is lower than it is in an atomic orbital.
 An **antibonding molecular orbital** places most of the electron density outside the bonding region. The energy of an electron in an antibonding MO is higher than it is in an atomic orbital.
nitrile A compound containing a cyano group, $-\mathrm{C{\equiv}N}$. (p. 75)
node In an orbital, a region of space with zero electron density. (p. 41)
pi bond (π bond) A bond formed by sideways overlap of two p orbitals. A pi bond has its electron density in two lobes, one above and one below the line joining the nuclei. (p. 45)

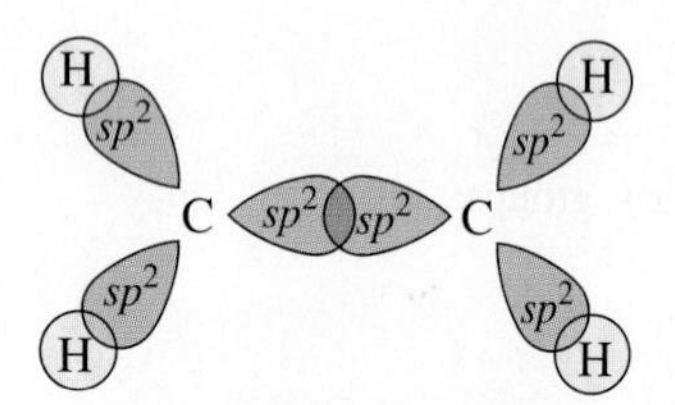

σ bond framework
(viewed from above the plane)

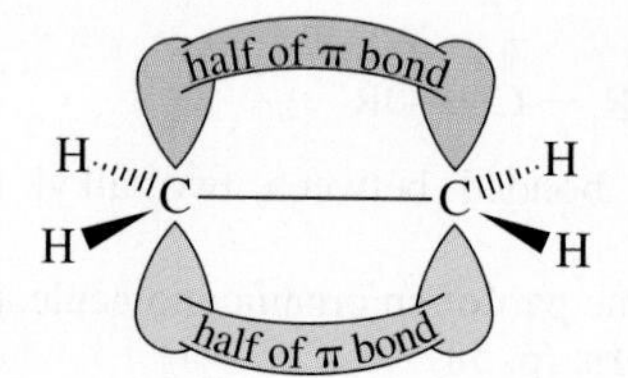

π bond
(viewed from alongside the plane)

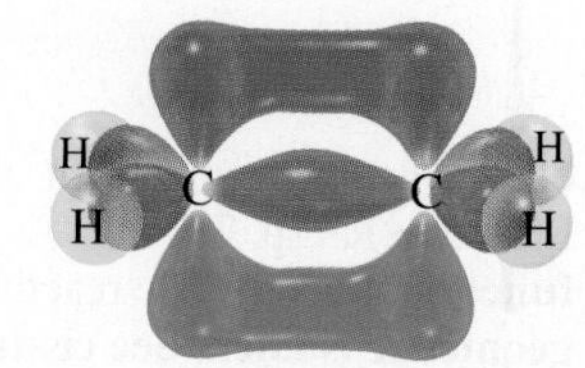

ethylene

sigma bond (σ bond) A bond with most of its electron density centered along the line joining the nuclei; a cylindrically symmetrical bond. Single bonds are normally sigma bonds. (p. 42)
stereochemistry The study of the structure and chemistry of stereoisomers. (p. 58)
stereoisomers Isomers that differ only in how their atoms are oriented in space. (p. 58)
structural isomers (IUPAC term: **constitutional isomers**) Isomers whose atoms are connected differently; they differ in their bonding sequence. (p. 57)
triple bond A bond containing six electrons between two nuclei. One pair of electrons forms a sigma bond and the other two pairs form two pi bonds at right angles to each other. (p. 53)
valence-shell electron-pair repulsion theory (VSEPR theory) Bonds and lone pairs around a central atom tend to be separated by the largest possible angles: about 180° for two, 120° for three, and 109.5° for four. (p. 46)
van der Waals forces The attractive forces between neutral molecules, including dipole–dipole forces and London dispersion forces. (p. 63)
 dipole–dipole forces: The forces between polar molecules resulting from the attraction of their permanent dipole moments.
 London forces: Intermolecular forces resulting from the attraction of correlated temporary dipole moments induced in adjacent molecules.
wave function (ψ) The mathematical description of an orbital. The square of the wave function (ψ^2) is proportional to the electron density. (p. 40)

Essential Problem-Solving Skills in Chapter 2

1. Draw the structure of a single bond, a double bond, and a triple bond.
2. Predict the hybridization and geometry of the atoms in a molecule.
3. Draw a three-dimensional representation of a given molecule.
4. Identify constitutional isomers and stereoisomers.
5. Identify polar and nonpolar molecules, and predict which ones can engage in hydrogen bonding.
6. Predict general trends in the boiling points and solubilities of compounds, based on their size, polarity, and hydrogen-bonding ability.
7. Identify the general classes of hydrocarbons, and draw structural formulas for examples.
8. Identify the classes of compounds containing oxygen or nitrogen, and draw structural formulas for examples.

Study Problems

2-23 Define and give examples of the following terms:

(a) bonding MO **(b)** antibonding MO **(c)** hybrid atomic orbital
(d) sigma bond **(e)** pi bond **(f)** double bond
(g) triple bond **(h)** constitutional isomers **(i)** cis-trans isomers
(j) stereoisomers **(k)** bond dipole moment **(l)** molecular dipole moment
(m) dipole–dipole forces **(n)** London forces **(o)** hydrogen bonding
(p) miscible liquids **(q)** hydrocarbons **(r)** alkyl group
(s) functional group

2-24 Give a definition and an example for each class of organic compounds.

(a) alkane **(b)** alkene **(c)** alkyne
(d) alcohol **(e)** ether **(f)** ketone
(g) aldehyde **(h)** aromatic hydrocarbon **(i)** carboxylic acid
(j) ester **(k)** amine **(l)** amide
(m) nitrile

2-25 If the carbon atom in CH_2Cl_2 were flat, there would be two stereoisomers. The carbon atom in CH_2Cl_2 is actually tetrahedral. Make a model of this compound, and determine whether there are any stereoisomers of CH_2Cl_2.

```
     H              H
     |              |
 H — C — Cl    Cl — C — Cl
     |              |
     Cl             H
```

2-26 Cyclopropane (C_3H_6, a three-membered ring) is more reactive than most other cycloalkanes.

(a) Draw a Lewis structure for cyclopropane.
(b) Compare the bond angles of the carbon atoms in cyclopropane with those in an acyclic (noncyclic) alkane.
(c) Suggest why cyclopropane is so reactive.

2-27 For each of the following compounds,

1. Give the hybridization and approximate bond angles around each atom except hydrogen.
2. Draw a three-dimensional diagram, including any lone pairs of electrons.

(a) H_3O^+ **(b)** ^-OH **(c)** CH_2CHCN
(d) $(CH_3)_3N$ **(e)** $[CH_3NH_3]^+$ **(f)** CH_3COOH
(g) CH_3CHNH **(h)** CH_3OH **(i)** CH_2O

2-28 For each of the following compounds and ions,
1. Draw a Lewis structure.
2. Show the kinds of orbitals that overlap to form each bond.
3. Give approximate bond angles around each atom except hydrogen.

(a) $[NH_2]^-$ **(b)** $[CH_2OH]^+$ **(c)** $CH_2{=}N{-}CH_3$
(d) $CH_3{-}CH{=}CH_2$ **(e)** $HC{\equiv}C{-}CHO$ **(f)** $H_2N{-}CH_2{-}CN$
(g) $CH_3{-}\overset{\overset{\displaystyle O}{\|}}{C}{-}OH$ **(h)** O, O **(i)** +, O

2-29 In most amines, the nitrogen atom is sp^3 hybridized, with a pyramidal structure and bond angles close to 109°. In formamide, the nitrogen atom is found to be planar, with bond angles close to 120°. Explain this surprising finding. (*Hint*: Consider resonance forms and the overlap needed in them.)

$$H{-}\overset{\overset{\displaystyle O}{\|}}{C}{-}\ddot{N}H_2$$
formamide

2-30 Predict the hybridization and geometry of the carbon and nitrogen atoms in the following ions. (*Hint*: Resonance.)

(a) $CH_3{-}\overset{\overset{\displaystyle O}{\|}}{C}{-}\ddot{\bar{C}}H_2$ **(b)** $H_2N{-}CH{=}CH{-}\overset{+}{C}H_2$ **(c)** $\overset{-}{C}H_2{-}C{\equiv}N$

2-31 Draw orbital pictures of the pi bonding in the following compounds:
(a) CH_3COCH_3 **(b)** HCN **(c)** $CH_2{=}CH{-}CH{=}CH{-}CN$
(d) $CH_3{-}C{\equiv}C{-}CHO$ **(e)** $CH_3{-}CH{=}C{=}CH{-}CH_3$

2-32 **(a)** Draw the structure of *cis*- $CH_3{-}CH{=}CH{-}CH_2CH_3$ showing the pi bond with its proper geometry.
(b) Circle the six coplanar atoms in this compound.
(c) Draw the trans isomer, and circle the coplanar atoms. Are there still six?
(d) Circle the coplanar atoms in the following structure.

CH_3

2-33 In 2-pentyne ($CH_3CCCH_2CH_3$) there are four atoms in a straight line. Use dashed lines and wedges to draw a three-dimensional representation of this molecule, and circle the four atoms that are in a straight line.

2-34 Which of the following compounds show cis-trans isomerism? Draw the cis and trans isomers of the ones that do.
(a) $CH_3CH{=}CHCH_3$ **(b)** $CH_3{-}C{\equiv}C{-}CH_3$ **(c)** $CH_2{=}C(CH_3)_2$
(d) cyclopentene, **(e)** $CH_3{-}CH{=}C(CH_2CH_2CH_3){-}CH_2{-}CH_3$ **(f)** $CH_3{-}CH{=}N{-}CH_3$

2-35 Give the relationships between the following pairs of structures. The possible relationships are: same compound, cis-trans isomers, constitutional (structural) isomers, not isomers (different molecular formula).
(a) $CH_3CH_2CH_2CH_3$ and $(CH_3)_3CH$ **(b)** $CH_2{=}CH{-}CH_2Cl$ and $CHCl{=}CH{-}CH_3$

(c)
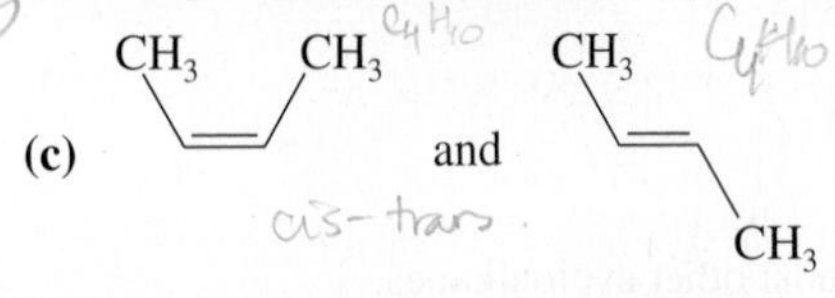

(d)
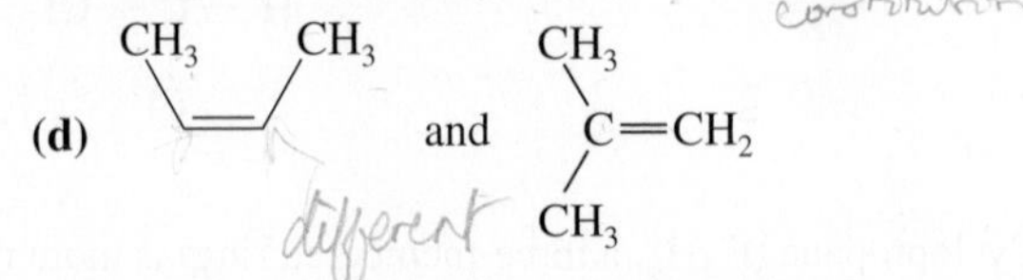

(e)
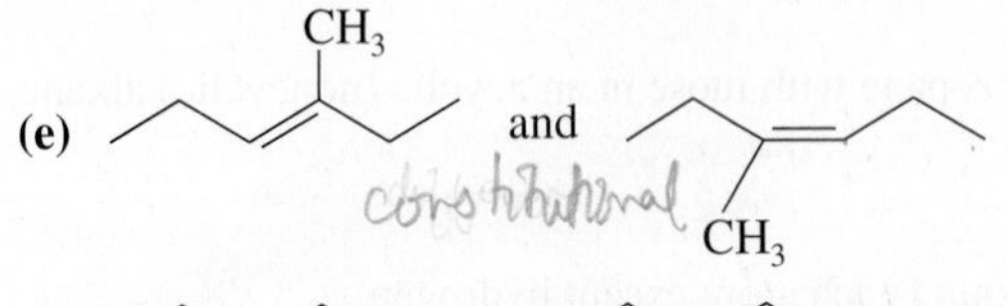

(f)
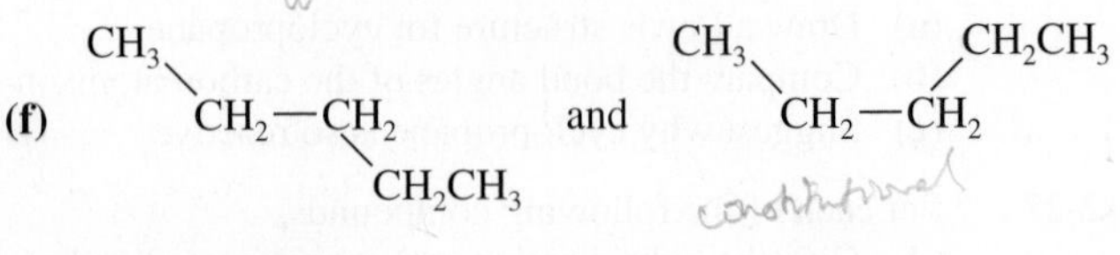

(g)
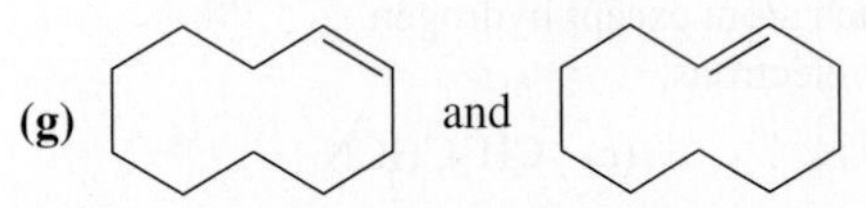

(h) and

2-36 Sulfur dioxide has a dipole moment of 1.60 D. Carbon dioxide has a dipole moment of zero, even though C—O bonds are more polar than S—O bonds. Explain this apparent contradiction.

2-37 For each of the following compounds,

1. Draw the Lewis structure.
2. Show how the bond dipole moments (and those of any nonbonding pairs of electrons) contribute to the molecular dipole moment.
3. Predict whether the compound will have a large (>1 D), small, or zero dipole moment.

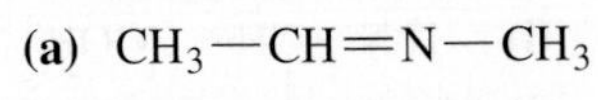

(b) $CH_3—CN$ **(c)** CBr_4 **(d)** $CH_3—C(=O)—CH_3$

(e) $(NC)_2C=C(CN)_2$ **(f)** piperidine (ring with N—H) **(g)** 1-chlorocyclohexene (Cl)

2-38 Diethyl ether and 1-butanol are isomers, and they have similar solubilities in water. Their boiling points are very different, however. Explain why these two compounds have similar solubility properties but dramatically different boiling points.

$CH_3CH_2—O—CH_2CH_3$	$CH_3CH_2CH_2CH_2—OH$
diethyl ether, bp 35 °C	1-butanol, bp 118 °C
8.4 mL dissolves in 100 mL H_2O	9.1 mL dissolves in 100 mL H_2O

2-39 *N*-methylpyrrolidine has a boiling point of 81 °C, and piperidine has a boiling point of 106 °C.

(a) Explain this large difference (25 °C) in boiling point for these two isomers.

(b) Tetrahydropyran has a boiling point of 88 °C, and cyclopentanol has a boiling point of 141 °C. These two isomers have a boiling point difference of 53 °C. Explain why the two oxygen-containing isomers have a much larger boiling point difference than the two amine isomers.

(c) *N*,*N*-dimethylformamide has a boiling point of 150 °C, and *N*-methylacetamide has a boiling point of 206 °C, for a difference of 56 °C. Explain why these two nitrogen-containing isomers have a much larger boiling point difference than the two amine isomers. Also explain why these two amides have higher boiling points than any of the other four compounds shown (two amines, an ether, and an alcohol).

N-methylpyrrolidine, bp 81 °C — tetrahydropyran, bp 88 °C — $H—C(=O)—N(CH_3)_2$ *N*,*N*-dimethylformamide, bp 150 °C

piperidine, bp 106 °C — cyclopentanol, bp 141 °C — $CH_3—C(=O)—N(CH_3)H$ *N*-methylacetamide, bp 206 °C

2-40 Which of the following pure compounds can form hydrogen bonds? Which can form hydrogen bonds with water?

(a) $(CH_3CH_2)_2NH$ **(b)** $(CH_3CH_2)_3N$ **(c)** $CH_3CH_2CH_2OH$
(d) $(CH_3CH_2CH_2)_2O$ **(e)** $CH_3(CH_2)_3CH_3$ **(f)** $CH_2=CH—CH_2CH_3$
(g) CH_3COCH_3 **(h)** CH_3CH_2COOH **(i)** CH_3CH_2CHO
(j) tetrahydrofuran (O) **(k)** γ-butyrolactone (O, =O) **(l)** $CH_3—C(=O)—NH_2$

2-41 Predict which compound in each pair has the higher boiling point. Explain your prediction.

(a) $CH_3CH_2OCH_3$ or $CH_3CH(OH)CH_3$ **(b)** $CH_3CH_2CH_2CH_3$ or $CH_3CH_2CH_2CH_2CH_3$
(c) $CH_3CH_2CH_2CH_2CH_3$ or $(CH_3)_2CHCH_2CH_3$ **(d)** $CH_3CH_2CH_2CH_2CH_3$ or $CH_3CH_2CH_2CH_2CH_2Cl$

2-42 Circle the functional groups in the following structures. State to which class (or classes) of compounds the structure belongs.

(a)

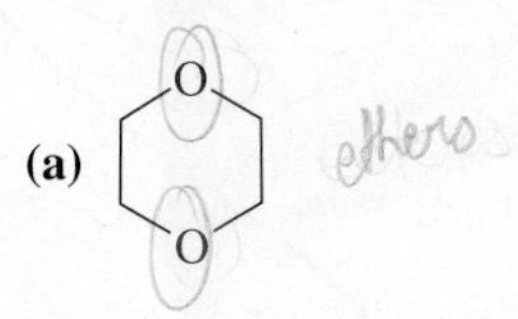

(b) cyclohexene with COOH **(c)** cyclopentyl–CH=CH–CHO

(d) O

(e) O O

(f) O N—H

(g) CH_2OCH_3 CN

(h) $CH_3—CH(NH_2)—COOCH_3$

(i) $H_2N—CH(CH_2—OH)—COOH$

2-43 Dimethyl sulfoxide (DMSO) has been used as an anti-inflammatory rub for race horses. DMSO and acetone seem to have similar structures, but the C=O carbon atom in acetone is planar, while the S=O sulfur atom in DMSO is pyramidal. Draw Lewis structures for DMSO and acetone, predict the hybridizations, and explain these observations.

$CH_3—S(=O)—CH_3$ DMSO

$CH_3—C(=O)—CH_3$ acetone

2-44 Many naturally occurring compounds contain more than one functional group. Identify the functional groups in the following compounds:

(a) Penicillin G is a naturally occurring antibiotic.
(b) Dopamine is the neurotransmitter that is deficient in Parkinson's disease.
(c) Capsaicin gives the fiery taste to chili peppers.
(d) Thyroxine is the principal thyroid hormone.
(e) Testosterone is a male sex hormone.

$CH_2—C(=O)—NH$ S N O COOH

penicillin G

HO HO NH_2 CH_2CH_2

dopamine

CH_3O HO N H O

capsaicin

I I HO O I I NH_2 $CH_2—CH—COOH$

thyroxine

OH O

testosterone

CHAPTER

3 STRUCTURE AND STEREOCHEMISTRY OF ALKANES

An **alkane** is a hydrocarbon that contains only single bonds. The alkanes are the simplest and least reactive class of organic compounds because they contain only hydrogen and sp^3 hybridized carbon, and they have no reactive functional groups. Alkanes contain no double or triple bonds and no heteroatoms (atoms other than carbon or hydrogen). They are poor acids and bases, and they are poor electrophiles and nucleophiles as well. Although alkanes undergo reactions such as cracking and combustion at high temperatures, they are much less reactive than other classes of compounds that have functional groups.

3-1 Classification of Hydrocarbons (Review)

We classify hydrocarbons according to their bonding (Section 2-12), as shown in Table 3-1. Alkanes have only single bonds. A hydrocarbon with a carbon–carbon double bond (such as ethylene) is an *alkene*. If a hydrocarbon has a carbon–carbon triple bond (like acetylene), it is an *alkyne*. Hydrocarbons with aromatic rings (resembling benzene) are called *aromatic hydrocarbons*.

A hydrocarbon with no double or triple bonds is said to be **saturated** because it has the maximum number of bonded hydrogens. Another way to describe *alkanes*, then, is as the class of **saturated hydrocarbons**.

TABLE 3-1

Hydrocarbon Classifications

Compound Type	Functional Group	Example
alkanes	none (no double or triple bonds)	$CH_3—CH_2—CH_3$, propane
alkenes	$>C=C<$ double bond	$CH_2=CH—CH_3$, propene
alkynes	$—C\equiv C—$ triple bond	$H—C\equiv C—CH_3$, propyne
aromatics	benzene ring	CH_2CH_3 (on benzene ring), ethylbenzene

3-2 Molecular Formulas of Alkanes

Table 3-2 shows the structures and formulas of the first 20 unbranched alkanes. Any isomers of these compounds have the same molecular formulas even though their structures are different. Notice how the molecular formulas increase by two hydrogen atoms each time a carbon atom is added.

The structures of the alkanes in Table 3-2 are purposely written as chains of $-CH_2-$ groups (**methylene groups**), terminated at each end by a hydrogen atom. This is the general formula for the unbranched (straight-chain) alkanes. These alkanes differ only by the number of methylene groups in the chain. If the molecule contains n carbon atoms, it must contain $(2n + 2)$ hydrogen atoms. Figure 3-1 shows how this pattern appears in structures and how it leads to formulas of the form C_nH_{2n+2}.

A series of compounds, like the unbranched alkanes, that differ only by the number of $-CH_2-$ groups, is called a *homologous series*, and the individual members of the series are called **homologs**. For example, butane is a homolog of propane, and both of these are homologs of hexane and decane.

Although we have derived the C_nH_{2n+2} formula using the unbranched *n*-alkanes, it applies to branched alkanes as well. Any isomer of one of these *n*-alkanes has the same molecular formula. Just as butane and pentane follow the C_nH_{2n+2} rule, their branched isomers isobutane, isopentane, and neopentane also follow the rule.

PROBLEM 3-1

Using the general molecular formula for alkanes,

(a) Predict the molecular formula of the C_{28} straight-chain alkane.

(b) Predict the molecular formula of 4,6-diethyl-12-(3,5-dimethyloctyl)triacontane, an alkane containing 44 carbon atoms.

TABLE 3-2

Formulas and Physical Properties of the Unbranched Alkanes, Called the *n*-Alkanes

Alkane	Number of Carbons	Structure	Formula	Boiling Point (°C)	Melting Point (°C)	Density[a]
methane	1	$H-CH_2-H$	CH_4	−164	−183	0.55
ethane	2	$H-(CH_2)_2-H$	C_2H_6	−89	−183	0.51
propane	3	$H-(CH_2)_3-H$	C_3H_8	−42	−189	0.50
butane	4	$H-(CH_2)_4-H$	C_4H_{10}	0	−138	0.58
pentane	5	$H-(CH_2)_5-H$	C_5H_{12}	36	−130	0.63
hexane	6	$H-(CH_2)_6-H$	C_6H_{14}	69	−95	0.66
heptane	7	$H-(CH_2)_7-H$	C_7H_{16}	98	−91	0.68
octane	8	$H-(CH_2)_8-H$	C_8H_{18}	126	−57	0.70
nonane	9	$H-(CH_2)_9-H$	C_9H_{20}	151	−51	0.72
decane	10	$H-(CH_2)_{10}-H$	$C_{10}H_{22}$	174	−30	0.73
undecane	11	$H-(CH_2)_{11}-H$	$C_{11}H_{24}$	196	−26	0.74
dodecane	12	$H-(CH_2)_{12}-H$	$C_{12}H_{26}$	216	−10	0.75
tridecane	13	$H-(CH_2)_{13}-H$	$C_{13}H_{28}$	235	−5	0.76
tetradecane	14	$H-(CH_2)_{14}-H$	$C_{14}H_{30}$	254	6	0.76
pentadecane	15	$H-(CH_2)_{15}-H$	$C_{15}H_{32}$	271	10	0.77
hexadecane	16	$H-(CH_2)_{16}-H$	$C_{16}H_{34}$	287	18	0.77
heptadecane	17	$H-(CH_2)_{17}-H$	$C_{17}H_{36}$	303	23	0.76
octadecane	18	$H-(CH_2)_{18}-H$	$C_{18}H_{38}$	317	28	0.76
nonadecane	19	$H-(CH_2)_{19}-H$	$C_{19}H_{40}$	330	32	0.78
eicosane	20	$H-(CH_2)_{20}-H$	$C_{20}H_{42}$	343	37	0.79
triacontane	30	$H-(CH_2)_{30}-H$	$C_{30}H_{62}$	>450	66	0.81

[a]Densities are given in g/mL at 20 °C, except for methane and ethane, whose densities are given at their boiling points.

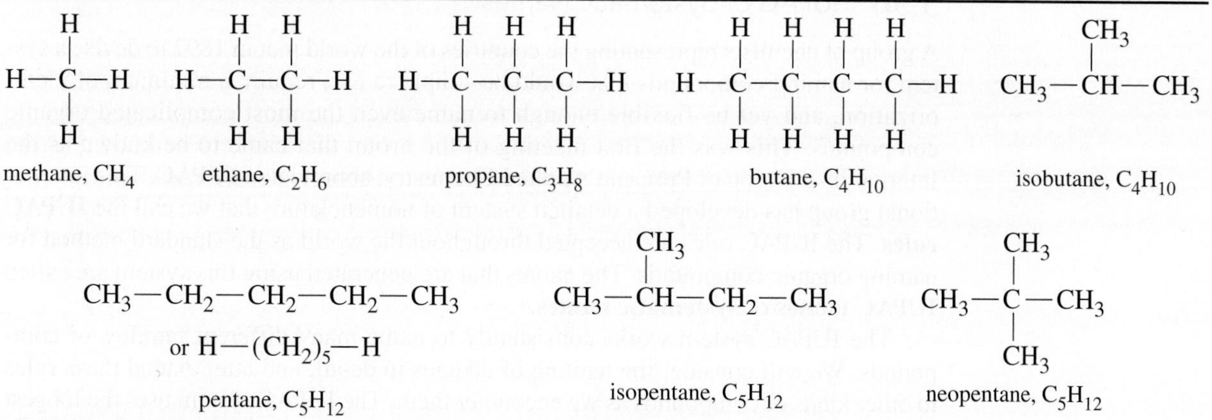

$$H{-}\underset{H}{\overset{H}{C}}{-}H \qquad H{-}\underset{H}{\overset{H}{C}}{-}\underset{H}{\overset{H}{C}}{-}H \qquad H{-}\underset{H}{\overset{H}{C}}{-}\underset{H}{\overset{H}{C}}{-}\underset{H}{\overset{H}{C}}{-}H \qquad H{-}\underset{H}{\overset{H}{C}}{-}\underset{H}{\overset{H}{C}}{-}\underset{H}{\overset{H}{C}}{-}\underset{H}{\overset{H}{C}}{-}H \qquad CH_3{-}\overset{CH_3}{CH}{-}CH_3$$

methane, CH_4 ethane, C_2H_6 propane, C_3H_8 butane, C_4H_{10} isobutane, C_4H_{10}

$$CH_3{-}CH_2{-}CH_2{-}CH_2{-}CH_3 \quad \text{or } H{-}(CH_2)_5{-}H \qquad CH_3{-}\overset{CH_3}{CH}{-}CH_2{-}CH_3 \qquad CH_3{-}\underset{CH_3}{\overset{CH_3}{C}}{-}CH_3$$

pentane, C_5H_{12} isopentane, C_5H_{12} neopentane, C_5H_{12}

FIGURE 3-1
Examples of the general alkane molecular formula, C_nH_{2n+2}.

3-3 Nomenclature of Alkanes

The names *methane, ethane, propane*, and *butane* have historical roots. From pentane on, alkanes are named using the Greek word for the number of carbon atoms, plus the suffix *-ane* to identify the molecule as an alkane. Table 3-2 gives the names and physical properties of the *n*-alkanes up to 20 carbon atoms.

3-3A Common Names

If all alkanes had unbranched (straight-chain) structures, their nomenclature would be simple. Most alkanes have structural isomers, however, and we need a way of naming all the different isomers. For example, there are two isomers of formula C_4H_{10}. The unbranched isomer is simply called *butane* (or *n-butane*, meaning "normal" butane), and the branched isomer is called *isobutane*, meaning an "isomer of butane."

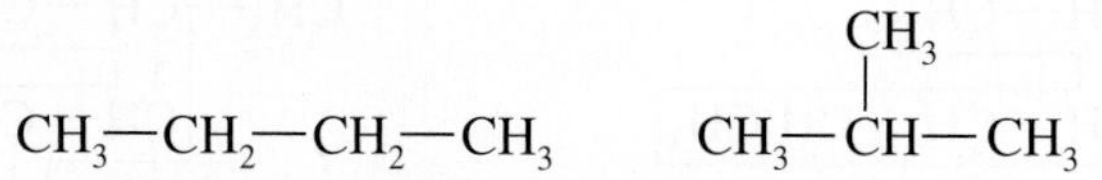

$$CH_3{-}CH_2{-}CH_2{-}CH_3 \qquad CH_3{-}\overset{CH_3}{CH}{-}CH_3$$

butane (*n*-butane) isobutane

The three isomers of C_5H_{12} are called *pentane* (or *n-pentane*), *isopentane*, and *neopentane*.

$$CH_3{-}CH_2{-}CH_2{-}CH_2{-}CH_3 \qquad CH_3{-}\overset{CH_3}{CH}{-}CH_2{-}CH_3 \qquad CH_3{-}\underset{CH_3}{\overset{CH_3}{C}}{-}CH_3$$

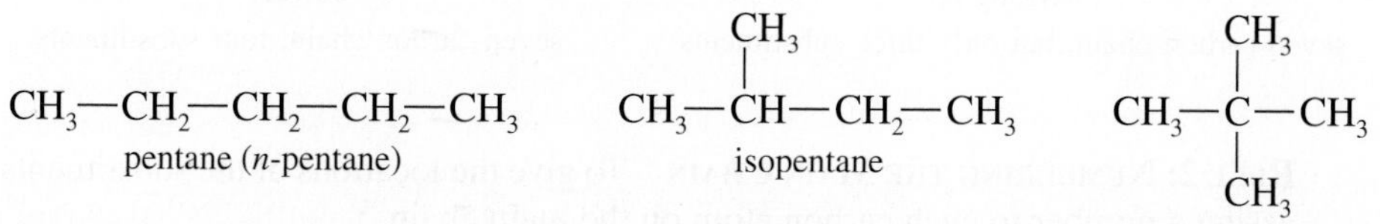

pentane (*n*-pentane) isopentane neopentane

Isobutane, isopentane, and *neopentane* are **common names** or **trivial names**, meaning historical names arising from common usage. Common names cannot easily describe the larger, more complicated molecules having many isomers, however. The number of isomers for any molecular formula grows rapidly as the number of carbon atoms increases. For example, there are 5 structural isomers of hexane, 18 isomers of octane, and 75 isomers of decane! We need a system of nomenclature that enables us to name complicated molecules without having to memorize hundreds of these historical common names.

3-3B IUPAC or Systematic Names

A group of chemists representing the countries of the world met in 1892 to devise a system for naming compounds that would be simple to use, require a minimum of memorization, and yet be flexible enough to name even the most complicated organic compounds. This was the first meeting of the group that came to be known as the International Union of Pure and Applied Chemistry, abbreviated **IUPAC**. This international group has developed a detailed system of nomenclature that we call the **IUPAC rules**. The IUPAC rules are accepted throughout the world as the standard method for naming organic compounds. The names that are generated using this system are called **IUPAC names** or **systematic names**.

The IUPAC system works consistently to name many different families of compounds. We will consider the naming of alkanes in detail, and later extend these rules to other kinds of compounds as we encounter them. The IUPAC system uses the longest chain of carbon atoms as the main chain, which is numbered to give the locations of side chains. Four rules govern this process.

RULE 1: THE MAIN CHAIN The first rule of nomenclature gives the base name of the compound.

> Find the longest continuous chain of carbon atoms, and use the name of this chain as the base name of the compound.

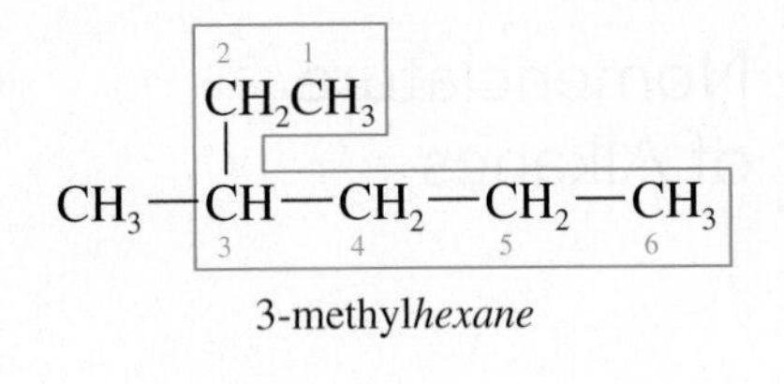

3-methyl*hexane*

For example, the longest chain of carbon atoms in the compound at left contains six carbons, so the compound is named as a *hexane* derivative. The longest chain is rarely drawn in a straight line; look carefully to find it.

The groups attached to the main chain are called **substituents** because they are substituted (in place of a hydrogen atom) on the main chain. *When there are two longest chains of equal length, use the chain with the greater number of substituents as the main chain.* The following compound contains two different seven-carbon chains and is named as a *heptane*. We choose the chain on the right as the main chain because it has more substituents (in red) attached to the chain.

problem-solving Hint

> When looking for the longest continuous chain (to give the base name), look to find all the different chains of that length. Often, the longest chain with the most substituents is not obvious.

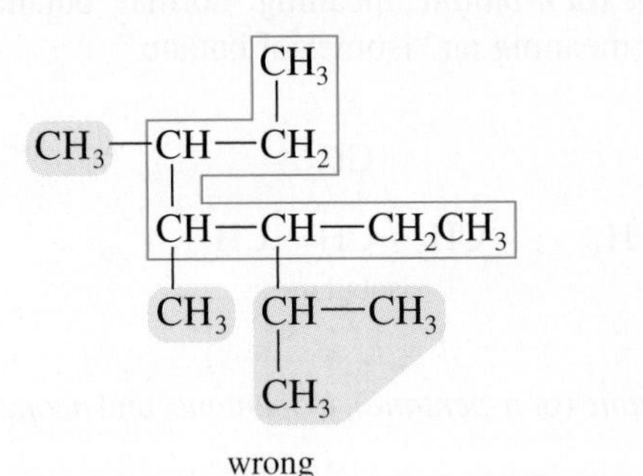

wrong
seven-carbon chain, but only three substituents

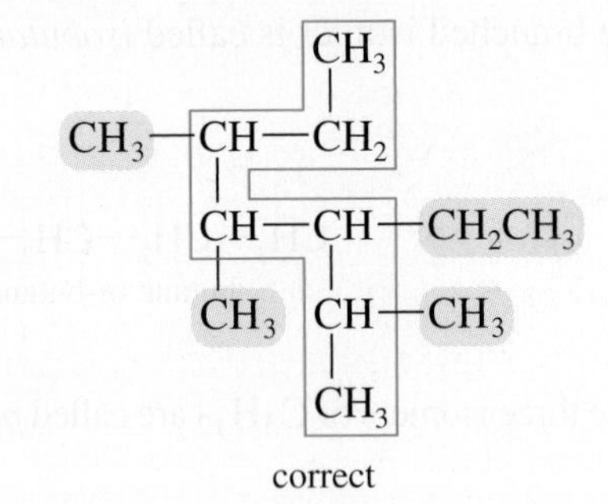

correct
seven-carbon chain, four substituents

RULE 2: NUMBERING THE MAIN CHAIN To give the locations of the substituents, assign a number to each carbon atom on the main chain.

> Number the longest chain, beginning with the end of the chain nearest a substituent.

We start the numbering from the end nearest a branch so the numbers of the substituted carbons will be as low as possible. In the preceding heptane structure on the right, numbering from top to bottom gives the first branch at C3 (carbon atom 3), but numbering from bottom to top gives the first branch at C2. Numbering from bottom to top is correct. (If each end had a substituent the same distance in, we would start at the end nearer the second branch point.)

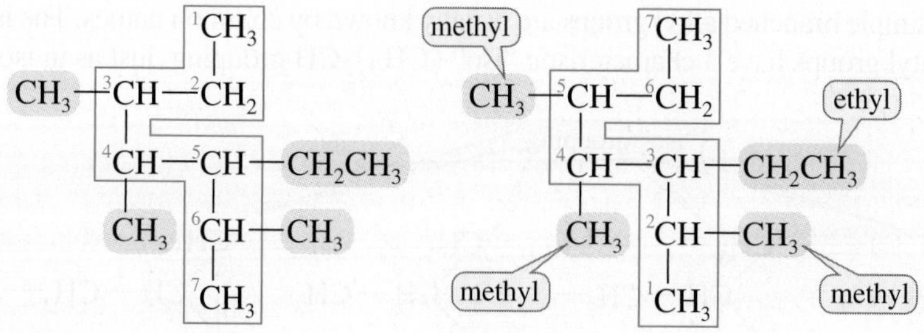

$$\begin{array}{l} {}^{1}CH_3 \\ CH_3-{}^{2}CH-{}^{3}CH_2 \\ {}^{4}CH-{}^{5}CH-CH_2CH_3 \\ CH_3\quad {}^{6}CH-CH_3 \\ \quad {}^{7}CH_3 \end{array}$$

incorrect

$$\begin{array}{l} {}^{7}CH_3 \\ CH_3-{}^{5}CH-{}^{6}CH_2 \\ {}^{4}CH-{}^{3}CH-CH_2CH_3 \\ CH_3\quad {}^{2}CH-CH_3 \\ \quad {}^{1}CH_3 \end{array}$$

correct (labels: methyl, ethyl, methyl, methyl)

3-ethyl-2,4,5-trimethylheptane

Rule 3: Naming Alkyl Groups Next, name the substituent groups.

> Name the substituent groups attached to the longest chain as **alkyl groups**. Give the location of each alkyl group by the number of the main-chain carbon atom to which it is attached.

Alkyl groups are named by replacing the *-ane* suffix of the alkane name with *-yl*. *Methane* becomes *methyl; ethane* becomes *ethyl*. You may encounter the word *amyl*, which is an archaic term for a pentyl (five-carbon) group.

Alkane	Name	Alkyl group	Name
CH_4	methane	CH_3-	methyl group
CH_3-CH_3	ethane	CH_3-CH_2-	ethyl group
$CH_3-CH_2-CH_3$	propane	$CH_3-CH_2-CH_2-$	propyl group
$CH_3-(CH_2)_2-CH_3$	butane	$CH_3-(CH_2)_2-CH_2-$	butyl group
$CH_3-(CH_2)_3-CH_3$	pentane	$CH_3-(CH_2)_3-CH_2-$	pentyl group (*n*-amyl group)

The following alkanes show the use of alkyl group nomenclature.

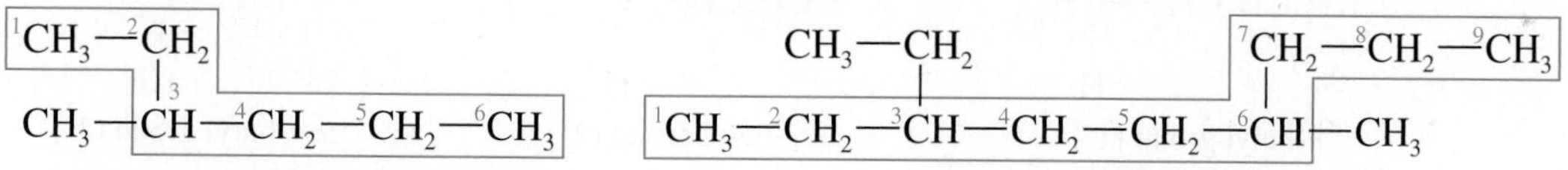

$$\begin{array}{l} {}^{1}CH_3-{}^{2}CH_2 \\ CH_3-{}^{3}CH-{}^{4}CH_2-{}^{5}CH_2-{}^{6}CH_3 \end{array}$$

3-methylhexane

$$\begin{array}{l} \qquad\qquad CH_3-CH_2 \qquad\qquad {}^{7}CH_2-{}^{8}CH_2-{}^{9}CH_3 \\ {}^{1}CH_3-{}^{2}CH_2-{}^{3}CH-{}^{4}CH_2-{}^{5}CH_2-{}^{6}CH-CH_3 \end{array}$$

3-ethyl-6-methylnonane

Figure 3-2 gives the names of the most common alkyl groups, those having up to four carbon atoms. The *propyl* and *butyl* groups are simply unbranched three- and four-carbon alkyl groups. These groups are sometimes named as "*n*-propyl" and "*n*-butyl" groups, to distinguish them from other kinds of (branched) propyl and butyl groups.

One carbon

CH_3- methyl group

Two carbons

CH_3-CH_2- ethyl group

Three carbons

$CH_3-CH_2-CH_2-$ propyl group (or "*n*-propyl group")

$CH_3-CH(CH_3)-$ isopropyl group

Four carbons

$CH_3-CH_2-CH_2-CH_2-$ butyl group (or "*n*-butyl group")

$CH_3-CH(CH_3)-CH_2-$ isobutyl group

$CH_3-CH_2-CH(CH_3)-$ *sec*-butyl group

$CH_3-C(CH_3)_2-$ *tert*-butyl group (or "*t*-butyl group")

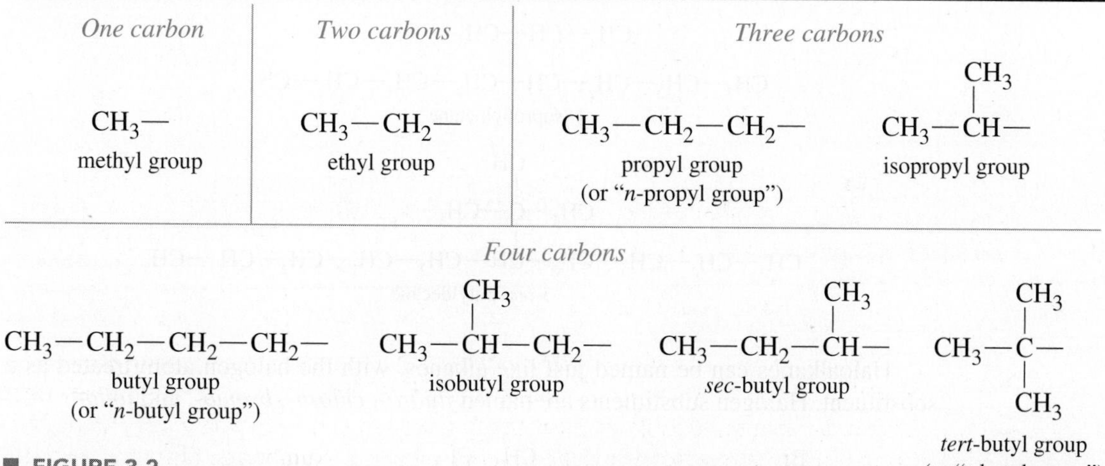

■ **FIGURE 3-2**
Some common alkyl groups.

The simple branched alkyl groups are usually known by common names. The isopropyl and isobutyl groups have a characteristic "iso" $(CH_3)_2CH$ grouping, just as in isobutane.

"iso" grouping

$(CH_3)_2CH-$ isopropyl group

$(CH_3)_2CH-CH_2-$ isobutyl group

$(CH_3)_2CH-CH_3$ isobutane

$(CH_3)_2CH-CH_2-CH_2-$ isopentyl group (isoamyl group)

The names of the *secondary*-butyl (*sec*-butyl) and *tertiary*-butyl (*tert*-butyl or *t*-butyl) groups are based on the **degree of alkyl substitution** of the carbon atom attached to the main chain. In the *sec*-butyl group, the carbon atom bonded to the main chain is **secondary** (2°), or bonded to two other carbon atoms. In the *tert*-butyl group, it is **tertiary** (3°), or bonded to three other carbon atoms. In both the *n*-butyl group and the isobutyl group, the carbon atoms bonded to the main chain are **primary** (1°), bonded to only one other carbon atom.

$R-CH_2-$ a *primary* (1°) carbon

R_2CH- a *secondary* (2°) carbon

R_3C- a *tertiary* (3°) carbon

$CH_3CH_2CH_2-CH_2-$ *n*-butyl group (1°)

$CH_3CH_2-CH(CH_3)-$ *sec*-butyl group (2°)

$CH_3-C(CH_3)_2-$ *tert*-butyl group (3°)

SOLVED PROBLEM 3-1

Give the structures of 4-isopropyloctane and 5-*tert*-butyldecane.

SOLUTION

4-Isopropyloctane has a chain of eight carbons, with an isopropyl group on the fourth carbon. 5-*tert*-Butyldecane has a chain of ten carbons, with a *tert*-butyl group on the fifth.

$CH_3-CH_2-CH_2-CH(CH(CH_3)_2)-CH_2-CH_2-CH_2-CH_3$

4-isopropyloctane

$CH_3-CH_2-CH_2-CH_2-CH(C(CH_3)_3)-CH_2-CH_2-CH_2-CH_2-CH_3$

5-*tert*-butyldecane

Haloalkanes can be named just like alkanes, with the halogen atom treated as a substituent. Halogen substituents are named *fluoro-*, *chloro-*, *bromo-*, and *iodo-*.

$CH_3-CHBr-CH_2CH_3$ 2-bromobutane

$CH_3-CH(CH_3)-CHCl-CH_2CH_3$ 3-chloro-2-methylpentane

$CH_3-CHF-CH_2F$ 1,2-difluoropropane

PROBLEM 3-2

Name the following alkanes and haloalkanes.

(a) $CH_3-CH(CH_2-CH_3)-CH_2-CH_3$

(b) $CH_3-CH(Br)-CH(CH_2CH_3)-CH_3$

(c) $CH_3-CH_2-CH(CH_3-CH_2)-CH(CH_2CH(CH_3)_2)-CH_2-CH_2-CH_3$

(d) $CH_3-CH_2-CH_2-CH_2-CH_2-CH_2-CH(CH_2-CH(CH_3)-CH_3)-CH(CH_3)-CH_3$

problem-solving **Hint**

Please remember the alkyl groups in Figure 3-2. You will encounter them many times throughout this course.

Rule 4: Organizing Multiple Groups The final rule deals with naming compounds with more than one substituent.

> When two or more substituents are present, list them in alphabetical order. When two or more of the *same* alkyl substituent are present, use the prefixes *di-*, *tri-*, *tetra-*, etc. to avoid having to name the alkyl group twice.
>
> | | |
> |---|---|
> | *di-* means 2 | *penta-* means 5 |
> | *tri-* means 3 | *hexa-* means 6 |
> | *tetra-* means 4 | |

Using this rule, we can construct names for some complicated structures. Let's finish naming the heptane on p. 86. This compound (at right) has an ethyl group on C3 and three methyl groups on C2, C4, and C5. The ethyl group is listed alphabetically before the methyl groups.

$^{7}CH_3-{}^{6}CH_2-{}^{5}CH(CH_3)-{}^{4}CH(CH_3)-{}^{3}CH(CH_2CH_3)-{}^{2}CH(CH_3)-{}^{1}CH_3$

3-ethyl-2,4,5-trimethylheptane

SOLVED PROBLEM 3-2

Give a systematic (IUPAC) name for the following compound.

$CH_3-CH(C(CH_3)_3)-CH(CH(CH_3)-CH_3)-CH_2-CH(CH_2CH_3)-CH_3$

SOLUTION

The longest carbon chain contains eight carbon atoms, so this compound is named as an octane. Numbering from left to right gives the first branch on C2; numbering from right to left gives the first branch on C3, so we number from left to right.

$^{1}CH_3-{}^{2}C(CH_3)_2-{}^{3}CH(CH_3)-{}^{4}CH(CH(CH_3)_2)-{}^{5}CH_2-{}^{6}CH(CH_3)-{}^{7}CH_2{}^{8}CH_3$

There are four methyl groups: two on C2, one on C3, and one on C6. These four groups will be listed as "2,2,3,6-tetramethyl. . . ." There is an isopropyl group on C4. Listing the isopropyl group and the methyl groups alphabetically, we have

4-isopropyl-2,2,3,6-tetramethyloctane

problem-solving **Hint**

When substituents are alphabetized, *iso-* is used as part of the alkyl group name, but the hyphenated prefixes are not. Thus *isobutyl* is alphabetized with *i*, but *n*-butyl, *tert*-butyl, and *sec*-butyl are alphabetized with *b*. The number prefixes *di-*, *tri-*, *tetra-*, etc. are ignored in alphabetizing.

SUMMARY Rules for Naming Alkanes

To name an alkane, we follow four rules:

1. Find the longest continuous chain of carbon atoms, and use this chain as the base name.
2. Number the longest chain, beginning with the end nearest a branch.
3. Name the substituents on the longest chain (as alkyl groups). Give the location of each substituent by the number of the main-chain carbon atom to which it is attached.
4. When two or more substituents are present, list them in alphabetical order. When two or more of the *same* alkyl substituent are present, use the prefixes *di-*, *tri-*, *tetra-*, and so on (ignored in alphabetizing) to avoid having to name the alkyl group twice.

problem-solving Hint

Always compare the total number of carbon atoms in the name with the number in the structure to make sure they match. For example, an *isopropyldimethyloctane* should have 3 + 2 + 8 carbon atoms.

problem-solving Hint

To draw all alkanes of a given molecular formula, start with a straight chain, then go to shorter chains with more branches. To draw all C_6H_{14} alkanes, for example, start with a C6 chain, then go to a C5 chain with a methyl group in each possible position. Next, draw a C4 chain with an ethyl group in each possible position, followed by two methyls in all possible combinations. To guard against duplicated structures, name each compound, and if a name appears twice, you have either duplicated a structure or named something wrong.

PROBLEM 3-3

Write structures for the following compounds.

(a) 3-ethyl-4-methylhexane **(b)** 3-ethyl-5-isobutyl-3-methylnonane
(c) 4-*tert*-butyl-2-methylheptane **(d)** 5-isopropyl-3,3,4-trimethyloctane

PROBLEM 3-4

Provide IUPAC names for the following compounds.

(a) $(CH_3)_2CHCH_2CH_3$ **(b)** $CH_3—C(CH_3)_2—CH_3$

(c) $CH_3CH_2CH_2CH(CH_2CH_3)—CH(CH_3)_2$ (the CH_2CH_3 is drawn above the CH)

(d) $CH_3—CH(CH_3)—CH_2—CH(CH_2CH_3)—CH_3$ (the CH_3 and CH_2CH_3 are drawn above the CH groups)

(e) $CH_3CH_2CHCHCH_3$ with $C(CH_3)_3$ above and $CH(CH_3)_2$ below

(f) $(CH_3)_3C—CH(CH_3—CHCH_2CH_3)—CH_2CH_2CH_3$ (the $CH_3—CHCH_2CH_3$ group is drawn above the CH)

PROBLEM 3-5

Give structures and names for

(a) the five isomers of C_6H_{14} **(b)** the nine isomers of C_7H_{16}

Complex Substituents Complex alkyl groups are named by a systematic method using the longest alkyl chain as the base alkyl group. The base alkyl group is numbered beginning with the carbon atom (the "head carbon") bonded to the main chain. The substituents on the base alkyl group are listed with appropriate numbers, and parentheses are used to set off the name of the complex alkyl group. The following examples illustrate the systematic method for naming complex alkyl groups.

$—\overset{1}{C}H(CH_2CH_3)—\overset{2}{C}H(CH_3)—\overset{3}{C}H_3$

a (1-ethyl-2-methylpropyl) group

$—\overset{1}{C}(CH_3)_2—\overset{2}{C}H_2—\overset{3}{C}H(CH_3)—\overset{4}{C}H_3$

a (1,1,3-trimethylbutyl) group

$\overset{1}{C}H_3\overset{2}{C}H_2—\overset{3}{C}H(CH_2CH_3)—\overset{4}{C}H_2—\overset{5}{C}H(\overset{1}{C}H(CH_2CH_3)—\overset{2}{C}H(CH_3)—\overset{3}{C}H_3)—\overset{6}{C}H_2\overset{7}{C}H_2\overset{8}{C}H_2\overset{9}{C}H_3$

3-ethyl-5-(1-ethyl-2-methylpropyl)nonane

1,1-dimethyl-3-(1,1,3-trimethylbutyl)cyclooctane

PROBLEM 3-6

Draw the structures of the following groups, and give their more common names.
(a) the (1-methylethyl) group
(b) the (2-methylpropyl) group
(c) the (1-methylpropyl) group
(d) the (1,1-dimethylethyl) group
(e) the (3-methylbutyl) group, sometimes called the "isoamyl" group

PROBLEM 3-7

Draw the structures of the following compounds.
(a) 4-(1,1-dimethylethyl)octane
(b) 5-(1,2,2-trimethylpropyl)nonane
(c) 3,3-diethyl-4-(2,2-dimethylpropyl)octane

PROBLEM 3-8

Without looking at the structures, give molecular formulas for the compounds in Problem 3-7 (a) and (b). Use the names of the groups to determine the number of carbon atoms, then use the $(2n+2)$ rule.

3-4 Physical Properties of Alkanes

Alkanes are used primarily as fuels, solvents, and lubricants. Natural gas, gasoline, kerosene, heating oil, lubricating oil, and paraffin "wax" are all composed primarily of alkanes, with different physical properties resulting from different ranges of molecular weights.

3-4A Solubilities and Densities of Alkanes

Alkanes are nonpolar, so they dissolve in nonpolar or weakly polar organic solvents. Alkanes are said to be **hydrophobic** ("water hating") because they do not dissolve in water. Alkanes are good lubricants and preservatives for metals because they keep water from reaching the metal surface and causing corrosion.

Densities of the *n*-alkanes are listed in Table 3-2 (p. 84). Alkanes have densities around 0.7 g/mL, compared with a density of 1.0 g/mL for water. Because alkanes are less dense than water and insoluble in water, a mixture of an alkane (such as gasoline or oil) and water quickly separates into two phases, with the alkane on top.

Oil floats on water. Note how the oil slick (from the leaking Exxon *Valdez*) spreads across the top of the water. Oil recovery booms, containing nonpolar fibers, are used to soak up and contain the spilled oil. Note how most of the oil slick ends at the oil recovery booms.

3-4B Boiling Points of Alkanes

Table 3-2 also gives the boiling points and melting points of the unbranched alkanes. The boiling points increase smoothly with increasing numbers of carbon atoms and increasing molecular weights. Larger molecules have larger surface areas, resulting in increased intermolecular van der Waals attractions. These increased attractions must be overcome for vaporization and boiling to occur. Thus, a larger molecule, with greater surface area and greater van der Waals attractions, boils at a higher temperature.

A graph of *n*-alkane boiling points versus the number of carbon atoms (the blue line in Figure 3-3) shows that boiling points increase with increasing molecular weight. Each additional CH_2 group increases the boiling point by about 30 °C up to about ten carbons, and by about 20 °C in higher alkanes.

The green line in Figure 3-3 represents the boiling points of some branched alkanes. In general, a branched alkane boils at a lower temperature than the *n*-alkane with the same number of carbon atoms. This difference in boiling points arises because branched alkanes are more compact, with less surface area for London force interactions.

3-4C Melting Points of Alkanes

The blue line in Figure 3-4 is a graph of the melting points of the *n*-alkanes. Like their boiling points, the melting points increase with increasing molecular weight. The melting point graph is not smooth, however. Alkanes with even numbers of carbon atoms pack better into a solid structure, so that higher temperatures are needed to melt them. Alkanes

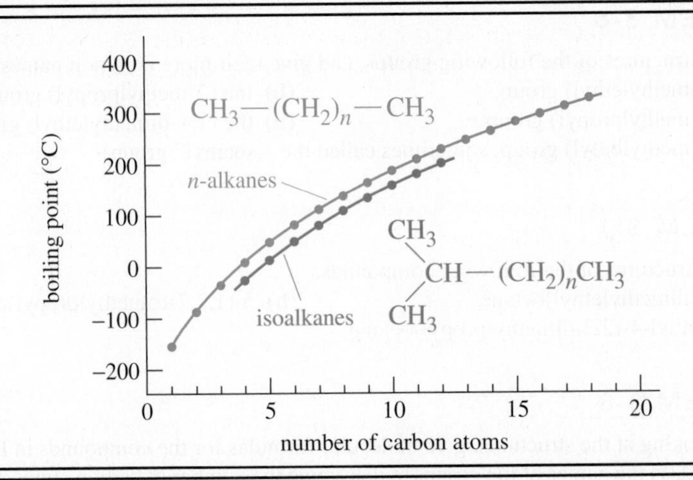

■ **FIGURE 3-3**
Alkane boiling points. The boiling points of the unbranched alkanes (blue) are compared with those of some branched alkanes (green). Because of their smaller surface areas, branched alkanes have lower boiling points than unbranched alkanes.

with odd numbers of carbon atoms do not pack as well, and they melt at lower temperatures. The sawtooth-shaped graph of melting points is smoothed by drawing separate lines (green and red) for the alkanes with even and odd numbers of carbon atoms.

Branching of the chain also affects an alkane's melting point. A branched alkane generally melts at a *higher* temperature than the *n*-alkane with the same number of carbon atoms. Branching of an alkane gives it a more compact three-dimensional structure, which packs more easily into a solid structure and increases the melting point. The boiling points and melting points of three isomers of formula C_6H_{14} show that the boiling points decrease and the melting points increase as the shape of the molecule becomes more highly branched and compact.

$(CH_3)_2CH—CH_2—CH_2—CH_3$	$(CH_3)_2CH—CH(CH_3)_2$	$CH_3—C(CH_3)_2—CH_2—CH_3$
bp 60 °C	bp 58 °C	bp 50 °C
mp −154 °C	mp −135 °C	mp −98 °C

PROBLEM 3-9

List each set of compounds in order of increasing boiling point.
(a) hexane, octane, and decane
(b) octane, $(CH_3)_3C—C(CH_3)_3$, and $CH_3CH_2C(CH_3)_2CH_2CH_2CH_3$

PROBLEM 3-10

Repeat Problem 3-9, listing the compounds in order of increasing melting point.

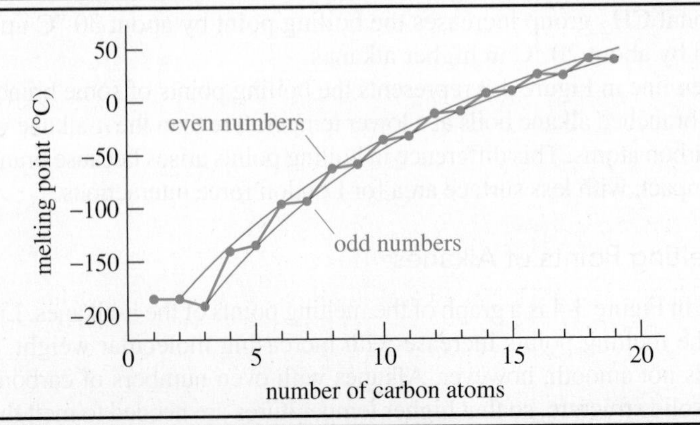

■ **FIGURE 3-4**
Alkane melting points. The melting point curve for *n*-alkanes with even numbers of carbon atoms is slightly higher than the curve for alkanes with odd numbers of carbons.

3-5 Uses and Sources of Alkanes

Distillation of petroleum separates alkanes into fractions with similar boiling points. These fractions are suited for different uses based on their physical properties, such as volatility and viscosity.

3-5A Major Uses of Alkanes

C_1–C_2 Methane and ethane are gases at room temperature and atmospheric pressure. They are difficult to liquefy, so they are usually handled as compressed gases. Upon cooling to cryogenic (very low) temperatures, however, methane and ethane become liquids. *Liquefied natural gas*, mostly methane, can be transported in special refrigerated tankers more easily than it can be transported as a compressed gas.

C_3–C_4 Propane and butane are also gases at room temperature and pressure, but they are easily liquefied at room temperature under modest pressure. These gases, often obtained along with liquid petroleum, are stored in low-pressure cylinders of *liquefied petroleum gas (LPG)*. Propane and butane are good fuels, both for heating and for internal combustion engines. They burn cleanly, and pollution-control equipment is rarely necessary. In many agricultural areas, propane and butane are more cost-effective tractor fuels than gasoline and diesel fuel. Propane and butane have largely replaced Freons® (see Section 6-3D) as propellants in aerosol cans. Unlike alkanes, the chlorofluorocarbon Freon propellants are implicated in damaging the earth's protective ozone layer.

Clean-burning propane-powered vehicles help to reduce air pollution in urban areas.

C_5–C_8 The next four alkanes are free-flowing, volatile liquids. Isomers of pentane, hexane, heptane, and octane are the primary constituents of gasoline. Their volatility is crucial for this use because the injection system simply squirts a stream of gasoline into the intake air as it rushes through. If gasoline did not evaporate easily, it would reach the cylinder in the form of droplets. Droplets cannot burn as efficiently as a vapor, so the engine would smoke and give low mileage.

In addition to being volatile, gasoline must resist the potentially damaging explosive combustion known as *knocking*. The antiknock properties of gasoline are rated by an **octane number** that is assigned by comparing the gasoline to a mixture of *n*-heptane (which knocks badly) and isooctane (2,2,4-trimethylpentane, which is not prone to knocking). The gasoline being tested is used in a test engine with a variable compression ratio. Higher compression ratios induce knocking, so the compression ratio is increased until knocking begins. Tables are available that show the percentage of isooctane in an isooctane/heptane blend that begins to knock at any given compression ratio. The octane number assigned to the gasoline is simply the percentage of isooctane in an isooctane/heptane mixture that begins to knock at that same compression ratio.

$$CH_3CH_2CH_2CH_2CH_2CH_2CH_3$$

n-heptane (0 octane)
prone to knocking

$$CH_3-C(CH_3)_2-CH_2-CH(CH_3)-CH_3$$

2,2,4-trimethylpentane (100 octane)
"isooctane," resists knocking

C_9–C_{16} The nonanes (C_9) through about the hexadecanes (C_{16}) are higher-boiling liquids that are somewhat viscous. These alkanes are used in kerosene, jet fuel, and diesel fuel. **Kerosene**, the lowest-boiling of these fuels, was once widely available but is now harder to find. It is less volatile than gasoline and less prone to forming explosive mixtures. Kerosene was used in kerosene lamps and heaters, which use wicks to allow this heavier fuel to burn. Jet fuel is similar to kerosene, but more highly refined and less odorous.

Diesel fuel is not very volatile, so it does not evaporate in the intake air. In a diesel engine, the fuel is sprayed directly into the cylinder right at the top of the compression stroke. The hot, highly compressed air in the cylinder causes the fuel to burn quickly, swirling and vaporizing as it burns. Some of the alkanes in diesel fuel have fairly high freezing points, and they may solidify in cold weather. This partial

Incomplete combustion of gasoline and other motor fuels releases significant quantities of volatile organic compounds (VOCs) into the atmosphere. VOCs are composed of short-chained alkanes, alkenes, aromatic compounds, and a variety of other hydrocarbons. VOCs are components of air pollution and contribute to cardiac and respiratory diseases.

The large distillation tower at left is used to separate petroleum into fractions based on their boiling points. The "cat cracker" at right uses catalysts and high temperatures to crack large molecules into smaller ones.

solidification causes the diesel fuel to turn into a waxy, semisolid mass. Owners of diesel engines in cold climates often mix a small amount of gasoline with their diesel fuel in the winter. The added gasoline dissolves the frozen alkanes, diluting the slush and allowing it to be pumped to the cylinders.

C_{16} and Up Alkanes with more than 16 carbon atoms are most often used as lubricating and heating oils. These are sometimes called "mineral" oils because they come from petroleum, which was once considered a mineral.

Paraffin "wax" is not a true wax, but a purified mixture of high-molecular-weight alkanes with melting points well above room temperature. The true waxes are long-chain esters, discussed in Chapter 25.

3-5B Alkane Sources; Petroleum Refining

Alkanes are derived mostly from petroleum and petroleum by-products. *Petroleum*, often called *crude oil*, is pumped from wells that reach into pockets containing the remains of prehistoric plants. The principal constituents of crude oil are alkanes, some aromatics, and some undesirable compounds containing sulfur and nitrogen. The composition of petroleum and the amounts of contaminants vary from one source to another, and a refinery must be carefully adjusted to process a particular type of crude oil. Because of their different qualities, different prices are paid for light Arabian crude, West Texas crude, and other classes of crude petroleum.

The first step in refining petroleum is a careful fractional distillation. The products of that distillation are not pure alkanes but mixtures of alkanes with useful ranges of boiling points. Table 3-3 shows the major fractions obtained from the distillation of crude petroleum.

After distillation, **catalytic cracking** converts some of the less valuable fractions to more valuable products. Catalytic cracking involves heating alkanes in the presence of materials that catalyze the cleavage of large molecules into smaller ones. Cracking is often used to convert higher-boiling fractions into mixtures that can be blended with gasoline. When cracking is done in the presence of hydrogen **(hydrocracking)**, the product is a mixture of alkanes free of sulfur and nitrogen impurities. The following reaction shows the catalytic hydrocracking of a molecule of tetradecane into two molecules of heptane.

$$CH_3-(CH_2)_{12}-CH_3 \; + \; H_2 \xrightarrow[SiO_2 \text{ or } Al_2O_3 \text{ catalyst}]{\text{heat}} 2\,CH_3-(CH_2)_5-CH_3$$

3-5C Natural Gas; Methane

Natural gas was once treated as a waste product of petroleum production and destroyed by flaring it off. Now natural gas is an equally valuable natural resource, pumped and stored throughout the world. Natural gas is about 70% methane, 10% ethane, and 15% propane, depending on the source of the gas. Small amounts of other hydrocarbons and contaminants are also present. Natural gas is often found above pockets of petroleum or coal, although it is also found in places where there is little or no recoverable

Methane hydrate, consisting of methane molecules surrounded by water molecules, is formed under high pressure on the cold seafloor. When brought to the surface, it quickly melts and releases the methane.

TABLE 3-3

Major Fractions Obtained from Distillation of Crude Petroleum

Boiling Range (°C)	Number of Carbons	Fraction	Use
under 30°	2–4	petroleum gas	LP gas for heating
30°–180°	4–9	gasoline	motor fuel
160°–230°	8–16	kerosene	heating, jet fuel
200°–320°	10–18	diesel	motor fuel
300°–450°	16–30	heavy oil	heating, lubrication
>300° (vacuum)	>25	petroleum "jelly," paraffin "wax"	
residue	>35	asphalt	

petroleum or coal. Natural gas is used primarily as a fuel to heat buildings and to generate electricity. It is also important as a starting material for the production of fertilizers.

Although the methane we burn as natural gas is millions of years old, another 300 million tons per year (estimated) of new methane is synthesized by microbes in diverse places such as the stomachs of plant-eating animals and the mud under the seafloor. Most of the undersea methane is eaten by other microbes, but some escapes at methane seeps. Under the sea, cold, high-pressure conditions may allow formation of **methane hydrate**, with individual methane molecules trapped inside cages of water molecules. When methane hydrate is brought to the surface, it quickly melts and the methane escapes. We currently have no practical methods for capturing and using microbial methane or methane hydrate. Much of this methane escapes to the atmosphere, where it acts as a greenhouse gas and contributes to global warming.

Methane is a stronger greenhouse gas than carbon dioxide. If all the methane trapped in methane hydrates were suddenly released into the atmosphere (by warming of the ocean, for example), the rate of global warming could increase dramatically.

3-6 Reactions of Alkanes

Alkanes are the least reactive class of organic compounds. Their low reactivity is reflected in another term for alkanes: **paraffins**. The name *paraffin* comes from two Latin terms, *parum*, meaning "too little," and *affinis*, meaning "affinity." Chemists found that alkanes do not react with strong acids or bases or with most other reagents. They attributed this low reactivity to a lack of affinity for other reagents, so they coined the name "paraffins."

Most useful reactions of alkanes take place under energetic or high-temperature conditions. These conditions are inconvenient in a laboratory because they require specialized equipment, and the rate of the reaction is difficult to control. Alkane reactions often form mixtures of products that are difficult to separate. These mixtures may be commercially important for an industry, however, where the products may be separated and sold separately. Newer methods of selective functionalization may eventually change this picture. For now, however, the following alkane reactions are rarely seen in laboratory applications, but they are widely used in the chemical industry and even in your home and car.

3-6A Combustion

Combustion is a rapid oxidation that takes place at high temperatures, converting alkanes to carbon dioxide and water. Little control over the reaction is possible, except for moderating the temperature and controlling the fuel/air ratio to achieve efficient burning.

$$C_nH_{(2n+2)} \quad + \text{excess } O_2 \xrightarrow{\text{heat}} n\, CO_2 \quad + (n+1)\, H_2O$$

Example

$$CH_3CH_2CH_3 \quad + 5\, O_2 \xrightarrow{\text{heat}} 3\, CO_2 \quad + 4\, H_2O$$

Unfortunately, the burning of gasoline and fuel oil pollutes the air and depletes the petroleum resources needed for lubricants and chemical feedstocks. Solar and nuclear heat sources cause less pollution, and they do not deplete these important natural resources. Facilities that use these more environment-friendly heat sources are currently more expensive than those that rely on the combustion of alkanes.

Combustion is the most common reaction of alkanes. Lightning initiated this fire in a tank containing 3 million gallons of gasoline at the Shell Oil storage facility in Woodbridge, NJ (June 11, 1996).

3-6B Cracking and Hydrocracking

As discussed in Section 3-5B, catalytic **cracking** of large hydrocarbons at high temperatures produces smaller hydrocarbons. The cracking process usually operates under conditions that give the maximum yields of gasoline. In **hydrocracking**, hydrogen is added to give saturated hydrocarbons; cracking without hydrogen gives mixtures of alkanes and alkenes.

Catalytic hydrocracking

$C_{12}H_{26}$
long-chain alkane

$\xrightarrow[\text{catalyst}]{H_2,\ \text{heat}}$

C_5H_{12}

C_7H_{16}
shorter-chain alkanes

Catalytic cracking

$C_{12}H_{26}$
long-chain alkane

$\xrightarrow[\text{catalyst}]{\text{heat}}$

C_5H_{10}

C_7H_{16}
shorter-chain alkanes and alkenes

3-6C Halogenation

Alkanes can react with halogens (F_2, Cl_2, Br_2, I_2) to form alkyl halides. For example, methane reacts with chlorine (Cl_2) to form chloromethane (methyl chloride), dichloromethane (methylene chloride), trichloromethane (chloroform), and tetrachloromethane (carbon tetrachloride).

$$CH_4 + Cl_2 \xrightarrow{\text{heat or light}} CH_3Cl + CH_2Cl_2 + CHCl_3 + CCl_4 + HCl$$

Heat or light is usually needed to initiate this **halogenation**. Reactions of alkanes with chlorine and bromine proceed at moderate rates and are easily controlled. Reactions with fluorine are often too fast to control, however. Iodine reacts very slowly or not at all. We will discuss the halogenation of alkanes in Chapter 4.

3-7 Structure and Conformations of Alkanes

Although alkanes are not as reactive as other classes of organic compounds, they have many of the same structural characteristics. We will use simple alkanes as examples to study some of the properties of organic compounds, including the structure of sp^3 hybridized carbon atoms and properties of C—C and C—H single bonds.

3-7A Structure of Methane

The simplest alkane is *methane*, CH_4. Methane is perfectly tetrahedral, with the 109.5° bond angles predicted for an sp^3 hybridized carbon. Four hydrogen atoms are covalently bonded to the central carbon atom, with bond lengths of 1.09 Å.

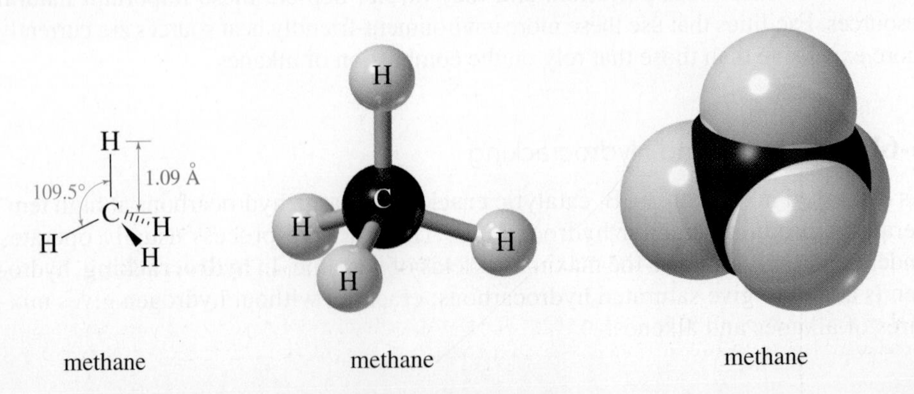

3-7B Conformations of Ethane

Ethane, the two-carbon alkane, is composed of two methyl groups with overlapping sp^3 hybrid orbitals forming a sigma bond between them.

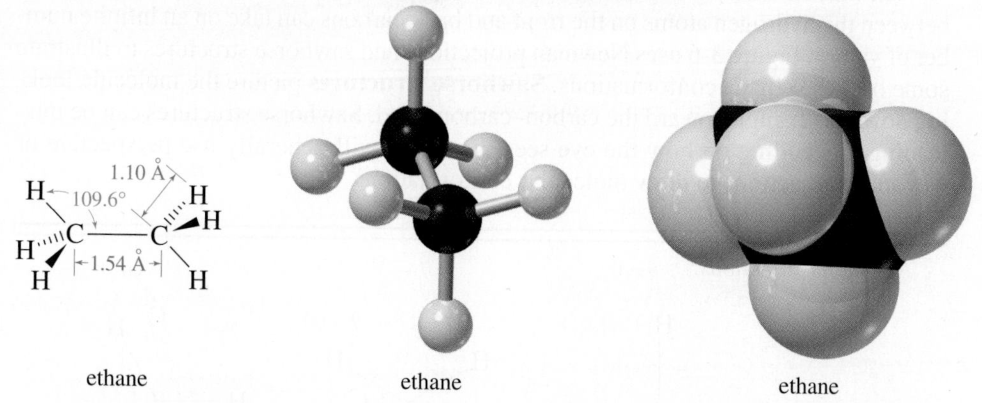

The two methyl groups are not fixed in a single position but are relatively free to rotate about the sigma bond connecting the two carbon atoms. The bond maintains its linear bonding overlap as the carbon atoms turn. The different arrangements formed by rotations about a single bond are called **conformations**, and a specific conformation is called a **conformer** ("**conform**ational iso**mer**").* Pure conformers cannot be isolated in most cases, because the molecules are constantly rotating through all the possible conformations.

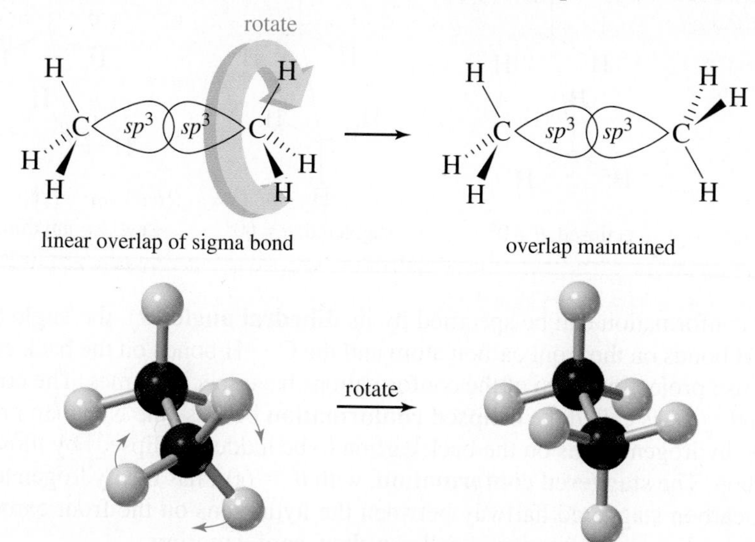

In drawing conformations, we often use **Newman projections**, a way of drawing a molecule looking straight down the bond connecting two carbon atoms (Figure 3-5). The front carbon atom is represented by three lines (three bonds) coming together in a

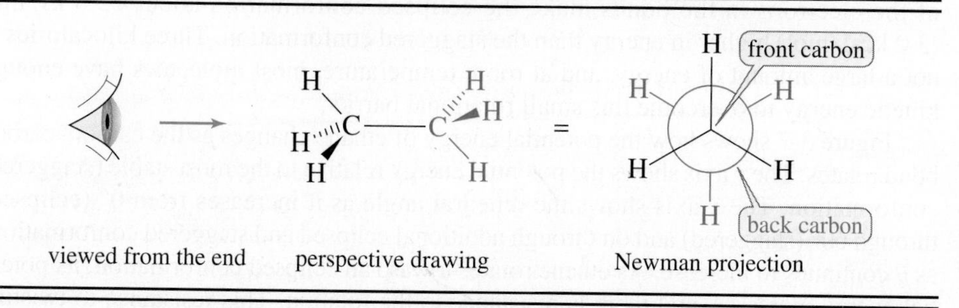

■ **FIGURE 3-5**
The Newman projection looks straight down the carbon–carbon bond.

*This is the common definition of conformers. The IUPAC definition also requires that a conformer correspond to a distinct potential energy minimum, such as the anti and gauche conformations of butane.

Y shape. The back carbon is represented by a circle with three bonds pointing out from it. Until you become familiar with Newman projections, you should make models and compare your models with the drawings.

An infinite number of conformations are possible for ethane, because the angle between the hydrogen atoms on the front and back carbons can take on an infinite number of values. Figure 3-6 uses Newman projections and sawhorse structures to illustrate some of these ethane conformations. **Sawhorse structures** picture the molecule looking down at an angle toward the carbon–carbon bond. Sawhorse structures can be misleading, depending on how the eye sees them. We will generally use perspective or Newman projections to draw molecular conformations.

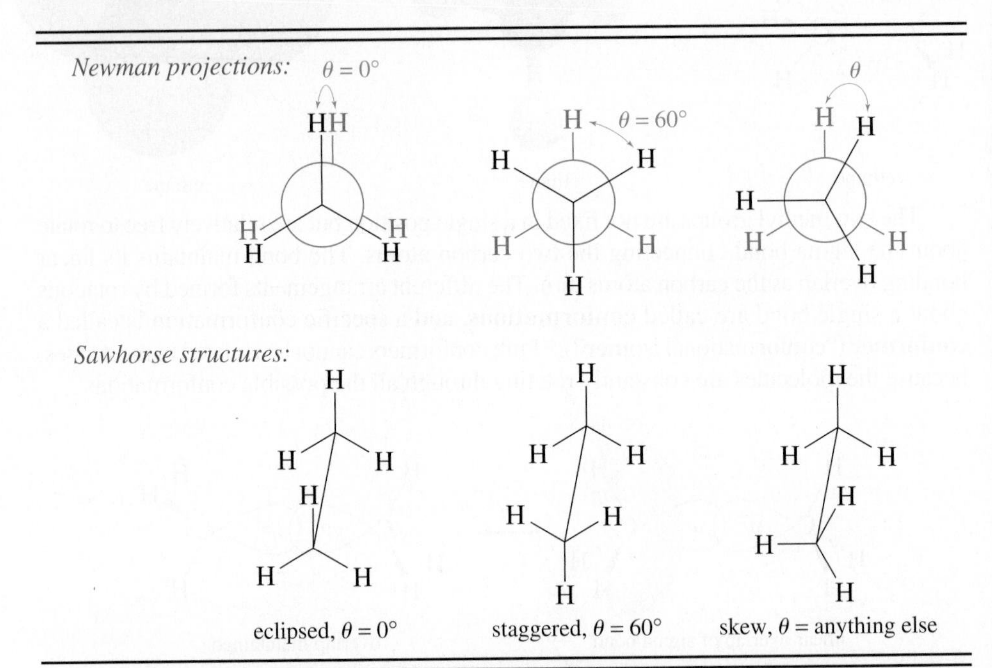

■ **FIGURE 3-6**
Ethane conformations. The eclipsed conformation has a dihedral angle $\theta = 0°$, and the staggered conformation has $\theta = 60°$. Any other conformation is called a *skew* conformation.

Any conformation can be specified by its **dihedral angle** (θ), the angle between the C—H bonds on the front carbon atom and the C—H bonds on the back carbon in the Newman projection. Two of the conformations have special names. The conformation with $\theta = 0°$ is called the **eclipsed conformation** because the Newman projection shows the hydrogen atoms on the back carbon to be hidden (eclipsed) by those on the front carbon. The **staggered conformation**, with $\theta = 60°$, has the hydrogen atoms on the back carbon staggered halfway between the hydrogens on the front carbon. Any other intermediate conformation is called a **skew conformation**.

In a sample of ethane gas at room temperature, the ethane molecules are rotating, and their conformations are constantly changing. These conformations are not all equally favored, however. The lowest-energy conformation is the staggered conformation, with the electron clouds in the C—H bonds separated as much as possible. The interactions of the electrons in the bonds make the eclipsed conformation about 12.6 kJ/mol (3.0 kcal/mol) higher in energy than the staggered conformation. Three kilocalories is not a large amount of energy, and at room temperature, most molecules have enough kinetic energy to overcome this small rotational barrier.

Figure 3-7 shows how the potential energy of ethane changes as the carbon–carbon bond rotates. The *y* axis shows the potential energy relative to the most stable (staggered) conformation. The *x* axis shows the dihedral angle as it increases from 0° (eclipsed) through 60° (staggered) and on through additional eclipsed and staggered conformations as θ continues to increase. As ethane rotates toward an eclipsed conformation, its potential energy increases, and there is resistance to the rotation. This resistance to twisting (torsion) is called **torsional strain**, and the 12.6 kJ/mol (3.0 kcal/mol) of energy required is called **torsional energy**.

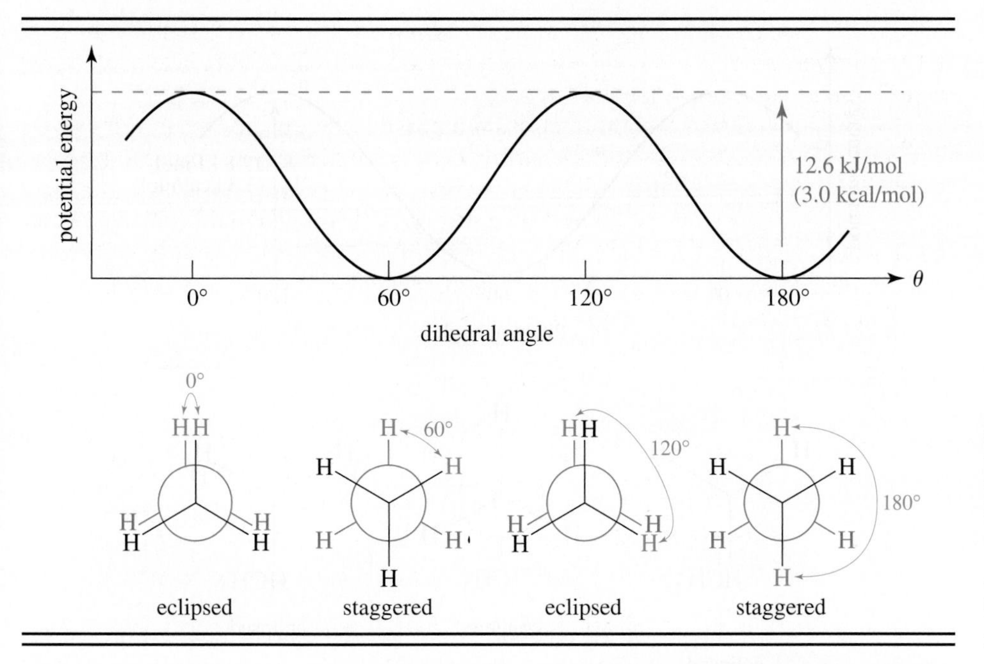

■ **FIGURE 3-7**
The torsional energy of ethane is lowest in the staggered conformation. The eclipsed conformation is about 12.6 kJ/mol (3.0 kcal/mol) higher in energy. At room temperature, this barrier is easily overcome and the molecules rotate constantly.

Conformational analysis is the study of the energetics of different conformations. Many reactions depend on a molecule's ability to twist into a particular conformation; conformational analysis can help to predict which conformations are favored and which reactions are more likely to take place. We will apply conformational analysis to propane and butane first, and later to some interesting cycloalkanes.

3-7C Conformations of Propane

Propane is the three-carbon alkane, with formula C_3H_8. Figure 3-8 shows a three-dimensional representation of propane and a Newman projection looking down one of the carbon–carbon bonds.

Figure 3-9 shows a graph of the torsional energy of propane as one of the carbon–carbon bonds rotates. The torsional energy of the eclipsed conformation is about 13.8 kJ/mol (3.3 kcal/mol), only 1.2 kJ (0.3 kcal) more than that required for ethane. Apparently, the torsional strain resulting from eclipsing a carbon–hydrogen bond with a carbon–methyl bond is only 1.2 kJ (0.3 kcal) more than the strain of eclipsing two carbon–hydrogen bonds.

problem-solving **Hint**

A C—H bond eclipsed with another C—H bond contributes 4.2 kJ/mol (1.0 kcal/mol) torsional energy (one-third of eclipsed ethane). A C—H bond eclipsed with a C—CH_3 bond contributes 5.4 kJ/mol (1.3 kcal/mol).

PROBLEM 3-11

Draw a graph, similar to Figure 3-9, of the torsional strain of 2-methylpropane as it rotates about the bond between C1 and C2. Show the dihedral angle and draw a Newman projection for each staggered and eclipsed conformation.

viewed from the end — perspective drawing = Newman projection

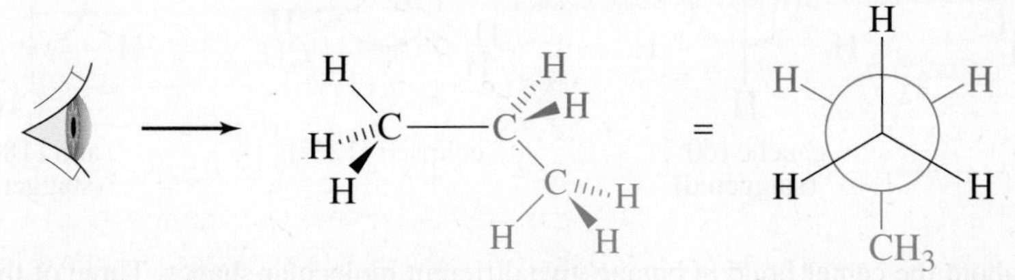

■ **FIGURE 3-8**
Propane is shown here as a perspective drawing and as a Newman projection looking down one of the carbon–carbon bonds.

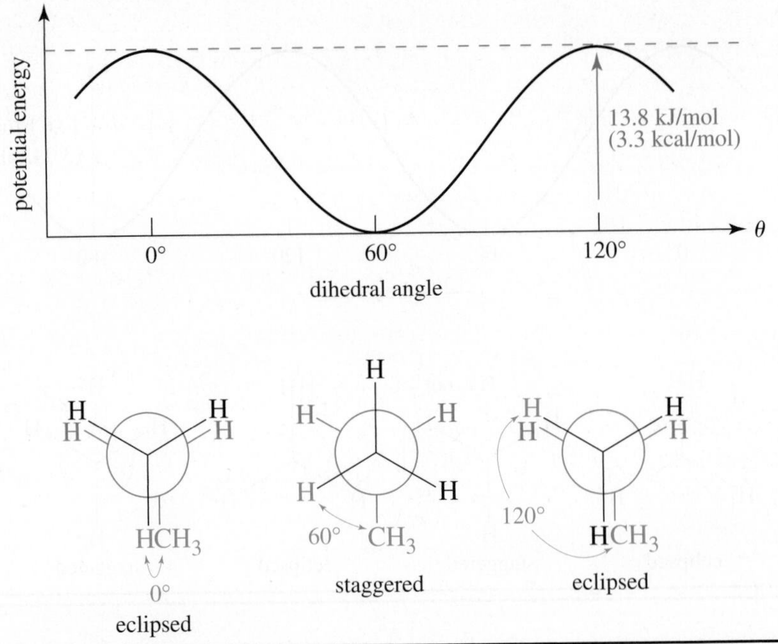

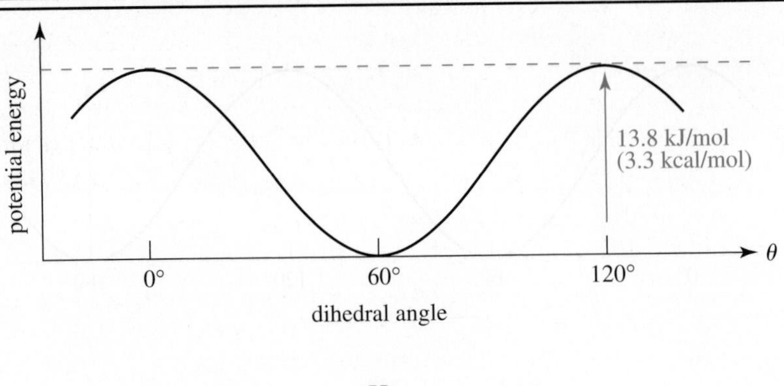

eclipsed (0°) — staggered (60°) — eclipsed (120°)

■ **FIGURE 3-9**
Torsional energy of propane. When a C—C bond of propane rotates, the torsional energy varies much like it does in ethane, but with 13.8 kJ/mol (3.3 kcal/mol) torsional energy in the eclipsed conformation.

3-8 Conformations of Butane

Butane is the four-carbon alkane, with molecular formula C_4H_{10}. We refer to *n*-butane as a straight-chain alkane, but the chain of carbon atoms is not really straight. The angles between the carbon atoms are close to the tetrahedral angle, about 109.5°. Rotations about any of the carbon–carbon bonds are possible. Rotations about either of the end bonds (C1—C2 or C3—C4) just rotate a methyl group like in ethane or propane. Rotations about the central C2—C3 bond are more interesting, however. Figure 3-10 shows Newman projections, looking along the central C2—C3 bond, for four conformations of butane. Construct butane with your molecular models, and sight down the C2—C3 bond. Notice that we have defined the dihedral angle θ as the angle between the two end methyl groups.

Three of the conformations shown in Figure 3-10 are given special names. When the methyl groups are pointed in the same direction ($\theta = 0°$), they eclipse each other. This conformation is called **totally eclipsed**, to distinguish it from the other eclipsed

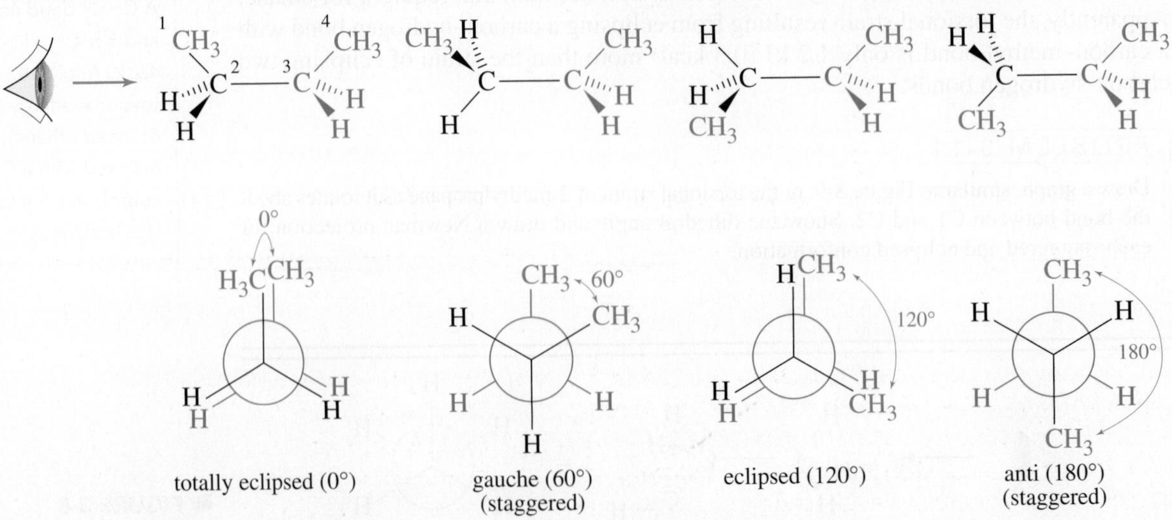

totally eclipsed (0°) — gauche (60°) (staggered) — eclipsed (120°) — anti (180°) (staggered)

■ **FIGURE 3-10**
Butane conformations. Rotations about the center bond in butane give different molecular shapes. Three of these conformations have specific names.

conformations like the one at $\theta = 120°$. At $\theta = 60°$, the butane molecule is staggered and the methyl groups are toward the left and right of each other. This 60° conformation is called **gauche** (pronounced gōsh), a French word meaning "left" or "awkward."

Another staggered conformation occurs at $\theta = 180°$, with the methyl groups pointing in opposite directions. This conformation is called **anti** because the methyl groups are "opposed."

3-8A Torsional Energy of Butane

A graph of the relative torsional energies of the butane conformations is shown in Figure 3-11. All the staggered conformations (anti and gauche) are lower in energy than any of the eclipsed conformations. The anti conformation is lowest in energy because it places the bulky methyl groups as far apart as possible. The gauche conformations, with the methyl groups separated by just 60°, are 3.8 kJ (0.9 kcal) higher in energy than the anti conformation because the methyl groups are close enough that their electron clouds begin to repel each other. Use your molecular models to compare the crowding of the methyl groups in these conformations.

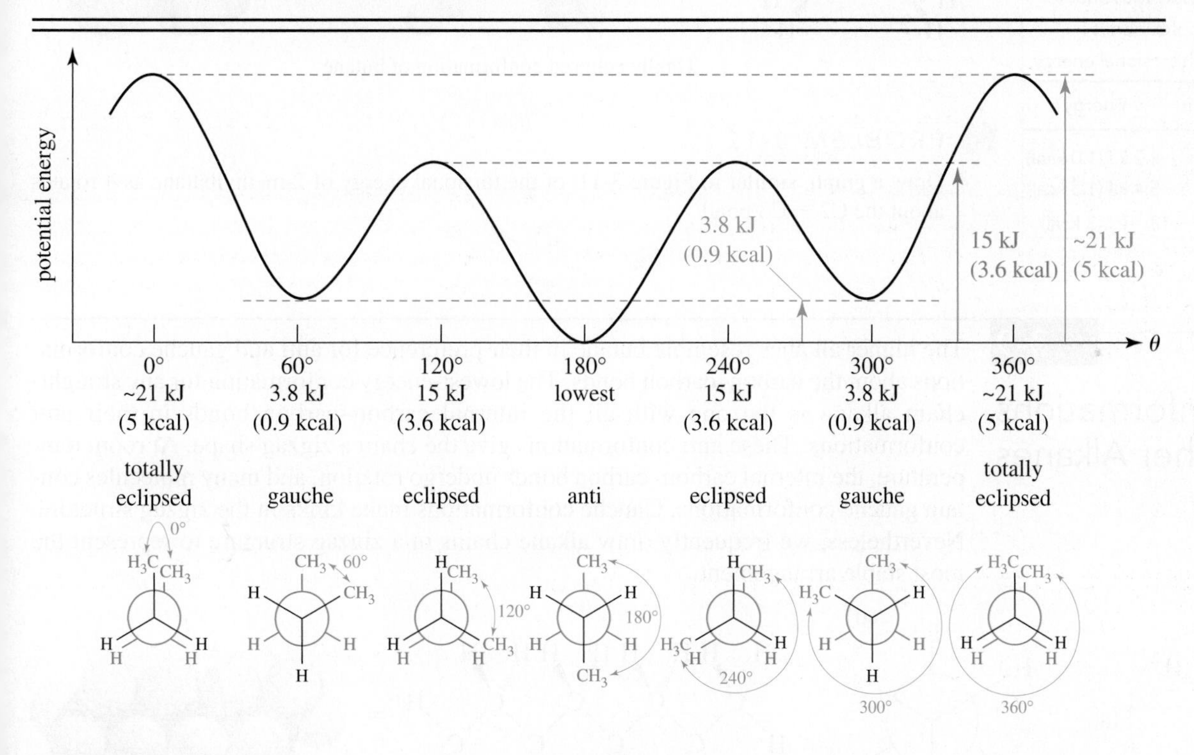

FIGURE 3-11
Torsional energy of butane. The anti conformation is lowest in energy, and the totally eclipsed conformation is highest in energy.

3-8B Steric Strain

The totally eclipsed conformation is about 6 kJ (1.4 kcal) higher in energy than the other eclipsed conformations because it forces the two end methyl groups so close together that their electron clouds experience a strong repulsion. This kind of interference between two bulky groups is called **steric strain**.* The following structure shows the interference between the methyl groups in the totally eclipsed conformation.

*"Steric strain" is sometimes called "steric hindrance," a term that more appropriately refers to the slowing (hindrance) of a reaction because bulky groups interfere.

Rotating the totally eclipsed conformation 60° to a gauche conformation releases most, but not all, of this steric strain. The gauche conformation is still 3.8 kJ (0.9 kcal) higher in energy than the most stable anti conformation.

What we have learned about the conformations of butane can be applied to other alkanes. We can predict that carbon–carbon single bonds will assume staggered conformations whenever possible to avoid eclipsing of the groups attached to them. Among the staggered conformations, the anti conformation is preferred because it has the lowest torsional energy. We must remember, however, that there is enough thermal energy present at room temperature for the molecules to rotate rapidly among all the different conformations. The relative stabilities are important because more molecules will be found in the more stable conformations than in the less stable ones.

problem-solving Hint

A C—CH_3 bond eclipsed with another C—CH_3 bond contributes about 13 kJ/mol (3 kcal/mol) torsional energy.

Bond	Eclipsed with	Energy
C—H	C—H	4.2 kJ (1.0 kcal)
C—H	C—CH_3	5.4 kJ (1.3 kcal)
C—CH_3	C—CH_3	13 kJ (3 kcal)

Totally eclipsed conformation of butane

PROBLEM 3-12

Draw a graph, similar to Figure 3-11, of the torsional energy of 2-methylbutane as it rotates about the C2—C3 bond.

3-9 Conformations of Higher Alkanes

The higher alkanes resemble butane in their preference for anti and gauche conformations about the carbon–carbon bonds. The lowest-energy conformation for any straight-chain alkane is the one with all the internal carbon–carbon bonds in their anti conformations. These anti conformations give the chain a zigzag shape. At room temperature, the internal carbon–carbon bonds undergo rotation, and many molecules contain gauche conformations. Gauche conformations make kinks in the zigzag structure. Nevertheless, we frequently draw alkane chains in a zigzag structure to represent the most stable arrangement.

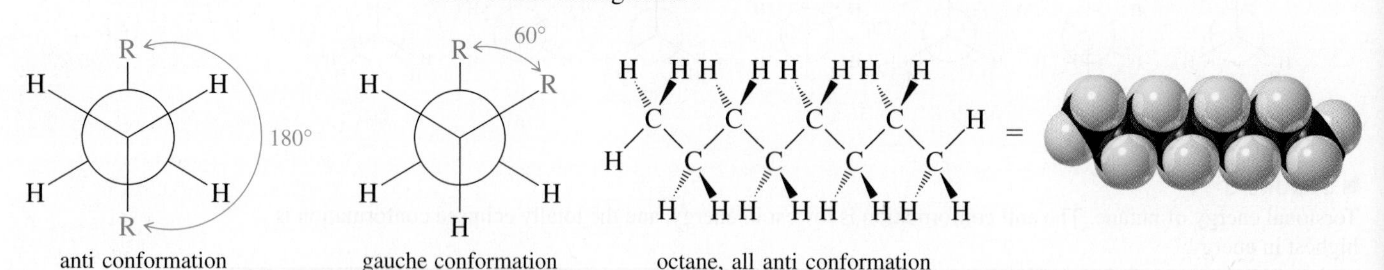

anti conformation gauche conformation octane, all anti conformation

PROBLEM 3-13

Draw a perspective representation of the most stable conformation of 3-methylhexane.

3-10 Cycloalkanes

Many organic compounds are **cyclic**: They contain rings of atoms. The carbohydrates we eat are cyclic, the nucleotides that make up our DNA and RNA are cyclic, and the antibiotics we use to treat diseases are cyclic. In this chapter, we use the *cycloalkanes* to illustrate the properties and stability of cyclic compounds.

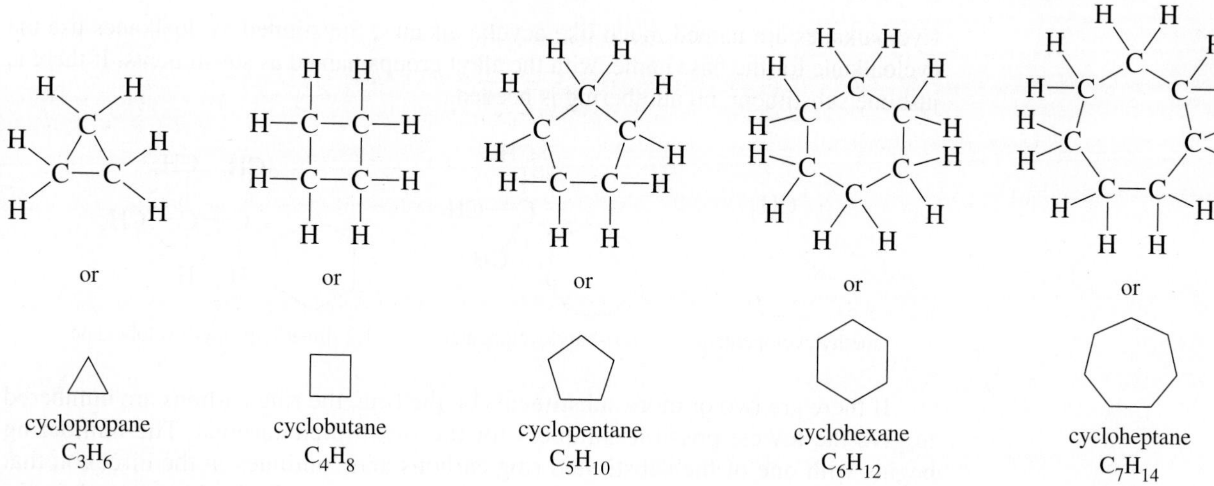

FIGURE 3-12
Structures of some cycloalkanes.

Cycloalkanes are alkanes that contain rings of carbon atoms. Simple cycloalkanes are named like acyclic (noncyclic) alkanes, with the prefix *cyclo-* indicating the presence of a ring. For example, the cycloalkane with four carbon atoms in a ring is called *cyclobutane*. The cycloalkane with seven carbon atoms in a ring is *cycloheptane*. Line–angle formulas are often used for drawing the rings of cycloalkanes (Figure 3-12).

3-10A General Molecular Formulas of Cycloalkanes

Simple cycloalkanes are rings of CH_2 groups (methylene groups). Each one has exactly twice as many hydrogen atoms as carbon atoms, giving the general molecular formula C_nH_{2n}. This general formula has two fewer hydrogen atoms than the $(2n + 2)$ formula for an acyclic alkane because a ring has no ends, and no hydrogens are needed to cap off the ends of the chain.

Cyclopropane was once used as general anesthetic because its vapors, like those of other simple alkanes and cycloalkanes, cause sleepiness and a loss of consciousness. After inhalation into the lungs, cyclopropane goes into the blood. Due to its nonpolar nature, it rapidly leaves the blood and passes through the nonpolar membranes surrounding the central nervous system, where it produces anesthesia. Cyclopropane is no longer used as an anesthetic because it is highly flammable (like ether) and can cause explosions when mixed with air.

3-10B Physical Properties of Cycloalkanes

Most cycloalkanes resemble the **acyclic** (noncyclic), open-chain alkanes in their physical properties and in their chemistry. They are nonpolar, relatively inert compounds with boiling points and melting points that depend on their molecular weights. The cycloalkanes are held in a more compact cyclic shape, so their physical properties are similar to those of the compact, branched alkanes. The physical properties of some common cycloalkanes are listed in Table 3-4.

TABLE 3-4
Physical Properties of Some Simple Cycloalkanes

Cycloalkane	Formula	Boiling Point (°C)	Melting Point (°C)	Density
cyclopropane	C_3H_6	−33	−128	0.72
cyclobutane	C_4H_8	−12	−50	0.75
cyclopentane	C_5H_{10}	49	−94	0.75
cyclohexane	C_6H_{12}	81	7	0.78
cycloheptane	C_7H_{14}	118	−12	0.81
cyclooctane	C_8H_{16}	148	14	0.83

3-10C Nomenclature of Cycloalkanes

Cycloalkanes are named much like acyclic alkanes. Substituted cycloalkanes use the cycloalkane for the base name, with the alkyl groups named as substituents. If there is just one substituent, no numbering is needed.

methylcyclopentane   *tert*-butylcycloheptane   (1,2-dimethylpropyl)cyclohexane

If there are two or more substituents on the ring, the ring carbons are numbered to give the lowest possible numbers for the substituted carbons. The numbering begins with one of the substituted ring carbons and continues in the direction that gives the lowest possible numbers to the other substituents. In the name, the substituents are listed in alphabetical order. When the numbering could begin with either of two alkyl groups (as in a disubstituted cycloalkane), begin with the one that is alphabetically first.

1-ethyl-2-methylcyclobutane   1,1,3-trimethylcyclopentane   1,1-diethyl-4-isopropylcyclohexane

When the acyclic portion of the molecule contains more carbon atoms than the cyclic portion (or when it contains an important functional group), the cyclic portion is sometimes named as a cycloalkyl substituent.

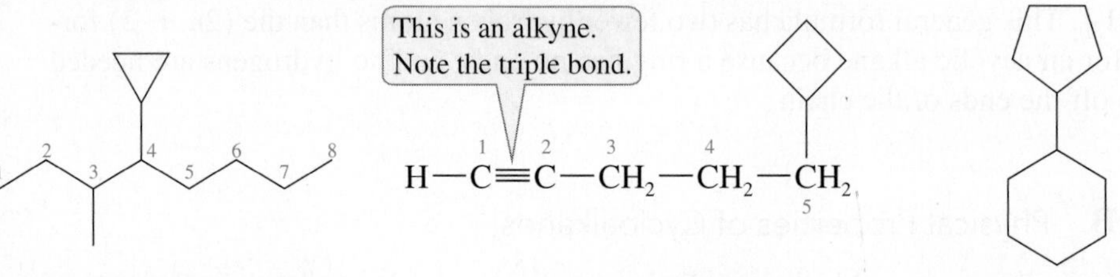
This is an alkyne.
Note the triple bond.
$H—C≡C—CH_2—CH_2—CH_2$

4-cyclopropyl-3-methyloctane   5-cyclobutyl-1-pentyne   cyclopentylcyclohexane

problem-solving Hint

Students accidentally draw cyclic structures when acyclic structures are intended, and *vice versa*. Always verify whether the name contains the prefix **cyclo-**.

PROBLEM 3-14

Give IUPAC names for the following compounds.

(a) (b) (c)

PROBLEM 3-15

Draw the structure and give the molecular formula for each of the following compounds.

(a) 1-ethyl-3-methylcycloheptane
(b) isobutylcyclohexane
(c) cyclopropylcyclopentane
(d) 3-ethyl-1,1-dimethylcyclohexane
(e) 3-ethyl-2,4-dimethylhexane
(f) 1,1-diethyl-4-(3,3-dimethylbutyl)cyclohexane

3-11 Cis-trans Isomerism in Cycloalkanes

Open-chain (acyclic) alkanes undergo rotations about their carbon–carbon single bonds, so they are free to assume any of an infinite number of conformations. Alkenes have rigid double bonds that prevent rotation, giving rise to cis and trans isomers with different orientations of the groups on the double bond (Section 2-8). Cycloalkanes are similar to alkenes in this respect. A cycloalkane has two distinct faces. If two substituents point toward the same face, they are **cis**. If they point toward opposite faces, they are **trans**. These **geometric isomers** cannot interconvert without breaking and re-forming bonds.

Figure 3-13 compares the cis-trans isomers of 2-butene with those of 1,2-dimethylcyclopentane. Make models of these compounds to convince yourself that *cis*- and *trans*-1,2-dimethylcyclopentane cannot interconvert by simple rotations about the bonds.

PROBLEM 3-16

Which of the following cycloalkanes are capable of geometric (cis-trans) isomerism? Draw the cis and trans isomers.

(a) 3-ethyl-1,1-dimethylcyclohexane **(b)** 1-ethyl-3-methylcycloheptane
(c) 1-ethyl-3-methylcyclopentane **(d)** 1-cyclopropyl-2-methylcyclohexane

PROBLEM 3-17

Give IUPAC names for the following cycloalkanes.

(a) 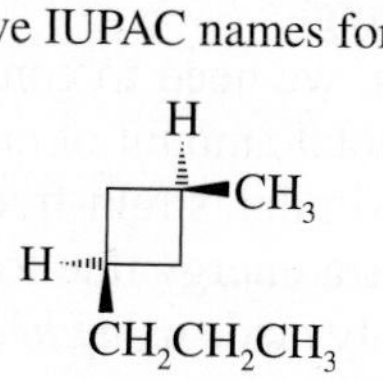 H, CH_3, H, $CH_2CH_2CH_3$ (b) $C(CH_3)_3$, H, H, CH_2CH_3 (c) H, CH_3, H, H_3C

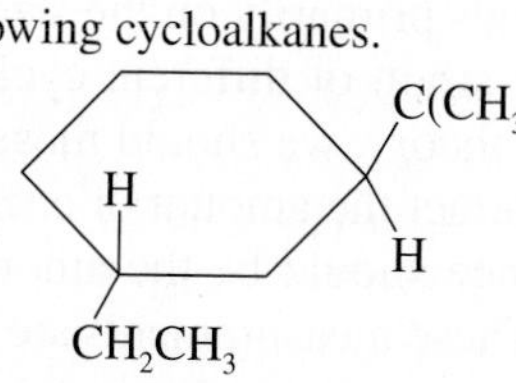

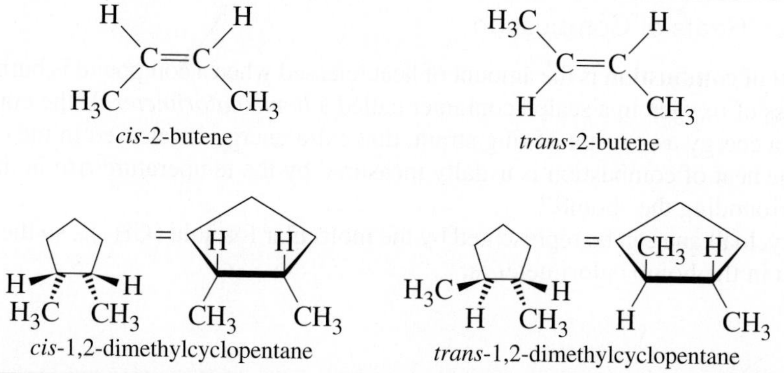

H, H, C=C, H_3C, CH_3
cis-2-butene

H_3C, H, C=C, H, CH_3
trans-2-butene

H, H, H_3C, CH_3 = H, H, CH_3, CH_3
cis-1,2-dimethylcyclopentane

H_3C, H, H, CH_3 = CH_3, H, H, CH_3
trans-1,2-dimethylcyclopentane

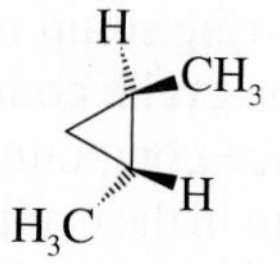

■ **FIGURE 3-13**
Cis-trans isomerism in cycloalkanes. Like alkenes, cycloalkane rings are restricted from free rotation. Two substituents on a cycloalkane must be either on the same side (cis) or on opposite sides (trans) of the ring.

3-12 Stabilities of Cycloalkanes; Ring Strain

Although all the simple cycloalkanes (up to about C_{20}) have been synthesized, the most common rings contain five or six carbon atoms. We will study the stabilities and conformations of these rings in detail because they help to determine the properties of many important organic compounds.

Why are five-membered and six-membered rings more common than the other sizes? Adolf von Baeyer first attempted to explain the relative stabilities of cyclic molecules in the late nineteenth century, and he was awarded a Nobel Prize for this work in 1905. Baeyer reasoned that the carbon atoms in acyclic alkanes have bond angles of 109.5°. (We now explain this bond angle by the tetrahedral geometry of the sp^3 hybridized carbon atoms.)

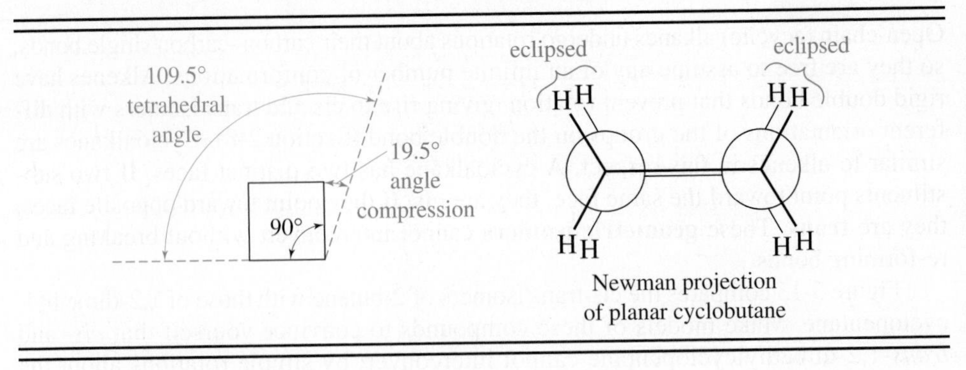

■ **FIGURE 3-14**
The ring strain of a planar cyclobutane results from two factors: angle strain from the compressing of the bond angles to 90° rather than the tetrahedral angle of 109.5°, and torsional strain from eclipsing of the bonds.

If a cycloalkane requires bond angles other than 109.5°, the orbitals of its carbon–carbon bonds cannot achieve optimum overlap, and the cycloalkane must have some **angle strain** (sometimes called **Baeyer strain**) associated with it. Figure 3-14 shows that a planar cyclobutane, with 90° bond angles, is expected to have significant angle strain.

In addition to this angle strain, the Newman projection in Figure 3-14 shows that the bonds are eclipsed, resembling the *totally eclipsed* conformation of butane (Section 3-7). This eclipsing of bonds gives rise to torsional strain. Together, the angle strain and the torsional strain add to give what we call the **ring strain** of the cyclic compound. The amount of ring strain depends primarily on the size of the ring.

Before we discuss the ring strain of different cycloalkanes, we need to consider how ring strain is measured. In theory, we should measure the total amount of energy in the cyclic compound and subtract the amount of energy in a similar, strain-free reference compound. The difference should be the amount of extra energy due to ring strain in the cyclic compound. These measurements are commonly made using *heats of combustion*.

3-12A Heats of Combustion

The **heat of combustion** is the amount of heat released when a compound is burned with an excess of oxygen in a sealed container called a *bomb calorimeter*. If the compound has extra energy as a result of ring strain, that extra energy is released in the combustion. The heat of combustion is usually measured by the temperature rise in the water bath surrounding the "bomb."

A cycloalkane can be represented by the molecular formula $(CH_2)_n$, so the general reaction in the bomb calorimeter is:

$$\text{cycloalkane, } (CH_2)_n + \tfrac{3}{2}n\,O_2 \longrightarrow n\,CO_2 + n\,H_2O + n(\text{energy per } CH_2)$$

(cycloalkane ring drawn as CH_2 groups; n(energy per CH_2) = heat of combustion)

The molar heat of combustion of cyclohexane is nearly twice that of cyclopropane, simply because cyclohexane contains twice as many methylene (CH_2) groups per mole. To compare the relative stabilities of cycloalkanes, we divide the heat of combustion by the number of methylene (CH_2) groups. The result is the energy per CH_2 group. These normalized energies allow us to compare the relative amounts of ring strain (per methylene group) in the cycloalkanes.

TABLE 3-5

Heats of Combustion (per Mole) for Some Simple Cycloalkanes

Ring Size	Cycloalkane	Molar Heat of Combustion	Heat of Combustion per CH_2 Group	Ring Strain per CH_2 Group	Total Ring Strain
3	cyclopropane	2091 kJ (499.8 kcal)	697.1 kJ (166.6 kcal)	38.5 kJ (9.2 kcal)	115 kJ (27.6 kcal)
4	cyclobutane	2744 kJ (655.9 kcal)	686.1 kJ (164.0 kcal)	27.5 kJ (6.6 kcal)	110 kJ (26.3 kcal)
5	cyclopentane	3320 kJ (793.5 kcal)	664.0 kJ (158.7 kcal)	5.4 kJ (1.3 kcal)	27 kJ (6.5 kcal)
6	cyclohexane	3951 kJ (944.4 kcal)	658.6 kJ (157.4 kcal)	0.0 kJ (0.0 kcal)	0.0 kJ (0.0 kcal)
7	cycloheptane	4637 kJ (1108.2 kcal)	662.4 kJ (158.3 kcal)	3.8 kJ (0.9 kcal)	27 kJ (6.4 kcal)
8	cyclooctane	5309 kJ (1268.9 kcal)	663.6 kJ (158.6 kcal)	5.1 kJ (1.2 kcal)	41 kJ (9.7 kcal)
reference: long-chain alkane			658.6 kJ (157.4 kcal)	0.0 kJ (0.0 kcal)	0.0 kJ (0.0 kcal)

All units are per mole.

Table 3-5 lists the heats of combustion for some simple cycloalkanes. The reference value of 658.6 kJ (157.4 kcal) per mole of CH_2 groups comes from an unstrained long-chain alkane. The values show large amounts of ring strain in cyclopropane and cyclobutane. Cyclopentane, cycloheptane, and cyclooctane have much smaller amounts of ring strain, and cyclohexane has no ring strain at all. We will discuss several of these rings in detail to explain this pattern of ring strain.

3-12B Cyclopropane

Table 3-5 shows that cyclopropane bears more ring strain per methylene group than any other cycloalkane. Two factors contribute to this large ring strain. First is the angle strain required to compress the bond angles from the tetrahedral angle of 109.5° to the 60° angles of cyclopropane. The bonding overlap of the carbon–carbon sp^3 orbitals is weakened when the bond angles differ so much from the tetrahedral angle. The sp^3 orbitals cannot point directly toward each other, and they overlap at an angle to form weaker "bent bonds" (Figure 3-15).

Torsional strain is the second factor in cyclopropane's large ring strain. The three-membered ring is planar, and all the bonds are eclipsed. A Newman projection of one of the carbon–carbon bonds (Figure 3-16) shows that the conformation resembles the totally eclipsed conformation of butane. The torsional strain in cyclopropane is not as great as its angle strain, but it helps to account for the large total ring strain.

Cyclopropane is generally more reactive than other alkanes. Reactions that open the cyclopropane ring release 115 kJ (27.6 kcal) per mole of ring strain, which provides an additional driving force for these reactions.

PROBLEM 3-18

The heat of combustion of *cis*-1,2-dimethylcyclopropane is larger than that of the trans isomer. Which isomer is more stable? Use drawings to explain this difference in stability.

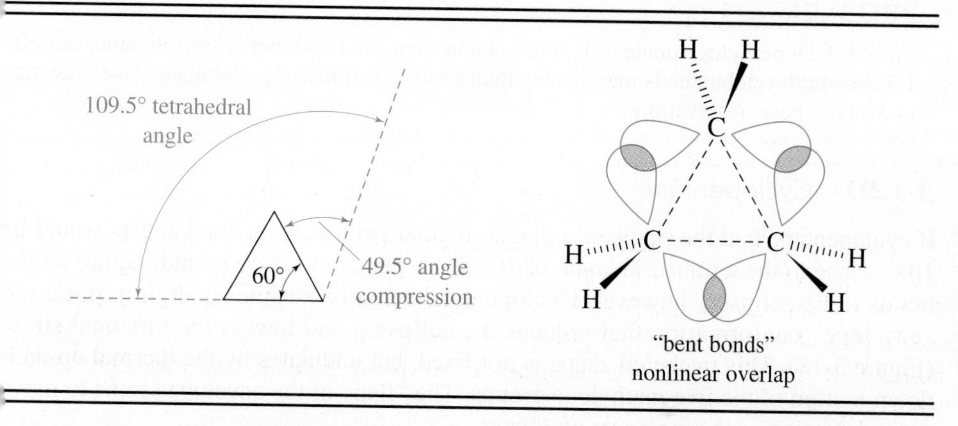

FIGURE 3-15
Angle strain in cyclopropane. The bond angles are compressed to 60° from the usual 109.5° bond angle of sp^3 hybridized carbon atoms. This severe angle strain leads to nonlinear overlap of the sp^3 orbitals and "bent bonds."

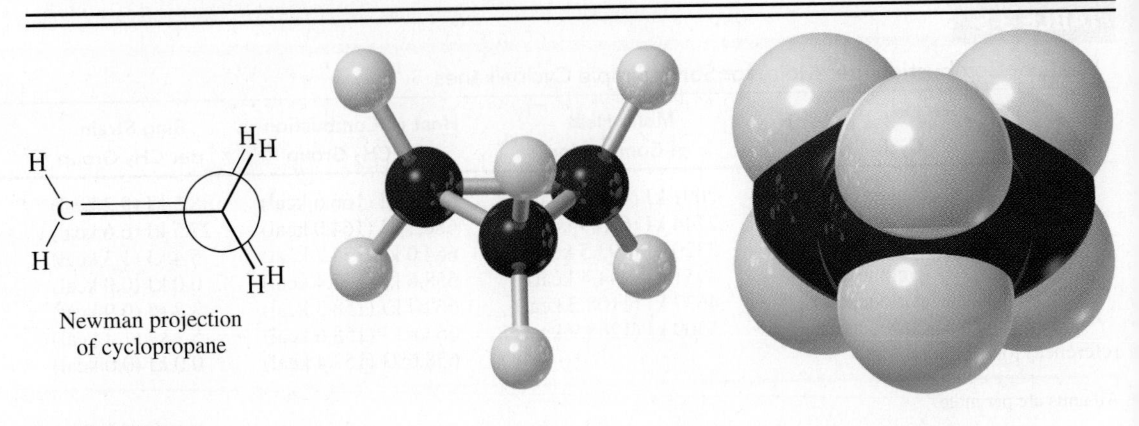

■ **FIGURE 3-16**
Torsional strain in cyclopropane. All the carbon–carbon bonds are eclipsed, generating torsional strain that contributes to the total ring strain.

3-12C Cyclobutane

The total ring strain in cyclobutane is almost as great as that in cyclopropane, but is distributed over four carbon atoms. If cyclobutane were perfectly planar and square, it would have 90° bond angles. A planar geometry requires eclipsing of all the bonds, however, as in cyclopropane. To reduce this torsional strain, cyclobutane actually assumes a slightly folded form, with bond angles of 88°. These smaller bond angles require slightly more angle strain than 90° angles, but the relief of some of the torsional strain appears to compensate for a small increase in angle strain (Figure 3-17).

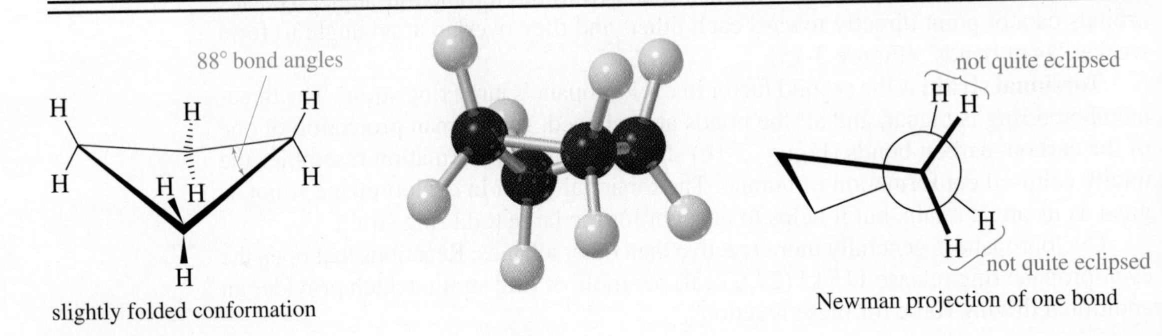

■ **FIGURE 3-17**
The conformation of cyclobutane is slightly folded. Folding gives partial relief from the eclipsing of bonds, as shown in the Newman projection. Compare this actual structure with the hypothetical planar structure in Figure 3-14.

PROBLEM 3-19

trans-1,2-Dimethylcyclobutane is more stable than *cis*-1,2-dimethylcyclobutane, but *cis*-1,3-dimethylcyclobutane is more stable than *trans*-1,3-dimethylcyclobutane. Use drawings to explain these observations.

The conformation of cyclopentane is important because ribose and deoxyribose, the sugar components of RNA and DNA, respectively, assume cyclopentane-like ring conformations. These conformations are crucial to the properties and reactions of RNA and DNA.

3-12D Cyclopentane

If cyclopentane had the shape of a planar, regular pentagon, its bond angles would be 108°, close to the tetrahedral angle of 109.5°. A planar structure would require all the bonds to be eclipsed, however. Cyclopentane actually assumes a slightly puckered "envelope" conformation that reduces the eclipsing and lowers the torsional strain (Figure 3-18). This puckered shape is not fixed, but undulates by the thermal up-and-down motion of the five methylene groups. The "flap" of the envelope seems to move around the ring as the molecule undulates.

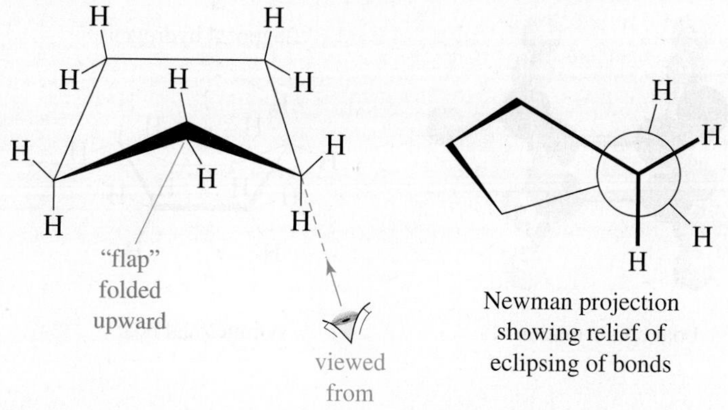

■ FIGURE 3-18
The conformation of cyclopentane is slightly folded, like the shape of an envelope. This puckered conformation reduces the eclipsing of adjacent CH_2 groups.

3-13 Cyclohexane Conformations

We will cover the conformations of cyclohexane in more detail than other cycloalkanes because cyclohexane ring systems are particularly common. Carbohydrates, steroids, plant products, pesticides, and many other important compounds contain cyclohexane-like rings whose conformations and stereochemistry are critically important to their reactivity. The abundance of cyclohexane rings in nature is probably due to both their stability and the selectivity offered by their predictable conformations.

The combustion data (Table 3-5) show that cyclohexane has *no* ring strain. Cyclohexane must have bond angles that are near the tetrahedral angle (no angle strain) and also have no eclipsing of bonds (no torsional strain). A planar, regular hexagon would have bond angles of 120° rather than 109.5°, implying some angle strain. A planar ring would also have torsional strain because the bonds on adjacent CH_2 groups would be eclipsed. Therefore, the cyclohexane ring cannot be planar.

3-13A Chair and Boat Conformations

Cyclohexane achieves tetrahedral bond angles and staggered conformations by assuming a puckered conformation. The most stable conformation is the **chair conformation** shown in Figure 3-19. Build a molecular model of cyclohexane, and compare its shape with the drawings in Figure 3-19. In the chair conformation, the angles between

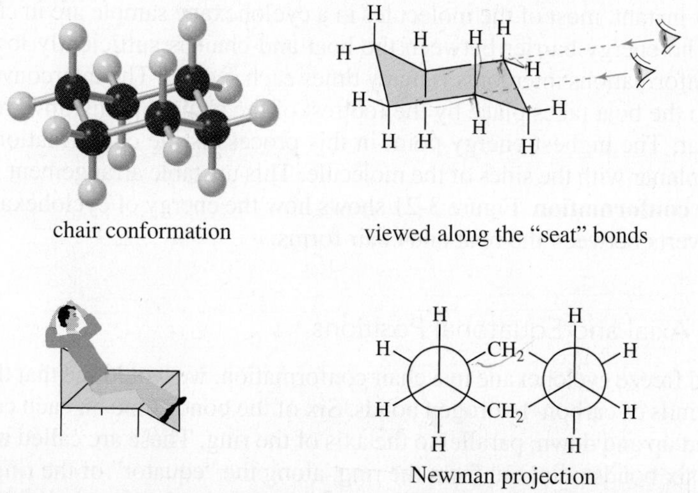

■ FIGURE 3-19
The chair conformation of cyclohexane has one methylene group puckered upward and another puckered downward. Viewed from the Newman projection, the chair has no eclipsing of the carbon–carbon bonds. The bond angles are 109.5°.

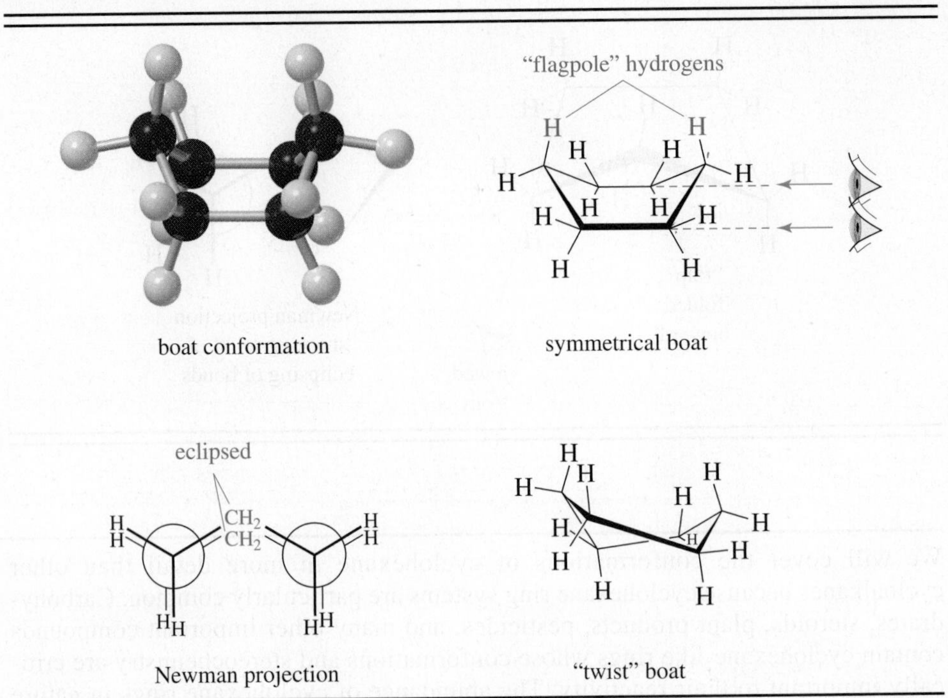

■ **FIGURE 3-20**
In the symmetrical boat conformation of cyclohexane, eclipsing of bonds results in torsional strain. In the actual molecule, the boat is skewed to give the twist boat, a conformation with less eclipsing of bonds and less interference between the two flagpole hydrogens.

the carbon–carbon bonds are all 109.5°. The Newman projection looking down the "seat" bonds shows all the bonds in staggered conformations.

The **boat conformation** of cyclohexane (Figure 3-20) also has bond angles of 109.5° and avoids angle strain. The boat conformation resembles the chair conformation except that the "footrest" methylene group is folded upward. The boat conformation suffers from torsional strain, however, because there is eclipsing of bonds.

This eclipsing forces two of the hydrogens on the ends of the "boat" to interfere with each other. These hydrogens are called **flagpole hydrogens** because they point upward from the ends of the boat like two flagpoles. The Newman projection in Figure 3-20 shows this eclipsing of the carbon–carbon bonds along the sides of the boat.

A cyclohexane molecule in the boat conformation actually exists as a slightly skewed **twist boat conformation**, also shown in Figure 3-20. If you assemble your molecular model in the boat conformation and twist it slightly, the flagpole hydrogens move away from each other and the eclipsing of the bonds is reduced. Even though the twist boat is lower in energy than the symmetrical boat, it is still about 23 kJ/mol (5.5 kcal/mol) higher in energy than the chair conformation. When someone refers to the "boat conformation," the twist boat (or simply **twist**) conformation is often intended.

The conformations of biological molecules are critical for their activities. For example, steroids fit into their receptors in only one conformation. The correct fit activates the receptor, resulting in a biological response.

At any instant, most of the molecules in a cyclohexane sample are in chair conformations. The energy barrier between the boat and chair is sufficiently low, however, that the conformations interconvert many times each second. The interconversion from the chair to the boat takes place by the footrest of the chair flipping upward and forming the boat. The highest-energy point in this process is the conformation where the footrest is planar with the sides of the molecule. This unstable arrangement is called the **half-chair conformation**. Figure 3-21 shows how the energy of cyclohexane varies as it interconverts between the boat and chair forms.

3-13B Axial and Equatorial Positions

If we could freeze cyclohexane in a chair conformation, we would see that there are two different kinds of carbon–hydrogen bonds. Six of the bonds (one on each carbon atom) are directed up and down, parallel to the axis of the ring. These are called **axial bonds**. The other six bonds point out from the ring, along the "equator" of the ring. These are

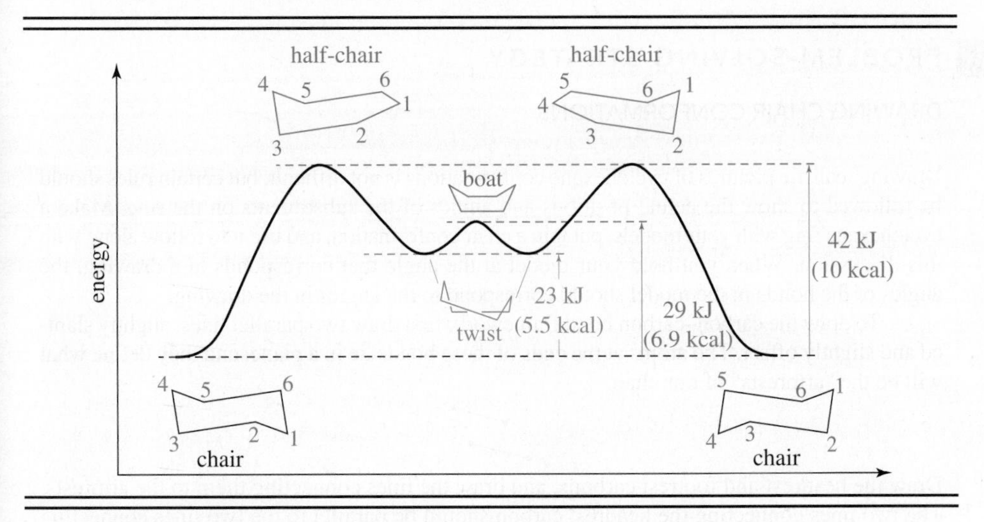

■ **FIGURE 3-21**
Conformational energy of cyclohexane. The chair conformation is most stable, followed by the twist boat. To convert between these two conformations, the molecule must pass through the unstable half-chair conformation.

called **equatorial bonds**. The axial bonds and hydrogens are shown in red in Figure 3-22, and the equatorial bonds and hydrogens are shown in green.

Each carbon atom in cyclohexane is bonded to two hydrogen atoms, one directed upward and one downward. As the carbon atoms are numbered in Figure 3-22, C1 has an axial bond upward and an equatorial bond downward. C2 has an equatorial bond upward and an axial bond downward. The pattern alternates. The odd-numbered carbon atoms have axial bonds up and equatorial bonds down, like C1. The even-numbered carbons have equatorial bonds up and axial bonds down, like C2. This pattern of alternating axial and equatorial bonds is helpful for predicting the conformations of substituted cyclohexanes, as we see in Sections 3-13 and 3-14.

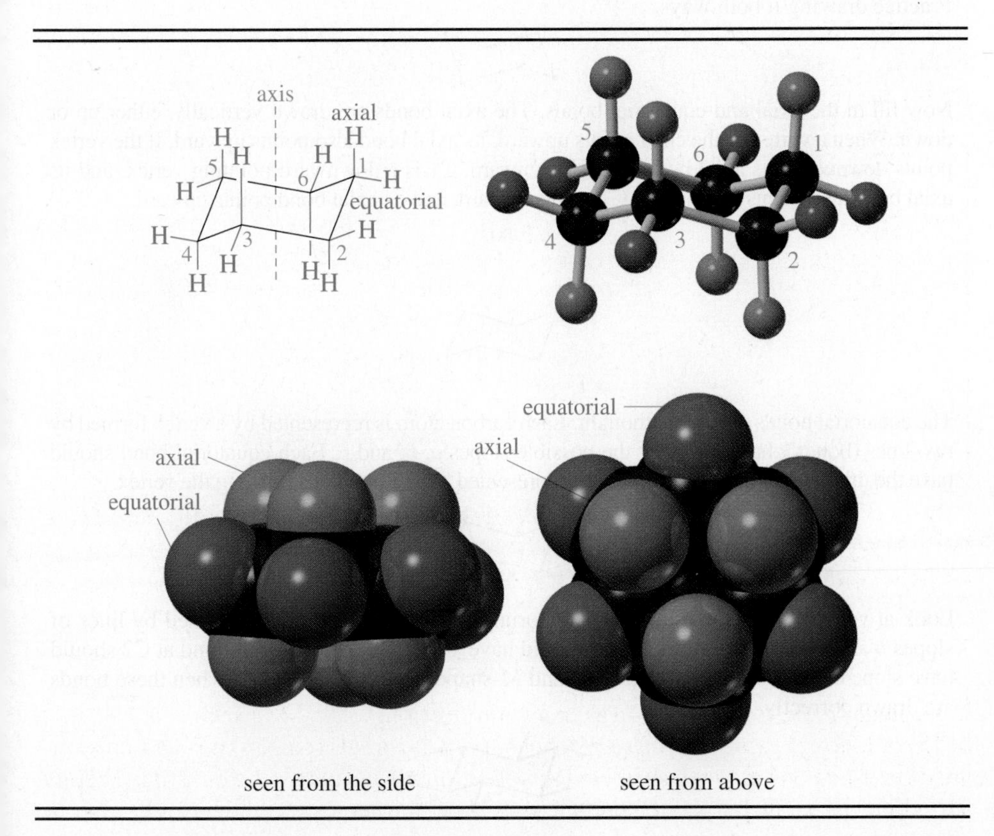

■ **FIGURE 3-22**
Axial bonds are directed vertically, parallel to the axis of the ring. Equatorial bonds are directed outward, toward the equator of the ring. As they are numbered here, the odd-numbered carbons have their *upward* bonds axial and their *downward* bonds equatorial. The even-numbered carbons have their *downward* bonds axial and their *upward* bonds equatorial.

PROBLEM-SOLVING STRATEGY

DRAWING CHAIR CONFORMATIONS

Drawing realistic pictures of cyclohexane conformations is not difficult, but certain rules should be followed to show the actual positions and angles of the substituents on the ring. Make a cyclohexane ring with your models, put it in a chair conformation, and use it to follow along with this discussion. When you hold your model at the angle that corresponds to a drawing, the angles of the bonds in the model should correspond to the angles in the drawing.

To draw the carbon–carbon bond framework, first draw two parallel lines, slightly slanted and slightly offset. The atoms at the ends of these bonds lie in a plane, and they define what will be the "armrests" of our chair.

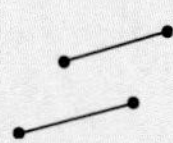

Draw the headrest and footrest carbons, and draw the lines connecting them to the armrests. The two lines connecting the headrest carbon should be parallel to the two lines connecting the footrest.

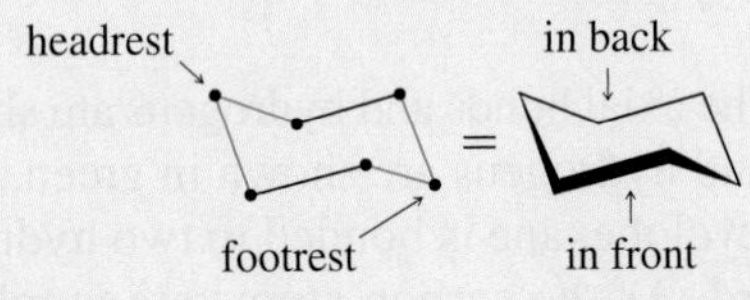

Notice that the carbon–carbon bond framework uses lines with only three different slopes, labeled *a, b,* and *c*. Compare this drawing with your model, and notice the pairs of carbon–carbon bonds with three distinct slopes.

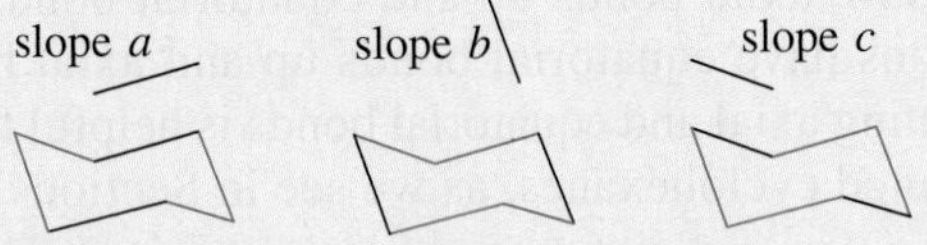

We can draw the chair with the headrest to the left and the footrest to the right, or vice versa. Practice drawing it both ways.

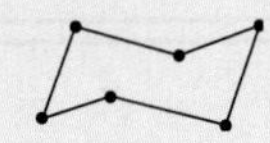

Now fill in the axial and equatorial bonds. The axial bonds are drawn vertically, either up or down. When a vertex of the chair points upward, its axial bond also points upward. If the vertex points downward, its axial bond points downward. C1 is a downward-pointing vertex, and its axial bond also points downward. C2 points upward, and its axial bond points upward.

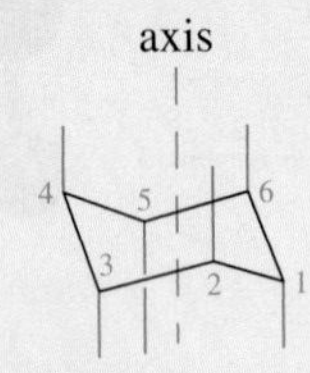

The equatorial bonds take more thought. Each carbon atom is represented by a vertex formed by two lines (bonds), having two of the possible slopes *a, b,* and *c*. Each equatorial bond should have the third slope: the slope that is *not* represented by the two lines forming the vertex.

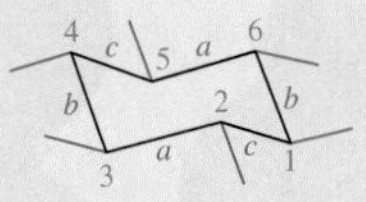

Look at your model as you add the equatorial bonds. The vertex C1 is formed by lines of slopes *b* and *c*, so its equatorial bond should have slope *a*. The equatorial bond at C2 should have slope *b*, and so on. Notice the W- and M-shaped patterns that result when these bonds are drawn correctly.

PROBLEM 3-20

The cyclohexane chair just drawn has the headrest to the left and the footrest to the right. Draw a cyclohexane chair with its axial and equatorial bonds, having the headrest to the right and the footrest to the left.

PROBLEM 3-21

Draw 1,2,3,4,5,6-hexamethylcyclohexane with all the methyl groups
(a) in axial positions. **(b)** in equatorial positions.

If your cyclohexane rings look awkward or slanted when using the analytical approach just shown, then try the artistic approach:* Draw a wide M, and draw a wide W below it, displaced about half a bond length to one side or the other. Connect the second atoms and the fourth atoms to give the cyclohexane ring with four equatorial bonds.

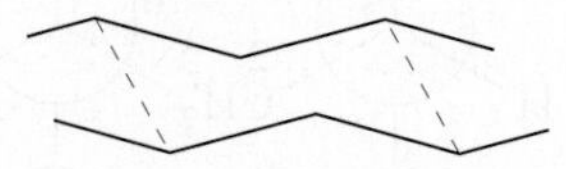

W displaced to the right

W displaced to the left

The other two equatorial bonds are drawn parallel to the ring connections. The axial bonds are then drawn vertically.

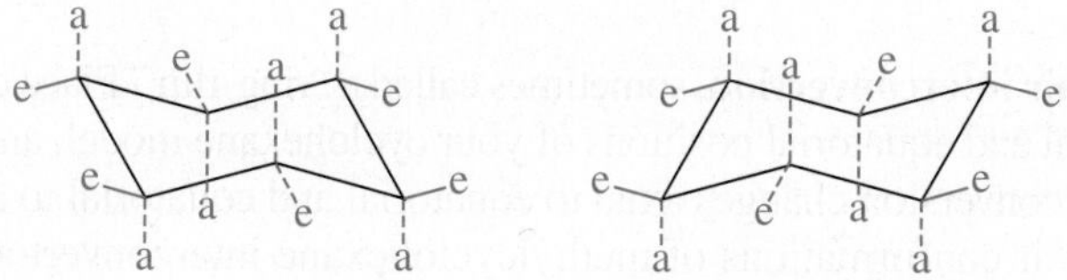

3-14 Conformations of Monosubstituted Cyclohexanes

A substituent on a cyclohexane ring (in the chair conformation) can occupy either an axial or an equatorial position. In many cases, the reactivity of the substituent depends on whether its position is axial or equatorial. The two possible chair conformations for methylcyclohexane are shown in Figure 3-23. These conformations are in equilibrium because they interconvert at room temperature. The boat (actually the twist boat) serves as an intermediate

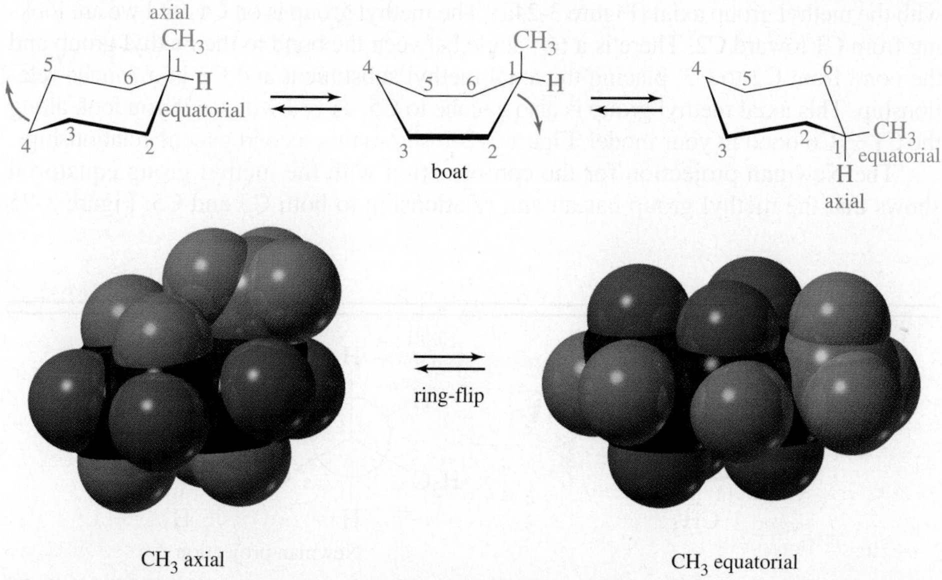

CH$_3$ axial

ring-flip

CH$_3$ equatorial

■ **FIGURE 3-23**
Chair–chair interconversion of methylcyclohexane. The methyl group is axial in one conformation, and equatorial in the other.

*See V. Dragojlovic, *J. Chem. Educ.* 2001, *78*, 923.

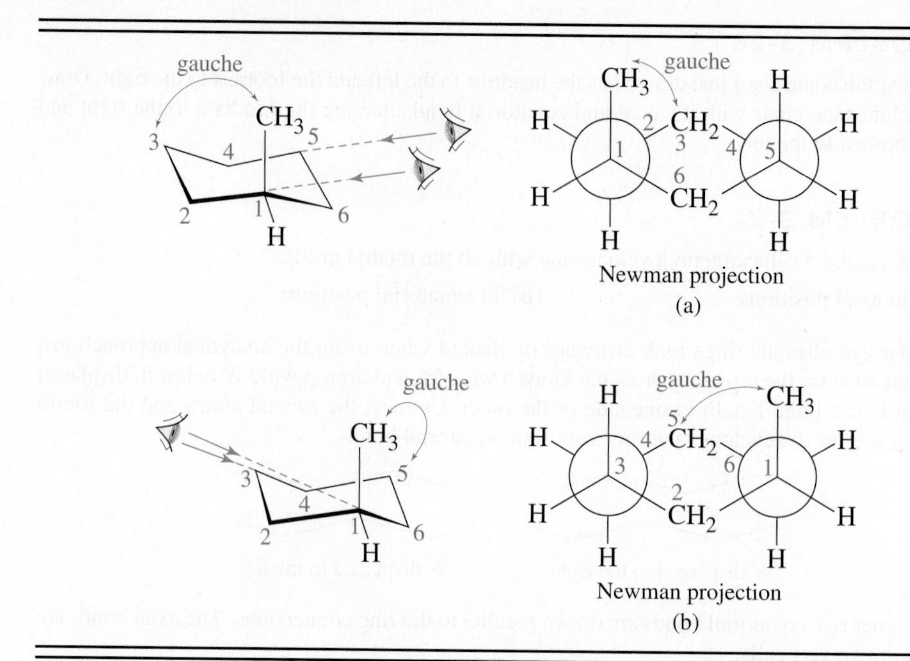

■ **FIGURE 3-24**
(a) When the methyl substituent is in an axial position on C1, it is gauche to C3. (b) The axial methyl group on C1 is also gauche to C5 of the ring.

in this **chair–chair interconversion**, sometimes called a "ring-flip." Place different-colored atoms in the axial and equatorial positions of your cyclohexane model, and notice that the chair–chair interconversion changes axial to equatorial and equatorial to axial.

The two chair conformations of methylcyclohexane interconvert at room temperature, so the one that is lower in energy predominates. Careful measurements have shown that the chair with the methyl group in an equatorial position is the most stable conformation. It is about 7.6 kJ/mol (1.8 kcal/mol) lower in energy than the conformation with the methyl group in an axial position. Both of these chair conformations are lower in energy than any boat conformation. We can show how the 7.6 kJ energy difference between the axial and equatorial positions arises by examining molecular models and Newman projections of the two conformations. First, make a model of methylcyclohexane and use it to follow this discussion.

Consider a Newman projection looking along the armrest bonds of the conformation with the methyl group axial (Figure 3-24a): The methyl group is on C1, and we are looking from C1 toward C2. There is a 60° angle between the bond to the methyl group and the bond from C2 to C3, placing the axial methyl substituent and C3 in a gauche relationship. This axial methyl group is also gauche to C5, as you will see if you look along the C1—C6 bond in your model. Figure 3-24b shows this second gauche relationship.

The Newman projection for the conformation with the methyl group equatorial shows that the methyl group has an anti relationship to both C3 and C5. Figure 3-25

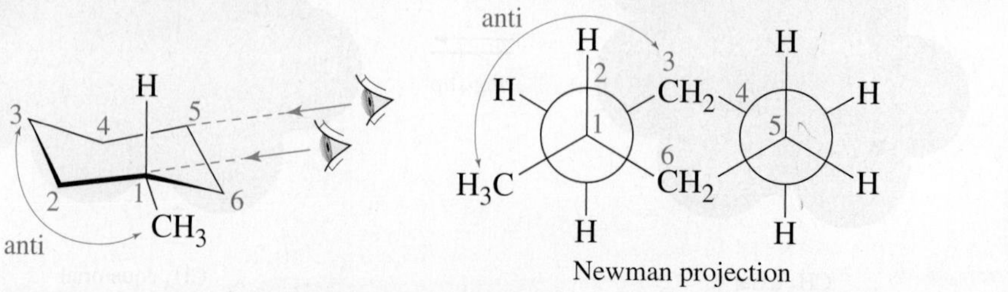

■ **FIGURE 3-25**
Looking down the C1—C2 bond of the equatorial conformation. Notice that the methyl group is anti to C3.

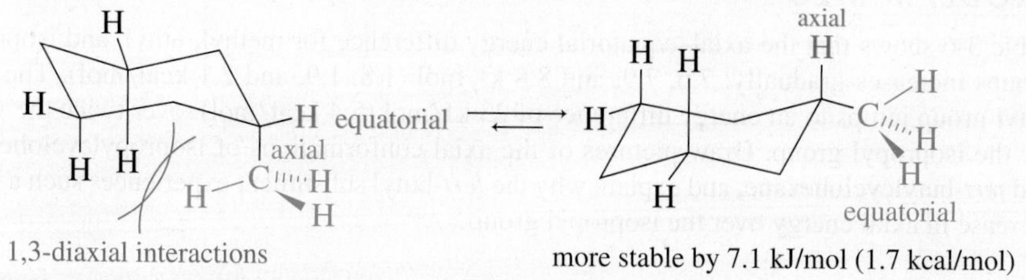

1,3-diaxial interactions

more stable by 7.1 kJ/mol (1.7 kcal/mol)

■ **FIGURE 3-26**
The axial substituent interferes with the axial hydrogens on C3 and C5. This interference is called a 1,3-diaxial interaction.

shows the Newman projection along the C1—C2 bond, with the anti relationship of the methyl group to C3.

PROBLEM 3-22

Draw a Newman projection, similar to Figure 3-25, down the C1—C6 bond in the equatorial conformation of methylcyclohexane. Show that the equatorial methyl group is also anti to C5. (Using your models will help.)

The axial methylcyclohexane conformation has two gauche interactions, each representing about 3.8 kJ (0.9 kcal) of additional energy. The equatorial methyl group has no gauche interactions. Therefore, we predict that the axial conformation is higher in energy by 7.6 kJ (1.8 kcal) per mole, in good agreement with the experimental value. Figure 3-26 shows that the gauche relationship of the axial methyl group with C3 and C5 places the methyl hydrogens close to the axial hydrogens on these carbons, causing their electron clouds to interfere. This form of steric strain is called a **1,3-diaxial interaction** because it involves substituents on carbon atoms of the ring that bear a 1,3 relationship. These 1,3-diaxial interactions are not present in the equatorial conformation.

A larger group usually has a larger energy difference between the axial and equatorial positions, because the 1,3-diaxial interaction shown in Figure 3-26 is stronger for larger groups. Table 3-6 lists the energy differences between the axial and equatorial positions for several alkyl groups and functional groups. The axial position is higher in energy in each case.

TABLE 3-6

Energy Differences Between the Axial and Equatorial Conformations of Monosubstituted Cyclohexanes

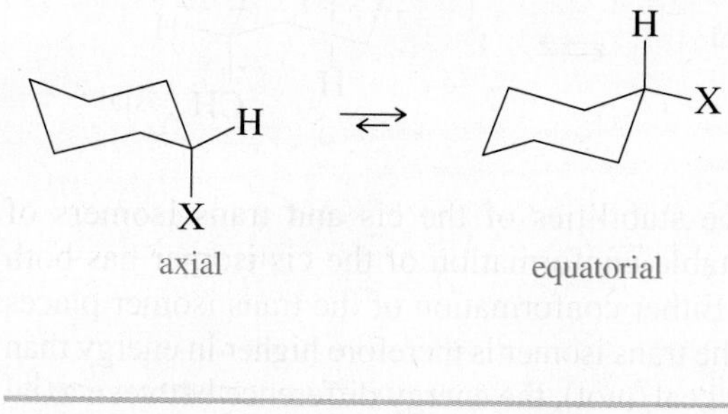

axial ⇌ equatorial

X	ΔG (axial–equatorial) (kJ/mol)	ΔG (axial–equatorial) (kcal/mol)
—F	0.8	0.2
—CN	0.8	0.2
—Cl	2.1	0.5
—Br	2.5	0.6
—OH	4.1	1.0
—COOH	5.9	1.4
$—CH_3$	7.6	1.8
$—CH_2CH_3$	7.9	1.9
$—CH(CH_3)_2$	8.8	2.1
$—C(CH_3)_3$	23	5.4

PROBLEM 3-23

Table 3-6 shows that the axial–equatorial energy difference for methyl, ethyl, and isopropyl groups increases gradually: 7.6, 7.9, and 8.8 kJ/mol (1.8, 1.9, and 2.1 kcal/mol). The *tert*-butyl group jumps to an energy difference of 23 kJ/mol (5.4 kcal/mol), over twice the value for the isopropyl group. Draw pictures of the axial conformations of isopropylcyclohexane and *tert*-butylcyclohexane, and explain why the *tert*-butyl substituent experiences such a large increase in axial energy over the isopropyl group.

PROBLEM 3-24

Draw the most stable conformation of

(a) ethylcyclohexane
(b) 3-isopropyl-1,1-dimethylcyclohexane
(c) *cis*-1-*tert*-butyl-4-isopropylcyclohexane

3-15 Conformations of Disubstituted Cyclohexanes

The steric interference between substituents in axial positions is particularly severe when there are large groups on two carbon atoms that bear a 1,3-diaxial relationship (*cis* on C1 and C3, or C1 and C5), as in the two chair conformations of *cis*-1,3-dimethylcyclohexane shown here. The less stable conformation has both methyl groups in axial positions. The more stable conformation has both methyl groups in equatorial positions. Note the strongly unfavorable 1,3-diaxial interaction between the two methyl groups in the diaxial conformation. The molecule can relieve this 1,3-diaxial interference by flipping to the diequatorial conformation. Use your models to compare the diaxial and diequatorial forms of *cis*-1,3-dimethylcyclohexane.

1,3-diaxial interaction
axial
axial
diaxial—very unfavorable
equatorial
equatorial
diequatorial—much more stable

trans-1,3-Dimethylcyclohexane does not have a conformation with a 1,3-diaxial interaction. Either of its chair conformations places one methyl group in an axial position and one in an equatorial position. These conformations have equal energies, and they are present in equal amounts.

Chair conformations of trans-*1,3-dimethylcyclohexane*

axial
CH_3
H
H
CH_3
equatorial
same energy
equatorial
CH_3
H
H
CH_3 axial

Now we can compare the relative stabilities of the cis and trans isomers of 1,3-dimethylcyclohexane. The most stable conformation of the cis isomer has both methyl groups in equatorial positions. Either conformation of the trans isomer places one methyl group in an axial position. The trans isomer is therefore higher in energy than the cis isomer by about 7.6 kJ/mol (1.8 kcal/mol), the energy difference between axial and equatorial methyl groups. Remember that the cis and trans isomers cannot interconvert, and there is no equilibrium between these isomers.

problem-solving Hint

Ring-flips change the axial or equatorial positioning of groups, but they cannot change their cis-trans relationships. Converting cis into trans would require breaking and re-forming bonds.

problem-solving Hint

If you number the carbons in a cyclohexane, the odd-numbered carbons are similar, as are the even-numbered carbons. If the odd-numbered carbons all have their *up* bond axial and their *down* bond equatorial, the even-numbered carbons will all have their *down* bond axial and their *up* bond equatorial. For example, *cis*-1,3 (both up, both odd) will be both axial or both equatorial; *cis*-1,2 (both up, one odd, one even) will be one axial, one equatorial. This tip allows you to predict the answers before you draw them.

SOLVED PROBLEM 3-3

(a) Draw both chair conformations of *cis*-1,2-dimethylcyclohexane, and determine which conformer is more stable.
(b) Repeat for the trans isomer.
(c) Predict which isomer (cis or trans) is more stable.

SOLUTION

(a) The two possible chair conformations for the cis isomer interconvert at room temperature. Each of these conformations places one methyl group axial and one equatorial, giving them the same energy.

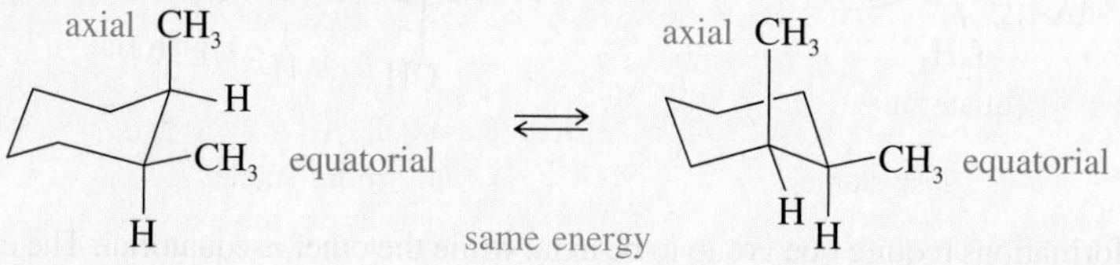

axial CH_3 / H / CH_3 equatorial / H ⇌ axial CH_3 / CH_3 equatorial / H / H

same energy

(b) The two chair conformations of the trans isomer interconvert at room temperature. Both methyl groups are axial in one, and both are equatorial in the other. The diequatorial conformation is more stable because neither methyl group occupies the more strained axial position.

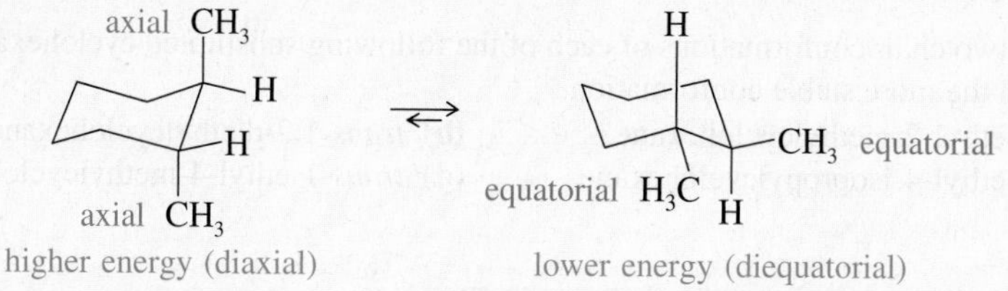

axial CH_3 / H / H / axial CH_3 ⇌ H / CH_3 equatorial / equatorial H_3C / H

higher energy (diaxial) — lower energy (diequatorial)

(c) The trans isomer is more stable. The most stable conformation of the trans isomer is diequatorial and therefore about 7.6 kJ/mol (1.8 kcal/mol) lower in energy than either conformation of the cis isomer, each having one methyl axial and one equatorial. Remember that cis and trans are distinct isomers and cannot interconvert.

PROBLEM 3-25

(a) Draw both chair conformations of *cis*-1,4-dimethylcyclohexane, and determine which conformer is more stable.
(b) Repeat for the trans isomer.
(c) Predict which isomer (cis or trans) is more stable.

PROBLEM 3-26

Use your results from Problem 3-25 to complete the following table. Each entry shows the positions of two groups arranged as shown. For example, two groups that are trans on adjacent carbons (*trans*-1,2) must be both equatorial (e,e) or both axial (a,a).

Positions	cis	trans
1,2	(e,a) or (a,e)	(e,e) or (a,a)
1,3		
1,4		

3-15A Substituents of Different Sizes

In many substituted cyclohexanes, the substituents are different sizes. As shown in Table 3-6 (p. 115), the energy difference between the axial and equatorial positions for a larger group is greater than that for a smaller group. In general, if both groups cannot be equatorial, the most stable conformation has the larger group equatorial and the smaller group axial.

SOLVED PROBLEM 3-4

Draw the most stable conformation of *trans*-1-ethyl-3-methylcyclohexane.

SOLUTION

First, we draw the two conformations.

axial
H CH_2CH_3
H
CH_3
equatorial
less stable
⇄
H
CH_2CH_3
equatorial
CH_3 H
axial
more stable

Both conformations require one group to be axial while the other is equatorial. The ethyl group is bulkier than the methyl group, so the conformation with the ethyl group equatorial is more stable. These chair conformations are in equilibrium at room temperature, and the one with the equatorial ethyl group predominates.

PROBLEM 3-27

Draw the two chair conformations of each of the following substituted cyclohexanes. In each case, label the more stable conformation.

(a) *cis*-1-ethyl-2-methylcyclohexane
(b) *trans*-1,2-diethylcyclohexane
(c) *cis*-1-ethyl-4-isopropylcyclohexane
(d) *trans*-1-ethyl-4-methylcyclohexane

PROBLEM-SOLVING STRATEGY

RECOGNIZING CIS AND TRANS ISOMERS

Some students find it difficult to look at a chair conformation and tell whether a disubstituted cyclohexane is the cis isomer or the trans isomer. In the following drawing, the two methyl groups appear to be oriented in similar directions. They are actually trans but are often mistaken for cis.

up H
1 down
CH_3
2 CH_3
up
down H
=
CH_3
1
2
CH_3

trans-1,2-dimethylcyclohexane

This ambiguity is resolved by recognizing that each of the ring carbons has two available bonds, one upward and one downward. In this drawing, the methyl group on C1 is on the downward bond, and the methyl on C2 is on the upward bond. Because one is down and one is up, their relationship is trans. A cis relationship would require both groups to be upward or both to be downward.

PROBLEM 3-28

Name the following compounds. Remember that two *up* bonds are cis; two *down* bonds are cis; one *up* bond and one *down* bond are trans.

(a) H H CH_3 H_3C
(b) H H_3C H CH_3
(c) CH_3 H H CH_3

(d) H_3C ... CH_3 (e) ... CH_3 ... CH_3 (f) H_3C ... CH_3

3-15B Extremely Bulky Groups

Some groups, such as *tertiary*-butyl groups, are so bulky that they are extremely strained in axial positions. Regardless of the other groups present, cyclohexanes with *tert*-butyl substituents are most stable when the *tert*-butyl group is in an equatorial position. The following figure shows the severe steric interactions in a chair conformation with a *tert*-butyl group axial.

extremely crowded — axial ⇌ equatorial — strongly preferred conformation

If two *tert*-butyl groups are attached to the ring, both of them are much less strained in equatorial positions. When neither chair conformation allows both bulky groups to be equatorial, they may force the ring into a twist boat conformation. For example, both chair conformations of *cis*-1,4-di-*tert*-butylcyclohexane require one of the bulky *tert*-butyl groups to occupy an axial position. This compound is more stable in a twist boat conformation that allows both bulky groups to avoid axial positions.

tert-butyl group moves out of the axial position — twist boat

PROBLEM 3-29

Draw the most stable conformation of

(a) *cis*-1-*tert*-butyl-3-ethylcyclohexane
(b) *trans*-1-*tert*-butyl-2-methylcyclohexane
(c) *trans*-1-*tert*-butyl-3-(1,1-dimethylpropyl)cyclohexane

3-16 Bicyclic Molecules

Two or more rings can be joined into *bicyclic* or *polycyclic* systems. There are three ways that two rings may be joined. **Fused rings** are most common, sharing two adjacent carbon atoms and the bond between them. **Bridged rings** are also common, sharing two nonadjacent carbon atoms (the **bridgehead carbons**) and one or more carbon atoms (the bridge) between them. **Spirocyclic compounds**, in which the two rings share only one carbon atom, are relatively rare.

fused bicyclic

bicyclo[4.4.0]decane
(decalin)

bridged bicyclic

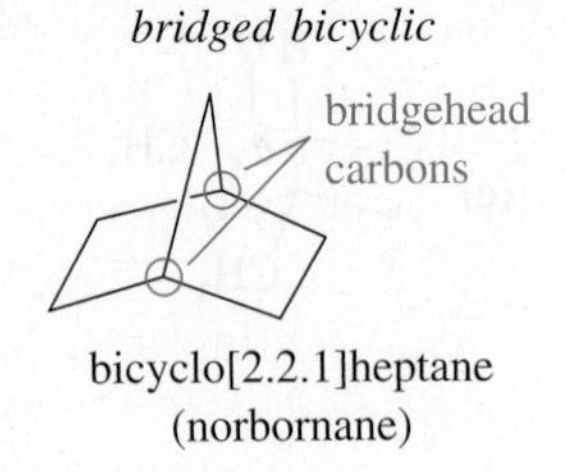

bicyclo[2.2.1]heptane
(norbornane)

spirocyclic

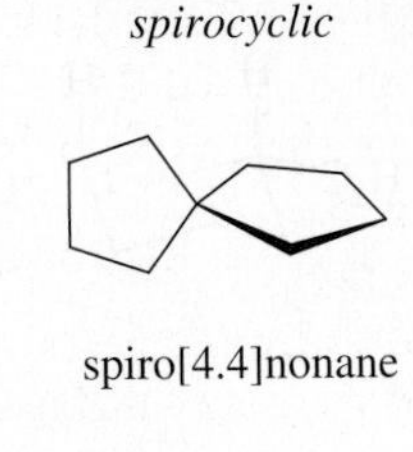

spiro[4.4]nonane

Bicyclic molecules are found in many natural product structures. Cocaine is a derivative of bicyclo[3.2.1]octane in which nitrogen replaces the carbon at the one-carbon bridge.

cocaine
in coca leaves

3-16A Nomenclature of Bicyclic Alkanes

The name of a bicyclic compound is based on the name of the alkane having the same number of carbons as there are in the ring system. This name follows the prefix *bicyclo* and a set of brackets enclosing three numbers. The following examples contain eight carbon atoms and are named bicyclo[4.2.0]octane and bicyclo[3.2.1]octane, respectively.

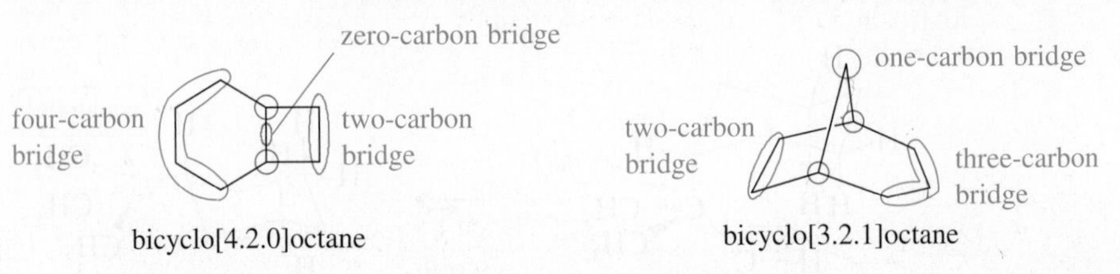

All fused and bridged bicyclic systems have three bridges connecting the two bridgehead atoms (red circles) where the rings connect. The numbers in the brackets give the number of carbon atoms in each of the three bridges connecting the bridgehead carbons, in order of decreasing size.

PROBLEM 3-30

Name the following compounds.

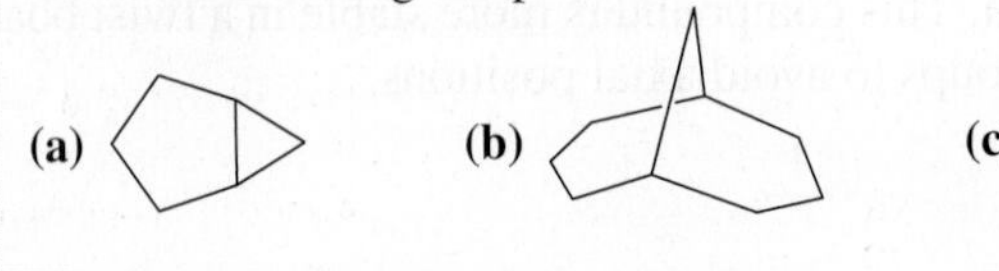

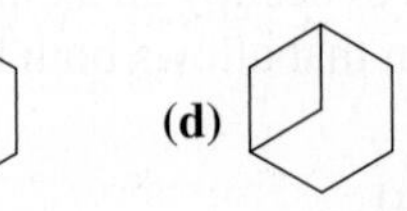

3-16B *cis*- and *trans*-Decalin

Decalin (bicyclo[4.4.0]decane) is the most common example of a fused-ring system. Two geometric isomers of decalin exist, as shown in Figure 3-27. In one isomer the rings are fused using two cis bonds, while the other is fused using two trans bonds. You should make a model of decalin to follow this discussion.

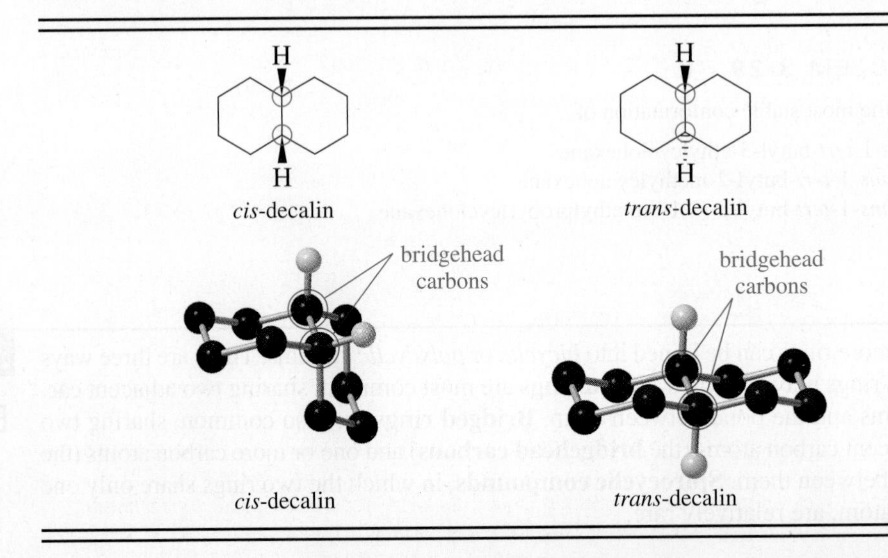

■ **FIGURE 3-27**
cis-Decalin has a ring fusion where the second ring is attached by two cis bonds. *trans*-Decalin is fused using two trans bonds. (The other hydrogens are omitted for clarity.)

If we consider the left ring in the drawing of *cis*-decalin, the bonds to the right ring are both directed downward (and the attached hydrogens are directed upward). These bonds are therefore cis, and this is a cis ring fusion. One of the bonds to the right ring must be axial, and the other is equatorial. In *trans*-decalin, one of the bonds to the right ring is directed upward and the other downward. These bonds are trans, and this is a trans ring fusion. Both of the bonds to the right ring are equatorial. The six-membered rings in both isomers assume chair conformations, as shown in Figure 3-27.

The conformation of *cis*-decalin is somewhat flexible, but the trans isomer is quite rigid. If one of the rings in the trans isomer did a chair–chair interconversion, the bonds to the second ring would both become axial and would be directed 180° apart. This is an impossible conformation, and it prevents any chair–chair interconversion in *trans*-decalin.

PROBLEM 3-31

Use your models to do a chair–chair interconversion on each ring of the conformation of *cis*-decalin shown in Figure 3-27. Draw the conformation that results.

Glossary 3

acyclic Not cyclic. (p. 103)
alkane A hydrocarbon having only single bonds; a **saturated hydrocarbon;** general formula: C_nH_{2n+2}. (p. 83)
alkyl group The group of atoms remaining after a hydrogen atom is removed from an alkane; an alkane-like substituent. Symbolized by R. (p. 87)
amyl An older common name for **pentyl.** (p. 87)
angle strain or **Baeyer strain** The strain associated with distorting bond angles to smaller (or larger) angles. (p. 106)
anti conformation A conformation with a 180° dihedral angle between the largest groups. Usually the lowest-energy conformation. (p. 101)
aromatic hydrocarbon A hydrocarbon having a benzene-like aromatic ring. (p. 71)
axial bond One of six bonds (three up and three down) on the chair conformation of the cyclohexane ring that are parallel to the "axis" of the ring. The axial bonds are shown in red, and the equatorial bonds in green, in the drawing on page 123. (p. 110)
bridged bicyclic compound A compound containing two rings joined at nonadjacent carbon atoms. (p. 119)

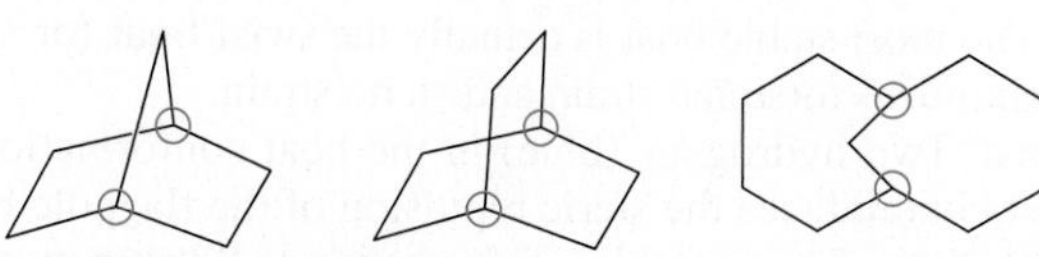

bridged bicyclic systems (bridgeheads circled)

bridgehead carbons The carbon atoms shared by two or more rings. Three chains of carbon atoms (bridges) connect the bridgeheads. (p. 119)
chair–chair interconversion (ring-flip) The process of one chair conformation of a cyclohexane flipping into another one, with all the axial and equatorial positions reversed. The boat (or twist boat) conformation is an intermediate for the chair–chair interconversion. (p. 114)

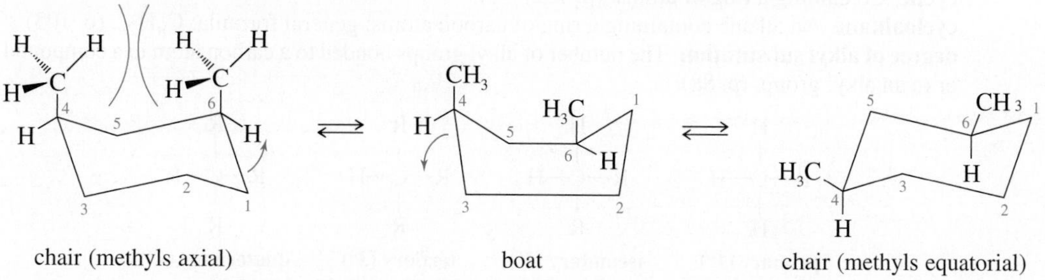

chair (methyls axial) boat chair (methyls equatorial)

cis-trans isomers (geometric isomers) Stereoisomers that differ only with respect to their cis or trans arrangement on a ring or double bond. (p. 105)
cis: Having two similar groups directed toward the same face of a ring or double bond.
trans: Having two similar groups directed toward opposite faces of a ring or double bond.

cis-2-butene *trans*-2-butene *cis*-1,2-dimethylcyclopentane *trans*-1,2-dimethylcyclopentane

combustion A rapid oxidation at high temperatures in the presence of air or oxygen. (p. 95)
common names The names that have developed historically, generally with a specific name for each compound; also called **trivial names.** (p. 85)
conformational analysis The study of the energetics of different conformations. (p. 99)
conformations and **conformers** Structures that are related by rotations about single bonds. Strictly speaking, a **conformer** is a conformation that corresponds to a relative minimum in energy, usually a staggered conformation. In most cases, conformations and conformers interconvert at room temperature, and they are not true isomers. (p. 97)

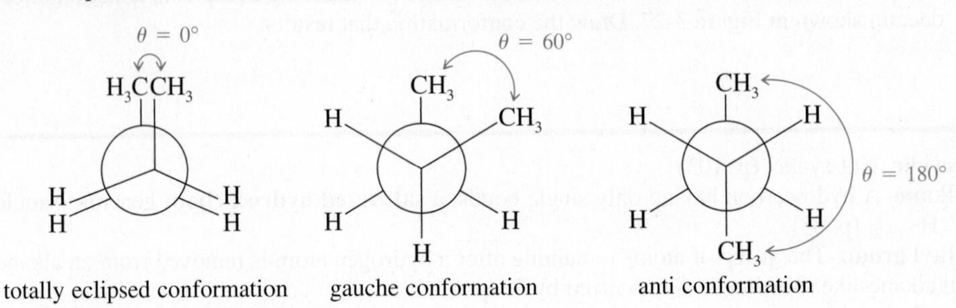

conformations of cyclohexanes (p. 109)

chair half-chair boat twist boat

chair conformation: The most stable conformation of cyclohexane, with one part puckered upward and another part puckered downward.
boat conformation: The less stable puckered conformation of cyclohexane, with both parts puckered upward. The most stable boat is actually the **twist boat** (or simply **twist**) conformation. Twisting minimizes torsional strain and steric strain.
flagpole hydrogens: Two hydrogens (blue) in the boat conformation point upward like flagpoles. The twist boat reduces the steric repulsion of the flagpole hydrogens.
half-chair conformation: The unstable conformation halfway between the chair conformation and the boat conformation. Part of the ring is flat in the half-chair conformation.

constitutional isomers (structural isomers) Isomers whose atoms are connected differently; they differ in their bonding sequence. (p. 55)
cracking Heating large alkanes to cleave them into smaller molecules. (p. 95)
catalytic cracking: Cracking in the presence of a catalyst.
hydrocracking: Catalytic cracking in the presence of hydrogen to give mixtures of alkanes.
cyclic Containing a ring of atoms. (p. 102)
cycloalkane An alkane containing a ring of carbon atoms; general formula: C_nH_{2n}. (p. 103)
degree of alkyl substitution The number of alkyl groups bonded to a carbon atom in a compound or in an alkyl group. (p. 88)

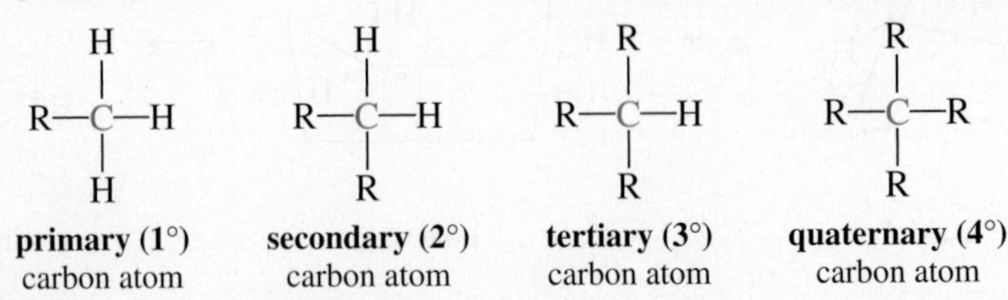

1,3-diaxial interaction The strong steric strain between two axial groups on cyclohexane carbons with one carbon between them. (p. 115)
dihedral angle (θ) (see also **conformations**) The angle between two specified groups in a Newman projection. (p. 98)

eclipsed conformation Any conformation with bonds directly lined up with each other, one behind the other, in the Newman projection. The conformation with $\theta = 0°$ is an eclipsed conformation. See also **staggered conformation**. (p. 98)

equatorial bond One of the six bonds (three down and three up) on the cyclohexane ring that are directed out toward the "equator" of the ring. The equatorial bonds are shown in green in the drawing at right. (p. 111)

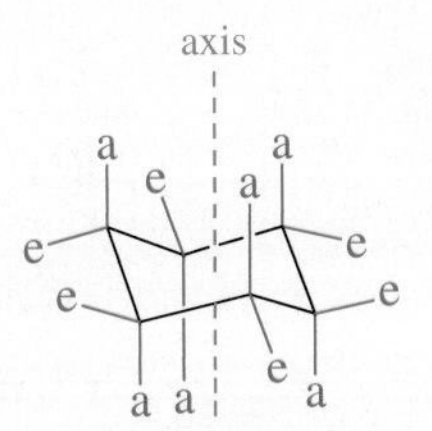

axial bonds in red; equatorial bonds in green

fused ring system A molecule in which two or more rings share two adjacent carbon atoms. (p. 119)

fused ring systems

gauche conformation A conformation with a 60° dihedral angle between the largest groups. (p. 101)

geometric isomers See **cis-trans isomers**, the IUPAC term. (p. 105)

halogenation The reaction of alkanes with halogens, in the presence of heat or light, to give products with halogen atoms substituted for hydrogen atoms. (p. 96)

$$R{-}H + X_2 \xrightarrow{\text{heat or light}} R{-}X + XH \qquad X = F, Cl, Br$$

heat of combustion The heat given off when a mole of a compound is burned with excess oxygen to give CO_2 and H_2O in a *bomb calorimeter*. A measure of the energy content of a molecule. (p. 106)

homologs Two compounds that differ only by one or more $-CH_2-$ groups. (p. 84)

hydrophilic Attracted to water, soluble in water.

hydrophobic Repelled by water; insoluble in water. (p. 91)

IUPAC names The systematic names that follow the rules adopted by the International Union of Pure and Applied Chemistry. (p. 86)

kerosene A thin, volatile oil distilled from petroleum, with a boiling range higher than that of gasoline and lower than that of diesel fuel. Kerosene was once used in lanterns and heaters, but now most of this petroleum fraction is further refined for use as jet fuel. (p. 93)

methane hydrate An ice-like substance consisting of individual methane molecules trapped inside cages of water molecules. (p. 95)

methine group The $-\overset{|}{C}H-$ group.

methylene group The $-CH_2-$ group. (p. 84)

methyl group The $-CH_3$ group. (p. 87)

***n*-alkane, normal alkane,** or **straight-chain alkane** An alkane with all its carbon atoms in a single chain, with no branching or alkyl substituents. (p. 85)

Newman projections A way of drawing the conformations of a molecule by looking straight down the bond connecting two carbon atoms. (p. 97)

180° dihedral angle

a Newman projection of butane in the anti conformation

octane number A rating of the antiknock properties of a gasoline blend. Its octane number is the percentage of isooctane (2,2,4-trimethylpentane) in an isooctane/heptane blend that begins to knock at the same compression ratio as the gasoline being tested. (p. 93)

paraffins Another term for alkanes. (p. 95)

ring strain The extra strain associated with the cyclic structure of a compound, as compared with a similar acyclic compound; composed of angle strain and torsional strain. (p. 106)

- **angle strain** or **Baeyer strain:** The strain associated with distorting bond angles to smaller (or larger) angles.
- **torsional strain:** The strain associated with eclipsing of bonds in the ring.

saturated Having no double or triple bonds. (p. 83)

sawhorse structures A way of picturing conformations by looking down at an angle toward the carbon–carbon bond. (p. 98)

skew conformation Any conformation that is not precisely staggered or eclipsed. (p. 98)

spirocyclic compounds Bicyclic compounds in which the two rings share only one carbon atom. (p. 119)

staggered conformation Any conformation with the bonds equally spaced in the Newman projection. The conformation with $\theta = 60°$ is a staggered conformation. (p. 98)

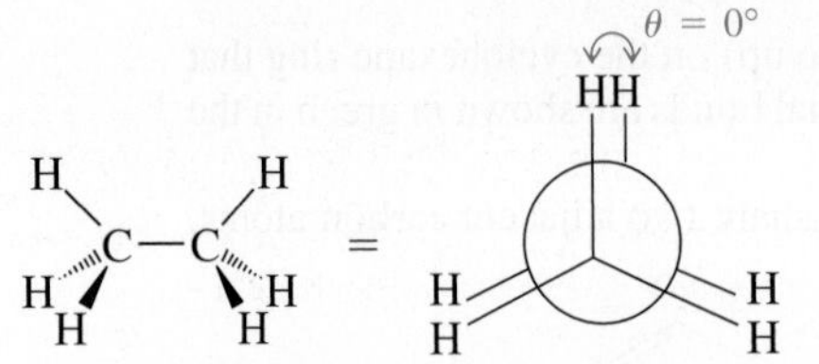

$\theta = 0°$ $\theta = 60°$

eclipsed conformation of ethane

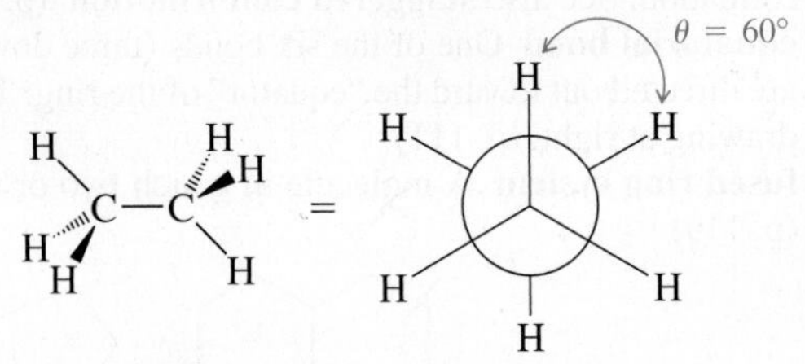

staggered conformation of ethane

steric strain The interference between two bulky groups that are so close together that their electron clouds experience a repulsion. (p. 101)
substituent A side chain or appendage on the main chain. (p. 86)
systematic names Same as IUPAC names, the names that follow the rules adopted by the International Union of Pure and Applied Chemistry. (p. 86)
torsional energy or **conformational energy** The energy required to twist a bond into a specific conformation. (p. 98)
torsional strain The resistance to twisting about a bond. (p. 98)
totally eclipsed conformation A conformation with a 0° dihedral angle between the largest groups. Usually the highest-energy conformation. (p. 100)

Essential Problem-Solving Skills in Chapter 3

1. Explain and predict trends in the physical properties of alkanes.
2. Correctly name alkanes, cycloalkanes, and bicyclic alkanes.
3. Given the name of an alkane, draw the structure and give the molecular formula.
4. Compare the energies of alkane conformations and predict the most stable conformation.
5. Compare the energies of cycloalkanes, and explain ring strain.
6. Identify and draw cis and trans stereoisomers of cycloalkanes.
7. Draw accurate cyclohexane conformations, and predict the most stable conformations of substituted cyclohexanes.

Study Problems

3-32 Define and give an example for each term.

(a) *n*-alkane (b) alkene (c) alkyne
(d) saturated (e) hydrophobic (f) aromatic
(g) hydrophilic (h) combustion (i) methylene group
(j) methyl group (k) common name (l) IUPAC name
(m) conformations (n) Newman projection (o) eclipsed
(p) staggered (q) gauche conformer (r) anti conformer
(s) catalytic cracking (t) cis-trans isomers on a ring (u) chair conformation
(v) boat conformation (w) twist boat (x) half-chair conformation
(y) axial position (z) equatorial position (aa) chair–chair interconversion
(bb) fused ring system (cc) bridged bicyclic compound (dd) bridgehead carbon atoms

3-33 Which of the following structures represent the same compound? Which ones represent different compounds?

(a) 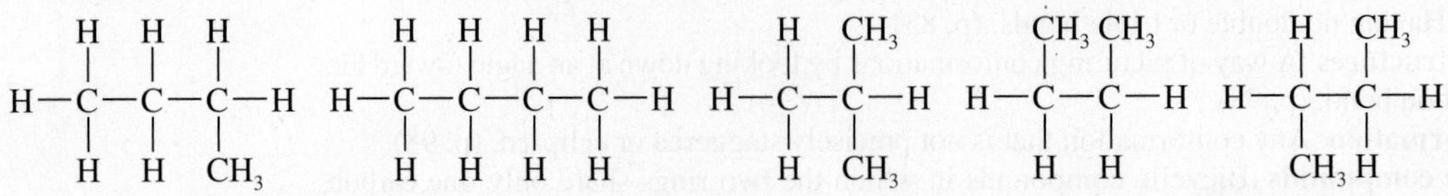 $H-\overset{H}{\underset{H}{C}}-\overset{H}{\underset{H}{C}}-\overset{H}{\underset{CH_3}{C}}-H$ $H-\overset{H}{\underset{H}{C}}-\overset{H}{\underset{H}{C}}-\overset{H}{\underset{H}{C}}-\overset{H}{\underset{H}{C}}-H$ $H-\overset{H}{\underset{H}{C}}-\overset{CH_3}{\underset{CH_3}{C}}-H$ $H-\overset{CH_3}{\underset{H}{C}}-\overset{CH_3}{\underset{H}{C}}-H$ $H-\overset{H}{\underset{CH_3}{C}}-\overset{CH_3}{\underset{H}{C}}-H$

(b)

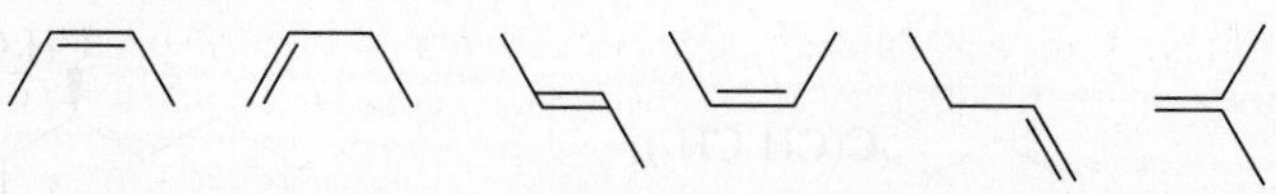

(c)

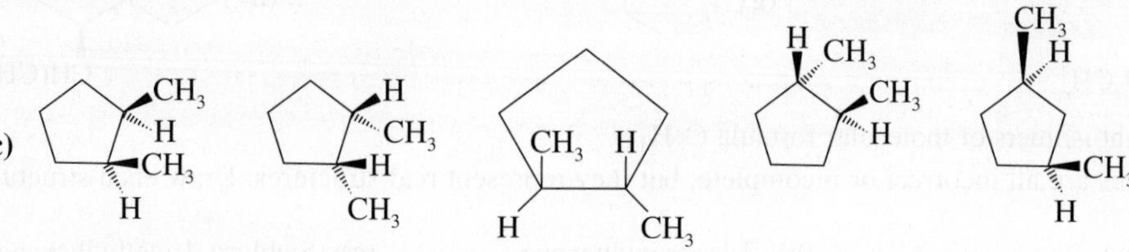

(d)

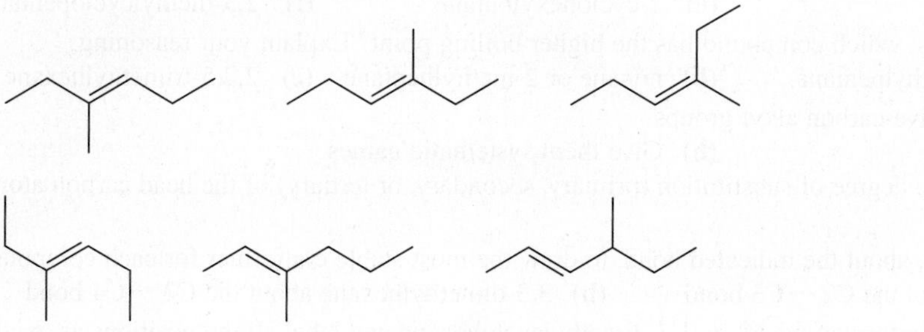

(e)

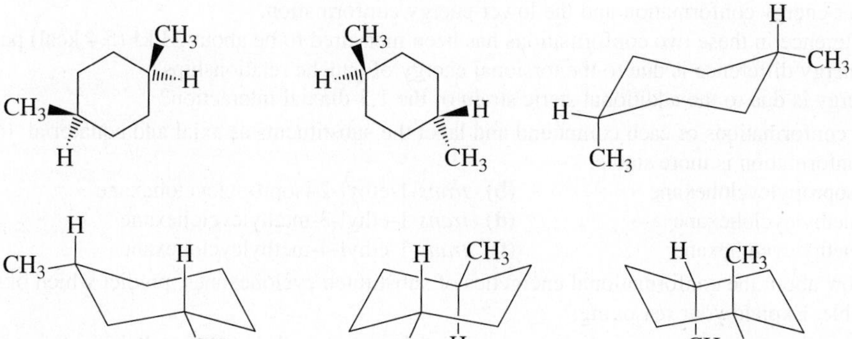

(f)

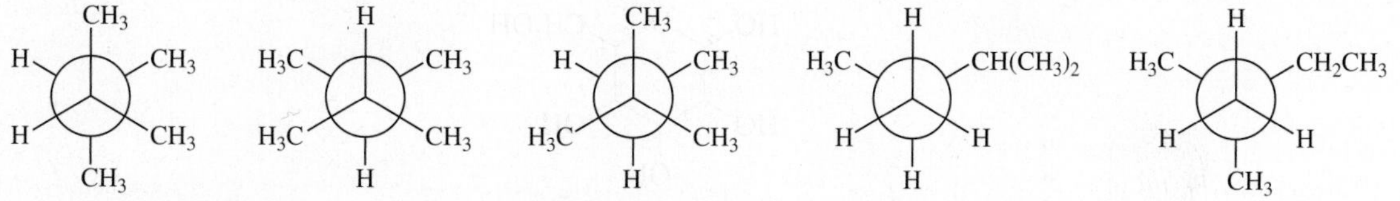

3-34 Draw the structure that corresponds with each name.

(a) 3-ethyloctane
(b) 4-isopropyldecane
(c) *sec*-butylcycloheptane
(d) 2,3-dimethyl-4-propylnonane
(e) 2,2,4,4-tetramethylhexane
(f) *trans*-1,3-diethylcyclopentane
(g) *cis*-1-ethyl-4-methylcyclohexane
(h) isobutylcyclopentane
(i) *tert*-butylcyclohexane
(j) pentylcyclohexane
(k) cyclobutylcyclohexane
(l) *cis*-1-bromo-3-chlorocyclohexane

3-35 Each of the following descriptions applies to more than one alkane. In each case, draw and name two structures that match the description.

(a) an isopropylheptane
(b) a diethyldecane
(c) a *cis*-diethylcyclohexane
(d) a *trans*-dihalocyclopentane
(e) a (2,3-dimethylpentyl)cycloalkane
(f) a bicyclononane

3-36 Write structures for a homologous series of alcohols (R—OH) having from one to six carbons.

3-37 Give the IUPAC names of the following alkanes.

(a) $CH_3C(CH_3)_2CH(CH_2CH_3)CH_2CH_2CH(CH_3)_2$

(b) $CH_3CH_2—CH(CH_3CHCH_3)—CH_2CH_2—CH(CH_3CHCH_3)—CH_3$

(c)

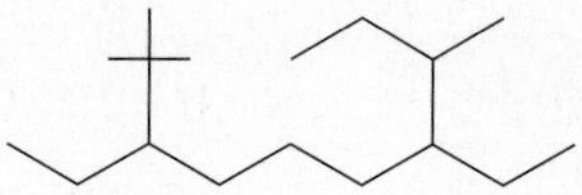

(d) 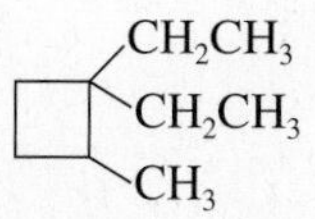 cyclobutane with CH_2CH_3, CH_2CH_3, CH_3

(e)

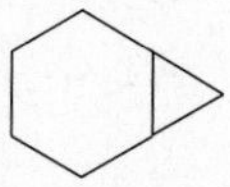

(f) [cyclopentane with CH_2CH_3 and $CH_2CH_2CH_3$]

(g) [cyclohexane with $C(CH_2CH_3)_3$]

(h) [ring with CH_2CH_3 and $CH(CH_3)_2$]

3-38 Draw and name eight isomers of molecular formula C_8H_{18}.

3-39 The following names are all incorrect or incomplete, but they represent real structures. Draw each structure and name it correctly.
(a) 2-ethylpentane (b) 3-isopropylhexane (c) 5-chloro-4-methylhexane
(d) 2-dimethylbutane (e) 2-cyclohexylbutane (f) 2,3-diethylcyclopentane

3-40 In each pair of compounds, which compound has the higher boiling point? Explain your reasoning.
(a) octane or 2,2,3-trimethylpentane (b) nonane or 2-methylheptane (c) 2,2,5-trimethylhexane or nonane

3-41 There are eight different five-carbon alkyl groups.
(a) Draw them. (b) Give them systematic names.
(c) In each case, label the degree of substitution (primary, secondary, or tertiary) of the head carbon atom, bonded to the main chain.

3-42 Use a Newman projection, about the indicated bond, to draw the most stable conformer for each compound.
(a) 3-methylpentane about the C2—C3 bond (b) 3,3-dimethylhexane about the C3—C4 bond

3-43 (a) Draw the two chair conformations of *cis*-1,3-dimethylcyclohexane and label all the positions as axial or equatorial.
(b) Label the higher-energy conformation and the lower-energy conformation.
(c) The energy difference in these two conformations has been measured to be about 23 kJ (5.4 kcal) per mole. How much of this energy difference is due to the torsional energy of gauche relationships?
(d) How much energy is due to the additional steric strain of the 1,3-diaxial interaction?

3-44 Draw the two chair conformations of each compound and label the substituents as axial and equatorial. In each case, determine which conformation is more stable.
(a) *cis*-1-ethyl-2-isopropylcyclohexane (b) *trans*-1-ethyl-2-isopropylcyclohexane
(c) *cis*-1-ethyl-3-methylcyclohexane (d) *trans*-1-ethyl-3-methylcyclohexane
(e) *cis*-1-ethyl-4-methylcyclohexane (f) *trans*-1-ethyl-4-methylcyclohexane

3-45 Using what you know about the conformational energetics of substituted cyclohexanes, predict which of the two decalin isomers is more stable. Explain your reasoning.

3-46 The most stable form of the common sugar glucose contains a six-membered ring in the chair conformation with all the substituents equatorial. Draw this most stable conformation of glucose.

[structure: HO, O, CH_2OH, HO, OH, OH]

glucose

***3-47** Draw Newman projections along the C3—C4 bond to show the most stable and least stable conformations of 3-ethyl-2,4,4-trimethylheptane.

***3-48** Conformational studies on ethane-1,2-diol ($HOCH_2—CH_2OH$) have shown the most stable conformation about the central C—C bond to be the gauche conformation, which is 9.6 kJ/mol (2.3 kcal/mol) more stable than the anti conformation. Draw Newman projections of these conformers and explain this curious result.

C H A P T E R

THE STUDY OF CHEMICAL REACTIONS

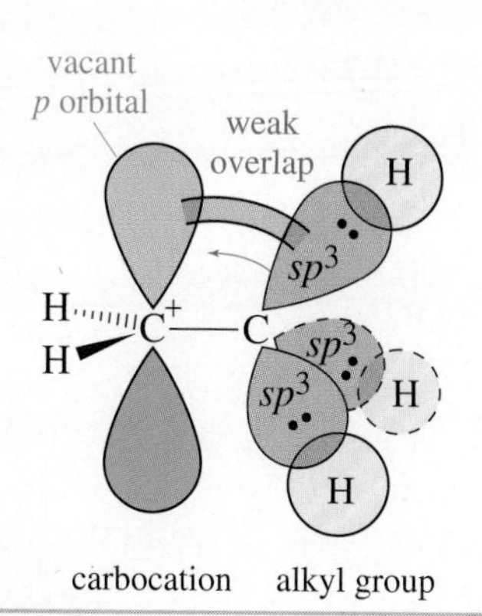

4-1 Introduction

The most interesting and useful aspect of organic chemistry is the study of reactions. We cannot remember thousands of specific organic reactions, but we can organize the reactions into logical groups based on how the reactions take place and what intermediates are involved. We begin our study by considering the *halogenation* of alkanes, a relatively simple reaction that takes place in the gas phase, without a solvent to complicate the reaction. In practice, alkanes are so unreactive that they are rarely used as starting materials for most organic syntheses. We start with them because we have already studied their structure and properties, and their reactions are relatively uncomplicated. Once we have used alkanes to introduce the tools for studying reactions, we will apply those tools to a variety of more useful reactions.

Writing the overall equation, with the reactants on the left and the products on the right, is only the first step in our study of a reaction. If we truly want to understand a reaction, we must also know the **mechanism**, the step-by-step pathway from reactants to products. To know how well the reaction goes to products, we study its **thermodynamics**, the energetics of the reaction at equilibrium. The amounts of reactants and products present at equilibrium depend on their relative stabilities.

Even though the equilibrium may favor the formation of a product, the reaction may not take place at a useful rate. To use a reaction in a realistic time period (and to keep the reaction from becoming violent), we study its **kinetics**, the variation of reaction rates with different conditions and concentrations of reagents. Understanding the reaction's kinetics helps us to propose reaction mechanisms that are consistent with the behavior we observe.

4-2 Chlorination of Methane

The chlorination of methane is an important industrial reaction, with a relatively simple mechanism that illustrates many of the important principles of a reaction. The reaction of methane with chlorine produces a mixture of chlorinated products, whose composition depends on the amount of chlorine added and also on the reaction conditions. Either light or heat is needed for the reaction to take place at a useful rate. When chlorine is added to methane, the first reaction is

$$\underset{\text{methane}}{CH_4} + \underset{\text{chlorine}}{Cl{-}Cl} \xrightarrow{\text{heat or light}} \underset{\substack{\text{chloromethane}\\ \text{(methyl chloride)}}}{H_3C{-}Cl} + \underset{\substack{\text{hydrogen}\\ \text{chloride}}}{H{-}Cl}$$

This reaction may continue; heat or light is needed for each step:

$$\begin{array}{c}\text{H}\\|\\\text{H—C—Cl}\\|\\\text{H}\end{array}\xrightarrow{Cl_2}\begin{array}{c}\text{Cl}\\|\\\text{H—C—Cl}\\|\\\text{H}\end{array}\xrightarrow{Cl_2}\begin{array}{c}\text{Cl}\\|\\\text{Cl—C—Cl}\\|\\\text{H}\end{array}\xrightarrow{Cl_2}\begin{array}{c}\text{Cl}\\|\\\text{Cl—C—Cl}\\|\\\text{Cl}\end{array}$$

$$\qquad\qquad + \ HCl \qquad\qquad\qquad + \ HCl \qquad\qquad\qquad + \ HCl$$

This sequence raises several questions about the chlorination of methane. Why is heat or light needed for the reaction to go? Why do we get a mixture of products? Is there any way to modify the reaction to get just one pure product? Are the observed products formed because they are the most stable products possible? Or are they favored because they are formed faster than any other products?

The answers to these questions involve three aspects of the reaction: the mechanism, the thermodynamics, and the kinetics.

1. The **mechanism** is the complete, step-by-step description of exactly which bonds break and which bonds form in what order to give the observed products.
2. **Thermodynamics** is the study of the energy changes that accompany chemical and physical transformations. It allows us to compare the stability of reactants and products and predict which compounds are favored by the equilibrium.
3. **Kinetics** is the study of reaction rates, determining which products are formed fastest. Kinetics also helps to predict how the rate will change if we change the reaction conditions.

We will use the chlorination of methane to show how we study a reaction. Before we can propose a detailed mechanism for the chlorination, we must learn everything we can about how the reaction works and what factors affect the reaction rate and the product distribution.

A careful study of the chlorination of methane has established three important characteristics:

1. *The chlorination does not occur at room temperature in the absence of light.* The reaction begins when light falls on the mixture or when it is heated. Thus, we know this reaction requires some form of energy to *initiate* it.
2. *The most effective wavelength of light is a blue color that is strongly absorbed by chlorine gas.* This finding implies that light is absorbed by the chlorine molecule, activating chlorine so that it initiates the reaction with methane.
3. *The light-initiated reaction has a high quantum yield.* This means that many molecules of the product are formed for every photon of light absorbed. Our mechanism must explain how hundreds of individual reactions of methane with chlorine result from the absorption of a single photon by a single molecule of chlorine.

4-3 The Free-Radical Chain Reaction

A **chain reaction** mechanism has been proposed to explain the chlorination of methane. A chain reaction consists of three kinds of steps:

1. The **initiation step**, which generates a reactive intermediate.
2. **Propagation steps**, in which the reactive intermediate reacts with a stable molecule to form a product and another reactive intermediate, allowing the chain to continue until the supply of reactants is exhausted or the reactive intermediate is destroyed.
3. **Termination steps**, side reactions that destroy reactive intermediates and tend to slow or stop the reaction.

In studying the chlorination of methane, we will consider just the first reaction to form chloromethane (common name *methyl chloride*). This reaction is a **substitution**: Chlorine does not add to methane, but a chlorine atom *substitutes* for one of the hydrogen atoms, which becomes part of the HCl by-product.

$$\underset{\text{methane}}{CH_3-\text{(H)}} + \underset{\text{chlorine}}{\text{(Cl)}-Cl} \xrightarrow{\text{heat or light } (h\nu)} \underset{\substack{\text{chloromethane}\\ \text{(methyl chloride)}}}{CH_3-\text{(Cl)}} + \text{(H)}-Cl$$

substitution

4-3A The Initiation Step: Generation of Radicals

Blue light, absorbed by chlorine but not by methane, promotes this reaction. Therefore, initiation probably results from the absorption of light by a molecule of chlorine. Blue light has about the right energy to split a chlorine molecule (Cl_2) into two chlorine atoms, which requires 242 kJ/mol (58 kcal/mol).* The splitting of a chlorine molecule by absorption of a photon is shown as follows:

Initiation: Formation of reactive intermediates.

$$:\ddot{Cl}:\ddot{Cl}: + \text{photon } (h\nu) \longrightarrow :\ddot{Cl}\cdot + \cdot\ddot{Cl}:$$

Notice the fishhook-shaped half-arrows used to show the movement of single unpaired electrons. Just as we use curved arrows to represent the movement of electron *pairs*, we use these curved half-arrows to represent the movement of single electrons. These half-arrows show that the two electrons in the Cl—Cl bond separate, and one leaves with each chlorine atom.

The splitting of a Cl_2 molecule is an initiation step that produces two highly reactive chlorine atoms. A chlorine atom is an example of a **reactive intermediate**, a short-lived species that is never present in high concentration because it reacts as quickly as it is formed. Each Cl· atom has an odd number of valence electrons (seven), one of which is unpaired. The unpaired electron is called the *odd electron* or the *radical electron*. Species with unpaired electrons are called **radicals** or **free radicals**. Radicals are electron-deficient because they lack an octet. The odd electron readily combines with an electron in another atom to complete an octet and form a bond. Figure 4-1 shows the Lewis structures of some free radicals. Radicals are often represented by a structure with a single dot representing the unpaired odd electron.

Free radicals may play a role in diseases and accelerate aging. In the course of everyday life, reactive oxygen species are encountered in the environment and produced in the body. These compounds break down into short-lived hydroxyl radicals, which can react with the body's proteins and DNA. The resulting damage accumulates and may result in heart disease, cancer, and premature aging.

Lewis structures				
$:\ddot{\underset{..}{Cl}}\cdot$	$:\ddot{\underset{..}{Br}}\cdot$	$H:\ddot{\underset{..}{O}}\cdot$	H:C· (with H above and below)	H:C:C· (with H H above and below)
Written				
Cl·	Br·	HO·	$CH_3\cdot$	$CH_3CH_2\cdot$
chlorine atom	bromine atom	hydroxyl radical	methyl radical	ethyl radical

■ **FIGURE 4-1**
Free radicals are reactive species with odd numbers of electrons. The unpaired electron is represented by a dot in the formula.

*The energy of a photon of light is related to its frequency ν by the relationship $E = h\nu$, where h is Planck's constant. Blue light has an energy of about 250 kJ (60 kcal) per einstein (an einstein is a mole of photons).

PROBLEM 4-1

Draw Lewis structures for the following free radicals.

(a) The ethyl radical, $CH_3—\dot{C}H_2$ **(b)** The *tert*-butyl radical, $(CH_3)_3C\cdot$

(c) The isopropyl radical (2-propyl radical) **(d)** The iodine atom

4-3B Propagation Steps

Propagation: Formation of products with regeneration of reactive intermediates.

When a chlorine radical collides with a methane molecule, it abstracts (removes) a hydrogen atom from methane. One of the electrons in the C—H bond remains on carbon while the other combines with the odd electron on the chlorine atom to form the H—Cl bond.

First propagation step

$$CH_4 + Cl\cdot \longrightarrow \cdot CH_3 + H—Cl$$

methane, chlorine atom, methyl radical, hydrogen chloride

This step forms only one of the final products: the molecule of HCl. A later step must form chloromethane. Notice that the first propagation step begins with one free radical (the chlorine atom) and produces another free radical (the methyl radical). The regeneration of a free radical is characteristic of a propagation step of a chain reaction. The reaction can continue because another reactive intermediate is produced.

In the second propagation step, the methyl radical reacts with a molecule of chlorine to form chloromethane. The odd electron of the methyl radical combines with one of the two electrons in the Cl—Cl bond to give the $Cl—CH_3$ bond, and the chlorine atom is left with the odd electron.

Second propagation step

$$\cdot CH_3 + Cl—Cl \longrightarrow H_3C—Cl + Cl\cdot$$

methyl radical, chlorine molecule, chloromethane, chlorine atom

In addition to forming chloromethane, the second propagation step produces another chlorine radical. The chlorine radical can react with another molecule of methane, giving HCl and a methyl radical, which reacts with Cl_2 to give chloromethane and regenerate yet another chlorine radical. In this way, the chain reaction continues until the supply of the reactants is exhausted or some other reaction consumes the radical intermediates. The chain reaction explains why many molecules of methyl chloride and HCl are formed by each photon of light that is absorbed. We can summarize the reaction mechanism as follows.

KEY MECHANISM 4-1 Free-Radical Halogenation

Like many other radical reactions, free-radical halogenation is a chain reaction. Chain reactions usually require one or more initiation steps to form radicals, followed by propagation steps that produce products and regenerate radicals.

Initiation: Radicals are formed.

Light supplies the energy to split a chlorine molecule.

$$Cl—Cl + h\nu \text{ (light)} \longrightarrow 2\ Cl\cdot$$

Propagation: A radical reacts to generate another radical.

Step 1: A chlorine radical abstracts a hydrogen to generate an alkyl radical.

$$\mathrm{H{-}CH_2{-}H} + \mathrm{Cl\cdot} \longrightarrow \mathrm{H{-}CH_2\cdot} + \mathrm{H{-}Cl}$$

methyl radical

continues the chain

Step 2: The alkyl radical reacts with Cl_2 to generate the product and a chlorine radical.

$$\mathrm{H{-}CH_2\cdot} + \mathrm{Cl{-}Cl} \longrightarrow \mathrm{H{-}CH_2{-}Cl} + \mathrm{Cl\cdot}$$

chloromethane

The chlorine radical generated in step 2 goes on to react in step 1, continuing the chain.

The overall reaction is simply the sum of the propagation steps:

$$\mathrm{H{-}CH_2{-}H} + \mathrm{Cl{-}Cl} \longrightarrow \mathrm{H{-}CH_2{-}Cl} + \mathrm{H{-}Cl}$$

QUESTION: What factors characterize the propagation steps of a chain reaction?

PROBLEM 4-2

(a) Write the propagation steps leading to the formation of dichloromethane (CH_2Cl_2) from chloromethane.
(b) Explain why free-radical halogenation usually gives mixtures of products.
(c) How could an industrial plant control the proportions of methane and chlorine to favor production of CCl_4? To favor CH_3Cl?

4-3C Termination Reactions

Termination: Destruction of reactive intermediates.

If anything happens to consume some of the free-radical intermediates without generating new ones, the chain reaction will slow or stop. Such a side reaction is called a **termination reaction**: a step that produces fewer reactive intermediates (free radicals) than it consumes. The following are some of the possible termination reactions in the chlorination of methane:

$$\mathrm{H{-}CH_2\cdot} + \mathrm{Cl\cdot} \longrightarrow \mathrm{H{-}CH_2{-}Cl}$$

$$\mathrm{Cl\cdot} + \mathrm{Cl\cdot} \longrightarrow \mathrm{Cl{-}Cl}$$

$$H_3C\cdot + \cdot CH_3 \longrightarrow H_3C{-}CH_3$$

$$H_3C\cdot \text{ collides with wall} \longrightarrow H_3C{-}\text{wall}$$

$$Cl\cdot \text{ collides with wall} \longrightarrow Cl{-}\text{wall}$$

The combination of any two free radicals is a termination step because it decreases the number of free radicals. Other termination steps involve reactions of free radicals with the walls of the vessel or other contaminants. Although the first of these termination steps gives chloromethane, one of the products, it consumes the free radicals that are necessary for the reaction to continue, thus breaking the chain. Its contribution to the amount of product obtained from the reaction is small compared with the contribution of the propagation steps.

Some anti-cancer agents act by generating highly reactive hydroxyl radicals, which damage and degrade the DNA of the rapidly dividing tumor cells. As a result, the cells die and the tumor shrinks. One example of a radical generator is bleomycin, which is used for the treatment of testicular cancer.

While a chain reaction is in progress, the concentration of radicals is very low. The probability that two radicals will combine in a termination step is lower than the probability that each will encounter a molecule of reactant and give a propagation step. The termination steps become important toward the end of the reaction, when there are relatively few molecules of reactants available. At this point, the free radicals are less likely to encounter a molecule of reactant than they are to encounter each other (or the wall of the container). The chain reaction quickly stops.

problem-solving **Hint**

In a free-radical chain reaction, initiation steps generally create new free radicals. Propagation steps usually combine a free radical and a reactant to give a product and another free radical. Termination steps generally decrease the number of free radicals.

PROBLEM 4-3

Each of the following proposed mechanisms for the free-radical chlorination of methane is wrong. Explain how the experimental evidence disproves each mechanism.

(a) $Cl_2 + h\nu \rightarrow Cl_2^*$ (an "activated" form of Cl_2)

$Cl_2^* + CH_4 \rightarrow HCl + CH_3Cl$

(b) $CH_4 + h\nu \rightarrow \cdot CH_3 + H\cdot$

$\cdot CH_3 + Cl_2 \rightarrow CH_3Cl + Cl\cdot$

$Cl\cdot + H\cdot \rightarrow HCl$

PROBLEM 4-4

Free-radical chlorination of hexane gives very poor yields of 1-chlorohexane, while cyclohexane can be converted to chlorocyclohexane in good yield.

(a) How do you account for this difference?

(b) What ratio of reactants (cyclohexane and chlorine) would you use for the synthesis of chlorocyclohexane?

4-4 Equilibrium Constants and Free Energy

Now that we have determined a mechanism for the chlorination of methane, we can consider the energetics of the individual steps. Let's begin by reviewing some of the principles needed for this discussion.

Thermodynamics is the branch of chemistry that deals with the energy changes accompanying chemical and physical transformations. These energy changes are most useful for describing the properties of systems at **equilibrium**. Let's review how energy and entropy variables describe an equilibrium.

The equilibrium concentrations of reactants and products are governed by the **equilibrium constant** of the reaction. For example, if A and B react to give C and D, then the equilibrium constant K_{eq} is defined by the following equation:

$$A + B \rightleftharpoons C + D$$

$$K_{eq} = \frac{[\text{products}]}{[\text{reactants}]} = \frac{[C][D]}{[A][B]}$$

The value of K_{eq} tells us the position of the equilibrium: whether the products or the reactants are more stable, and therefore energetically favored. If K_{eq} is larger than 1, the reaction is favored as written from left to right. If K_{eq} is less than 1, the reverse reaction is favored (from right to left as written).

The chlorination of methane has a large equilibrium constant of about 1.1×10^{19}.

$$CH_4 + Cl_2 \rightleftharpoons CH_3Cl + HCl$$

$$K_{eq} = \frac{[CH_3Cl][HCl]}{[CH_4][Cl_2]} = 1.1 \times 10^{19}$$

The equilibrium constant for chlorination is so large that the remaining amounts of the reactants are close to zero at equilibrium. Such a reaction is said to *go to completion*, and the value of K_{eq} is a measure of the reaction's tendency to go to completion.

From the value of K_{eq} we can calculate the change in **free energy** (sometimes called **Gibbs free energy**) that accompanies the reaction. Free energy is represented by G, and the change (Δ) in free energy associated with a reaction is represented by ΔG, the difference between the free energy of the products and the free energy of the reactants. ΔG is a measure of the amount of energy available to do work.

$$\Delta G = (\text{free energy of products}) - (\text{free energy of reactants})$$

If the energy levels of the products are lower than the energy levels of the reactants (a "downhill" reaction), then the reaction is energetically favored; and this equation gives a negative value of ΔG, corresponding to a decrease in the energy of the system.

Some chemists use the terms "exergonic" and "endergonic" to describe changes in free energy.
exergonic = having a negative $\Delta G°$
endergonic = having a positive $\Delta G°$

The **standard Gibbs free energy change**, $\Delta G°$, is most commonly used. The symbol ° designates a reaction involving reactants and products in their standard states (pure substances in their most stable states at 25 °C and 1 atm pressure). The relationship between $\Delta G°$ and K_{eq} is given by the expression

$$K_{eq} = e^{-\Delta G°/RT}$$

or, conversely, by

$$\Delta G° = -RT(\ln K_{eq}) = -2.303RT(\log_{10} K_{eq})$$

where

R = 8.314 J/kelvin-mol (1.987 cal/kelvin-mol), the gas constant
T = absolute temperature, in kelvins*
e = 2.718, the base of natural logarithms

The value of RT at 25 °C is about 2.48 kJ/mol (0.592 kcal/mol).

The formula shows that a reaction is favored ($K_{eq} > 1$) if it has a *negative* value of $\Delta G°$ (energy is released). A reaction that has a positive value of $\Delta G°$ (energy must be added) is unfavorable. These predictions agree with our intuition that reactions should go from higher-energy states to lower-energy states, with a net decrease in free energy.

problem-solving Hint

A reaction with a negative ΔG is favorable.

A reaction with a positive ΔG is unfavorable.

---

*Absolute temperatures (in kelvins) are correctly given without a degree sign, as in the equation 25 °C = 298 K. We will include the degree sign, however, to distinguish absolute temperatures (K) from equilibrium constants (K) as in 25 °C = 298 °K.

SOLVED PROBLEM 4-1

Calculate the value of $\Delta G°$ for the chlorination of methane.

SOLUTION

$$\Delta G° = -2.303RT(\log K_{eq})$$

K_{eq} for the chlorination is 1.1×10^{19}, and $\log K_{eq} = 19.04$

At 25 °C (about 298 °K), the value of RT is

$$RT = (8.314 \text{ J/kelvin-mol})(298 \text{ kelvins}) = 2478 \text{ J/mol, or } 2.48 \text{ kJ/mol}$$

Substituting, we have

$$\Delta G° = (-2.303)(2.478 \text{ kJ/mol})(19.04) = -108.7 \text{ kJ/mol } (-25.9 \text{ kcal/mol})$$

This is a large negative value for $\Delta G°$, showing that this chlorination has a large driving force that pushes it toward completion.

In general, a reaction goes nearly to completion (>99%) for values of $\Delta G°$ that are more negative than about −12 kJ/mol or −3 kcal/mol. Table 4-1 shows what percentages of the starting materials are converted to products at equilibrium for reactions with various values of $\Delta G°$.

PROBLEM 4-5

The following reaction has a value of $\Delta G° = -2.1$ kJ/mol (−0.50 kcal/mol).

$$CH_3Br + H_2S \rightleftharpoons CH_3SH + HBr$$

(a) Calculate K_{eq} at room temperature (25 °C) for this reaction as written.
(b) Starting with a 1 M solution of CH_3Br and H_2S, calculate the final concentrations of all four species at equilibrium.

PROBLEM 4-6

Under base-catalyzed conditions, two molecules of acetone can condense to form diacetone alcohol. At room temperature (25 °C), about 5% of the acetone is converted to diacetone alcohol. Determine the value of $\Delta G°$ for this reaction.

$$2\,CH_3-\overset{O}{\overset{\|}{C}}-CH_3 \xrightleftharpoons{^{-}OH} CH_3-\overset{O}{\overset{\|}{C}}-CH_2-\overset{OH}{\overset{|}{C}}(CH_3)_2$$

acetone → diacetone alcohol

TABLE 4-1

Product Composition as a Function of $\Delta G°$ at 25 °C

$\Delta G°$ kJ/mol	$\Delta G°$ kcal/mol	K	Conversion to Products
+4.0	(+1.0)	0.20	17%
+2.0	(+0.5)	0.45	31%
0.0	(0.0)	1.0	50%
−2.0	(−0.5)	2.2	69%
−4.0	(−1.0)	5.0	83%
−8.0	(−1.9)	25	96%
−12.0	(−2.9)	127	99.2%
−16.0	(−3.8)	638	99.8%
−20.0	(−4.8)	3200	99.96%

4-5 Enthalpy and Entropy

Two factors contribute to the change in free energy: the change in **enthalpy** and the change in **entropy** multiplied by the temperature.

$$\Delta G° = \Delta H° - T\Delta S°$$

$$\Delta G° = (\text{free energy of products}) - (\text{free energy of reactants})$$
$$\Delta H° = (\text{enthalpy of products}) - (\text{enthalpy of reactants})$$
$$\Delta S° = (\text{entropy of products}) - (\text{entropy of reactants})$$

At low temperatures, the enthalpy term $(\Delta H°)$ is usually much larger than the entropy term $(-T\Delta S°)$, and the entropy term is sometimes ignored.

4-5A Enthalpy

The **change in enthalpy** $(\Delta H°)$ is the heat of reaction—the amount of heat evolved or consumed in the course of a reaction, usually given in kilojoules (or kilocalories) per mole. The enthalpy change is a measure of the relative strength of bonding in the products and reactants. Reactions tend to favor products with the lowest enthalpy (those with the strongest bonds).

If weaker bonds are broken and stronger bonds are formed, heat is evolved and the reaction is **exothermic** (negative value of $\Delta H°$). In an exothermic reaction, the enthalpy term makes a favorable negative contribution to $\Delta G°$. If stronger bonds are broken and weaker bonds are formed, then energy is consumed in the reaction, and the reaction is **endothermic** (positive value of $\Delta H°$). In an endothermic reaction, the enthalpy term makes an unfavorable positive contribution to $\Delta G°$.

The value of $\Delta H°$ for the chlorination of methane is about -105.1 kJ/mol $(-25.0$ kcal/mol$)$. This is a highly exothermic reaction, with the decrease in enthalpy serving as the primary driving force.

4-5B Entropy

Entropy is often described as randomness, disorder, or freedom of motion. Reactions tend to favor products with the greatest entropy. Notice the negative sign in the entropy term $(-T\Delta S°)$ of the free-energy expression. A positive value of the entropy change $(\Delta S°)$, indicating that the products have more freedom of motion than the reactants, makes a favorable (negative) contribution to $\Delta G°$.

In many cases, the enthalpy change $(\Delta H°)$ is much larger than the entropy change $(\Delta S°)$, and the enthalpy term dominates the equation for $\Delta G°$. Thus, a negative value of $\Delta S°$ does not necessarily mean that the reaction has an unfavorable value of $\Delta G°$. The formation of strong bonds (the change in enthalpy) is usually the most important component in the driving force for a reaction.

In the chlorination of methane, the value of $\Delta S°$ is $+12.1$ J/kelvin-mole $(2.89$ cal/kelvin-mole$)$. The $-T\Delta S°$ term in the free energy is

$$-T\Delta S° = -(298\ °\text{K})(12.1\ \text{J/kelvin-mol}) = -3610\ \text{J/mol}$$
$$= -3.61\ \text{kJ/mol}\ (-0.86\ \text{kcal/mol})$$

The value of $\Delta G° = -108.7$ kJ/mol is divided into enthalpy and entropy terms:

$$\Delta G° = \Delta H° - T\Delta S° = -105.1\ \text{kJ/mol} - 3.61\ \text{kJ/mol}$$
$$= -108.7\ \text{kJ/mol}\ (-25.9\ \text{kcal/mol})$$

The enthalpy change is the largest factor in the driving force for chlorination. This is the case in most organic reactions: The entropy term is often small in relation to the enthalpy term. When we discuss chemical reactions involving the breaking and forming of bonds, we can often use the values of the enthalpy changes $(\Delta H°)$, under the assumption that $\Delta G° \cong \Delta H°$. We must be cautious in making this approximation, however, because some reactions have relatively small changes in enthalpy and larger changes in entropy.

SOLVED PROBLEM 4-2

Predict whether the value of $\Delta S°$ for the dissociation of Cl_2 is positive (favorable) or negative (unfavorable). What effect does the entropy term have on the sign of the value of $\Delta G°$ for this reaction?

$$Cl_2 \xrightarrow{h\nu} 2\,Cl\cdot$$

SOLUTION

Two isolated chlorine atoms have more freedom of motion than a single chlorine molecule. Therefore, the change in entropy is positive, and the entropy term $(-T\Delta S°)$ is negative. This negative (favorable) value of $(-T\Delta S°)$ is small, however, compared with the much larger, positive (unfavorable) value of $\Delta H°$ required to break the Cl—Cl bond. The chlorine molecule is much more stable than two chlorine atoms, showing that the positive enthalpy term predominates.

problem-solving Hint

In general, two smaller molecules (or fragments, such as radicals) have more freedom of motion (greater entropy) than one larger molecule.

PROBLEM 4-7

When ethene is mixed with hydrogen in the presence of a platinum catalyst, hydrogen adds across the double bond to form ethane. At room temperature, the reaction goes to completion. Predict the signs of $\Delta H°$ and $\Delta S°$ for this reaction. Explain these signs in terms of bonding and freedom of motion.

$$H_2C{=}CH_2 + H_2 \xrightarrow{\text{Pt catalyst}} H{-}CH_2{-}CH_2{-}H$$

ethene → ethane

PROBLEM 4-8

For each reaction, estimate whether $\Delta S°$ for the reaction is positive, negative, or impossible to predict.

(a) $C_{10}H_{22}$ (n-decane) $\xrightarrow[\text{catalyst}]{\text{heat}}$ C_3H_6 (propene) + C_7H_{16} (heptane) (catalytic cracking)

(b) The formation of diacetone alcohol:

$$2\,CH_3{-}C({=}O){-}CH_3 \overset{^-OH}{\rightleftharpoons} CH_3{-}C({=}O){-}CH_2{-}C(OH)(CH_3)_2$$

(c) $$CH_3{-}C({=}O){-}OH + CH_3OH \overset{H^+}{\rightleftharpoons} CH_3{-}C({=}O){-}OCH_3 + H_2O$$

4-6 Bond-Dissociation Enthalpies

We can put known amounts of methane and chlorine into a bomb calorimeter and use a hot wire to initiate the reaction. The temperature rise in the calorimeter is used to calculate the precise value of the heat of reaction, $\Delta H°$. This measurement shows that 105 kJ (25 kcal) of heat is evolved (exothermic) for each mole of methane converted to chloromethane. Thus, $\Delta H°$ for the reaction is negative, and the heat of reaction is given as

$$\Delta H° = -105 \text{ kJ/mol } (-25 \text{ kcal/mol})$$

In many cases, we want to predict whether a particular reaction will be endothermic or exothermic, without actually measuring the heat of reaction. We can calculate an approximate heat of reaction by adding and subtracting the energies involved in the breaking and forming of bonds. To do this calculation, we need to know the energies of the affected bonds.

The **bond-dissociation enthalpy** (**BDE**, also called **bond-dissociation energy**) is the amount of enthalpy required to break a particular bond **homolytically**—that is, in such a way that each bonded atom retains one of the bond's two electrons. In contrast, when a bond is broken **heterolytically**, one of the atoms retains both electrons.

Homolytic cleavage (free radicals result)

$$A{:}B \longrightarrow A\cdot + \cdot B \qquad \Delta H^\circ = \text{bond-dissociation enthalpy}$$

$$:\ddot{Cl}:\ddot{Cl}: \longrightarrow 2\,:\ddot{Cl}\cdot \qquad \Delta H^\circ = 242 \text{ kJ/mol (58 kcal/mol)}$$

Heterolytic cleavage (ions result)

$$A{:}B \longrightarrow A^+ + {}^-{:}B$$

$$(CH_3)_3C-\ddot{Cl}: \longrightarrow (CH_3)_3C^+ + :\ddot{Cl}:^- \quad (\Delta H^\circ \text{ varies with solvent})$$

Homolytic cleavage (radical cleavage) forms free radicals, while **heterolytic cleavage (ionic cleavage)** forms ions. Enthalpies for heterolytic (ionic) cleavage depend strongly on the solvent's ability to solvate the ions that result. Homolytic cleavage is used to define bond-dissociation enthalpies because the values do not vary so much with different solvents or with no solvent. Note that a curved arrow is used to show the movement of the electron pair in an ionic cleavage, and curved half-arrows are used to show the separation of individual electrons in a homolytic cleavage.

Energy is released when bonds are formed, and energy is consumed to break bonds. Therefore, bond-dissociation enthalpies are always positive (endothermic). The overall enthalpy change for a reaction is the sum of the dissociation enthalpies of the bonds broken minus the sum of the dissociation enthalpies of the bonds formed.

$$\Delta H^\circ = \Sigma(\text{BDE of bonds broken}) - \Sigma(\text{BDE of bonds formed})$$

For the hypothetical reaction

$$A-B + C-D \rightleftharpoons A-C + B-D$$

$$\Delta H^\circ = (\text{BDE of } A-B) + (\text{BDE of } C-D) - (\text{BDE of } A-C) - (\text{BDE of } B-D)$$

By studying the heats of reaction for many different reactions, chemists have developed reliable tables of bond-dissociation enthalpies. Table 4-2 gives the bond-dissociation enthalpies for the homolysis of bonds in a variety of molecules.

4-7 Enthalpy Changes in Chlorination

We can use values from Table 4-2 to predict the heat of reaction for the chlorination of methane. This reaction involves the breaking (positive values) of a CH_3-H bond and a $Cl-Cl$ bond, and the formation (negative values) of a CH_3-Cl bond and a $H-Cl$ bond.

Overall reaction

$$CH_3-H + Cl-Cl \longrightarrow CH_3-Cl + H-Cl$$

Bonds broken	ΔH° *(per mole)*	*Bonds formed*	ΔH° *(per mole)*
$Cl-Cl$	+242 kJ (+58 kcal)	$H-Cl$	−431 kJ (−103 kcal)
CH_3-H	+435 kJ (+104 kcal)	CH_3-Cl	−351 kJ (−84 kcal)
Total	+677 kJ (+162 kcal)	Total	−782 kJ (−187 kcal)

$$\Delta H^\circ = +677 \text{ kJ/mol} + (-782) \text{ kJ/mol} = -105 \text{ kJ/mol } (-25 \text{ kcal/mol})$$

The bond-dissociation enthalpies also provide the heat of reaction for each individual step:

First propagation step

$$Cl\cdot + CH_4 \longrightarrow \cdot CH_3 + HCl$$

Breaking a CH_3-H bond	+435 kJ/mol (+104 kcal/mol)
Forming an $H-Cl$ bond	−431 kJ/mol (−103 kcal/mol)
Step total	+4 kJ/mol (+1 kcal/mol)

TABLE 4-2

Bond-Dissociation Enthalpies for Homolytic Cleavages

$$\mathrm{A{:}B} \longrightarrow \mathrm{A\cdot} + \mathrm{\cdot B}$$

Bond	Bond-Dissociation Enthalpy kJ/mol	kcal/mol
H—X bonds and X—X bonds		
H—H	435	104
D—D	444	106
F—F	159	38
Cl—Cl	242	58
Br—Br	192	46
I—I	151	36
H—F	569	136
H—Cl	431	103
H—Br	368	88
H—I	297	71
HO—H	498	119
HO—OH	213	51
Methyl bonds		
CH_3—H	435	104
CH_3—F	456	109
CH_3—Cl	351	84
CH_3—Br	293	70
CH_3—I	234	56
CH_3—OH	381	91
Bonds to primary carbons		
CH_3CH_2—H	410	98
CH_3CH_2—F	448	107
CH_3CH_2—Cl	339	81
CH_3CH_2—Br	285	68
CH_3CH_2—I	222	53
CH_3CH_2—OH	381	91
$CH_3CH_2CH_2$—H	410	98
$CH_3CH_2CH_2$—F	448	107
$CH_3CH_2CH_2$—Cl	339	81
$CH_3CH_2CH_2$—Br	285	68
$CH_3CH_2CH_2$—I	222	53
$CH_3CH_2CH_2$—OH	381	91
Bonds to secondary carbons		
$(CH_3)_2CH$—H	397	95
$(CH_3)_2CH$—F	444	106
$(CH_3)_2CH$—Cl	335	80
$(CH_3)_2CH$—Br	285	68
$(CH_3)_2CH$—I	222	53
$(CH_3)_2CH$—OH	381	91
Bonds to tertiary carbons		
$(CH_3)_3C$—H	381	91
$(CH_3)_3C$—F	444	106
$(CH_3)_3C$—Cl	331	79
$(CH_3)_3C$—Br	272	65
$(CH_3)_3C$—I	209	50
$(CH_3)_3C$—OH	381	91
Other C—H bonds		
$PhCH_2$—H (benzylic)	356	85
$CH_2{=}CHCH_2$—H (allylic)	364	87
$CH_2{=}CH$—H (vinyl)	464	111
Ph—H (aromatic)	473	113
C—C bonds		
CH_3—CH_3	368	88
CH_3CH_2—CH_3	356	85
CH_3CH_2—CH_2CH_3	343	82
$(CH_3)_2CH$—CH_3	351	84
$(CH_3)_3C$—CH_3	339	81

Second propagation step

$$\cdot CH_3 + Cl_2 \longrightarrow CH_3Cl + Cl\cdot$$

Breaking a Cl—Cl bond	+243 kJ/mol (+58 kcal/mol)
Forming a CH_3—Cl bond	−352 kJ/mol (−84 kcal/mol)
Step total	−109 kJ/mol (−26 kcal/mol)

Grand total = +4 kJ/mol + (−109 kJ/mol) = −105 kJ/mol (−25 kcal/mol)

The sum of the values of ΔH° for the individual propagation steps gives the overall enthalpy change for the reaction. The initiation step, $Cl_2 \rightarrow 2\,Cl\cdot$, is not added to give the overall enthalpy change because it is not necessary for each molecule of product formed. The first splitting of a chlorine molecule simply begins the chain reaction, which generates hundreds or thousands of molecules of chloromethane. The energy needed to break the Cl—Cl bond is already included in the second propagation step.

problem-solving Hint

Bond-dissociation enthalpies are for breaking bonds, which costs energy. In calculating values of ΔH°, use positive BDE values for bonds that are broken and negative values for bonds that are formed.

PROBLEM 4-9

(a) Propose a mechanism for the free-radical chlorination of ethane,

$$CH_3{-}CH_3 + Cl_2 \xrightarrow{h\nu} CH_3{-}CH_2Cl + HCl$$

(b) Calculate $\Delta H°$ for each step in this reaction.
(c) Calculate the overall value of $\Delta H°$ for this reaction.

Alternative Mechanism The mechanism we have used is not the only one that might be proposed to explain the reaction of methane with chlorine. We know that the initiating step must be the splitting of a molecule of Cl_2, but there are other propagation steps that would form the correct products:

(a) $Cl\cdot + CH_3{-}H \longrightarrow CH_3{-}Cl + H\cdot$ $\Delta H° = +435\text{ kJ} - 351\text{ kJ} = +84\text{ kJ}$ ($+104\text{ kcal} - 84\text{ kcal} = +20\text{ kcal}$)

(b) $H\cdot + Cl{-}Cl \longrightarrow H{-}Cl + Cl\cdot$ $\Delta H° = +242\text{ kJ} - 431\text{ kJ} = -189\text{ kJ}$ ($+58\text{ kcal} - 103\text{ kcal} = -45\text{ kcal}$)

Total -105 kJ (-25 kcal)

This alternative mechanism seems plausible, but step (a) is endothermic by 84 kJ/mol (20 kcal/mol). The previous mechanism provides a lower-energy alternative. When a chlorine atom collides with a methane molecule, it will not react to give methyl chloride and a hydrogen atom ($\Delta H° = +84\text{ kJ} = +20\text{ kcal}$); it will react to give HCl and a methyl radical ($\Delta H° = +4\text{ kJ} = +1\text{ kcal}$), the first propagation step of the correct mechanism.

PROBLEM 4-10

(a) Using bond-dissociation enthalpies from Table 4-2 (page 138), calculate the heat of reaction for each step in the free-radical bromination of methane.

$$Br_2 + CH_4 \xrightarrow{\text{heat or light}} CH_3Br + HBr$$

(b) Calculate the overall heat of reaction.

4-8 Kinetics and the Rate Equation

Kinetics is the study of reaction rates. How fast a reaction goes is just as important as the position of its equilibrium. Just because thermodynamics favors a reaction (negative $\Delta G°$) does not necessarily mean the reaction will actually occur. For example, a mixture of gasoline and oxygen does not react without a spark or a catalyst. Similarly, a mixture of methane and chlorine does not react if it is kept cold and dark.

The **rate of a reaction** is a measure of how fast the products appear and the reactants disappear. We can determine the rate by measuring the increase in the concentrations of the products with time, or the decrease in the concentrations of the reactants with time.

Reaction rates depend on the concentrations of the reactants. The greater the concentrations, the more often the reactants collide and the greater the chance of reaction. A **rate equation** (sometimes called a **rate law**) is the relationship between the concentrations of the reactants and the observed reaction rate. Each reaction has its own rate equation, *determined experimentally* by changing the concentrations of the reactants and measuring the change in the rate. For example, consider the general reaction

$$A + B \longrightarrow C + D$$

The reaction rate is usually proportional to the concentrations of the reactants ([A] and [B]) raised to some powers, *a* and *b*. We can use a general rate expression to represent this relationship as

$$\text{rate} = k_r[A]^a[B]^b$$

where k_r is the **rate constant**, and the values of the powers (*a* and *b*) must be determined experimentally. We cannot guess or calculate the rate equation from just the stoichiometry of the reaction. The rate equation depends on the mechanism of the reaction and on the rates of the individual steps.

In the general rate equation, the power *a* is called the **order** of the reaction with respect to reactant A, and *b* is the order of the reaction with respect to B. The sum of these powers, $(a + b)$, is called the **overall order** of the reaction.

The following reaction has a simple rate equation:

$$CH_3{-}Br + {}^{-}OH \xrightarrow{H_2O/\text{acetone}} CH_3{-}OH + Br^-$$

Experiments show that doubling the concentration of methyl bromide, $[CH_3Br]$, doubles the rate of reaction. Doubling the concentration of hydroxide ion, $[^-OH]$, also doubles the rate. Thus, the rate is proportional to both $[CH_3Br]$ and $[^-OH]$, so the rate equation has the following form:

$$\text{rate} = k_r[CH_3Br][^-OH]$$

This rate equation is *first order* in each of the two reagents because it is proportional to the first power of their concentrations. The rate equation is *second order overall* because the sum of the powers of the concentrations in the rate equation is 2; that is, (first order) + (first order) = second order overall.

Reactions of the same overall type do not necessarily have the same form of rate equation. For example, the following similar reaction has a different kinetic order:

$$(CH_3)_3C{-}Br \;+\; ^-OH \xrightarrow{H_2O/\text{acetone}} (CH_3)_3C{-}OH \;+\; Br^-$$

Doubling the concentration of *tert*-butyl bromide $[(CH_3)_3C{-}Br]$ causes the rate to double, but doubling the concentration of hydroxide ion $[^-OH]$ has no effect on the rate of this particular reaction. The rate equation is

$$\text{rate} = k_r[(CH_3)_3C{-}Br]$$

This reaction is first order in *tert*-butyl bromide, and zeroth order in hydroxide ion (proportional to $[^-OH]$ to the zeroth power). It is first order overall. This reaction is zeroth order in hydroxide ion because the slow step involves only *tert*-butyl bromide and not hydroxide ion:

$$(CH_3)_3C{-}Br \rightleftharpoons (CH_3)_3C^+ + Br^-$$

The most important fact to remember is that *the rate equation must be determined experimentally*. We cannot predict the form of the rate equation from the stoichiometry of the reaction. We determine the rate equation experimentally, then use that information to propose consistent mechanisms.

SOLVED PROBLEM 4-3

Chloromethane reacts with dilute sodium cyanide ($Na^+ \; ^-C{\equiv}N$) according to the following equation:

$$\underset{\text{chloromethane}}{CH_3{-}Cl} \;+\; \underset{\text{cyanide}}{^-C{\equiv}N} \longrightarrow \underset{\text{acetonitrile}}{CH_3{-}C{\equiv}N} \;+\; \underset{\text{chloride}}{Cl^-}$$

When the concentration of chloromethane is doubled, the rate is observed to double. When the concentration of cyanide ion is tripled, the rate is observed to triple.

(a) What is the kinetic order with respect to chloromethane?
(b) What is the kinetic order with respect to cyanide ion?
(c) What is the kinetic order overall?
(d) Write the rate equation for this reaction.

SOLUTION

(a) When $[CH_3Cl]$ is doubled, the rate doubles, which is 2 to the first power. The reaction is first order with respect to chloromethane.
(b) When $[^-CN]$ is tripled, the reaction rate triples, which is 3 to the first power. The reaction is first order with respect to cyanide ion.
(c) First order plus first order equals second order overall.
(d) rate = $k_r[CH_3Cl][^-CN]$

PROBLEM 4-11

The reaction of *tert*-butyl chloride with methanol

$$\underset{\textit{tert}\text{-butyl chloride}}{(CH_3)_3C{-}Cl} \;+\; \underset{\text{methanol}}{CH_3{-}OH} \longrightarrow \underset{\text{methyl }\textit{tert}\text{-butyl ether}}{(CH_3)_3C{-}OCH_3} \;+\; HCl$$

is found to follow the rate equation

$$\text{rate} = k_r[(CH_3)_3C{-}Cl]$$

(a) What is the kinetic order with respect to *tert*-butyl chloride?
(b) What is the kinetic order with respect to methanol?
(c) What is the kinetic order overall?

PROBLEM 4-12

Under certain conditions, the bromination of cyclohexene follows an unusual rate law:

$$\text{cyclohexene} + Br_2 \longrightarrow \text{1,2-dibromocyclohexane} \qquad \text{rate} = k_r[\text{cyclohexene}][Br_2]^2$$

(a) What is the kinetic order with respect to cyclohexene?
(b) What is the kinetic order with respect to bromine?
(c) What is the overall kinetic order?

PROBLEM 4-13

When a small piece of platinum is added to a mixture of ethene and hydrogen, the following reaction occurs:

$$H_2C{=}CH_2 \;(\text{ethene}) + H_2 \;(\text{hydrogen}) \xrightarrow{\text{Pt catalyst}} H{-}CH_2{-}CH_2{-}H \;(\text{ethane})$$

Doubling the concentration of hydrogen has no effect on the reaction rate. Doubling the concentration of ethene also has no effect.
(a) What is the kinetic order of this reaction with respect to ethene? With respect to hydrogen? What is the overall order?
(b) Write the unusual rate equation for this reaction.
(c) Explain this strange rate equation, and suggest what one might do to accelerate the reaction.

4-9 Activation Energy and the Temperature Dependence of Rates

Each reaction has its own characteristic rate constant, k_r. Its value depends on the conditions of the reaction, especially the temperature. This temperature dependence is expressed by the *Arrhenius equation*,

$$k_r = Ae^{-E_a/RT}$$

where

A = a constant (the "frequency factor")
E_a = activation energy
R = the gas constant, 8.314 J/kelvin-mole (1.987 cal/kelvin-mole)
T = the absolute temperature

The **activation energy,** E_a, is the minimum kinetic energy the molecules must have to overcome the repulsions between their electron clouds when they collide. The exponential term $e^{-E_a/RT}$ corresponds to the fraction of collisions in which the particles have the minimum energy E_a needed to react. We can calculate E_a for a reaction by measuring how k_r varies with temperature, and substituting into the Arrhenius equation.

The *frequency factor A* accounts for the frequency of collisions and the fraction of collisions with the proper orientation for the reaction to occur. In most cases, only a small fraction of collisions occur between molecules with enough speed and with just the right orientation for reaction to occur. Far more collisions occur without enough kinetic energy or without the proper orientation, and the molecules simply bounce off each other.

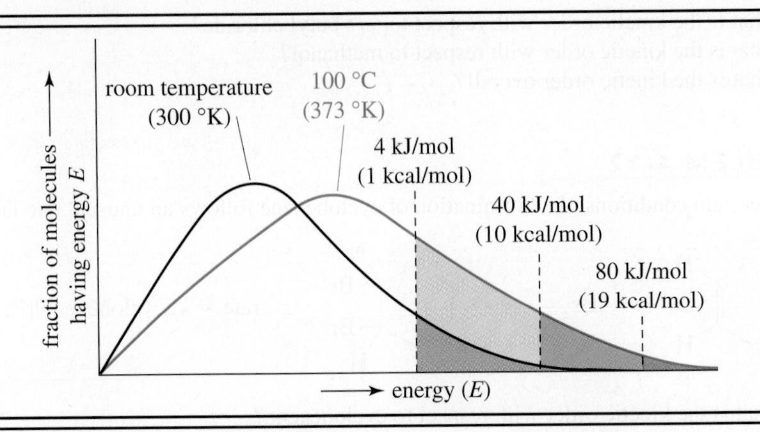

■ **FIGURE 4-2**
The dependence of kinetic energies on temperature. This graph shows how the fraction of molecules with a given activation energy decreases as the activation energy increases. At a higher temperature (red curve), more collisions have the needed energy.

The Arrhenius equation implies that the rate of a reaction depends on the fraction of collisions with kinetic energy of at least E_a. Figure 4-2 shows how the distribution of kinetic energies in a sample of a gas depends on the temperature. The black curved line shows the molecular energy distribution at room temperature, and the dashed lines show the energy needed to overcome barriers of 4 kJ/mol (1 kcal/mol), 40 kJ/mol (10 kcal/mol), and 80 kJ (19 kcal/mol). The area under the curve to the right of each barrier corresponds to the fraction of molecules with enough energy to overcome that barrier.

The red curve shows how the energy distribution is shifted at 100 °C. At 100 °C, many more molecules have the energy needed to overcome the energy barriers, especially the 80 kJ/mol barrier. For smaller temperature changes, chemists often use an approximation: For reactions with typical activation energies of about 40 to 60 kJ/mol (10 to 15 kcal/mol), the reaction rate approximately doubles when the temperature is raised by 10 °C, as from 27 °C (near room temperature) to 37 °C (body temperature).

Because the relative rate constant, k_{rel}, increases quickly when the temperature is raised, it might seem that raising the temperature would always be a good way to save time by making reactions go faster. The problem with raising the temperature is that *all* reactions are accelerated, including all the unwanted side reactions. We try to find a temperature that allows the desired reaction to go at a reasonable rate without producing unacceptable rates of side reactions.

4-10 Transition States

The activation energy E_a represents the energy difference between the reactants and the **transition state**, the highest-energy state in a molecular collision that leads to reaction. In effect, the activation energy is the barrier that must be overcome for the reaction to take place. The value of E_a is always positive, and its magnitude depends on the relative energy of the transition state. The term *transition state* implies that this configuration is the transition between the reactants and products, and the molecules can either go on to products or return to reactants.

Unlike the reactants or products, a transition state is unstable and cannot be isolated. It is not an intermediate, because an **intermediate** is a species that exists for some finite length of time, even if it is very short. An intermediate has at least some stability, but the transition state is a transient on the path from one intermediate to another. The transition state is often symbolized by a superscript double dagger (‡), and the changes in variables such as free energy, enthalpy, and entropy involved in achieving the transition state are symbolized $\Delta G^‡$, $\Delta H^‡$, and $\Delta S^‡$. $\Delta G^‡$ is similar to E_a, and the symbol $\Delta G^‡$ is often used in speaking of the activation energy.

Transition states have high energies because bonds must begin to break before other bonds can form. The following equation shows the reaction of a chlorine radical with methane. The transition state shows the C—H bond partially broken and the H—Cl bond partially formed. Transition states are often enclosed by brackets to emphasize their transient nature.

$$CH_4 + \cdot Cl \rightleftharpoons [H_3C\text{---}H\text{---}Cl]^{\ddagger} \longrightarrow \cdot CH_3 + H\text{—}Cl$$

transition state

transition state
‡
E_a
A + B
(reactants)
$\Delta H°$
C + D
(products)
energy
reaction coordinate

■ FIGURE 4-3
Reaction-energy diagram for a one-step exothermic reaction. The reactants are toward the left, and the products are toward the right. The vertical axis represents the potential energy. The transition state is the highest point on the graph, and the activation energy is the energy difference between the reactants and the transition state.

Reaction-Energy Diagrams The concepts of transition state and activation energy are easier to understand graphically. Figure 4-3 shows a **reaction-energy diagram** for a one-step exothermic reaction. The vertical axis of the energy diagram represents the total potential energy of all the species involved in the reaction. The horizontal axis is called the **reaction coordinate**. The reaction coordinate symbolizes the progress of the reaction, going from the reactants on the left to the products on the right. The transition state is the highest point on the graph, and the activation energy is the energy difference between the reactants and the transition state. The heat of reaction ($\Delta H°$) is the difference in energy between the reactants and the products.

If a **catalyst** were added to the reaction in Figure 4-3, it would create a transition state of lower energy, thereby lowering the activation energy and increasing the reaction rate. Addition of a catalyst would not change the energies of the reactants and products, however, so the heat of reaction and the equilibrium constant would be unaffected.

Enzymes serve as biological catalysts. They speed up reactions without changing the energies of the reactants (called substrates) and products. Without enzymes, most of the reactions in our cells would not go fast enough to keep us alive.

SOLVED PROBLEM 4-4

Consider the following reaction:

$$CH_4 + Cl\cdot \longrightarrow \cdot CH_3 + HCl$$

This reaction has an activation energy (E_a) of +17 kJ/mol (+4 kcal/mol) and a $\Delta H°$ of +4 kJ/mol (+1 kcal/mol). Draw a reaction-energy diagram for this reaction.

SOLUTION

We draw a diagram that shows the products to be 4 kJ *higher* in energy than the reactants. The barrier is made to be 17 kJ higher in energy than the reactants.

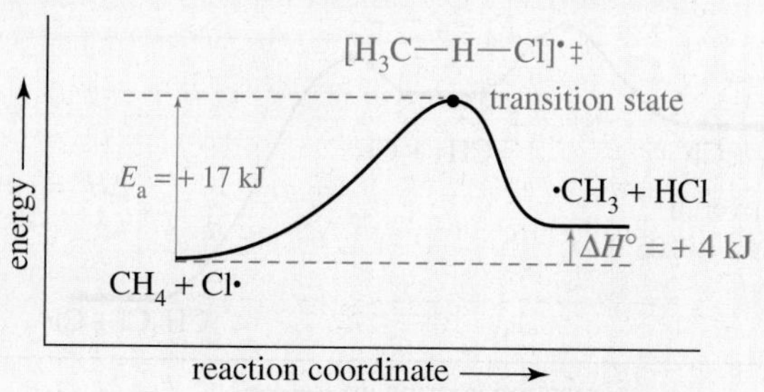

PROBLEM 4-14

(a) Draw the reaction-energy diagram for the reverse reaction:

$$\cdot CH_3 + HCl \longrightarrow CH_4 + Cl\cdot$$

(b) What is the activation energy for this reverse reaction?
(c) What is the heat of reaction ($\Delta H°$) for this reverse reaction?

PROBLEM 4-15

(a) Draw a reaction-energy diagram for the following reaction:

$$\cdot CH_3 + Cl_2 \longrightarrow CH_3Cl + Cl\cdot$$

The activation energy is 4 kJ/mol (1 kcal/mol), and the overall $\Delta H°$ for the reaction is -109 kJ/mol (-26 kcal/mol).
(b) Give the equation for the reverse reaction.
(c) What is the activation energy for the reverse reaction?

4-11 Rates of Multistep Reactions

Many reactions proceed by mechanisms involving several steps and several intermediates. As we saw in Section 4-7, for example, the reaction of methane with chlorine goes through two propagation steps. The propagation steps are shown here, along with their heats of reaction and their activation energies. Just the propagation steps are shown because the rate of the initiation step is controlled by the amount of light or heat available to split chlorine molecules.

Step	$\Delta H°$ (per mole)	E_a (per mole)
$CH_4 + Cl\cdot \longrightarrow \cdot CH_3 + HCl$	+4 kJ (+1 kcal)	17 kJ (4 kcal)
$\cdot CH_3 + Cl_2 \longrightarrow CH_3Cl + Cl\cdot$	−109 kJ (−26 kcal)	4 kJ (1 kcal)

In this reaction, $Cl\cdot$ and $CH_3\cdot$ are *reactive intermediates*. Unlike transition states, reactive intermediates are stable as long as they do not collide with other atoms or molecules. As free radicals, however, $Cl\cdot$ and $CH_3\cdot$ are quite reactive toward other molecules. Figure 4-4 shows a single reaction-energy profile that includes both propagation steps of the chlorination. The energy maxima (high points) are the unstable transition states, and the energy minima (low points) are the intermediates. This complete energy profile provides most of the important information about the energetics of the reaction.

The Rate-Limiting Step In a multistep reaction, each step has its own characteristic rate. There can be only one overall reaction rate, however, and it is controlled by the **rate-limiting step** (also called the **rate-determining step**). In general, the *highest-energy* step of a multistep reaction is the "bottleneck," and it determines the overall rate. How can we tell which step is rate limiting? If we have the reaction-energy diagram, it is simple: The highest point in the energy diagram is the transition state with the highest energy—generally the transition state for the rate-limiting step.

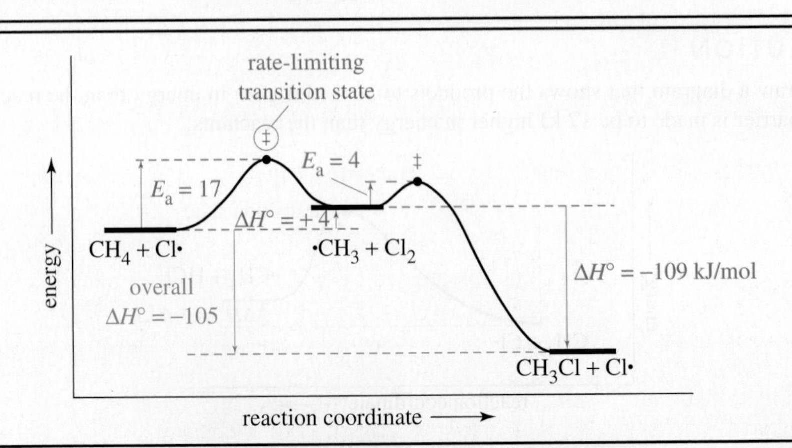

■ **FIGURE 4-4**
Combined reaction-energy diagram for the chlorination of methane. The energy maxima are transition states, and the energy minima are intermediates. (Units are kJ/mol.)

The highest point in the energy diagram of the chlorination of methane (Figure 4-4) is the transition state for the reaction of methane with a chlorine radical. This step must be rate limiting. If we calculate a rate for this slow step, it will be the rate for the overall reaction. The second, faster step will consume the products of the slow step as fast as they are formed.

4-12 Temperature Dependence of Halogenation

We now apply what we know about rates to the reaction of methane with halogens. The rate-limiting step for chlorination is the endothermic reaction of the chlorine atom with methane to form a methyl radical and a molecule of HCl.

Rate-limiting step

$$CH_4 + Cl\cdot \longrightarrow \cdot CH_3 + HCl$$

The activation energy for this step is 17 kJ/mol (4 kcal/mol). At room temperature, the value of $e^{-E_a/RT}$ is 1300×10^{-6}. This value represents a rate that is fast but controllable.

In a free-radical chain reaction, every propagation step must occur quickly, or the free radicals will undergo unproductive collisions and participate in termination steps. We can predict how quickly the various halogen atoms react with methane given relative rates based on the measured activation energies of the slowest steps:

Reaction	E_a (per mole)	Relative Rate ($e^{-E_a/RT} \times 10^6$) 27 °C (300 °K)	227 °C (500 °K)
$F\cdot + CH_4 \longrightarrow HF + \cdot CH_3$	5 kJ (1.2 kcal)	140,000	300,000
$Cl\cdot + CH_4 \longrightarrow HCl + \cdot CH_3$	17 kJ (4 kcal)	1300	18,000
$Br\cdot + CH_4 \longrightarrow HBr + \cdot CH_3$	75 kJ (18 kcal)	9×10^{-8}	0.015
$I\cdot + CH_4 \longrightarrow HI + \cdot CH_3$	140 kJ (34 kcal)	2×10^{-19}	2×10^{-9}

These relative rates suggest how easily and quickly methane reacts with the different halogen radicals. The reaction with fluorine should be difficult to control because its rate is very high. Chlorine should react moderately at room temperature, but it may become difficult to control if the temperature rises much (the rate at 500 °K is rather high). The reaction with bromine is very slow, but heating might give an observable rate. Iodination is probably out of the question because its rate is exceedingly slow, even at 500 °K.

Laboratory halogenations show that our predictions are right. In fact, fluorine reacts explosively with methane, and chlorine reacts at a moderate rate. A mixture of bromine and methane must be heated to react, and iodine does not react at all.

PROBLEM 4-16

The bromination of methane proceeds through the following steps:

	$\Delta H°$ (per mole)	E_a (per mole)
$Br_2 \xrightarrow{h\nu} 2\ Br\cdot$	+192 kJ (46 kcal)	192 kJ (46 kcal)
$CH_4 + Br\cdot \rightarrow \cdot CH_3 + HBr$	67 kJ (16 kcal)	75 kJ (18 kcal)
$\cdot CH_3 + Br_2 \rightarrow CH_3Br + Br\cdot$	−101 kJ (−24 kcal)	4 kJ (1 kcal)

(a) Draw a complete reaction-energy diagram for this reaction.
(b) Label the rate-limiting step.
(c) Draw the structure of each transition state.
(d) Compute the overall value of $\Delta H°$ for the bromination.

PROBLEM 4-17

(a) Using the BDEs in Table 4-2 (p. 138), compute the value of $\Delta H°$ for each step in the iodination of methane.
(b) Compute the overall value of $\Delta H°$ for iodination.
(c) Suggest *two* reasons why iodine does not react well with methane.

4-13 Selectivity in Halogenation

Up to now, we have limited our discussions to the halogenation of methane. Beginning our study with such a simple compound allowed us to concentrate on the thermodynamics and kinetics of the reaction. Now we consider halogenation of the "higher" alkanes, meaning those of higher molecular weight.

4-13A Chlorination of Propane: Product Ratios

Halogenation is a substitution, where a halogen atom replaces a hydrogen.

$$R—H + X_2 \longrightarrow R—X + H—X$$

In methane, all four hydrogen atoms are identical, and it does not matter which hydrogen is replaced. In the higher alkanes, replacement of different hydrogen atoms may lead to different products. In the chlorination of propane, for example, two monochlorinated (just one chlorine atom) products are possible. One has the chlorine atom on a primary carbon atom, and the other has the chlorine atom on the secondary carbon atom.

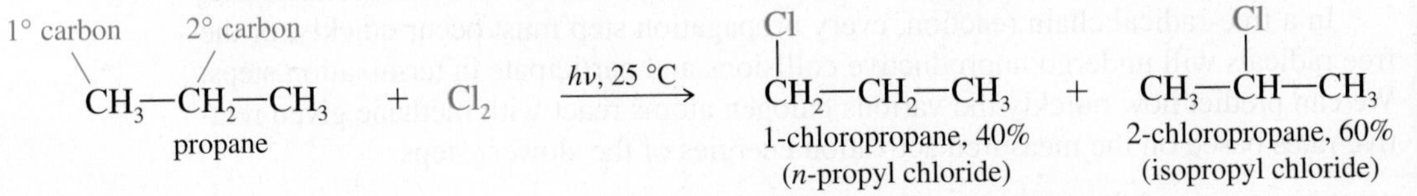

$$\underset{\text{propane}}{CH_3—CH_2—CH_3} + Cl_2 \xrightarrow{h\nu,\ 25\ °C} \underset{\text{1-chloropropane, 40\% (n-propyl chloride)}}{CH_2(Cl)—CH_2—CH_3} + \underset{\text{2-chloropropane, 60\% (isopropyl chloride)}}{CH_3—CH(Cl)—CH_3}$$

(1° carbon: CH_3; 2° carbon: CH_2)

The product ratio shows that replacement of hydrogen atoms by chlorine is not random. Propane has six primary hydrogens (hydrogens bonded to primary carbons) and only two secondary hydrogens (bonded to the secondary carbon), yet the major product results from substitution of a secondary hydrogen. We can calculate how reactive each kind of hydrogen is by dividing the amount of product observed by the number of hydrogens that can be replaced to give that product.

Figure 4-5 shows the definition of primary, secondary, and tertiary hydrogens and the calculation of their relative reactivity. Replacing either of the two secondary hydrogens accounts for 60% of the product, and replacing any of the six primary hydrogens accounts for 40% of the product. We calculate that each secondary hydrogen is 4.5 times as reactive as each primary hydrogen. To explain this preference for reaction at the secondary position, we must look carefully at the reaction mechanism (Figure 4-6).

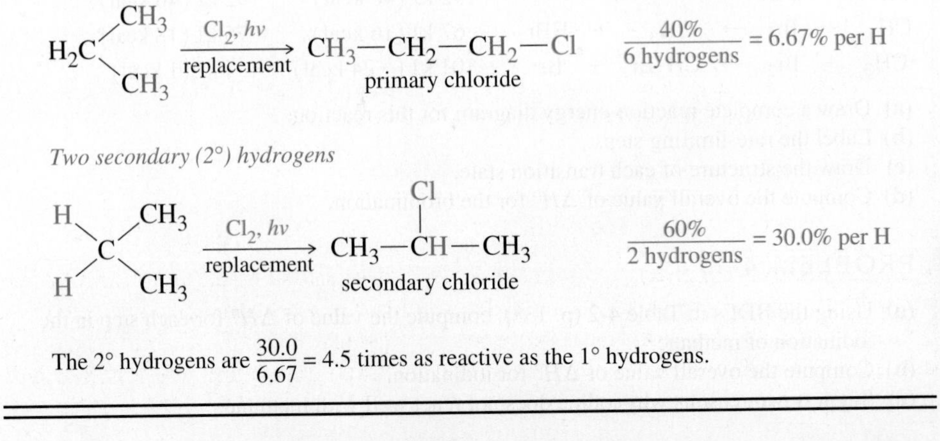

R—CH₂—H: primary (1°) hydrogens; $R_2CH—H$: secondary (2°) hydrogens; $R_3C—H$: tertiary (3°) hydrogen

Six primary (1°) hydrogens

$$H_2C(CH_3)_2 \xrightarrow[\text{replacement}]{Cl_2,\ h\nu} \underset{\text{primary chloride}}{CH_3—CH_2—CH_2—Cl} \qquad \frac{40\%}{6\text{ hydrogens}} = 6.67\%\text{ per H}$$

relative reactivity

Two secondary (2°) hydrogens

$$H_2C(CH_3)_2 \xrightarrow[\text{replacement}]{Cl_2,\ h\nu} \underset{\text{secondary chloride}}{CH_3—CH(Cl)—CH_3} \qquad \frac{60\%}{2\text{ hydrogens}} = 30.0\%\text{ per H}$$

The 2° hydrogens are $\frac{30.0}{6.67} = 4.5$ times as reactive as the 1° hydrogens.

■ **FIGURE 4-5**
Definitions of primary, secondary, and tertiary hydrogens. There are six primary hydrogens in propane and only two secondary hydrogens, yet the major product results from replacement of a secondary hydrogen.

Initiation: Splitting of the chlorine molecule

$$Cl_2 + h\nu \longrightarrow 2\ Cl\cdot$$

First propagation step: Abstraction (removal) of a primary or secondary hydrogen

$$CH_3{-}CH_2{-}CH_3 + Cl\cdot \longrightarrow \underset{\text{primary radical}}{\cdot CH_2{-}CH_2{-}CH_3} \text{ or } \underset{\text{secondary radical}}{CH_3{-}\dot{C}H{-}CH_3} + HCl$$

Second propagation step: Reaction with chlorine to form the alkyl chloride

$$\underset{\text{primary radical}}{\cdot CH_2{-}CH_2{-}CH_3} + Cl_2 \longrightarrow \underset{\substack{\text{primary chloride}\\\text{(1-chloropropane)}}}{Cl{-}CH_2{-}CH_2{-}CH_3} + Cl\cdot$$

$$\text{or } \underset{\text{secondary radical}}{CH_3{-}\dot{C}H{-}CH_3} + Cl_2 \longrightarrow \underset{\substack{\text{secondary chloride}\\\text{(2-chloropropane)}}}{CH_3{-}\overset{Cl}{\overset{|}{C}H}{-}CH_3} + Cl\cdot$$

FIGURE 4-6
The mechanism for free-radical chlorination of propane. The first propagation step forms either a primary radical or a secondary radical. This radical determines whether the final product will be the primary alkyl chloride or the secondary alkyl chloride.

When a chlorine atom reacts with propane, abstraction of a hydrogen atom can give either a primary radical or a secondary radical. The structure of the radical formed in this step determines the structure of the observed product, either 1-chloropropane or 2-chloropropane. The product ratio shows that the secondary radical is formed preferentially. This preference for reaction at the secondary position results from the greater stability of the secondary free radical and the transition state leading to it. Section 4-13B explains this preference in more detail.

PROBLEM 4-18

What would be the product ratio in the chlorination of propane if all the hydrogens were abstracted at equal rates?

PROBLEM 4-19

Classify each hydrogen atom in the following compounds as primary (1°), secondary (2°), or tertiary (3°).

(a) butane **(b)** isobutane **(c)** 2-methylbutane
(d) cyclohexane **(e)** norbornane (bicyclo[2.2.1]heptane)

4-13B Free-Radical Stabilities

Figure 4-7 shows the energy required (the bond-dissociation enthalpy) to form a free radical by breaking a bond between a hydrogen atom and a carbon atom. This energy is greatest for a methyl carbon, and it decreases for a primary carbon, a secondary carbon, and a tertiary carbon. The more highly substituted the carbon atom, the less energy is required to form the free radical.

Formation of a methyl radical — *Bond-dissociation enthalpy*

$$CH_4 \longrightarrow H\cdot + \cdot CH_3 \qquad \Delta H° = 435 \text{ kJ (104 kcal)}$$

Formation of a primary (1°) radical

$$CH_3{-}CH_2{-}CH_3 \longrightarrow H\cdot + CH_3{-}CH_2{-}\dot{C}H_2 \qquad \Delta H° = 410 \text{ kJ (98 kcal)}$$

Formation of a secondary (2°) radical

$$CH_3{-}CH_2{-}CH_3 \longrightarrow H\cdot + CH_3{-}\dot{C}H{-}CH_3 \qquad \Delta H° = 397 \text{ kJ (95 kcal)}$$

Formation of a tertiary (3°) radical

$$(CH_3)_3C{-}H \longrightarrow H\cdot + (CH_3)_3C\cdot \qquad \Delta H° = 381 \text{ kJ (91 kcal)}$$

■ **FIGURE 4-7**
Enthalpy required to form a free radical. Bond-dissociation enthalpies show that more highly substituted free radicals are more stable than less highly substituted ones.

From the information in Figure 4-7, we conclude that free radicals are more stable if they are more highly substituted. The following free radicals are listed in increasing order of stability.

$$H_3C\cdot \; < \; RCH_2\cdot \; < \; R_2CH\cdot \; < \; R_3C\cdot$$

Me· < 1° < 2° < 3°

methyl < primary < secondary < tertiary

In the chlorination of propane, the secondary hydrogen atom is abstracted more often because the secondary radical and the transition state leading to it are lower in energy than the primary radical and its transition state. Using the bond-dissociation enthalpies in Table 4-2 (page 138), we can calculate $\Delta H°$ for each of the possible reaction steps. Abstraction of the secondary hydrogen is 13 kJ/mol (3 kcal/mol) more exothermic than abstraction of the primary hydrogen.

problem-solving Hint

The first propagation step of chlorination is exothermic for all alkanes except methane. For methane it is slightly endothermic, about +4 kJ/mol (+1 kcal/mol).

1° H: $CH_3{-}CH_2{-}CH_3 + Cl\cdot \longrightarrow CH_3{-}CH_2{-}CH_2\cdot + H{-}Cl$

Energy required to break the $CH_3CH_2CH_2{-}H$ bond	+410 kJ/mol (+98 kcal/mol)
Energy released in forming the H—Cl bond	−431 kJ/mol (−103 kcal/mol)
Total energy for reaction at the primary position:	−21 kJ/mol (−5 kcal/mol)

2° H: $CH_3{-}CH(CH_3){-}H + Cl\cdot \longrightarrow CH_3{-}\dot{C}H{-}CH_3 + H{-}Cl$

Energy required to break the $CH_3{-}CH(CH_3){-}H$ bond	+397 kJ/mol (+95 kcal/mol)
Energy released in forming the H—Cl bond	−431 kJ/mol (−103 kcal/mol)
Total energy for reaction at the secondary position:	−34 kJ/mol (−8 kcal/mol)

A reaction-energy diagram for this rate-limiting first propagation step appears in Figure 4-8. The activation energy to form the secondary radical is slightly lower, so the secondary radical is formed faster than the primary radical.

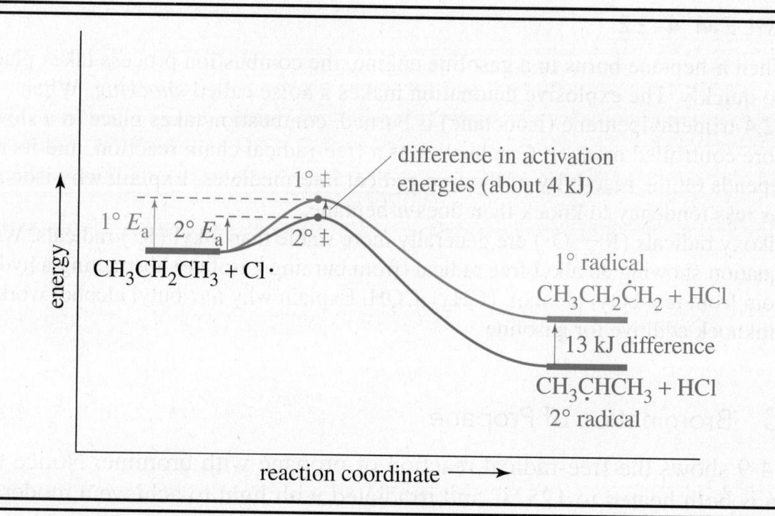

■ **FIGURE 4-8**
Reaction-energy diagram for the first propagation step in the chlorination of propane. Formation of the secondary radical has a lower activation energy than does formation of the primary radical.

SOLVED PROBLEM 4-5

Tertiary hydrogen atoms react with Cl· about 5.5 times as fast as primary ones. Predict the product ratios for chlorination of isobutane.

SOLUTION

Isobutane has nine primary hydrogens and one tertiary hydrogen.

nine primary hydrogens → $(H_3C)_3C{-}H$ ← one tertiary hydrogen

$$(9 \text{ primary hydrogens}) \times (\text{reactivity } 1.0) = 9.0 \text{ relative amount of reaction}$$

$$(1 \text{ tertiary hydrogen}) \times (\text{reactivity } 5.5) = 5.5 \text{ relative amount of reaction}$$

Even though the primary hydrogens are less reactive, there are so many of them that the primary product is the major product. The product ratio will be 9.0:5.5, or about 1.6:1.

$$\text{fraction of primary} = \frac{9.0}{9.0 + 5.5} = 62\%$$

$$\text{fraction of tertiary} = \frac{5.5}{9.0 + 5.5} = 38\%$$

$CH_3{-}CH(CH_2{-}Cl){-}CH_3$ — major product, 62%

$CH_3{-}C(CH_3)_2{-}Cl$ — minor product, 38%

PROBLEM 4-20

Use the bond-dissociation enthalpies in Table 4-2 (page 138) to calculate the heats of reaction for the two possible first propagation steps in the chlorination of isobutane. Use this information to draw a reaction-energy diagram like Figure 4-8, comparing the activation energies for formation of the two radicals.

PROBLEM 4-21

Predict the ratios of products that result from chlorination of isopentane (2-methylbutane).

PROBLEM 4-22

(a) When *n*-heptane burns in a gasoline engine, the combustion process takes place too quickly. The explosive detonation makes a noise called *knocking*. When 2,2,4-trimethylpentane (isooctane) is burned, combustion takes place in a slower, more controlled manner. Combustion is a free-radical chain reaction, and its rate depends on the reactivity of the free-radical intermediates. Explain why isooctane has less tendency to knock than does *n*-heptane.

(b) Alkoxy radicals (R—O·) are generally more stable than alkyl (R·) radicals. Write an equation showing an alkyl free radical (from burning gasoline) abstracting a hydrogen atom from *tert*-butyl alcohol, $(CH_3)_3COH$. Explain why *tert*-butyl alcohol works as an antiknock additive for gasoline.

4-13C Bromination of Propane

Figure 4-9 shows the free-radical reaction of propane with bromine. Notice that this reaction is both heated to 125 °C and irradiated with light to achieve a moderate rate. The secondary bromide (2-bromopropane) is favored by a 97:3 product ratio. From this product ratio, we calculate that the two secondary hydrogens are each 97 times as reactive as one of the primary hydrogens.

The 97:1 reactivity ratio for bromination is much larger than the 4.5:1 ratio for chlorination. We say that bromination is more *selective* than chlorination because the major reaction is favored by a larger amount. To explain this enhanced selectivity, we must consider the transition states and activation energies for the rate-limiting step.

As with chlorination, the rate-limiting step in bromination is the first propagation step: abstraction of a hydrogen atom by a bromine radical. The energetics of the two possible hydrogen abstractions are shown below. Compare these numbers with the energetics of the first propagation step of chlorination shown on page 148. The bond dissociation enthalpies are taken from Table 4-2 (page 138).

1° H: $CH_3-CH_2-CH_3 + Br\cdot \longrightarrow CH_3-CH_2-CH_2\cdot + H-Br$

Energy required to break the $CH_3CH_2CH_2$—H bond	+410 kJ/mol (+98 kcal/mol)
Energy released in forming the H—Br bond	−368 kJ/mol (−88 kcal/mol)
Total energy for reaction at the primary position:	+42 kJ/mol (+10 kcal/mol)

$$CH_3-CH_2-CH_3 + Br_2 \xrightarrow{h\nu,\ 125\ °C} \underset{\text{primary bromide, 3\%}}{CH_3-CH_2-CH_2Br} + \underset{\text{secondary bromide, 97\%}}{CH_3-CHBr-CH_3} + HBr$$

Relative reactivity

six primary hydrogens $\frac{3\%}{6} = 0.5\%$ per H

two secondary hydrogens $\frac{97\%}{2} = 48.5\%$ per H

The 2° hydrogens are $\frac{48.5}{0.5} = 97$ times as reactive as the 1° hydrogens.

FIGURE 4-9
The free-radical reaction of propane with bromine. This 97:3 ratio of products shows that bromine abstracts a secondary hydrogen 97 times as rapidly as a primary hydrogen. Bromination (reactivity ratio 97:1) is much more selective than chlorination (reactivity ratio 4.5:1).

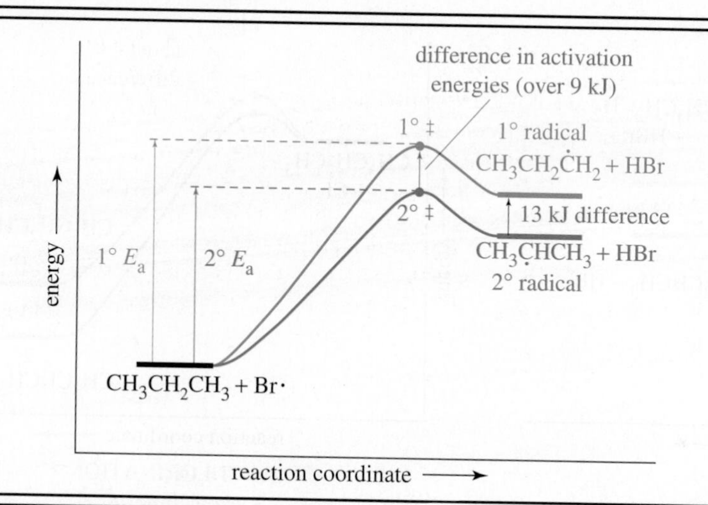

■ FIGURE 4-10
Reaction-energy diagram for the first propagation step in the bromination of propane. The energy difference in the transition states is nearly as large as the energy difference in the products.

$$\text{2° H:}\quad CH_3-\underset{}{\overset{CH_3}{|}}{CH_2} + Br\cdot \longrightarrow CH_3-\overset{CH_3}{|}{CH}\cdot + H-Br$$

Energy required to break the $CH_3-CH(CH_3)\!-\!\!\!\!\!\!\;\;H$ bond	+397 kJ/mol (+95 kcal/mol)
Energy released in forming the H—Br bond	−368 kJ/mol (−88 kcal/mol)
Total energy for reaction at the secondary position:	+29 kJ/mol (+7 kcal/mol)

The energy differences between chlorination and bromination result from the difference in the bond-dissociation enthalpies of H—Cl (431 kJ) and H—Br (368 kJ). The HBr bond is weaker, and abstraction of a hydrogen atom by Br· is endothermic. This endothermic step explains why bromination is much slower than chlorination, but it still does not explain the enhanced selectivity observed with bromination.

Consider the reaction-energy diagram for the first propagation step in the bromination of propane (Figure 4-10). Although the difference in values of $\Delta H°$ between abstraction of a primary hydrogen and a secondary hydrogen is still 13 kJ/mol (3 kcal/mol), the energy diagram for bromination shows a much larger difference in activation energies for abstraction of the primary and secondary hydrogens than we saw for chlorination (Figure 4-8).

In bromination, the rate-limiting first propagation step is endothermic, and the energy maxima (corresponding to the activation energies) are closer to the products than to the reactants. A smooth graph (Figure 4-10) shows the activation energies nearly as far apart as the product energies. In chlorination, on the other hand, this first step is exothermic, and the energy maxima are closer to the reactants, which are the same and have the same energy for either route. The graph for chlorination (Figure 4-8) shows the activation energies separated by only a small fraction of the difference in product energies. This intuitive, graphic principle is formalized in the **Hammond postulate**.

4-14 The Hammond Postulate

Figure 4-11 summarizes the energy diagrams for the first propagation steps in the bromination and chlorination of propane. Together, these energy diagrams explain the enhanced selectivity observed in bromination.

Two important differences are apparent in the reaction-energy diagrams for the first propagation steps of chlorination and bromination:

1. The first propagation step is endothermic for bromination but exothermic for chlorination.

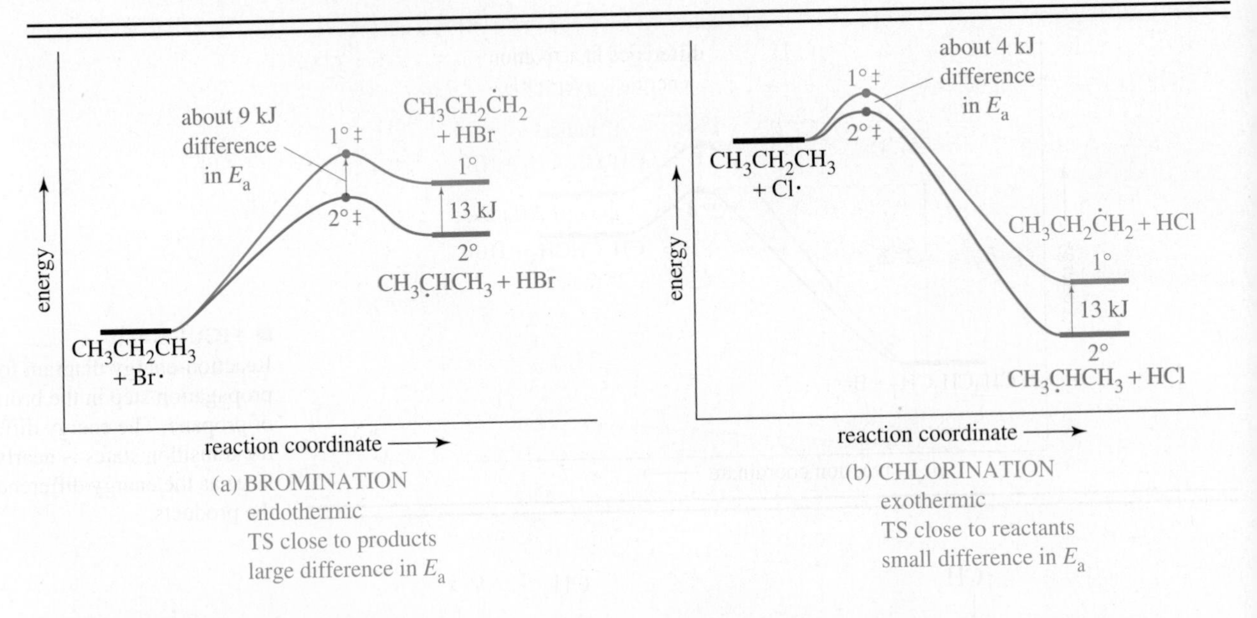

FIGURE 4-11
The energy diagrams for bromination and chlorination of propane. (**a**) In the endothermic bromination, the transition states are closer to the products (the radicals) in energy and in structure. The difference in the 1° and 2° activation energies is about 9 kJ (2.2 kcal), nearly the entire energy difference of the radicals. (**b**) In the exothermic chlorination, the transition states are closer to the reactants in energy and in structure. The difference in activation energies for chlorination is about 4 kJ (1 kcal), only a third of the energy difference of the radicals.

2. The transition states forming the 1° and 2° radicals for the endothermic bromination have a larger energy difference than those for the exothermic chlorination, even though the energy difference of the products is the same (13 kJ, or 3 kcal) in both reactions.

In general, we will find that these differences are related:

> In an endothermic reaction, the transition state is closer to the products in energy and in structure. In an exothermic reaction, the transition state is closer to the reactants in energy and in structure.

Figure 4-12 compares the transition states for bromination and chlorination. In the product-like transition state for bromination, the C—H bond is nearly broken and the carbon atom has a great deal of radical character. The energy of this transition state

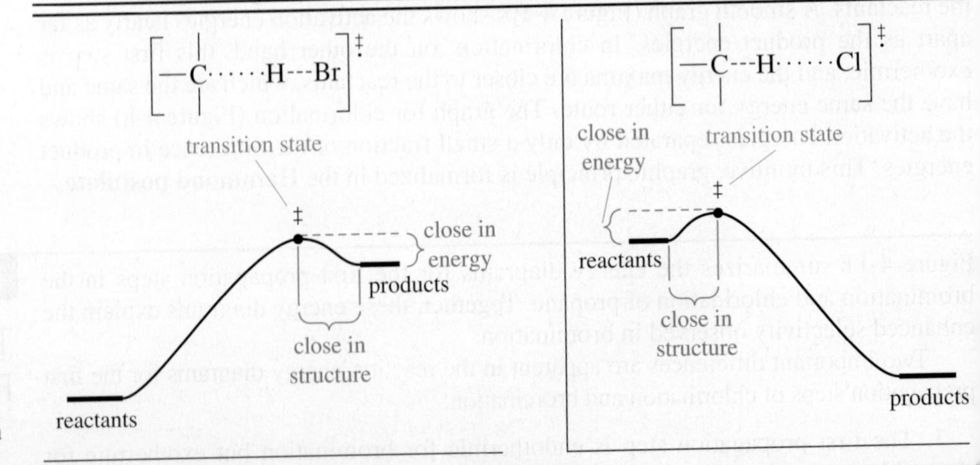

FIGURE 4-12
Comparison of transition states for bromination and chlorination. In the endothermic bromination, the transition state resembles the products (the free radical and HBr). In the exothermic chlorination, the free radical has just begun to form in the transition state, so the transition state resembles the reactants.

reflects most of the energy difference of the radical products. In the reactant-like transition state for chlorination, the C—H bond is just beginning to break, and the carbon atom has little radical character. This transition state reflects only a small part (about a third) of the energy difference of the radical products. Therefore, chlorination is less selective.

These reactions are examples of a more general principle called the **Hammond postulate**.

> HAMMOND POSTULATE: Related species that are closer in energy are also closer in structure. The structure of a transition state resembles the structure of the closest stable species.

This general rule tells us something about the transition states in endothermic and exothermic reactions. The transition state is always the point of highest energy on the energy diagram. Its structure resembles either the reactants or the products, whichever ones are higher in energy. In an endothermic reaction, the products are higher in energy, and the transition state is product-like. In an exothermic reaction, the reactants are higher in energy, and the transition state is reactant-like. Thus, the Hammond postulate helps us understand why exothermic processes tend to be less selective than similar endothermic processes.

PROBLEM 4-23

(a) Compute the heats of reaction for abstraction of a primary hydrogen and a secondary hydrogen from propane by a fluorine radical.

$$CH_3-CH_2-CH_3 + F\cdot \longrightarrow CH_3-CH_2-\dot{C}H_2 + HF$$

$$CH_3-CH_2-CH_3 + F\cdot \longrightarrow CH_3-\dot{C}H-CH_3 + HF$$

(b) How selective do you expect free-radical fluorination to be?

(c) What product distribution would you expect to obtain from the free-radical fluorination of propane?

PROBLEM-SOLVING STRATEGY

PROPOSING REACTION MECHANISMS

Throughout this course, we will propose mechanisms to explain reactions. We will discuss methods for dealing with different types of mechanisms as we encounter them. These techniques for dealing with a variety of mechanisms are collected in Appendix 4. At this point, however, we focus on free-radical mechanisms like those in this chapter.

Free-Radical Reactions

General principles: Free-radical reactions generally proceed by chain-reaction mechanisms, using an initiator with an easily broken bond (such as chlorine, bromine, or a peroxide) to start the chain reaction. In drawing the mechanism, expect free-radical intermediates (especially highly substituted or resonance-stabilized intermediates). Watch for the most stable free radicals, and avoid any high-energy radicals such as hydrogen atoms.

1. **Draw a step that breaks the weak bond in the initiator.**
   A free-radical reaction usually begins with an initiation step in which the initiator undergoes homolytic (free-radical) cleavage to give two radicals.
2. **Draw a reaction of the initiator with one of the starting materials.**
   One of the initiator radicals reacts with one of the starting materials to give a free-radical version of the starting material. The initiator might abstract a hydrogen atom or add to a double bond, depending on what reaction leads to formation of the observed product. You might want to consider bond-dissociation enthalpies to see which reaction is energetically favored.
3. **Draw a reaction of the free-radical version of the starting material with another starting-material molecule to form a bond needed in the product and generate a new radical intermediate.**
   Check your intermediates to be sure that you have used the most stable radical intermediates. For a realistic chain reaction, no new initiation steps should be required; a radical should be regenerated in each propagation step.
4. **Draw termination step(s).**
   The reaction ends with termination steps, which are side reactions rather than part of the product-forming mechanism. The reaction of any two free radicals to give a stable molecule is a termination step, as is a collision of a free radical with the container.

Before we illustrate this procedure, let's consider a few common mistakes. Avoiding these mistakes will help you to draw correct mechanisms throughout this course.

(Continued)

Common Mistakes to Avoid

1. Do not use condensed or line–angle formulas for reaction sites. Draw all the bonds and all the substituents of each carbon atom affected throughout the mechanism. Three-bonded carbon atoms in intermediates are most likely to be radicals in the free-radical reactions we have studied. If you draw condensed formulas or line–angle formulas, you will likely misplace a hydrogen atom and show a reactive species on the wrong carbon.
2. Do not show more than one step occurring at once, unless they really do occur at once.

Sample Problem

Draw a mechanism for the reaction of methylcyclopentane with bromine under irradiation with light. Predict the major product.

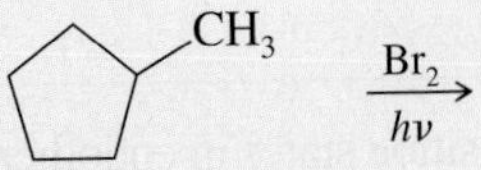

CH_3 $\xrightarrow[h\nu]{Br_2}$

In every mechanism problem, we first draw what we know, showing all the bonds and all the substituents of each carbon atom that may be affected throughout the mechanism.

$\xrightarrow[h\nu]{Br_2}$

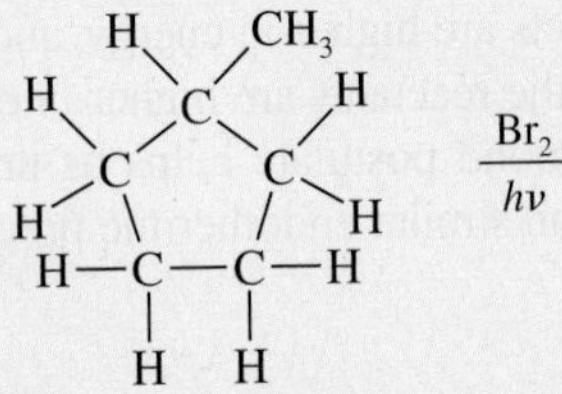

1. Draw a step involving cleavage of the weak bond in the initiator.
The use of light with bromine suggests a free-radical reaction, with light providing the energy for dissociation of Br_2. This homolytic cleavage initiates the chain reaction by generating two Br· radicals.

Initiation step

$$Br{-}Br \xrightarrow{h\nu} Br\cdot + \cdot Br$$

2. Draw a reaction of the initiator with one of the starting materials.
One of these initiator radicals should react with methylcyclopentane to give a free-radical version of methylcyclopentane. As we have seen, a bromine or chlorine radical can abstract a hydrogen atom from an alkane to generate an alkyl radical. The bromine radical is highly selective, and the most stable alkyl radical should result. Abstraction of the tertiary hydrogen atom gives a tertiary radical.

First propagation step

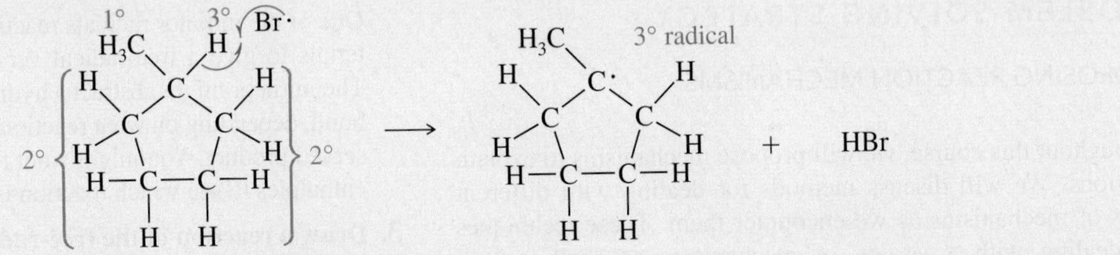

1° 3° Br· 2° 2° → 3° radical + HBr

3. Draw a reaction of the free-radical version of the starting material with another starting-material molecule to form a bond needed in the product and to generate a new radical intermediate.
The alkyl radical should react with another starting-material molecule, in another propagation step, to generate a product and another radical. Reaction of the alkyl radical with Br_2 gives 1-bromo-1-methylcyclopentane (the major product) and another bromine radical to continue the chain.

Second propagation step

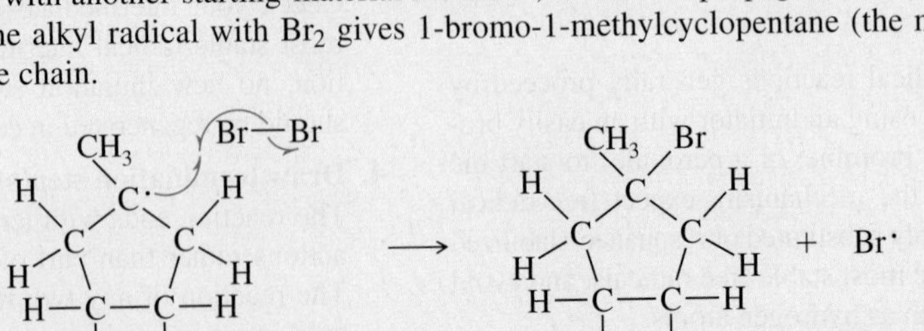

Br—Br → + Br·

major product

4. Draw termination step(s).
It is left to you to add some possible termination steps and summarize the mechanism developed here.

As practice in using a systematic approach to proposing mechanisms for free-radical reactions, work Problem 4-24 by going through the four steps just outlined.

PROBLEM 4-24

2,3-Dimethylbutane reacts with bromine in the presence of light to give a good yield of a monobrominated product. Further reaction gives a dibrominated product. Predict the structures of these products, and propose a mechanism for the formation of the monobrominated product.

problem-solving Hint

Free-radical bromination is highly selective, chlorination is moderately selective, and fluorination is nearly nonselective.

PROBLEM 4-25

In the presence of a small amount of bromine, cyclohexene undergoes the following light-promoted reaction:

cyclohexene + trace Br_2 $\xrightarrow{h\nu}$ 3-bromocyclohexene + HBr

(a) Propose a mechanism for this reaction.
(b) Draw the structure of the rate-limiting transition state.
(c) Use the Hammond postulate to predict which intermediate most closely resembles this transition state.
(d) Explain why cyclohexene reacts with bromine much faster than cyclohexane, which must be heated to react.

4-15 Radical Inhibitors

We often want to prevent or retard free-radical reactions. For example, oxygen in the air oxidizes and spoils foods, solvents, and other compounds mostly by free-radical chain reactions. Chemical intermediates may decompose or polymerize by free-radical chain reactions. Even the cells in living systems are damaged by radical reactions, which can lead to aging, cancerous mutations, or cell death.

Radical inhibitors are often added to foods and chemicals to retard spoilage by radical chain reactions. Chain reactions depend on the individual steps being fast, so that each initiation step results in many molecules reacting, as in the reaction-energy diagram at the left of the following figure. (Only the radicals are shown.)

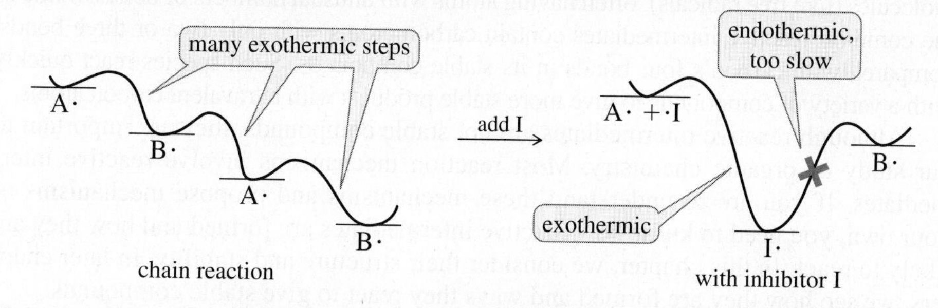

The diagram at right in the figure shows how an inhibitor (I) can stop the chain by reacting with a radical intermediate in a fast, highly exothermic step to form an intermediate that is relatively stable. The next step in the chain becomes endothermic and very slow.

"Butylated hydroxyanisole" (BHA) is often added to foods as an antioxidant. It stops oxidation by reacting with radical intermediates to form a relatively stable free-radical intermediate (BHA radical). The BHA radical can react with a second free radical to form an even more stable quinone with all its electrons paired.

RO· or R· + BHA ⟶ ROH or RH + BHA radical $\xrightarrow{\text{RO· or R·}}$ $ROCH_3$ or RCH_3 + a quinone

BHA (OH, OCH_3) — BHA radical (O·, OCH_3) — a quinone (O, O)

Radical inhibitors also help to protect the cells of living systems. Like BHA, vitamin E is a *phenol* (an aromatic ring with an —OH group), and it is thought to react with radicals by losing the OH hydrogen atom as just shown for BHA. Ascorbic acid (vitamin C) is also thought to protect cells from free radicals, possibly by the following mechanism:

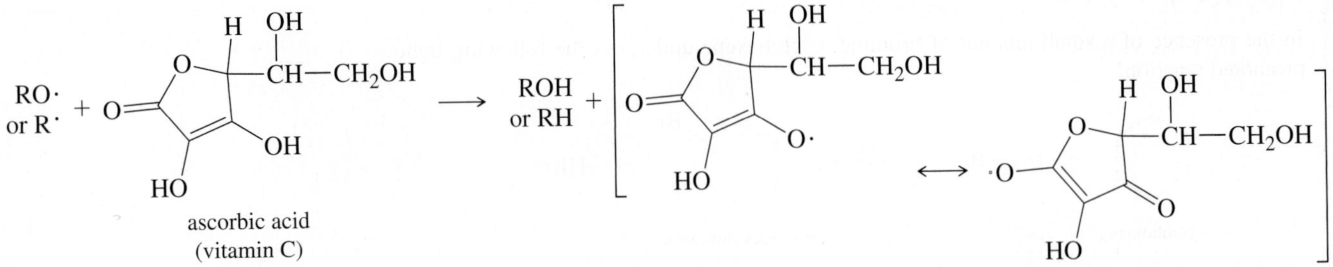

RO· or R· + ascorbic acid (vitamin C) ⟶ ROH or RH + [stabilized free radical]

ascorbic acid
(vitamin C)

stabilized free radical

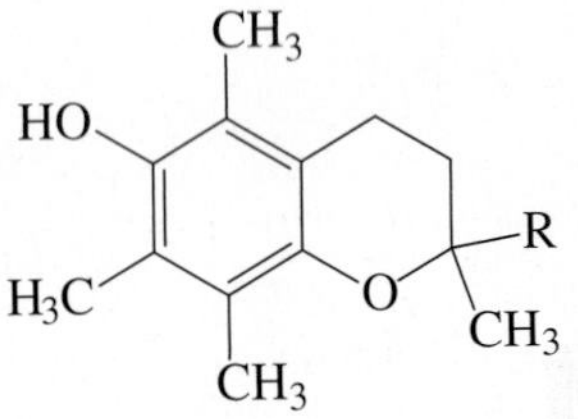

vitamin E
(R = alkyl chain)

PROBLEM 4-26

Draw resonance forms to show how the BHA radical is stabilized by delocalization of the radical electron over other atoms in the molecule.

PROBLEM 4-27

Write an equation for the reaction of vitamin E with an oxidizing radical (RO·) to give ROH and a less reactive free radical.

4-16 Reactive Intermediates

The free radicals we have studied are one class of reactive intermediates. **Reactive intermediates** are short-lived species that are never present in high concentrations because they react as quickly as they are formed. In most cases, reactive intermediates are fragments of molecules (like free radicals), often having atoms with unusual numbers of bonds. Some of the common reactive intermediates contain carbon atoms with only two or three bonds, compared with carbon's four bonds in its stable compounds. Such species react quickly with a variety of compounds to give more stable products with tetravalent carbon atoms.

Although reactive intermediates are not stable compounds, they are important to our study of organic chemistry. Most reaction mechanisms involve reactive intermediates. If you are to understand these mechanisms and propose mechanisms of your own, you need to know how reactive intermediates are formed and how they are likely to react. In this chapter, we consider their structure and stability. In later chapters, we see how they are formed and ways they react to give stable compounds.

Species with trivalent (three-bonded) carbon are classified according to their charge, which depends on the number of nonbonding electrons. The *carbocations* have no nonbonding electrons and are positively charged. The *radicals* have one nonbonding electron and are neutral. The *carbanions* have a pair of nonbonding electrons and are negatively charged.

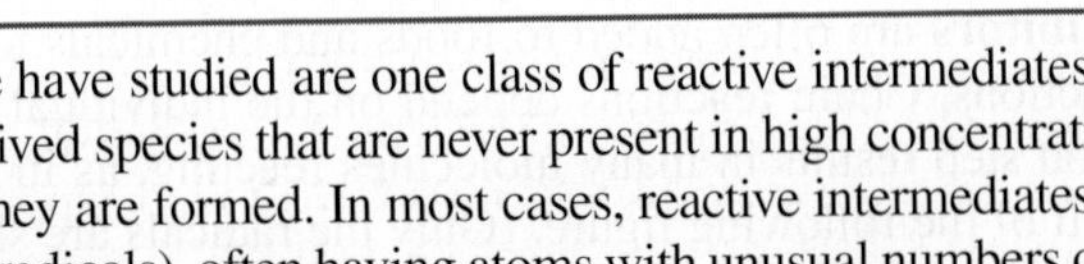

carbocation CH_3^+ — radical $CH_3\cdot$ — carbanion $CH_3:^-$ — carbene $H_2C:$

The most common intermediates with a divalent (two-bonded) carbon atom are the *carbenes*. A carbene has two nonbonding electrons on the divalent carbon atom, making it uncharged.

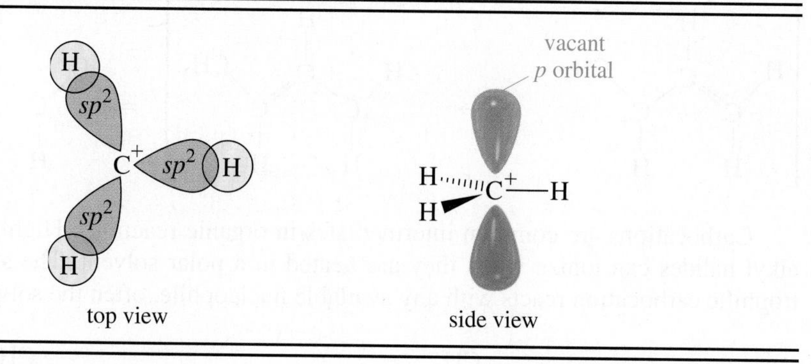

■ **FIGURE 4-13**
Orbital diagram of the methyl cation. The methyl cation is similar to BH_3. The carbon atom is σ bonded to three hydrogen atoms by overlap of its sp^2 hybrid orbitals with the s orbitals of hydrogen. A vacant p orbital lies perpendicular to the plane of the three C—H bonds.

4-16A Carbocations

A **carbocation** (also called a **carbonium ion** or a **carbenium ion**) is a species that contains a carbon atom bearing a positive charge. The positively charged carbon atom is bonded to three other atoms, and it has no nonbonding electrons, so it has only six electrons in its valence shell. It is sp^2 hybridized, with a planar structure and bond angles of about 120°. For example, the methyl cation (CH_3^+) is planar, with bond angles of exactly 120°. The unhybridized p orbital is vacant and lies perpendicular to the plane of the C—H bonds (Figure 4-13). The structure of CH_3^+ is similar to the structure of BH_3, discussed in Chapter 2.

With only six electrons in the positive carbon's valence shell, a carbocation is a powerful electrophile (Lewis acid), and it may react with any nucleophile it encounters. Like other strong acids, carbocations are unlikely to be found in basic solutions. Carbocations are proposed as intermediates in many types of organic reactions, some of which we will encounter in Chapter 6.

Like free radicals, carbocations are *electron-deficient* species: They have fewer than eight electrons in the valence shell. Also like free radicals, carbocations are stabilized by alkyl substituents. An alkyl group stabilizes an electron-deficient carbocation in two ways: (1) through an inductive effect, and (2) through the partial overlap of filled orbitals with empty ones. The **inductive effect** is a donation of electron density through the sigma (σ) bonds of the molecule. The positively charged carbon atom withdraws some electron density from the polarizable alkyl groups bonded to it.

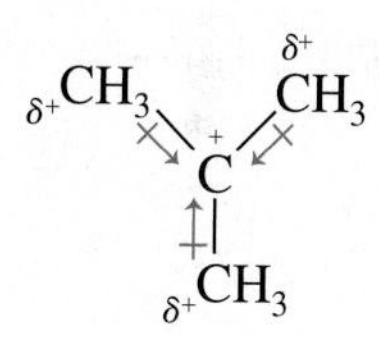

Alkyl substituents also have filled sp^3 orbitals that can overlap with the empty p orbital on the positively charged carbon atom, further stabilizing the carbocation (Figure 4-14). Even though the attached alkyl group rotates, one of its sigma bonds is always aligned with the empty p orbital on the carbocation. The pair of electrons in this σ bond spreads out into the empty p orbital, stabilizing the electron-deficient carbon atom. This type of overlap between a p orbital and a sigma bond is called *hyperconjugation*.

In general, more highly substituted carbocations are more stable.

Stability of carbocations

$$R_3C^+ > R_2CH^+ > RCH_2^+ > H_3C^+$$

most stable ... least stable

3° > 2° > 1° > methyl

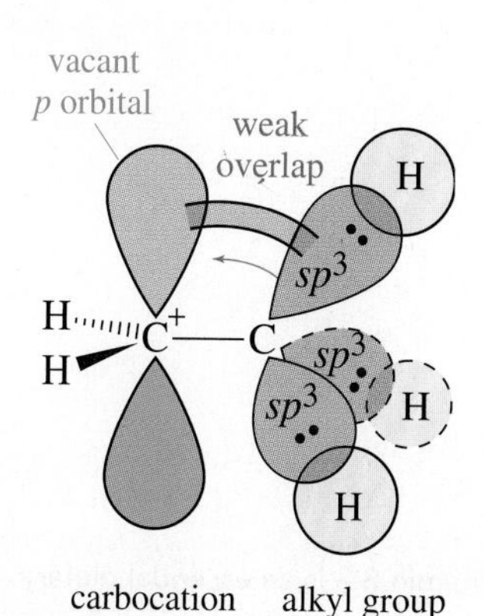

■ **FIGURE 4-14**
Effect of alkyl substituent on carbocation stability. A carbocation is stabilized by overlap of filled orbitals on an adjacent alkyl group with the vacant p orbital of the carbocation. Overlap between a σ bond and a p orbital is called *hyperconjugation*.

Unsaturated carbocations are also stabilized by **resonance stabilization**. If a pi (π) bond is adjacent to a carbocation, the filled p orbitals of the π bond will overlap with the empty p orbital of the carbocation. The result is a delocalized ion, with the positive charge shared by two atoms. Resonance delocalization is particularly effective in stabilizing carbocations.

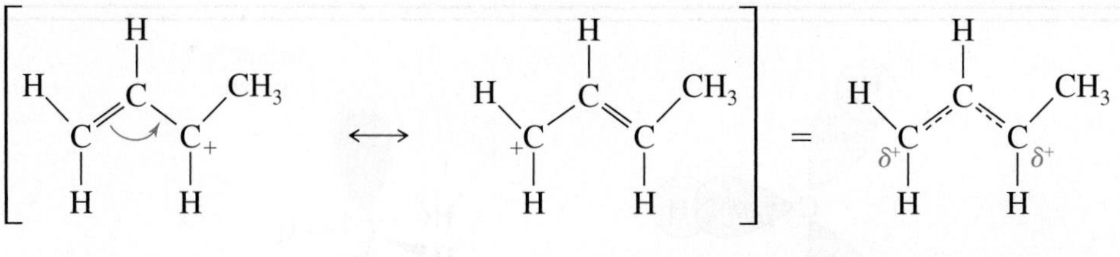

Carbocations are common intermediates in organic reactions. Highly substituted alkyl halides can ionize when they are heated in a polar solvent. The strongly electrophilic carbocation reacts with any available nucleophile, often the solvent.

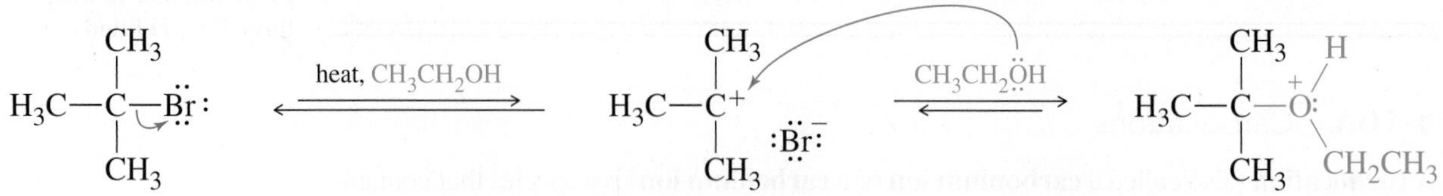

tert-butyl bromide

heat, CH_3CH_2OH

tert-butyl cation

$CH_3CH_2\ddot{O}H$

Carbocations are also strong proton acids. The *tert*-butyl cation shown above can also lose a proton to a weak base, often the solvent.

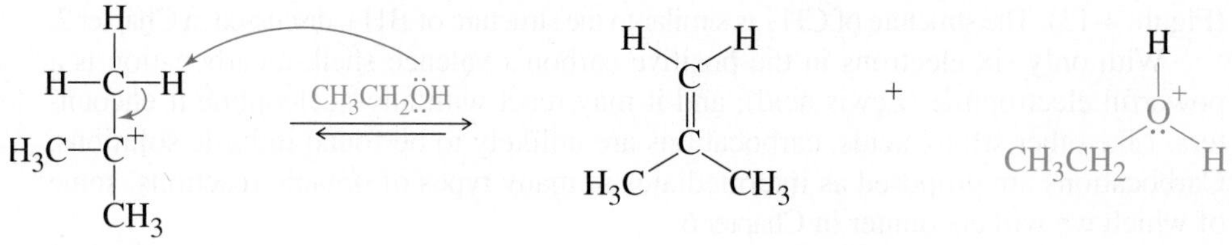

$CH_3CH_2\ddot{O}H$

tert-butyl cation

PROBLEM 4-28

The triphenylmethyl cation is so stable that some of its salts can be stored for months. Explain why this cation is so stable.

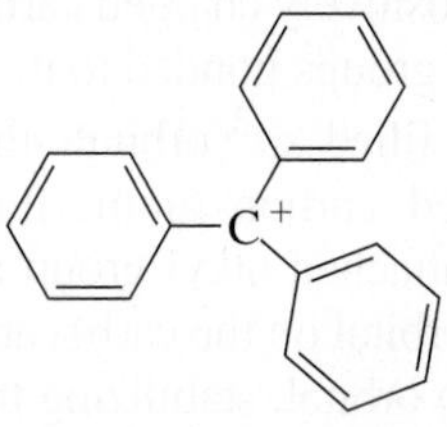

triphenylmethyl cation

PROBLEM 4-29

Rank the following carbocations in decreasing order of stability. Classify each as primary, secondary, or tertiary.

(a) The isopentyl cation, $(CH_3)_2CHCH_2—\overset{+}{C}H_2$

(b) The 3-methyl-2-butyl cation, $CH_3—\overset{+}{C}H—CH(CH_3)_2$

(c) The 2-methyl-2-butyl cation, $CH_3—\overset{+}{C}(CH_3)CH_2CH_3$

(d)

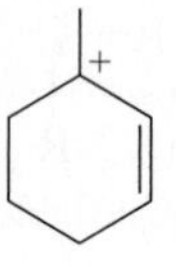

Vitamin B_{12} is an essential dietary factor, and a deficiency results in anemia and neurological damage. The vitamin assists two different enzymes in the production and the stabilization of methyl radicals. These methyl radicals are then used for the synthesis of important cellular components.

4-16B Free Radicals

Like carbocations, **free radicals** are sp^2 hybridized and planar (or nearly planar). Unlike carbocations, however, the *p* orbital perpendicular to the plane of the C—H bonds of the radical is not empty; it contains the odd electron. Figure 4-15 shows the structure of the methyl radical.

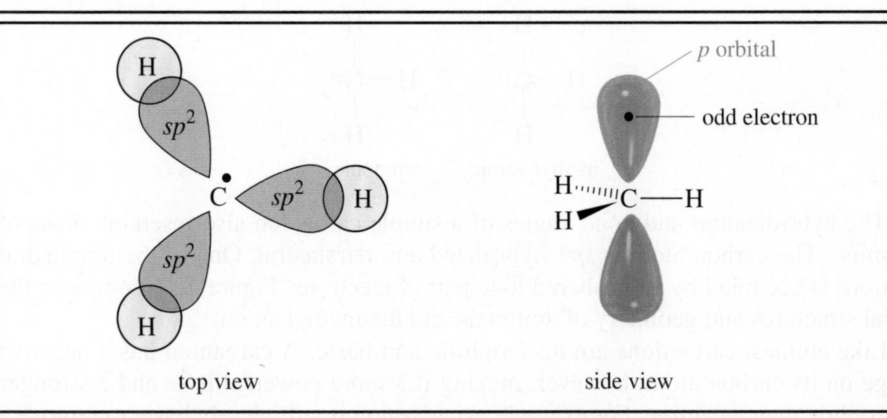

■ FIGURE 4-15
Orbital diagram of the methyl radical. The structure of the methyl radical is like that of the methyl cation (Figure 4-13), except there is an additional electron. The odd electron is in the p orbital perpendicular to the plane of the three C—H bonds.

Both radicals and carbocations are electron deficient because they lack an octet around the carbon atom. Like carbocations, radicals are stabilized by the electron-donating effect of alkyl groups, making more highly substituted radicals more stable. This effect is confirmed by the bond-dissociation enthalpies shown in Figure 4-7: Less energy is required to break a C—H bond to form a more highly substituted radical.

Stability of radicals

$$R_3C\cdot \;>\; R_2CH\cdot \;>\; RCH_2\cdot \;>\; H_3C\cdot$$

most stable ... least stable

3° > 2° > 1° > methyl

Like carbocations, radicals can be stabilized by resonance. Overlap with the p orbitals of a π bond allows the odd electron to be delocalized over two carbon atoms. Resonance delocalization is particularly effective in stabilizing a radical.

$$\left[\; H_2C{=}CH{-}\dot{C}H{-}CH_3 \;\longleftrightarrow\; H_2\dot{C}{-}CH{=}CH{-}CH_3 \;\right] \quad \text{or} \quad H_2\overset{\delta\cdot}{C}{\cdots}CH{\cdots}\overset{\delta\cdot}{C}H{-}CH_3$$

PROBLEM 4-30

Rank the following radicals in decreasing order of stability. Classify each as primary, secondary, or tertiary.

(a) The isopentyl radical, $(CH_3)_2CHCH_2{-}\dot{C}H_2$

(b) The 3-methyl-2-butyl radical, $CH_3{-}\dot{C}H{-}CH(CH_3)_2$

(c) The 2-methyl-2-butyl radical, $CH_3{-}\dot{C}(CH_3)CH_2CH_3$

(d)

4-16C Carbanions

A **carbanion** has a trivalent carbon atom that bears a negative charge. There are eight electrons around the carbon atom (three bonds and one lone pair), so it is not electron deficient; rather, it is electron rich and a strong nucleophile (Lewis base). A carbanion has the same electronic structure as an amine. Compare the structures of a methyl carbanion and ammonia:

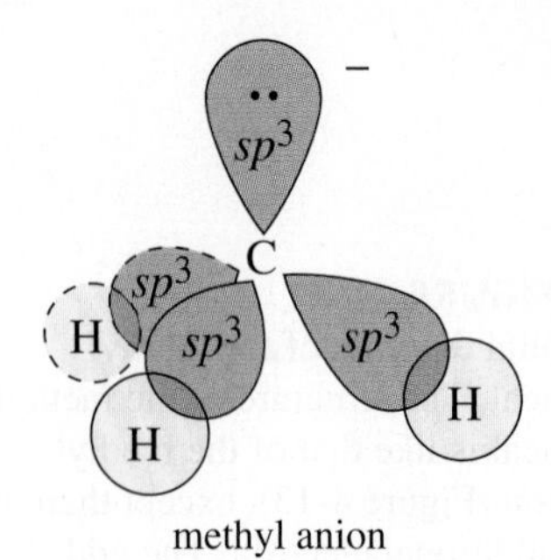

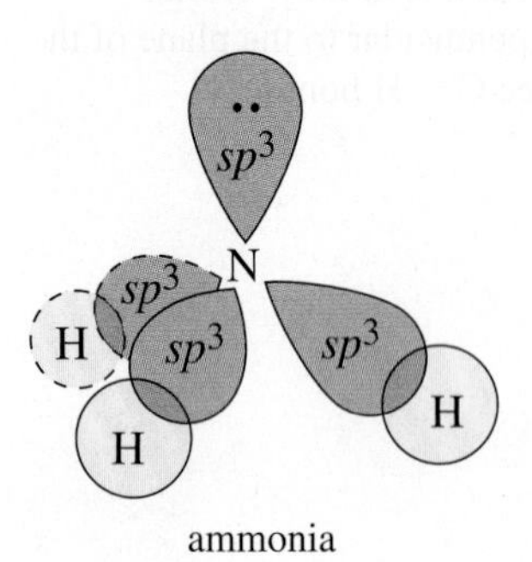

■ **FIGURE 4-16**
Comparison of orbital structures of methyl anion and ammonia. Both the methyl anion and ammonia have an sp^3 hybridized central atom, with a nonbonding pair of electrons occupying one of the tetrahedral positions.

methyl anion ($H_3C:^-$) ammonia ($H_3N:$)

The hybridization and bond angles of a simple carbanion also resemble those of an amine. The carbon atom is sp^3 hybridized and tetrahedral. One of the tetrahedral positions is occupied by an unshared lone pair of electrons. Figure 4-16 compares the orbital structures and geometry of ammonia and the methyl anion.

Like amines, carbanions are nucleophilic and basic. A carbanion has a negative charge on its carbon atom, however, making it a more powerful base and a stronger nucleophile than an amine. For example, a carbanion is sufficiently basic to remove a proton from ammonia.

$$R_3C:^- + :NH_3 \longrightarrow R_3CH + {}^-:\ddot{N}H_2$$

Like other strong bases, carbanions are unlikely to be found in acidic solutions. The stability order of carbanions reflects their high electron density. Alkyl groups and other electron-donating groups slightly destabilize a carbanion. The order of stability is usually the opposite of that for carbocations and free radicals.

Stability of carbanions

$$R_3C:^- < R_2HC:^- < RH_2C:^- < H_3C:^-$$

least stable — most stable

3° < 2° < 1° < methyl

Carbanions that occur as intermediates in organic reactions are almost always stabilized by neighboring groups. They can be stabilized either by inductive effects or by resonance. For example, halogen atoms are electron withdrawing, so they stabilize carbanions through the inductive withdrawal of electron density. Resonance also plays an important role in stabilizing carbanions. A carbonyl group (C=O) stabilizes an adjacent carbanion by overlap of its π bond with the nonbonding electrons of the carbanion. The negative charge is delocalized onto the electronegative oxygen atom of the carbonyl group.

$$HC(=O)-CH_3 + {}^-:\ddot{O}H \rightleftharpoons \left[HC(=O)-CH_2:^- \longleftrightarrow HC(-O:^-)=CH_2 \right] + H_2O$$

resonance-stabilized carbanion

This resonance-stabilized carbanion must be sp^2 hybridized and planar for effective delocalization of the negative charge onto oxygen (Section 2-6). Resonance-stabilized carbanions are the most common type of carbanions we will encounter in organic reactions.

PROBLEM 4-31

Acetylacetone (2,4-pentanedione) reacts with sodium hydroxide to give water and the sodium salt of a carbanion. Write a complete structural formula for the carbanion, and use resonance forms to show the stabilization of the carbanion.

$$H_3C-\overset{\overset{\displaystyle O}{\|}}{C}-CH_2-\overset{\overset{\displaystyle O}{\|}}{C}-CH_3$$

acetylacetone (2,4-pentanedione)

PROBLEM 4-32

Acetonitrile ($CH_3C{\equiv}N$) is deprotonated by very strong bases. Write resonance forms to show the stabilization of the carbanion that results.

4-16D Carbenes

Carbenes are uncharged reactive intermediates containing a divalent carbon atom. The simplest carbene has the formula $:CH_2$ and is called *methylene*, just as a $-CH_2-$ group in a molecule is called a *methylene group*. One way of generating carbenes is to form a carbanion that can expel a halide ion. For example, a strong base can abstract a proton from tribromomethane ($CHBr_3$) to give an inductively stabilized carbanion. This carbanion expels bromide ion to give dibromocarbene.

$$CHBr_3 + {}^-OH \rightleftarrows H_2O + Br_3C:^- \longrightarrow Br_2C: + Br^-$$

tribromomethane — a carbanion — dibromocarbene

The electronic structure of dibromocarbene is shown next. The carbon atom has only six electrons in its valence shell. It is sp^2 hybridized, with trigonal geometry. An unshared pair of electrons occupies one of the sp^2 hybrid orbitals, and there is an empty p orbital extending above and below the plane of the atoms. A carbene has both a lone pair of electrons and an empty p orbital, so it can react as a nucleophile or as an electrophile.

empty p orbital

nonbonding electrons paired in this sp^2 orbital

sp^2 hybridized

Methylene itself is formed when diazomethane (CH_2N_2) is heated or irradiated with light. The diazomethane molecule splits to form a stable nitrogen molecule and the very reactive carbene.

$$H_2\overset{-}{C}-\overset{+}{N}{\equiv}N: \xrightarrow{\text{heat or light}} H_2C: + :N{\equiv}N:$$

diazomethane — methylene — nitrogen

The most common synthetic reaction of carbenes is their addition to double bonds to form cyclopropane rings. For example, dibromocarbene adds to cyclohexene to give an interesting bicyclic compound.

$$\text{cyclohexene} + :CBr_2 \text{ (dibromocarbene)} \longrightarrow \text{(7,7-dibromobicyclo[4.1.0]heptane)}$$

cyclohexene dibromocarbene

No simple carbenes have ever been purified or even made in a high concentration, because when two carbenes collide, they immediately dimerize (two of them bond together) to give an alkene.

$$R_2C: + :CR_2 \xrightarrow{\text{very fast}} R_2C{=}CR_2$$

Carbenes and carbenoids (carbene-like reagents) are useful both for the synthesis of other compounds and for the investigation of reaction mechanisms. The carbene intermediate is generated in the presence of its target compound, so that it can react immediately, and the concentration of the carbene is always low. Reactions using carbenes are discussed in Chapter 8.

PROBLEM 4-33

When it is strongly heated, ethyl diazoacetate decomposes to give nitrogen gas and a carbene. Draw a Lewis structure of the carbene.

$$:\overset{+}{N}{\equiv}N{-}\overset{-}{C}H{-}\overset{O}{\overset{\|}{C}}{-}O{-}CH_2CH_3$$

ethyl diazoacetate

SUMMARY Reactive Intermediates

	Structure	*Stability*	*Properties*
carbocations	$-\overset{\mid}{\underset{\mid}{C}}{}^{+}$	3° > 2° > 1° > $^{+}CH_3$	electrophilic strong acids
radicals	$-\overset{\mid}{\underset{\mid}{C}}\cdot$	3° > 2° > 1° > $\cdot CH_3$	electron deficient
carbanions	$-\overset{\mid}{\underset{\mid}{C}}:^{-}$	$^{-}:CH_3$ > 1° > 2° > 3°	nucleophilic strong bases
carbenes	$>C:$		both nucleophilic and electrophilic

4 Glossary

activation energy (E_a) The energy difference between the reactants and the transition state; the minimum energy the reactants must have for the reaction to occur. (p. 141)

bond-dissociation enthalpy (BDE) The amount of enthalpy required to break a particular bond homolytically, to give radicals. (p. 136)

$$A{:}B \longrightarrow A\cdot + B\cdot \qquad \Delta H° = \text{BDE}$$

carbanion A strongly nucleophilic species with a negatively charged carbon atom having only three bonds. The carbon atom has a nonbonding pair of electrons. (p. 159)
carbene A highly reactive species with only two bonds to an uncharged carbon atom with a nonbonding pair of electrons. The simplest carbene is methylene, $:CH_2$. (p. 161)
carbocation (carbonium ion, carbenium ion) A strongly electrophilic species with a positively charged carbon atom having only three bonds. (p. 157)
catalyst A substance that increases the rate of a reaction (by lowering E_a) without being consumed in the reaction. (p. 143)
chain reaction A multistep reaction where a reactive intermediate formed in one step brings about a second step that generates the intermediate needed for the following step. (p. 128)

initiation step: The preliminary step in a chain reaction, where the reactive intermediate is first formed.

propagation steps: The steps in a chain reaction that are repeated over and over to form the product. The sum of the propagation steps should give the net reaction.
termination steps: Any steps where a reactive intermediate is consumed without another one being generated.

enthalpy (heat content; *H*) A measure of the heat energy in a system. In a reaction, the heat absorbed or evolved is called the *heat of reaction*, $\Delta H°$. A decrease in enthalpy (negative $\Delta H°$) is favorable for a reaction. (p. 135)

endothermic: Consuming heat (having a positive $\Delta H°$).
exothermic: Giving off heat (having a negative $\Delta H°$).

entropy (*S*) A measure of disorder or freedom of motion. An increase in entropy (positive $\Delta S°$) is favorable for a reaction. (p. 135)
equilibrium A state of a system such that no more net change is taking place; the rate of the forward reaction equals the rate of the reverse reaction. (p. 132)
equilibrium constant A quantity calculated from the relative amounts of the products and reactants present at equilibrium. (p. 133) For the reaction

$$aA + bB \longleftrightarrow cC + dD$$

the equilibrium constant is

$$K_{eq} = \frac{[C]^c[D]^d}{[A]^a[B]^b}$$

free energy (Gibbs free energy; *G*) A measure of a reaction's tendency to go in the direction written. A decrease in free energy (negative ΔG) is favorable for reaction. (p. 133)

$$\text{Free-energy change is defined:} \quad \Delta G = \Delta H - T\Delta S$$

standard Gibbs free energy change: ($\Delta G°$) The free-energy change corresponding to reactants and products in their standard states (pure substances in their most stable states) at 25 °C and 1 atm pressure. $\Delta G°$ is related to K_{eq} by

$$K_{eq} = e^{-\Delta G°/RT} \quad \text{(p. 133)}$$

endergonic: Having a positive $\Delta G°$ (unfavorable).
exergonic: Having a negative $\Delta G°$ (favorable).

Hammond postulate Related species (on a reaction-energy diagram) that are closer in energy are also closer in structure. In an exothermic reaction, the transition state is closer to the reactants in energy and in structure. In an endothermic reaction, the transition state is closer to the products in energy and in structure. (p. 151)
heterolytic cleavage (ionic cleavage) The breaking of a bond in such a way that one of the atoms retains both of the bond's electrons. A heterolytic cleavage forms two ions. (p. 136)

$$A{:}B \longrightarrow A{:}^- + B^+$$

homolytic cleavage (radical cleavage) The breaking of a bond in such a way that each atom retains one of the bond's two electrons. A homolytic cleavage produces two radicals. (p. 136)

$$A{:}B \longrightarrow A\cdot + \cdot B$$

inductive effect A donation (or withdrawal) of electron density through sigma bonds. (p. 157)

intermediate A molecule or a fragment of a molecule that is formed in a reaction and exists for a finite length of time before it reacts in the next step. An intermediate corresponds to a relative minimum (a low point) in the reaction-energy diagram. (p. 142)

reactive intermediate: A short-lived species that is never present in high concentration because it reacts as quickly as it is formed. (pp. 129, 156)

kinetics The study of reaction rates. (p. 139)

mechanism The step-by-step pathway from reactants to products, showing which bonds break and which bonds form in what order. The mechanism should include the structures of all intermediates and curved arrows to show the movement of electrons. (p. 127)

potential-energy diagram See **reaction-energy diagram.** (p. 143)

radical (free radical) A highly reactive species in which one of the atoms has an odd number of electrons. Most commonly, a radical contains a carbon atom with three bonds and an "odd" (unpaired) electron. (p. 129)

radical inhibitor A compound added to prevent the propagation of free-radical chain reactions. In most cases, the inhibitor reacts to form a radical that is too stable to propagate the chain. (p. 155)

rate equation (rate law) The relationship between the concentrations of the reagents and the observed reaction rate. (p. 139)

A general rate law for the reaction $A + B \longrightarrow C + D$ is

$$\text{rate} = k_r[A]^a[B]^b$$

kinetic order: The power of a concentration term in the rate equation. The preceding rate equation is ath order in [A], bth order in [B], and $(a + b)$th order overall.

rate constant: The proportionality constant k_r in the rate equation.

rate-limiting step (rate-determining step) The slowest step in a multistep sequence of reactions. In general, the rate-limiting step is the step with the highest-energy transition state. (p. 144)

rate of a reaction The amount of product formed or reactant consumed per unit of time. (p. 139)

reaction-energy diagram (potential-energy diagram) A plot of potential-energy changes as the reactants are converted to products. The vertical axis is potential energy (usually free energy, but occasionally enthalpy). The horizontal axis is the **reaction coordinate**, a measure of the progress of the reaction. (p. 143)

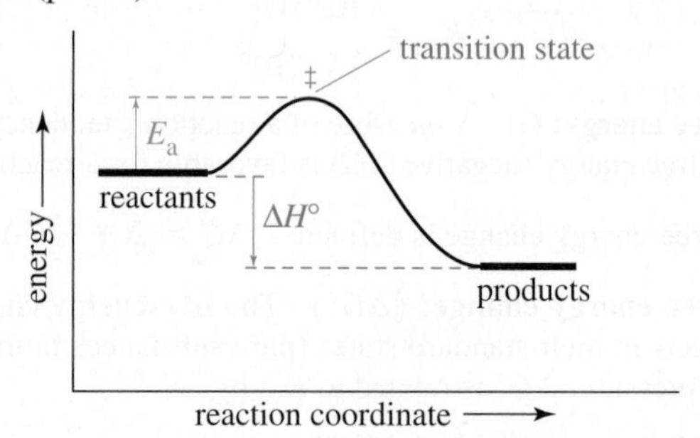

resonance stabilization Stabilization that takes place by delocalization of electrons in a π bonded system. Cations, radicals, and anions are often stabilized by resonance delocalization. (p. 157)

resonance-stabilized carbanion

substitution A reaction in which one atom replaces another, usually as a substituent on a carbon atom. (p. 129)

thermodynamics The study of the energy changes accompanying chemical transformations. Thermodynamics is generally concerned with systems at equilibrium. (p. 132)

transition state **(activated complex)** The state of highest energy between reactants and products. A relative maximum (high point) on the reaction-energy diagram. (p. 142)

Essential Problem-Solving Skills in Chapter 4

1. Explain the mechanism and energetics of free-radical halogenations of alkanes.
2. Based on the selectivity of halogenation, predict the products of halogenation of an alkane.
3. Calculate free-energy changes from equilibrium constants.
4. Calculate enthalpy changes from bond-dissociation enthalpies.
5. Determine the order of a reaction, and suggest a possible mechanism based on its rate equation.
6. Use energy diagrams to discuss transition states, activation energies, intermediates, and the rate-limiting step of a multistep reaction.
7. Use the Hammond postulate to predict whether a transition state will be reactant-like or product-like.
8. Describe the structures of carbocations, carbanions, free radicals, and carbenes and the structural features that stabilize them. Explain which are electrophilic and which are nucleophilic.

Study Problems

4-34 Define and give an example for each term.

(a) homolytic cleavage **(b)** heterolytic cleavage **(c)** free radical
(d) carbocation **(e)** carbanion **(f)** carbene
(g) reaction-energy diagram **(h)** intermediate **(i)** catalyst
(j) transition state **(k)** rate equation **(l)** equilibrium constant
(m) rate constant **(n)** reaction mechanism **(o)** chain reaction
(p) substitution reaction **(q)** activation energy **(r)** bond-dissociation enthalpy
(s) rate-limiting step **(t)** Hammond postulate **(u)** resonance stabilization
(v) exothermic reaction **(w)** endothermic reaction **(x)** free energy
(y) enthalpy **(z)** entropy

4-35 Consider the following reaction-energy diagram.

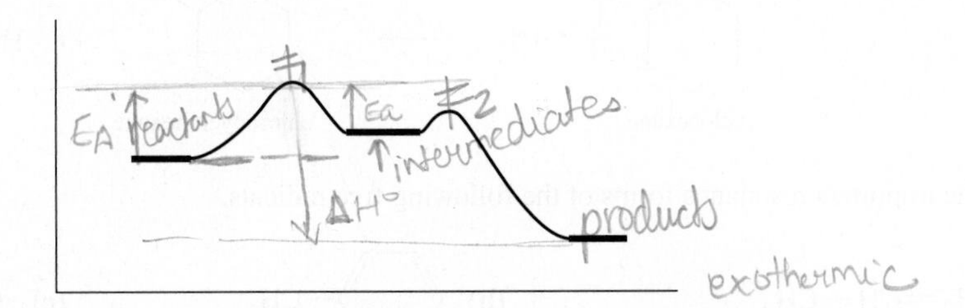

(a) Label the reactants and the products. Label the activation energy for the first step and the second step.
(b) Is the overall reaction endothermic or exothermic? What is the sign of $\Delta H°$? negative
(c) Which points in the curve correspond to intermediates? Which correspond to transition states?
(d) Label the transition state of the rate-limiting step. Does its structure resemble the reactants, the products, or an intermediate? ‡1 Reactants

4-36 Draw a reaction-energy diagram for a one-step exothermic reaction. Label the parts that represent the reactants, products, transition state, activation energy, and heat of reaction.

4-37 Draw a reaction-energy diagram for a two-step endothermic reaction with a rate-limiting second step.

4-38 Treatment of *tert*-butyl alcohol with concentrated HCl gives *tert*-butyl chloride.

$$(CH_3)_3C{-}OH + H^+ + Cl^- \longrightarrow (CH_3)_3C{-}Cl + H_2O$$

tert-butyl alcohol → *tert*-butyl chloride

When the concentration of H^+ is doubled, the reaction rate doubles. When the concentration of *tert*-butyl alcohol is tripled, the reaction rate triples. When the chloride ion concentration is quadrupled, however, the reaction rate is unchanged. Write the rate equation for this reaction.

4-39 Label each hydrogen atom in the following compounds as primary (1°), secondary (2°), or tertiary (3°).

(a) $CH_3CH_2CH(CH_3)_2$ (b) $(CH_3)_3CCH_2CH_3$ (c) $(CH_3)_2CHCH(CH_3)CH_2CH_3$

(d) methylcyclopentane (CH_3 on cyclopentane) (e) (f) H, CH_3

4-40 Use bond-dissociation enthalpies (Table 4-2, p. 138) to calculate values of $\Delta H°$ for the following reactions.

(a) $CH_3{-}CH_3 + I_2 \longrightarrow CH_3CH_2I + HI$
(b) $CH_3CH_2Cl + HI \longrightarrow CH_3CH_2I + HCl$
(c) $(CH_3)_3C{-}OH + HCl \longrightarrow (CH_3)_3C{-}Cl + H_2O$
(d) $CH_3CH_2CH_3 + H_2 \longrightarrow CH_3CH_3 + CH_4$
(e) $CH_3CH_2OH + HBr \longrightarrow CH_3CH_2{-}Br + H_2O$

4-41 Use the information in Table 4-2 (p. 138) to rank the following radicals in decreasing order of stability.

$\cdot CH_3$ $CH_3\dot{C}H_2$ $C_6H_5\dot{C}H_2$ $(CH_3)_3C\cdot$ $(CH_3)_2\dot{C}H$ $CH_2{=}CH{-}\dot{C}H_2$

4-42 For each alkane,

1. Draw all the possible monochlorinated derivatives.
2. Determine whether free-radical chlorination would be a good way to make any of these monochlorinated derivatives. (Will the reaction give mostly one major product?)
3. Which monobrominated derivatives could you form in good yield by free-radical bromination?

(a) cyclopentane (b) methylcyclopentane
(c) 2,3-dimethylbutane (d) 2,2,3,3-tetramethylbutane

4-43 Write a mechanism for the light-initiated reaction of cyclohexane with chlorine to give chlorocyclohexane. Label the initiation and propagation steps.

$$\text{cyclohexane} + Cl_2 \xrightarrow{h\nu} \text{chlorocyclohexane} + HCl$$

4-44 Draw the important resonance forms of the following free radicals.

(a) $CH_2{=}CH{-}\dot{C}H_2$ (b) $C_6H_5{-}\dot{C}H_2$ (c) $CH_3{-}\overset{O}{\overset{\|}{C}}{-}O\cdot$

(d) (e) (f) O·

***4-45** In the presence of a small amount of bromine, the following light-promoted reaction has been observed.

$$\text{H}_3\text{C}, \text{CH}_3\text{-cyclopentene} + Br_2 \xrightarrow{h\nu} \text{H}_3\text{C}, \text{CH}_3, \text{Br product} + \text{H}_3\text{C}, \text{CH}_3, \text{H}, \text{Br product}$$

(a) Write a mechanism for this reaction. Your mechanism should explain how both products are formed. (*Hint*: Notice which H atom has been lost in both products.)
(b) Explain why only this one type of hydrogen atom has been replaced, in preference to any of the other hydrogen atoms in the starting material.

4-46 For each compound, predict the major product of free-radical bromination. Remember that bromination is highly selective, and only the most stable radical will be formed.
(a) cyclohexane **(b)** methylcyclopentane **(c)** decalin **(d)** hexane
(e) 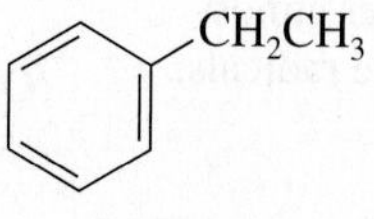 ethylbenzene (CH_2CH_3) **(f)** 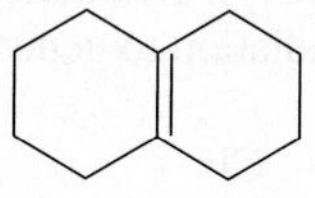 (2 products)

4-47 When exactly 1 mole of methane is mixed with exactly 1 mole of chlorine and light is shone on the mixture, a chlorination reaction occurs. The products are found to contain substantial amounts of di-, tri-, and tetrachloromethane, as well as unreacted methane.
(a) Explain how a mixture is formed from this stoichiometric mixture of reactants, and propose mechanisms for the formation of these compounds from chloromethane.
(b) How would you run this reaction to get a good conversion of methane to CH_3Cl? Of methane to CCl_4?

4-48 The chlorination of pentane gives a mixture of three monochlorinated products.
(a) Draw their structures.
(b) Predict the ratios in which these monochlorination products will be formed, remembering that a chlorine atom abstracts a secondary hydrogen about 4.5 times as fast as it abstracts a primary hydrogen.

4-49 **(a)** Draw the structure of the transition state for the second propagation step in the chlorination of methane.

$$\cdot CH_3 + Cl_2 \longrightarrow CH_3Cl + Cl\cdot$$

Show whether the transition state is product-like or reactant-like, and which of the two partial bonds is stronger.
(b) Repeat for the second propagation step in the bromination of methane.

4-50 Peroxides are often added to free-radical reactions as initiators because the oxygen–oxygen bond cleaves homolytically rather easily. For example, the bond-dissociation enthalpy of the O—O bond in hydrogen peroxide (H—O—O—H) is only 212 kJ/mol (51 kcal/mol). Give a mechanism for the hydrogen peroxide–initiated reaction of cyclopentane with chlorine. The BDE for HO—Cl is 210 kJ/mol (50 kcal/mol).

***4-51** When dichloromethane is treated with strong NaOH, an intermediate is generated that reacts like a carbene. Draw the structure of this reactive intermediate, and propose a mechanism for its formation.

***4-52** When ethene is treated in a calorimeter with H_2 and a Pt catalyst, the heat of reaction is found to be -137 kJ/mol (-32.7 kcal/mol), and the reaction goes to completion. When the reaction takes place at 1400 °K, the equilibrium is found to be evenly balanced, with $K_{eq} = 1$. Compute the value of ΔS for this reaction.

$$CH_2{=}CH_2 + H_2 \xrightleftharpoons{\text{Pt catalyst}} CH_3{-}CH_3 \qquad \Delta H = -137 \text{ kJ/mol } (-32.7 \text{ kcal/mol})$$

***4-53** When a small amount of iodine is added to a mixture of chlorine and methane, it prevents chlorination from occurring. Therefore, iodine is a *free-radical inhibitor* for this reaction. Calculate $\Delta H°$ values for the possible reactions of iodine with species present in the chlorination of methane, and use these values to explain why iodine inhibits the reaction. (The I—Cl bond-dissociation enthalpy is 211 kJ/mol or 50 kcal/mol.)

***4-54** Tributyltin hydride (Bu_3SnH) is used synthetically to reduce alkyl halides, replacing a halogen atom with hydrogen. Free-radical initiators promote this reaction, and free-radical inhibitors are known to slow it or stop it. Your job is to develop a mechanism, using the following reaction as the example.

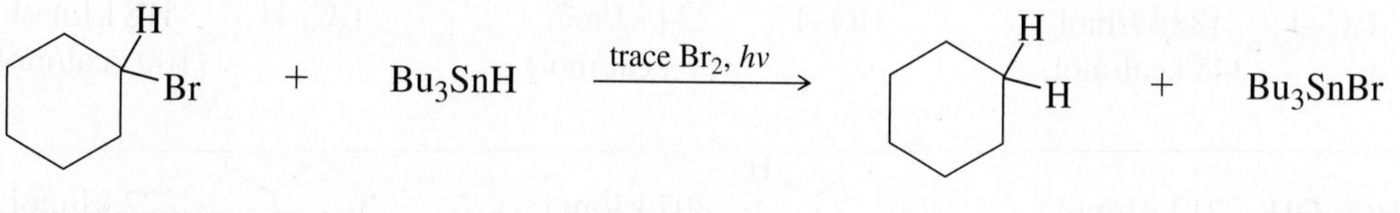

$$\text{C}_6\text{H}_{11}\text{Br} + Bu_3SnH \xrightarrow{\text{trace } Br_2,\ h\nu} \text{C}_6\text{H}_{11}\text{H} + Bu_3SnBr$$

The following bond-dissociation enthalpies may be helpful:

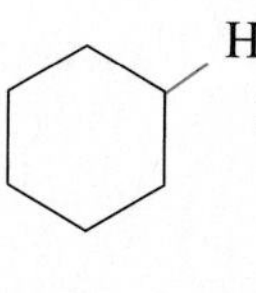

Bond	BDE
cyclohexyl—H	397 kJ/mol
cyclohexyl—Br	285 kJ/mol
Br—Br	192 kJ/mol
H—Br	368 kJ/mol
Bu_3Sn—H	310 kJ/mol
Bu_3Sn—Br	552 kJ/mol

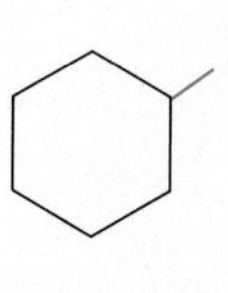

(a) Propose initiation and propagation steps to account for this reaction.
(b) Calculate values of ΔH for your proposed steps to show that they are energetically feasible. (*Hint*: A trace of Br_2 and light suggests it's there only as an initiator, to create Br· radicals. Then decide which atom can be abstracted most favorably from the starting materials by the Br· radical. That should complete the initiation. Now decide what energetically favored propagation steps will accomplish the reaction.)

*4-55 When healthy, Earth's stratosphere contains a low concentration of ozone (O_3) that absorbs potentially harmful ultraviolet (UV) radiation by the cycle shown at right.

Chlorofluorocarbon refrigerants, such as Freon 12 (CF_2Cl_2), are stable in the lower atmosphere, but in the stratosphere they absorb high-energy UV radiation to generate chlorine radicals.

$O_3 \xrightarrow{h\nu} O_2 + O$; $O_2 + O \xrightarrow{\text{heat}} O_3$

$$CF_2Cl_2 \xrightarrow{h\nu} \cdot CF_2Cl + Cl\cdot$$

The presence of a small number of chlorine radicals appears to lower ozone concentrations dramatically. The following reactions are all known to be exothermic (except the one requiring light) and to have high rate constants. Propose two mechanisms to explain how a small number of chlorine radicals can destroy large numbers of ozone molecules. Which of the two mechanisms is more likely when the concentration of chlorine atoms is very small?

$$Cl{-}O{-}O{-}Cl \xrightarrow{h\nu} O_2 + 2\,Cl\cdot \qquad Cl{-}O\cdot + O \longrightarrow O_2 + Cl\cdot$$

$$Cl\cdot + O_3 \longrightarrow Cl{-}O\cdot + O_2 \qquad 2\,Cl{-}O\cdot \longrightarrow Cl{-}O{-}O{-}Cl$$

*4-56 Deuterium (D) is the hydrogen isotope of mass number 2, with a proton and a neutron in its nucleus. The chemistry of deuterium is nearly identical to the chemistry of hydrogen, except that the C—D bond is slightly stronger than the C—H bond by 5.0 kJ/mol (1.2 kcal/mol). Reaction rates tend to be slower if a C—D bond (as opposed to a C—H bond) is broken in a rate-limiting step.

This effect, called a *kinetic isotope effect*, is clearly seen in the chlorination of methane. Methane undergoes free-radical chlorination 12 times as fast as tetradeuteriomethane (CD_4).

Faster: $CH_4 + Cl\cdot \longrightarrow CH_3Cl + HCl$ relative rate = 12

Slower: $CD_4 + Cl\cdot \longrightarrow CD_3Cl + DCl$ relative rate = 1

(a) Draw the transition state for the rate-limiting step of each of these reactions, showing how a bond to hydrogen or deuterium is being broken in this step.
(b) Monochlorination of deuterioethane (C_2H_5D) leads to a mixture containing 93% C_2H_4DCl and 7% C_2H_5Cl. Calculate the relative rates of abstraction per hydrogen and deuterium in the chlorination of deuterioethane.
(c) Consider the thermodynamics of the chlorination of methane and the chlorination of ethane, and use the Hammond postulate to explain why one of these reactions has a much larger isotope effect than the other.

*4-57 Iodination of alkanes using iodine (I_2) is usually an unfavorable reaction. (See Prob. 4-17, for example.) Tetraiodomethane (CI_4) can be used as the iodine source for iodination, in the presence of a free-radical initiator. Propose a mechanism (involving mildly exothermic propagation steps) for the following proposed reaction. Calculate the value of ΔH for each of the steps in your proposed mechanism.

$$\text{cyclopentane} + CI_4 \xrightarrow[\text{heat}]{H_2O_2} \text{iodocyclopentane} + HCI_3$$

The following bond-dissociation energies may be helpful:

Bond	Energy	Bond	Energy	Bond	Energy
I_3C--I	188 kJ/mol (45 kcal/mol)	HO--I	234 kJ/mol (56 kcal/mol)	I_3C--H	418 kJ/mol (100 kcal/mol)
HO--OH	213 kJ/mol (51 kcal/mol)	cyclopentyl--H	397 kJ/mol (95 kcal/mol)	cyclopentyl--I	222 kJ/mol (53 kcal/mol)

CHAPTER

5 STEREOCHEMISTRY

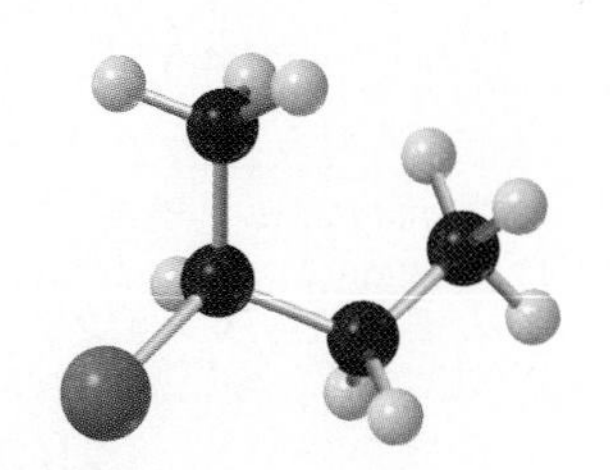

5-1 Introduction

Stereochemistry is the study of the three-dimensional structure of molecules. No one can understand organic chemistry, biochemistry, or biology without using stereochemistry. Biological systems are exquisitely selective, and they often discriminate between molecules with subtle stereochemical differences. We have seen (Section 2-8) that isomers are grouped into two broad classes: constitutional isomers and stereoisomers. **Constitutional isomers (structural isomers)** differ in their bonding sequence; their atoms are connected differently. **Stereoisomers** have the same bonding sequence, but they differ in the orientation of their atoms in space.

Differences in spatial orientation might seem unimportant, but stereoisomers often have remarkably different physical, chemical, and biological properties. For example, the cis and trans isomers of butenedioic acid are a special type of stereoisomers called *cis-trans isomers* (or *geometric isomers*). Both compounds have the formula HOOC—CH=CH—COOH, but they differ in how these atoms are arranged in space. The cis isomer is called *maleic acid*, and the trans isomer is called *fumaric acid.* Fumaric acid is an essential metabolic intermediate in both plants and animals, but maleic acid is toxic and irritating to tissues.

fumaric acid, mp 287 °C
essential metabolite

maleic acid, mp 138 °C
toxic irritant

A double bond in rhodopsin, a visual pigment found in your eyes that enables you to see at night, is converted from the cis isomer to the trans isomer when light strikes the eye. As a result, a nerve impulse travels to the brain and you see the source of the light.

N—opsin

rhodopsin

The discovery of stereochemistry was one of the most important breakthroughs in the structural theory of organic chemistry. Stereochemistry explained why several types of isomers exist, and it forced scientists to propose the tetrahedral carbon atom. In this chapter, we study the three-dimensional structures of molecules to understand their stereochemical relationships. We compare the various types of stereoisomers and study ways to differentiate among stereoisomers. In future chapters, we will see how stereochemistry plays a major role in the properties and reactions of organic compounds.

5-2 Chirality

What is the difference between your left hand and your right hand? They look similar, yet a left-handed glove does not fit the right hand. The same principle applies to your feet. They look almost identical, yet the left shoe fits painfully on the right foot. The relationship between your two hands or your two feet is that they are nonsuperimposable (nonidentical) mirror images of each other. Objects that have left-handed and right-handed forms are called **chiral** (*kī′rel*, rhymes with "spiral"), the Greek word for "handed."

We can tell whether an object is chiral by looking at its mirror image (Figure 5-1). Every physical object (with the possible exception of a vampire) has a mirror image, but *a chiral object has a mirror image that is different from the original object*. For example, a chair and a spoon and a glass of water all look the same in a mirror. Such objects are called **achiral**, meaning "not chiral." A hand looks different in the mirror. If the original hand were the right hand, it would look like a left hand in the mirror.

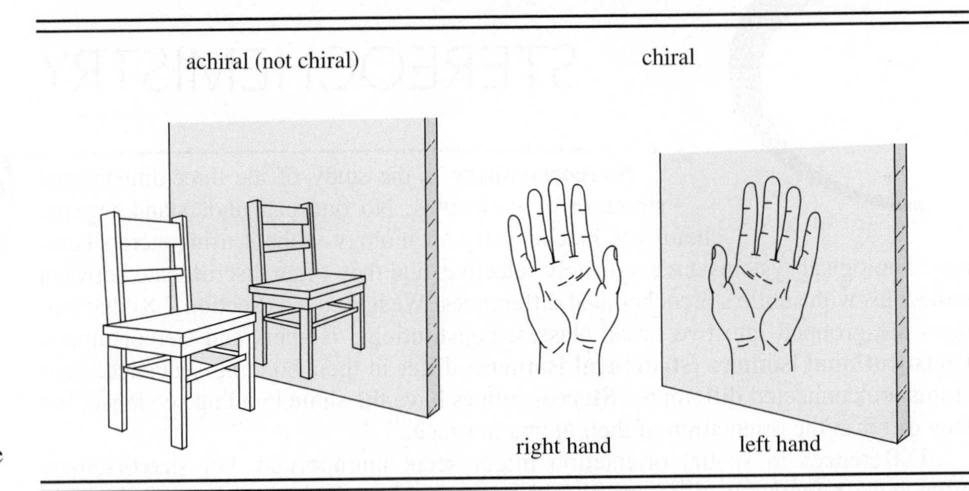

■ **FIGURE 5-1**
Use of a mirror to test for chirality. An object is chiral if its mirror image is different from the original object.

Besides shoes and gloves, we encounter many other chiral objects every day (Figure 5-2). What is the difference between an English car and an American car? The English car has the steering wheel on the right-hand side, while the American car has it on the left. To a first approximation, the English and American cars are nonsuperimposable mirror images. Most screws have right-hand threads and are turned clockwise to tighten. The mirror image of a right-handed screw is a left-handed screw, turned counterclockwise to tighten. Those of us who are left-handed realize that scissors are chiral. Most scissors are right-handed. If you use them in your left hand, they cut poorly, if at all. A left-handed person must go to a well-stocked store to find a pair of left-handed scissors, the mirror image of the "standard" right-handed scissors.

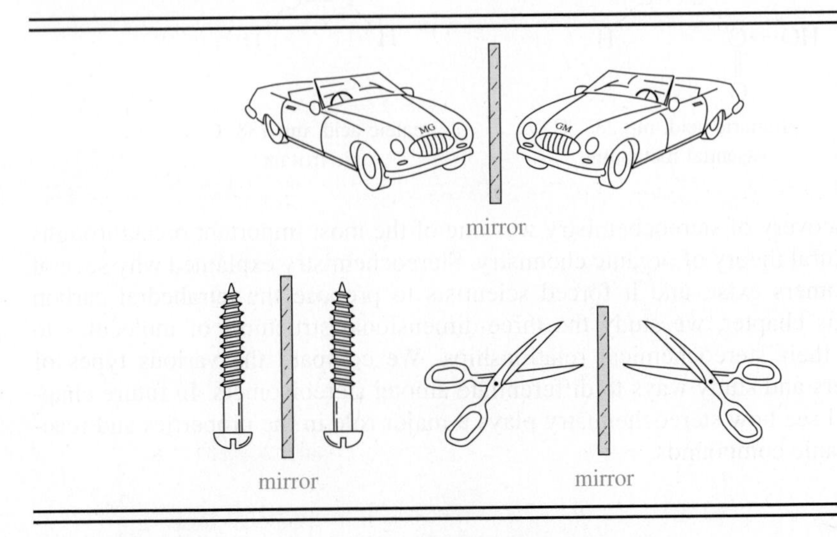

■ **FIGURE 5-2**
Common chiral objects. Many objects come in "left-handed" and "right-handed" versions.

PROBLEM 5-1

Determine whether the following objects are chiral or achiral.

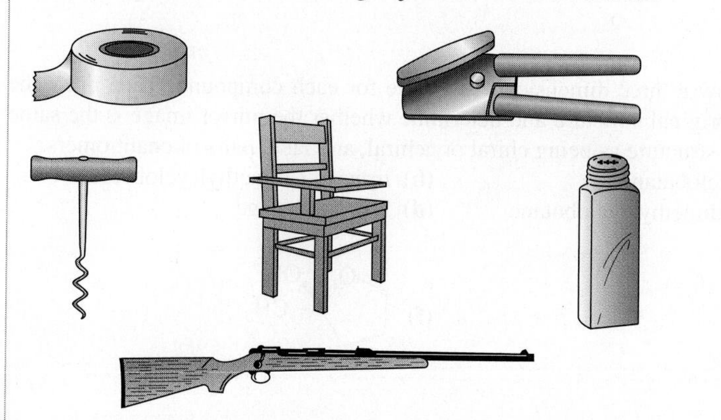

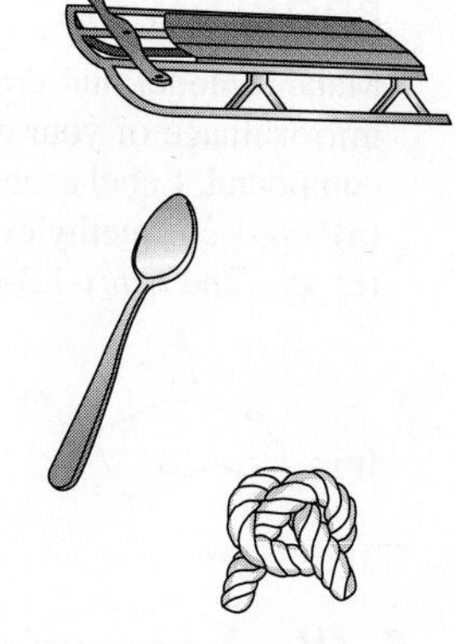

5-2A Chirality and Enantiomerism in Organic Molecules

Like other objects, molecules are either chiral or achiral. For example, consider the two geometric isomers of 1,2-dichlorocyclopentane (Figure 5-3). The cis isomer is achiral because its mirror image is superimposable on the original molecule. Two molecules are said to be **superimposable** if they can be placed on top of each other and the three-dimensional position of each atom of one molecule coincides with the equivalent atom of the other molecule. To draw the mirror image of a molecule, simply draw the same structure with left and right reversed. The up-and-down and front-and-back directions are unchanged. These two mirror-image structures are identical (superimposable), and *cis*-1,2-dichlorocyclopentane is achiral.

The mirror image of *trans*-1,2-dichlorocyclopentane is different from (nonsuperimposable with) the original molecule. These are two different compounds, and we should expect to discover two mirror-image isomers of *trans*-1,2-dichlorocyclopentane. Make models of these isomers to convince yourself that they are different no matter how you twist and turn them. Nonsuperimposable mirror-image molecules are called **enantiomers**. A chiral compound always has an enantiomer (a nonsuperimposable mirror image). An achiral compound always has a mirror image that is the same as the original molecule. Let's review the definitions of these words.

***problem-solving* Hint**

Every object has a mirror image. Is its mirror image the same or different? Different: The object is chiral. Same: The object is achiral.

enantiomers:	mirror-image isomers; pairs of compounds that are nonsuperimposable mirror images
chiral:	("handed") different from its mirror image; having an enantiomer
achiral:	("not handed") identical with its mirror image; not chiral

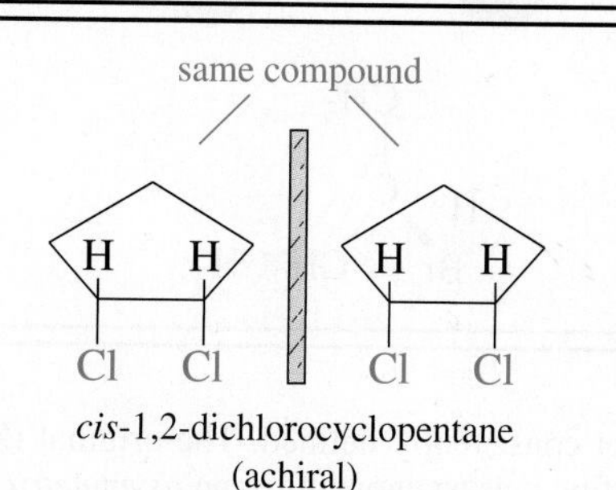

cis-1,2-dichlorocyclopentane (achiral)

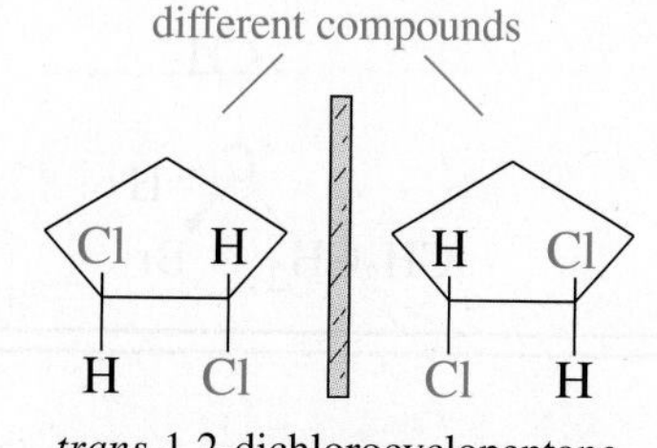

trans-1,2-dichlorocyclopentane (chiral)

■ **FIGURE 5-3** Stereoisomers of 1,2-dichlorocyclopentane. The cis isomer has no enantiomers; it is achiral. The trans isomer is chiral; it can exist in either of two nonsuperimposable enantiomeric forms.

Any compound that is chiral must have an enantiomer. Any compound that is achiral cannot have an enantiomer.

problem-solving Hint

Stereochemistry is a difficult topic for many students. Use your models to help you see the relationships between structures. Once you have experience working with these three-dimensional relationships, you may (or may not) be able to visualize them without constructing models.

PROBLEM 5-2

Make a model and draw a three-dimensional structure for each compound. Then draw the mirror image of your original structure and determine whether the mirror image is the same compound. Label each structure as being chiral or achiral, and label pairs of enantiomers.

(a) *cis*-1,2-dimethylcyclobutane
(b) *trans*-1,2-dimethylcyclobutane
(c) *cis*- and *trans*-1,3-dimethylcyclobutane
(d) 2-bromobutane
(e) O
(f) O OH CH_3

5-2B Asymmetric Carbon Atoms, Chirality Centers, and Stereocenters

The three-dimensional drawing of 2-bromobutane in Figure 5-4 shows that 2-bromobutane cannot be superimposed on its mirror image. This simple molecule is chiral, with two distinct enantiomers. What is it about a molecule that makes it chiral? The most common feature (but not the only one) that lends chirality is a carbon atom that is bonded to four different groups. Such a carbon atom is called an **asymmetric carbon atom** or a **chiral carbon atom**, and is often designated by an asterisk (*). Carbon atom 2 of 2-bromobutane is bonded to a hydrogen atom, a bromine atom, a methyl group, and an ethyl group. It is an asymmetric carbon atom, and it is responsible for the chirality of 2-bromobutane.

An asymmetric carbon atom is the most common example of a **chirality center**, the IUPAC term for any atom holding a set of ligands in a spatial arrangement that is not superimposable on its mirror image. Chirality centers belong to an even broader group called *stereocenters*. A **stereocenter** (or **stereogenic atom**) is any atom at which the interchange of two groups gives a stereoisomer.[1] Asymmetric carbons and the double-bonded carbon atoms in cis-trans isomers are the most common types of stereocenters. Figure 5-5 compares these successively broader definitions.

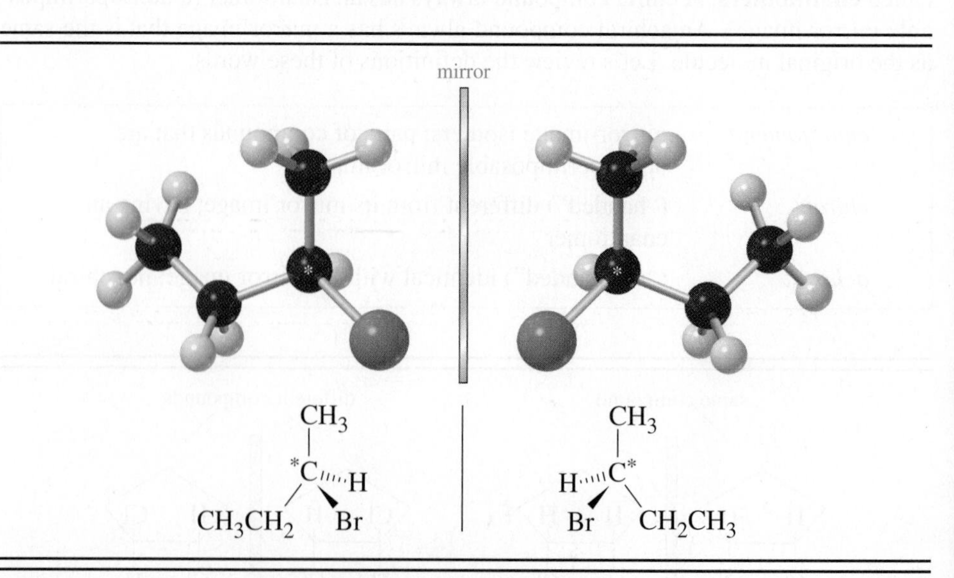

■ **FIGURE 5-4**
2-Bromobutane is chiral by virtue of an asymmetric carbon atom (chiral carbon atom), marked by an*.

[1]The term *stereocenter* (*stereogenic atom*) is not consistently defined. The original (Mislow) definition is given here. Some sources simply define it as a synonym for an *asymmetric carbon* (*chiral carbon*) or for a *chirality center.*

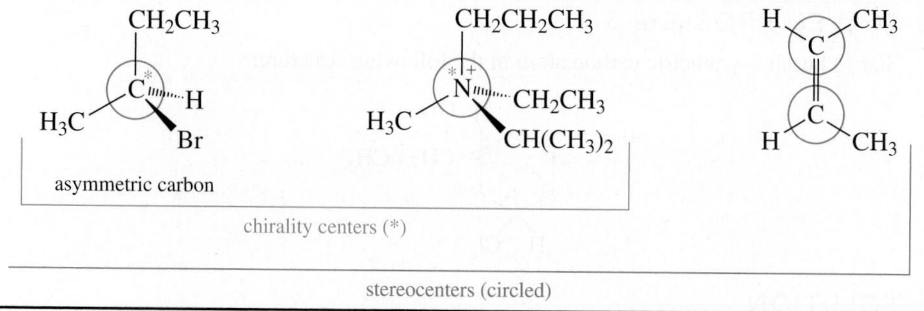

CH_2CH_3 — H_3C–C*–H, Br (asymmetric carbon)

$CH_2CH_2CH_3$ — H_3C–N*+–CH_2CH_3, $CH(CH_3)_2$

H, CH_3 C=C H, CH_3

asymmetric carbon

chirality centers (*)

stereocenters (circled)

■ **FIGURE 5-5**
Asymmetric carbon atoms are examples of chirality centers, which are examples of stereocenters.

Make a model of an asymmetric carbon atom, bonded to four different-colored atoms. Also make its mirror image, and try to superimpose the two (Figure 5-6). No matter how you twist and turn the models, they never look exactly the same.

If two of the four groups on a carbon atom are the same, however, the arrangement usually is not chiral. Figure 5-7 shows the mirror image of a tetrahedral structure with only three different groups; two of the four groups are the same. If the structure on the right is rotated 180°, it can be superimposed on the left structure.

We can generalize at this point, but keep in mind that the ultimate test for chirality is always whether the molecule's mirror image is the same or different.

1. If a compound has no asymmetric carbon atom, it is usually achiral. (We will see exceptions in Section 5-9.)
2. If a compound has just one asymmetric carbon atom, it must be chiral.
3. If a compound has more than one asymmetric carbon, it may or may not be chiral. (We will see examples in Section 5-12.)

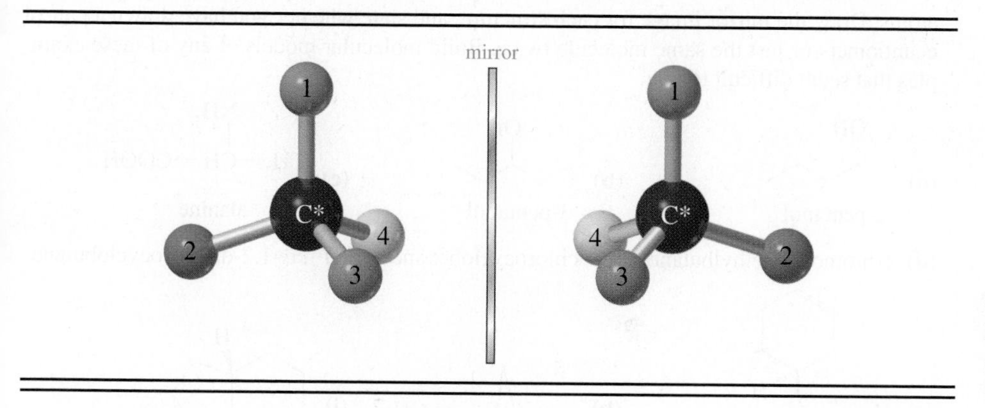

■ **FIGURE 5-6**
Enantiomers of an asymmetric carbon atom. These two mirror images are nonsuperimposable.

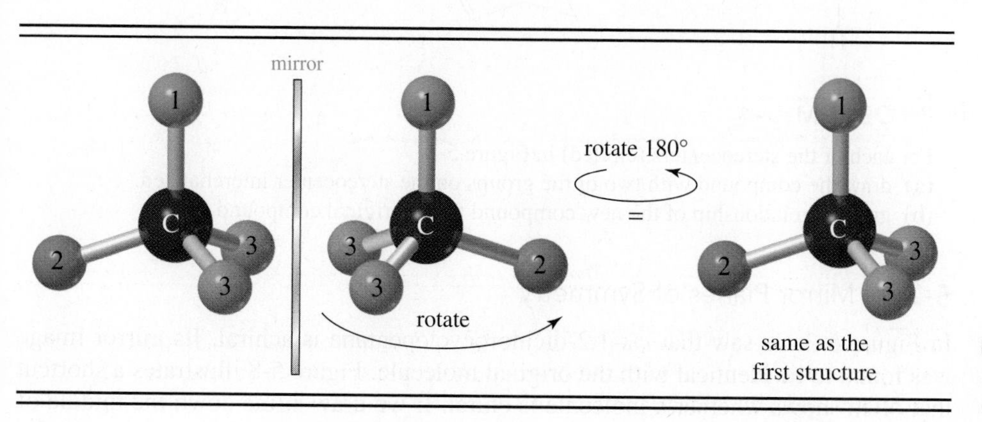

■ **FIGURE 5-7**
A carbon atom bonded to just three different types of groups is not chiral.

SOLVED PROBLEM 5-1

Star (*) each asymmetric carbon atom in the following structure:

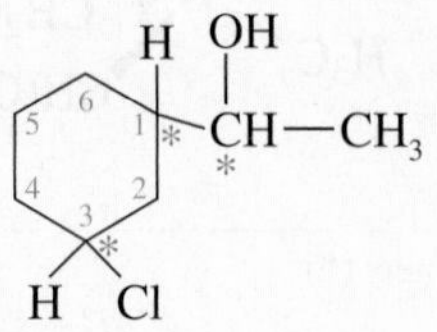

H OH
CH—CH_3
H Cl

SOLUTION

There are three asymmetric carbons, starred in red.

1. The (CHOH) carbon of the side chain is asymmetric. Its four substituents are the ring, a hydrogen atom, a hydroxyl group, and a methyl group.
2. Carbon atom C1 of the ring is asymmetric. Its four substituents are the side chain, a hydrogen atom, the part of the ring closer to the chlorine atom ($-CH_2-CHCl-$), and the part of the ring farther from the chlorine atom ($-CH_2-CH_2-CH_2-CHCl-$).
3. The ring carbon bearing the chlorine atom is asymmetric. Its four substituents are the chlorine atom, a hydrogen atom, the part of the ring closer to the side chain, and the part of the ring farther from the side chain.

Notice that different groups might be different in any manner. For example, the ring carbon bearing the chlorine atom is asymmetric even though two of its ring substituents initially appear to be $-CH_2-$ groups. These two parts of the ring are different because one is closer to the side chain and one is farther away. The *entire* structure of the group must be considered.

***problem-solving* Hint**

To draw the mirror image of a structure, keep up-and-down and front-and-back aspects as they are in the original structure, but reverse left and right.

PROBLEM 5-3

Draw a three-dimensional structure for each compound, and star all asymmetric carbon atoms. Draw the mirror image for each structure, and state whether you have drawn a pair of enantiomers or just the same molecule twice. Build molecular models of any of these examples that seem difficult to you.

(a) 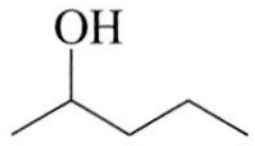 OH — 2-pantanol

(b) 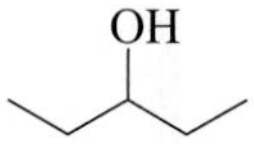 OH — 3-pentanol

(c) $CH_3-CH(NH_2)-COOH$ — alanine

(d) 1-bromo-2-methylbutane **(e)** chlorocyclohexane **(f)** *cis*-1,2-dichlorocyclobutane

(g) 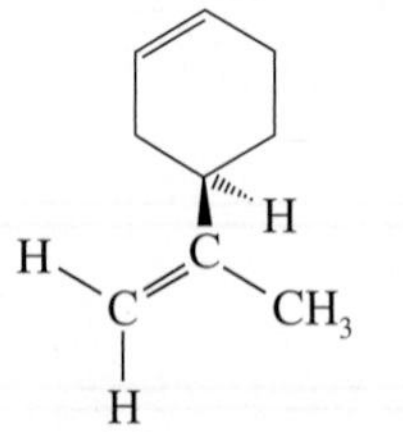 H, 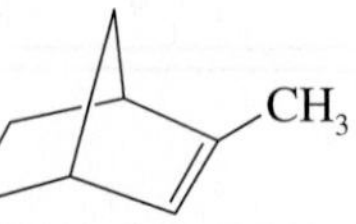 C, H, C, H, CH_3

(h) CH_3

(i) 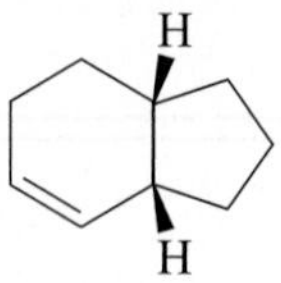 H, H

***problem-solving* Hint**

To determine whether a ring carbon is asymmetric, see if there is a difference in the path around the ring in each direction. If there is, then the two ring bonds are "different groups."

PROBLEM 5-4

For each of the stereocenters (circled) in Figure 5-5,
(a) draw the compound with two of the groups on the stereocenter interchanged.
(b) give the relationship of the new compound to the original compound.

5-2C Mirror Planes of Symmetry

In Figure 5-3 we saw that *cis*-1,2-dichlorocyclopentane is achiral. Its mirror image was found to be identical with the original molecule. Figure 5-8 illustrates a shortcut that often shows whether a molecule is chiral. If we draw a line down the middle of

internal mirror plane of symmetry (σ)

■ **FIGURE 5-8**
Internal mirror plane. *cis*-1,2-Dichlorocyclopentane has an internal mirror plane of symmetry. Any compound with an internal mirror plane of symmetry *cannot* be chiral.

cis-1,2-dichlorocyclopentane, bisecting a carbon atom and two hydrogen atoms, the part of the molecule that appears to the right of the line is the mirror image of the part on the left. This kind of symmetry is called an **internal mirror plane**, sometimes symbolized by the Greek lowercase letter sigma (σ). Since the right-hand side of the molecule is the reflection of the left-hand side, the molecule's mirror image is the same as the original molecule.

Notice in the following figure that the chiral trans isomer of 1,2-dichlorocyclopentane does not have a mirror plane of symmetry. The chlorine atoms do not reflect into each other across our hypothetical mirror plane. One of them is directed up, the other down.

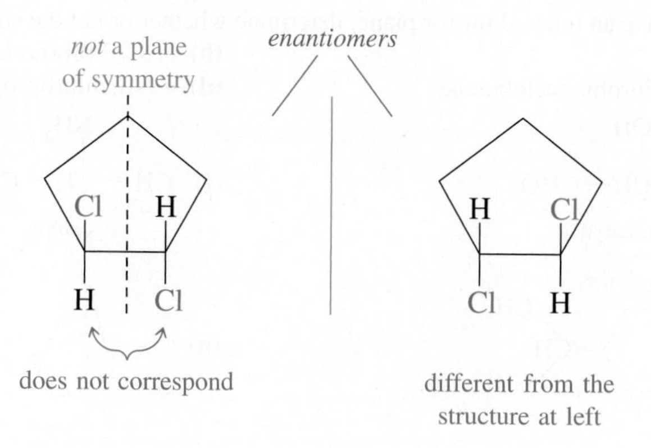

We can generalize from these and other examples to state the following principle:

> *Any molecule that has an internal mirror plane of symmetry cannot be chiral*, even though it may contain asymmetric carbon atoms.

The converse is not true, however. When we cannot find a mirror plane of symmetry, that does not necessarily mean that the molecule must be chiral. The following example has no internal mirror plane of symmetry, yet the mirror image is superimposable on the original molecule. You may need to make models to show that these mirror images are just two drawings of the same compound.

(hydrogens are omitted for clarity)

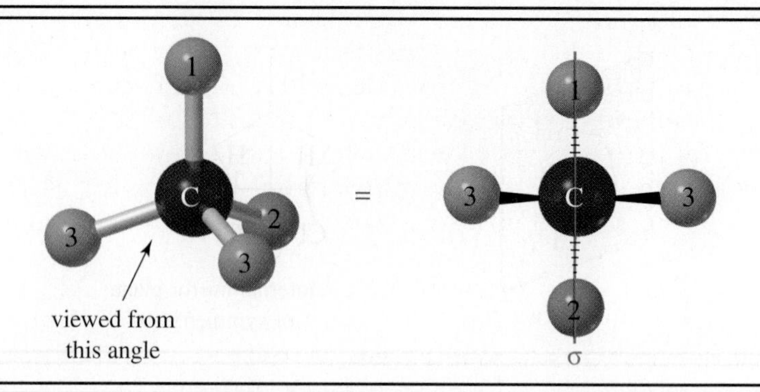

■ **FIGURE 5-9**
A carbon atom with two identical substituents (only three different substituents) usually has an internal mirror plane of symmetry. The structure is not chiral.

Using what we know about mirror planes of symmetry, we can see why a chiral (asymmetric) carbon atom is special. Figure 5-4 showed that an asymmetric carbon has a mirror image that is nonsuperimposable on the original structure; it has no internal mirror plane of symmetry. If a carbon atom has only three different kinds of substituents, however, it has an internal mirror plane of symmetry (Figure 5-9). Therefore, it cannot contribute to chirality in a molecule.

PROBLEM 5-5

For each compound, determine whether the molecule has an internal mirror plane of symmetry. If it does, draw the mirror plane on a three-dimensional drawing of the molecule. If the molecule does not have an internal mirror plane, determine whether or not the structure is chiral.

(a) methane
(b) *cis*-1,2-dibromocyclobutane
(c) *trans*-1,2-dibromocyclobutane
(d) 1,2-dichloropropane
(e) $HOCH_2-CH(OH)-CHO$
glyceraldehyde
(f) $CH_3-CH(NH_2)-COOH$
alanine
(g) CH_3–(cyclohexane)–$CH(CH_3)_2$
(h) (bicyclic structure)

5-3 (R) and (S) Nomenclature of Asymmetric Carbon Atoms

Alanine, from Problem 5-5(f), is one of the amino acids found in common proteins. Alanine has an asymmetric carbon atom, and it exists in two enantiomeric forms.

natural alanine | unnatural alanine

These mirror images are different, and this difference is reflected in their biochemistry. Only the enantiomer on the left can be metabolized by the usual enzyme; the one on the right is not recognized as a useful amino acid. Both are named alanine, however, or 2-aminopropanoic acid in the IUPAC system. We need a simple way to distinguish between enantiomers and to give each of them a unique name.

The difference between the two enantiomers of alanine lies in the three-dimensional arrangement of the four groups around the asymmetric carbon atom. Any asymmetric carbon has two possible (mirror-image) spatial arrangements, which we call **configurations**. The alanine enantiomers represent the two possible arrangements of its four groups around the asymmetric carbon atom. If we can name the two configurations of any asymmetric carbon atom, then we have a way of specifying and naming the enantiomers of alanine or any other chiral compound.

The **Cahn–Ingold–Prelog convention** is the most widely accepted system for naming the configurations of chirality centers. Each asymmetric carbon atom is assigned a letter (*R*) or (*S*) based on its three-dimensional configuration. To determine the name, we follow a two-step procedure that assigns "priorities" to the four substituents and then assigns the name based on the relative positions of these substituents. Here is the procedure:

1. *Assign a "priority" to each group bonded to the asymmetric carbon.* We speak of group 1 as having the highest priority, group 2 second, group 3 third, and group 4 as having the lowest priority.

(a) Look at the first atom of the group—the atom bonded to the asymmetric carbon. *Atoms with higher atomic numbers receive higher priorities.* For example, if the four groups bonded to an asymmetric carbon atom were H, CH_3, NH_2, and F, the fluorine atom (atomic number 9) would have the highest priority, followed by the nitrogen atom of the NH_2 group (atomic number 7), then by the carbon atom of the methyl group (atomic number 6). Note that we look only at the atomic number of the atom directly attached to the asymmetric carbon, not the entire group. Hydrogen would have the lowest priority.

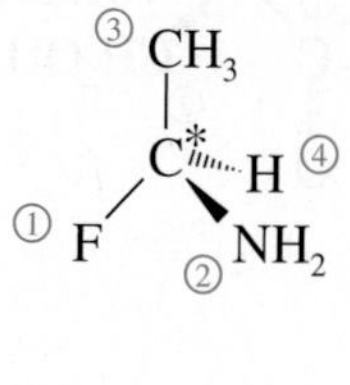

③ CH_3; C*; H ④; ① F; NH_2 ②

With different isotopes of the same element, the heavier isotopes have higher priorities. For example, tritium (^3H) receives a higher priority than deuterium (^2H), followed by hydrogen (^1H).

Examples of priority for atoms bonded to an asymmetric carbon:

$$I > Br > Cl > S > F > O > N > {}^{13}C > {}^{12}C > Li > {}^{3}H > {}^{2}H > {}^{1}H$$

(b) *In case of ties, use the next atoms along the chain of each group as tiebreakers.* For example, we assign a higher priority to isopropyl $-CH(CH_3)_2$ than to ethyl $-CH_2CH_3$ or bromoethyl $-CH_2CH_2Br$. The first carbon in the isopropyl group is bonded to two carbons, while the first carbon in the ethyl group (or the bromoethyl group) is bonded to only one carbon. An ethyl group and a $-CH_2CH_2Br$ have identical first atoms and second atoms, but the bromine atom in the third position gives $-CH_2CH_2Br$ a higher priority than $-CH_2CH_3$. One high-priority atom takes priority over any number of lower-priority atoms.

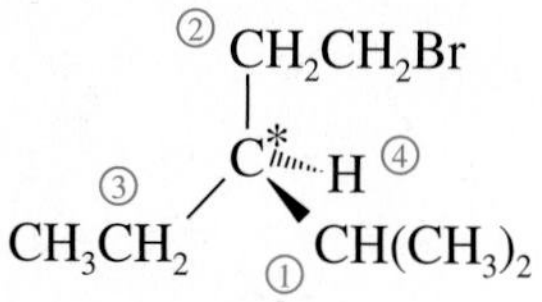

② CH_2CH_2Br; C*; H ④; ③ CH_3CH_2; $CH(CH_3)_2$ ①

Examples

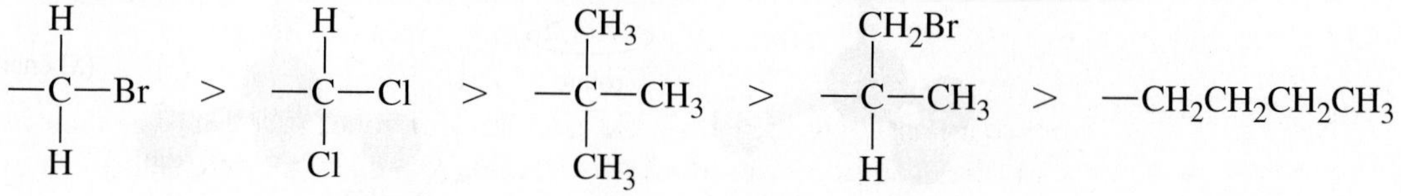

$$-CH_2Br > -CHCl_2 > -C(CH_3)_2H > -CH(CH_2Br)CH_3 > -CH_2CH_2CH_2CH_3$$

(drawn as: H–C(–Br)–H > H–C(–Cl)–Cl > CH_3–C(–CH_3)–CH_3 > CH_2Br–C(–CH_3)–H > $-CH_2CH_2CH_2CH_3$)

(c) *Treat double and triple bonds as if each were a bond to a separate atom.* For this method, imagine that each pi bond is broken and the atoms at both ends duplicated. Note that when you break a bond, you always add *two* imaginary atoms. (Imaginary atoms are circled below.)

alanine

R—C=C(H)(H), H on C — becomes R—C(H)(C)—C(H)(C)—H
break and duplicate

R—C=N, H on each — becomes R—C(H)(N)—N(H)(C)
break and duplicate

R—C≡C—H becomes R—C(C)(C)—C(C)(C)—H
break and duplicate

R—C(OH)=O becomes R—C(OH)(O)—O(C)
break and duplicate

2. *Using a three-dimensional drawing or a model, put the fourth-priority group away from you and view the molecule along the bond from the asymmetric carbon to the fourth-priority group. Draw an arrow from the first-priority group, through the second, to the third.* If the arrow points clockwise, the asymmetric carbon atom is called (*R*) (Latin, *rectus*, "upright"). If the arrow points counterclockwise, the chiral carbon atom is called (*S*) (Latin, *sinister*, "left").

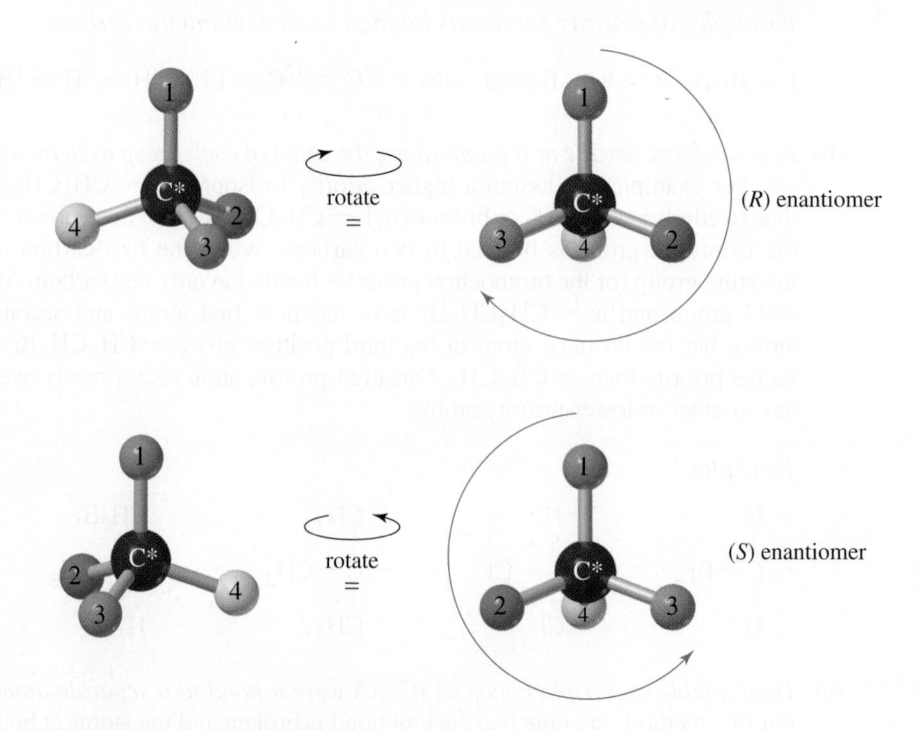

Alternatively, you can draw the arrow and imagine turning a car's steering wheel in that direction. If the car would go to the left, the asymmetric carbon atom is designated (*S*). If the car would go to the right, the asymmetric carbon atom is designated (*R*).

Let's use the enantiomers of alanine as an example. The naturally occurring enantiomer is the one on the left, determined to have the (*S*) configuration. Of the four atoms attached to the asymmetric carbon in alanine, nitrogen has the largest atomic number, giving it the highest priority. Next is the $-COOH$ carbon atom, since it is bonded to oxygen atoms. Third is the methyl group, followed by the hydrogen atom. When we position the natural enantiomer with its hydrogen atom pointing away from us, the arrow from $-NH_2$ to $-COOH$ to $-CH_3$ points counterclockwise. Thus, the naturally occurring enantiomer of alanine has the (*S*) configuration. Make models of these enantiomers to illustrate how they are named (*R*) and (*S*).

problem-solving Hint

Until you become comfortable working with drawings, use models to help you assign (*R*) and (*S*) configurations.

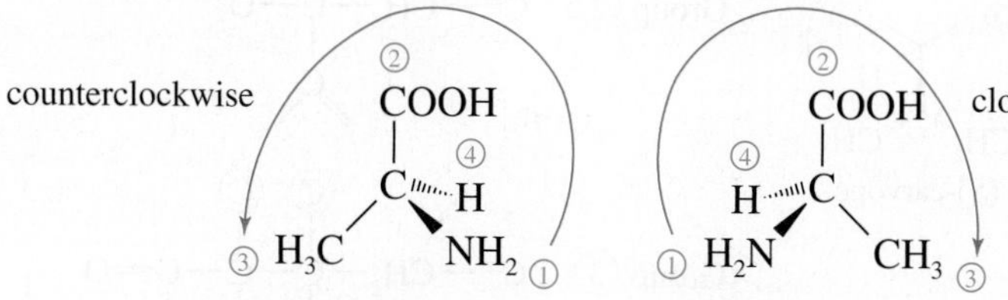

counterclockwise ... clockwise

natural (*S*)-alanine   unnatural (*R*)-alanine

SOLVED PROBLEM 5-2

Draw the enantiomers of 1,3-dibromobutane and label them as (*R*) and (*S*). (Making a model is particularly helpful for this type of problem.)

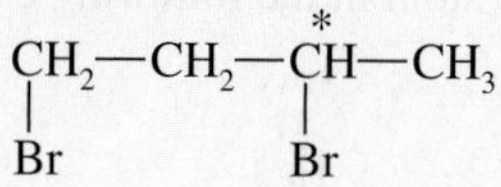

$$\underset{\text{Br}}{CH_2}-CH_2-\overset{*}{\underset{\text{Br}}{CH}}-CH_3$$

SOLUTION

The third carbon atom in 1,3-dibromobutane is asymmetric. The bromine atom receives first priority, the ($-CH_2CH_2Br$) group second priority, the methyl group third, and the hydrogen fourth. The following mirror images are drawn with the hydrogen atom back, ready to assign (*R*) or (*S*) as shown.

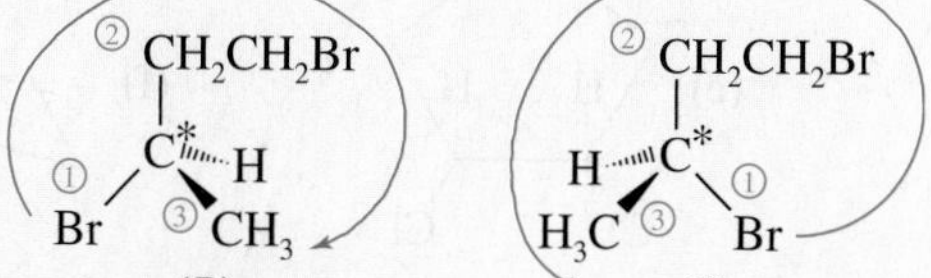

(*R*)   (*S*)

SOLVED PROBLEM 5-3

The structure of one of the enantiomers of carvone is shown here. Find the asymmetric carbon atom, and determine whether it has the (*R*) or the (*S*) configuration.

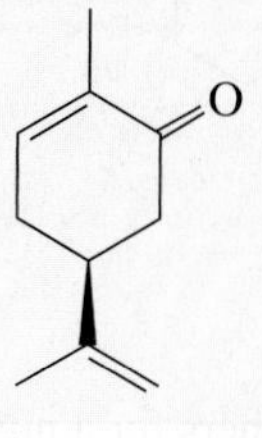

problem-solving Hint

In assigning priorities for a ring carbon, go around the ring in each direction until you find a point of difference; then use the difference to determine which ring carbon has higher priority than the other.

(*Continued*)

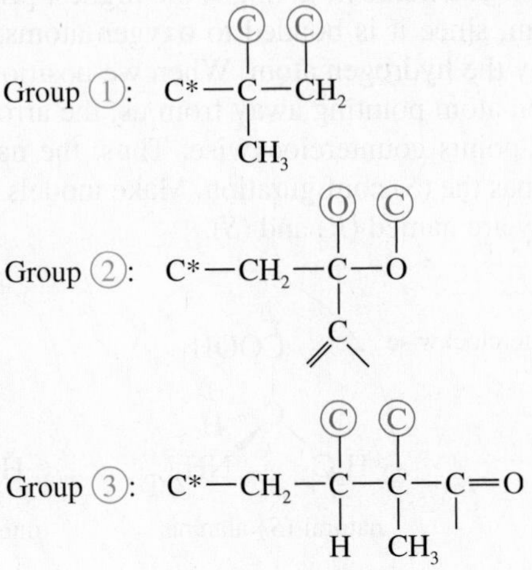

Scientists frequently use the isotopes of hydrogen to assign the configuration of the products of biological reactions. Ethanol, made chiral by the presence of a deuterium (D or ^{2}H), is one of the early examples.

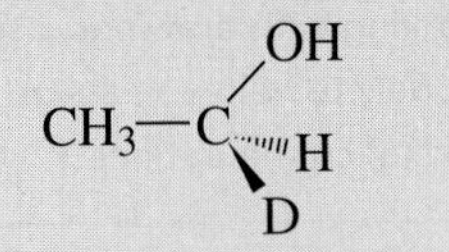

CH_3—C(OH)(H)(D)

(*S*)-1-deuterioethanol

SOLUTION

The asymmetric carbon atom is one of the ring carbons, as indicated by the asterisk in the following structure. Although there are two $-CH_2-$ groups bonded to the carbon, they are different $-CH_2-$ groups. One is a $-CH_2-CO-$ group, and the other is a $-CH_2-CH{=}C$ group. The groups are assigned priorities, and this is found to be the (*S*) enantiomer.

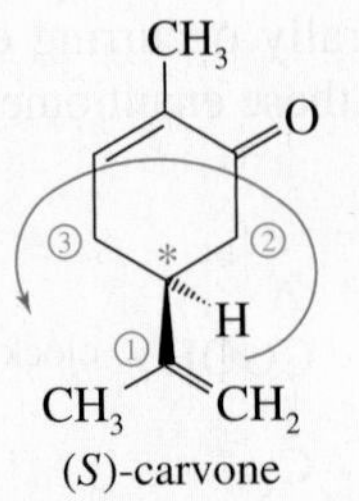

(*S*)-carvone

Group ①: C*—C(C)(C)—CH_2, CH_3

Group ②: C*—CH_2—C(O)(C)—O, C

Group ③: C*—CH_2—C(C)(H)—C(C)(CH_3)—C=O

PROBLEM 5-6

Star (*) each asymmetric carbon atom in the following examples, and determine whether it has the (*R*) or (*S*) configuration.

(a) 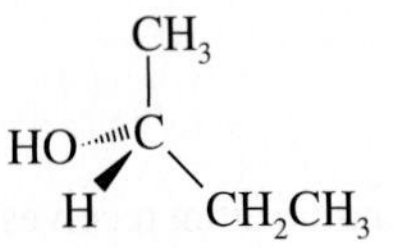 HO—C(CH_3)(H)—CH_2CH_3

(b) 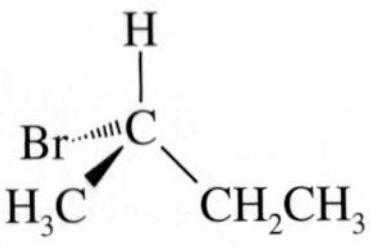 Br—C(H)(H_3C)—CH_2CH_3

(c)

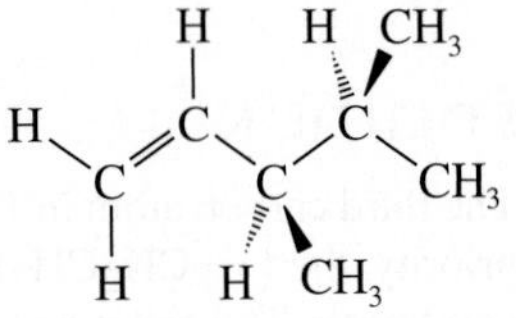

(d)

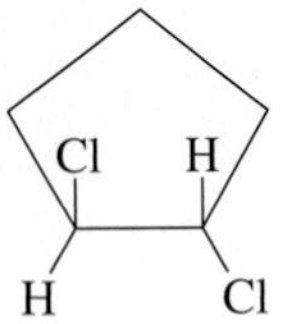

(e)

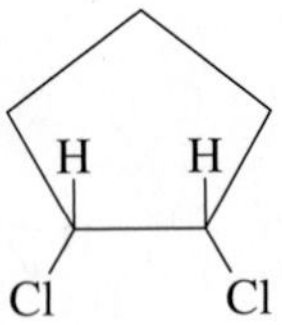

(f)

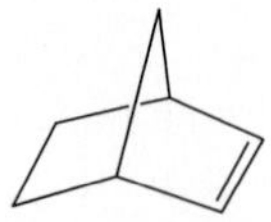

(g)

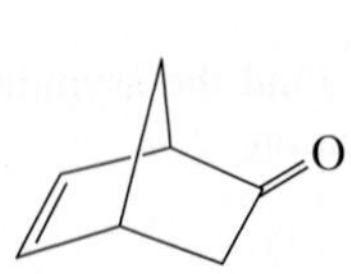

(h)

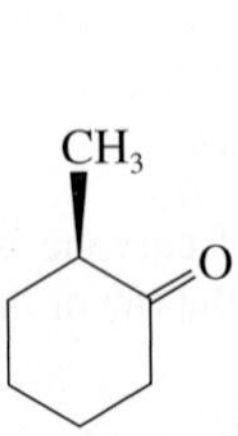

(*i) CHO—C(CH=CH_2)(CH(CH_3)$_2$)—(CH_3O)$_2$CH

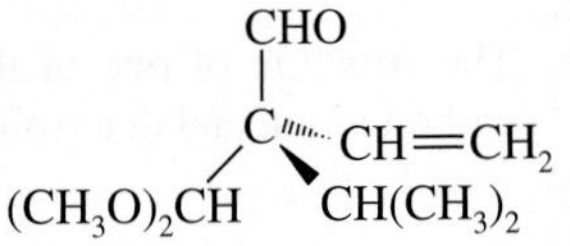

problem-solving Hint

If the lowest-priority atom (usually H) is oriented toward you, you don't need to turn the structure around. You can leave it as it is with the H toward you and apply the *R*/*S* rule backward.

problem-solving Hint

Interchanging any two substituents on an asymmetric carbon atom inverts its (*R*) or (*S*) configuration. If there is only one chirality center in a molecule, inverting its configuration gives the enantiomer.

PROBLEM 5-7

In Problem 5-3, you drew the enantiomers for a number of chiral compounds. Now go back and designate each asymmetric carbon atom as either (*R*) or (*S*).

5-4 Optical Activity

Mirror-image molecules have nearly identical physical properties. Compare the following properties of (*R*)-2-bromobutane and (*S*)-2-bromobutane.

	(*R*)-2-Bromobutane	(*S*)-2-Bromobutane
boiling point (° C)	91.2	91.2
melting point (° C)	−112	−112
refractive index	1.436	1.436
density	1.253	1.253

Differences in enantiomers become apparent in their interactions with other chiral molecules, such as enzymes. Still, we need a simple method to distinguish between enantiomers and measure their purity in the laboratory. **Polarimetry** is a common method used to distinguish between enantiomers, based on their ability to rotate the plane of polarized light in opposite directions. For example, the two enantiomers of thyroid hormone are shown below. The (*S*) enantiomer has a powerful effect on the metabolic rate of all the cells in the body. The (*R*) enantiomer is useless. In the laboratory, we distinguish between the enantiomers by observing that the active one rotates the plane of polarized light to the left.

thyroid hormone (*S*)
rotates polarized light to the left

wrong enantiomer (*R*)
rotates polarized light to the right

5-4A Plane-Polarized Light

Most of what we see is unpolarized light, vibrating randomly in all directions. **Plane-polarized light** is composed of waves that vibrate in only one plane. Although there are other types of "polarized light," the term usually refers to plane-polarized light.

When unpolarized light passes through a polarizing filter, the randomly vibrating light waves are filtered so that most of the light passing through is vibrating in one direction (Figure 5-10). The direction of vibration is called the *axis* of the filter. Polarizing filters may be made from carefully cut calcite crystals or from specially treated plastic sheets. Plastic polarizing filters are often used as lenses in sunglasses, because the axis of the filters can be positioned to filter out reflected glare.

When light passes first through one polarizing filter and then through another, the amount of light emerging depends on the relationship between the axes of the two

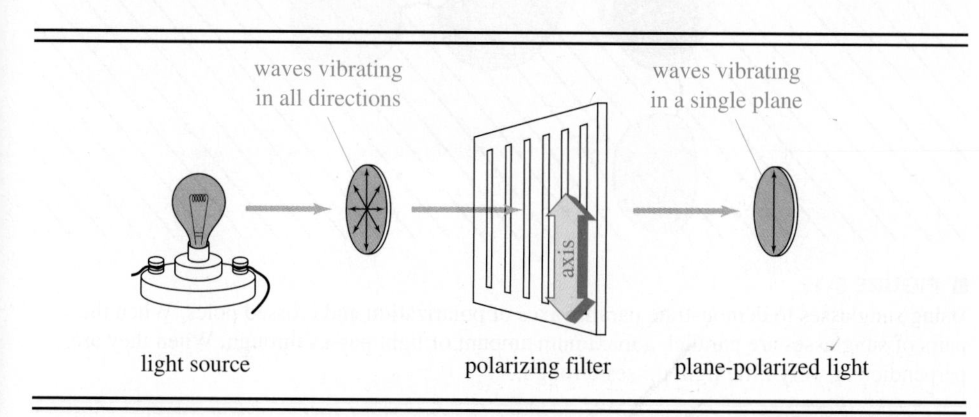

■ **FIGURE 5-10**
Function of a polarizing filter. The waves of plane-polarized light vibrate primarily in a single plane.

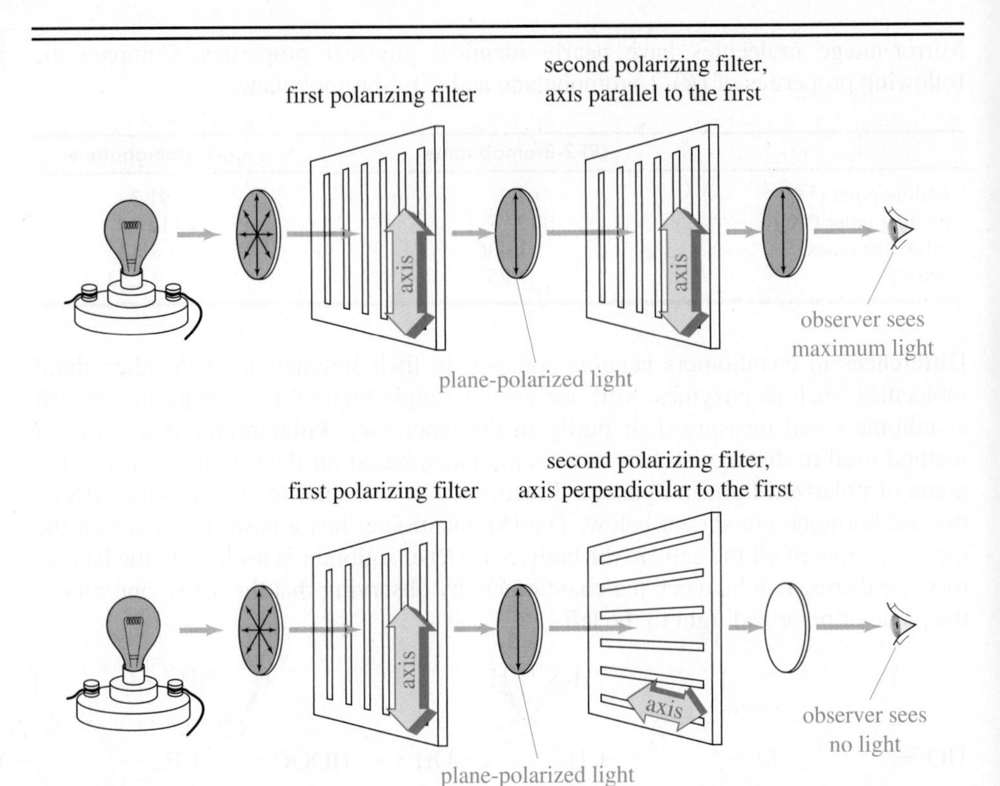

■ **FIGURE 5-11**
Crossed poles. When the axis of a second polarizing filter is parallel to the first, a maximum amount of light passes through. When the axes of the filters are perpendicular (crossed poles), no light passes through.

filters (Figure 5-11). If the axes of the two filters are lined up (parallel), then nearly all the light that passes through the first filter also passes through the second. If the axes of the two filters are perpendicular (*crossed poles*), however, all the polarized light that emerges from the first filter is stopped by the second. At intermediate angles of rotation, intermediate amounts of light pass through.

You can demonstrate this effect for yourself by wearing a pair of polarized sunglasses while looking at a light source through another pair (Figure 5-12). The second pair seems to be transparent, as long as its axis is lined up with the pair you are wearing. When the second pair is rotated to 90°, however, the lenses become opaque, as if they were covered with black ink.

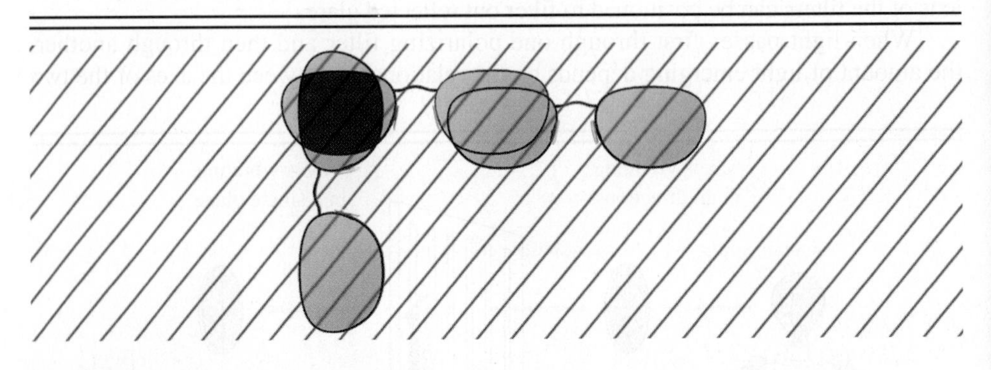

■ **FIGURE 5-12**
Using sunglasses to demonstrate parallel axes of polarization and crossed poles. When the pairs of sunglasses are parallel, a maximum amount of light passes through. When they are perpendicular, very little light passes through.

5-4B Rotation of Plane-Polarized Light

When polarized light passes through a solution containing a chiral compound, the chiral compound causes the plane of vibration to rotate. Rotation of the plane of polarized light is called **optical activity**, and substances that rotate the plane of polarized light are said to be **optically active**.

Before the relationship between chirality and optical activity was known, enantiomers were called **optical isomers** because they seemed identical except for their opposite optical activity. The term was loosely applied to more than one type of isomerism among optically active compounds, however, and this ambiguous term has been replaced by the well-defined term *enantiomers*.

Two enantiomers have identical physical properties, except for the direction they rotate the plane of polarized light.

> Enantiomeric compounds rotate the plane of polarized light by exactly the same amount but in opposite directions.

If the (*R*) enantiomer rotates the plane 30° clockwise, the (*S*) enantiomer will rotate it 30° counterclockwise. If the (*R*) enantiomer rotates the plane 5° counterclockwise, the (*S*) enantiomer will rotate it 5° clockwise.

> We cannot predict which direction a particular enantiomer [either (*R*) or (*S*)] will rotate the plane of polarized light.

(*R*) and (*S*) are simply names, but the direction and magnitude of rotation are physical properties that must be measured.

problem-solving Hint

Don't confuse the process for *naming* a structure (*R*) or (*S*) with the process for *measuring* an optical rotation. Just because we use the terms *clockwise* and *counterclockwise* in naming (*R*) and (*S*) does not mean that light follows our naming rules.

5-4C Polarimetry

A **polarimeter** measures the rotation of polarized light. It has a tubular cell filled with a solution of the optically active material and a system for passing polarized light through the solution and measuring the rotation as the light emerges (Figure 5-13). The light from a sodium lamp is filtered so that it consists of just one wavelength (one color), because most compounds rotate different wavelengths of light by different amounts. The wavelength of light most commonly used for polarimetry is a yellow emission line in the spectrum of sodium, called the *sodium D line*.

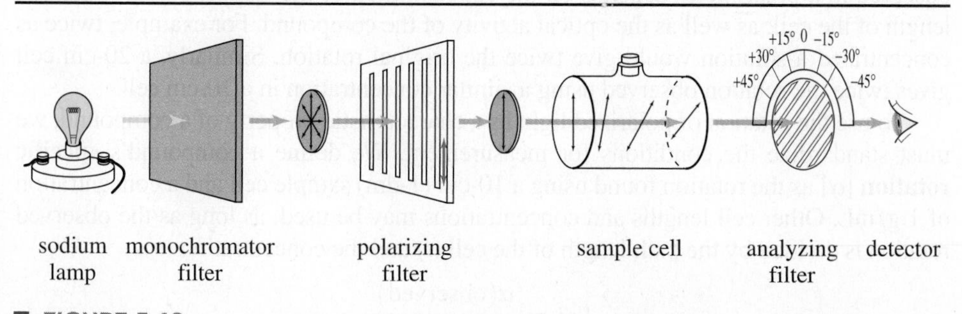

FIGURE 5-13
Schematic diagram of a polarimeter. The light originates at a source (usually a sodium lamp) and passes through a polarizing filter and the sample cell. An optically active solution rotates the plane of polarized light. The analyzing filter is another polarizing filter equipped with a protractor. It is turned until a maximum amount of light is observed, and the rotation is read from the protractor.

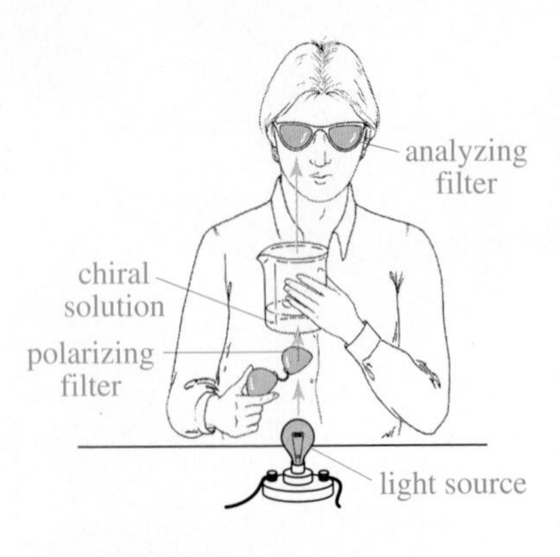

■ **FIGURE 5-14**
Apparatus for using a lightbulb and two pairs of polarized sunglasses as a simple polarimeter.

Monochromatic (one-color) light from the source passes through a polarizing filter, then through the sample cell containing a solution of the optically active compound. On leaving the sample cell, the polarized light encounters another polarizing filter. This filter is movable, with a scale allowing the operator to read the angle between the axis of the second (analyzing) filter and the axis of the first (polarizing) filter. The operator rotates the analyzing filter until the maximum amount of light is transmitted, then reads the observed rotation from the protractor. The observed rotation is symbolized by α, the Greek letter alpha.

Compounds that rotate the plane of polarized light toward the right (clockwise) are called **dextrorotatory**, from the Greek word *dexios*, meaning "toward the right." Compounds that rotate the plane toward the left (counterclockwise) are called **levorotatory**, from the Latin word *laevus*, meaning "toward the left." These terms are sometimes abbreviated by a lowercase *d* or *l*. Using IUPAC notation, the direction of rotation is specified by the (+) or (−) sign of the rotation:

> Dextrorotatory (clockwise) rotations are (+) or (*d*).
> Levorotatory (counterclockwise) rotations are (−) or (*l*).

For example, the isomer of 2-butanol that rotates the plane of polarized light clockwise is named (+)-2-butanol or *d*-2-butanol. Its enantiomer, (−)-2-butanol or *l*-2-butanol, rotates the plane counterclockwise by exactly the same amount.

You can see the principle of polarimetry by using two pairs of polarized sunglasses, a beaker, and some corn syrup or sugar solution. Wear one pair of sunglasses, look down at a light, and hold another pair of sunglasses above the light. Notice that the most light is transmitted through the two pairs of sunglasses when their axes are parallel. Very little light is transmitted when their axes are perpendicular.

Put syrup into the beaker, and hold the beaker above the bottom pair of sunglasses so the light passes through one pair of sunglasses (the polarizing filter), then the beaker (the optically active sample), and then the other pair of sunglasses (the analyzing filter); see Figure 5-14. Again, check the angles giving maximum and minimum light transmission. Is the syrup solution dextrorotatory or levorotatory? Did you notice the color variation as you rotated the filter? You can see why just one color of light should be used for accurate work.

5-4D Specific Rotation

The angular rotation of polarized light by a chiral compound is a characteristic physical property of that compound, just like the boiling point or the density. The rotation (α) observed in a polarimeter depends on the concentration of the sample solution and the length of the cell, as well as the optical activity of the compound. For example, twice as concentrated a solution would give twice the original rotation. Similarly, a 20-cm cell gives twice the rotation observed using a similar concentration in a 10-cm cell.

To use the rotation of polarized light as a characteristic property of a compound, we must standardize the conditions for measurement. We define a compound's **specific rotation** $[\alpha]$ as the rotation found using a 10-cm (1-dm) sample cell and a concentration of 1 g/mL. Other cell lengths and concentrations may be used, as long as the observed rotation is divided by the path length of the cell (l) and the concentration (c).

$$[\alpha] = \frac{\alpha(\text{observed})}{c \cdot l}$$

where

$\alpha(\text{observed})$ = rotation observed in the polarimeter
c = concentration in grams per mL
l = length of sample cell (path length) in decimeters (dm)

SOLVED PROBLEM 5-4

When one of the enantiomers of 2-butanol is placed in a polarimeter, the observed rotation is 4.05° counterclockwise. The solution was made by diluting 6.00 g of 2-butanol to a total of 40.0 mL, and the solution was placed into a 200-mm polarimeter tube for the measurement. Determine the specific rotation for this enantiomer of 2-butanol.

SOLUTION

Since it is levorotatory, this must be (−)-2-butanol. The concentration is 6.00 g per 40.0 mL = 0.150 g/mL, and the path length is 200 mm = 2.00 dm. The specific rotation is

$$[\alpha]_{D}^{25} = \frac{-4.05°}{(0.150)(2.00)} = -13.5°$$

A rotation depends on the wavelength of light used and also on the temperature, so these data are given together with the rotation. In Solved Problem 5-4, the "25" means that the measurement was made at 25 °C, and the "D" means that the light used was the D line of the sodium spectrum.

Without even measuring it, we can predict that the specific rotation of the other enantiomer of 2-butanol will be

$$[\alpha]_{D}^{25} = +13.5°$$

where the (+) refers to the clockwise direction of the rotation. This enantiomer would be called (+)-2-butanol. We could refer to this pair of enantiomers as (+)-2-butanol and (−)-2-butanol or as (*R*)-2-butanol and (*S*)-2-butanol.

Does this mean that (*R*)-2-butanol is the dextrorotatory isomer because it is named (*R*), and (*S*)-2-butanol is levorotatory because it is named (*S*)? Not at all! The rotation of a compound, (+) or (−), is something that we measure in the polarimeter, depending on how the molecule interacts with light. The (*R*) and (*S*) nomenclature is our own artificial way of describing how the atoms are arranged in space.

In the laboratory, we can measure a rotation and see whether a particular substance is (+) or (−). On paper, we can determine whether a particular drawing is named (*R*) or (*S*). But it is difficult to predict whether a structure we call (*R*) will rotate polarized light clockwise or counterclockwise. Similarly, it is difficult to predict whether a dextrorotatory substance in a flask has the (*R*) or (*S*) configuration.

PROBLEM 5-8

A solution of 2.0 g of (+)-glyceraldehyde, $HOCH_2-CHOH-CHO$, in 10.0 mL of water was placed in a 100-mm cell. Using the sodium D line, a rotation of +1.74° was found at 25 °C. Determine the specific rotation of (+)-glyceraldehyde.

PROBLEM 5-9

A solution of 0.50 g of (−)-epinephrine (see Figure 5-15) dissolved in 10.0 mL of dilute aqueous HCl was placed in a 20-cm polarimeter tube. Using the sodium D line, the rotation was found to be −5.1° at 25 °C. Determine the specific rotation of epinephrine.

PROBLEM 5-10

A chiral sample gives a rotation that is close to 180°. How can one tell whether this rotation is +180° or −180°?

5-5 Biological Discrimination of Enantiomers

If the direction of rotation of polarized light were the only difference between enantiomers, one might ask whether the difference would be important. Biological systems commonly distinguish between enantiomers, and two enantiomers may have totally different biological properties. In fact, any **chiral probe** can distinguish between enantiomers, and a polarimeter is only one example of a chiral probe. Another example is your hand. If you needed to sort a box of gloves into right-handed gloves and left-handed gloves, you could distinguish between them by checking to see which ones fit your right hand.

Enzymes in living systems are chiral, and they are capable of distinguishing between enantiomers. Usually, only one enantiomer of a pair fits properly into the chiral active site of an enzyme. For example, the levorotatory form of epinephrine is one of the principal hormones secreted by the adrenal medulla. When synthetic epinephrine is given to a patient, the (−) form has the same stimulating effect as the natural hormone. The (+) form lacks this effect and is mildly toxic. Figure 5-15 shows a simplified picture of how only the (−) enantiomer fits into the enzyme's active site.

Biological systems are capable of distinguishing between the enantiomers of many different chiral compounds. In general, just one of the enantiomers produces the characteristic effect; the other either produces no effect or has a different effect. Even your nose is capable of distinguishing between some enantiomers. For example, (−)-carvone is the fragrance associated with spearmint oil; (+)-carvone has the tangy

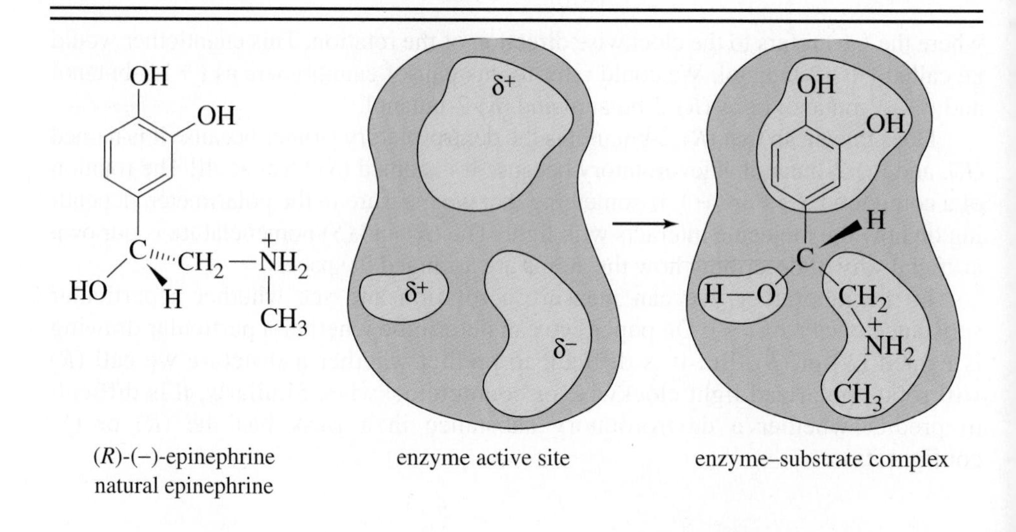

OH
OH
$\overset{+}{N}H_2-CH_2$ C OH
H
CH_3
OH
OH
H
C
H_2C
O
H
$^+NH_2$
CH_3

(S)-(+)-epinephrine
unnatural epinephrine

does not fit the enzyme's active site

■ **FIGURE 5-15**
Chiral recognition of epinephrine by an enzyme. Only the levorotatory enantiomer fits into the active site of the enzyme.

odor of caraway seed. The receptor sites for the sense of smell must be chiral, therefore, just as the active sites in most enzymes are chiral. In general, enantiomers do not interact identically with other chiral molecules, whether or not they are of biological origin.

(+)-carvone (caraway seed) (−)-carvone (spearmint)

Enzymes can exist as two enantiomers, although only one enantiomer is found in nature. In 1992, Stephen Kent and co-workers reported the synthesis of both enantiomers of an enzyme that cuts peptide substrates, and showed for the first time that each enzyme acts only on the corresponding enantiomeric peptide substrate.

PROBLEM 5-11

If you had the two enantiomers of carvone in unmarked bottles, could you use just your nose and a polarimeter to determine

(a) whether it is the (+) or (−) enantiomer that smells like spearmint?

(b) whether it is the (*R*) or (*S*) enantiomer that smells like spearmint?

(c) With the information given in the drawings of carvone above, what can you add to your answers to (a) or (b)?

5-6 Racemic Mixtures

Suppose we had a mixture of equal amounts of (+)-2-butanol and (−)-2-butanol. The (+) isomer would rotate polarized light clockwise with a specific rotation of +13.5°, and the (−) isomer would rotate the polarized light counterclockwise by exactly the same amount. We would observe a rotation of zero, just as though 2-butanol were achiral. A solution of equal amounts of two enantiomers, so that the mixture is optically inactive, is called a **racemic mixture**. Sometimes a racemic mixture is called a **racemate**, a (±) **pair**, or a **(*d,l*) pair**. A racemic mixture is symbolized by placing (±) or (*d,l*) in front of the name of the compound. For example, racemic 2-butanol would be symbolized by "(±)-2-butanol" or "(*d,l*)-2-butanol."

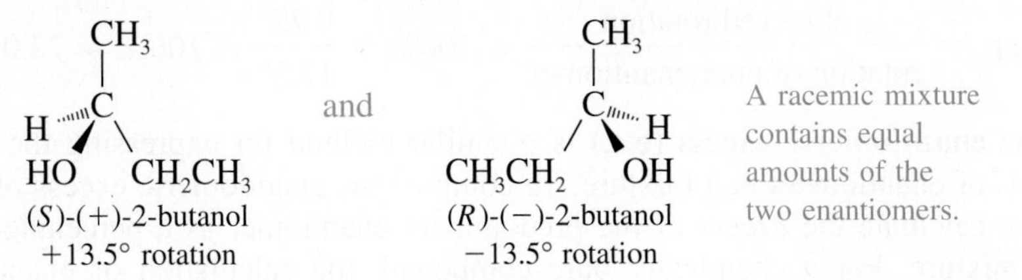

You might think that a racemic mixture would be unusual, since it requires exactly equal amounts of the two enantiomers. This is not the case, however. Many reactions lead to racemic products, especially when an achiral molecule is converted to a chiral molecule.

A reaction that uses optically inactive reactants and catalysts cannot produce a product that is optically active. Any chiral product must be formed as a racemic mixture.

For example, hydrogen adds across the C=O double bond of a ketone to produce an alcohol.

$$RR'C{=}O \xrightarrow{H_2,\ Ni} RR'CH{-}OH$$

Many drugs currently on the market are racemic mixtures. Ketamine, for example, is a potent anesthetic agent, but its use is limited because it is hallucinogenic (making it a drug of abuse widely known as "K"). The (*S*) isomer is responsible for the anesthetic effects, and the (*R*) isomer causes the hallucinogenic effects.

ketamine

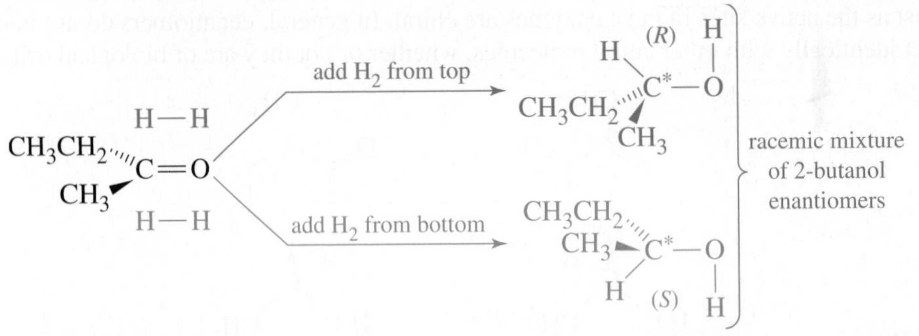

$$CH_3CH_2(CH_3)C{=}O \xrightarrow[\text{add } H_2 \text{ from bottom}]{\text{add } H_2 \text{ from top}} \text{racemic mixture of 2-butanol enantiomers: } (R)\text{ and } (S)\ CH_3CH_2C^*H(CH_3)OH$$

■ FIGURE 5-16
Hydrogenation of 2-butanone forms racemic 2-butanol. Hydrogen adds to either face of the double bond. Addition of H_2 to one face gives the (*R*) product, while addition to the other face gives the (*S*) product.

Because the carbonyl group is flat, a simple ketone such as 2-butanone is achiral. Hydrogenation of 2-butanone gives 2-butanol, a chiral molecule (Figure 5-16). This reaction involves adding hydrogen atoms to the C=O carbon atom and oxygen atom. If the hydrogen atoms are added to one face of the double bond, the (*S*) enantiomer results. Addition of hydrogen to the other face forms the (*R*) enantiomer. It is equally probable for hydrogen to add to either face of the double bond, and equal amounts of the (*R*) and (*S*) enantiomers are formed.

Logically, it makes sense that optically inactive reagents and catalysts cannot form optically active products. If the starting materials and reagents are optically inactive, there is no reason for the dextrorotatory product to be favored over a levorotatory one or vice versa. The (+) product and the (−) product are favored equally, and they are formed in equal amounts: a racemic mixture.

5-7 Enantiomeric Excess and Optical Purity

Sometimes we deal with mixtures that are neither optically pure (all one enantiomer) nor racemic (equal amounts of two enantiomers). In these cases, we specify the **optical purity (o.p.)** of the mixture. The optical purity of a mixture is defined as the ratio of its rotation to the rotation of a pure enantiomer. For example, if we have some [mostly (+)] 2-butanol with a specific rotation of +9.72°, we compare this rotation with the +13.5° rotation of the pure (+) enantiomer.

$$\text{o.p.} = \frac{\text{observed rotation}}{\text{rotation of pure enantiomer}} \times 100\% = \frac{9.72^\circ}{13.5^\circ} \times 100\% = 72.0\%$$

The **enantiomeric excess (e.e.)** is a similar method for expressing the relative amounts of enantiomers in a mixture. To compute the enantiomeric excess of a mixture, we calculate the *excess* of the predominant enantiomer as a percentage of the entire mixture. For a chemically pure compound, the calculation of enantiomeric excess generally gives the same result as the calculation of optical purity, and we often use the two terms interchangeably. Algebraically, we use the following formula:

$$\text{o.p.} = \text{e.e.} = \frac{|d - l|}{d + l} \times 100\% = \frac{(\text{excess of one over the other})}{(\text{entire mixture})} \times 100\%$$

The units cancel out in the calculation of either e.e. or o.p., so these formulas can be used whether the amounts of the enantiomers are expressed in concentrations, grams, or percentages. For the 2-butanol mixture just described, the optical purity of 72% (+) implies that $d - l = 72\%$, and we know that $d + l = 100\%$. Adding the equations gives $2d = 172\%$. We conclude that the mixture contains 86% of the *d* or (+) enantiomer and 14% of the *l* or (−) enantiomer.

SOLVED PROBLEM 5-5

Calculate the e.e. and the specific rotation of a mixture containing 6.0 g of (+)-2-butanol and 4.0 g of (−)-2-butanol.

Several racemic drugs have recently become available as pure active enantiomers. For example, the drug Nexium® (for controlling acid reflux) contains just the active enantiomer of the racemic mixture in Prilosec®.

SOLUTION

In this mixture, there is a 2.0 g excess of the (+) isomer and a total of 10.0 g, for an e.e. of 20%. We can envision this mixture as 80% racemic [4.0 g(+) and 4.0 g(−)] and 20% pure (+).

$$\text{o.p.} = \text{e.e.} = \frac{|6.0 - 4.0|}{6.0 + 4.0} = \frac{2.0}{10.0} = 20\%$$

The specific rotation of enantiomerically pure (+)-2-butanol is +13.5°. The rotation of this mixture is

$$\text{observed rotation} = (\text{rotation of pure enantiomer}) \times (\text{o.p.})$$
$$= (+13.5°) \times (20\%) = +2.7°$$

PROBLEM 5-12

When optically pure (*R*)-2-bromobutane is heated with water, 2-butanol is the product. The reaction forms twice as much (*S*)-2-butanol as (*R*)-2-butanol. Calculate the e.e. and the specific rotation expected for the product.

PROBLEM 5-13

A chemist finds that the addition of (+)-epinephrine to the catalytic reduction of 2-butanone (Figure 5-16) gives a product that is slightly optically active, with a specific rotation of +0.45°. Calculate the percentages of (+)-2-butanol and (−)-2-butanol formed in this reaction.

5-8 Chirality of Conformationally Mobile Systems

Let's consider whether *cis*-1,2-dibromocyclohexane is chiral. If we did not know about chair conformations, we might draw a flat cyclohexane ring. With a flat ring, the molecule has an internal mirror plane of symmetry (σ), and it is achiral.

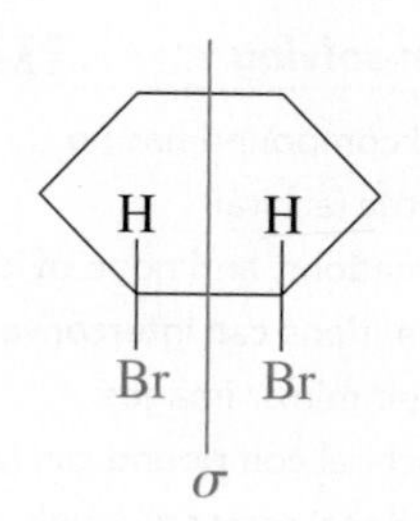

But we know the ring is puckered into a chair conformation with one bromine atom axial and one equatorial. A chair conformation of *cis*-1,2-dibromocyclohexane and its mirror image are shown below. These two mirror-image structures are nonsuperimposable. You may be able to see the difference more easily if you make models of these two conformations.

Does this mean that *cis*-1,2-dibromocyclohexane is chiral? No, it does not, because the chair–chair interconversion is rapid at room temperature. If we had a bottle of just the conformation on the left, the molecules would quickly undergo chair–chair interconversions. Since the two mirror-image conformations interconvert and have identical energies, any sample of *cis*-1,2-dibromocyclohexane must contain equal amounts of the two mirror images. Similarly, most achiral compounds can exist in transient chiral conformations that are in equilibrium with their mirror-image conformations.

A molecule cannot be optically active if its chiral conformations are in equilibrium with their mirror images. We consider such a molecule to be achiral.

cis-1,2-Dibromocyclohexane appears to exist as a racemic mixture, but with a major difference: It is impossible to create an optically active sample of *cis*-1,2-dibromocyclohexane. The molecule is incapable of showing optical activity. We could have predicted the correct result by imagining that the cyclohexane ring is flat.

This finding leads to a general principle we can use with conformationally mobile systems:

> To determine whether a conformationally mobile molecule can be optically active, consider its most symmetric conformation.

An alternative statement of this rule is that a molecule cannot be optically active if it is in equilibrium with a structure (or a conformation) that is achiral. Inherently chiral compounds have NO achievable achiral conformations. Because conformers differ only by rotations about single bonds, they are generally in equilibrium at room temperature. We can consider cyclohexane rings as though they were flat (the most symmetric conformation), and we should consider straight-chain compounds in their most symmetric conformations (often an eclipsed conformation).

Organic compounds commonly exist as rapidly interconverting chiral conformations. Even ethane is chiral in its skew conformations. When we speak of chirality, however, we intend to focus on observable, persistent properties rather than transient conformations. For example, butane exists in gauche conformations that are chiral, but they quickly interconvert. They are in equilibrium with the totally eclipsed conformation, which is symmetric, implying that butane must be achiral.

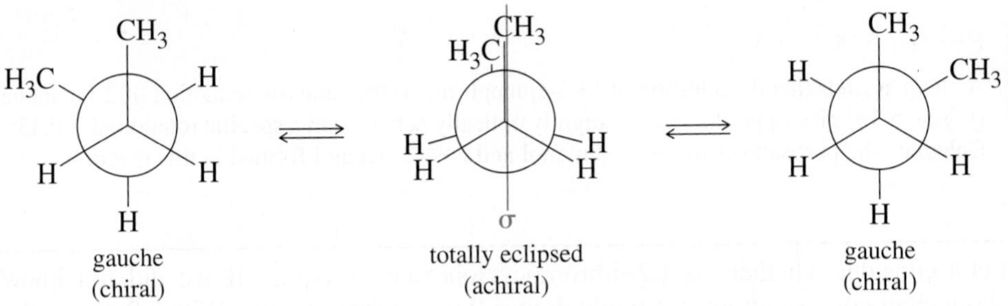

gauche (chiral) ⇌ totally eclipsed (achiral) ⇌ gauche (chiral)

SOLVED PROBLEM 5-6

Draw each compound in its most stable conformation(s). Then draw it in its most symmetric conformation, and determine whether it is capable of showing optical activity.
(a) 2-methylbutane

SOLUTION

problem-solving Hint

A chiral compound has no symmetric (achiral) conformations, and none of its conformations can interconvert with their mirror images.

An achiral compound can (and usually does) rotate through chiral conformations, but the chiral conformations can interconvert with their mirror images.

The most stable conformations of 2-methylbutane are two mirror-image conformations. These conformations are nonsuperimposable, but they can interconvert by rotation around the central bond. So they are not enantiomers.

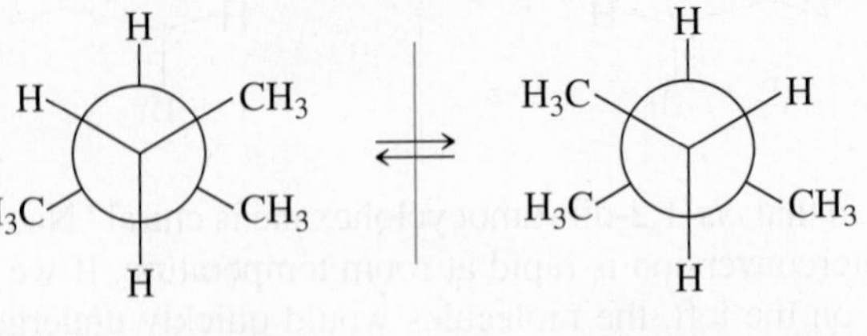

chiral conformation ⇌ chiral conformation

2-Methylbutane has two symmetric conformations: Either of these conformations is sufficient to show that 2-methylbutane is achiral.

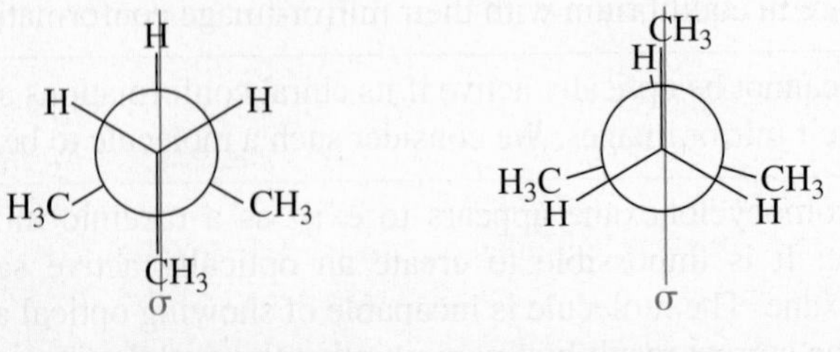

symmetric conformation   symmetric conformation

(b) *trans*-1,2-dibromocyclohexane

SOLUTION

We can draw two nonsuperimposable mirror images of the most stable chair conformation of *trans*-1,2-dibromocyclohexane with both bromines equatorial. These structures cannot interconvert by ring-flips or other rotations about bonds, however. They are mirror-image isomers: enantiomers.

This molecule's chirality is more apparent when drawn in its most symmetric conformation. Drawn flat, the two mirror-image structures of *trans*-1,2-dibromocyclohexane are still nonsuperimposable. This compound is inherently chiral, and no conformational changes can interconvert the two enantiomers.

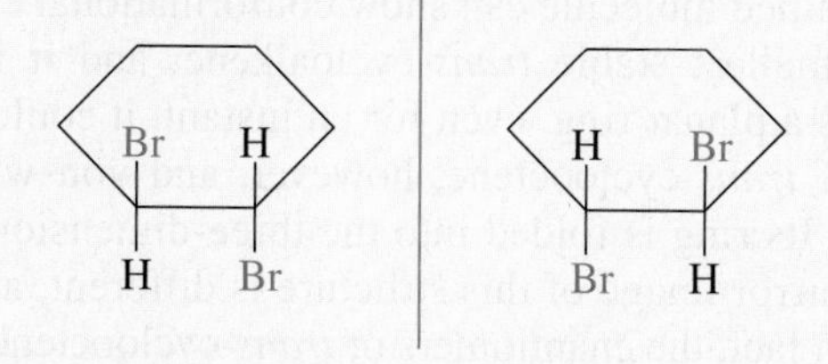

problem-solving Hint

Consider the most symmetric accessible conformation. You can also consider the most stable conformation and see if it can interconvert with its mirror image.

PROBLEM 5-14

1. Make a model of each compound, draw it in its most symmetric conformation, and determine whether it is capable of showing optical activity.
 (a) 1-bromo-1-chloroethane
 (b) 1-bromo-2-chloroethane
 (c) 1,2-dichloropropane
 (d) *cis*-1,3-dibromocyclohexane
 (e) *trans*-1,3-dibromocyclohexane
 (f) *trans*-1,4-dibromocyclohexane

2. Star (*) each asymmetric carbon atom, label each as (*R*) or (*S*), and compare your result from part (1) with the prediction you would make based on the asymmetric carbons.

5-9 Chiral Compounds without Asymmetric Atoms

Most chiral organic compounds have at least one asymmetric carbon atom. Some compounds are chiral because they have another asymmetric atom, such as phosphorus, sulfur, or nitrogen, serving as a chirality center. Some compounds are chiral even though they have no asymmetric atoms at all. In these types of compounds, special characteristics of the molecules' shapes lend chirality to the structure.

5-9A Conformational Enantiomerism

Some molecules are so bulky or so highly strained that they cannot easily convert from one chiral conformation to the mirror-image conformation. They cannot achieve the most symmetric conformation because it has too much steric strain or ring strain. Since these molecules are "locked" into a conformation, we must evaluate the individual locked-in conformation to determine whether the molecule is chiral.

Figure 5-17 shows three conformations of a sterically crowded derivative of biphenyl. The center drawing shows the molecule in its most symmetric conformation. This conformation is planar, and it has a mirror plane of symmetry. If the molecule could achieve this conformation, or even pass through it for an instant, it would not be optically active. This planar conformation is very high in energy, however, because the iodine and bromine atoms are too large to be forced so close together. The molecule is *conformationally locked*. It can exist only in one of the two staggered conformations shown on the left and

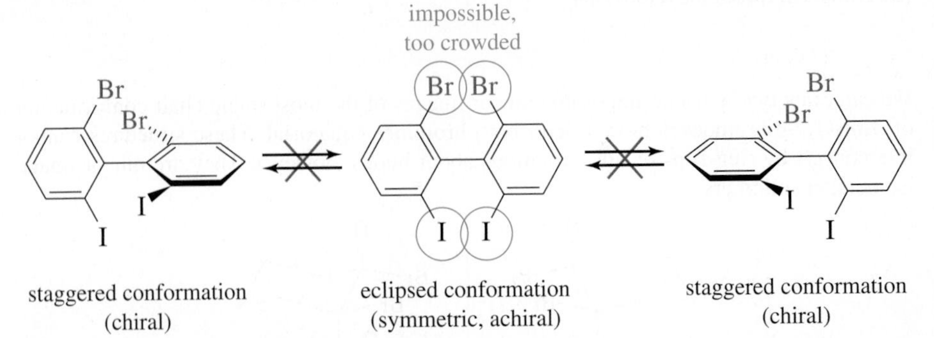

impossible, too crowded

staggered conformation (chiral) | eclipsed conformation (symmetric, achiral) | staggered conformation (chiral)

■ **FIGURE 5-17**
Three conformations of a biphenyl. This biphenyl cannot pass through its symmetric conformation because there is too much crowding of the iodine and bromine atoms. The molecule is "locked" into one of the two chiral, enantiomeric, staggered conformations.

right. These conformations are nonsuperimposable mirror images, and they do not interconvert. They are enantiomers, and they can be separated and isolated. Each of them is optically active, and they have equal and opposite specific rotations.

Even a simple strained molecule can show conformational enantiomerism. *trans*-Cyclooctene is the smallest stable *trans*-cycloalkene, and it is strained. If *trans*-cyclooctene existed as a planar ring, even for an instant, it could not be chiral. Make a molecular model of *trans*-cyclooctene, however, and you will see that it cannot exist as a planar ring. Its ring is folded into the three-dimensional structure pictured in Figure 5-18. The mirror image of this structure is different, and *trans*-cyclooctene is a chiral molecule. In fact, the enantiomers of *trans*-cyclooctene have been separated and characterized, and they are optically active.

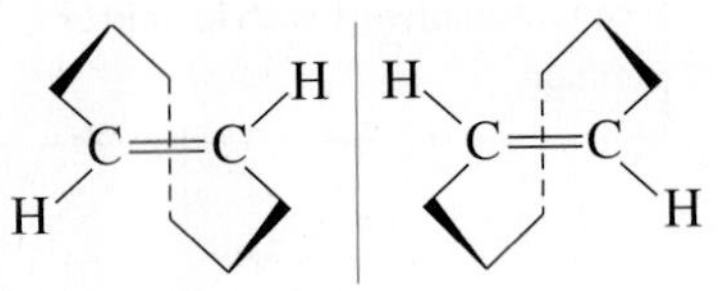

■ **FIGURE 5-18**
Conformational enantiomerism. *trans*-Cyclooctene is strained, unable to achieve a symmetric planar conformation. It is locked into one of these two enantiomeric conformations.

5-9B Allenes

Allenes are compounds that contain the C=C=C unit, with two C=C double bonds meeting at a single carbon atom. The parent compound, propadiene, has the common name *allene*.

$$H_2C{=}C{=}CH_2$$

allene (central carbon: *sp* hybridized)

In allene, the central carbon atom is *sp* hybridized and linear (Section 2-4), and the two outer carbon atoms are sp^2 hybridized and trigonal. We might imagine that the whole molecule lies in a plane, but this is not correct. The central *sp* hybrid carbon atom must use different *p* orbitals to form the pi bonds with the two outer carbon atoms. The two unhybridized *p* orbitals on the *sp* hybrid carbon atom are perpendicular, so the two pi bonds must also be perpendicular. Figure 5-19 shows the bonding and three-dimensional structure of allene. Allene itself is achiral. If you make a model of its mirror image, you will find it identical with the original molecule. If we add some substituents to allene, however, the molecule may be chiral.

Make a model of the following compound:

$$\overset{1}{CH_3}-\overset{2}{CH}=\overset{3}{C}=\overset{4}{CH}-\overset{5}{CH_3}$$

2,3-pentadiene

Carbon atom 3 is the *sp* hybrid allene-type carbon atom. Carbons 2 and 4 are both sp^2 and planar, but their planes are perpendicular to each other. None of the carbon atoms is attached to four different atoms, so there is no asymmetric carbon atom. Nevertheless, 2,3-pentadiene is chiral, as you should see from your models and from the following drawings of the enantiomers.

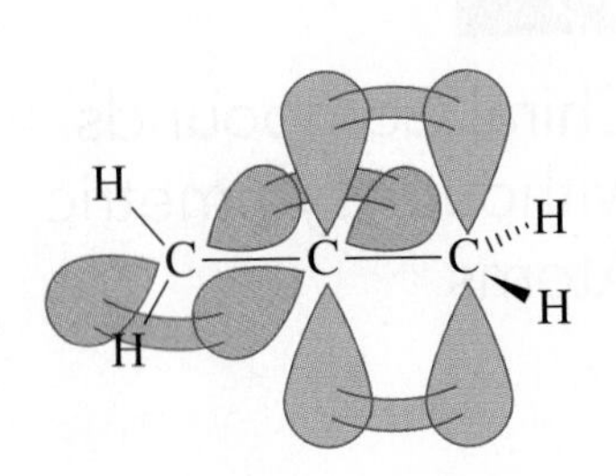

■ **FIGURE 5-19**
Structure of allene. The two ends of the allene molecule are perpendicular.

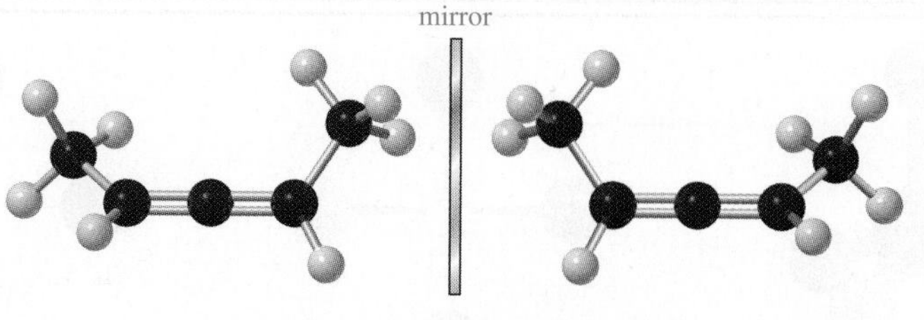

mirror

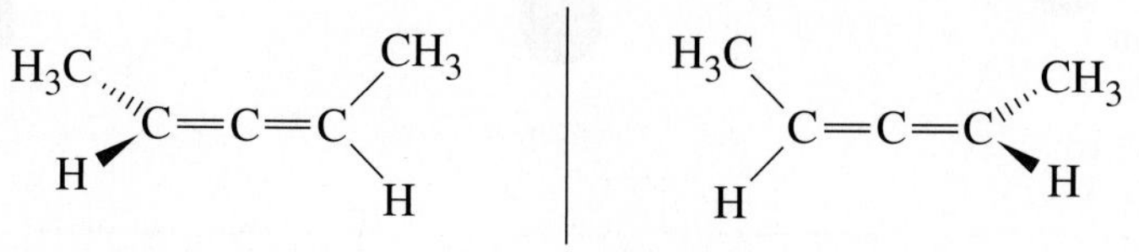

H_3C C=C=C CH_3 H H | H_3C C=C=C CH_3 H H

enantiomers of 2,3-pentadiene

PROBLEM 5-15

Draw three-dimensional representations of the following compounds. Which have asymmetric carbon atoms? Which have no asymmetric carbons but are chiral anyway? Use your models for parts (a) through (d) and any others that seem unclear.

(a) 1,3-dichloropropadiene
(b) 1-chloro-1,2-butadiene
(c) 1-chloro-3-methyl-1,2-butadiene
(d) 1-chloro-1,3-butadiene
(e) 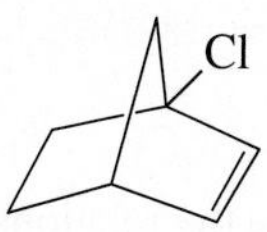 Cl
(f) 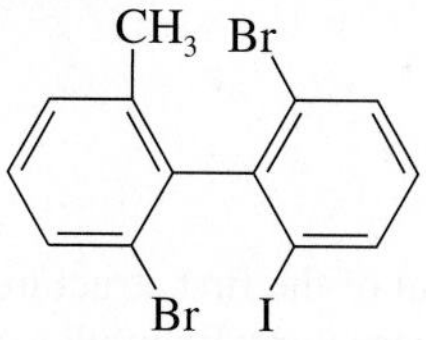 CH_3 Br Br I
(g) 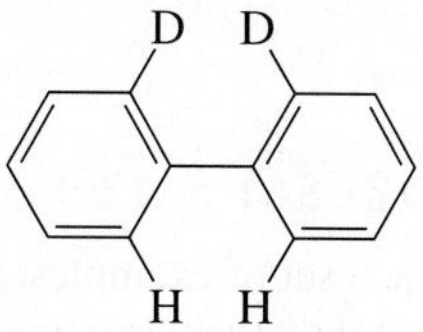 D D H H

problem-solving Hint

Dienes are compounds with two double bonds. In the name, each double bond is given the lower number of its two carbon atoms. *Allenes* are dienes with the two double bonds next to each other, joined at one carbon atom. An allene is chiral if each end has two distinct substituents.

5-10 Fischer Projections

We have been using dashed lines and wedges to indicate perspective in drawing the stereochemistry of asymmetric carbon atoms. When we draw molecules with several asymmetric carbons, perspective drawings become time-consuming and cumbersome. In addition, the complicated drawings make it difficult to see the similarities and differences in groups of stereoisomers.

At the turn of the twentieth century, Emil Fischer was studying the stereochemistry of sugars (Chapter 23), which contain as many as seven asymmetric carbon atoms. To draw these structures in perspective would have been difficult, and to pick out minor stereochemical differences in the drawings would have been nearly impossible. Fischer developed a symbolic way of drawing asymmetric carbon atoms, allowing them to be drawn rapidly. The **Fischer projection** also facilitates comparison of stereoisomers, holding them in their most symmetric conformation and emphasizing any differences in stereochemistry.

5-10A Drawing Fischer Projections

The Fischer projection looks like a cross, with the asymmetric carbon (usually not drawn in) at the point where the lines cross. The horizontal lines are taken to be wedges—that is, bonds that project out toward the viewer. The vertical lines are taken to project away from the viewer, as dashed lines. Figure 5-20 shows the perspective implied by the Fischer projection. The center drawing, with the wedged horizontal bonds looking like a bow tie, illustrates why this projection is sometimes called the "bow-tie convention." Problem 5-16 should help you to visualize how the Fischer projection is used.

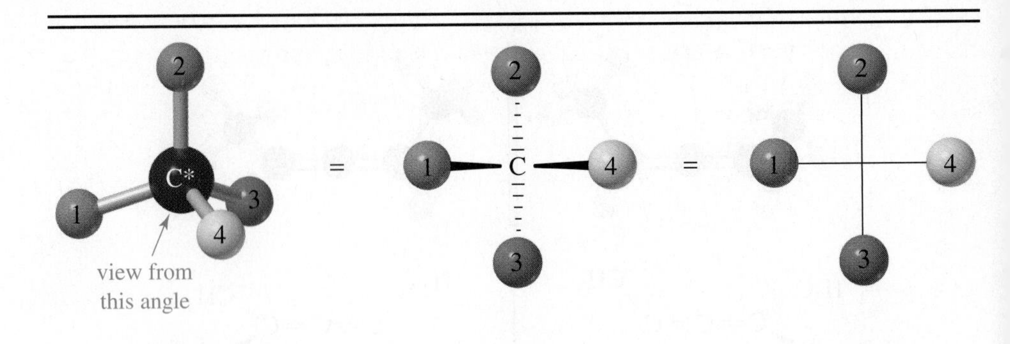

COOH
C····CH$_3$
HO H
view from this angle
(*S*)-lactic acid
perspective drawing

=

COOH
HO ▸ C ◂ H
CH$_3$

=

COOH
HO ┼ H
CH$_3$
(*S*)-lactic acid
Fischer projection

■ FIGURE 5-20
Perspective in a Fischer projection. The Fischer projection uses a cross to represent an asymmetric carbon atom. The horizontal lines project toward the viewer, and the vertical lines project away from the viewer.

PROBLEM 5-16

For each set of examples, make a model of the first structure, and indicate the relationship of each of the other structures to the first structure. Examples of relationships: same compound, enantiomer, structural isomer.

(a)

COOH	COOH	H	CH$_3$
H ┼ OH	HO ┼ H	H$_3$C ┼ COOH	HO ┼ H
CH$_3$	CH$_3$	OH	COOH

(b)

CH$_2$CH$_3$	CH$_3$	CH$_2$CH$_3$	CH$_3$
H ┼ Br	Br ┼ H	Br ┼ H	H ┼ Br
CH$_3$	CH$_2$CH$_3$	CH$_3$	CH$_2$CH$_3$

(c)

	CH$_3$	CH$_3$	CH$_2$CH$_3$
(*R*)-2-butanol	H ┼ OH	HO ┼ H	H ┼ OH
	CH$_2$CH$_3$	CH$_2$CH$_3$	CH$_3$

In working Problem 5-16, you may have noticed that Fischer projections that differ by a 180° rotation are the same. When we rotate a Fischer projection by 180°, the vertical (dashed line) bonds still end up vertical, and the horizontal (wedged) lines still end up horizontal. The "horizontal lines forward, vertical lines back" convention is maintained.

Rotation by 180° is allowed.

COOH
H ┼ OH
CH$_3$

=

COOH
H ▸ C ◂ OH
CH$_3$

= (rotate 180°)

CH$_3$
HO ▸ C ◂ H
COOH

=

CH$_3$
HO ┼ H
COOH

On the other hand, if we were to rotate a Fischer projection by 90°, we would change the configuration and confuse the viewer. The original projection has the vertical groups back (dashed lines) and the horizontal groups forward. When we rotate the projection by 90°, the vertical bonds become horizontal and the horizontal bonds become vertical. The viewer assumes that the horizontal bonds come forward and that the vertical bonds go back. The viewer sees a different molecule (actually, the enantiomer of the original molecule).

A 90° rotation is NOT allowed.

COOH / H—OH / CH_3 = COOH / H▸C◂OH / CH_3 (90° rotation) = H / H_3C···C···COOH / OH ≠ H / H_3C—COOH / OH

incorrect orientation — enantiomer

In comparing Fischer projections, we cannot rotate them by 90° and we cannot flip them over. Either of these operations gives an incorrect representation of the molecule. The Fischer projection must be kept in the plane of the paper, and it may be rotated only by 180°.

The final rule for drawing Fischer projections helps to ensure that we do not rotate the drawing by 90°. This rule is that the carbon chain is drawn along the vertical line of the Fischer projection, usually with the IUPAC numbering from top to bottom. In most cases, this numbering places the most highly oxidized carbon substituent at the top. For example, to represent (*R*)-1,2-propanediol with a Fischer projection, we should arrange the three carbon atoms along the vertical. C1 is placed at the top, and C3 at the bottom.

$^1CH_2OH$ / ^2C···$^3CH_3$, H, OH = $^1CH_2OH$ / H▸^2C◂OH / $^3CH_3$ = $^1CH_2OH$ / H—^{2}—OH / $^3CH_3$

viewed from this angle

(*R*)-1,2-propanediol

PROBLEM 5-17

Draw a Fischer projection for each compound. Remember that the cross represents an asymmetric carbon atom, and the carbon chain should be along the vertical, with the IUPAC numbering from top to bottom.

(a) (*S*)-1,2-propanediol
(b) (*R*)-2-bromo-1-butanol
(c) (*S*)-1,2-dibromobutane
(d) (*R*)-2-butanol
(e) (*R*)-glyceraldehyde, HO—$^3CH_2$—^2CH(OH)—^1CHO

problem-solving **Hint**

Interchanging any two groups on a Fischer projection (or on a perspective drawing) inverts the configuration of that asymmetric carbon from (*R*) to (*S*) or from (*S*) to (*R*).

5-10B Drawing Mirror Images of Fischer Projections

How does one draw the mirror image of a molecule drawn in Fischer projection? With our perspective drawings, the rule was to reverse left and right while keeping the other directions (up and down, front and back) in their same positions. This rule still applies to Fischer projections. Interchanging the groups on the horizontal part of the cross reverses left and right while leaving the other directions unchanged.

COOH / H—OH / CH_3 — (*R*)-lactic acid

COOH / HO—H / CH_3 — (*S*)-lactic acid

Testing for enantiomerism is particularly simple using Fischer projections. If the Fischer projections are properly drawn (carbon chain along the vertical), and if the mirror image cannot be made to look the same as the original structure with a 180° rotation in the plane of the paper, the two mirror images are enantiomers. In the following examples, any groups that fail to superimpose after a 180° rotation are circled in red.

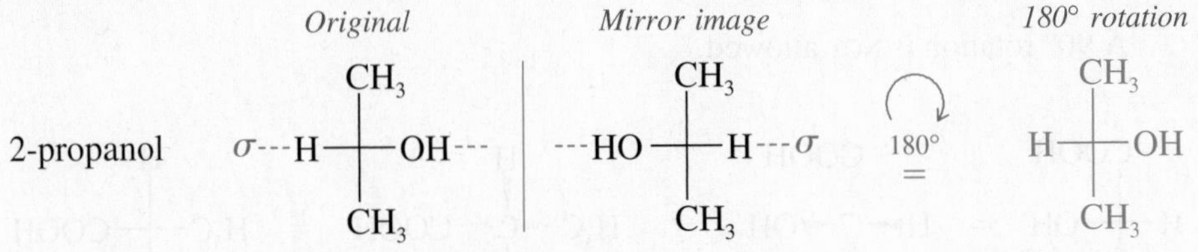

Original *Mirror image* *180° rotation*

2-propanol

These mirror images are the same. 2-Propanol is achiral.

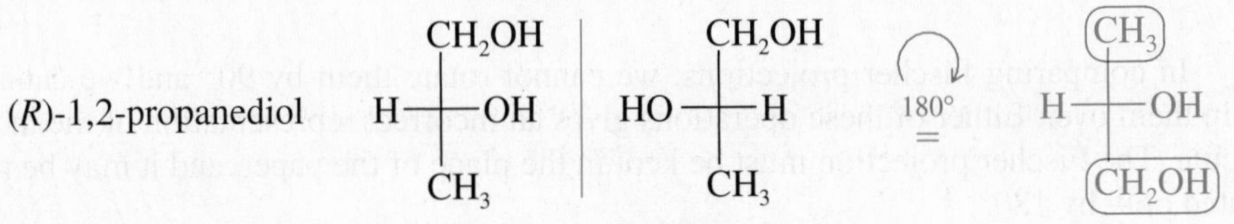

(R)-1,2-propanediol

These mirror images are different. 1,2-Propanediol is chiral.

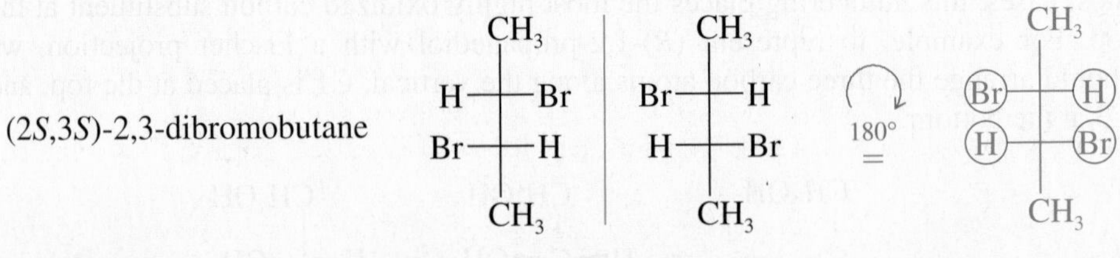

(2S,3S)-2,3-dibromobutane

These mirror images are different. This structure is chiral.

Mirror planes of symmetry are particularly easy to identify from the Fischer projection because this projection is normally the most symmetric conformation. In the first preceding example (2-propanol) and in the following example [(2S,3R)-2,3-dibromobutane], the symmetry planes are indicated in red; these molecules with symmetry planes cannot be chiral.

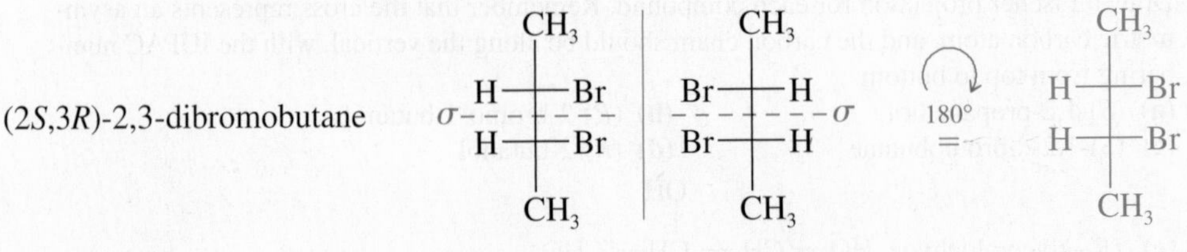

(2S,3R)-2,3-dibromobutane

These mirror images are the same. This structure is achiral.

PROBLEM 5-18

For each Fischer projection

1. Make a model.
2. Draw the mirror image.
3. Determine whether the mirror image is the same as, or different from, the original structure.
4. Draw any mirror planes of symmetry that are apparent from the Fischer projections.

(a) CHO; H—|—OH; CH_2OH

(b) CH_2OH; H—|—Br; CH_2OH

(c) CH_2Br; Br—|—Br; CH_3

(d) CHO; H—|—OH; H—|—OH; CH_2OH

(e) CH_2OH; H—|—OH; H—|—OH; CH_2OH

(f) CH_2OH; HO—|—H; H—|—OH; CH_2OH

5-10C Assigning (*R*) and (*S*) Configurations from Fischer Projections

The Cahn–Ingold–Prelog convention (Section 5-3) can be applied to structures drawn using Fischer projections. Let's review the two rules for assigning (*R*) and (*S*): (1) Assign priorities to the groups bonded to the asymmetric carbon atom; (2) put the lowest-priority group (usually H) in back, and draw an arrow from group 1 to group 2 to group 3. Clockwise is (*R*), and counterclockwise is (*S*).

The (*R*) or (*S*) configuration can also be determined directly from the Fischer projection, without having to convert it to a perspective drawing. The lowest-priority atom is usually hydrogen. In the Fischer projection, the carbon chain is along the vertical line, so the hydrogen atom is usually on the horizontal line and projects out in front. Once we have assigned priorities, we can draw an arrow from group 1 to group 2 to group 3 and see which way it goes. If the molecule were turned around so that the hydrogen would be in back [as in the definition of (*R*) and (*S*)], the arrow would rotate in the other direction. By mentally turning the arrow around (or simply applying the rule backward), we can assign the configuration.

As an example, consider the Fischer projection formula of one of the enantiomers of glyceraldehyde. First priority goes to the —OH group, followed by the —CHO group and the —CH_2OH group. The hydrogen atom receives the lowest priority. The arrow from group 1 to group 2 to group 3 appears counterclockwise in the Fischer projection. If the molecule is turned over so the hydrogen is in back, the arrow is clockwise, so this is the (*R*) enantiomer of glyceraldehyde.

counterclockwise: ② CHO; H—|—OH ①; CH_2OH ③ = CHO; [H]—C—OH; CH_2OH (hydrogen in front) = clockwise: ② CHO; H····C; ① HO, ③ CH_2OH

Fischer projection
(*R*)-(+)-glyceraldehyde

perspective drawing
(*R*)-(+)-glyceraldehyde

PROBLEM 5-19

For each Fischer projection, label each asymmetric carbon atom as (*R*) or (*S*).
(a)–(f) the structures in Problem 5-18

(g) CH_2CH_3; H—|—Br; CH_3

(h) COOH; H_2N—|—H; CH_3

(i) CH_2OH; Br—|—Cl; CH_3 (careful—no hydrogen)

problem-solving **Hint**

When naming (*R*) and (*S*) from Fischer projections with the hydrogen on a horizontal bond (toward you instead of away from you), just apply the normal rules backward.

SUMMARY Fischer Projections and Their Use

1. They are most useful for compounds with two or more asymmetric carbon atoms.
2. Asymmetric carbons are at the centers of crosses.
3. The vertical lines project away from the viewer, the horizontal lines toward the viewer (like a bow tie).
4. The carbon chain is placed along the vertical, with the IUPAC numbering from top to bottom. In most cases, this places the more oxidized end (the carbon with the most bonds to O or halogen) at the top.
5. The entire projection can be rotated 180° (but not 90°) in the plane of the paper without changing its stereochemistry.
6. Interchanging any two groups on an asymmetric carbon (for example, those on the horizontal line) inverts its stereochemistry.

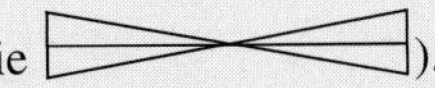

5-11 Diastereomers

We have defined *stereoisomers* as isomers whose atoms are bonded together in the same order but differ in how the atoms are directed in space. We have also considered enantiomers (mirror-image isomers) in detail. All other stereoisomers are classified as **diastereomers**, which are defined as *stereoisomers that are not mirror images*. Most diastereomers are either geometric isomers or compounds containing two or more chirality centers.

5-11A Cis-trans Isomerism on Double Bonds

We have already seen one class of diastereomers, the **cis-trans isomers**, or **geometric isomers**. For example, there are two isomers of 2-butene:

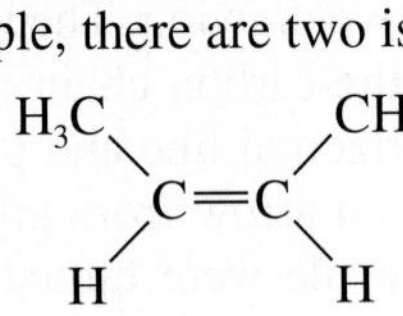

$H_3C(H)C=C(H)CH_3$ — *cis*-2-butene

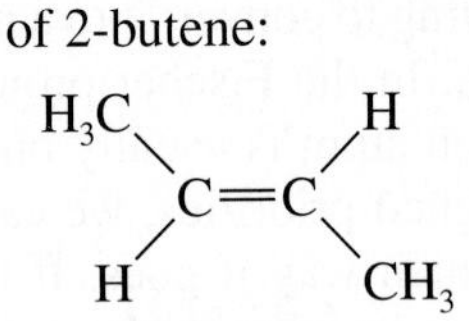

$H_3C(H)C=C(CH_3)H$ — *trans*-2-butene

These stereoisomers are not mirror images of each other, so they are not enantiomers. They are diastereomers.

5-11B Cis-trans Isomerism on Rings

Cis-trans isomerism is also possible when there is a ring present. *Cis*- and *trans*-1,2-dimethylcyclopentane are geometric isomers, and they are also diastereomers. The trans diastereomer has an enantiomer, but the cis diastereomer has an internal mirror plane of symmetry, so it is achiral.

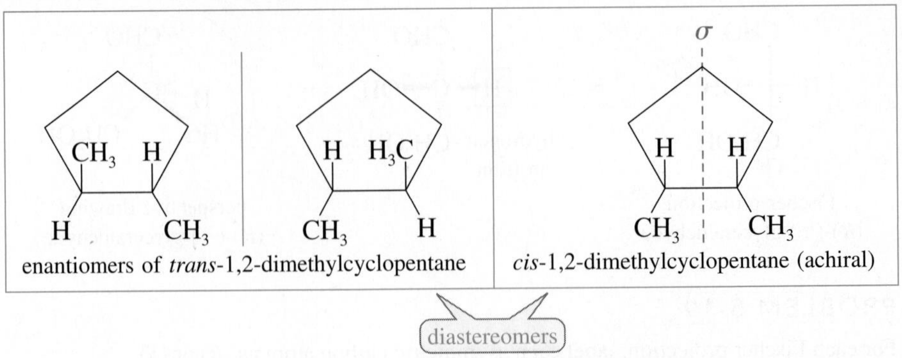

enantiomers of *trans*-1,2-dimethylcyclopentane

cis-1,2-dimethylcyclopentane (achiral)

diastereomers

5-11C Diastereomers of Molecules with Two or More Chirality Centers

Apart from geometric isomers, most other compounds that show diastereomerism have two or more chirality centers, usually asymmetric carbon atoms. For example, 2-bromo-3-chlorobutane has two asymmetric carbon atoms, and it exists in two diastereomeric forms (shown next). Make molecular models of these two stereoisomers.

not mirror images

diastereomers

These two structures are not the same; they are stereoisomers because they differ in the orientation of their atoms in space. They are not enantiomers, however, because they are not mirror images of each other: C2 has the (*S*) configuration in both structures, while C3 is (*R*) in the structure on the left and (*S*) in the structure on the right. The C3 carbon atoms are mirror images of each other, but the C2 carbon atoms are not. If these two compounds were mirror images of each other, both asymmetric carbons would have to be mirror images of each other.

Since these compounds are stereoisomers but not enantiomers, they must be diastereomers. In fact, both of these diastereomers are chiral and each has an enantiomer. Thus, there is a total of four stereoisomeric 2-bromo-3-chlorobutanes: two pairs of enantiomers. Either member of one pair of enantiomers is a diastereomer of either member of the other pair.

(2*S*, 3*R*) (2*R*, 3*S*)
enantiomers

(2*S*, 3*S*) (2*R*, 3*R*)
enantiomers

diastereomers

We have now seen all the types of isomers we need to study, and we can diagram their relationships and summarize their definitions.

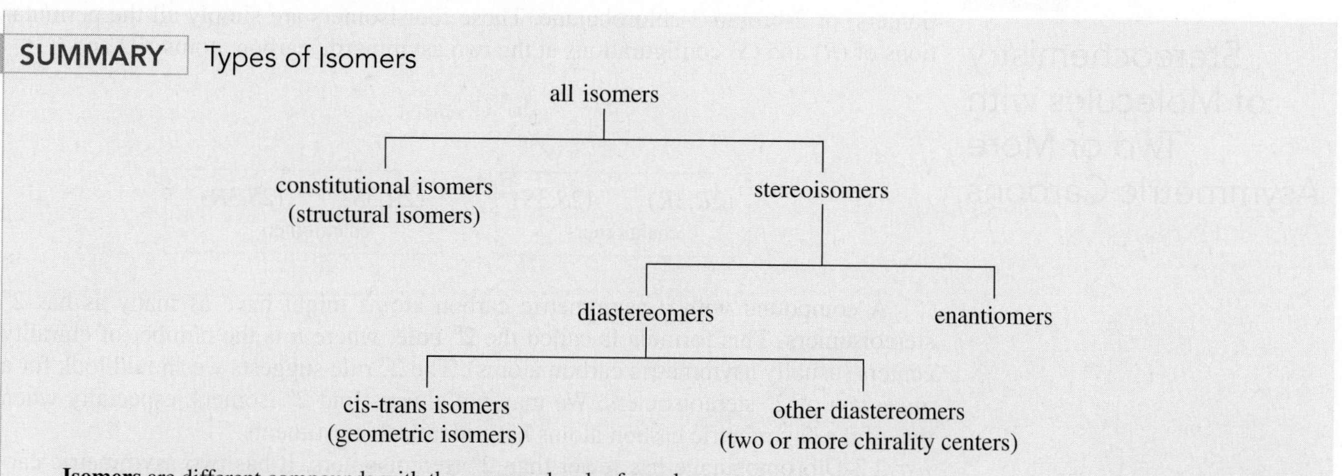

Isomers are different compounds with the same molecular formula.

Constitutional isomers are isomers that differ in the order in which atoms are bonded together. Constitutional isomers are sometimes called **structural isomers** because they have different connections among their atoms.

(Continued)

Stereoisomers are isomers that differ only in the orientation of the atoms in space.

Enantiomers are mirror-image isomers.

Diastereomers are stereoisomers that are not mirror images of each other.

Cis-trans isomers (geometric isomers) are diastereomers that differ in their cis-trans arrangement on a ring or double bond.

PROBLEM 5-20

For each pair, give the relationship between the two compounds. Making models will be helpful.

(a) (2*R*,3*S*)-2,3-dibromohexane and (2*S*,3*R*)-2,3-dibromohexane

(b) (2*R*,3*S*)-2,3-dibromohexane and (2*R*,3*R*)-2,3-dibromohexane

(c) 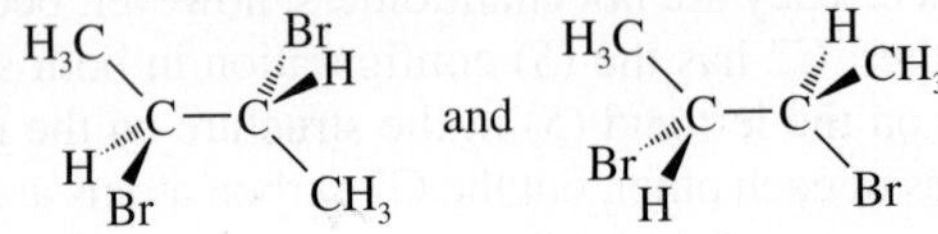 and

(d) 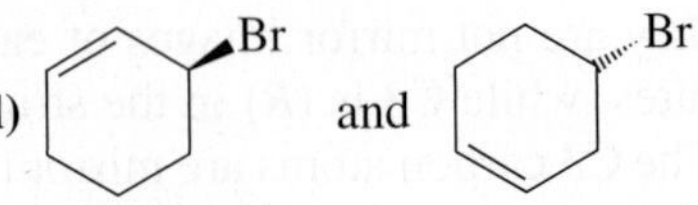 and

(e) 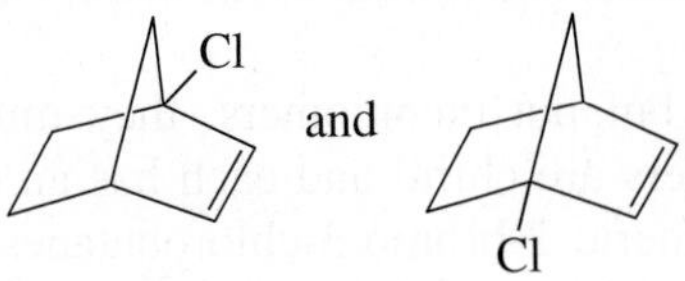 and

(f) 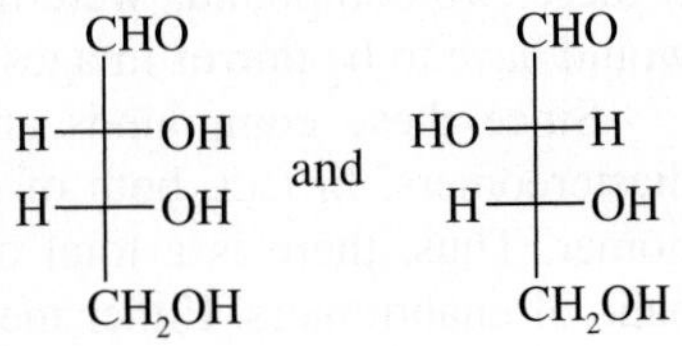 and

(g) 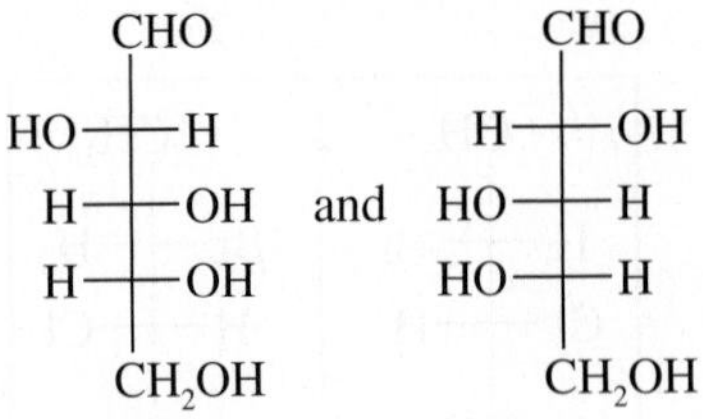 and

*(h) 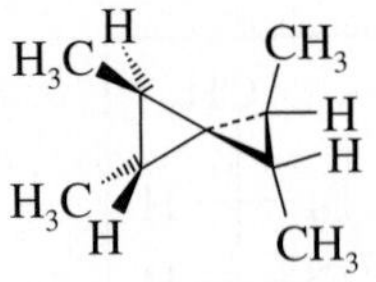 and its mirror image

(i) 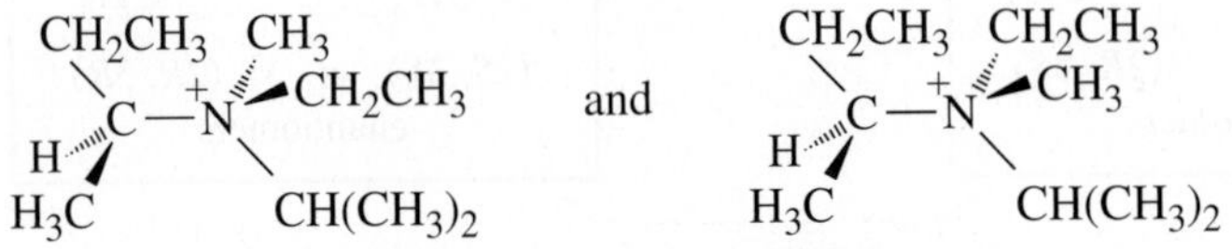 and

5-12 Stereochemistry of Molecules with Two or More Asymmetric Carbons

In the preceding section, we saw there are four stereoisomers (two pairs of enantiomers) of 2-bromo-3-chlorobutane. These four isomers are simply all the permutations of (*R*) and (*S*) configurations at the two asymmetric carbon atoms, C2 and C3:

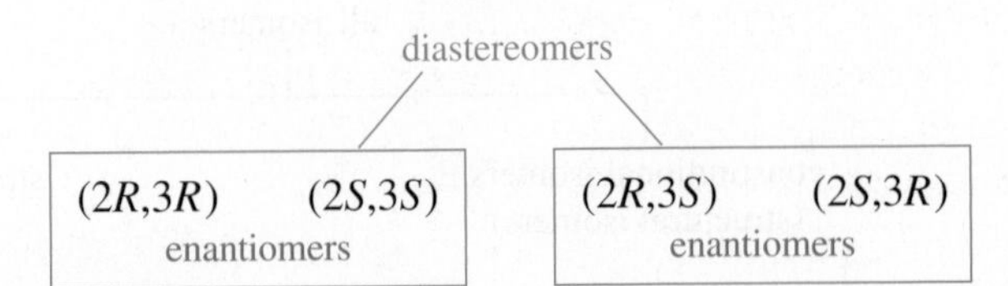

A compound with n asymmetric carbon atoms might have as many as has 2^n stereoisomers. This formula is called the **2^n rule**, where n is the number of chirality centers (usually asymmetric carbon atoms). The 2^n rule suggests we should look for a *maximum* of 2^n stereoisomers. We may not always find 2^n isomers, especially when two of the asymmetric carbon atoms have identical substituents.

2,3-Dibromobutane has fewer than 2^n stereoisomers. It has two asymmetric carbons (C2 and C3), so the 2^n rule predicts a maximum of four stereoisomers. The four permutations of (*R*) and (*S*) configurations at C2 and C3 are shown next. Make molecular models of these structures to compare them.

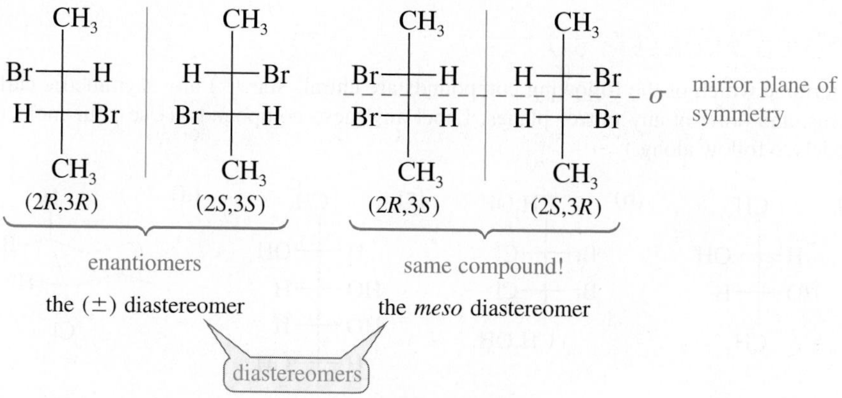

(2*R*,3*R*) (2*S*,3*S*) (2*R*,3*S*) (2*S*,3*R*)

mirror plane of symmetry

enantiomers — the (±) diastereomer

same compound! — the *meso* diastereomer

diastereomers

There are only three stereoisomers of 2,3-dibromobutane because two of the four structures are identical. The diastereomer on the right is achiral, having a mirror plane of symmetry. The asymmetric carbon atoms have identical substituents, and the one with (*R*) configuration reflects into the other having (*S*) configuration. It seems almost as though the molecule were a racemic mixture within itself.

5-13 Meso Compounds

Compounds that are achiral even though they have asymmetric carbon atoms are called **meso compounds**. The (2*R*,3*S*) isomer of 2,3-dibromobutane is a meso compound; most meso compounds have this kind of symmetric structure, with two similar halves of the molecule having opposite configurations. In speaking of the two diastereomers of 2,3-dibromobutane, the symmetric one is called the *meso diastereomer*, and the chiral one is called the (±) *diastereomer*, since one enantiomer is (+) and the other is (−).

> MESO COMPOUND: An achiral compound that has chirality centers (usually asymmetric carbons).

The term *meso* (Greek, "middle") was used to describe an achiral member of a set of diastereomers, some of which are chiral. The optically inactive isomer seemed to be in the "middle" between the dextrorotatory and levorotatory isomers. The definition just given ("an achiral compound with chirality centers") is nearly as complete, and more easily applied, especially when you remember that chirality centers are usually asymmetric carbon atoms.

We have already seen other meso compounds, although we have not yet called them that. For example, the cis isomer of 1,2-dichlorocyclopentane has two asymmetric carbon atoms, yet it is achiral. Thus it is a meso compound. *Cis*-1,2,-dibromocyclohexane is not symmetric in its chair conformation, but it consists of equal amounts of two enantiomeric chair conformations in a rapid equilibrium. We are justified in looking at the molecule in its symmetric flat conformation to show that it is achiral and meso. For acyclic compounds, the Fischer projection helps to show the symmetry of meso compounds.

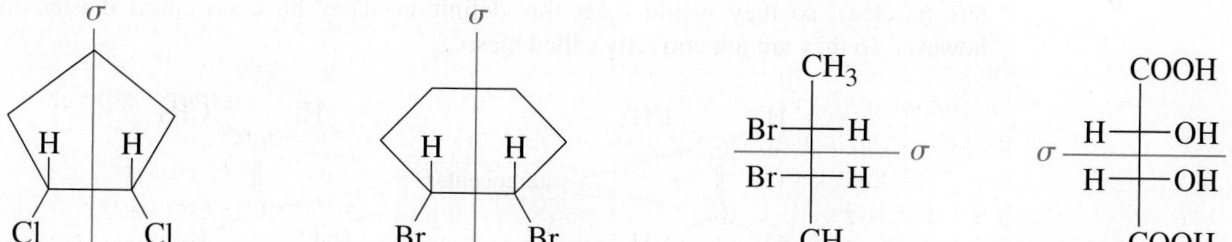

cis-1,2-dichlorocyclopentane — *cis*-1,2-dibromocyclohexane — *meso*-2,3-dibromobutane — *meso*-tartaric acid

SOLVED PROBLEM 5-7

Determine which of the following compounds are chiral. Star (*) any asymmetric carbon atoms, and draw in any mirror planes. Label any meso compounds. (Use your molecular models to follow along.)

(a)
CH_3
H—OH
HO—H
CH_3

(b)
CH_2OH
Br—Cl
Br—Cl
CH_2OH

(c)
CH_3
H—OH
HO—H
HO—H
H—OH
CH_3

(d)
H, Br, H, Cl (cyclohexane ring)

SOLUTION

(a)
CH_3 / H—*—OH / HO—*—H / CH_3 | CH_3 / HO—*—H / H—*—OH / CH_3

This compound does *not* have a plane of symmetry, and we suspect that it is chiral. Drawing the mirror image shows that it is nonsuperimposable on the original structure. These are the enantiomers of a chiral compound.

(b)
CH_2OH / Br—*—Cl / Br—*—Cl / CH_2OH (σ)
meso

(c)
CH_3 / H—*—OH / HO—*—H / HO—*—H / H—*—OH / CH_3 (σ)
meso

Both (b) and (c) have mirror planes of symmetry and are achiral. Because they have asymmetric carbon atoms yet are achiral, they are meso.

(d)

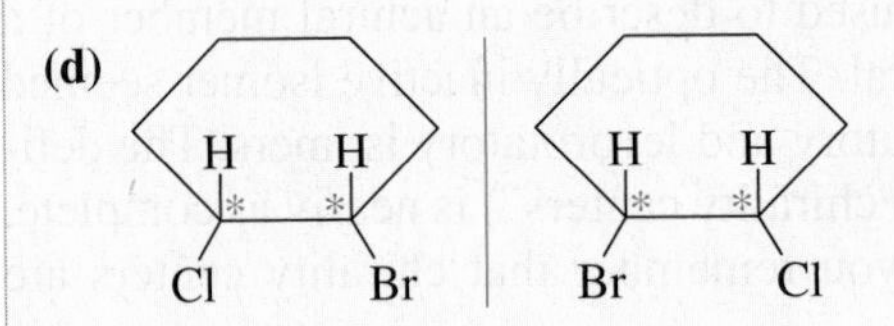

Drawing this compound in its most symmetric conformation (flat) shows that it does not have a mirror plane of symmetry. When we draw the mirror image, it is found to be an enantiomer.

SOLVED PROBLEM 5-8

One source defines a meso compound as "an achiral compound with stereocenters." Why is this a poor definition?

SOLUTION

A stereocenter is an atom at which the interchange of two groups gives a stereoisomer. Stereocenters include both chirality centers and double-bonded carbons giving rise to cis-trans isomers. For example, the isomers of 2-butene are achiral and they contain stereocenters (circled), so they would meet this definition. They have no chiral diastereomers, however, so they are not correctly called meso.

H, CH_3, C=C, H, CH_3 — stereocenters — H, CH_3, C=C, H_3C, H

PROBLEM 5-21

Which of the following compounds are chiral? Draw each compound in its most symmetric conformation, star (*) any asymmetric carbon atoms, and draw any mirror planes. Label any meso compounds. You may use Fischer projections if you prefer.

(a) *meso*-2,3-dibromo-2,3-dichlorobutane **(b)** (±)-2,3-dibromo-2,3-dichlorobutane
(c) (2*R*,3*S*)-2-bromo-3-chlorobutane **(d)** (2*R*,3*S*)-2,3-dibromobutane
(e) (*R*,*R*)-2,3-dibromobutane

(f) CHO; H—OH; HO—H; CH_2OH **(g)** Br, H, H, H, Br, CH_3, CH_3, H ***(h)** H, CH_3, Br, H, H, Br, CH_3, H

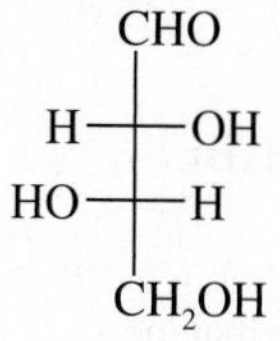

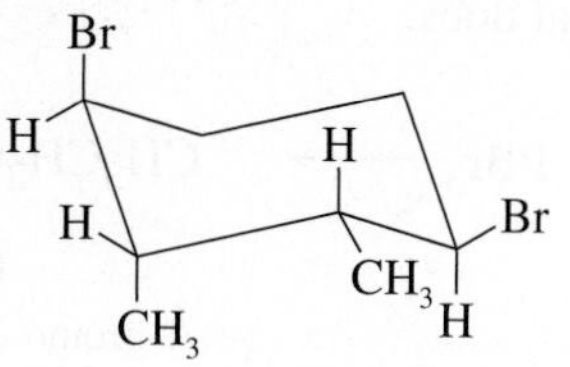

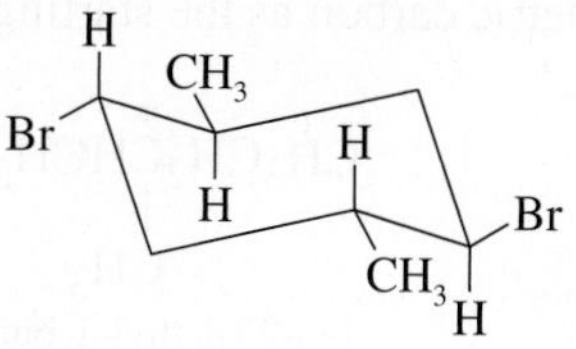

PROBLEM 5-22

Draw all the distinct stereoisomers for each structure. Show the relationships (enantiomers, diastereomers, etc.) between the isomers. Label any meso isomers, and draw any mirror planes of symmetry.

(a) $CH_3—CHCl—CHOH—COOH$
(b) tartaric acid, HOOC—CHOH—CHOH—COOH
(c) HOOC—CHBr—CHOH—CHOH—COOH
(d) **(e)** HO— (cyclopropane with CH_3, CH_3)

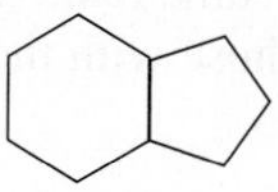

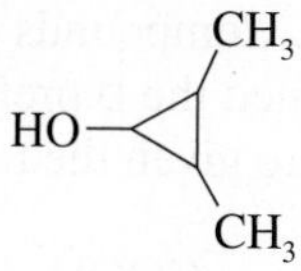

problem-solving **Hint**

In part (e), the carbon bearing the OH group is not asymmetric, but it can be a stereocenter if the methyl groups are cis to each other.

5-14 Absolute and Relative Configuration

Throughout our study of stereochemistry, we have drawn three-dimensional representations, and we have spoken of asymmetric carbons having the (*R*) or (*S*) configuration. These ways of describing the configuration of a chirality center are *absolute*; that is, they give the actual orientation of the atoms in space. We say that these methods specify the **absolute configuration** of the molecule. For example, given the name "(*R*)-2-butanol," any chemist can construct an accurate molecular model or draw a three-dimensional representation.

ABSOLUTE CONFIGURATION: The detailed stereochemical picture of a molecule, including how the atoms are arranged in space. Alternatively, the (*R*) or (*S*) configuration at each chirality center.

Chemists have determined the absolute configurations of many chiral compounds since 1951, when X-ray crystallography was first used to find the orientation of atoms in space. Before 1951, there was no way to link the stereochemical drawings with the actual enantiomers and their observed rotations. No absolute configurations were known. It was possible, however, to correlate the configuration of one compound with another and to show that two compounds had the same or opposite configurations. When we convert one compound into another using a reaction that does not break bonds at the asymmetric carbon atom, we know that the product must have the same **relative configuration** as the reactant, even if we cannot determine the absolute configuration of either compound.

RELATIVE CONFIGURATION: The experimentally determined relationship between the configurations of two molecules, even though we may not know the absolute configuration of either.

For example, optically active 2-methyl-1-butanol reacts with PBr_3 to give optically active 1-bromo-2-methylbutane. None of the bonds to the asymmetric carbon atom are broken in this reaction, so the product must have the same configuration at the asymmetric carbon as the starting material does.

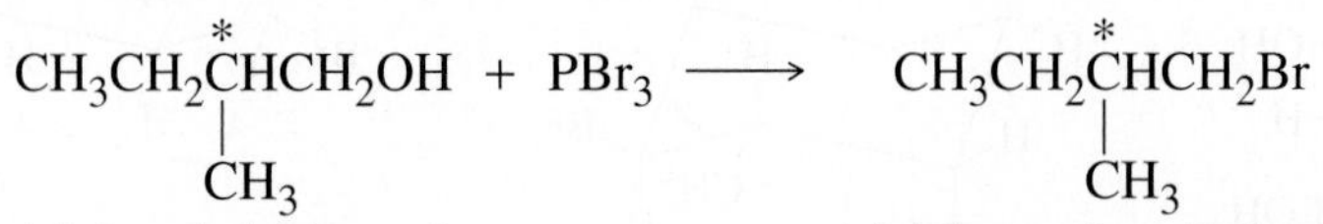

$$CH_3CH_2\overset{*}{C}H(CH_3)CH_2OH + PBr_3 \longrightarrow CH_3CH_2\overset{*}{C}H(CH_3)CH_2Br$$

(+)-2-methyl-1-butanol $[\alpha]^{25}_{d} = +5.8°$

(−)-1-bromo-2-methylbutane $[\alpha]^{25}_{d} = -4.0°$

We say that (+)-2-methyl-1-butanol and (−)-1-bromo-2-methylbutane have the same relative configuration, even though we don't have the foggiest idea whether either of these is (*R*) or (*S*) unless we relate them to a compound whose absolute configuration has been established by X-ray crystallography.

Before the advent of X-ray crystallography, several systems were used to compare the relative configurations of chiral compounds with those of standard compounds. Only one of these systems is still in common use today: the **D–L system**, also known as the *Fischer–Rosanoff convention*. The configurations of sugars and amino acids were related to the enantiomers of glyceraldehyde. Compounds with the same relative configuration as (+)-glyceraldehyde were assigned the D prefix, and those with the relative configuration of (−)-glyceraldehyde were given the L prefix.

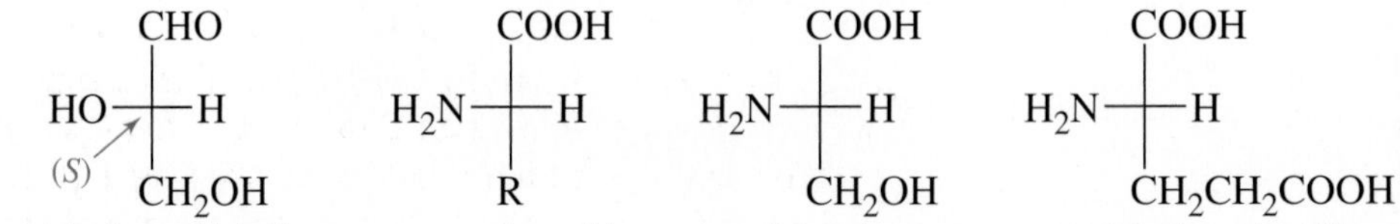

CHO / HO—C—H / CH_2OH (*S*) — L-(−)-glyceraldehyde

COOH / H_2N—C—H / R — an L-amino acid

COOH / H_2N—C—H / CH_2OH — L-(−)-serine

COOH / H_2N—C—H / CH_2CH_2COOH — L-(+)-glutamic acid

We now know the absolute configurations of the glyceraldehyde enantiomers: The (+) enantiomer has the (*R*) configuration, with the hydroxyl (OH) group on the right in the Fischer projection. The (−) enantiomer has the (*S*) configuration, with the hydroxyl group on the left. Most naturally occurring amino acids have the L configuration, with the amino (NH_2) group on the left in the Fischer projection.

Sugars have several asymmetric carbons, but they can all be degraded to glyceraldehyde by oxidizing them from the aldehyde end. (We discuss these reactions in Chapter 23.) Most naturally occurring sugars degrade to (+)-glyceraldehyde, so they are given the D prefix. This means that the bottom asymmetric carbon of the sugar has its hydroxyl (OH) group on the right in the Fischer projection.

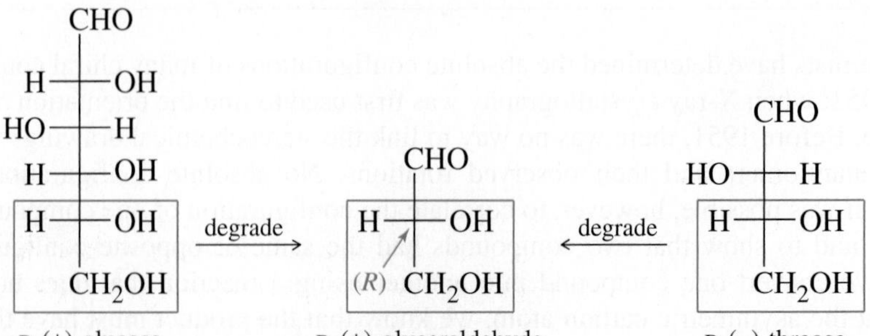

CHO / H—OH / HO—H / H—OH / H—OH / CH_2OH — D-(+)-glucose —degrade→ CHO / H—OH / (*R*) CH_2OH — D-(+)-glyceraldehyde ←degrade— CHO / HO—H / H—OH / CH_2OH — D-(−)-threose

5-15 Physical Properties of Diastereomers

We have seen that enantiomers have identical physical properties except for the direction in which they rotate polarized light. Diastereomers, on the other hand, generally have different physical properties. For example, consider the diastereomers of 2-butene (shown next). The symmetry of *trans*-2-butene causes the dipole moments of the bonds to cancel. The dipole moments in *cis*-2-butene do not cancel but add together to create a molecular dipole moment. The dipole–dipole attractions of *cis*-2-butene give it a higher boiling point than *trans*-2-butene.

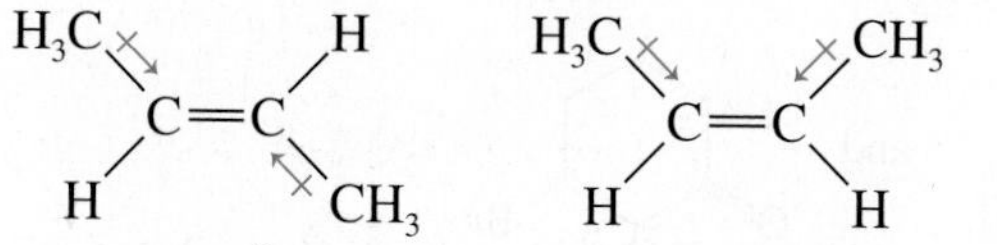

H_3C, H, C=C, H, CH_3
$\mu = 0$
trans-2-butene
bond dipoles cancel
bp = 0.9 °C

H_3C, CH_3, C=C, H, H
$\mu = 0.33$ D
cis-2-butene
vector sum dipole
bp = 3.7 °C

Diastereomers that are not geometric isomers also have different physical properties. The two diastereomers of 2,3-dibromosuccinic acid have melting points that differ by nearly 100 °C!

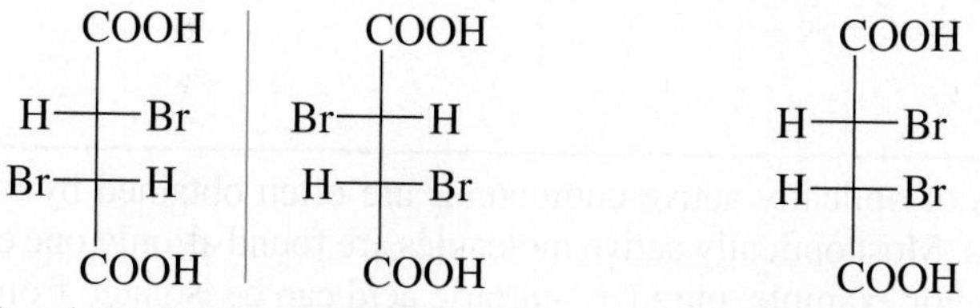

COOH / H–Br / Br–H / COOH | COOH / Br–H / H–Br / COOH
(+) and (−)-2,3-dibromosuccinic acid
mp for either is 158 °C

COOH / H–Br / H–Br / COOH
meso-2,3-dibromosuccinic acid
mp 256 °C

Most of the common sugars are diastereomers of glucose. All these diastereomers have different physical properties. For example, glucose and galactose are diastereomeric sugars that differ only in the stereochemistry of one asymmetric carbon atom, C4.

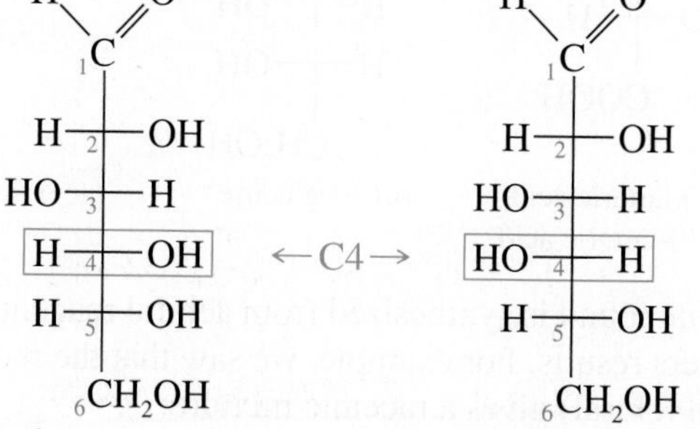

H, O, ^{1}C / H–2–OH / HO–3–H / H–4–OH / H–5–OH / $_6CH_2OH$
D-(+)-glucose, mp 148 °C

←C4→

H, O, ^{1}C / H–2–OH / HO–3–H / HO–4–H / H–5–OH / $_6CH_2OH$
D-(+)-galactose, mp 167 °C

Because diastereomers have different physical properties, we can separate them by ordinary means such as distillation, recrystallization, and chromatography. As we will see in the next section, the separation of enantiomers is a more difficult process.

PROBLEM 5-23

Which of the following pairs of compounds could be separated by recrystallization or distillation?

(a) *meso*-tartaric acid and (±)-tartaric acid (HOOC—CHOH—CHOH—COOH)

(b) CH_2CH_3 / H—O—C(=O) with H—OH / CH_3 ... and ... C(=O)—O—H with CH_2CH_3, CH_3 / H—OH / CH_3

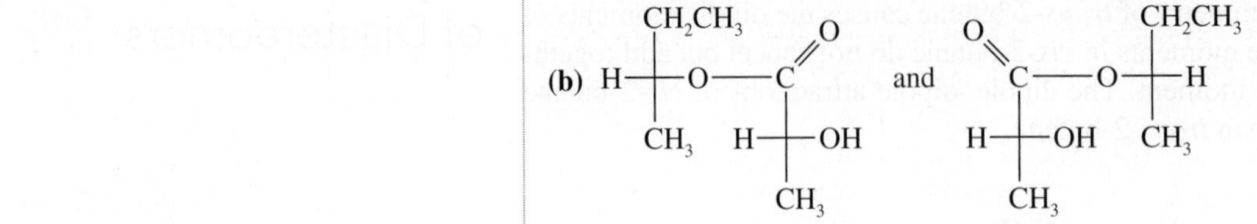

(c) O, Br, Br and O, Br, Br

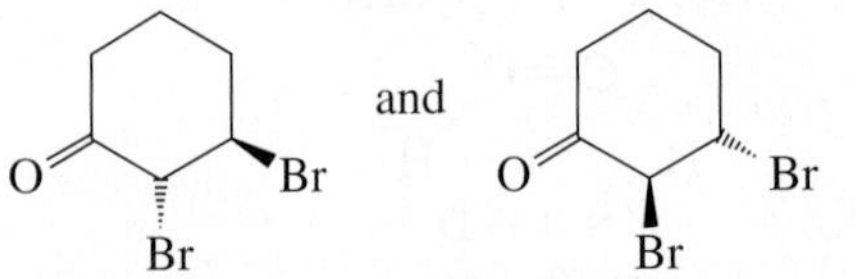

(d)* CH_3, C—H, PhCH$_2$, NH_3^+ ; COOH, H—OH, HO—H, COO^- and CH_3, C—NH_3^+, PhCH$_2$, H ; COOH, H—OH, HO—H, COO^-

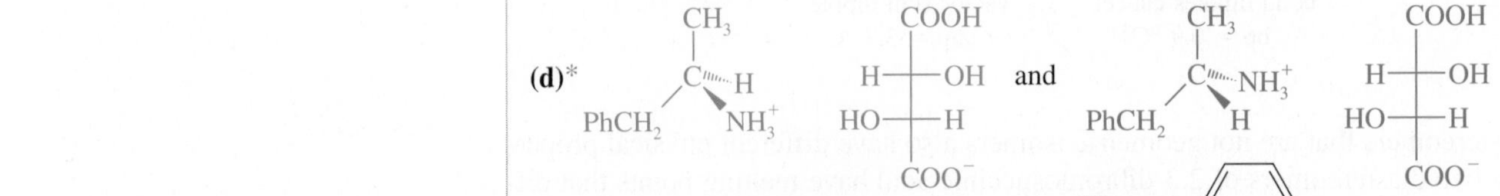

(an acid–base salt)

Ph =

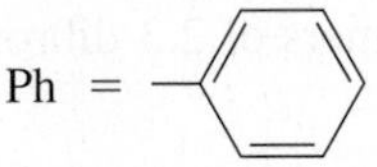

5-16 Resolution of Enantiomers

Pure enantiomers of optically active compounds are often obtained by isolation from biological sources. Most optically active molecules are found as only one enantiomer in living organisms. For example, pure (+)-tartaric acid can be isolated from the precipitate formed by yeast during the fermentation of wine. Pure (+)-glucose is obtained from many different sugar sources, such as grapes, sugar beets, sugarcane, and honey. Alanine is a common amino acid found in protein as the pure (+) enantiomer.

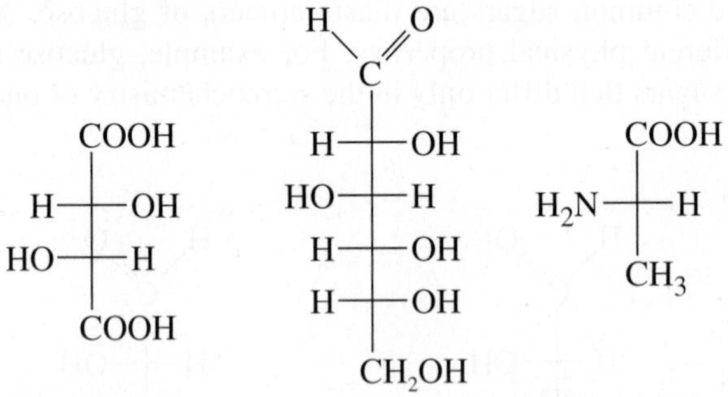

COOH; H—OH; HO—H; COOH — L-(+)-tartaric acid, (2*R*,3*R*)-tartaric acid

H, O, C; H—OH; HO—H; H—OH; H—OH; CH_2OH — D-(+)-glucose

COOH; H_2N—H; CH_3 — L-(+)-alanine

When a chiral compound is synthesized from achiral reagents, however, a racemic mixture of enantiomers results. For example, we saw that the reduction of 2-butanone (achiral) to 2-butanol (chiral) gives a racemic mixture:

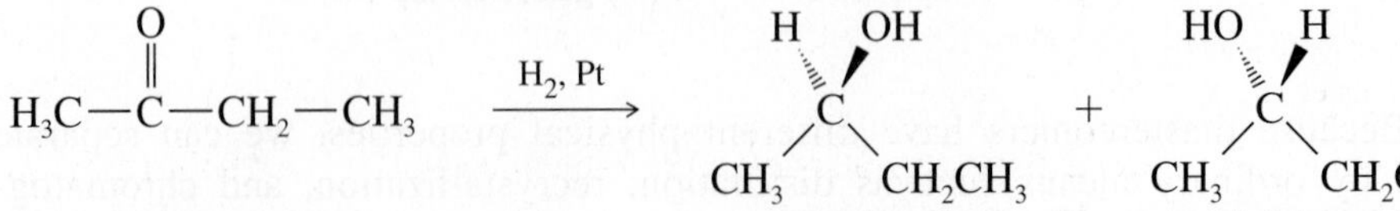

$$H_3C—C(=O)—CH_2—CH_3 \xrightarrow{H_2,\ Pt} (R)\text{-2-butanol} + (S)\text{-2-butanol}$$

2-butanone; H, OH, C, CH_3, CH_2CH_3 (*R*)-2-butanol; HO, H, C, CH_3, CH_2CH_3 (*S*)-2-butanol

If we need one pure enantiomer of 2-butanol, we must find a way of separating it from the other enantiomer. The separation of enantiomers is called **resolution**, and it is a different process from the usual physical separations. A chiral probe is necessary for the resolution of enantiomers; such a chiral compound or apparatus is called a **resolving agent**.

In 1848, Louis Pasteur noticed that a salt of racemic (±)-tartaric acid crystallizes into mirror-image crystals. Using a microscope and a pair of tweezers, he physically separated the enantiomeric crystals. He found that solutions made from the "left-handed" crystals rotate polarized light in one direction and solutions made from the "right-handed" crystals rotate polarized light in the opposite direction. Pasteur had accomplished the first artificial resolution of enantiomers. Unfortunately, few racemic compounds crystallize as separate enantiomers, and other methods of separation are required.

Wine sediments often contain salts of tartaric acid. This wine cork bears crystals of the potassium salt of L-(+)-tartaric acid.

5-16A Chemical Resolution of Enantiomers

The traditional method for resolving a racemic mixture into its enantiomers is to use an enantiomerically pure natural product that bonds with the compound to be resolved. When the enantiomers of the racemic compound bond to the pure resolving agent, a pair of diastereomers results. The diastereomers are separated, then the resolving agent is cleaved from the separated enantiomers.

Let's consider how we might resolve a racemic mixture of (*R*)- and (*S*)-2-butanol. We need a resolving agent that reacts with an alcohol and that is readily available in an enantiomerically pure state. A carboxylic acid combines with an alcohol to form an ester. Although we have not yet studied the chemistry of esters (Chapter 21), the following equation shows how an acid and an alcohol can combine with the loss of water to form an ester.

$$\underset{\text{acid}}{\text{R—C(=O)—OH}} + \underset{\text{alcohol}}{\text{R}'\text{—OH}} \xrightleftharpoons{(\text{H}^+ \text{ catalyst})} \underset{\text{ester}}{\text{R—C(=O)—O—R}'} + \underset{\text{water}}{\text{H—O—H}}$$

For our resolving agent, we need an optically active chiral acid to react with 2-butanol. Any winery can provide large amounts of pure (+)-tartaric acid. Figure 5-21 shows that diastereomeric esters are formed when (*R*)- and (*S*)-2-butanol react with (+)-tartaric acid. We can represent the reaction schematically as follows:

$$\begin{array}{c}\boxed{(R)\text{- and }(S)\text{-2-butanol}}\\ \text{plus}\\ \boxed{(R,R)\text{-tartaric acid}}\end{array} \xrightarrow{\text{H}^+} \underbrace{\boxed{\begin{array}{c}(R)\text{-2-butyl}\\(R,R)\text{-tartrate}\end{array}} + \boxed{\begin{array}{c}(S)\text{-2-butyl}\\(R,R)\text{-tartrate}\end{array}}}_{\text{diastereomers, } not \text{ mirror images}}$$

An illustration of Louis Pasteur working in the laboratory. He is, no doubt, contemplating the implications of enantiomerism in tartaric acid crystals.

The diastereomers of 2-butyl tartrate have different physical properties, and they can be separated by conventional distillation, recrystallization, or chromatography. Separation of the diastereomers leaves us with two flasks, each containing one of the diastereomeric esters. The resolving agent is then cleaved from the separated enantiomers of 2-butanol by the reverse of the reaction used to make the ester. Adding an acid catalyst and an excess of water to an ester drives the equilibrium toward the acid and the alcohol:

$$\underset{\text{ester}}{\text{R—C(=O)—O—R}'} + \underset{\text{water}}{\text{H—O—H}} \xrightleftharpoons{(\text{H}^+ \text{ catalyst})} \underset{\text{acid}}{\text{R—C(=O)—OH}} + \underset{\text{alcohol}}{\text{R}'\text{—OH}}$$

Hydrolysis of (*R*)-2-butyl tartrate gives (*R*)-2-butanol and (+)-tartaric acid, and hydrolysis of (*S*)-2-butyl tartrate gives (*S*)-2-butanol and (+)-tartaric acid. The recovered tartaric acid would probably be thrown away, since it is cheap and nontoxic. Many other chiral resolving agents are expensive, so they must be carefully recovered and recycled.

(S)-2-butanol + (R)-2-butanol + (R,R)-(+)-tartaric acid $\xrightarrow{H^+}$ (S)-2-butyl (R,R)-tartrate + (R)-2-butyl (R,R)-tartrate (diastereomers)

(S)-2-butyl (R,R)-tartrate $\xrightarrow[H_2O]{\text{separating then } H^+}$ (R,R)-(+)-tartaric acid + (S)-2-butanol

(R)-2-butyl (R,R)-tartrate $\xrightarrow[H_2O]{\text{separating then } H^+}$ (R,R)-(+)-tartaric acid + (R)-2-butanol

■ **FIGURE 5-21**
Formation of (*R*)- and (*S*)-2-butyl tartrate. The reaction of a pure enantiomer of one compound with a racemic mixture of another compound produces a mixture of diastereomers. Separation of the diastereomers, followed by hydrolysis, gives the resolved enantiomers.

PROBLEM 5-24

To show that (*R*)-2-butyl (*R*,*R*)-tartrate and (*S*)-2-butyl (*R*,*R*)-tartrate are not enantiomers, draw and name the mirror images of these compounds.

5-16B Chromatographic Resolution of Enantiomers

Chromatography is a powerful method for separating compounds. One type of chromatography involves passing a solution through a column containing particles whose surface tends to adsorb organic compounds. Compounds that are adsorbed strongly spend more time on the stationary particles; they come off the column later than less strongly adsorbed compounds, which spend more time in the mobile solvent phase.

In some cases, enantiomers may be resolved by passing the racemic mixture through a column containing particles whose surface is coated with chiral molecules (Figure 5-22). As the solution passes through the column, the enantiomers form weak complexes, usually through hydrogen bonding, with the chiral column packing. The solvent flows continually through the column, and the dissolved enantiomers gradually move along, retarded by the time they spend complexed with the column packing.

The special feature of this chromatography is the fact that the enantiomers form diastereomeric complexes with the chiral column packing. These diastereomeric complexes have different physical properties. They also have different binding energies and different equilibrium constants for complexation. One of the two enantiomers will spend more time complexed with the chiral column packing. The more strongly complexed enantiomer passes through the column more slowly and emerges from the column after the faster-moving (more weakly complexed) enantiomer.

Enzymes can also be used to eliminate an undesired stereoisomer. The enzyme will process only one isomer in a racemic mixture and leave the other stereoisomer untouched.

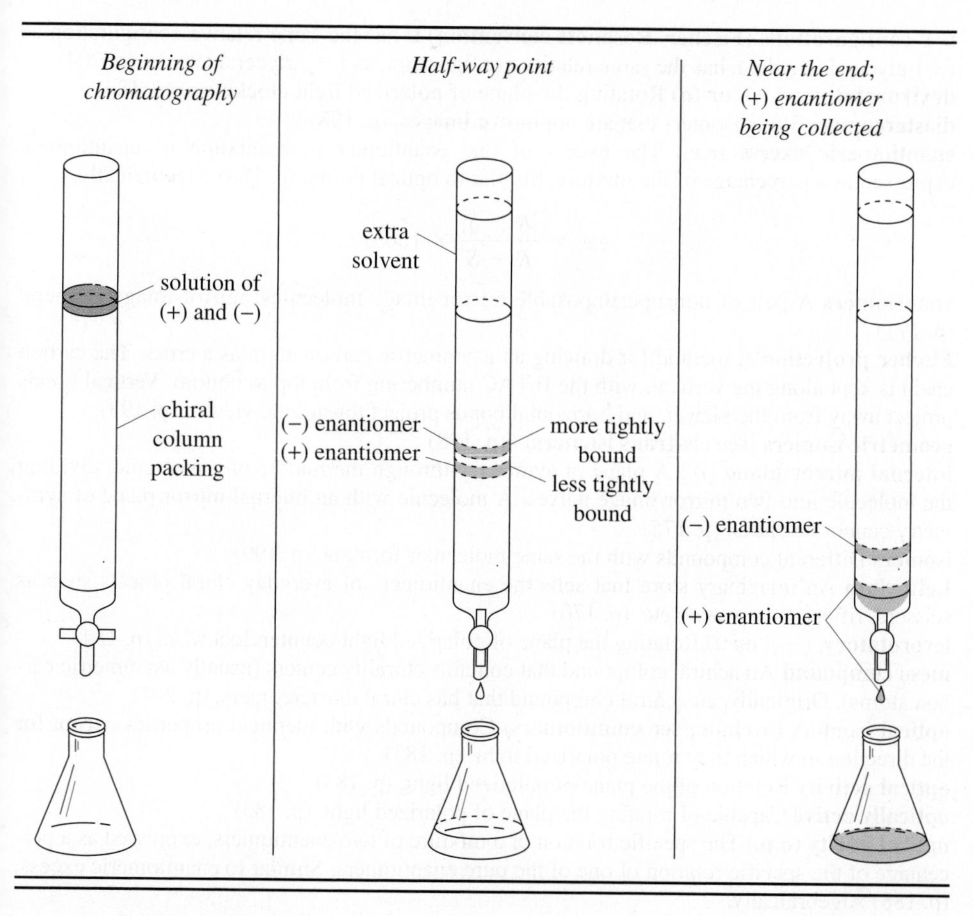

■ **FIGURE 5-22**
Chromatographic resolution of enantiomers. The enantiomers of the racemic compound form diastereomeric complexes with the chiral material on the column packing. One of the enantiomers binds more tightly than the other, so it moves more slowly through the column.

Glossary 5

absolute configuration The detailed stereochemical picture of a molecule, including how the atoms are arranged in space. Alternatively, the (*R*) or (*S*) configuration at each asymmetric carbon atom. (p. 203)

achiral Not chiral. (p. 170)

allenes Compounds having two C═C double bonds that meet at a single carbon atom, C═C═C. The two outer carbon atoms are trigonal planar, with their planes perpendicular to each other. Many substituted allenes are chiral. (p. 192)

asymmetric carbon atom (chiral carbon atom) A carbon atom that is bonded to four different groups. (p. 172)

Cahn–Ingold–Prelog convention The accepted method for designating the absolute configuration of a chirality center (usually an asymmetric carbon) as either (*R*) or (*S*). (p. 177)

chiral Different from its mirror image. (p. 170)

chiral carbon atom (asymmetric carbon atom) A carbon atom that is bonded to four different groups. (p. 172)

chirality center The IUPAC term for an atom holding a set of ligands in a spatial arrangement that is not superimposable on its mirror image. Asymmetric carbon atoms are the most common chirality centers. (p. 172)

chiral probe A molecule or an object that is chiral and can use its own chirality to differentiate between mirror images. (p. 186)

cis On the same side of a ring or double bond. (p. 198)

cis-trans isomers (geometric isomers) Isomers that differ in their geometric arrangement on a ring or double bond; cis-trans isomers are a subclass of diastereomers. (p. 198)

configurations The two possible spatial arrangements around a chirality center or other stereocenter. (p. 177)

configurational isomers (see stereoisomers)

conformers (conformational isomers) Structures that differ only by rotations about single bonds. In most cases, conformers interconvert at room temperature; thus, they are not different compounds and not true isomers. (p. 189)

constitutional isomers (structural isomers) Isomers that differ in the order in which their atoms are bonded together. (p. 169)

D–L configurations (Fischer–Rosanoff convention) D has the same relative configuration as (+)-glyceraldehyde. L has the same relative configuration as (−)-glyceraldehyde. (p. 204)
dextrorotatory, (+), or (*d*) Rotating the plane of polarized light clockwise. (p. 184)
diastereomers Stereoisomers that are not mirror images. (p. 198)
enantiomeric excess (e.e.) The excess of one enantiomer in a mixture of enantiomers expressed as a percentage of the mixture. Similar to optical purity. (p. 188) Algebraically,

$$\text{e.e.} = \frac{|R - S|}{R + S} \times 100\%$$

enantiomers A pair of nonsuperimposable mirror-image molecules: mirror-image isomers. (p. 171)
Fischer projection A method for drawing an asymmetric carbon atom as a cross. The carbon chain is kept along the vertical, with the IUPAC numbering from top to bottom. Vertical bonds project away from the viewer, and horizontal bonds project toward the viewer. (p. 193)
geometric isomers (see cis-trans isomers) (p. 198)
internal mirror plane (σ) A plane of symmetry through the middle of a molecule, dividing the molecule into two mirror-image halves. A molecule with an internal mirror plane of symmetry cannot be chiral. (p. 175)
isomers Different compounds with the same molecular formula. (p. 199)
Leftorium An imaginary store that sells the enantiomers of everyday chiral objects such as scissors, rifles, can openers, etc. (p. 170)
levorotatory, (−), or (*l*) Rotating the plane of polarized light counterclockwise. (p. 184)
meso compound An achiral compound that contains chirality centers (usually asymmetric carbon atoms). Originally, an achiral compound that has chiral diastereomers. (p. 201)
optical isomers (archaic; see enantiomers) Compounds with identical properties except for the direction in which they rotate polarized light. (p. 183)
optical activity Rotation of the plane of polarized light. (p. 183)
optically active Capable of rotating the plane of polarized light. (p. 183)
optical purity (o.p.) The specific rotation of a mixture of two enantiomers, expressed as a percentage of the specific rotation of one of the pure enantiomers. Similar to enantiomeric excess. (p. 188) Algebraically,

$$\text{o.p.} = \frac{\text{observed rotation}}{\text{rotation of pure enantiomer}} \times 100\%$$

plane-polarized light Light composed of waves that vibrate in only one plane. (p. 181)
polarimeter An instrument that measures the rotation of plane-polarized light by an optically active compound. (p. 183)
racemic mixture [racemate, racemic modification, (±) pair, (*d,l*) pair] A mixture of equal quantities of enantiomers, such that the mixture is optically inactive. (p. 187)
relative configuration The experimentally determined relationship between the configurations of two molecules, even though the absolute configuration of either may not be known. (p. 203)
resolution The process of separating a racemic mixture into the pure enantiomers. Resolution requires a chiral resolving agent. (p. 206)
resolving agent A chiral compound (or chiral material on a chromatographic column) used for separating enantiomers. (p. 207)
2^n rule A molecule with n chiral carbon atoms might have as many as 2^n stereoisomers. (p. 200)
specific rotation A measure of a compound's ability to rotate the plane of polarized light, given by

$$[\alpha]_{\text{D}}^{25} = \frac{\alpha(\text{observed})}{c \cdot l}$$

where c is concentration in g/mL and l is length of sample cell (path length) in decimeters. (p. 184)
stereocenter (stereogenic atom) An atom that gives rise to stereoisomers when its groups are interchanged. Asymmetric carbon atoms and double-bonded carbons in cis-trans alkenes are the most common stereocenters. (p. 172)

examples of stereocenters (circled)

stereochemistry The study of the three-dimensional structure of molecules. (p. 169)
stereoisomers (configurational isomers) Isomers whose atoms are bonded together in the same order but differ in how the atoms are oriented in space. (p. 169)
structural isomers (see constitutional isomers) Isomers that differ in the order in which their atoms are bonded together. (p. 169)
superimposable Identical in all respects. The three-dimensional positions of all atoms coincide when the molecules are placed on top of each other. (p. 171)
trans On opposite sides of a ring or double bond. (p. 198)

Essential Problem-Solving Skills in Chapter 5

1. Classify molecules as chiral or achiral, and identify mirror planes of symmetry.
2. Identify asymmetric carbon atoms, and name them using the (*R*) and (*S*) nomenclature.
3. Calculate specific rotations from polarimetry data.
4. Draw all stereoisomers of a given structure.
5. Identify enantiomers, diastereomers, and meso compounds.
6. Draw correct Fischer projections of asymmetric carbon atoms.
7. Explain how the physical properties differ for different types of stereoisomers.
8. Suggest how to separate different types of stereoisomers.

Study Problems

5-25 Briefly define each term and give an example.

(a) (*R*) and (*S*) **(b)** chiral and achiral **(c)** optical activity
(d) cis and trans **(e)** asymmetric carbon atom **(f)** isomers
(g) constitutional isomers **(h)** stereoisomers **(i)** enantiomers
(j) Fischer projection **(k)** diastereomers **(l)** chirality center
(m) optical isomers **(n)** meso **(o)** stereocenter
(p) racemic mixture **(q)** specific rotation **(r)** dextrorotatory
(s) (+) and (−) **(t)** absolute configuration **(u)** relative configuration
(v) D and L configurations **(w)** enantiomeric excess **(x)** resolution of enantiomers

5-26 For each structure,
1. Star (*) any asymmetric carbon atoms.
2. Label each asymmetric carbon as (*R*) or (*S*).
3. Draw any internal mirror planes of symmetry.
4. Label the structure as chiral or achiral.
5. Label any meso structures.

(a)
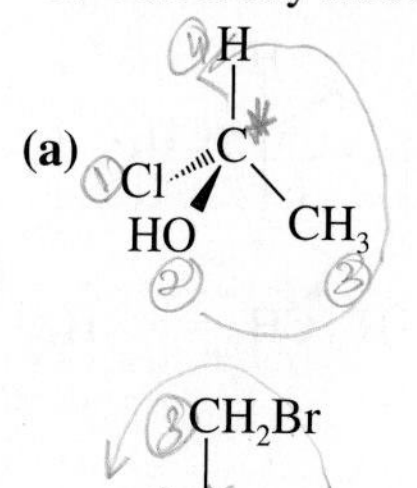

(b) CH_2OH; H—C—OH; CH_3

(c) H H H Cl; H, C, C, C, Br; H OH

(d) H CH_3 H; H_3C, C, C, C, CH_2; H CH_3

(e) CH_2Br; H—C—Br; H—C—Br; CH_2Br

(f) CH_2Br; H—C—Br; Br—C—H; CH_2Br

(g) CH_3; H—C—Br; H—C—OH; CH_3

(h) CH_3; H—C—OH; H—C—OH; H—C—OH; CH_2CH_3

(i) 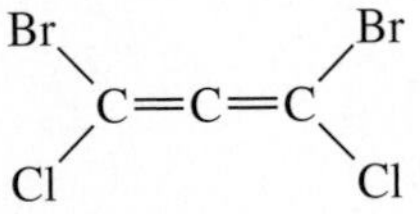 (j) 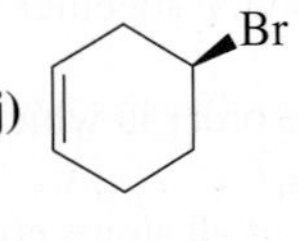 (k) 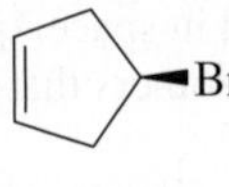 (l)

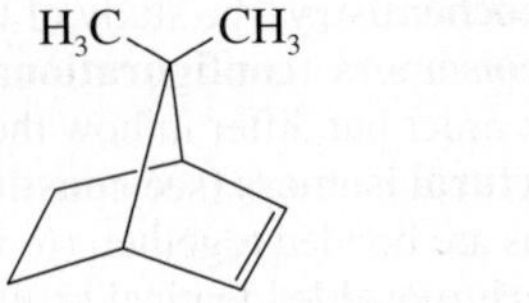

(m) 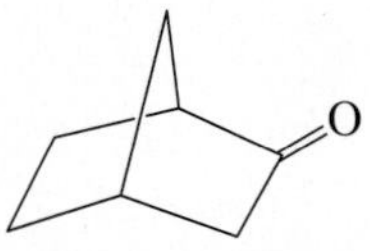 (n) 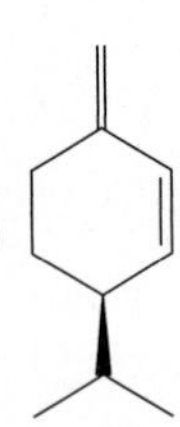 (o) 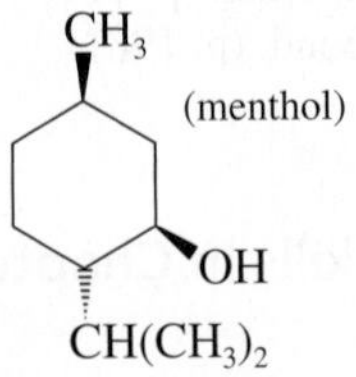 (menthol) *(p)

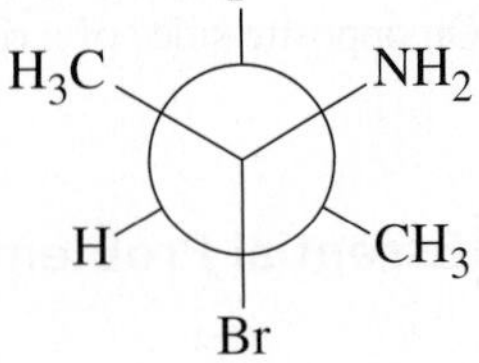

5-27 For each of the compounds described by the following names,

1. Draw a three-dimensional representation.
2. Star (*) each chirality center.
3. Draw any planes of symmetry.
4. Draw any enantiomer.
5. Draw any diastereomers.
6. Label each structure you have drawn as chiral or achiral.

(a) (*S*)-2-chlorobutane
(b) (*R*)-1,1,2-trimethylcyclohexane
(c) (2*R*,3*S*)-2,3-dibromohexane
(d) (1*R*,2*R*)-1,2-dibromocyclohexane
(e) *meso*-3,4-hexanediol, $CH_3CH_2CH(OH)CH(OH)CH_2CH_3$
(f) (±)-3,4-hexanediol

5-28 Convert the following perspective formulas to Fischer projections.

(a) 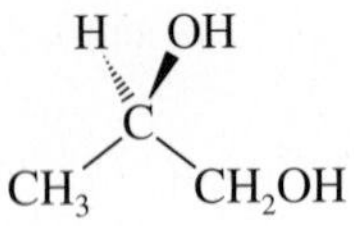 (b) 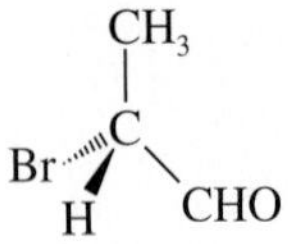 (c) 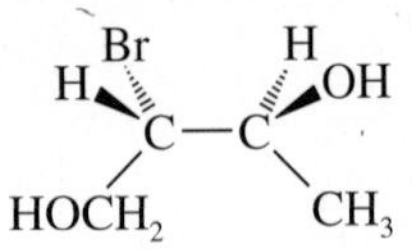 (d)

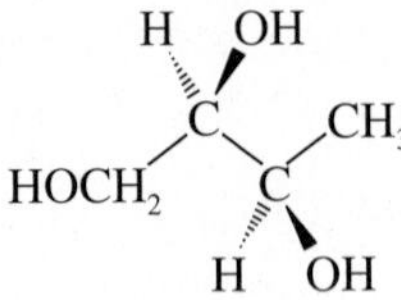

5-29 Convert the following Fischer projections to perspective formulas.

(a) 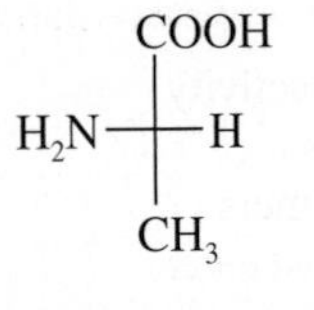 (b) 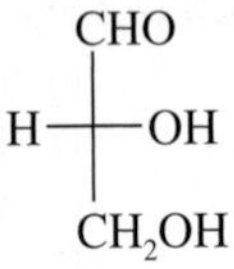 (c) 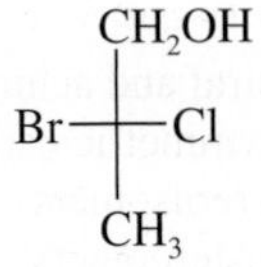 (d)

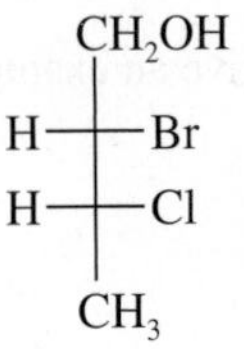

5-30 Give the stereochemical relationships between each pair of structures. Examples are same compound, structural isomers, enantiomers, diastereomers.

(a) 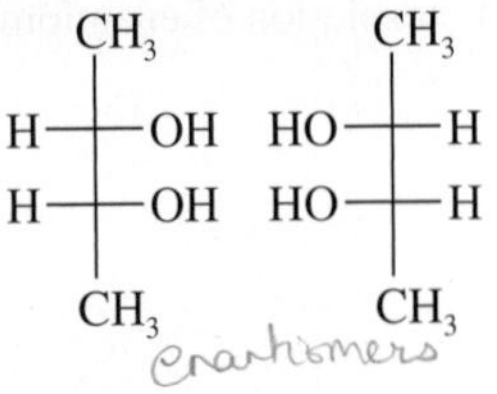 (b) 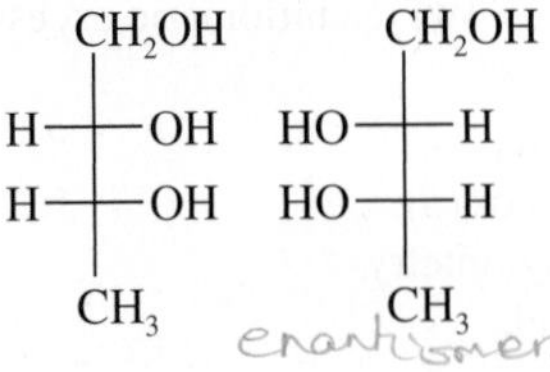 (c)

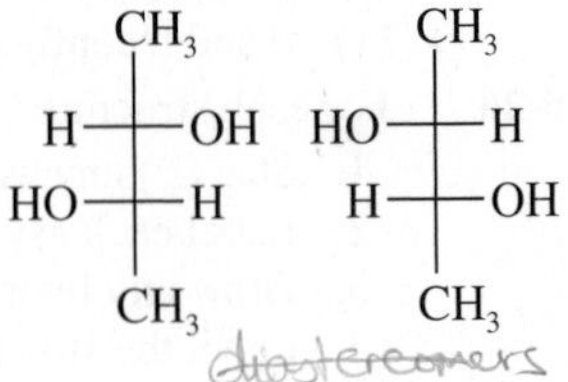

enantiomers enantiomers diastereomers enantiomers

(d) 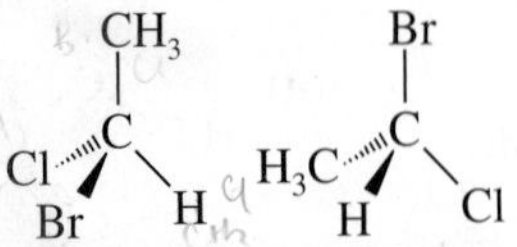 (e) 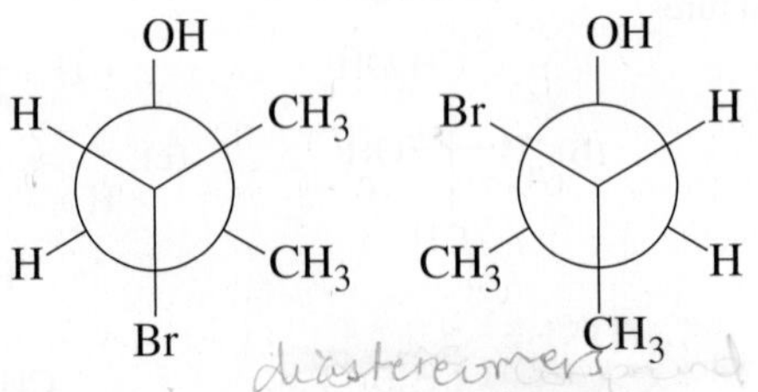 (f)

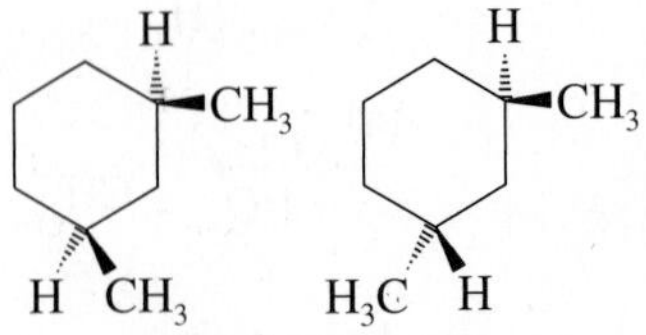

enantiomers diastereomers diastereomers

(g) 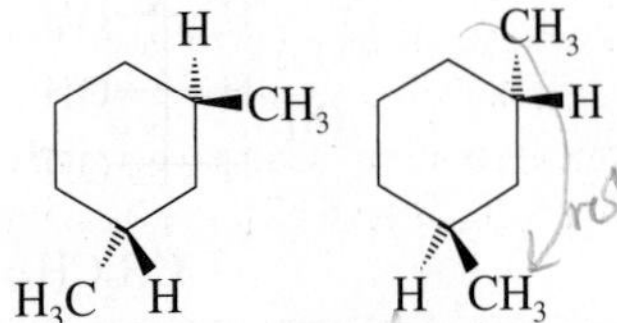 rotate *(h)

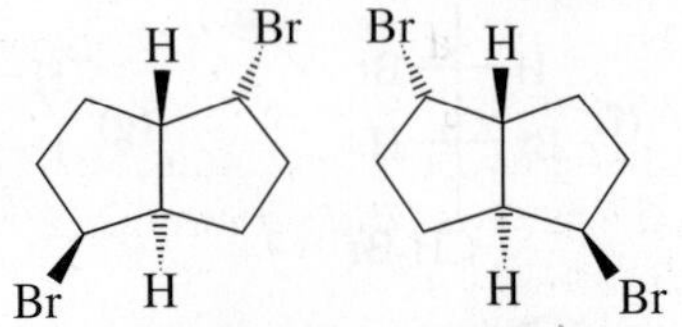

enantiomer same compound

5-31 Draw the enantiomer, if any, for each structure.

(a) (b) (c) (d)

(e) (f) (g)

(h) (i) (j)

5-32 Calculate the specific rotations of the following samples taken at 25 °C using the sodium D line.

(a) 1.00 g of sample is dissolved in 20.0 mL of ethanol. Then 5.00 mL of this solution is placed in a 20.0-cm polarimeter tube. The observed rotation is 1.25° counterclockwise.

(b) 0.050 g of sample is dissolved in 2.0 mL of ethanol, and this solution is placed in a 2.0-cm polarimeter tube. The observed rotation is clockwise 0.043°.

5-33 (+)-Tartaric acid has a specific rotation of +12.0°. Calculate the specific rotation of a mixture of 68% (+)-tartaric acid and 32% (−)-tartaric acid.

5-34 The specific rotation of (*S*)-2-iodobutane is +15.90°.

(a) Draw the structure of (*S*)-2-iodobutane.

(b) Predict the specific rotation of (*R*)-2-iodobutane.

(c) Determine the percentage composition of a mixture of (*R*)- and (*S*)-2-iodobutane with a specific rotation of −7.95°.

***5-35** For each structure,

1. Draw all the stereoisomers.
2. Label each structure as chiral or achiral.
3. Give the relationships between the stereoisomers (enantiomers, diastereomers).

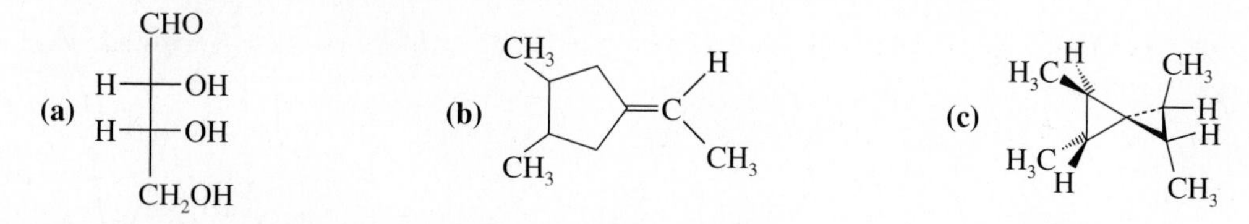

***5-36** Draw all the stereoisomers of 1,2,3-trimethylcyclopentane, and give the relationships between them.

***5-37** If you think you know your definitions, try this difficult problem.

(a) Draw all the stereoisomers of 2,3,4-tribromopentane. (Using Fischer projections may be helpful.) You should find two meso structures and one pair of enantiomers.

(b) Star (*) the asymmetric carbon atoms, and label each as (*R*) or (*S*).

(c) In the meso structures, show how C3 is not asymmetric, nor is it a chirality center, yet it is a stereocenter.

(d) In the enantiomers, show how C3 is not a stereocenter in this diastereomer.

***5-38** 3,4-Dimethyl-1-pentene has the formula $CH_2{=}CH{-}CH(CH_3){-}CH(CH_3)_2$. When pure (*R*)-3,4-dimethyl-1-pentene is treated with hydrogen over a platinum catalyst, the product is (*S*)-2,3-dimethylpentane.

(a) Draw the equation for this reaction. Show the stereochemistry of the reactant and the product.

(b) Has the chirality center retained its configuration during this hydrogenation, or has it been inverted?

(c) The reactant is named (*R*), but the product is named (*S*). Does this name change imply a change in the spatial arrangement of the groups around the chirality center? So why does the name switch from (*R*) to (*S*)?

(d) How useful is the (*R*) or (*S*) designation for predicting the sign of an optical rotation? Can you predict the sign of the rotation of the reactant? Of the product? (*Hint* from Juliet Capulet: "What's in a name? That which we call a rose/By any other name would smell as sweet.")

*5-39 A graduate student was studying enzymatic reductions of cyclohexanones when she encountered some interesting chemistry. When she used an enzyme and NADPH to reduce the following ketone, she was surprised to find that the product was optically active. She carefully repurified the product so that no enzyme, NADPH, or other contaminants were present. Still, the product was optically active.

COOH H NADPH enzyme HO H COOH H

optically active?

(a) Does the product have any asymmetric carbon atoms or other stereocenters?
(b) Is the product capable of showing optical activity? If it is, explain how.
(c) If this reaction could be accomplished using H_2 and a nickel catalyst, would the product be optically active? Explain.

*5-40 D-(−)-Erythrose has the formula $HOCH_2—CH(OH)—CH(OH)—CHO$, and the D in its name implies that it can be degraded to D-(+)-glyceraldehyde. The (−) in its name implies that D-(−)-erythrose is optically active (levorotatory). When D-(−)-erythrose is reduced (using H_2 and a nickel catalyst), it gives an optically inactive product of formula $HOCH_2—CH(OH)—CH(OH)—CH_2OH$. Knowing the absolute configuration of D-(+)-glyceraldehyde (Section 5-14), determine the absolute configuration of D-(−)-erythrose.

*5-41 The original definition of *meso* is "an achiral compound that has chiral diastereomers." Our working definition of *meso* is "an achiral compound that has chirality centers (usually asymmetric carbon atoms)." The working definition is much easier to apply, because we don't have to envision all possible chiral diastereomers of the compound. Still, the working definition is not quite as complete as the original definition.

(a) Show how *cis*-cyclooctene is defined as a *meso* compound under the original definition, but not under our working definition. (Review Figure 5-18.)
(b) See if you can construct a double allene that is achiral, although it has chiral diastereomers, and is therefore a *meso* compound under the original definition. The allene structure is not a chirality center, but it can be a *chirality axis*.

CHAPTER 6

ALKYL HALIDES: NUCLEOPHILIC SUBSTITUTION AND ELIMINATION

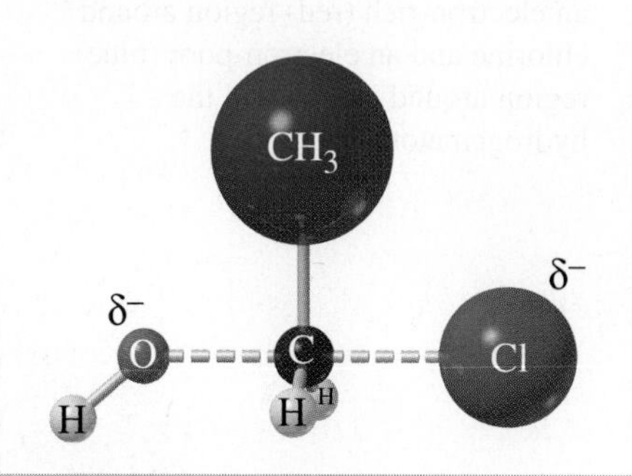

6-1 Introduction

Our study of organic chemistry is organized into families of compounds classified by their functional groups. In this chapter, we consider the properties and reactions of alkyl halides. We use alkyl halides to introduce substitution and elimination, two of the most important types of reactions in organic chemistry. Stereochemistry (Chapter 5) will play a major role in our study of these reactions. Many other reactions show similarities to substitution and elimination, and the techniques introduced in this chapter will be used throughout our study of organic reactions.

There are three major classes of halogenated organic compounds: the alkyl halides, the vinyl halides, and the aryl halides. An **alkyl halide** simply has a halogen atom bonded to one of the sp^3 hybrid carbon atoms of an alkyl group. A **vinyl halide** has a halogen atom bonded to one of the sp^2 hybrid carbon atoms of an alkene. An **aryl halide** has a halogen atom bonded to one of the sp^2 hybrid carbon atoms of an aromatic ring. The chemistry of vinyl halides and aryl halides is different from that of alkyl halides because their bonding and hybridization are different. We consider the reactions of vinyl halides and aryl halides in later chapters. The structures of some representative alkyl halides, vinyl halides, and aryl halides are shown here, with their most common names and uses.

Alkyl halides

$CHCl_3$	$CHClF_2$	$CCl_3—CH_3$	$CF_3—CHClBr$
chloroform	Freon-22®	1,1,1-trichloroethane	Halothane
solvent	refrigerant	cleaning fluid	nonflammable anesthetic

Vinyl halides

$$\mathrm{(Cl)(H)C{=}C(H)(H)}$$

vinyl chloride
monomer for poly(vinyl chloride)

$$\mathrm{F_2C{=}CF_2}$$

tetrafluoroethylene (TFE)
monomer for Teflon®

Aryl halides

$$\mathrm{Cl{-}C_6H_4{-}Cl}\ (para)$$

para-dichlorobenzene
mothballs

$$\mathrm{HO{-}C_6H_2I_2{-}O{-}C_6H_2I_2{-}CH_2{-}CH(NH_2){-}COOH}$$

thyroxine
thyroid hormone

■ **FIGURE 6-1**
Chloromethane and its electrostatic potential map (EPM). The polar C—Cl bond is seen in the EPM as an electron-rich (red) region around chlorine and an electron-poor (blue) region around carbon and the hydrogen atoms.

chloromethane

EPM of chloromethane

The carbon–halogen bond in an alkyl halide is polar because halogen atoms are more electronegative than carbon atoms. Most reactions of alkyl halides result from breaking this polarized bond. The electrostatic potential map of chloromethane (Figure 6-1) shows higher electron density (red) around the chlorine atom and relatively low electron density (blue) around the carbon and hydrogen atoms. The carbon atom has a partial positive charge, making it somewhat electrophilic. A nucleophile can attack this electrophilic carbon, and the halogen atom can leave as a halide ion, taking the bonding pair of electrons with it. By serving as a leaving group, the halogen can be eliminated from the alkyl halide, or it can be replaced (substituted for) by a wide variety of functional groups. This versatility allows alkyl halides to serve as intermediates in the synthesis of many other functional groups.

PROBLEM 6-1

Classify each compound as an alkyl halide, a vinyl halide, or an aryl halide.

(a) $CH_3CHCFCH_3$ **(b)** $(CH_3)_3CBr$ **(c)** CH_3CCl_3

(d) bromocyclohexane **(e)** 1-bromocyclohexene **(f)**

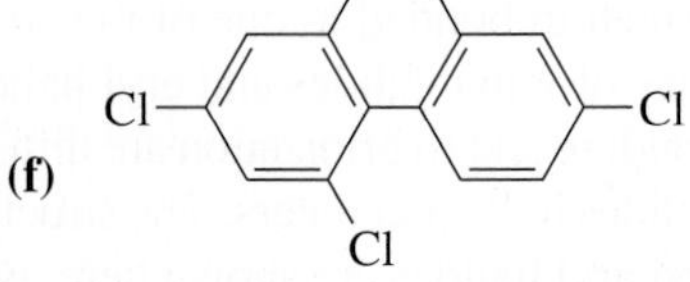

a PCB (polychlorinated biphenyl)

6-2 Nomenclature of Alkyl Halides

There are two ways of naming alkyl halides. The systematic (IUPAC) nomenclature treats an alkyl halide as an alkane with a *halo-* substituent: Fluorine is *fluoro-*, chlorine is *chloro-*, bromine is *bromo-*, and iodine is *iodo-*. The result is a systematic **haloalkane** name, as in 1-chlorobutane or 2-bromopropane. Common or "trivial" names are constructed by naming the alkyl group and then the halide, as in "isopropyl bromide." This is the origin of the term *alkyl halide*. Common names are useful only for simple alkyl halides, such as the following:

	$CH_3CH_2—F$	$CH_2(Cl)CH_2CH_2CH_3$	$CH_3—CH(Br)—CH_3$
IUPAC name:	fluoroethane	1-chlorobutane	2-bromopropane
common name:	ethyl fluoride	*n*-butyl chloride	isopropyl bromide

IUPAC name:	iodocyclohexane	*trans*-1-chloro-3-methylcyclopentane
common name:	cyclohexyl iodide	(none)

$$\underset{\text{3-(iodomethyl)pentane}}{CH_3CH_2-\underset{|}{\overset{CH_2-I}{CH}}-CH_2CH_3} \qquad \underset{\text{4-(2-fluoroethyl)heptane}}{CH_3CH_2CH_2-\overset{CH_2CH_2-F}{CH}-CH_2CH_2CH_3}$$

IUPAC name: 3-(iodomethyl)pentane; 4-(2-fluoroethyl)heptane

Some of the halomethanes have acquired common names that are not clearly related to their structures. A compound of formula CH_2X_2 (a methylene group with two halogens) is called a *methylene halide*; a compound of formula CHX_3 is called a *haloform*; and a compound of formula CX_4 is called a *carbon tetrahalide*.

	CH_2Cl_2	$CHCl_3$	CCl_4
IUPAC name:	dichloromethane	trichloromethane	tetrachloromethane
common name:	methylene chloride	chloroform	carbon tetrachloride

PROBLEM 6-2

Give the structures of the following compounds.
(a) methylene iodide
(b) carbon tetrabromide
(c) 3-bromo-2-methylpentane
(d) iodoform
(e) 2-bromo-3-ethyl-2-methylhexane
(f) isobutyl bromide
(g) *cis*-1-fluoro-3-(fluoromethyl)cyclohexane
(h) *tert*-butyl chloride

Alkyl halides are classified according to the nature of the carbon atom bonded to the halogen. If the halogen-bearing carbon is bonded to one carbon atom, it is primary (1°) and the alkyl halide is a **primary halide**. If two carbon atoms are bonded to the halogen-bearing carbon, it is secondary (2°) and the compound is a **secondary halide**. A **tertiary halide** (3°) has three other carbon atoms bonded to the halogen-bearing carbon atom. If the halogen-bearing carbon atom is a methyl group (bonded to no other carbon atoms), the compound is a *methyl halide*.

$$\underset{\text{methyl halide}}{CH_3-X} \qquad \underset{\text{primary (1°) halide}}{R-CH_2-X} \qquad \underset{\text{secondary (2°) halide}}{R-\overset{R}{\overset{|}{CH}}-X} \qquad \underset{\text{tertiary (3°) halide}}{R-\overset{R}{\underset{R}{C}}-X}$$

Examples

	CH_3-Br	$CH_3CH_2CH_2-F$ (1°)	$CH_3-\overset{I}{CH}-CH_2CH_3$ (2°)	$(CH_3)_3C-Cl$ (3°)
IUPAC name:	bromomethane	1-fluoropropane	2-iodobutane	2-chloro-2-methylpropane
common name:	methyl bromide	*n*-propyl fluoride	*sec*-butyl iodide	*tert*-butyl chloride

A **geminal dihalide** (Latin, *geminus* "twin") has the two halogen atoms bonded to the same carbon atom. A **vicinal dihalide** (Latin, *vicinus*, "neighboring") has the two halogens bonded to adjacent carbon atoms.

$$\underset{\text{a geminal dibromide}}{\overset{Br\quad Br}{C}} \qquad \underset{\text{a vicinal dichloride}}{-\overset{Cl}{\underset{|}{C}}-\overset{Cl}{\underset{|}{C}}-}$$

PROBLEM 6-3

For each of the following compounds,

1. Give the IUPAC name.
2. Give the common name (if possible).
3. Classify the compound as a methyl, primary, secondary, or tertiary halide.

(a) $(CH_3)_2CHCH_2Cl$

(b) $(CH_3)_3CBr$

(c) $CH_3CH_2CHBrCH_3$

(d) $CH_3—CH(CH_2CH_3)—CH_2Cl$

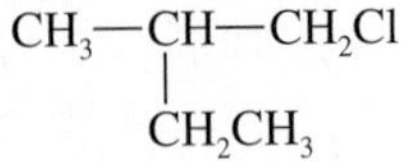

(e) Br, H, Cl, H (cyclobutane structure)

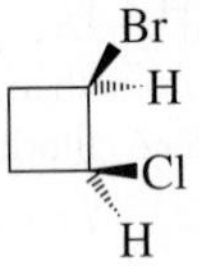

(f) Br (skeletal structure)

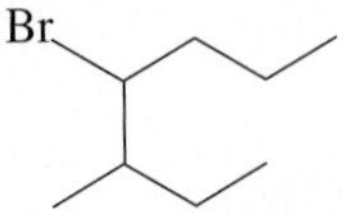

(g) CH_3, CH_3, H, F (cyclohexane structure)

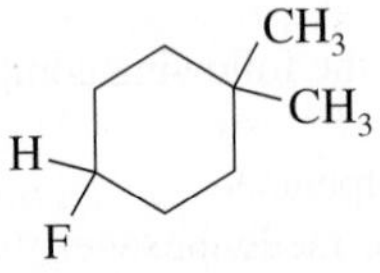

6-3 Common Uses of Alkyl Halides

6-3A Solvents

Alkyl halides are used primarily as industrial and household solvents. Carbon tetrachloride (CCl_4) was once used for dry cleaning, spot removing, and other domestic cleaning. Carbon tetrachloride is toxic and carcinogenic (causes cancer), however, so dry cleaners now use 1,1,1-trichloroethane and other solvents instead.

Methylene chloride (CH_2Cl_2) and chloroform ($CHCl_3$) are also good solvents for cleaning and degreasing work. Methylene chloride was once used to dissolve the caffeine from coffee beans to produce decaffeinated coffee. Concerns about the safety of coffee with residual traces of methylene chloride prompted coffee producers to use liquid carbon dioxide instead. Chloroform is more toxic and carcinogenic than methylene chloride; it has been replaced by methylene chloride and other solvents in most industrial degreasers and paint removers.

Even the safest halogenated solvents, such as methylene chloride and 1,1,1-trichloroethane, should be used carefully. They are all potentially toxic and carcinogenic, and they dissolve the fatty oils that protect skin, causing a form of dermatitis.

Chloroform can be converted to phosgene, a very reactive acid chloride, in the presence of oxygen at room temperature. Phosgene is extremely toxic because it reacts with and deactivates many biological molecules. A small amount of alcohol is sometimes added to bottles of chloroform to destroy any phosgene that might be formed.

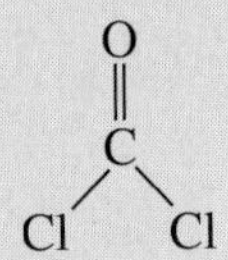

$Cl_2C{=}O$

phosgene

6-3B Reagents

Many syntheses use alkyl halides as starting materials for making more complex molecules. The conversion of alkyl halides to organometallic reagents (compounds containing carbon–metal bonds) is a particularly important tool for organic synthesis. We discuss the formation of organometallic compounds in Section 10-8.

6-3C Anesthetics

Chloroform ($CHCl_3$) was the first substance found to produce general anesthesia, opening new possibilities for careful surgery with a patient who is unconscious and relaxed. Chloroform is toxic and carcinogenic, however, and it was soon abandoned in favor of safer anesthetics, such as diethyl ether. A less toxic halogenated anesthetic is a mixed alkyl halide, $CF_3CHClBr$, which goes by the trade name Halothane. Ethyl chloride is often used as a topical anesthetic for minor procedures. When sprayed on the skin, its evaporation (bp 12 °C) cools the area and enhances the numbing effect.

6-3D Freons: Refrigerants and Foaming Agents

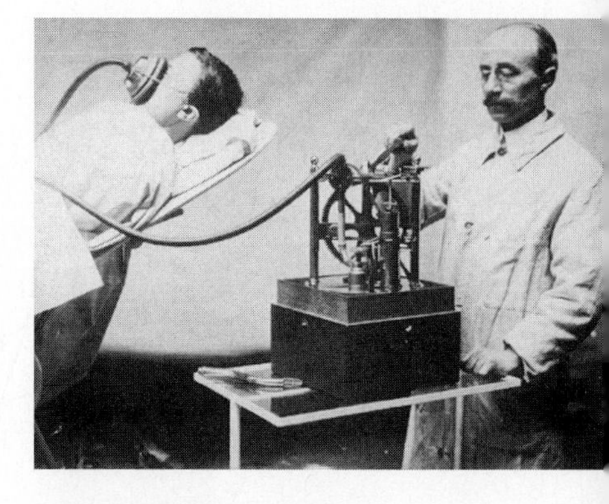

Use of the Dubois chloroform inhaler to produce surgical anesthesia, around 1850.

The **freons** (also called *chlorofluorocarbons*, or CFCs) are fluorinated haloalkanes that were developed to replace ammonia as a refrigerant gas. Ammonia is toxic, and leaking refrigerators often killed people who were working or sleeping nearby. Freon-12®, CF_2Cl_2, was at one time the most widely used refrigerant. Low-boiling freons (such as Freon-11®, CCl_3F) were once used as *foaming agents* that were added to a plastic to vaporize and form a froth that hardens into a plastic foam. The release of freons into the atmosphere has raised concerns about their reactions with the earth's protective ozone layer. CFCs gradually diffuse up into the stratosphere, where the chlorine atoms catalyze the decomposition of ozone (O_3) into oxygen (O_2). Most scientists blame the freon-catalyzed depletion of ozone for the "hole" in the ozone layer that has been detected over the South Pole.

International treaties have limited the future production and use of the ozone-destroying freons. Freon-12 has been replaced in aerosol cans by low-boiling hydrocarbons or carbon dioxide. In refrigerators and automotive air conditioners, Freon-12 has been replaced by Freon-22®, $CHClF_2$. Freons with C—H bonds (such as Freon-22), called HCFCs, are generally destroyed at lower altitudes before they reach the stratosphere. Propane, CO_2, and HCFC-123 ($CHCl_2CF_3$) are used as substitutes for Freon-11 in making plastic foams.

Halogenated compounds persist in the environment because they resist breakdown by soil bacteria. Many are chemically unreactive and insoluble in water, hindering bacterial degradation. Nevertheless, there are strains of bacteria that can use halogenated compounds as their source of food.

6-3E Pesticides

Alkyl halides have contributed to human health through their use as insecticides. Since antiquity, people have died from famine and disease caused or carried by mosquitoes, fleas, lice, and other vermin. The "black death" of the Middle Ages wiped out nearly a third of the population of Europe through infection by the flea-borne bubonic plague. Whole regions of Africa and tropical America were uninhabited and unexplored because people could not survive insect-borne diseases such as malaria, yellow fever, and sleeping sickness.

Arsenic compounds, nicotine, and other crude insecticides were developed in the nineteenth century, but these compounds are just as toxic to birds, animals, and people as they are to insects. Their use is extremely hazardous, but a hazardous insecticide was still preferable to certain death by disease or starvation.

The war against insects changed dramatically in 1939 with the discovery of DDT (Figure 6-2). DDT is extremely toxic to insects, but its toxicity in mammals is quite low. About an ounce of DDT is required to kill a person, but that same amount of insecticide protects an acre of land against locusts or mosquitoes. In 1970, the U.S. National Academy of Sciences reported, "in little more than two decades DDT has prevented 500 million deaths due to malaria." Similar advances were made against the mosquitoes carrying yellow fever and the tsetse flies carrying sleeping sickness. Using DDT as a body dust protected people against louse-borne typhus, and dusting rodent burrows controlled the threat of plague.

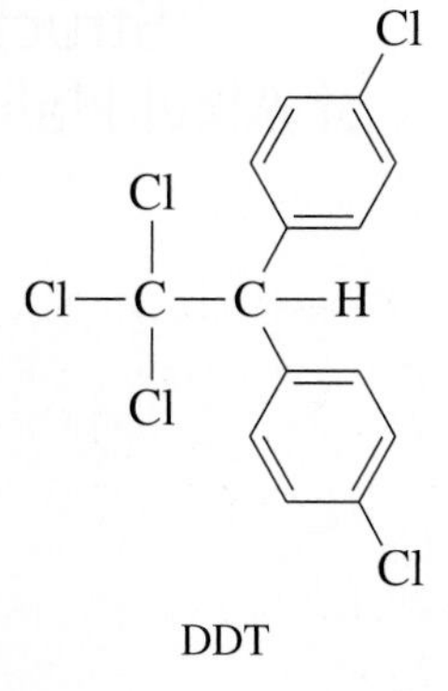

■ **FIGURE 6-2**
Structure of DDT. DDT is DichloroDiphenylTrichloroethane, or 1,1,1-trichloro-2,2-bis-(*p*-chlorophenyl)ethane. DDT was the first chlorinated insecticide. Its use rendered large parts of the world safe from insect-borne disease and starvation, but it has accumulated in the environment.

As with many inventions, DDT showed undesired side effects. It is a long-lasting insecticide, and its residues accumulate in the environment. The widespread use of DDT as an agricultural insecticide led to the development of substantial DDT concentrations in wildlife, causing declines in several species. In 1972, DDT was banned by the U.S. Environmental Protection Agency for use as an agricultural insecticide. It is still used, however, in places where insect-borne diseases threaten human life. DDT-treated bed netting is still the most cost-effective protection against malaria, and careful spraying of DDT around dwellings and in rodent burrows has helped to control the spread of deadly diseases.

Many other chlorinated insecticides have been developed. Some of them also accumulate in the environment, gradually producing toxic effects in wildlife. Others can be used with little adverse impact if they are applied properly. Because of their persistent toxic effects, chlorinated insecticides are rarely used in agriculture. They are generally used when a potent insecticide is needed to protect life or property. For example, lindane is used in shampoos to kill lice, and chlordane is used to protect wooden buildings from termites. The structures of some chlorinated insecticides are shown next.

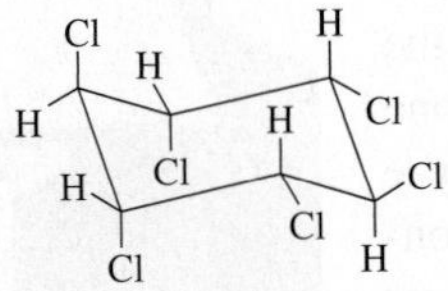

lindane 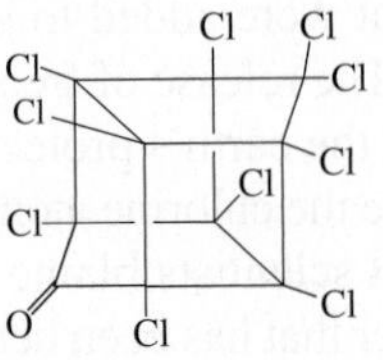 kepone 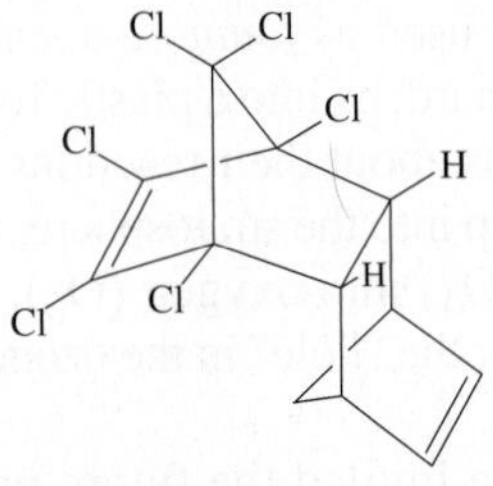 aldrin 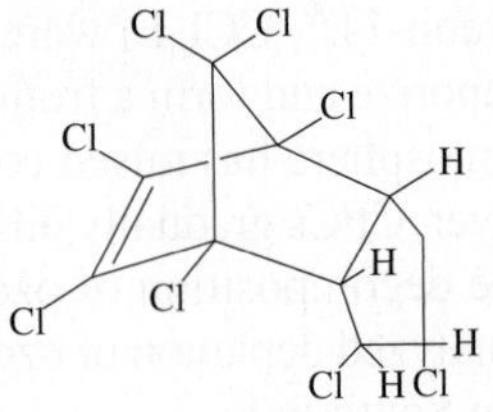 chlordane

PROBLEM 6-4

Kepone and chlordane are synthesized from hexachlorocyclopentadiene and other five-membered-ring compounds. Show how these two pesticides are composed of two five-membered rings.

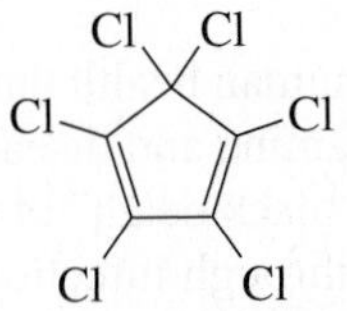

hexachlorocyclopentadiene

6-4 Structure of Alkyl Halides

In an alkyl halide, the halogen atom is bonded to an sp^3 hybrid carbon atom. The halogen is more electronegative than carbon, and the C—X bond is polarized with a partial positive charge on carbon and a partial negative charge on the halogen.

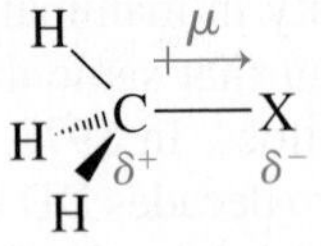

$$\mu = 4.8 \times \delta \times d$$

where δ is the amount of charge separation, and d is the bond length.

The electronegativities of the halogens *increase* in the order

	I	<	Br	<	Cl	<	F
electronegativity:	2.7		3.0		3.2		4.0

The carbon–halogen bond lengths *increase* as the halogen atoms become bigger (larger atomic radii) in the order

	C—F	<	C—Cl	<	C—Br	<	C—I
bond length:	1.38 Å		1.78 Å		1.94 Å		2.14 Å

These two effects oppose each other, with the larger halogens having longer bonds but weaker electronegativities. The overall result is that the bond dipole moments increase in the order

	C—I	<	C—Br	<	C—F	<	C—Cl
dipole moment, μ:	1.29 D		1.48 D		1.51 D		1.56 D

Cl
Cl C Cl
Cl
carbon tetrachloride

TABLE 6-1

Molecular Dipole Moments of Methyl Halides

X	CH_3X	CH_2X_2	CHX_3	CX_4
F	1.82 D	1.97 D	1.65 D	0
Cl	1.94 D	1.60 D	1.03 D	0
Br	1.79 D	1.45 D	1.02 D	0
I	1.64 D	1.11 D	1.00 D	0

A *molecular* dipole moment is the vector sum of the individual bond dipole moments. Molecular dipole moments are not easy to predict because they depend on the bond angles and other factors that vary with the specific molecule. Table 6-1 lists the experimentally measured dipole moments of the halogenated methanes. Notice how the four symmetrically oriented polar bonds of the carbon tetrahalides cancel to give a molecular dipole moment of zero.

PROBLEM 6-5

For each pair of compounds, predict which one has the higher molecular dipole moment, and explain your reasoning.
(a) ethyl chloride or ethyl iodide
(b) 1-bromopropane or cyclopropane
(c) cyclopentene or *trans*-2-butene

6-5 Physical Properties of Alkyl Halides

6-5A Boiling Points

Two types of intermolecular forces influence the boiling points of alkyl halides. The London force is the strongest intermolecular attraction in alkyl halides. London forces are *surface* attractions, resulting from coordinated temporary dipoles. Molecules with larger surface areas have larger London attractions, resulting in higher boiling points. Dipole–dipole attractions (arising from the polar C—X bond) also affect the boiling points, but to a smaller extent.

Molecules with higher molecular weights generally have higher boiling points because they are heavier (and therefore slower moving), and they have greater surface area. The surface areas of the alkyl halides vary with the surface areas of halogens. We can get an idea of the relative surface areas of halogen atoms by considering their van der Waals radii. Figure 6-3 shows that an alkyl fluoride has nearly the same surface area as the corresponding alkane; thus its London attractive forces are similar. The alkyl fluoride has a larger dipole moment, however, so the total attractive forces are slightly greater in the alkyl fluoride, giving it a higher boiling point. For example, the boiling point of *n*-butane is 0 °C, while that of *n*-butyl fluoride is 33 °C.

The other halogens are considerably larger than fluorine, giving them more surface area and raising the boiling points of their alkyl halides. With a boiling point of 78 °C, *n*-butyl chloride shows the influence of chlorine's much larger surface area. This trend continues with *n*-butyl bromide (bp 102 °C) and *n*-butyl iodide (bp 131 °C). Table 6-2 lists the boiling points and densities of some simple alkyl halides. Notice that compounds with branched, more spherical shapes have lower boiling points as a result of their smaller surface areas. For example, *n*-butyl bromide has a boiling point of 102 °C, while the more spherical *tert*-butyl bromide has a boiling point of only 73 °C. This effect is similar to the one we saw with alkanes.

PROBLEM 6-6

For each pair of compounds, predict which compound has the higher boiling point. Check Table 6-2 to see if your prediction was right, then explain why that compound has the higher boiling point.
(a) isopropyl bromide and *n*-butyl bromide
(b) isopropyl chloride and *tert*-butyl bromide
(c) 1-bromobutane and 1-chlorobutane

Halogen	van der Waals Radius (10^{-8} cm)
F	1.35
Cl	1.8
Br	1.95
I	2.15
H (for comparison)	1.2

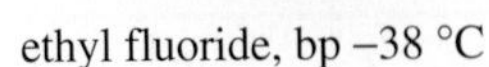

ethyl fluoride, bp −38 °C

ethyl chloride, bp 12 °C

ethyl bromide, bp 38 °C

ethyl iodide, bp 72 °C

■ **FIGURE 6-3**
Space-filling drawings of the ethyl halides. The heavier halogens are larger, with much greater surface areas. As a result, the boiling points of the ethyl halides increase in the order F < Cl < Br < I.

TABLE 6-2
Physical Properties of Alkyl Halides

Compound	Molecular Weight	Boiling Point (°C)	Density (g/mL)
$CH_3—F$	34	−78	
$CH_3—Cl$	50.5	−24	0.92
$CH_3—Br$	95	4	1.68
$CH_3—I$	142	42	2.28
CH_2Cl_2	85	40	1.34
$CHCl_3$	119	61	1.50
CCl_4	154	77	1.60
$CH_3CH_2—F$	48	−38	0.72
$CH_3CH_2—Cl$	64.5	12	0.90
$CH_3CH_2—Br$	109	38	1.46
$CH_3CH_2—I$	156	72	1.94
$CH_3CH_2CH_2—F$	62	3	0.80
$CH_3CH_2CH_2—Cl$	78.5	47	0.89
$CH_3CH_2CH_2—Br$	123	71	1.35
$CH_3CH_2CH_2—I$	170	102	1.75
$(CH_3)_2CH—Cl$	78.5	36	0.86
$(CH_3)_2CH—Br$	123	59	1.31
$(CH_3)_2CH—I$	170	89	1.70
$CH_3CH_2CH_2CH_2—F$	76	33	0.78
$CH_3CH_2CH_2CH_2—Cl$	92.5	78	0.89
$CH_3CH_2CH_2CH_2—Br$	137	102	1.28
$CH_3CH_2CH_2CH_2—I$	184	131	1.62
$(CH_3)_3C—Cl$	92.5	52	0.84
$(CH_3)_3C—Br$	137	73	1.23
$(CH_3)_3C—I$	184	100	1.54

6-5B Densities

Table 6-2 also lists the densities of common alkyl halides. Like their boiling points, their densities follow a predictable trend. Alkyl fluorides and alkyl chlorides (those with just one chlorine atom) are less dense than water (1.00 g/mL). Alkyl chlorides with two or more chlorine atoms are denser than water, and all alkyl bromides and alkyl iodides are denser than water.

PROBLEM 6-7

When water is shaken with hexane, the two liquids separate into two phases. Which compound is present in the top phase, and which is present in the bottom phase? When water is shaken with chloroform, a similar two-phase system results. Again, which compound is present in each phase? Explain the difference in the two experiments. What do you expect to happen when water is shaken with ethanol (CH_3CH_2OH)?

6-6 Preparation of Alkyl Halides

Most syntheses of alkyl halides exploit the chemistry of functional groups we have not yet covered. For now, we review free-radical halogenation and only summarize other, often more useful, syntheses of alkyl halides. The other syntheses are discussed in subsequent chapters.

6-6A Free-Radical Halogenation

Although we discussed its mechanism at length in Section 4-3, free-radical halogenation is rarely an effective method for the synthesis of alkyl halides. It usually produces mixtures of products because there are different kinds of hydrogen atoms that can be abstracted. Also, more than one halogen atom may react, giving multiple substitutions. For example, the chlorination of propane can give a messy mixture of products.

$$CH_3{-}CH_2{-}CH_3 \;+\; Cl_2 \xrightarrow{h\nu} \left\{\begin{array}{l} CH_3{-}CH_2{-}CH_2Cl \;+\; CH_3{-}CHCl{-}CH_3 \\ +\; CH_3{-}CHCl{-}CH_2Cl \;+\; CH_3{-}CCl_2{-}CH_3 \\ +\; CH_3{-}CH_2{-}CHCl_2 \;+\; \text{others} \end{array}\right.$$

In industry, free-radical halogenation is sometimes useful because the reagents are cheap, the mixture of products can be separated by distillation, and each of the individual products is sold separately. In a laboratory, however, we need a good yield of one particular product. Free-radical halogenation rarely provides good selectivity and yield, so it is seldom used in the laboratory. Laboratory syntheses using free-radical halogenation are generally limited to specialized compounds that give a single major product, such as the following examples.

$$\text{cyclohexane } (C_6H_{11}{-}H) \;+\; Cl_2 \xrightarrow{h\nu} \text{chlorocyclohexane } (C_6H_{11}{-}Cl)\ (50\%)$$

$$\underset{\text{isobutane}}{(CH_3)_3C{-}H} \;+\; Br_2 \xrightarrow{h\nu} \underset{\textit{tert}\text{-butyl bromide } (90\%)}{(CH_3)_3C{-}Br}$$

All the hydrogen atoms in cyclohexane are equivalent, and free-radical chlorination gives a usable yield of chlorocyclohexane. Formation of dichlorides and trichlorides is possible, but these side reactions are controlled by using only a small amount of chlorine and an excess of cyclohexane. Free-radical bromination is highly selective (Section 4-14), and it gives good yields of products that have one type of hydrogen atom that is more reactive than the others. Isobutane has only one tertiary hydrogen atom, and this atom is preferentially abstracted to give a tertiary free radical. In general, however, we are not inclined to use free-radical halogenation in the laboratory because it tends to be plagued by mixtures of products.

6-6B Allylic Bromination

Although free-radical halogenation is a poor synthetic method in most cases, free-radical bromination of alkenes can be carried out in a highly selective manner. An **allylic** position is a carbon atom next to a carbon–carbon double bond. Allylic intermediates (cations, radicals, and anions) are stabilized by resonance with the double bond, allowing the charge or radical to be delocalized. The following bond dissociation enthalpies show that less energy is required to form a resonance-stabilized primary allylic radical than a typical secondary radical.

$$(CH_3)_2CH_2 \longrightarrow (CH_3)_2\dot{C}H + H\cdot \qquad \Delta H = +397 \text{ kJ/mol} \quad (95 \text{ kcal/mol})$$

(2° radical)

$$H_2C{=}CH{-}CH_3 \longrightarrow \left[H_2C{=}CH{-}\dot{C}H_2 \longleftrightarrow H_2\dot{C}{-}CH{=}CH_2\right] + H\cdot \qquad \Delta H = +364 \text{ kJ/mol} \quad (87 \text{ kcal/mol})$$

(1° allylic radical)

Recall from Section 4-13C that bromination is highly selective, with only the most stable radical being formed. If there is an allylic hydrogen, the allylic radical is usually the most stable of the radicals that might be formed. For example, consider the free-radical bromination of cyclohexene. Under the right conditions, free-radical bromination of cyclohexene can give a good yield of 3-bromocyclohexene, where bromine has substituted for an allylic hydrogen on the carbon atom next to the double bond.

allylic positions

cyclohexene

allylic hydrogens

cyclohexene + Br_2 $\xrightarrow{h\nu}$ 3-bromocyclohexene (80%) + HBr

The mechanism is similar to other free-radical halogenations. A bromine radical abstracts an allylic hydrogen atom to give a resonance-stabilized allylic radical. This radical reacts with Br_2, regenerating a bromine radical that continues the chain reaction.

abstraction of allylic H

cyclohexene $\xrightarrow{Br\cdot}$ Br—H + [allylic radical ⟷ allylic radical] $\xrightarrow{Br—Br}$ allylic bromide + Br·

cyclohexene — allylic radical — allylic bromide

MECHANISM 6-1 Allylic Bromination

Initiation Step: Bromine absorbs light, causing formation of radicals.

$$:\ddot{Br}-\ddot{Br}: \xrightarrow{h\nu} 2\ :\ddot{Br}\cdot$$

First Propagation Step: A bromine radical abstracts an allylic hydrogen.

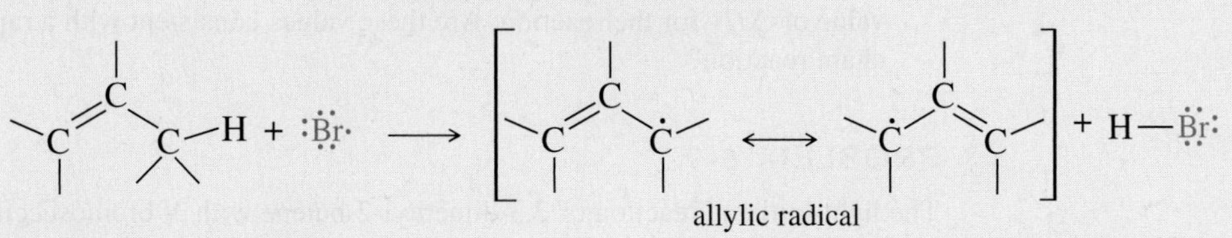

C=C–C–H + :Br· ⟶ [C=C–Ċ ⟷ Ċ–C=C] + H—Br:

allylic radical

Second Propagation Step: Either radical carbon can react with bromine.

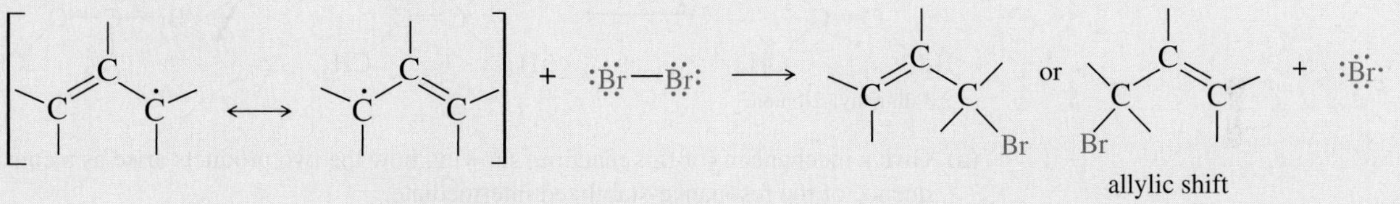

[C=C–Ċ ⟷ Ċ–C=C] + :Br—Br: ⟶ C=C–C–Br or Br–C–C=C + :Br·

allylic shift

Overall reaction

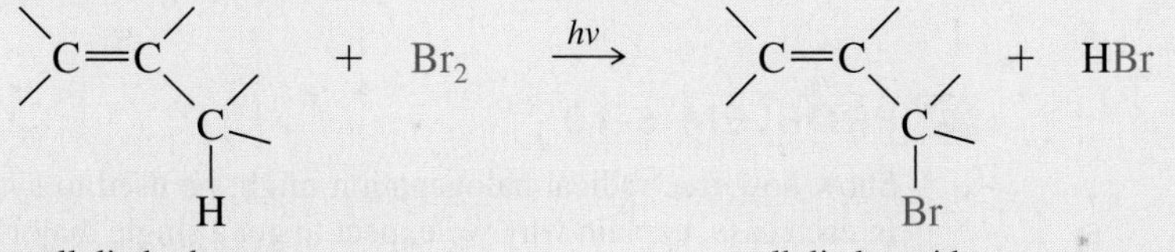

$$C{=}C{-}C{-}H + Br_2 \xrightarrow{h\nu} C{=}C{-}C{-}Br + HBr$$

an allylic hydrogen — an allylic bromide

The general mechanism for allylic bromination shows that either end of the resonance-stabilized allylic radical can react with bromine to give products. In one of the products, the bromine atom appears in the same position where the hydrogen atom was abstracted. The other product results from reaction at the carbon atom that bears the radical in the second resonance form of the allylic radical. This second compound is said to be the product of an **allylic shift**.

For efficient allylic bromination, a large concentration of bromine must be avoided because bromine can also add to the double bond (Chapter 8). *N*-Bromosuccinimide (NBS) is often used as the bromine source in free-radical brominations because it combines with the HBr side product to regenerate a constant low concentration of bromine. No additional bromine is needed because most samples of NBS contain traces of Br_2 to initiate the reaction.

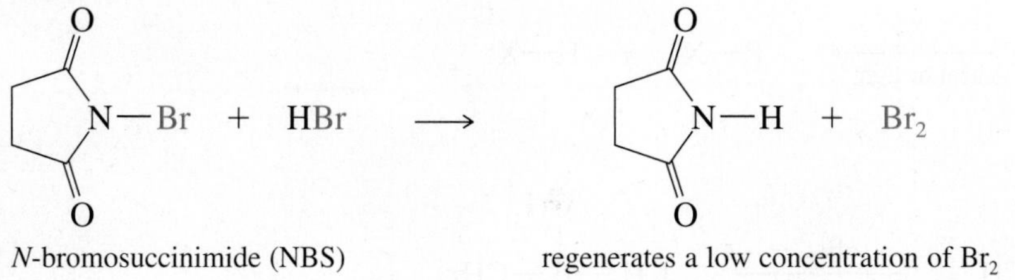

N—Br + HBr ⟶ N—H + Br_2

N-bromosuccinimide (NBS) — regenerates a low concentration of Br_2

Allylic halogenation is discussed in more detail in Chapter 15.

PROBLEM 6-8

(a) Propose a mechanism for the following reaction:

$$H_2C{=}CH{-}CH_3 + Br_2 \xrightarrow{h\nu} H_2C{=}CH{-}CH_2Br + HBr$$

(b) Use the bond-dissociation enthalpies given in Table 4-2 (page 138) to calculate the value of $\Delta H°$ for each step shown in your mechanism. (The BDE for $CH_2{=}CHCH_2{-}Br$ is about 280 kJ/mol, or 67 kcal/mol.) Calculate the overall value of $\Delta H°$ for the reaction. Are these values consistent with a rapid free-radical chain reaction?

PROBLEM 6-9

The light-initiated reaction of 2,3-dimethyl-2-butene with *N*-bromosuccinimide (NBS) gives two products:

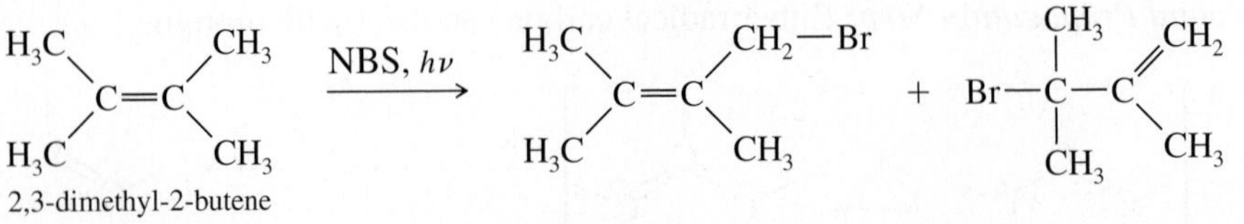

$$(CH_3)_2C{=}C(CH_3)_2 \xrightarrow{\text{NBS},\ h\nu} (CH_3)_2C{=}C(CH_3){-}CH_2{-}Br \; + \; Br{-}C(CH_3)_2{-}C(CH_3){=}CH_2$$

2,3-dimethyl-2-butene

(a) Give a mechanism for this reaction, showing how the two products arise as a consequence of the resonance-stabilized intermediate.

(b) The bromination of cyclohexene using NBS gives only one major product, as shown on page 224. Explain why there is no second product from an allylic shift.

PROBLEM 6-10

Show how free-radical halogenation might be used to synthesize the following compounds. In each case, explain why we expect to get a single major product.

(a) 1-chloro-2,2-dimethylpropane (neopentyl chloride)

(b) 2-bromo-2-methylbutane

(c) 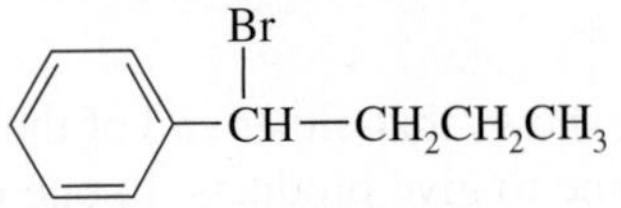 $C_6H_5{-}CH(Br){-}CH_2CH_2CH_3$
1-bromo-1-phenylbutane

(d) 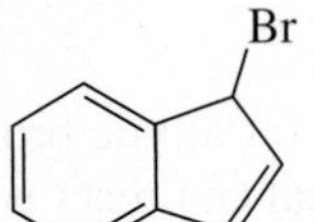 1-bromoindene structure (five-membered ring fused to benzene, Br on the sp^3 carbon)

Following is a brief summary of the most important methods of making alkyl halides. Many of them are more general and more useful than free-radical halogenation. Several of these methods are not discussed until later in the text (note the appropriate section references). They are listed here so that you can use this summary for reference throughout the course.

SUMMARY Methods for Preparing Alkyl Halides

1. *From alkanes: free-radical halogenation (synthetically useful only in certain cases)* (Sections 4-13 and 6-6)

$$R{-}H \xrightarrow[\text{heat or light}]{X_2} R{-}X + H{-}X$$

Example

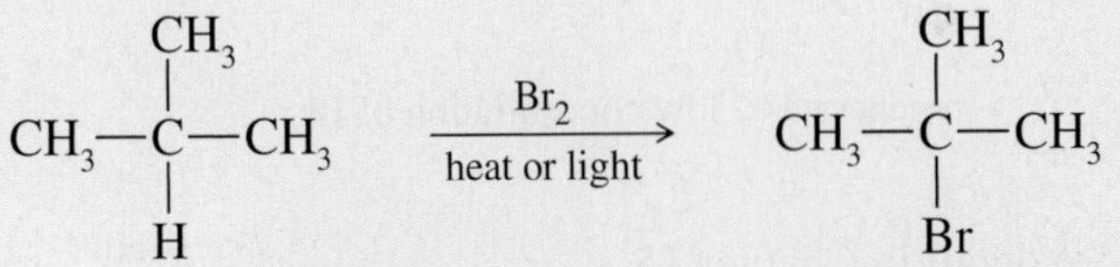

$$CH_3{-}CH(CH_3){-}CH_3 \xrightarrow[\text{heat or light}]{Br_2} CH_3{-}CBr(CH_3){-}CH_3$$

isobutane → *tert*-butyl bromide

2. *From alkenes and alkynes*

$$\rangle C{=}C\langle \xrightarrow{HX} -\overset{|}{\underset{H}{C}}-\overset{|}{\underset{X}{C}}- \quad \text{(Section 8-8)}$$

$$\rangle C{=}C\langle \xrightarrow{X_2} -\overset{X}{\underset{|}{C}}-\overset{|}{\underset{X}{C}}- \quad \text{(Section 8-8)}$$

$$-C{\equiv}C- \xrightarrow{2\,HX} -\overset{H}{\underset{H}{C}}-\overset{X}{\underset{X}{C}}- \quad \text{(Section 9-9)}$$

$$-C{\equiv}C- \xrightarrow{2\,X_2} -\overset{X}{\underset{X}{C}}-\overset{X}{\underset{X}{C}}- \quad \text{(Section 9-9)}$$

$$\rangle C{=}C\langle\!-C{-}H \xrightarrow[\text{light}]{\text{NBS: N-bromosuccinimide (N}-\text{Br)}} \rangle C{=}C\langle\!-C{-}Br \quad \text{(Sections 6-6, 15-7)}$$

(allylic bromination)

Examples

$$\underset{\text{2-methyl-2-butene}}{CH_3{-}CH{=}C(CH_3)_2} \xrightarrow{HBr} \underset{\text{2-bromo-2-methylbutane}}{CH_3{-}CH_2{-}\overset{CH_3}{\underset{Br}{C}}{-}CH_3}$$

$$\underset{\text{2-butene}}{CH_3{-}CH{=}CH{-}CH_3} \xrightarrow{Cl_2} \underset{\text{2,3-dichlorobutane}}{CH_3{-}CHCl{-}CHCl{-}CH_3}$$

$$\underset{\text{1-pentyne}}{H{-}C{\equiv}C{-}CH_2CH_2CH_3} \xrightarrow{2\,HBr} \underset{\text{2,2-dibromopentane}}{CH_3{-}CBr_2{-}CH_2CH_2CH_3}$$

3. *From alcohols* (Sections 11-7, 11-8, 11-9)

$$R{-}OH \xrightarrow{HX,\ PX_3,\ \text{or others}} R{-}X$$

Example

$$\underset{\text{1-butanol}}{CH_3CH_2CH_2CH_2OH} \xrightarrow{HBr,\ H_2SO_4} \underset{\text{1-bromobutane}}{CH_3CH_2CH_2CH_2Br}$$

4. *From other halides* (Section 6-9)

$$R{-}X + I^- \xrightarrow[\text{acetone}]{} R{-}I + X^-$$

$$R{-}Cl + KF \xrightarrow[CH_3CN]{\text{18-crown-6}} R{-}F$$

Example

$$\underset{\text{allyl chloride}}{H_2C{=}CH{-}CH_2Cl} + NaI \xrightarrow[\text{acetone}]{} \underset{\text{allyl iodide}}{H_2C{=}CH{-}CH_2I}$$

6-7 Reactions of Alkyl Halides: Substitution and Elimination

Alkyl halides are easily converted to many other functional groups. The halogen atom can leave with its bonding pair of electrons to form a stable halide ion; we say that a halide is a good **leaving group**. When another atom replaces the halide ion, the reaction is a **substitution**. When the halide ion leaves with another atom or ion (often H^+), the reaction is an **elimination**. In many eliminations, a molecule of H—X is lost from the alkyl halide to give an alkene. These eliminations are called **dehydrohalogenations** because a hydrogen halide has been removed from the alkyl halide. Substitution and elimination reactions often compete with each other.

In a **nucleophilic substitution**, a nucleophile (Nuc:$^-$) replaces a leaving group (:X:$^-$) from a carbon atom, using its lone pair of electrons to form a new bond to the carbon atom.

Nucleophilic substitution

$$\text{H–C–C–X (—C—C—, H on one C, :X: on the other)} + \text{Nuc:}^- \longrightarrow \text{—C—C— (H, Nuc)} + \text{:X:}^-$$

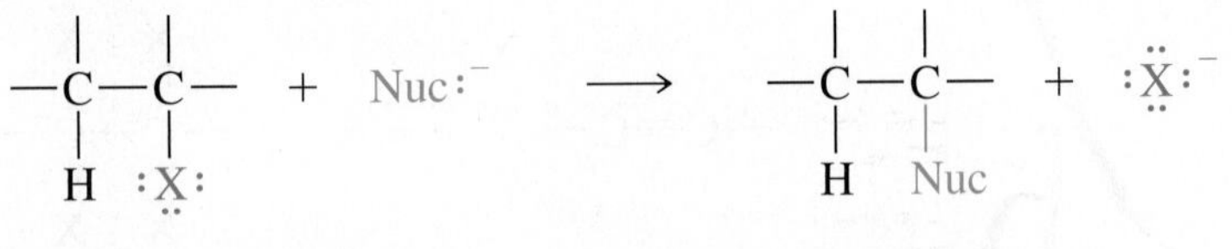

In an elimination, both the halide ion and another substituent are lost. A new π bond is formed.

Elimination

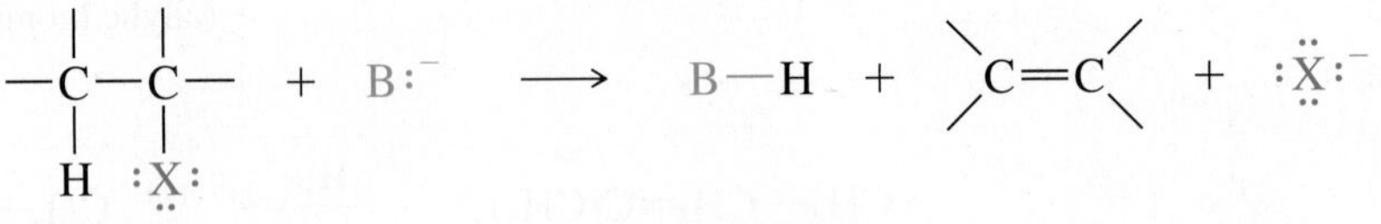

$$\text{—C—C— (H, :X:)} + \text{B:}^- \longrightarrow \text{B—H} + \text{C=C} + \text{:X:}^-$$

In the elimination (a dehydrohalogenation), the reagent (B:$^-$) reacts as a base, abstracting a proton from the alkyl halide. Most nucleophiles are also basic and can engage in either substitution or elimination, depending on the alkyl halide and the reaction conditions.

Besides alkyl halides, many other types of compounds undergo substitution and elimination reactions. Substitutions and eliminations are introduced in this chapter using the alkyl halides as examples. In later chapters, we encounter substitutions and eliminations of other types of compounds.

PROBLEM 6-11

Classify each reaction as a substitution, elimination, or neither. Identify the leaving group and the nucleophile (for substitutions) or base (for eliminations).

(a) cyclohexyl (H, Br) $\xrightarrow{Na^+\ ^-OCH_3}$ cyclohexyl (H, OCH_3) + NaBr

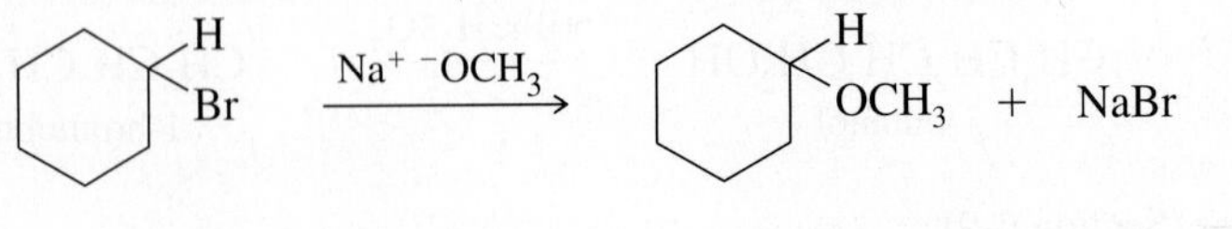

(b) cyclohexyl (H, OH) $\xrightarrow{H_2SO_4}$ cyclohexene + H_3O^+ + HSO_4^-

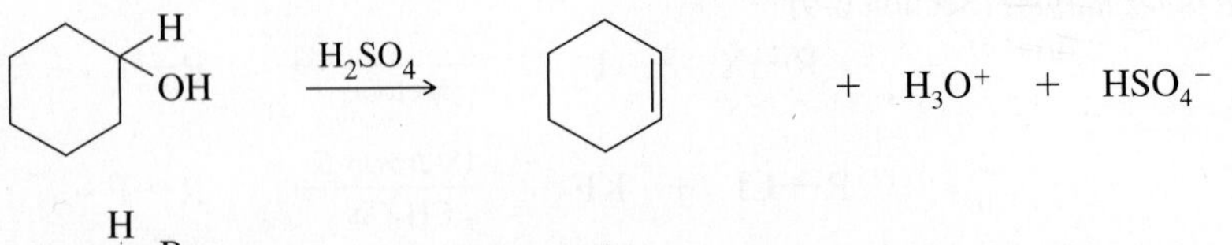

(c) 1,2-dibromocyclohexane (H, Br; H, Br) $\xrightarrow{KI}$ cyclohexene + IBr + KBr

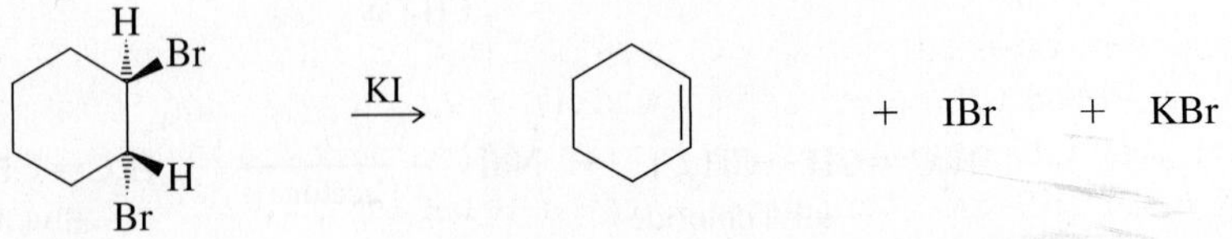

PROBLEM 6-12

Give the structures of the substitution products expected when 1-bromohexane reacts with
(a) $NaOCH_2CH_3$ (b) KCN (c) NaOH

6-8 Second-Order Nucleophilic Substitution: The S_N2 Reaction

A nucleophilic substitution has the general form

$$\text{Nuc:}^- + \text{—C—X:} \longrightarrow \text{Nuc—C—} + \text{:X:}^-$$

nucleophile substrate product leaving group

where Nuc:$^-$ is the nucleophile and :X:$^-$ is the leaving halide ion. An example is the reaction of iodomethane (CH_3I) with hydroxide ion. The product is methanol.

$$\text{H—O:}^- + \text{H—CH}_2\text{—I:} \longrightarrow \text{H—O—CH}_2\text{—H} + \text{:I:}^-$$

hydroxide (nucleophile) iodomethane (substrate) methanol (product) iodide (leaving group)

Hydroxide ion is a strong **nucleophile** (donor of an electron pair) because the oxygen atom has unshared pairs of electrons and a negative charge. Iodomethane is called the **substrate**, meaning the compound that is attacked by the reagent. The carbon atom of iodomethane is electrophilic because it is bonded to an electronegative iodine atom. Electron density is drawn away from carbon by the halogen atom, giving the carbon atom a partial positive charge. The negative charge of hydroxide ion is attracted to this partial positive charge.

$$\text{HO:}^- + \overset{\delta+}{\text{C}}\text{H}_3\text{—}\overset{\delta-}{\text{I:}} \longrightarrow [\text{HO---CH}_3\text{---I:}]^{\ddagger -} \longrightarrow \text{HO—CH}_3 + \text{:I:}^-$$

nucleophile electrophile (substrate) transition state product leaving group

Hydroxide ion attacks the back side of the electrophilic carbon atom, donating a pair of electrons to form a new bond. (In general, nucleophiles are said to attack electrophiles, not the other way around.) Notice that curved arrows are used to show the movement of electron pairs, from the electron-rich nucleophile to the electron-poor carbon atom of the electrophile. Carbon can accommodate only eight electrons in its valence shell, so the carbon–iodine bond must begin to break as the carbon–oxygen bond begins to form. Iodide ion is the leaving group; it leaves with the pair of electrons that once bonded it to the carbon atom.

This one-step mechanism is supported by kinetic information. One can vary the concentrations of the reactants and observe the effects on the reaction rate (how much methanol is formed per second). The rate is found to double when the concentration of *either* reactant is doubled. The reaction is therefore first order in each of the reactants and second order overall. The rate equation has the following form:

$$\text{rate} = k_r[CH_3I][^-OH]$$

This rate equation is consistent with a mechanism that requires a collision between a molecule of methyl iodide and a hydroxide ion. Both of these species are present in the transition state, and the collision frequency is proportional to both concentrations. The rate constant k_r depends on several factors, including the energy of the transition state and the temperature (Section 4-9).

■ FIGURE 6-4
The reaction-energy diagram for the S_N2 reaction of methyl iodide with hydroxide shows only one energy maximum: the transition state. There are no intermediates.

The electrostatic potential maps of the reactants, transition state, and products show that the negatively charged nucleophile (red) attacks the electrophilic (blue) region of the substrate. In the transition state, the negative charge (red) is delocalized over the nucleophile and the leaving group. The negative charge leaves with the leaving group.

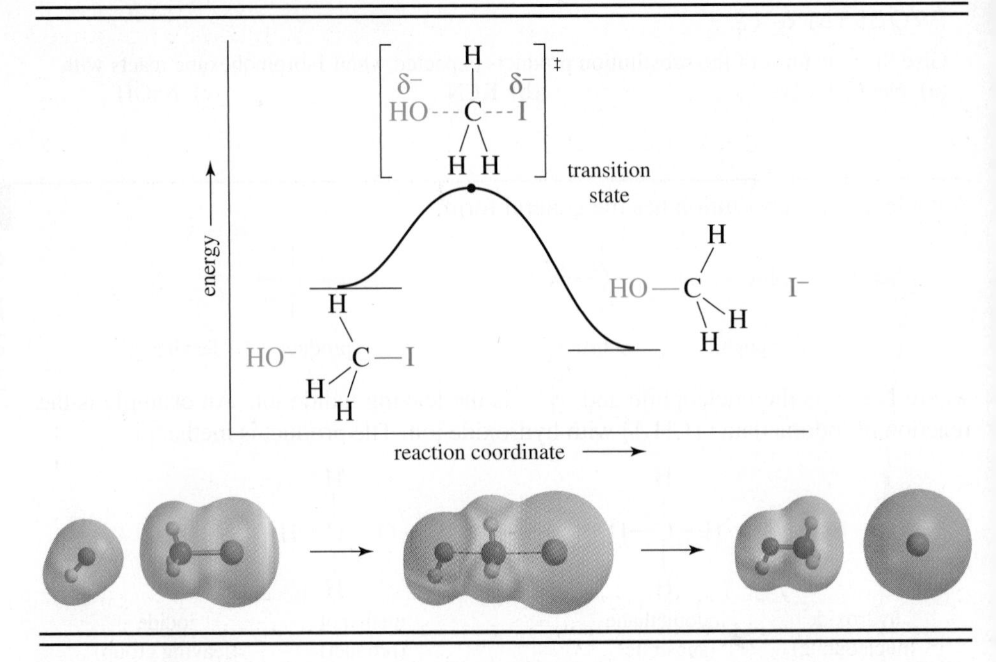

This one-step nucleophilic substitution is an example of the **S_N2 mechanism**. The abbreviation S_N2 stands for *Substitution, Nucleophilic, bimolecular*. The term *bimolecular* means that the transition state of the rate-limiting step (the only step in this reaction) involves the collision of *two* molecules. Bimolecular reactions usually have rate equations that are second order overall.

The S_N2 reaction of methyl iodide (iodomethane) with hydroxide ion is a **concerted reaction**, taking place in a single step with bonds breaking and forming at the same time. The middle structure is a **transition state**, a point of maximum energy, rather than an intermediate. In this transition state, the bond to the nucleophile (hydroxide) is partially formed, and the bond to the leaving group (iodide) is partially broken. Remember that a transition state is not a discrete molecule that can be isolated; it exists for only an instant.

The reaction-energy diagram for this substitution (Figure 6-4) shows only one transition state and no intermediates between the reactants and the products. The reactants are shown slightly higher in energy than the products because this reaction is known to be exothermic. The transition state is much higher in energy because it involves a five-coordinate carbon atom with two partial bonds.

problem-solving **Hint**

A transition state is unstable and cannot be isolated. It exists for only an instant.

The following mechanism shows a general S_N2 reaction. A nucleophile attacks the substrate to give a transition state in which a bond to the nucleophile is forming at the same time as the bond to the leaving group is breaking.

KEY MECHANISM 6-2 The S_N2 Reaction

The S_N2 reaction takes place in a single (concerted) step. A strong nucleophile attacks the electrophilic carbon, forcing the leaving group to leave.

$$\text{Nuc:}^- + \text{C—X:} \longrightarrow [\text{Nuc---C---X:}]^{\ddagger} \longrightarrow \text{Nuc—C} + \text{:X:}^-$$

nucleophile — substrate (electrophile) — transition state — product — leaving group

The order of reactivity for substrates is $CH_3X > 1° > 2°$. (3° alkyl halides cannot react by this mechanism.)

(Continued)

EXAMPLE: Reaction of 1-bromobutane with sodium methoxide gives 1-methoxybutane.

$$\underset{\text{sodium methoxide}}{NaOCH_3} + \underset{\text{1-bromobutane}}{CH_3CH_2CH_2CH_2Br} \longrightarrow \underset{\text{1-methoxybutane}}{CH_3CH_2CH_2CH_2OCH_3} + NaBr$$

CH_3—Ö:⁻ (nucleophile) + $CH_3CH_2CH_2$–C(H)(H)–Br: (electrophile (substrate)) ⟶ [CH_3—Ö---C($CH_2CH_2CH_3$)(H)(H)---Br:]‡ (transition state) ⟶ CH_3—Ö—C($CH_2CH_2CH_3$)(H)(H) (product) + Na^+ :Br:⁻ (leaving group)

PROBLEM 6-13

(a) Under certain conditions, the reaction of 0.5 M 1-bromobutane with 1.0 M sodium methoxide forms 1-methoxybutane at a rate of 0.05 mol/L per second. What would be the rate if 0.1 M 1-bromobutane and 2.0 M $NaOCH_3$ were used?

(b) Consider the reaction of 1-bromobutane with a large excess of ammonia (NH_3). Draw the reactants, the transition state, and the products. Note that the initial product is the salt of an amine ($RNH_3^+ Br^-$), which is deprotonated by the excess ammonia to give the amine.

6-9 Generality of the S_N2 Reaction

Many useful reactions take place by the S_N2 mechanism. The reaction of an alkyl halide, such as methyl iodide, with hydroxide ion gives an alcohol. Other nucleophiles convert alkyl halides to a wide variety of functional groups. The following table summarizes some of the types of compounds that can be formed by nucleophilic displacement of alkyl halides.

SUMMARY S_N2 Reactions of Alkyl Halides

$$Nuc:^- + R{-}X \longrightarrow Nuc{-}R + X^-$$

Nucleophile		Product	Class of Product
R—X + ⁻:Ï:	⟶	R—Ï:	alkyl halide
R—X + ⁻:ÖH	⟶	R—ÖH	alcohol
R—X + ⁻:ÖR′	⟶	R—ÖR′	ether
R—X + ⁻:S̈H	⟶	R—S̈H	thiol (mercaptan)
R—X + ⁻:S̈R′	⟶	R—S̈R′	thioether (sulfide)
R—X + :NH_3	⟶	R—NH_3^+ X^-	amine salt
R—X + ⁻:N̈=N⁺=N̈:⁻	⟶	R—N̈=N⁺=N̈:⁻	azide
R—X + ⁻:C≡C—R′	⟶	R—C≡C—R′	alkyne
R—X + ⁻:C≡N:	⟶	R—C≡N:	nitrile
R—X + R′—COÖ:⁻	⟶	R′—COO—R	ester
R—X + :PPh_3	⟶	$[R{-}PPh_3]^+$ ^-X	phosphonium salt

Examples

benzyl chloride ($C_6H_5CH_2Cl$)	+	$^{-}$:ÖH: hydroxide	⟶	benzyl alcohol ($C_6H_5CH_2OH$)	+	Cl^-
CH_3I iodomethane (methyl iodide)	+	phenoxide ($C_6H_5O^-$)	⟶	methoxybenzene (methylphenyl ether) ($C_6H_5OCH_3$)	+	I^-
$CH_3CH_2CH_2CH_2CH_2Br$ 1-bromopentane	+	$^{-}$:SH	⟶	$CH_3CH_2CH_2CH_2CH_2SH$ 1-pentanethiol	+	Br^-
$CH_3CH_2CH_2CH_2Cl$ 1-chlorobutane (*n*-butyl chloride)	+	:NH_3 ammonia (excess)	⟶	$CH_3CH_2CH_2CH_2NH_2$ 1-butanamine (*n*-butylamine)	+	NH_4Cl
CH_3CH_2Br bromoethane (ethyl bromide)	+	$Na^{+}\,^{-}$:C≡C—H sodium acetylide	⟶	CH_3CH_2—C≡C—H 1-butyne (ethylacetylene)	+	NaBr
$CH_3CH_2CH_2I$ 1-iodopropane (*n*-propyl iodide)	+	$^{-}$:C≡N cyanide	⟶	$CH_3CH_2CH_2$—C≡N butanenitrile (butyronitrile)	+	I^-

Halogen Exchange Reactions The S_N2 reaction provides a useful method for synthesizing alkyl iodides and fluorides, which are more difficult to make than alkyl chlorides and bromides. Halides can be converted to other halides by **halogen exchange reactions**, in which one halide displaces another.

Iodide is a good nucleophile, and many alkyl chlorides react with sodium iodide to give alkyl iodides. Alkyl fluorides are difficult to synthesize directly, and they are often made by treating alkyl chlorides or bromides with KF under conditions that use a crown ether and an aprotic solvent to enhance the normally weak nucleophilicity of the fluoride ion (see Section 6-10).

$$R{-}X + I^- \longrightarrow R{-}I + X^-$$

$$R{-}X + KF \xrightarrow[CH_3CN]{\text{18-crown-6}} R{-}F + KX$$

Examples

$$H_2C{=}CH{-}CH_2Cl \text{ (allyl chloride)} + NaI \longrightarrow H_2C{=}CH{-}CH_2I \text{ (allyl iodide)} + NaCl$$

$$CH_3CH_2Cl \text{ (ethyl chloride)} + KF \xrightarrow[CH_3CN]{\text{18-crown-6}} CH_3CH_2F \text{ (ethyl fluoride)} + KCl$$

PROBLEM 6-14

Predict the major products of the following substitutions.

(a) CH_3CH_2Br + $(CH_3)_3CO^- \ ^+K \longrightarrow$
ethyl bromide, potassium *tert*-butoxide

(b) $HC{\equiv}C{:}^- \ ^+Na$ + $CH_3CH_2CH_2CH_2Cl \longrightarrow$
sodium acetylide, 1-chlorobutane

(c) $(CH_3)_2CHCH_2Br$ + excess $NH_3 \longrightarrow$

(d) $CH_3CH_2CH_2I$ + $NaCN \longrightarrow$

(e) 1-chloropentane + NaI $\longrightarrow$

(f) 1-chloropentane + KF $\xrightarrow[CH_3CN]{\text{18-crown-6}}$

PROBLEM 6-15

Show how you might use S_N2 reactions to convert 1-chlorobutane into the following compounds.

(a) 1-butanol
(b) 1-fluorobutane
(c) 1-iodobutane
(d) $CH_3{-}(CH_2)_3{-}CN$
(e) $CH_3{-}(CH_2)_3{-}C{\equiv}CH$
(f) $CH_3CH_2{-}O{-}(CH_2)_3{-}CH_3$
(g) $CH_3{-}(CH_2)_3{-}NH_2$

6-10 Factors Affecting S_N2 Reactions: Strength of the Nucleophile

We will use the S_N2 reaction as an example of how we study the properties of the species that participate in the reaction. Both the nucleophile and the substrate (the alkyl halide) are important, as well as the type of solvent used. We begin by considering what makes a good nucleophile.

The nature of the nucleophile strongly affects the rate of the S_N2 reaction. A strong nucleophile is much more effective than a weak one in attacking an electrophilic carbon atom. For example, both methanol (CH_3OH) and methoxide ion (CH_3O^-) have easily shared pairs of nonbonding electrons, but methoxide ion reacts with electrophiles in the S_N2 reaction about 1 million times faster than methanol. It is generally true that a species with a negative charge is a stronger nucleophile than a similar, neutral species.

Methoxide ion has nonbonding electrons that are readily available for bonding. In the transition state, the negative charge is shared by the oxygen of methoxide ion and by the halide leaving group. Methanol, however, has no negative charge; the transition state has a partial negative charge on the halide but a partial positive charge on the methanol oxygen atom. We can generalize the case of methanol and the methoxide ion to say that

> A base is always a stronger nucleophile than its conjugate acid.

$CH_3{-}\ddot{O}{:}^- + CH_3I \longrightarrow [CH_3{-}\overset{\delta-}{O}{\cdots}CH_3{\cdots}\overset{\delta-}{I}]^{\ddagger} \longrightarrow CH_3{-}O{-}CH_3 + {:}\ddot{I}{:}^-$

conjugate base (stronger nucleophile); lower E_a

$CH_3{-}\ddot{O}H + CH_3I \longrightarrow [CH_3{-}\overset{\delta+}{O}(H){\cdots}CH_3{\cdots}\overset{\delta-}{I}]^{\ddagger} \longrightarrow CH_3{-}\overset{+}{O}(H){-}CH_3 + {:}\ddot{I}{:}^-$

conjugate acid (weaker nucleophile); higher E_a

The "nitrogen mustard" anticancer drugs are believed to alkylate DNA using two S_N2 reactions. First, the nitrogen nucleophile displaces chloride on the primary alkyl chloride portion to generate a reactive intermediate that alkylates a nitrogen atom of DNA. The process is repeated, linking the two strands of the double-helix DNA, and thereby preventing replication of the DNA.

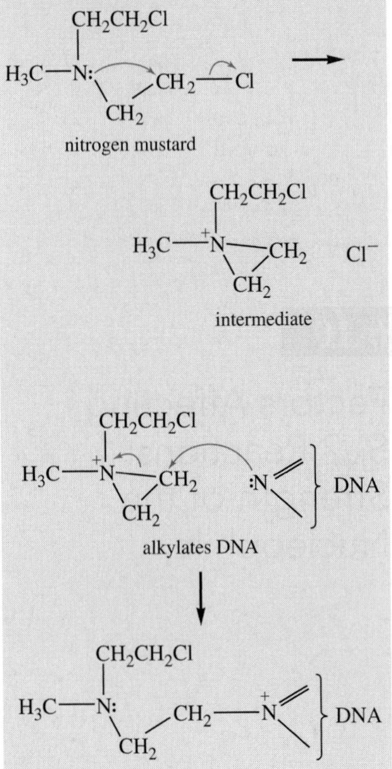

nitrogen mustard

intermediate

alkylates DNA

TABLE 6-3

Some Common Nucleophiles. Listed in Decreasing Order of Nucleophilicity in Hydroxylic Solvents Such as Water and Alcohols

strong nucleophiles	$(CH_3CH_2)_3P:$	moderate nucleophiles	$:Br:^-$
	$^-:SH$		$:NH_3$
	$:I:^-$		CH_3-S-CH_3
	$(CH_3CH_2)_2NH$		$:Cl:^-$
	$^-:C\equiv N$		$CH_3C(=O)-O:^-$
	$(CH_3CH_2)_3N:$	weak nucleophiles	$:F:^-$
	$H-O:^-$		$H-O-H$
	$CH_3-O:^-$		CH_3-O-H

We might be tempted to say that methoxide is a much better nucleophile because it is much more basic. This would be a mistake because basicity and nucleophilicity are different properties. **Basicity** is defined by the *equilibrium constant* for abstracting a *proton*. **Nucleophilicity** is defined by the *rate* of attack on an electrophilic *carbon atom*. In both cases, the nucleophile (or base) forms a new bond. If the new bond is to a proton, it has reacted as a **base**; if the new bond is to carbon, it has reacted as a **nucleophile**. Predicting which way a species will react may be difficult; most (but not all) good nucleophiles are also strong bases, and vice versa.

Basicity

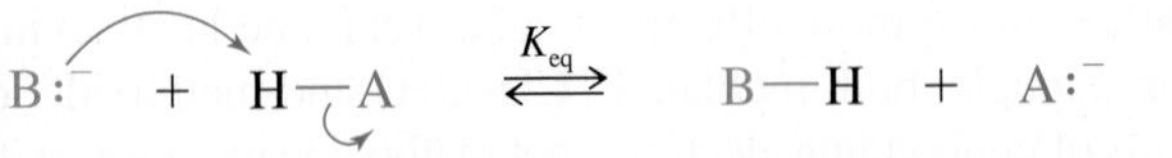

$$B:^- + H-A \overset{K_{eq}}{\rightleftharpoons} B-H + A:^-$$

Nucleophilicity

$$B:^- + -C-X \xrightarrow{k_r} B-C- + X:^-$$

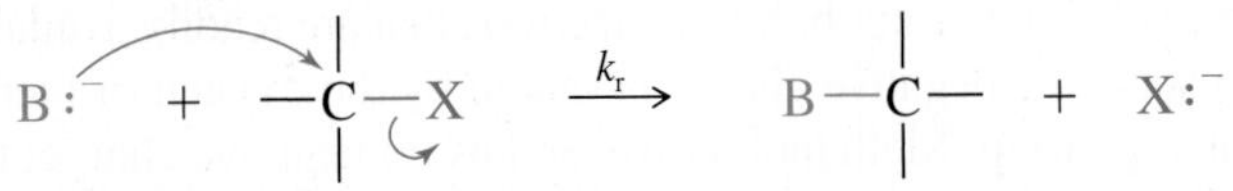

Table 6-3 lists some common nucleophiles in decreasing order of their nucleophilicity in hydroxylic solvents such as water and alcohols. The strength of nucleophiles in these solvents shows three major trends:

SUMMARY Trends in Nucleophilicity

1. A species with a negative charge is a stronger nucleophile than a similar neutral species. In particular, a base is a stronger nucleophile than its conjugate acid.

$$^-:OH > H_2O: \qquad ^-:SH > H_2S: \qquad ^-:NH_2 > :NH_3$$

2. Nucleophilicity decreases from left to right in the periodic table, following the increase in electronegativity from left to right. The more electronegative elements have more tightly held nonbonding electrons that are less reactive toward forming new bonds.

$$^-:NH_2 > ^-:OH > :F:^- \qquad :NH_3 > H_2O: \qquad (CH_3CH_2)_3P: > (CH_3CH_2)_2S:$$

3. Nucleophilicity increases down the periodic table, following the increase in size and polarizability, and the decrease in electronegativity.

$$:I:^- > :Br:^- > :Cl:^- > :F:^- \qquad ^-:SeH > ^-:SH > ^-:OH \qquad (CH_3CH_2)_3P: > (CH_3CH_2)_3N:$$

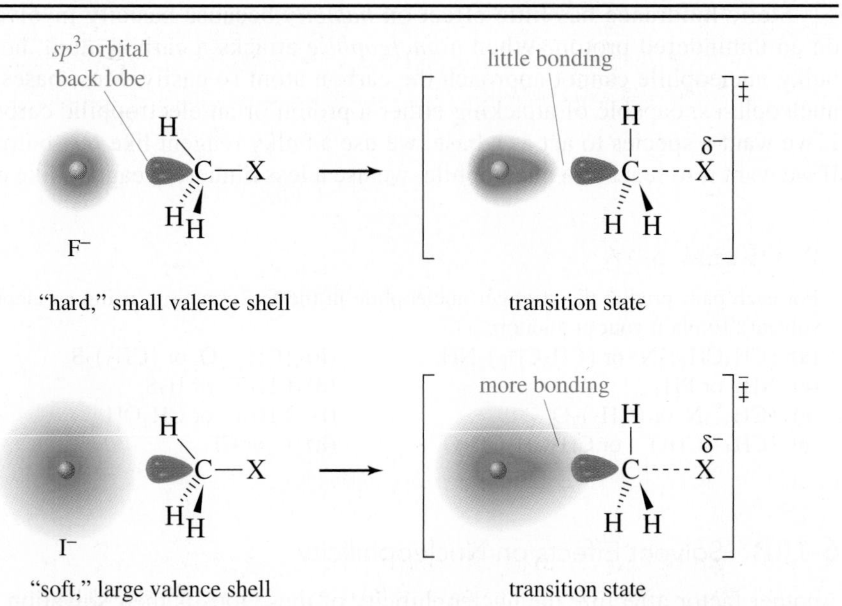

sp^3 orbital back lobe

little bonding

"hard," small valence shell — transition state

more bonding

"soft," large valence shell — transition state

■ **FIGURE 6-5**
Comparison of fluoride ion and iodide ion as nucleophiles in the S_N2 reaction. Fluoride has tightly bound electrons that cannot begin to form a C—F bond until the atoms are close together. Iodide has more loosely bound outer electrons that begin bonding earlier in the reaction.

The third trend (size and polarizability) reflects an atom's ability to engage in partial bonding as it begins to attack an electrophilic carbon atom. As we go down a column in the periodic table, the atoms become larger, with more electrons at a greater distance from the nucleus. The electrons are more loosely held, and the atom is more **polarizable**: Its electrons can move more freely toward a positive charge, resulting in stronger bonding in the transition state. The increased mobility of its electrons enhances the atom's ability to begin to form a bond at a relatively long distance.

Figure 6-5 illustrates this polarizability effect by comparing the attack of iodide ion and fluoride ion on a methyl halide. The outer shell of the fluoride ion is the second shell. These electrons are tightly held, close to the nucleus. Fluoride is a "hard" (low-polarizability) nucleophile, and its nucleus must approach the carbon nucleus quite closely before the electrons can begin to overlap and form a bond. In the transition state, there is little bonding between fluorine and carbon. In contrast, the outer shell of the iodide ion is the fifth shell. These electrons are loosely held, making the iodide ion a "soft" (high-polarizability) nucleophile. The outer electrons begin to shift and overlap with the carbon atom from farther away. There is a great deal of bonding between iodine and carbon in the transition state, which lowers the energy of the transition state.

6-10A Steric Effects on Nucleophilicity

To serve as a nucleophile, an ion or molecule must get in close to a carbon atom to attack it. Bulky groups on the nucleophile hinder this close approach, and they slow the reaction rate. For example, the *tert*-butoxide ion is a stronger *base* (for abstracting protons) than ethoxide ion, but *tert*-butoxide ion has three methyl groups that hinder any close approach to a more crowded carbon atom. Therefore, ethoxide ion is a stronger nucleophile than *tert*-butoxide ion. When bulky groups interfere with a reaction by virtue of their size, we call the effect **steric hindrance**.

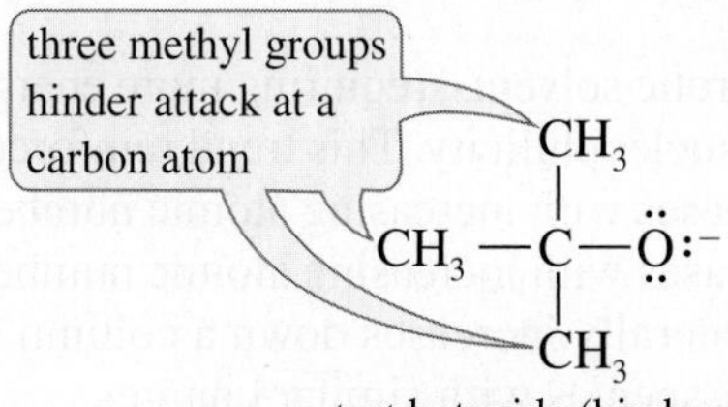

three methyl groups hinder attack at a carbon atom

$(CH_3)_3C-\ddot{O}:^-$

tert-butoxide (hindered)
stronger base, yet weaker nucleophile

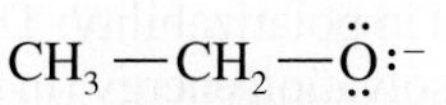

$CH_3-CH_2-\ddot{O}:^-$

ethoxide (unhindered)
weaker base, yet stronger nucleophile

Steric hindrance has little effect on *basicity* because basicity involves attack on an unhindered proton. When a *nucleophile* attacks a carbon atom, however, a bulky nucleophile cannot approach the carbon atom so easily. Most bases are also nucleophiles, capable of attacking either a proton or an electrophilic carbon atom. If we want a species to act as a base, we use a bulky reagent like *tert*-butoxide ion. If we want it to react as a nucleophile, we use a less hindered reagent, like ethoxide.

problem-solving Hint

Steric hindrance (bulkiness) hinders nucleophilicity (S_N2) more than it hinders basicity.

PROBLEM 6-16

For each pair, predict the stronger nucleophile in the S_N2 reaction (using an alcohol as the solvent). Explain your prediction.

(a) $(CH_3CH_2)_3N$ or $(CH_3CH_2)_2NH$
(b) $(CH_3)_2O$ or $(CH_3)_2S$
(c) NH_3 or PH_3
(d) CH_3S^- or H_2S
(e) $(CH_3)_3N$ or $(CH_3)_2O$
(f) CH_3S^- or CH_3OH
(g) $(CH_3)_2CHO^-$ or $CH_3CH_2CH_2O^-$
(h) I^- or Cl^-

6-10B Solvent Effects on Nucleophilicity

Another factor affecting the nucleophilicity of these ions is their solvation, particularly in protic solvents. A **protic solvent** is one that has acidic protons, usually in the form of O—H or N—H groups. These groups form hydrogen bonds to negatively charged nucleophiles. Protic solvents, especially alcohols, are convenient solvents for nucleophilic substitutions because the reagents (alkyl halides, nucleophiles, etc.) tend to be quite soluble.

Small anions are solvated more strongly than large anions in a protic solvent because the solvent approaches a small anion more closely and forms stronger hydrogen bonds. When an anion reacts as a nucleophile, energy is required to "strip off" some of the solvent molecules, breaking some of the hydrogen bonds that stabilized the solvated anion. More energy is required to strip off solvent from a small, strongly solvated ion such as fluoride than from a large, diffuse, less strongly solvated ion like iodide.

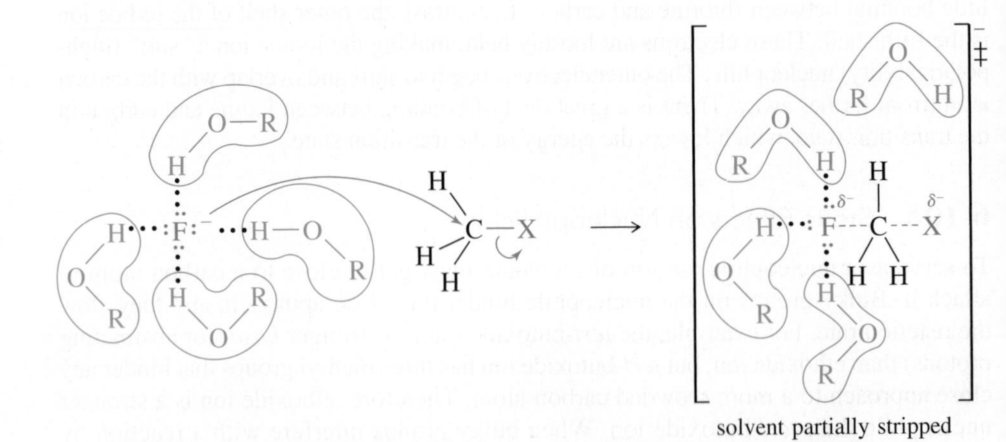

solvent partially stripped off in the transition state

The enhanced solvation of smaller anions in protic solvents, requiring more energy to strip off their solvent molecules, reduces their nucleophilicity. This trend reinforces the trend in polarizability: The polarizability increases with increasing atomic number, and the solvation energy (in protic solvents) decreases with increasing atomic number. Therefore, nucleophilicity (in protic solvents) generally increases down a column in the periodic table, as long as we compare similar species with similar charges.

In contrast with protic solvents, **aprotic solvents** (solvents without O—H or N—H groups) enhance the nucleophilicity of anions. An anion is more reactive in an aprotic solvent because it is not so strongly solvated. There are no hydrogen bonds to be broken when solvent must make way for the nucleophile to approach an electrophilic carbon atom. The relatively weak solvating ability of aprotic solvents is also a disadvantage: Most polar, ionic reagents are insoluble in simple aprotic solvents such as alkanes.

Polar aprotic solvents have strong dipole moments to enhance solubility, yet they have no O—H or N—H groups to form hydrogen bonds with anions. Examples of useful polar aprotic solvents are acetonitrile, dimethylformamide, and acetone. We can add specific solvating reagents to enhance solubility without affecting the reactivity of the nucleophile. For example, the "crown ether" 18-crown-6 solvates potassium ions. Using the potassium salt of a nucleophile and solvating the potassium ions causes the nucleophilic anion to be dragged along into solution.

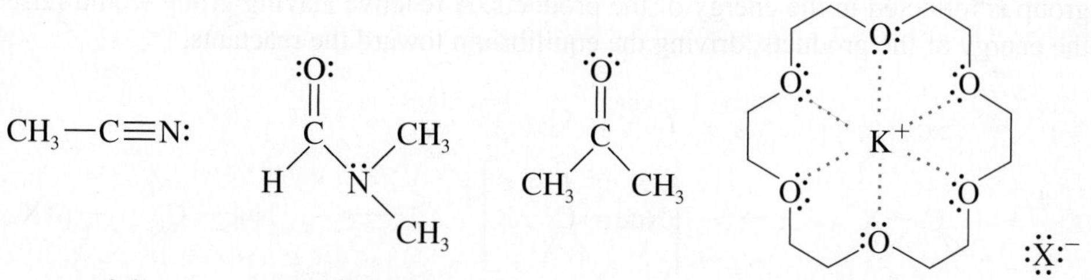

$CH_3—C≡N:$ acetonitrile

dimethylformamide (DMF)

acetone

18-crown-6 solvates K^+ ions

The following example shows how fluoride ion, normally a poor nucleophile in hydroxylic (protic) solvents, can be a good nucleophile in an aprotic solvent. Although KF is not very soluble in acetonitrile, 18-crown-6 solvates the potassium ions, and the poorly solvated (and therefore nucleophilic) fluoride ion follows.

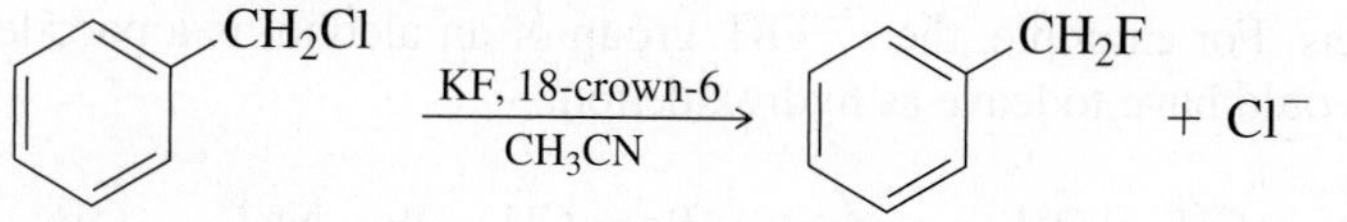

$$C_6H_5CH_2Cl \xrightarrow[CH_3CN]{KF,\ 18\text{-crown-6}} C_6H_5CH_2F + Cl^-$$

6-11 Reactivity of the Substrate in S_N2 Reactions

Just as the nucleophile is important in the S_N2 reaction, the structure of the alkyl halide is equally important. We will often refer to the alkyl halide as the **substrate**: literally, the compound that is being attacked by the reagent. Besides alkyl halides, a variety of other types of compounds serve as substrates in S_N2 reactions. To be a good substrate for S_N2 attack by a nucleophile, a molecule must have an electrophilic carbon atom with a good leaving group, and that carbon atom must not be too sterically hindered for a nucleophile to attack.

6-11A Leaving-Group Effects on the Substrate

A leaving group serves two purposes in the S_N2 reaction:

1. It polarizes the C—X bond, making the carbon atom electrophilic.
2. It leaves with the pair of electrons that once bonded it to the electrophilic carbon atom.

To fill these roles, a good leaving group should be:

1. electron withdrawing, to polarize the carbon atom,
2. stable (not a strong base) once it has left, and
3. polarizable, to stabilize the transition state.

1. The leaving group must be *electron withdrawing* to create a partial positive charge on the carbon atom, making the carbon electrophilic. An electron-withdrawing leaving group also stabilizes the negatively charged transition state. Halogen atoms are strongly electronegative, so alkyl halides are common substrates for S_N2 reactions. Oxygen, nitrogen, and sulfur also form strongly polarized bonds with carbon; given the right substituents, they can form the basis for excellent leaving groups.

Strongly polarized

$$C \overset{+\!\to}{—} X \ (X = \text{halogen}) \qquad C \overset{+\!\to}{—} O \quad C \overset{+\!\to}{—} N \quad C \overset{+\!\to}{—} S$$

2. The leaving group must be *stable* once it has left with the pair of electrons that bonded it to carbon. A stable leaving group is needed for favorable energetics. The leaving group is leaving in the transition state; a reactive leaving group would raise the energy of the transition state, slowing the reaction. Also, the energy of the leaving group is reflected in the energy of the products. A reactive leaving group would raise the energy of the products, driving the equilibrium toward the reactants.

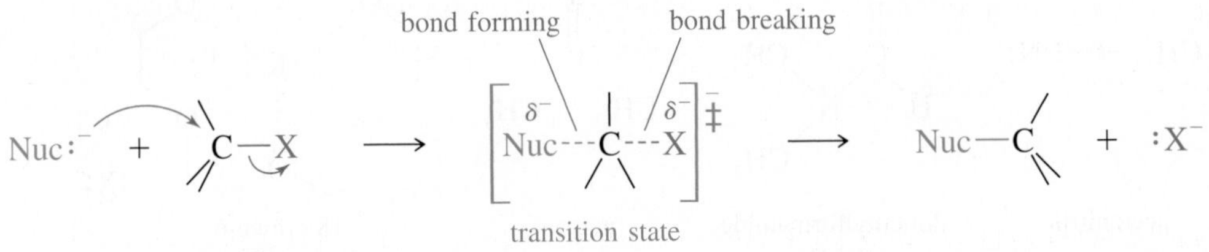

$$\text{Nuc}:^- + \ C—X \longrightarrow \left[\overset{\delta^-}{\text{Nuc}}\text{---}C\text{---}\overset{\delta^-}{X}\right]^{\ddagger} \longrightarrow \text{Nuc}—C \ + \ :X^-$$

bond forming   bond breaking

transition state

problem-solving Hint

Do not write S_N2 reactions that show hydroxide ions, alkoxide ions, or other strong bases serving as leaving groups.

Good leaving groups should be *weak bases*; therefore, they are the conjugate bases of strong acids. The hydrohalic acids HCl, HBr, and HI are strong, and their conjugates bases (Cl^-, Br^-, and I^-) are all weak bases. Other weak bases, such as sulfate ions, sulfonate ions, and phosphate ions, can also serve as good leaving groups. Table 6-4 lists examples of good leaving groups.

Hydroxide ion, alkoxide ions, and other strong bases are poor leaving groups for S_N2 reactions. For example, the —OH group of an alcohol is a poor leaving group because it would have to leave as hydroxide ion.

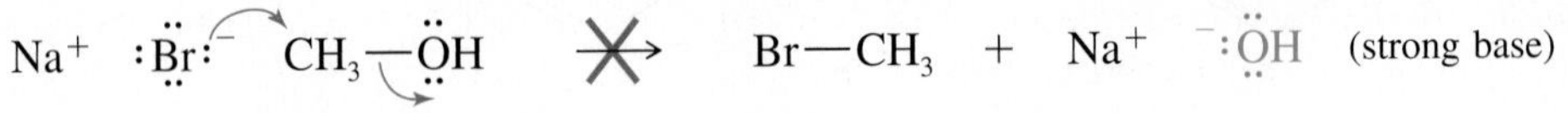

$$Na^+ \ :\ddot{Br}:^- \quad CH_3—\ddot{O}H \quad \not\longrightarrow \quad Br—CH_3 \ + \ Na^+ \ ^-:\ddot{O}H \ \text{(strong base)}$$

Ions that are strong bases and poor leaving groups:

$$^-:\ddot{O}H \qquad ^-:\ddot{O}R \qquad ^-:\ddot{N}H_2$$

hydroxide   alkoxide   amide

Table 6-4 also lists some neutral molecules that can be good leaving groups. A neutral molecule often serves as the leaving group from a *positively charged* species.

TABLE 6-4

Weak Bases That Are Common Leaving Groups

Ions:	$^-:\ddot{Cl}:$ $^-:\ddot{Br}:$ $^-:\ddot{I}:$	$^-:\ddot{O}—S(=O)_2—R$	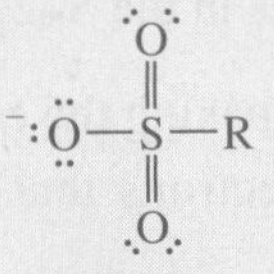 $^-:\ddot{O}—S(=O)_2—OR$	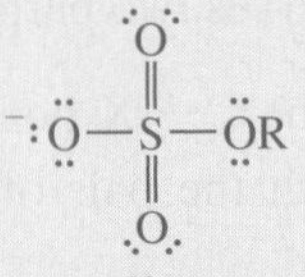 $^-:\ddot{O}—P(=O)(O^-)—OR$	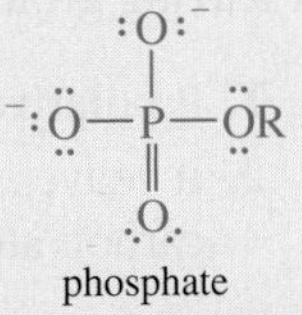
	halides	sulfonate	sulfate	phosphate	
Neutral molecules:	$:\ddot{O}(H)—H$	$:\ddot{O}(H)—R$	$:N(R)(R)—R$	$:P(R)(R)—R$	$:\ddot{S}(R)—R$
	water	alcohols	amines	phosphines	sulfides

For example, if an alcohol is placed in an acidic solution, the hydroxyl group is protonated. Water then serves as the leaving group. Note that the need to protonate the alcohol (requiring acid) limits the choice of nucleophiles to those few that are weak bases, such as bromide and iodide. A strongly basic nucleophile would become protonated in acid.

$$CH_3-\ddot{O}H + H^+ \overset{HBr}{\rightleftharpoons} :\ddot{Br}:^- \; CH_3-\overset{+}{O}(H)-H \longrightarrow :\ddot{Br}-CH_3 + :\ddot{O}(H)-H$$

protonated alcohol — water

3. Finally, a good leaving group should be *polarizable*, to maintain partial bonding with the carbon atom in the transition state. This bonding helps stabilize the transition state and reduce the activation energy. The departure of a leaving group is much like the attack of a nucleophile, except that the bond is breaking rather than forming. Polarizable nucleophiles and polarizable leaving groups both stabilize the transition state by engaging in more bonding at a longer distance. Iodide ion, one of the most polarizable ions, is both a good nucleophile and a good leaving group. In contrast, fluoride ion is a small, "hard" ion. Fluoride is both a poor nucleophile (in protic solvents) and a poor leaving group in S_N2 reactions.

PROBLEM 6-17

When diethyl ether ($CH_3CH_2OCH_2CH_3$) is treated with concentrated HBr, the initial products are CH_3CH_2Br and CH_3CH_2OH. Propose a mechanism to account for this reaction.

6-11B Steric Effects on the Substrate

Different alkyl halides undergo S_N2 reactions at vastly different rates. The structure of the substrate is the most important factor in its reactivity toward S_N2 displacement. The reaction goes rapidly with methyl halides and with most primary substrates. It is more sluggish with secondary halides. Tertiary halides fail to react at all by the S_N2 mechanism. Table 6-5 shows the effect of alkyl substitution on the rate of S_N2 displacements.

For simple alkyl halides, the relative rates for S_N2 displacement are

$$\text{Relative rates for } S_N2: \quad CH_3X > 1° > 2° \gg 3°$$

The physical explanation for this order of reactivity is suggested by the information in Table 6-5. All the slow-reacting compounds have one property in common: The back side of the electrophilic carbon atom is crowded by the presence of bulky groups. Tertiary halides are more hindered than secondary halides, which are more hindered than primary halides. Even a bulky primary halide (like neopentyl bromide) undergoes S_N2 reaction at a rate similar to that of a tertiary halide. The relative rates show that it is the

TABLE 6-5

Effect of Substituents on the Rates of S_N2 Reactions

Class of Halide	Example	Relative Rate
methyl	CH_3-Br	>1000
primary (1°)	CH_3CH_2-Br	50
secondary (2°)	$(CH_3)_2CH-Br$	1
tertiary (3°)	$(CH_3)_3C-Br$	<0.001
n-butyl (1°)	$CH_3CH_2CH_2CH_2-Br$	20
isobutyl (1°)	$(CH_3)_2CHCH_2-Br$	2
neopentyl (1°)	$(CH_3)_3CCH_2-Br$	0.0005

Note: Two or three alkyl groups, or even a single bulky alkyl group, slow the reaction rate. The rates listed are compared to the secondary case (isopropyl bromide), assigned a relative rate of 1.

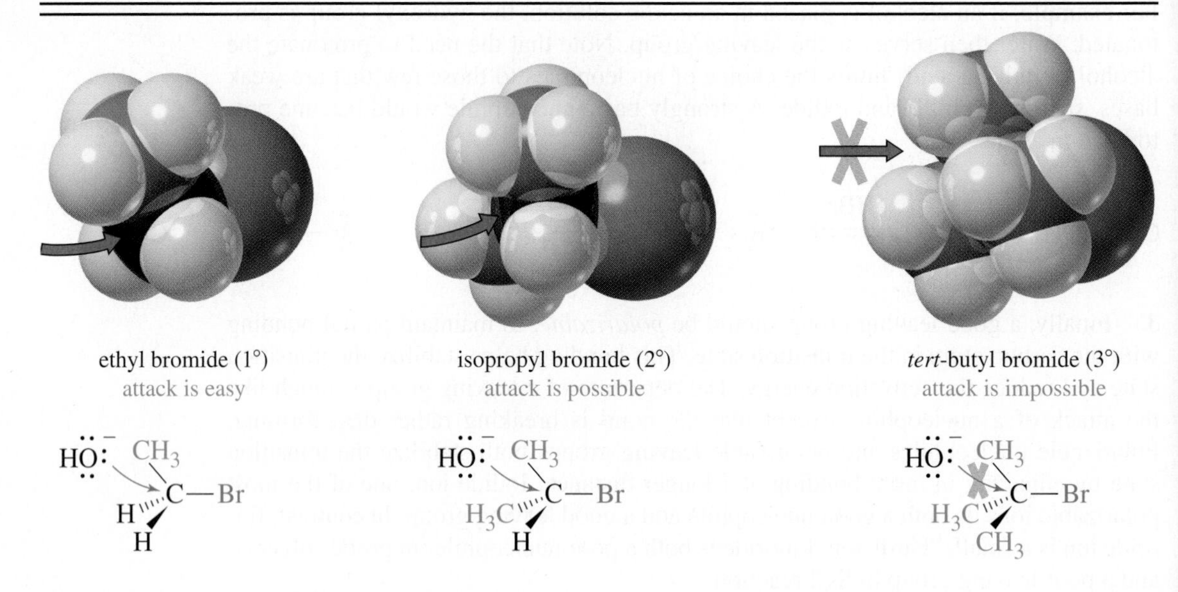

■ **FIGURE 6-6**
S_N2 attack on a simple primary alkyl halide is unhindered. Attack on a secondary halide is hindered, and attack on a tertiary halide is impossible.

bulk of the alkyl groups, rather than an electronic effect, that hinders the reactivity of bulky alkyl halides in the S_N2 displacement.

This effect on the rate is another example of **steric hindrance**. When the nucleophile approaches the back side of the electrophilic carbon atom, it must come within bonding distance of the back lobe of the C—X sp^3 orbital. If there are two alkyl groups bonded to the carbon atom, this process is difficult. Three alkyl groups make it impossible. Just one alkyl group can produce a large amount of steric hindrance if it is unusually bulky, like the *tert*-butyl group of neopentyl bromide.

Figure 6-6 shows the S_N2 reaction of hydroxide ion with ethyl bromide (1°), isopropyl bromide (2°), and *tert*-butyl bromide (3°). The nucleophile can easily approach the electrophilic carbon atom of ethyl bromide. In isopropyl bromide, the approach is hindered, but still possible. In contrast, S_N2 approach to the tertiary carbon of *tert*-butyl bromide is impossible because of the steric hindrance of the three methyl groups. Make models of ethyl bromide, isopropyl bromide, and *tert*-butyl bromide, and compare the ease of bringing in an atom for a back-side attack.

problem-solving **Hint**

Do not write (S_N2) reactions occurring on tertiary alkyl halides.

PROBLEM 6-18

Rank the following compounds in decreasing order of their reactivity toward the S_N2 reaction with sodium ethoxide ($Na^+ \ ^-OCH_2CH_3$) in ethanol.

methyl chloride   *tert*-butyl iodide   neopentyl bromide
isopropyl bromide   methyl iodide   ethyl chloride

PROBLEM 6-19

For each pair of compounds, state which compound is the better S_N2 substrate.

(a) 2-methyl-1-iodopropane or *tert*-butyl iodide
(b) cyclohexyl bromide or 1-bromo-1-methylcyclohexane
(c) 2-bromobutane or isopropyl bromide
(d) 1-chloro-2,2-dimethylbutane or 2-chlorobutane
(e) 1-iodobutane or 2-iodopropane

6-12 Stereochemistry of the S_N2 Reaction

As we have seen, the S_N2 reaction requires attack by a nucleophile on the back side of an electrophilic carbon atom (Figure 6-7). A carbon atom can have only four filled bonding orbitals (an octet), so the leaving group must leave as the nucleophile bonds to the carbon atom. The nucleophile's electrons insert into the back lobe of carbon's sp^3 hybrid orbital in its antibonding combination with the orbital of the leaving group (because the bonding MO is already filled). These electrons in the antibonding MO help to weaken the C—Br bond as bromide leaves. The transition state shows partial bonding to both the nucleophile and the leaving group.

Back-side attack literally turns the tetrahedron of the carbon atom inside out, like an umbrella caught by the wind (Figure 6-7). In the product, the nucleophile assumes a stereochemical position opposite the position the leaving group originally occupied. We call this result an **inversion of configuration** at the carbon atom.

In the case of an asymmetric carbon atom, back-side attack gives the opposite configuration of the carbon atom. The S_N2 displacement is the most common example of a **Walden inversion**, a step (in a reaction sequence) where an asymmetric carbon atom undergoes inversion of configuration. In the 1890s, Paul Walden, of the University of Tübingen (Germany), was one of the first to study reactions giving inversion of configuration.

MECHANISM 6-3 Inversion of Configuration in the S_N2 Reaction

Back-side attack inverts the configuration of the carbon atom.

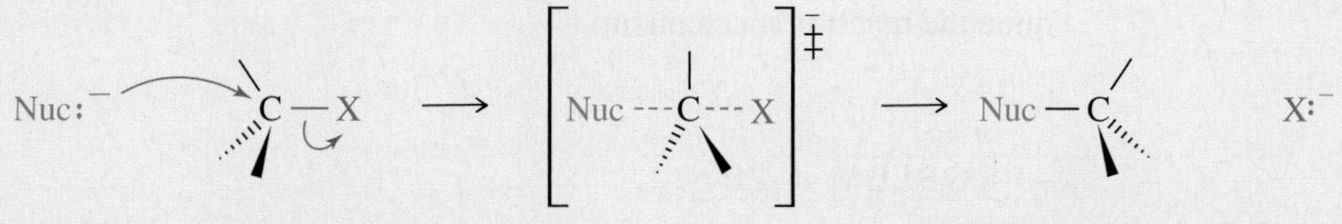

$$\text{Nuc}:^- \; + \; \text{C—X} \longrightarrow [\text{Nuc}\text{---C---X}]^{\ddagger} \longrightarrow \text{Nuc—C} \quad \text{X}:^-$$

EXAMPLE:

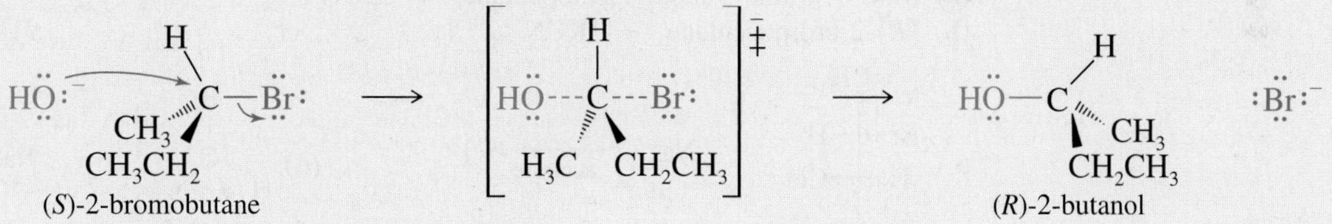

$$\text{H}\ddot{\text{O}}:^- + \text{(S)-2-bromobutane} \longrightarrow [\text{H}\ddot{\text{O}}\text{---C(H)(H}_3\text{C)(CH}_2\text{CH}_3\text{)---}\ddot{\text{Br}}:]^{\ddagger} \longrightarrow \text{(R)-2-butanol} \quad :\ddot{\text{Br}}:^-$$

(S)-2-bromobutane (H, CH_3, CH_3CH_2 on C—Br); (R)-2-butanol (HO—C with H, CH_3, CH_2CH_3)

back-side attack on the C—Br sp^3 orbital — transition state — product

HO:$^-$ + H, H, H tetrahedral carbon—Br: $\xrightarrow{\text{inversion}}$ HO—C(H)(H)(H) :Br:$^-$

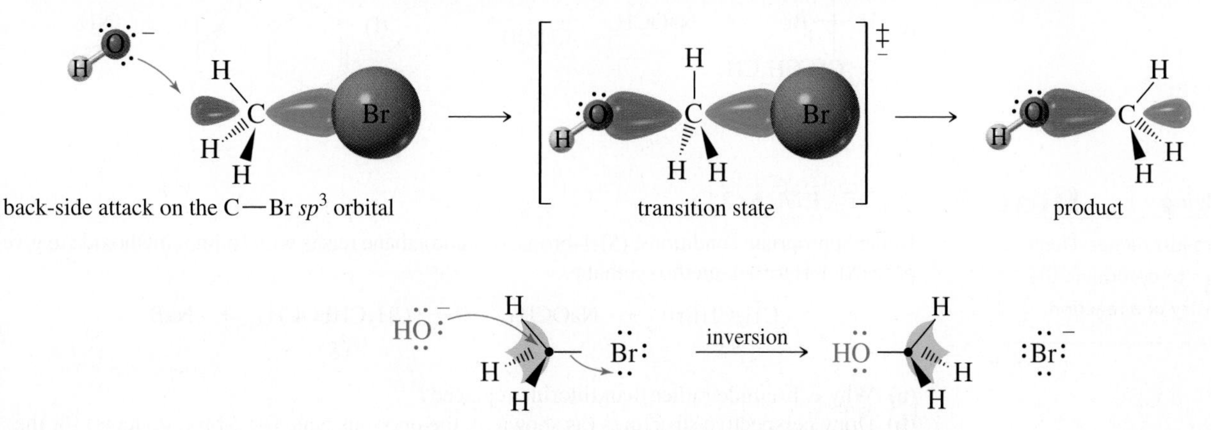

■ **FIGURE 6-7**
Back-side attack in the S_N2 reaction. The S_N2 reaction takes place through nucleophilic attack on the back lobe of carbon's sp^3 hybrid orbital. This back-side attack inverts the carbon atom's tetrahedron, like a strong wind inverts an umbrella.

In some cases, inversion of configuration is readily apparent. For example, when *cis*-1-bromo-3-methylcyclopentane undergoes S_N2 displacement by hydroxide ion, inversion of configuration gives *trans*-3-methylcyclopentanol.

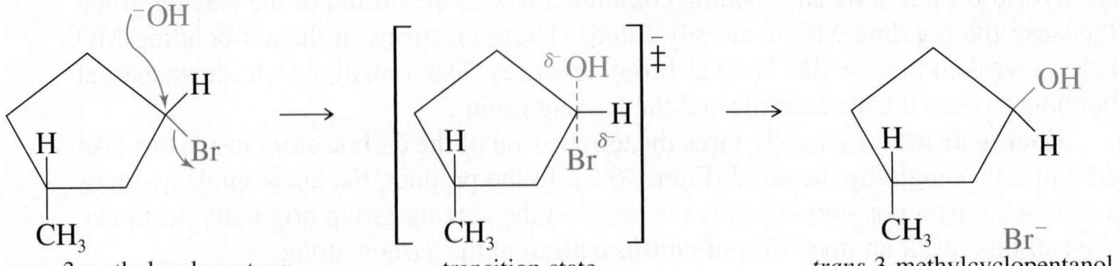

cis-1-bromo-3-methylcyclopentane → transition state → *trans*-3-methylcyclopentanol

The S_N2 displacement is a good example of a **stereospecific reaction**: one in which different stereoisomers react to give different stereoisomers of the product. To study the mechanism of a nucleophilic substitution, we often look at the product to see if the reaction is stereospecific, with inversion of configuration. If it is, the S_N2 mechanism is a good possibility, especially if the reaction kinetics are second order. In many cases (no asymmetric carbon or ring, for example), it is impossible to determine whether inversion has occurred. In these cases, we use kinetics and other evidence to help determine the reaction mechanism.

PROBLEM 6-20

Draw a perspective structure or a Fischer projection for the products of the following S_N2 reactions.

(a) *trans*-1-bromo-3-methylcyclopentane + KOH

(b) (*R*)-2-bromopentane + KCN

(c) 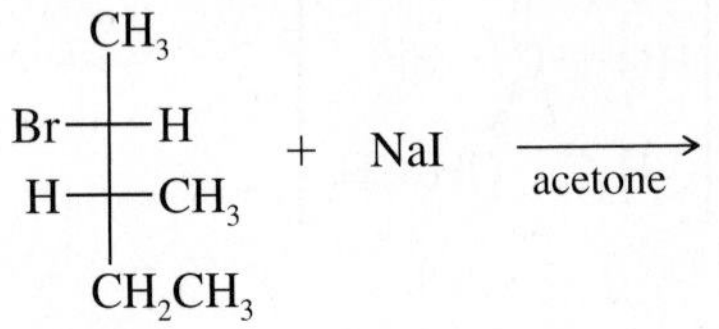 Fischer projection (CH_3 top; Br–H; H–CH_3; CH_2CH_3 bottom) + NaI $\xrightarrow{\text{acetone}}$

(d) 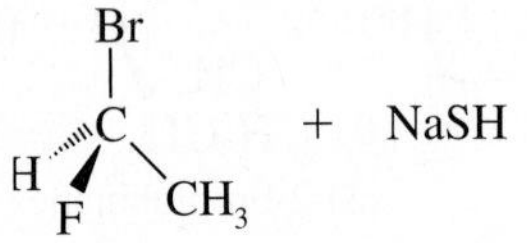 C with Br, H, F, CH_3 + NaSH

(e) 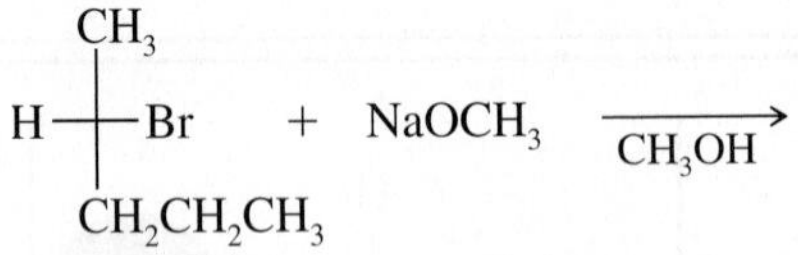 Fischer projection (CH_3 top; H–Br; $CH_2CH_2CH_3$ bottom) + $NaOCH_3$ $\xrightarrow{CH_3OH}$

(f) phenyl–C(H)(D)(Cl) + NH_3 excess

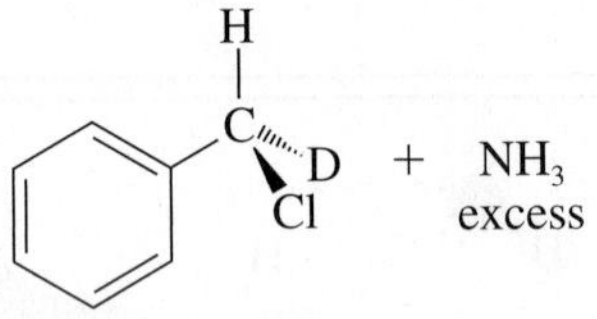

problem-solving Hint

(*R*) and (*S*) are just names. Don't rely on names to determine the stereochemistry of a reaction.

PROBLEM 6-21

Under appropriate conditions, (*S*)-1-bromo-1-fluoroethane reacts with sodium methoxide to give pure (*S*)-1-fluoro-1-methoxyethane.

$$\underset{(S)}{CH_3CHBrF} + NaOCH_3 \longrightarrow \underset{(S)}{CH_3CHFOCH_3} + NaBr$$

(a) Why is bromide rather than fluoride replaced?

(b) Draw perspective structures (as shown on the previous page for 2-bromobutane) for the starting material, the transition state, and the product.

(c) Does the product show retention or inversion of configuration?

(d) Is this result consistent with reaction by the S_N2 mechanism?

6-13 First-Order Nucleophilic Substitution: The S_N1 Reaction

When *tert*-butyl bromide is placed in boiling methanol, methyl *tert*-butyl ether can be isolated from the reaction mixture. Because this reaction takes place with the solvent acting as the nucleophile, it is called a **solvolysis** (*solvo* for "solvent," plus *lysis*, meaning "cleavage").

$$\underset{tert\text{-butyl bromide}}{(CH_3)_3C—Br} + \underset{\text{methanol}}{CH_3—OH} \xrightarrow{\text{boil}} \underset{\text{methyl } tert\text{-butyl ether}}{(CH_3)_3C—O—CH_3} + HBr$$

This solvolysis is a substitution because methoxide has replaced bromide on the *tert*-butyl group. It does not go through the S_N2 mechanism, however. The S_N2 requires a strong nucleophile and a substrate that is not too hindered. Methanol is a weak nucleophile, and *tert*-butyl bromide is a hindered tertiary halide—a poor S_N2 substrate.

If this substitution cannot go by the S_N2 mechanism, what kind of mechanism might be involved? An important clue is kinetic: Its rate does not depend on the concentration of methanol, the nucleophile. The rate depends only on the concentration of the substrate, *tert*-butyl bromide.

$$S_N1 \text{ rate} = k_r[(CH_3)_3C—Br]$$

This rate equation is first order overall: first order in the concentration of the alkyl halide and zeroth order in the concentration of the nucleophile. Because the rate does not depend on the concentration of the nucleophile, we infer that the nucleophile is not present in the transition state of the rate-limiting step. The nucleophile must react *after* the slow step.

This type of substitution is called an **S_N1 reaction**, for *Substitution, Nucleophilic, unimolecular*. The term *unimolecular* means there is only one molecule involved in the transition state of the rate-limiting step. The mechanism of the S_N1 reaction of *tert*-butyl bromide with methanol is shown here. Ionization of the alkyl halide (first step) is the rate-limiting step.

Step 1: Formation of carbocation (rate limiting)

$$(CH_3)_3C—\ddot{\underset{..}{Br}}: \rightleftharpoons (CH_3)_3C^+ + :\ddot{\underset{..}{Br}}:^- \quad \text{(slow)}$$

Step 2: Nucleophilic attack on the carbocation

$$(CH_3)_3C^+ \; :\ddot{O}(H)—CH_3 \rightleftharpoons (CH_3)_3C—\overset{+}{\ddot{O}}(H)—CH_3 \quad \text{(fast)}$$

Final Step: Loss of proton to solvent

$$(CH_3)_3C—\overset{+}{\ddot{O}}(H)—CH_3 + CH_3—\ddot{\underset{..}{O}}H \rightleftharpoons (CH_3)_3C—\ddot{\underset{..}{O}}—CH_3 + CH_3—\overset{+}{\ddot{O}}(H)—H \quad \text{(fast)}$$

The S_N1 mechanism is a multistep process. The first step is a slow ionization to form a carbocation. The second step is a fast attack on the carbocation by a nucleophile. The carbocation is a strong electrophile; it reacts very fast with nucleophiles, including weak nucleophiles. The nucleophile in S_N1 reactions is usually weak, because a strong nucleophile would be more likely to attack the substrate and force some kind of second-order reaction. If the nucleophile is an uncharged molecule like water or an alcohol, the positively charged product must lose a proton to give the final uncharged product. The general mechanism for the S_N1 reaction is summarized in Key Mechanism 6-4.

KEY MECHANISM 6-4 The S_N1 Reaction

The S_N1 reaction involves a two-step mechanism. A slow ionization gives a carbocation that reacts quickly with a (usually weak) nucleophile. Reactivity: 3° > 2° > 1°.

Step 1. Formation of the carbocation (rate-limiting).

$$R-\ddot{X}: \rightleftharpoons R^+ + :\ddot{X}:^-$$

Step 2. Nucleophilic attack on the carbocation (fast).

$$R^+ + Nuc:^- \longrightarrow R-Nuc$$

If the nucleophile is water or an alcohol, a third step is needed to deprotonate the product.

EXAMPLE: Solvolysis of 1-iodo-1-methylcyclohexane in methanol.

Step 1: Formation of a carbocation (rate-limiting).

CH₃ on cyclohexane with :I: ⇌ cyclohexyl cation (+) with CH₃ + :I:⁻

Step 2: Nucleophilic attack by the solvent (methanol).

cyclohexyl cation (+) with CH₃ + $CH_3-\ddot{O}-H$ ⇌ cyclohexane bearing CH₃ and $^+\ddot{O}$(CH₃)(H)

Step 3: Deprotonation to form the product.

cyclohexane bearing CH₃ and $^+\ddot{O}$(CH₃)(H) + $CH_3-\ddot{O}-H$ ⇌ cyclohexane bearing CH₃ and $\ddot{O}CH_3$ + $CH_3-\overset{+}{\ddot{O}}H_2$

product (protonated methanol)

problem-solving Hint

Never show a proton falling off into thin air. Show a possible base (often the solvent) abstracting the proton.

PROBLEM 6-22

Propose an S_N1 mechanism for the solvolysis of 3-bromo-2,3-dimethylpentane in ethanol.

The reaction-energy diagram of the S_N1 reaction (Figure 6-8) shows why the rate does not depend on the strength or concentration of the nucleophile. The ionization (first step) is highly endothermic, and its large activation energy determines the overall reaction rate. The nucleophilic attack (second step) is strongly exothermic, with a lower-energy transition state. In effect, a nucleophile reacts with the carbocation almost as soon as it forms.

The reaction-energy diagrams of the S_N1 mechanism and the S_N2 mechanism are compared in Figure 6-8. The S_N1 has a true intermediate, the carbocation. The intermediate appears as a relative minimum (a low point) in the reaction-energy diagram. Reagents and conditions that favor formation of the carbocation (the slow step) accelerate the S_N1 reaction; reagents and conditions that hinder its formation retard the reaction.

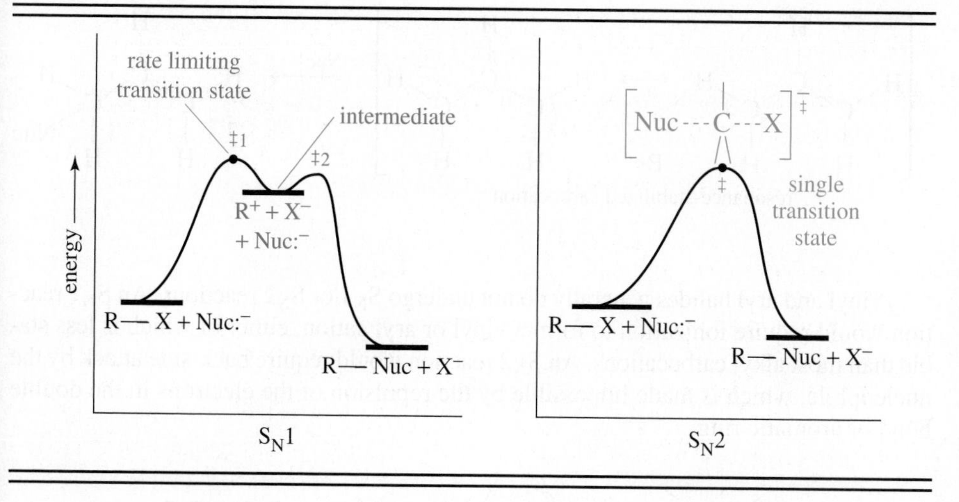

■ **FIGURE 6-8**
Reaction-energy diagrams of the S_N1 and S_N2 reactions. The S_N1 is a two-step mechanism with two transition states (‡1 and ‡2) and a carbocation intermediate. The S_N2 has only one transition state and no intermediate.

6-13A Substituent Effects

The rate-limiting step of the S_N1 reaction is ionization to form a carbocation, a strongly endothermic process. The first transition state resembles the carbocation (Hammond postulate, Section 4-14); consequently, rates of S_N1 reactions depend strongly on carbocation stability. In Section 4-16A, we saw that alkyl groups stabilize carbocations by donating electrons through sigma bonds (the *inductive effect*) and through overlap of filled orbitals with the empty *p* orbital of the carbocation *(hyperconjugation)*. Highly substituted carbocations are therefore more stable.

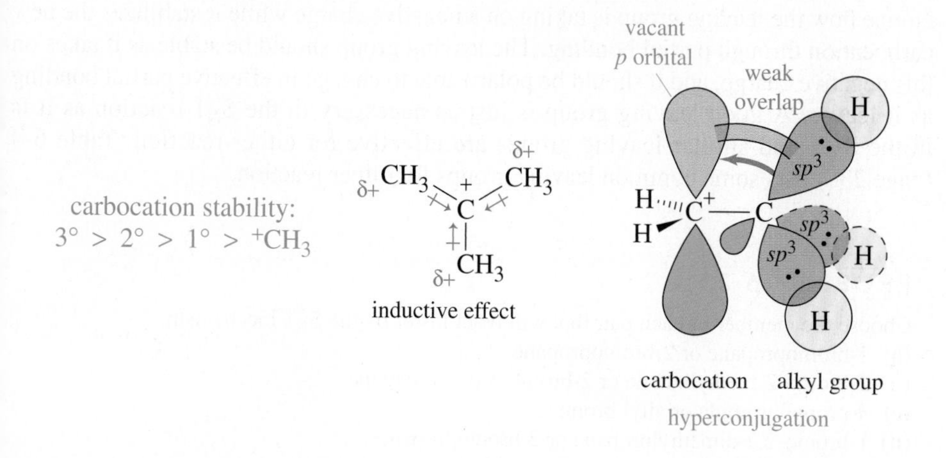

Reactivity toward S_N1 substitution mechanisms follows the stability of carbocations:

S_N1 reactivity:	3° > 2° > 1° > CH_3X

This order is *opposite* that of the S_N2 reaction. Alkyl groups hinder the S_N2 by blocking attack of the strong nucleophile, but alkyl groups enhance the S_N1 by stabilizing the carbocation intermediate.

Resonance stabilization of the carbocation can also promote the S_N1 reaction. For example, allyl bromide is a primary halide, but it undergoes the S_N1 reaction about as fast as a secondary halide. The carbocation formed by ionization is resonance stabilized, with the positive charge spread equally over two carbon atoms.

allyl bromide

resonance-stabilized carbocation

Vinyl and aryl halides generally do not undergo S_N1 or S_N2 reactions. An S_N1 reaction would require ionization to form a vinyl or aryl cation, either of which is less stable than most alkyl carbocations. An S_N2 reaction would require back-side attack by the nucleophile, which is made impossible by the repulsion of the electrons in the double bond or aromatic ring.

a vinyl halide or an aryl halide — no S_N1, no S_N2

6-13B Leaving-Group Effects

The leaving group is breaking its bond to carbon in the rate-limiting ionization step of the S_N1 mechanism. A highly polarizable leaving group helps stabilize the rate-limiting transition state through partial bonding as it leaves. The leaving group should be a weak base, very stable after it leaves with the pair of electrons that bonded it to carbon.

Figure 6-9 shows the transition state of the ionization step of the S_N1 reaction. Notice how the leaving group is taking on a negative charge while it stabilizes the new carbocation through partial bonding. The leaving group should be stable as it takes on this negative charge, and it should be polarizable to engage in effective partial bonding as it leaves. A good leaving group is just as necessary in the S_N1 reaction as it is in the S_N2, and similar leaving groups are effective for either reaction. Table 6-4 (page 238) lists some common leaving groups for either reaction.

problem-solving **Hint**

Primary cations are rarely formed in solution unless they are resonance-stabilized.

PROBLEM 6-23

Choose the member of each pair that will react faster by the S_N1 mechanism.

(a) 1-bromopropane or 2-bromopropane
(b) 2-bromo-2-methylbutane or 2-bromo-3-methylbutane
(c) *n*-propyl bromide or allyl bromide
(d) 1-bromo-2,2-dimethylpropane or 2-bromopropane
(e) 2-iodo-2-methylbutane or *tert*-butyl chloride
(f) 2-bromo-2-methylbutane or ethyl iodide

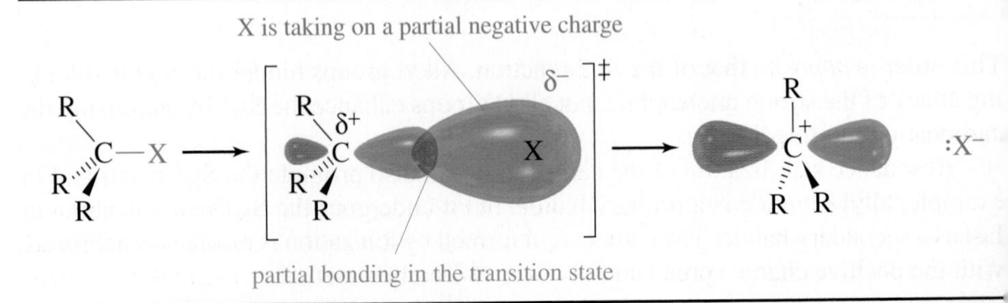
X is taking on a partial negative charge
partial bonding in the transition state

■ **FIGURE 6-9**
In the transition state of the S_N1 ionization, the leaving group is taking on a negative charge. The C—X bond is breaking, and a polarizable leaving group can still maintain substantial overlap.

PROBLEM 6-24

3-Bromocyclohexene is a secondary halide, and benzyl bromide is a primary halide. Both halides undergo S_N1 substitution about as fast as most tertiary halides. Use resonance structures to explain this enhanced reactivity.

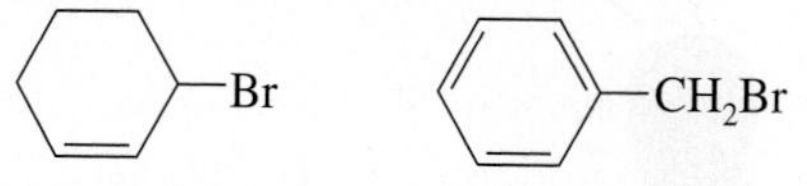

Br　　　CH_2Br

3-bromocyclohexene　　benzyl bromide

6-13C Solvent Effects

The S_N1 reaction goes much more readily in polar solvents that stabilize ions. The rate-limiting step forms two ions, and ionization is taking place in the transition state. Polar solvents solvate these ions by an interaction of the solvent's dipole moment with the charge of the ion. Protic solvents such as alcohols and water are even more effective solvents because anions form hydrogen bonds with the —OH hydrogen atom, and cations complex with the nonbonding electrons of the —OH oxygen atom.

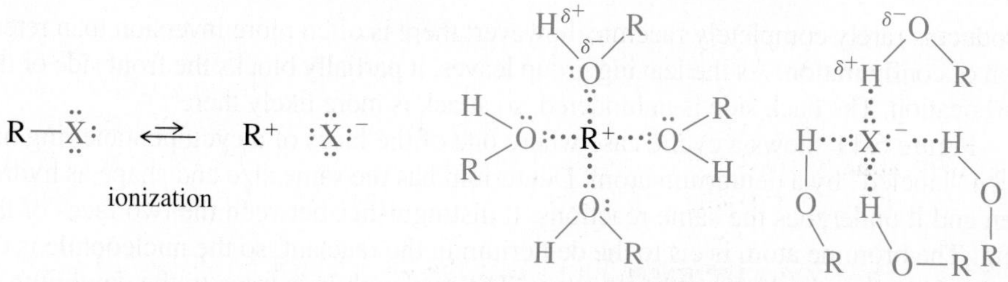

$$R{-}\ddot{X}: \;\xrightarrow{\text{ionization}}\; R^+ \;:\ddot{X}:^-$$

solvated ions

Ionization of an alkyl halide requires formation and separation of positive and negative charges, similar to what happens when sodium chloride dissolves in water. Therefore, S_N1 reactions require highly polar solvents that strongly solvate ions. One measure of a solvent's ability to solvate ions is its *dielectric constant* (ε), a measure of the solvent's polarity. Table 6-6 lists the dielectric constants of some common solvents and the relative ionization rates for *tert*-butyl chloride in these solvents. Note that ionization occurs much faster in highly polar solvents such as water and alcohols. Although most alkyl halides are not soluble in water, they often dissolve in highly polar mixtures of acetone and alcohols with water.

TABLE 6-6

Dielectric Constants (ϵ) and Ionization Rates of *tert*-Butyl Chloride in Common Solvents

Solvent	ϵ	Relative Rate
water	78	8000
methanol	33	1000
ethanol	24	200
acetone	21	1
diethyl ether	4.3	0.001
hexane	2.0	<0.0001

6-14 Stereochemistry of the S_N1 Reaction

Recall from Section 6-12 that the S_N2 reaction is stereospecific: The nucleophile attacks from the back side of the electrophilic carbon atom, giving inversion of configuration. In contrast, the S_N1 reaction is not stereospecific. In the S_N1 mechanism, the carbocation intermediate is sp^2 hybridized and planar. A nucleophile can attack the carbocation from either face. Figure 6-10 shows the S_N1 solvolysis of a chiral compound, (*S*)-3-bromo-2,3-dimethylpentane, in ethanol. The carbocation is planar and achiral; attack from both faces gives both enantiomers of the product. Such a process, giving both enantiomers of the product (whether or not the two enantiomers are produced in equal amounts), is called **racemization**. The product is either racemic or at least less optically pure than the starting material.

If a nucleophile attacks the carbocation in Figure 6-10 from the front side (the side the leaving group left), the product molecule shows **retention of configuration**. Attack from the back side gives a product molecule showing **inversion of configuration**. Racemization is simply a combination of retention and inversion. When racemization occurs, the

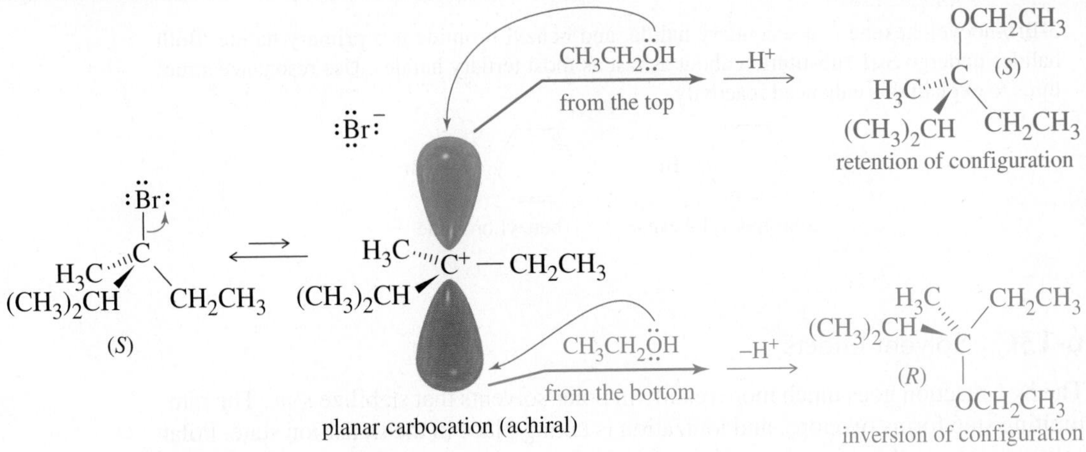

■ FIGURE 6-10
Racemization. An asymmetric carbon atom undergoes racemization when it ionizes to a planar, achiral carbocation. A nucleophile can attack the carbocation from either face, giving either enantiomer of the product.

product is rarely completely racemic, however; there is often more inversion than retention of configuration. As the leaving group leaves, it partially blocks the front side of the carbocation. The back side is unhindered, so attack is more likely there.

Figure 6-11 shows a cyclic case where one of the faces of a cyclopentane ring has been "labeled" by a deuterium atom. Deuterium has the same size and shape as hydrogen and it undergoes the same reactions. It distinguishes between the two faces of the ring: The bromine atom is cis to the deuterium in the reactant, so the nucleophile is cis to the deuterium in the retention product. The nucleophile is trans to the deuterium in the inversion product. The product mixture contains both cis and trans isomers, with the trans isomer slightly favored because the leaving group hinders approach of the nucleophilic solvent from the front side.

MECHANISM 6-5 Racemization in the S_N1 Reaction

The S_N1 reaction involves ionization to a flat carbocation, which can be attacked from either side.

Step 1: Ionization of a tetrahedral carbon gives a flat carbocation.

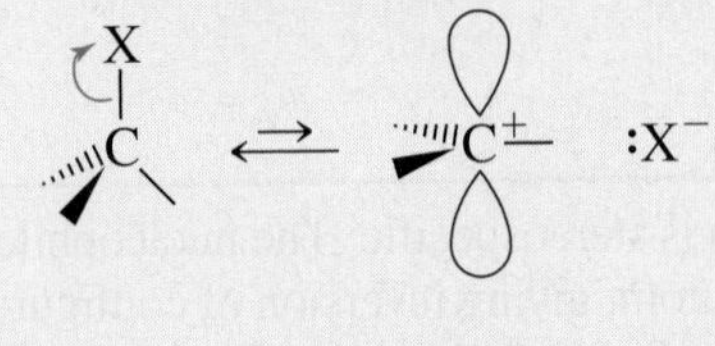

Step 2: A nucleophile may attack either side of the carbocation.

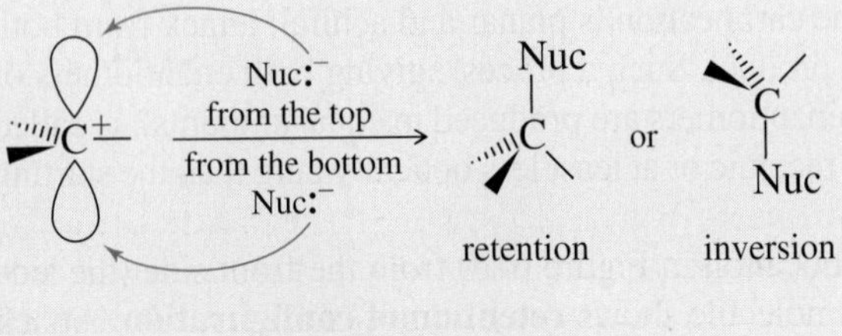

These two products may be different if the carbon atom is stereogenic.

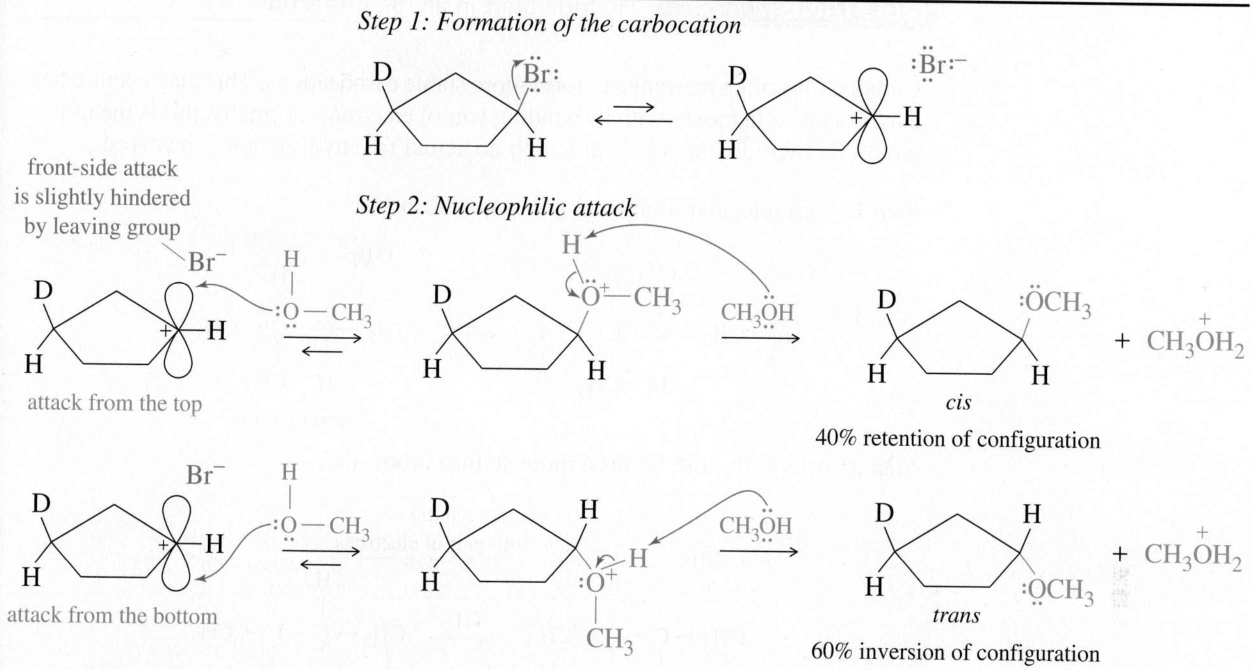

Step 1: Formation of the carbocation

front-side attack is slightly hindered by leaving group

Step 2: Nucleophilic attack

attack from the top

cis

40% retention of configuration

attack from the bottom

trans

60% inversion of configuration

FIGURE 6-11
In the S_N1 reaction of *cis*-1-bromo-3-deuteriocyclopentane with methanol, the carbocation can be attacked from either face. Because the leaving group (bromide) partially blocks the front side as it leaves, back-side attack (inversion of configuration) is slightly favored.

6-15 Rearrangements in S_N1 Reactions

Carbocations frequently undergo structural changes, called **rearrangements**, to form more stable ions. A rearrangement may occur after a carbocation has formed or it may occur as the leaving group is leaving. Rearrangements are not seen in S_N2 reactions, where no carbocation is formed and the one-step mechanism allows no opportunity for rearrangement.

An example of a reaction with rearrangement is the S_N1 reaction of 2-bromo-3-methylbutane in boiling ethanol. The product is a mixture of 2-ethoxy-3-methylbutane (not rearranged) and 2-ethoxy-2-methylbutane (rearranged).

$$CH_3-CH(Br)-CH(CH_3)-CH_3 \xrightarrow[\text{heat}]{CH_3CH_2OH} CH_3-CH(OCH_2CH_3)-CH(CH_3)-CH_3 + CH_3-CH_2-C(OCH_2CH_3)(CH_3)-CH_3 + HBr$$

2-bromo-3-methylbutane; (not rearranged) 2-ethoxy-3-methylbutane; (rearranged) 2-ethoxy-2-methylbutane

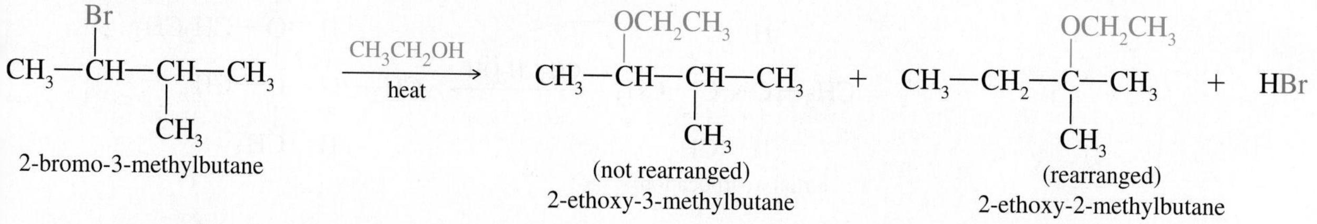

PROBLEM 6-25

Give the S_N1 mechanism for the formation of 2-ethoxy-3-methylbutane, the unrearranged product in this reaction.

The rearranged product, 2-ethoxy-2-methylbutane, results from a **hydride shift**, the movement of a hydrogen atom with its bonding pair of electrons. A hydride shift is represented by the symbol ~H. In this case, the hydride shift converts the initially formed secondary carbocation to a more stable tertiary carbocation. Attack by the solvent gives the rearranged product.

MECHANISM 6-6 Hydride Shift in an S_N1 Reaction

Carbocations often rearrange to form more stable carbocations. This may occur when a hydrogen atom moves with its bonding pair of electrons. Formally, this is the movement of a hydride ion ($H:^-$), although no actual free hydride ion is involved.

Step 1: Unimolecular ionization gives a carbocation.

$$CH_3-CH(Br)-CH(CH_3)-CH_3 \rightleftarrows CH_3-\overset{+}{C}H-CH(CH_3)-CH_3 + :\ddot{Br}:^-$$

2° carbocation

Step 2: A hydride shift forms a more stable carbocation.

hydrogen moves with pair of electrons

$$CH_3-\overset{+}{C}H-CH(CH_3)-CH_3 \xrightarrow{\sim H} CH_3-CH_2-\overset{+}{C}(CH_3)-CH_3$$

2° carbocation → 3° carbocation

This rearrangement involves movement of a hydrogen atom with its bonding pair of electrons over to the empty *p* orbital of the carbocation. In three dimensions, the rearrangement looks like this:

H, H_3C, H, CH_3, CH_3 $\xrightarrow{\sim H}$ H, H, H_3C, CH_3, CH_3

2° carbocation → 3° carbocation

Step 3: Solvent (a weak nucleophile) attacks the rearranged carbocation.

$$CH_3-CH_2-\overset{+}{C}(CH_3)-CH_3 \xrightarrow{CH_3CH_2\ddot{O}H} CH_3-CH_2-C(CH_3)(\overset{+}{O}H-CH_2CH_3)-CH_3$$

tertiary carbocation

Step 4: Deprotonation gives the rearranged product.

$$CH_3-CH_2-C(CH_3)(\overset{+}{O}H-CH_2CH_3)-CH_3 \xrightarrow{CH_3CH_2\ddot{O}H} CH_3-CH_2-C(CH_3)(\ddot{O}CH_2CH_3)-CH_3 + CH_3CH_2\overset{+}{O}H_2$$

rearranged product

When neopentyl bromide is boiled in ethanol, it gives *only* a rearranged substitution product. This product results from a **methyl shift** (represented by the symbol $\sim CH_3$), the migration of a methyl group together with its pair of electrons. Without rearrangement, ionization of neopentyl bromide would give a very unstable primary carbocation.

problem-solving Hint

Primary halides and methyl halides rarely ionize to carbocations in solution. If a primary halide ionizes, it will likely ionize with rearrangement.

$$(CH_3)_3C-CH_2-Br \not\leftrightarrow (CH_3)_3C-\overset{+}{C}H_2 \quad :Br:^-$$

neopentyl bromide → 1° carbocation

The methyl shift occurs *while* bromide ion is leaving, so that only the more stable tertiary carbocation is formed.

MECHANISM 6-7 Methyl Shift in an S_N1 Reaction

An alkyl group can rearrange to make a carbocation more stable.

Step 1: Ionization occurs with a methyl shift.

methyl moves with its pair of electrons

$$H-\underset{:Br:}{\overset{H}{C}}-\underset{CH_3}{\overset{CH_3}{C}}-CH_3 \xrightarrow{\sim CH_3} H-\underset{H}{\overset{CH_3}{C}}-\underset{CH_3}{\overset{+}{C}}-CH_3 \; + \; :Br:^-$$

In three dimensions,

$$\text{(H)(H)(Br)C}-C(CH_3)_3 \xrightarrow{\sim CH_3} \text{(H}_3\text{C)(H)(H)C}-\overset{+}{C}(CH_3)_2 \; + \; Br^-$$

3° carbocation

Step 2: Attack by ethanol gives a protonated version of the rearranged product.

$$H-\underset{H}{\overset{CH_3}{C}}-\underset{CH_3}{\overset{+}{C}}-CH_3 \xrightarrow{CH_3CH_2\ddot{O}H} H-\underset{H}{\overset{H_3C}{C}}-\underset{CH_3}{\overset{:\overset{+}{O}(H)-CH_2CH_3}{C}}-CH_3$$

protonated product

Step 3: Deprotonation gives the rearranged product.

H
H₃C :O⁺—CH₂CH₃
H—C—C—CH₃
H CH₃

$\xrightarrow{CH_3CH_2\ddot{O}H}$

H₃C :Ö—CH₂CH₃
H—C—C—CH₃ + $CH_3CH_2\overset{+}{O}H_2$
H CH₃
rearranged product

Because rearrangement is required for ionization, only rearranged products are observed.

In general, we should expect rearrangements in reactions involving carbocations whenever a hydride shift or an alkyl shift can form a more stable carbocation. Most rearrangements convert 2° (or incipient 1°) carbocations to 3° or resonance-stabilized carbocations.

The rearrangements of carbocations also play a role in the formation of terpene natural products. Menthol and camphor are examples of terpenes derived from plant oils. They are constructed using a common building block and undergo a series of rearrangements in the course of construction to generate the most stable carbocation.

CH₃ OH H H O

menthol camphor

problem-solving Hint

Most rearrangements convert 2° (or incipient 1°) carbocations to 3° or resonance-stabilized carbocations.

PROBLEM 6-26

Propose a mechanism involving a hydride shift or an alkyl shift for each solvolysis reaction. Explain how each rearrangement forms a more stable intermediate.

(a) $CH_3-C(CH_3)_2-CH(I)-CH_3 \xrightarrow[\text{heat}]{CH_3OH} CH_3-C(CH_3)_2-CH(OCH_3)-CH_3 + CH_3-C(OCH_3)(CH_3)-CH(CH_3)-CH_3$

(b) 1-chloro-2-methylcyclohexane $\xrightarrow[\text{heat}]{CH_3CH_2OH}$ 1-ethoxy-2-methylcyclohexane (OCH₂CH₃, CH₃) + 1-ethoxy-1-methylcyclohexane (OCH₂CH₃, CH₃)

(c) 3-iodocyclohexene (I) + $CH_3-\overset{O}{\overset{\|}{C}}-OH \xrightarrow{\text{heat}}$ cyclohexenyl acetate ($O-\overset{O}{\overset{\|}{C}}-CH_3$) + cyclohexenyl acetate ($O-\overset{O}{\overset{\|}{C}}-CH_3$)

(d) (iodomethyl)cyclohexane (CH₂I) $\xrightarrow[\text{heat}]{CH_3CH_2OH}$ 1-ethoxy-1-methylcyclohexane (CH₃, OCH₂CH₃) + ethoxycycloheptane (OCH₂CH₃)

6-16 Comparison of S_N1 and S_N2 Reactions

Let's compare what we know about the S_N1 and S_N2 reactions, then organize this material into a brief table.

Effect of the Nucleophile The nucleophile takes part in the slow step (the only step) of the S_N2 reaction but not in the slow step of the S_N1. Therefore, a strong nucleophile promotes the S_N2 but not the S_N1. Weak nucleophiles fail to promote the S_N2 reaction; therefore, reactions with weak nucleophiles often go by the S_N1 mechanism if the substrate is secondary or tertiary.

S_N1:	Nucleophile strength is unimportant (usually weak).
S_N2:	Strong nucleophiles are required.

Effect of the Substrate The structure of the substrate (the alkyl halide) is an important factor in determining which of these substitution mechanisms might operate. Methyl halides and primary halides are poor substrates for S_N1 substitutions because they cannot easily ionize to high-energy methyl and primary carbocations. They are relatively unhindered, however, so they make good S_N2 substrates.

Tertiary halides are too hindered to undergo S_N2 displacement, but they can ionize to form tertiary carbocations. Tertiary halides undergo substitution exclusively through the S_N1 mechanism. Secondary halides can undergo substitution by either mechanism, depending on the conditions.

S_N1 substrates:	$3° > 2°$	(1° and CH_3X are unlikely)
S_N2 substrates:	$CH_3X > 1° > 2°$	(3° is unsuitable)

If silver nitrate ($AgNO_3$) is added to an alkyl halide in a good ionizing solvent, it removes the halide ion to give a carbocation. This technique can force some unlikely ionizations, often giving interesting rearrangements (see Problem 6-29.)

Effect of the Solvent The slow step of the S_N1 reaction involves formation of two ions. Solvation of these ions is crucial to stabilizing them and lowering the activation energy for their formation. Very polar ionizing solvents such as water and alcohols are needed for the S_N1. The solvent may be heated to reflux (boiling) to provide the energy needed for ionization.

Less charge separation is generated in the transition state of the S_N2 reaction. Strong solvation may weaken the strength of the nucleophile because of the energy needed to strip off the solvent molecules. Thus, the S_N2 reaction often goes faster in less polar solvents if the nucleophile will dissolve. Polar aprotic solvents may enhance the strength of weak nucleophiles.

S_N1:	Good ionizing solvent required.
S_N2:	May go faster in a less polar solvent.

Kinetics The rate of the S_N1 reaction is proportional to the concentration of the alkyl halide but not the concentration of the nucleophile. It follows a first-order rate equation.

The rate of the S_N2 reaction is proportional to the concentrations of both the alkyl halide [R—X] and the nucleophile [Nuc:$^-$]. It follows a second-order rate equation.

$$S_N1 \text{ rate} = k_r[\text{R—X}]$$
$$S_N2 \text{ rate} = k_r[\text{R—X}][\text{Nuc:}^-]$$

Stereochemistry The S_N1 reaction involves a flat carbocation intermediate that can be attacked from either face. Therefore, the S_N1 usually gives a mixture of inversion and retention of configuration.

The S_N2 reaction takes place through a back-side attack, which inverts the stereochemistry of the carbon atom. Complete inversion of configuration is the result.

S_N1 stereochemistry:	Mixture of retention and inversion; racemization.
S_N2 stereochemistry:	Complete inversion.

Rearrangements The S_N1 reaction involves a carbocation intermediate. This intermediate can rearrange, usually by a hydride shift or an alkyl shift, to give a more stable carbocation.

The S_N2 reaction takes place in one step with no intermediates. No rearrangement is possible in the S_N2 reaction.

S_N1:	Rearrangements are common.
S_N2:	Rearrangements are impossible.

SUMMARY Nucleophilic Substitutions

	S_N1	S_N2
Promoting factors		
nucleophile	weak nucleophiles are OK	strong nucleophile needed
substrate (RX)	3° > 2°	CH_3X > 1° > 2°
solvent	good ionizing solvent needed	wide variety of solvents
leaving group	good one required	good one required
other	$AgNO_3$ forces ionization	
Characteristics		
kinetics	first order, k_r[RX]	second order, k_r[RX][Nuc:$^-$]
stereochemistry	mixture of inversion and retention	complete inversion
rearrangements	common	impossible

problem-solving Hint

The strength of the nucleophile (or base) usually determines the order of the reaction. Strong nucleophiles encourage second-order reactions, and weak nucleophiles more commonly react by first-order reactions. Also, (S_N2) is unlikely with 3° halides, and S_N1 is unlikely with 1° halides.

PROBLEM 6-27

For each reaction, give the expected substitution product, and predict whether the mechanism will be predominantly first order (S_N1) or second order (S_N2).

(a) 2-chloro-2-methylbutane + CH_3COOH
(b) isobutyl bromide + sodium methoxide
(c) 1-iodo-1-methylcyclohexane + ethanol
(d) cyclohexyl bromide + methanol
(e) cyclohexyl bromide + sodium ethoxide

PROBLEM 6-28

Under certain conditions, when (*R*)-2-bromobutane is heated with water, the S_N1 substitution proceeds twice as fast as the S_N2. Calculate the e.e. and the specific rotation expected for the product. The specific rotation of (*R*)-2 butanol is −13.5°. Assume that the S_N1 gives equal amounts of the two enantiomers.

PROBLEM 6-29

A reluctant first-order substrate can be forced to ionize by adding some silver nitrate (one of the few soluble silver salts) to the reaction. Silver ion reacts with the halogen to form a silver halide (a highly exothermic reaction), generating the cation of the alkyl group.

$$R{-}X + Ag^+ \longrightarrow R^+ + AgX\downarrow$$

Give mechanisms for the following silver-promoted rearrangements.

(a) $CH_3{-}C(CH_3)_2{-}CH_2{-}I \xrightarrow{AgNO_3,\ H_2O} CH_3{-}C(CH_3)(OH){-}CH_2{-}CH_3$

(b) (bicyclic compound bearing CH_2I) $\xrightarrow{AgNO_3,\ H_2O/CH_3CH_2OH}$ (ring-expanded bicyclic alcohol bearing OH)

6-17 First-Order Elimination: The E1 Reaction

An **elimination** involves the loss of two atoms or groups from the substrate, usually with formation of a pi bond. Elimination reactions frequently accompany and compete with substitutions. By varying the reagents and conditions, we can often modify a reaction to favor substitution or to favor elimination. First we will discuss eliminations by themselves. Then we consider substitutions and eliminations together, trying to predict what products and what mechanisms are likely with a given set of reactants and conditions.

Depending on the reagents and conditions involved, an elimination might be a first-order (E1) or second-order (E2) process. The following examples illustrate the types of eliminations we cover in this chapter.

E1:

$$H-C(H)(CH_3)-C(CH_2CH_3)(Br)-CH_2CH_3 \xrightarrow{CH_3OH} H-C(H)(CH_3)-C^{+}(CH_2CH_3)-CH_2CH_3 \;\; :Br:^- \xrightarrow{CH_3OH} (H)(H_3C)C=C(CH_2CH_3)_2 \;\; CH_3-\overset{+}{O}(H)-H$$

E2:

$$CH_3O:^- \;+\; H-C(H)(CH_3)-C(CH_2CH_3)(Br)-CH_2CH_3 \xrightarrow[CH_3OH]{Na^+ \; ^-OCH_3} CH_3OH \;+\; (H)(H_3C)C=C(CH_2CH_3)_2 \;+\; :Br:^-$$

6-17A Mechanism and Kinetics of the E1 Reaction

The abbreviation **E1** stands for *Elimination, unimolecular*. The mechanism is called *unimolecular* because the rate-limiting transition state involves a single molecule rather than a collision between two molecules. The slow step of an E1 reaction is the same as in the S_N1 reaction: unimolecular ionization to form a carbocation. In a fast second step, a base abstracts a proton from the carbon atom adjacent to the C^+. The electrons that once formed the carbon–hydrogen bond now form a pi bond between two carbon atoms. The general mechanism for the E1 reaction is shown in Key Mechanism 6-8.

KEY MECHANISM 6-8 The E1 Reaction

The E1 reaction requires ionization to a carbocation intermediate like the S_N1, so it follows the same order of reactivity: 3° > 2° >> 1°.

A base (usually weak) deprotonates the carbocation to give an alkene.

Step 1: Unimolecular ionization to give a carbocation (rate-limiting).

$$-\overset{|}{\underset{H}{C}}-\overset{|}{\underset{:X:}{C}}- \rightleftharpoons -\overset{|}{\underset{H}{C}}-\overset{+}{C}\lt \;+\; ^-:X:$$

Step 2: Deprotonation by a weak base (often the solvent) gives the alkene (fast).

$$B:^- \;+\; -\overset{|}{\underset{H}{C}}-\overset{+}{C}\lt \;\rightleftharpoons\; B-H \;+\; \gt C=C\lt$$

EXAMPLE: E1 elimination of bromocyclohexane in methanol.

Step 1: Ionization gives a carbocation and bromide ion in a slow step.

$$\text{bromocyclohexane} \xrightleftharpoons{CH_3OH,\ heat} \text{cyclohexyl cation} + :\ddot{Br}:^-$$

Step 2: Methanol abstracts a proton to give cyclohexene in a fast step.

$$\text{cyclohexyl cation} + CH_3\ddot{O}H \longrightarrow \text{cyclohexene} + CH_3\overset{+}{O}H_2$$

PROBLEM: Show what happens in step 2 of the Example (El elimination of bromocyclohexane in methanol) if the solvent acts as a *nucleophile* rather than as a *base*.

Because the rate-limiting step involves unimolecular ionization of the alkyl halide, the rate equation is first-order. The rate depends only on the concentration of the alkyl halide, and not on the strength or concentration of the base.

$$\text{E1 rate} = k_r[\text{RX}]$$

The weak base (often the solvent) takes part in the fast second step of the reaction.

6-17B Competition with the S_N1 Reaction

The E1 reaction almost always competes with the S_N1 reaction. Whenever a carbocation is formed, it can undergo either substitution or elimination, and mixtures of products often result. The following reaction shows the formation of both elimination and substitution products in the reaction of *tert*-butyl bromide with boiling ethanol.

$$(CH_3)_3C{-}Br + CH_3{-}CH_2{-}OH \xrightarrow{heat} H_2C{=}C(CH_3)_2 + CH_3{-}C(CH_3)_2{-}O{-}CH_2{-}CH_3$$

tert-butyl bromide; ethanol; 2-methylpropene (E1 product); ethyl *tert*-butyl ether (S_N1 product)

The 2-methylpropene product results from **dehydrohalogenation**, an elimination of hydrogen and a halogen atom. Under these first-order conditions (the absence of a strong base), dehydrohalogenation takes place by the E1 mechanism: Ionization of the alkyl halide gives a carbocation intermediate, which loses a proton to give the alkene. Substitution results from nucleophilic attack on the carbocation. Ethanol serves as a base in the elimination and as a nucleophile in the substitution.

Step 1: Ionization to form a carbocation.

$$CH_3{-}C(:\ddot{Br}:)(CH_3){-}CH_3 \rightleftarrows CH_3{-}\overset{+}{C}(CH_3){-}CH_3 + :\ddot{Br}:^-$$

Step 2 (by the E1 mechanism): Basic attack by the solvent abstracts a proton to give an alkene.

$$CH_3CH_2{-}\ddot{O}(H): + H{-}CH_2{-}\overset{+}{C}(CH_3){-}CH_3 \rightleftarrows H_2C{=}C(CH_3)_2 + CH_3CH_2{-}\overset{+}{\ddot{O}}H_2$$

or, step 2 (by the S_N1 *mechanism): Nucleophilic attack by the solvent on the carbocation.*

$$CH_3-\overset{+}{C}(CH_3)-CH_3 \xrightarrow{CH_3CH_2-\ddot{O}-H} CH_3-C(CH_3)(\overset{+}{\ddot{O}}(H)CH_2CH_3)-CH_3 \underset{}{\overset{CH_3CH_2-\ddot{O}-H}{\rightleftharpoons}} CH_3-C(CH_3)(\ddot{O}CH_2CH_3)-CH_3 \quad CH_3CH_2\overset{+}{O}H_2$$

Under ideal conditions, one of these first-order reactions provides a good yield of one product or the other. Often, however, carbocation intermediates react in two or more ways to give mixtures of products. For this reason, S_N1 and E1 reactions of alkyl halides are not often used for organic synthesis. They have been studied in great detail to learn about the properties of carbocations, however.

PROBLEM 6-30

S_N1 substitution and E1 elimination frequently compete in the same reaction.

(a) Propose a mechanism and predict the products for the solvolysis of 1-bromo-1-methyl-cyclopentane in ethanol.

(b) Compare the function of the solvent (ethanol) in the E1 and S_N1 reactions.

6-17C Orbitals and Energetics of the E1 Reaction

In the second step of the E1 mechanism, the carbon atom next to the C^+ must rehybridize to sp^2 as the base attacks the proton and electrons flow into the new pi bond.

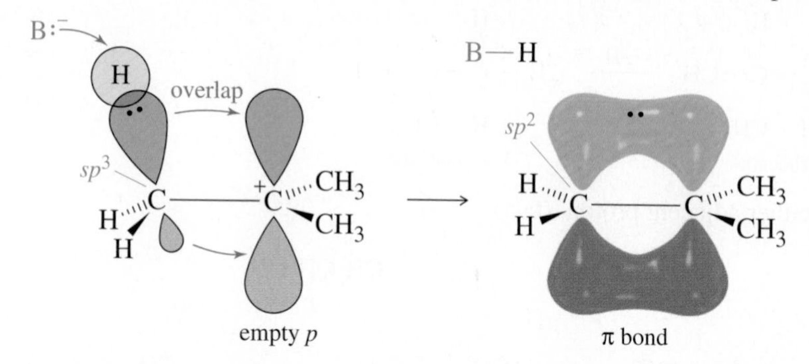

The potential-energy diagram for the E1 reaction (Figure 6-12) is similar to that for the S_N1 reaction. The ionization step is strongly endothermic, with a rate-limiting transition state. The second step is a fast exothermic deprotonation by a base. The base is

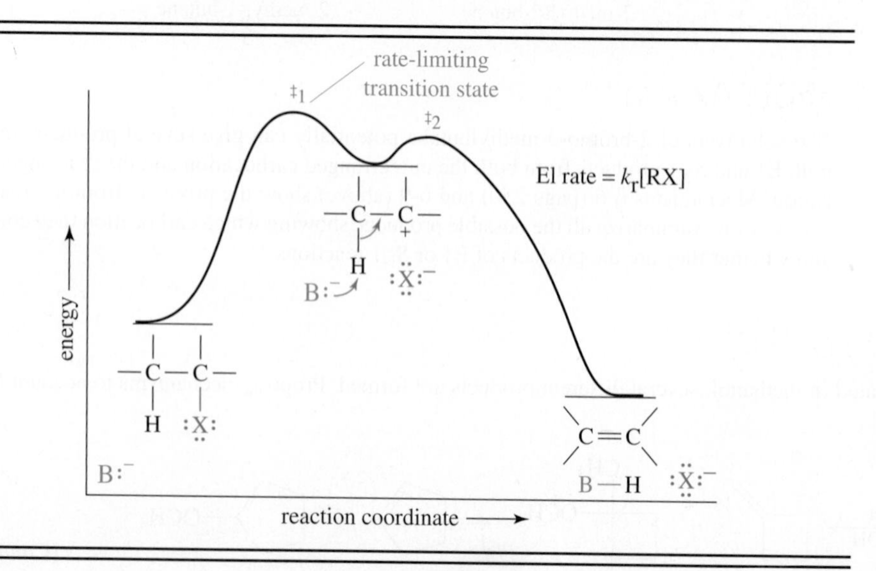

■ **FIGURE 6-12**
Reaction-energy diagram of the E1 reaction. The first step is a rate-limiting ionization. Compare this energy profile with that of the S_N1 reaction in Figure 6-8.

not involved in the reaction until *after* the rate-limiting step, so the rate depends only on the concentration of the alkyl halide. Weak bases are common in E1 reactions.

6-17D Rearrangements in E1 Reactions

Like other carbocation reactions, the E1 may be accompanied by rearrangement. Compare the following E1 reaction (with rearrangement) with the S_N1 reaction of the same substrate, shown in Mechanism 6-6. Note that the solvent acts as a *base* in the E1 reaction and a *nucleophile* in the S_N1 reaction.

MECHANISM 6-9 Rearrangement in an E1 Reaction

Like other reactions involving carbocations, the E1 may be accompanied by rearrangement.

Step 1: Ionization to form a carbocation. (slow)

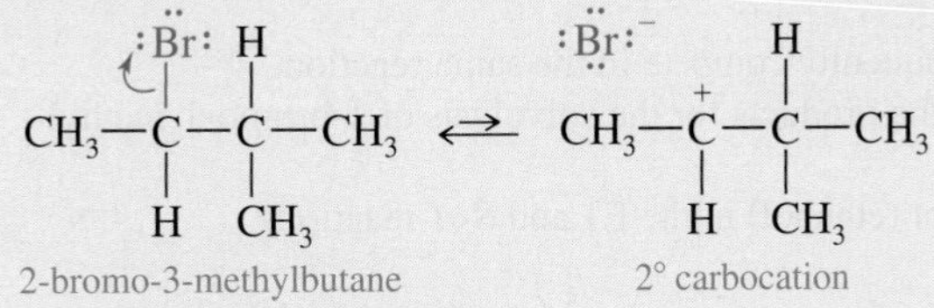

$CH_3-CHBr-CH(CH_3)-CH_3 \rightleftharpoons CH_3-\overset{+}{C}H-CH(CH_3)-CH_3 + :\ddot{Br}:^-$

2-bromo-3-methylbutane 2° carbocation

Step 2: A hydride shift forms a more stable carbocation. (fast)

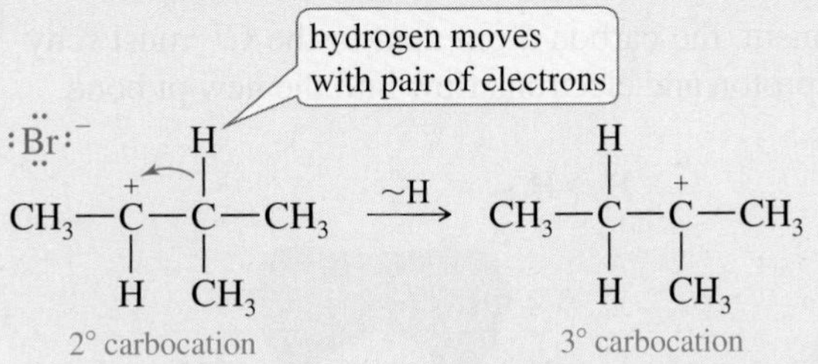

hydrogen moves with pair of electrons

$CH_3-\overset{+}{C}H-CH(CH_3)-CH_3 \xrightarrow{\sim H} CH_3-CH_2-\overset{+}{C}(CH_3)-CH_3$

2° carbocation 3° carbocation

Step 3: The weakly basic solvent removes either adjacent proton. (fast)

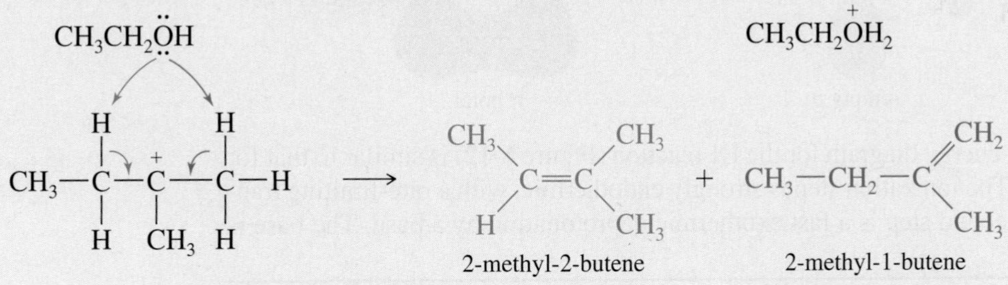

$CH_3CH_2\ddot{O}H$ ... $\longrightarrow (CH_3)_2C{=}CH(CH_3) + CH_3-CH_2-C(CH_3){=}CH_2$ + $CH_3CH_2\overset{+}{O}H_2$

2-methyl-2-butene 2-methyl-1-butene

PROBLEM 6-31

The solvolysis of 2-bromo-3-methylbutane potentially can give several products, including both E1 and S_N1 products from both the unrearranged carbocation and the rearranged carbocation. Mechanisms 6-6 (page 250) and 6-9 (above) show the products from the rearranged carbocation. Summarize all the possible products, showing which carbocation they come from and whether they are the products of E1 or S_N1 reactions.

PROBLEM 6-1 (PARTIALLY SOLVED)

When the following compound is heated in methanol, several different products are formed. Propose mechanisms to account for the four products shown.

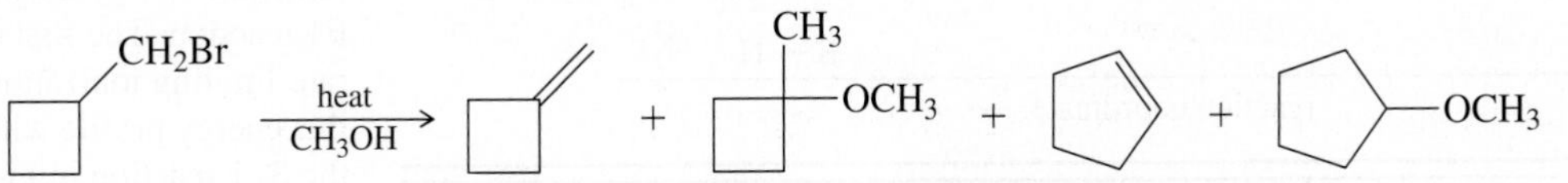

(bromomethyl)cyclobutane (CH_2Br) $\xrightarrow[CH_3OH]{heat}$ methylenecyclobutane + 1-methoxy-1-methylcyclobutane (CH_3, OCH_3) + cyclopentene + methoxycyclopentane (OCH_3)

(Continued)

Solution: With no strong base and a good ionizing solvent, we would expect a first-order reaction. But this is a primary alkyl halide, so ionization is difficult unless it rearranges. It might rearrange as it forms, but we'll imagine the cation forming then rearranging.

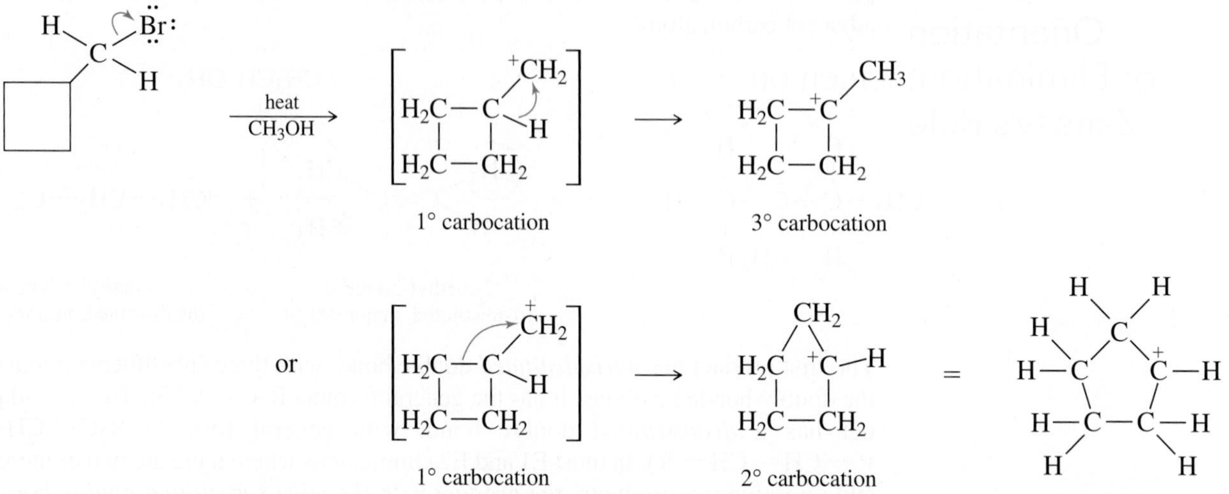

heat, CH_3OH

1° carbocation → 3° carbocation

or

1° carbocation → 2° carbocation

From these rearranged intermediates, either loss of a proton (E1) or attack by the solvent (S_N1) gives the observed products. Note that the actual reaction may give more than just these products, but the other products are not required for the problem.

PROBLEM 6-32

Finish Partially Solved Problem 6-1 by showing how the rearranged carbocations give the four products shown in the problem. Be careful when using curved arrows to show deprotonation and/or nucleophilic attack by the solvent. The curved arrows always show movement of electrons, not movement of protons or other species.

We can now summarize four ways that a carbocation can react to become more stable.

SUMMARY Carbocation Reactions

A carbocation can

1. **React with its own leaving group to return to the reactant:** $R^+ + :X^- \longrightarrow R{-}X$
2. **React with a nucleophile to form a substitution product (S_N1):** $R^+ + \text{Nuc:}^- \longrightarrow R{-}\text{Nuc}$
3. **Lose a proton to form an elimination product (an alkene) (E1):**

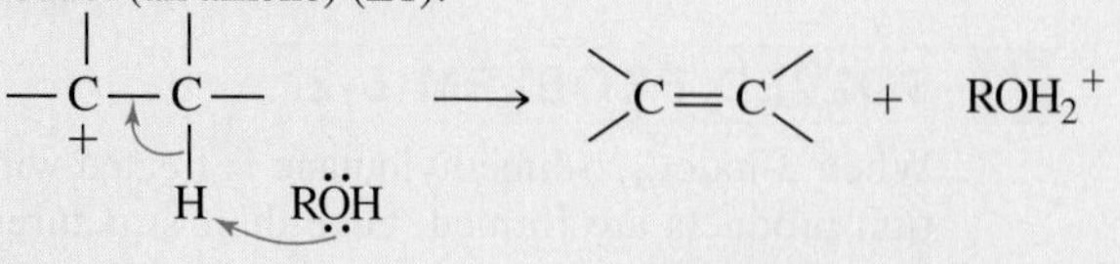

$$-\overset{|}{\underset{+}{C}}-\overset{|}{\underset{H}{C}}- \quad \ddot{R}\ddot{O}H \longrightarrow \;>C{=}C<\; + \; ROH_2^+$$

4. **Rearrange to a more stable carbocation, then react further.**

The order of stability of carbocations is: resonance-stabilized, 3° > 2° > 1°.

PROBLEM 6-33

Give the substitution and elimination products you would expect from the following reactions.

(a) 3-bromo-3-ethylpentane heated in methanol
(b) 1-iodo-1-methylcyclopentane heated in ethanol
(c) 3-bromo-2,2-dimethylbutane heated in ethanol
(d) 1-iodo-2-methylcyclohexane + silver nitrate in water (see Problem 6-29)

6-18 Positional Orientation of Elimination: Zaitsev's Rule

Many compounds can eliminate in more than one way, to give mixtures of alkenes. In many cases, we can predict which elimination product will predominate. In the example shown in Mechanism Box 6-9, the carbocation can lose a proton on either of two adjacent carbon atoms.

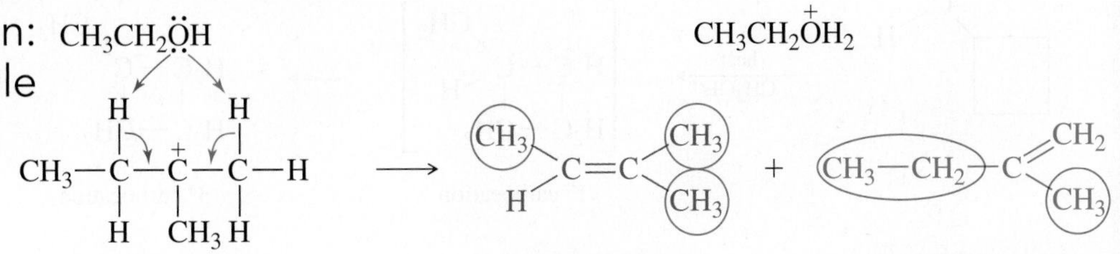

$$CH_3CH_2\ddot{O}H \qquad CH_3-CH(H)-\overset{+}{C}(CH_3)-CH_2(H) \longrightarrow (CH_3)_2C{=}CH(CH_3) + CH_3-CH_2-C(CH_3){=}CH_2 \qquad CH_3CH_2\overset{+}{O}H_2$$

2-methyl-2-butene, trisubstituted, major (90%) — 2-methyl-1-butene, disubstituted, minor (10%)

The first product has a *trisubstituted* double bond, with three substituents (circled) on the doubly bonded carbons. It has the general formula $R_2C{=}CHR$. The second product has a *disubstituted* double bond, with general formula $R_2C{=}CH_2$ (or $R-CH{=}CH-R$). In most E1 and E2 eliminations where there are two or more possible elimination products, *the product with the most substituted double bond will predominate*. This general principle is called **Zaitsev's rule**,* and reactions that give the most substituted alkene are said to follow **Zaitsev orientation**.

> **ZAITSEV'S RULE**: In elimination reactions, the most substituted alkene usually predominates.

$$\underset{\text{tetrasubstituted}}{R_2C{=}CR_2} > \underset{\text{trisubstituted}}{R_2C{=}CHR} > \underset{\text{disubstituted}}{RHC{=}CHR \text{ and } R_2C{=}CH_2} > \underset{\text{monosubstituted}}{RHC{=}CH_2}$$

This order of preference is the same as the order of stability of alkenes. We consider the stability of alkenes in more detail in Section 7-7, but for now, it is enough just to know that more substituted alkenes are more stable. In Chapter 7, we will study some unusual reactions where Zaitsev's rule does not apply.

PROBLEM 6-34

When 1-bromo-1-methylcyclohexane is heated in ethanol for an extended period of time, three products result: one ether and two alkenes. Predict the products of this reaction, and propose a mechanism for their formation. Predict which of the two alkenes is the major elimination product.

SOLVED PROBLEM 6-2

When 3-iodo-2,2-dimethylbutane is treated with silver nitrate in ethanol, three elimination products are formed. Give their structures, and predict which ones are formed in larger amounts.

SOLUTION

Silver nitrate reacts with the alkyl iodide to give silver iodide and a cation.

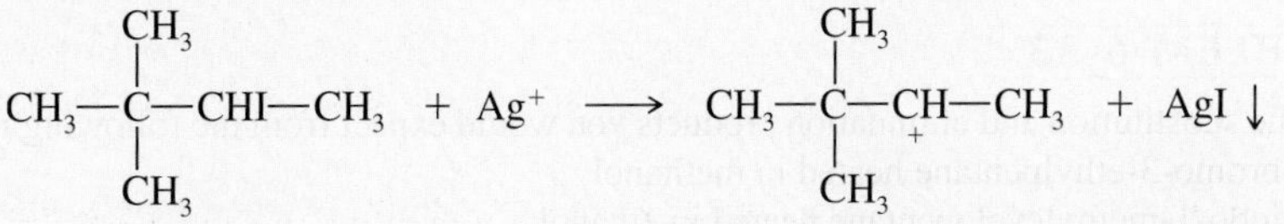

$$CH_3-C(CH_3)_2-CHI-CH_3 + Ag^+ \longrightarrow CH_3-C(CH_3)_2-\overset{+}{C}H-CH_3 + AgI\downarrow$$

(Continued)

__Zaitsev__ is transliterated from the Russian, and may also be spelled __Saytzeff__.

This secondary carbocation can lose a proton to give an unrearranged alkene (**A**), or it can rearrange to a more stable tertiary cation.

Loss of a proton

$$CH_3-C(CH_3)_2-C^+H-CH_3 \xrightarrow{CH_3CH_2\ddot{O}H} CH_3-C(CH_3)_2-CH=CH_2$$

Product (**A**) + $CH_3CH_2\overset{+}{O}H_2$

Rearrangement

$$CH_3-C(CH_3)_2-\overset{+}{C}H-CH_3 \xrightarrow[\text{(methyl shift)}]{\sim CH_3} CH_3-\overset{+}{C}(CH_3)-CH(CH_3)-CH_3$$

2° carbocation → 3° carbocation

The tertiary cation can lose a proton in either of two positions. One of the products (**B**) is a tetrasubstituted alkene, and the other (**C**) is disubstituted.

Formation of a tetrasubstituted alkene

$$CH_3-\overset{+}{C}(CH_3)-CH(CH_3)-CH_3 \xrightarrow{H\ddot{O}CH_2CH_3} (H_3C)_2C=C(CH_3)_2 + CH_3CH_2\overset{+}{O}H_2$$

(**B**)
(tetrasubstituted)

Formation of a disubstituted alkene

$$CH_3CH_2\ddot{O}H + CH_2H-\overset{+}{C}(CH_3)-CH(CH_3)-CH_3 \longrightarrow H_2C=C(CH_3)-CH(CH_3)-CH_3 + CH_3CH_2\overset{+}{O}H_2$$

(**C**)
(disubstituted)

Product **B** predominates over product **C** because the double bond in **B** is more substituted. Whether product **A** is a major product will depend on the specific reaction conditions and whether proton loss or rearrangement occurs faster.

problem-solving Hint

Whenever a carbocation is formed next to a more highly substituted carbon, consider whether a rearrangement might occur.

PROBLEM 6-35

Each of the two carbocations in Solved Problem 6-2 can also react with ethanol to give a substitution product. Give the structures of the two substitution products formed in this reaction.

6-19 Second-Order Elimination: The E2 Reaction

Eliminations can also take place under second-order conditions with a strong base present. As an example, consider the reaction of *tert*-butyl bromide with methoxide ion in methanol.

This is a second-order reaction because methoxide ion is a strong base as well as a strong nucleophile. It attacks the alkyl halide faster than the halide can ionize to give a first-order reaction. No substitution product (methyl *tert*-butyl ether) is observed, however. The S_N2 mechanism is blocked because the tertiary alkyl halide is too hindered.

The observed product is 2-methylpropene, resulting from elimination of HBr and formation of a double bond.

S_N2 is too hindered

$$\text{Rate} = k_r[(CH_3)_3C{-}Br][^{-}OCH_3]$$

The rate of this elimination is proportional to the concentrations of both the alkyl halide and the base, giving a second-order rate equation. This is a *bimolecular* process, with both the base and the alkyl halide participating in the transition state, so this mechanism is abbreviated **E2** for *Elimination, bimolecular*.

$$\text{E2 rate} = k_r[\text{RX}]\,[\text{B:}^-]$$

In the E2 reaction just shown, methoxide reacts as a *base* rather than as a *nucleophile*. Most strong nucleophiles are also strong bases, and elimination commonly results when a strong base/nucleophile is used with a poor S_N2 substrate such as a 3° or hindered 2° alkyl halide. Instead of attacking the back side of the hindered electrophilic carbon, methoxide abstracts a proton from one of the methyl groups. This reaction takes place in one step, with bromide leaving as the base abstracts a proton.

In the general mechanism of the E2 reaction, a strong base abstracts a proton on a carbon atom adjacent to the one with the leaving group. As the base abstracts a proton, a double bond forms and the leaving group leaves. Like the S_N2 reaction, the E2 is a *concerted* reaction in which bonds break and new bonds form at the same time, in a single step.

KEY MECHANISM 6-10 The E2 Reaction

The concerted E2 reaction takes place in a single step. A strong base abstracts a proton on a carbon next to the leaving group, and the leaving group leaves. The product is an alkene.

transition state

EXAMPLE: E2 elimination of 3-bromopentane with sodium ethoxide.

The order of reactivity for alkyl halides in E2 reactions is 3° > 2° > 1°.

PROBLEM 6-36

Under second-order conditions (strong base/nucleophile), S_N2 and E2 reactions may occur simultaneously and compete with each other. Show what products might be expected from the reaction of 2-bromo-3-methylbutane (a moderately hindered 2° alkyl halide) with sodium ethoxide.

Reactivity of the Substrate in the E2 The order of reactivity of alkyl halides toward E2 dehydrohalogenation is found to be

$$3° > 2° > 1°$$

This reactivity order reflects the greater stability of highly substituted double bonds. Elimination of a tertiary halide gives a more substituted alkene than elimination of a secondary halide, which gives a more substituted alkene than a primary halide. The stabilities of the alkene products are reflected in the transition states, giving lower activation energies and higher rates for elimination of alkyl halides that lead to highly substituted alkenes.

Mixtures of Products in the E2 The E2 reaction requires abstraction of a proton on a carbon atom next to the carbon bearing the halogen. If there are two or more possibilities, mixtures of products may result. In most cases, Zaitsev's rule predicts which of the possible products will be the major product: the most substituted alkene. For example, the E2 reaction of 2-bromobutane with potassium hydroxide gives a mixture of two products, 1-butene (a monosubstituted alkene) and 2-butene (a disubstituted alkene). As predicted by Zaitsev's rule, the disubstituted isomer 2-butene is the major product.

2-bromobutane $\xrightarrow[H_2O]{KOH}$ 1-butene + 2-butene + CH_3OH + NaBr

19% 1-butene, monosubstituted

81% 2-butene, disubstituted

Similarly, the reaction of 1-bromo-1-methylcyclohexane with sodium ethoxide gives a mixture of a disubstituted alkene and a trisubstituted alkene. The trisubstituted alkene is the major product.

1-bromo-1-methylcyclohexane $\xrightarrow[CH_3CH_2OH]{NaOCH_2CH_3}$ methylenecyclohexane + 1-methylcyclohexene + CH_3CH_2OH + NaBr

methylenecyclohexane, disubstituted, minor

1-methylcyclohexene, trisubstituted, major

PROBLEM 6-37

1. Predict the elimination products of the following reactions. When two alkenes are possible, predict which one will be the major product. Explain your answers, showing the degree of substitution of each double bond in the products.
2. Which of these reactions are likely to produce both elimination and substitution products?

(a) 2-bromopentane + $NaOCH_3$

(b) 3-bromo-3-methylpentane + NaOMe (Me = methyl, CH_3)

(c) 2-bromo-3-ethylpentane + NaOH

(d) *cis*-1-bromo-2-methylcyclohexane + NaOEt (Et = ethyl, CH_2CH_3)

problem-solving Hint

Zaitsev's rule usually applies in E2 reactions unless the base and/or the leaving group are unusually bulky.

6-20 Stereochemistry of the E2 Reaction

Like the S_N2 reaction, the E2 follows a **concerted mechanism**: Bond breaking and bond formation take place at the same time, and the partial formation of new bonds lowers the energy of the transition state. Concerted mechanisms require specific geometric arrangements so that the orbitals of the bonds being broken can overlap with those being formed and the electrons can flow smoothly from one bond to another. The geometric arrangement required by the S_N2 reaction is a back-side attack; with the E2 reaction, a coplanar arrangement of the orbitals is needed.

E2 elimination requires partial formation of a new pi bond, with its parallel *p* orbitals, in the transition state. The electrons that once formed a C—H bond must begin to overlap with the orbital that the leaving group is vacating. Formation of this new pi bond implies that these two sp^3 orbitals must be parallel so that pi overlap is possible as the hydrogen and halogen leave and the orbitals rehybridize to the *p* orbitals of the new pi bond.

Figure 6-13 shows two conformations that provide the necessary coplanar alignment of the leaving group, the departing hydrogen, and the two carbon atoms. When the hydrogen and the halogen are **anti** to each other ($\theta = 180°$), their orbitals are aligned. This is called the **anti-coplanar** conformation. When the hydrogen and the halogen eclipse each other ($\theta = 0°$), their orbitals are once again aligned. This is called the **syn-coplanar** conformation. Make a model corresponding to Figure 6-13, and use it to follow along with this discussion.

Enzyme-catalyzed eliminations generally proceed by E2 mechanisms and produce only one stereoisomer. Two catalytic groups are involved: One abstracts the hydrogen, and the other assists in the departure of the leaving group. The groups are positioned appropriately to allow an anti-coplanar elimination.

Of these possible conformations, the anti-coplanar arrangement is most commonly seen in E2 reactions. The transition state for the anti-coplanar arrangement is a staggered conformation, with the base far away from the leaving group. In most cases, this transition state is lower in energy than that for the syn-coplanar elimination.

The transition state for syn-coplanar elimination is an eclipsed conformation. In addition to the higher energy resulting from eclipsing interactions, the transition state suffers from interference between the attacking base and the leaving group. To abstract the proton, the base must approach quite close to the leaving group. In most cases, the leaving group is bulky and negatively charged, and the repulsion between the base and the leaving group raises the energy of the syn-coplanar transition state.

Base:⁻ Base—H

θ = 180° anti-coplanar transition state (staggered conformation—lower energy)

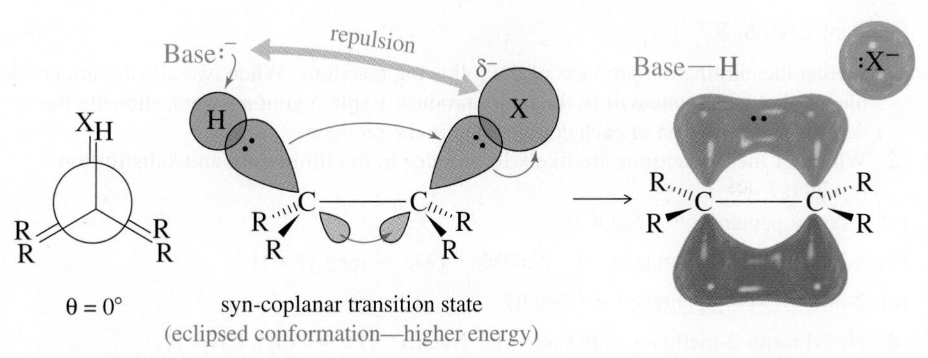

■ **FIGURE 6-13** Concerted transition states of the E2 reaction. The orbitals of the hydrogen atom and the halide must be aligned so they can begin to form a pi bond in the transition state.

Some molecules are rigidly held in eclipsed (or nearly eclipsed) conformations, with a hydrogen atom and a leaving group in a syn-coplanar arrangement. Such compounds are likely to undergo E2 elimination by a concerted syn-coplanar mechanism. Deuterium labeling (using D, the hydrogen isotope with mass number 2) is used in the following reaction to show which atom is abstracted by the base. Only the hydrogen atom is abstracted, because it is held in a syn-coplanar position with the bromine atom. Remember that syn-coplanar eliminations are unusual, however, and anti-coplanar eliminations are more common.

syn-coplanar

Br, H, H, D $\xrightarrow{Na^+ \ ^-OCH_3}$ H + $HOCH_3$, D + NaBr

The E2 is a **stereospecific** reaction, because different stereoisomers of the starting material react to give different stereoisomers of the product. This stereospecificity results from the anti-coplanar transition state that is usually involved in the E2. We consider more of the implications of the anti-coplanar transition state in Chapter 7. For now, Problem 6-38 will give you an opportunity to build models and see how the stereochemistry of an E2 elimination converts different stereoisomers of the reactants into different stereoisomers of the product.

problem-solving **Hint**

Models are helpful whenever complex stereochemistry is involved.

PROBLEM 6-38

When the first compound shown here is treated with sodium methoxide, the only elimination product is the trans isomer. The second diastereomer (blue) gives only the cis product. Use your models and careful drawings of the transition states to explain these results.

H, Br, Ph C—C H, CH_3, Ph $\xrightarrow[CH_3OH]{NaOCH_3}$ Ph, CH_3 C=C H, Ph (trans)

(Ph = phenyl group)

Br, H, Ph C—C H, CH_3, Ph $\xrightarrow[CH_3OH]{NaOCH_3}$ Ph, Ph C=C H, CH_3 (cis)

6-21 Comparison of E1 and E2 Elimination Mechanisms

Let's summarize the major points to remember about the E1 and E2 reactions, focusing on the factors that help us predict which of these mechanisms will operate under a given set of experimental conditions. Then we will organize these factors into a short table.

Effect of the Base The nature of the base is the single most important factor in determining whether an elimination will go by the E1 or E2 mechanism. If a strong base is present, the rate of the bimolecular reaction will be greater than the rate of ionization, and the E2 reaction will predominate (perhaps accompanied by the S_N2).

If no strong base is present, then a good solvent makes a unimolecular ionization likely. Subsequent loss of a proton to a weak base (such as the solvent) leads to elimination. Under these conditions, the E1 reaction usually predominates, usually accompanied by the S_N1.

E1: Base strength is unimportant (usually weak).
E2: Requires strong bases.

Effect of the Solvent The slow step of the E1 reaction is the formation of two ions. Like the S_N1, the E1 reaction critically depends on polar ionizing solvents such as water and the alcohols.

In the E2 reaction, the transition state spreads out the negative charge of the base over the entire molecule. There is no more need for solvation in the E2 transition state than in the reactants. The E2 is therefore less sensitive to the solvent; in fact, some reagents are stronger bases in less polar solvents.

E1:	Requires a good ionizing solvent.
E2:	Solvent polarity is not so important.

Effect of the Substrate For both the E1 and the E2 reactions, the order of reactivity is

E1, E2: 3° > 2° > 1° (1° usually will not go E1)

In the E1 reaction, the rate-limiting step is formation of a carbocation, and the reactivity order reflects the stability of carbocations. In the E2 reaction, the more substituted halides generally form more substituted, more stable alkenes.

Kinetics The rate of the E1 reaction is proportional to the concentration of the alkyl halide [RX] but not to the concentration of the base. It follows a first-order rate equation.

The rate of the E2 reaction is proportional to the concentrations of both the alkyl halide [RX] and the base [B:⁻]. It follows a second-order rate equation.

$$\text{E1 rate} = k_r[\text{RX}]$$
$$\text{E2 rate} = k_r[\text{RX}][\text{B:}^-]$$

Orientation of Elimination In most E1 and E2 eliminations with two or more possible products, the product with the most substituted double bond (the most stable product) predominates. This principle is called **Zaitsev's rule**, and the most highly substituted product is called the **Zaitsev product**.

Br — El or E2 → major (cis + trans) + minor

E1, E2: Usually Zaitsev orientation.

Stereochemistry The E1 reaction begins with an ionization to give a flat carbocation. No particular geometry is required for ionization.

The E2 reaction takes place through a concerted mechanism that requires a coplanar arrangement of the bonds to the atoms being eliminated. The transition state is usually anti-coplanar, although it may be syn-coplanar in rigid systems.

E1:	No particular geometry required for the slow step.
E2:	Coplanar arrangement (usually anti) required for the transition state.

Rearrangements The E1 reaction involves a carbocation intermediate. This intermediate can rearrange, usually by the shift of a hydride or an alkyl group, to give a more stable carbocation.

The E2 reaction takes place in one step with no intermediates. No rearrangement is possible in the E2 reaction.

E1:	Rearrangements are common.
E2:	No rearrangements.

SUMMARY Elimination Reactions

	E1	E2
Promoting factors		
base	weak bases work	strong base required
solvent	good ionizing solvent	wide variety of solvents
substrate	3° > 2°	3° > 2° > 1°
leaving group	good one required	good one required
Characteristics		
kinetics	first order, k_r[RX]	second order, k_r[RX][B:$^-$]
orientation	most substituted alkene	most substituted alkene
stereochemistry	no special geometry	coplanar transition state required
rearrangements	common	impossible

PROBLEM-SOLVING STRATEGY

PREDICTING SUBSTITUTIONS AND ELIMINATIONS

S_N1

$$\mathrm{R{-}\ddot{X}:} \rightleftarrows \mathrm{R^+} + \mathrm{:\ddot{X}:^-} \quad \text{(slow)}$$

$$\mathrm{R^+} + \mathrm{Nuc:^-} \longrightarrow \mathrm{R{-}Nuc} \quad \text{(fast)}$$

S_N2

$$\mathrm{Nuc:^-} + \mathrm{{>}C{-}\ddot{X}:} \longrightarrow \mathrm{Nuc{-}C{<}} + \mathrm{:\ddot{X}:^-}$$

E1

$$\mathrm{H{-}\overset{|}{C}{-}\overset{|}{C}{-}X} \rightleftarrows \mathrm{H{-}\overset{|}{C}{-}C^+{<}} + \mathrm{^-:\ddot{X}:} \quad \text{(slow)}$$

$$\mathrm{B:^-} + \mathrm{H{-}\overset{|}{C}{-}C^+{<}} \rightleftarrows \mathrm{B{-}H} + \mathrm{{>}C{=}C{<}} \quad \text{(fast)}$$

E2

$$\mathrm{B:^-} + \mathrm{H{-}\overset{|}{C}{-}\overset{|}{C}{-}\ddot{X}:} \longrightarrow \mathrm{{>}C{=}C{<}} + \mathrm{B{-}H} + \mathrm{:\ddot{X}:^-}$$

Given a set of reagents and solvents, how can we predict what products will result and which mechanisms will be involved? Should you memorize all this theory about substitutions and eliminations? Students sometimes feel overwhelmed at this point.

Memorizing is not the best way to approach this material because the answers are not absolute and too many factors are involved. Besides, the real world with its real reagents and solvents is not as clean as our equations on paper. Most nucleophiles are also basic, and most bases are also nucleophilic. Many solvents can solvate ions or react as nucleophiles, or both. We will review the most important factors that determine the reaction pathway and organize them in a sequence that allows you to predict as much as can be predicted.

The first principle you must understand is that *we cannot always predict one unique product or one unique mechanism.* Often, the best we can do is to eliminate some of the possibilities and make some good predictions. Remembering this limitation, here are some general guidelines:

1. The strength of the base or nucleophile determines the order of the reaction.
If a strong nucleophile (or base) is present, it will force second-order kinetics, either S_N2 or E2. A strong nucleophile attacks the electrophilic carbon atom or abstracts a proton faster than the molecule can ionize for first-order reactions.

Br

$\xrightarrow[CH_3OH]{NaOCH_3}$ S_N2 and E2

$(CH_3)_3C—Br$ $\xrightarrow[CH_3OH]{NaOCH_3}$ E2 (no S_N2 on 3° carbon)

If no strong base or nucleophile is present, the fastest reaction will probably be a first-order reaction, either S_N1 or E1. Addition of silver salts to the reaction can force some difficult ionizations.

Br

$\xrightarrow[heat]{CH_3OH}$ S_N1 and E1

2. Primary halides usually undergo the S_N2 reaction, occasionally the E2 reaction.
Primary halides rarely undergo first-order reactions, since primary carbocations are rarely formed. With good nucleophiles, S_N2 substitution is usually observed. With a strong base, E2 elimination may also be observed.

Br $\xrightarrow[CH_3OH]{NaOCH_3}$ S_N2 (and possibly E2)

Sometimes silver salts or high temperatures are used to force a primary halide to ionize, usually with rearrangement to give a more stable carbocation. In such a case, the rearranged S_N1 and E1 products may be observed.

Br $\xrightarrow[CH_3OH]{AgNO_3,\ heat}$ S_N1 and E1 (both with rearrangement)

3. Tertiary halides usually undergo the E2 reaction (strong base) or a mixture of S_N1 and E1 (weak base).
Tertiary halides cannot undergo the S_N2 reaction. A strong base forces second-order kinetics, resulting in elimination by the E2 mechanism. In the absence of a strong base, tertiary halides react by first-order processes, usually a mixture of S_N1 and E1. The specific reaction conditions determine the ratio of substitution to elimination.

$(CH_3)_3C—Br$ $\xrightarrow[CH_3OH]{NaOCH_3}$ E2 (no S_N2 on 3° carbon)

$(CH_3)_3C—Br$ $\xrightarrow[heat]{CH_3OH}$ S_N1 and E1

4. The reactions of secondary halides are the most difficult to predict.
With a strong base, either the S_N2 or the E2 reaction is possible. With a weak base and a good ionizing solvent, either the S_N1 or the E1 reaction is possible. Mixtures of products are common. Figure 6-14 shows these possibilities with a secondary halide under second-order and first-order conditions.

Br

$\xrightarrow[CH_3OH]{NaOCH_3}$ S_N2 and E2

Br

$\xrightarrow[heat]{CH_3OH}$ S_N1 and E1

(Continued)

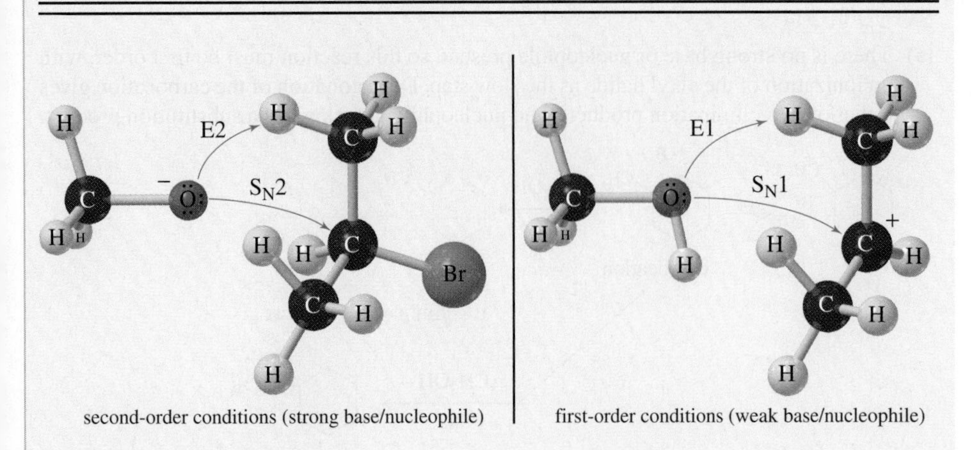

FIGURE 6-14
Under second-order conditions (strong base/nucleophile), a secondary alkyl halide might undergo either substitution (S_N2) or elimination (E2). Under first-order conditions (weak base/nucleophile), S_N1 and E1 are possible.

5. Some nucleophiles and bases favor substitution or elimination.
To promote elimination, the base should readily abstract a proton but not readily attack a carbon atom. A bulky strong base, such as *tert*-butoxide [$^-OC(CH_3)_3$], enhances elimination. Higher temperatures also favor elimination in most cases, because more molecules are formed, and $\Delta S > 0$. As the temperature increases, the free energy term, $-T\Delta S$, becomes more negative and more favorable for elimination. To promote substitution, we need a good nucleophile with limited basicity: a highly polarizable species that is the conjugate base of a strong acid. Bromide (Br^-) and iodide (I^-) are examples of good nucleophiles that are weak bases and favor substitution.

2-bromohexane $\xrightarrow{\text{NaI}}$ mostly S_N2

2-bromohexane $\xrightarrow[(CH_3)_3COH]{NaOC(CH_3)_3}$ mostly E2

PROBLEM 6-39

Give the structures of the products expected from the indicated mechanisms in the preceding examples.

SOLVED PROBLEM 6-3

Predict the mechanisms and products of the following reactions.

(a) 1-bromo-1-methylcyclohexane $\xrightarrow[\text{heat}]{CH_3OH}$

(b) $CH_3-CH(Br)-CH_2CH_2CH_2CH_3$ (2-bromohexane) $\xrightarrow[CH_3OH]{NaOCH_3}$

problem-solving **Hint**

The strength of the base/nucleophile usually determines the order of the reaction.

SOLUTION

(a) There is no strong base or nucleophile present, so this reaction must be first order, with an ionization of the alkyl halide as the slow step. Deprotonation of the carbocation gives either of two elimination products, and nucleophilic attack gives a substitution product.

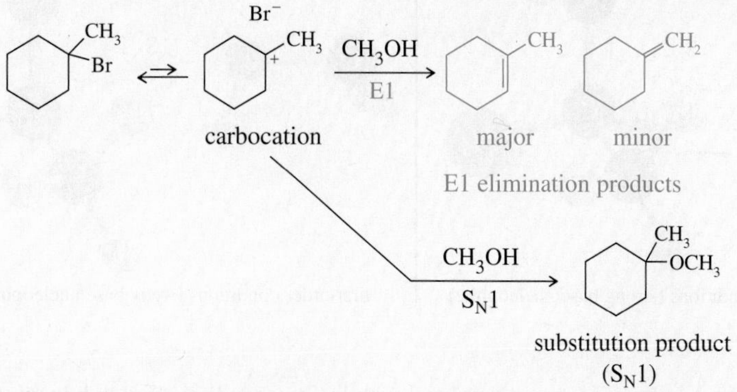

1-bromo-1-methylcyclohexane ⇄ carbocation (Br^-) $\xrightarrow[E1]{CH_3OH}$ 1-methylcyclohexene (major) + methylenecyclohexane (minor)

E1 elimination products

carbocation $\xrightarrow[S_N1]{CH_3OH}$ 1-methoxy-1-methylcyclohexane

substitution product (S_N1)

(b) This reaction takes place with a strong base, so it is second order. This secondary halide can undergo both S_N2 substitution and E2 elimination. Both products will be formed, with the relative proportions of substitution and elimination depending on the reaction conditions.

$CH_3-CH=CH-CH_2CH_2CH_3$ (major) $\quad CH_2=CH-CH_2CH_2CH_2CH_3$ (minor)

E2 products

$CH_3-CH(OCH_3)-CH_2CH_2CH_2CH_3$

S_N2 product

problem-solving **Hint**

Don't try to memorize your way through this chapter. Try to understand what happens in the different reactions. Some memorizing is necessary, but simply memorizing everything won't allow you to predict new reactions.

PROBLEM 6-40

Predict the products and mechanisms of the following reactions. When more than one product or mechanism is possible, explain which are most likely.

(a) 1-bromohexane + sodium ethoxide in ethanol
(b) 2-chlorohexane + $NaOCH_3$ in methanol
(c) 2-chloro-2-methylbutane + $NaOCH_2CH_3$ in ethanol
(d) 2-chloro-2-methylbutane heated in ethanol
(e) isobutyl iodide + KOH in ethanol/water
(f) isobutyl chloride + $AgNO_3$ in ethanol/water
(g) 1-bromo-1-methylcyclopentane + NaOEt in ethanol
(h) 1-bromo-1-methylcyclopentane heated in methanol

SUMMARY Reactions of Alkyl Halides

Some of these reactions have not yet been covered, but they are included here for completeness and for later reference. Notice the section numbers, indicating where each reaction is covered.

1. *Nucleophilic substitutions* (Section 6-9)

a. *Alcohol formation*

$$R-X \quad + \quad ^-:\ddot{\underset{..}{O}}H \quad \longrightarrow \quad R-OH \quad + \quad :X^-$$

Example

$$\underset{\text{ethyl bromide}}{CH_3CH_2-Br} \quad + \quad NaOH \quad \longrightarrow \quad \underset{\text{ethyl alcohol}}{CH_3CH_2-OH} \quad + \quad NaBr$$

b. *Halide exchange*

$$R{-}X + :\ddot{\underset{..}{I}}:^- \longrightarrow R{-}I + :X^-$$

$$R{-}Cl + KF \xrightarrow[CH_3CN]{\text{18-crown-6}} R{-}F + KCl$$

Example

$$\underset{\text{allyl chloride}}{H_2C{=}CH{-}CH_2Cl} + NaI \longrightarrow \underset{\text{allyl iodide}}{H_2C{=}CH{-}CH_2I} + NaCl$$

c. *Williamson ether synthesis*

$$R{-}X + R'\ddot{\underset{..}{O}}:^- \longrightarrow R{-}\ddot{\underset{..}{O}}{-}R' + :X^- \quad \text{ether synthesis}$$

$$R{-}X + R'\ddot{\underset{..}{S}}:^- \longrightarrow R{-}\ddot{\underset{..}{S}}{-}R' + :X^- \quad \text{thioether synthesis}$$

Example

$$\underset{\text{methyl iodide}}{CH_3{-}I} + \underset{\text{sodium ethoxide}}{CH_3CH_2{-}O^- \, Na^+} \longrightarrow \underset{\text{methyl ethyl ether}}{CH_3{-}O{-}CH_2CH_3} + Na^+ \, I^-$$

d. *Amine synthesis*

$$R{-}X + \underset{\text{excess}}{:NH_3} \longrightarrow R{-}NH_3^+ \, X^- \xrightarrow{:NH_3} \underset{\text{amine}}{R{-}\ddot{N}H_2} + NH_4^+ \, :X^-$$

Example

$$\underset{n\text{-propyl bromide}}{CH_3CH_2CH_2{-}Br} + :NH_3 \longrightarrow \underset{n\text{-propylamine}}{CH_3CH_2CH_2{-}NH_2} + NH_4^+ \, ^-Br$$

e. *Nitrile synthesis*

$$R{-}X + \underset{\text{cyanide}}{^-:C{\equiv}N:} \longrightarrow \underset{\text{nitrile}}{R{-}C{\equiv}N:} + :X^-$$

Example

$$\underset{\text{1-chloro-3-methylbutane}}{(CH_3)_2CHCH_2CH_2{-}Cl} + NaCN \longrightarrow \underset{\text{4-methylpentanenitrile}}{(CH_3)_2CHCH_2CH_2{-}CN} + NaCl$$

f. *Alkyne synthesis* (Section 9-7)

$$\underset{\text{acetylide ion}}{R{-}C{\equiv}C:^-} + R'{-}X \longrightarrow \underset{\text{alkyne}}{R{-}C{\equiv}C{-}R'} + :X^-$$

Example

$$\underset{\text{propyne}}{CH_3{-}C{\equiv}C{-}H} + \underset{\text{sodium amide}}{NaNH_2} \longrightarrow \underset{\text{sodium propynide}}{CH_3{-}C{\equiv}C:^- \, Na^+} + NH_3$$

$$\underset{\text{propynide ion}}{CH_3{-}C{\equiv}C:^- \, Na^+} + \underset{\text{ethyl iodide}}{CH_3CH_2{-}I} \longrightarrow \underset{\text{2-pentyne}}{CH_3{-}C{\equiv}C{-}CH_2CH_3} + NaI$$

2. *Eliminations*

a. *Dehydrohalogenation* (Sections 6-18 and 7-9A)

$$-\underset{|}{\overset{H}{\overset{|}{C}}}-\underset{\underset{X}{|}}{\overset{|}{C}}- \xrightarrow{KOH} \;\rangle C{=}C\langle\; + :X^-$$

Example

2-bromohexane $\xrightarrow[CH_3OH]{NaOCH_3}$ 2-hexene + 1-hexene

b. *Dehalogenation* (Section 7-9D)

$$-\overset{Br}{\overset{|}{C}}-\underset{Br}{\underset{|}{C}}- \xrightarrow{KI} >C{=}C< \;+\; I{-}Br \;+\; KBr$$

Example

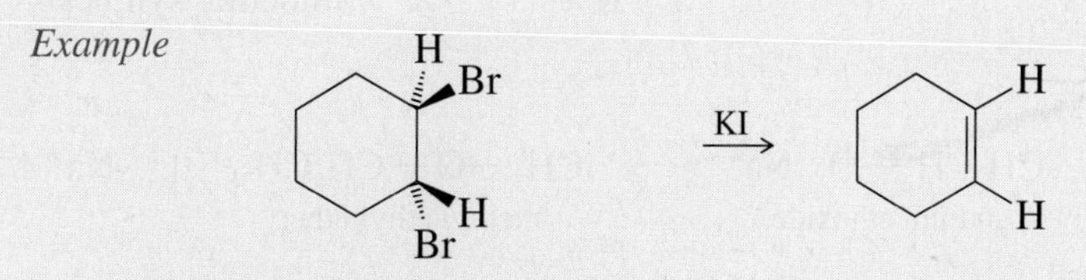

trans-1,2-dibromocyclohexane cyclohexene

3. *Formation of organometallic reagents* (Section 10-8)

a. *Grignard reagents*

$$R{-}X \;+\; Mg \xrightarrow{CH_3CH_2{-}O{-}CH_2CH_3} R{-}Mg{-}X$$

(X = Cl, Br, or I) organomagnesium halide (Grignard reagent)

Example

bromocyclohexane + Mg $\xrightarrow{\text{ether}}$ cyclohexylmagnesium bromide

b. *Organolithium reagents*

$$R{-}X \;+\; 2\,Li \longrightarrow R{-}Li \;+\; Li^+\,X^-$$

(X = Cl, Br, or I) organolithium

Example

$$CH_3CH_2CH_2CH_2{-}Br \;+\; 2\,Li \xrightarrow{\text{hexane}} CH_3CH_2CH_2CH_2{-}Li \;+\; LiBr$$

n-butyl bromide *n*-butyllithium

4. *Coupling of organocopper reagents* (Section 10-9)

$$2\,R{-}Li \;+\; CuI \longrightarrow R_2CuLi \;+\; LiI$$

$$R_2CuLi \;+\; R'{-}X \longrightarrow R{-}R' \;+\; R{-}Cu \;+\; LiX$$

Example

$$2\,CH_3I \xrightarrow{4\,Li} 2\,CH_3Li \;+\; 2\,LiI \xrightarrow{CuI} (CH_3)_2CuLi$$

$$(n\text{-}C_8H_{17})(H)C{=}C(H)(I) \xrightarrow{(CH_3)_2CuLi} (n\text{-}C_8H_{17})(H)C{=}C(H)(CH_3)$$

5. *Reduction* (Section 10-10)

$$R{-}X \xrightarrow[(2)\ H_2O]{(1)\ Mg\ or\ Li} R{-}H$$

Example

$$\underset{n\text{-decyl bromide}}{C_9H_{19}{-}CH_2{-}Br} \xrightarrow[(2)\ H_2O]{(1)\ Mg,\ ether} \underset{n\text{-decane}}{C_9H_{19}{-}CH_3}$$

Glossary 6

acid A species that can donate a proton.

acidity (acid strength): The thermodynamic reactivity of an acid, expressed quantitatively by the acid-dissociation constant K_a.

Lewis acid (electrophile): A species that can accept an electron pair from a nucleophile, forming a bond. (p. 29)

alkyl halide (haloalkane) A derivative of an alkane in which one (or more) of the hydrogen atoms has been replaced by a halogen. (p. 215)

alkyl shift (symbolized **~R**) Movement of an alkyl group with a pair of electrons from one atom (usually carbon) to another. Alkyl shifts are examples of rearrangements that convert carbocations into more stable carbocations. (p. 251)

allylic The saturated position adjacent to a carbon–carbon double bond. (p. 224)

allylic halogenation Substitution of a halogen for a hydrogen at the allylic position. (p. 224)

$H_2C{=}CH{-}CH_2{-}CH_3$ (allylic position) + N-bromosuccinimide $\xrightarrow{light}$ $H_2C{=}CH{-}CH(Br){-}CH_3$ (allylic bromide) + $BrH_2C{-}CH{=}CH{-}CH_3$ (rearranged allylic bromide (product of an allylic shift)) + succinimide

allylic shift A rearrangement that results from reaction at either end of a resonance-stabilized allylic intermediate. (p. 225)

anti Adding to (or eliminating from) opposite faces of a molecule. (p. 264)

anti-coplanar: Having a dihedral angle of 180°.

syn-coplanar: Having a dihedral angle of 0°.

anti-coplanar (H up, X down) syn-coplanar (HX eclipsed)

aprotic solvent A solvent that has no acidic protons; a solvent with no O—H or N—H groups. (p. 237)

aryl halide An aromatic compound (benzene derivative) in which a halogen is bonded to one of the carbon atoms of the aromatic ring. (p. 215)

base An electron-rich species that can abstract a proton. (p. 234)

basicity (base strength): The thermodynamic reactivity of a base, expressed quantitatively by the base-dissociation constant K_b.

Lewis base (nucleophile): An electron-rich species that can donate a pair of electrons to form a bond. (pp. 229, 234)

concerted reaction A reaction in which the breaking of bonds and the formation of new bonds occur at the same time (in one step). (pp. 230, 264)

dehydrohalogenation An elimination in which the two atoms lost are a hydrogen atom and a halogen atom. (pp. 228, 256)

electrophile (Lewis acid) A species that can accept an electron pair from a nucleophile, forming a bond. (p. 29)
electrophilicity (electrophile strength) The kinetic reactivity of an electrophile.
elimination A reaction that involves the loss of two atoms or groups from the substrate, usually resulting in the formation of a pi bond. (pp. 228, 255)

E1 reaction (elimination, unimolecular): A multistep elimination where the leaving group is lost in a slow ionization step, then a proton is lost in a second step. Zaitsev orientation is generally preferred. (p. 255)

E2 reaction (elimination, bimolecular): A concerted elimination involving a transition state where the base is abstracting a proton at the same time that the leaving group is leaving. The anti-coplanar transition state is generally preferred. Zaitsev orientation is usually preferred, unless the base or the leaving group is unusually bulky. (p. 261)

freons A generic name for a group of chlorofluorocarbons used as refrigerants, propellants, and solvents. Freon-12® is CF_2Cl_2, and Freon-22® is $CHClF_2$. (p. 219)
geminal dihalide A dihalide with both halogens on the same carbon atom. (p. 217)

$$CH_3-CH_2-CBr_2-CH_3$$
a geminal dibromide

haloalkane (alkyl halide) A derivative of an alkane in which one (or more) of the hydrogen atoms has been replaced by a halogen. (p. 216)
halogen exchange reaction A substitution where one halogen atom replaces another; commonly used to form fluorides and iodides. (p. 232)
hydride shift (symbolized ~H) Movement of a hydrogen atom with a pair of electrons from one atom (usually carbon) to another. Hydride shifts are examples of rearrangements that convert carbocations into more stable carbocations. (p. 249)
hydroxylic solvent A solvent containing OH groups (the most common type of protic solvents). (p. 237)
inversion of configuration (see also **Walden inversion**) A process in which the groups around an asymmetric carbon atom are changed to the opposite spatial configuration, usually as a result of **back-side attack**. (pp. 241, 247)

The S_N2 reaction goes with *inversion of configuration.*
leaving group The atom or group of atoms that departs during a substitution or elimination. The leaving group can be charged or uncharged, but it leaves with the pair of electrons that originally bonded the group to the remainder of the molecule. (p. 228)
Lewis acid See **electrophile**. (p. 29)
Lewis base See **nucleophile**. (p. 234)
methyl shift (symbolized $\sim CH_3$) Rearrangement of a methyl group with a pair of electrons from one atom (usually carbon) to another. A methyl shift (or any alkyl shift) in a carbocation generally results in a more stable carbocation. (p. 251)
nucleophile (Lewis base) An electron-rich species that can donate a pair of electrons to form a bond. (pp. 229, 234)

nucleophilicity (nucleophile strength) The kinetic reactivity of a nucleophile; a measure of the rate of substitution in a reaction with a standard substrate.

nucleophilic substitution A reaction where a nucleophile replaces another group or atom (the leaving group) in a molecule. (p. 228)

organic synthesis The preparation of desired organic compounds from readily available starting materials.
polarizable Having electrons that are easily displaced toward a positive charge. Polarizable atoms can begin to form a bond at a relatively long distance. (p. 235)
primary halide, secondary halide, tertiary halide These terms specify the substitution of the halogen-bearing carbon atom (sometimes called the ***head carbon***). If the head carbon is bonded to one other carbon, it is **primary**; if it is bonded to two carbons, it is **secondary**; and if bonded to three carbons, it is **tertiary**. (p. 217)

$CH_3{-}CH_2{-}Br$ — a primary halide (1°)

$CH_3{-}CH(CH_3){-}Br$ — a secondary halide (2°)

$CH_3{-}C(CH_3)_2{-}Br$ — a tertiary halide (3°)

protic solvent A solvent containing acidic protons, usually O—H or N—H groups. (p. 236)
racemization The loss of optical activity that occurs when a reaction shows neither clean retention of configuration nor clean inversion of configuration. (p. 247)
reagent The compound that serves as the attacking species in a reaction. (p. 225)
rearrangement A reaction involving a change in the bonding sequence within a molecule. Rearrangements are common in reactions such as the S_N1 and E1 involving carbocation intermediates. (p. 249)
retention of configuration Formation of a product with the same configuration as the reactant. In a nucleophilic substitution, retention of configuration occurs when the nucleophile assumes the same stereochemical position in the product as the leaving group occupied in the reactant. (p. 247)
solvolysis A nucleophilic substitution or elimination where the solvent serves as the attacking reagent. Solvolysis literally means "cleavage by the solvent." (p. 243)

$$(CH_3)_3C{-}Br \xrightarrow{CH_3OH,\ heat} (CH_3)_3C{-}OCH_3 + (CH_3)_2C{=}CH_2 + HBr$$

stereocenter An atom that gives rise to stereoisomers when its groups are interchanged. Asymmetric carbon atoms and double-bonded carbons in cis-trans alkenes are the most common stereocenters.
stereospecific reaction A reaction in which different stereoisomers react to give different stereoisomers of the product. (pp. 242, 265)
steric hindrance Interference by bulky groups that slow a reaction or prevent it from occurring. (p. 235, 270)
substitution (displacement) A reaction in which an attacking species (nucleophile, electrophile, or free radical) replaces another group. (p. 228)
  S_N2 reaction (Substitution, Nucleophilic, bimolecular): The concerted displacement of one nucleophile by another on an sp^3 hybrid carbon atom. (p. 230)
  S_N1 reaction (Substitution, Nucleophilic, unimolecular): A two-step interchange of nucleophiles, with bond breaking preceding bond formation. The first step is ionization to form a carbocation. The second step is the reaction of the carbocation with a nucleophile. (p. 243)
substrate The compound that is attacked by the reagent. (p. 225)
syn Adding to (or eliminating from) the same face of a molecule. (p. 264)
  syn-coplanar Having a dihedral angle of 0°. See **anti-coplanar** for a diagram.
transition state In each individual step of a reaction, the state of highest energy between reactants and products. The transition state is a relative maximum (high point) on the reaction-energy diagram. (p. 230)
vicinal dihalide A dihalide with the halogens on adjacent carbon atoms. (p. 217)

$CH_3{-}CHBr{-}CHBr{-}CH_3$ — a vicinal dibromide

$CH_3{-}CH{=}CBr{-}CH_3$ — a vinyl bromide

vinyl halide A derivative of an alkene in which one (or more) of the hydrogen atoms on the double-bonded carbon atoms has been replaced by a halogen. (p. 215)
Walden inversion (see also **inversion of configuration**) A step in a reaction sequence in which an asymmetric carbon atom undergoes inversion of configuration. (p. 241)
Zaitsev's rule (Saytzeff's rule) An elimination usually gives the most substituted alkene product. Zaitsev's rule does not always apply, but when it does, the reaction is said to give **Zaitsev orientation**. (p. 260)

Essential Problem-Solving Skills in Chapter 6

1. Correctly name alkyl halides, and identify them as 1°, 2°, or 3°.
2. Predict the products of S_N1, S_N2, E1, and E2 reactions, including stereochemistry.
3. Draw the mechanisms and energy profiles of S_N1, S_N2, E1, and E2 reactions.
4. Predict and explain the rearrangement of cations in first-order reactions.
5. Predict which substitutions or eliminations will be faster, based on differences in substrate, base/nucleophile, leaving group, or solvent.
6. Predict whether a reaction will be first-order or second-order.
7. When possible, predict predominance of substitution or elimination.
8. Use Zaitsev's rule to predict major and minor elimination products.

Study Problems

6-41 Define and give an example for each term.

(a) nucleophile **(b)** electrophile **(c)** leaving group
(d) substitution **(e)** S_N2 reaction **(f)** S_N1 reaction
(g) solvolysis **(h)** elimination **(i)** E2 reaction
(j) E1 reaction **(k)** rearrangement **(l)** base
(m) steric hindrance **(n)** substrate **(o)** aryl halide
(p) vinyl halide **(q)** allylic halide **(r)** primary halide
(s) secondary halide **(t)** hydride shift **(u)** anti elimination
(v) syn elimination **(w)** stereospecific reaction **(x)** methyl shift

6-42 Draw the structures of the following compounds.

(a) *sec*-butyl chloride **(b)** isobutyl bromide **(c)** 1,2-dibromo-3-methylpentane
(d) 2,2,2-trichloroethanol **(e)** *trans*-1-chloro-2-methylcyclohexane **(f)** methylene chloride
(g) chloroform **(h)** 1-chloro-1-isopropylcyclopentane **(i)** *tert*-pentyl iodide

6-43 Give systematic (IUPAC) names for the following compounds.

(a)  Br
(b) 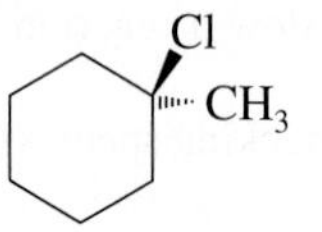 Cl CH_3
(c) 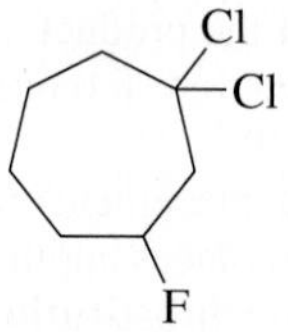 Cl Cl F
(d) 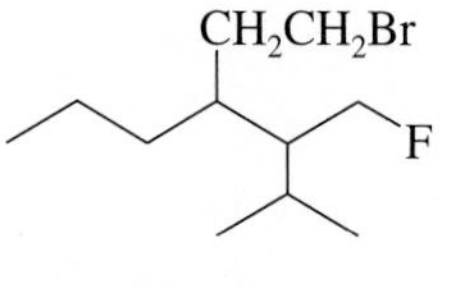 CH_2CH_2Br F
(e) 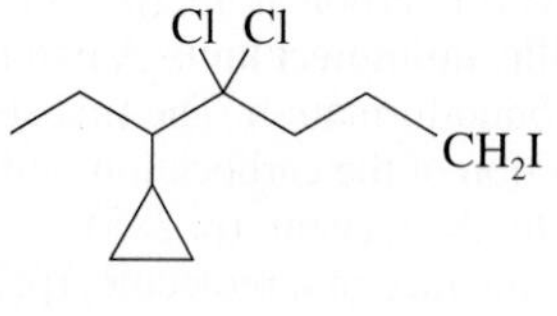 Cl Cl CH_2I
(f) Cl CH_3 Cl H

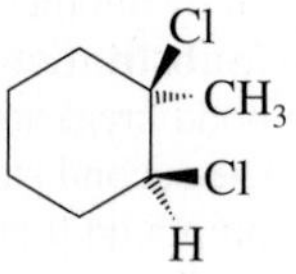

6-44 Predict the compound in each pair that will undergo the S_N2 reaction faster.

(a)  Cl or 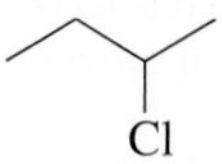 Cl
(b)  Cl or  I
(c) 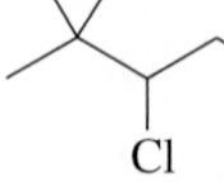 Cl or 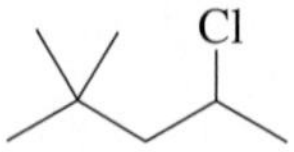 Cl
(d) 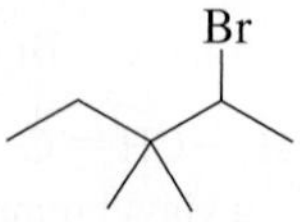 Br or 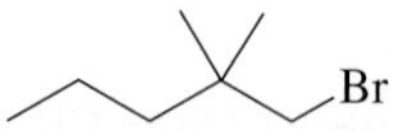 Br
(e) 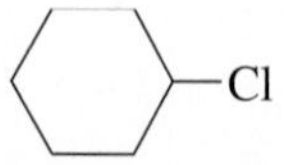 Cl or CH_2Cl
(f) 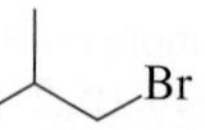 Br or Br

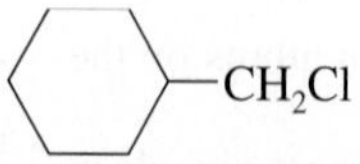

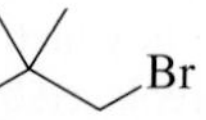

6-45 Predict the compound in each pair that will undergo solvolysis (in aqueous ethanol) more rapidly.

(a) $(CH_3CH_2)_2CH-Cl$ or $(CH_3)_3C-Cl$ **(b)**  Cl or Cl

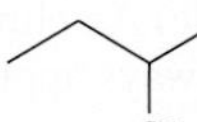

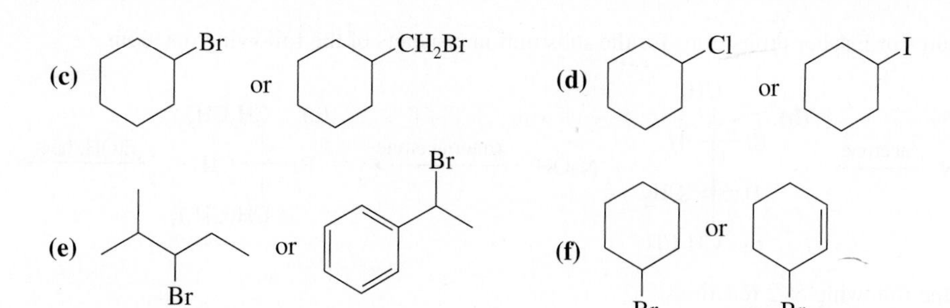

6-46 Show how each compound might be synthesized by the S_N2 displacement of an alkyl halide.

(a) $-CH_2OH$ **(b)** SCH_2CH_3 **(c)** O

(d) $-CH_2NH_2$ **(e)** $H_2C{=}CH{-}CH_2CN$ **(f)** $H{-}C{\equiv}C{-}CH_2CH_2CH_3$

6-47 **(a)** Give two syntheses for $(CH_3)_2CH{-}O{-}CH_2CH_3$, and explain which synthesis is better.
(b) A student wanted to synthesize methyl *tert*-butyl ether, $CH_3{-}O{-}C(CH_3)_3$. He attempted the synthesis by adding sodium methoxide (CH_3ONa) to *tert*-butyl chloride, but he obtained none of the desired product. Show what product is formed in this reaction, and give a better synthesis for methyl *tert*-butyl ether.

6-48 When ethyl bromide is added to potassium *tert*-butoxide, the product is ethyl *tert*-butyl ether.

$$\underset{\text{ethyl bromide}}{CH_3CH_2{-}Br} + \underset{\text{potassium } tert\text{-butoxide}}{(CH_3)_3C{-}O^{-}\,{}^{+}K} \longrightarrow \underset{\text{ethyl } tert\text{-butyl ether}}{(CH_3)_3C{-}O{-}CH_2CH_3}$$

(a) What happens to the reaction rate if the concentration of ethyl bromide is doubled?
(b) What happens to the rate if the concentration of potassium *tert*-butoxide is tripled and the concentration of ethyl bromide is doubled?
(c) What happens to the rate if the temperature is raised?

6-49 When *tert*-butyl bromide is heated with an equal amount of ethanol in an inert solvent, one of the products is ethyl *tert*-butyl ether.
(a) What happens to the reaction rate if the concentration of ethanol is doubled?
(b) What happens to the rate if the concentration of *tert*-butyl bromide is tripled and the concentration of ethanol is doubled?
(c) What happens to the rate if the temperature is raised?

6-50 Chlorocyclohexane reacts with sodium cyanide (NaCN) in ethanol to give cyanocyclohexane. The rate of formation of cyanocyclohexane increases when a small amount of sodium iodide is added to the solution. Explain this acceleration in the rate.

6-51 Give the solvolysis products expected when each compound is heated in ethanol.

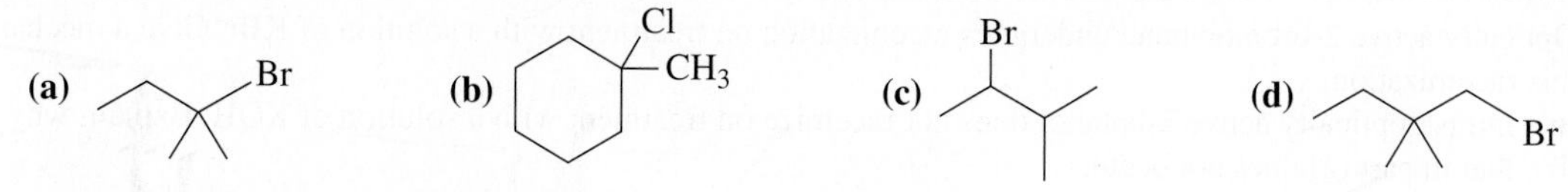

6-52 Allylic halides have the structure

$$\begin{matrix} & & | & | & \\ >C & = & C & - & C{-}X \\ & & & | & \end{matrix}$$

(a) Show how the first-order ionization of an allylic halide leads to a resonance-stabilized cation.
(b) Draw the resonance structures of the allylic cations formed by ionization of the following halides.
(c) Show the products expected from S_N1 solvolysis of these halides in ethanol.

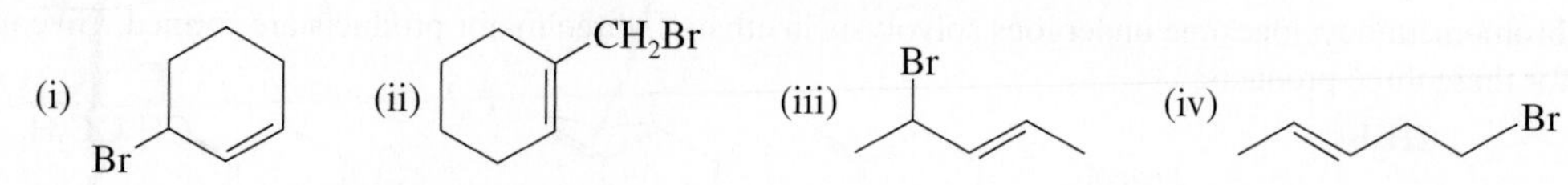

6-53 List the following carbocations in decreasing order of their stability.

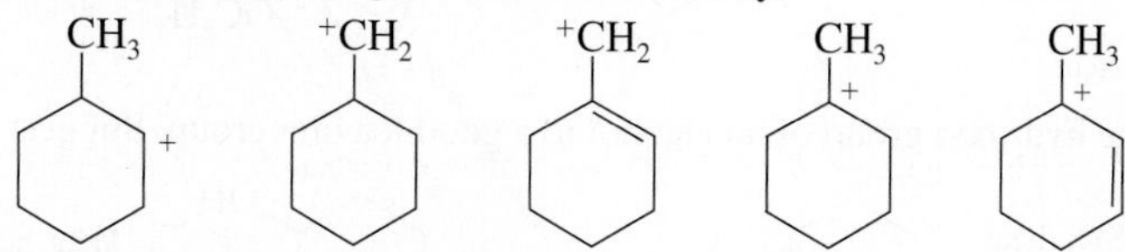

6-54 Two of the carbocations in Problem 6-53 are prone to rearrangement. Show how they might rearrange to more stable carbocations.

6-55 Draw perspective structures or Fischer projections for the substitution products of the following reactions.

(a) Fischer projection: CH_3 (top), H–C–Br, CH_2CH_3 (bottom) + NaCN $\xrightarrow{\text{acetone}}$

(b) Fischer projection: CH_3 (top), Br–C–H, H–C–CH_3, CH_2CH_3 (bottom) + NaOH $\xrightarrow{\text{water/acetone}}$

(c) Fischer projection: CH_2CH_3 (top), Br–C–CH_3, $CH(CH_3)_2$ (bottom) $\xrightarrow{\text{EtOH, heat}}$

6-56 Predict the products of the following S_N2 reactions.

(a) $CH_3CH_2ONa + CH_3CH_2Cl \longrightarrow$

(b) C_6H_5–CH_2CH_2Br + NaCN $\longrightarrow$

(c) C_6H_5–$S^-\ Na^+$ + $CH_3CH_2Br \longrightarrow$

(d) $CH_3(CH_2)_8CH_2Cl + Na^{+}\ {}^{-}\!:C\equiv CH \longrightarrow$

(e) pyridine (N:) + $CH_3I \longrightarrow$

(f) $(CH_3)_3C$—CH_2CH_2Br + excess $NH_3 \longrightarrow$

(g) $HOCH_2CH_2CH_2CH_2Cl$ (drawn as a chain with Cl and OH ends) + NaOH $\longrightarrow$

(h) Br (wedge)–cyclohexane–CH_3 (hashed) $\xrightarrow[\text{CH}_3\text{OH}]{\text{NaOH}}$

***6-57** When (±)-2,3-dibromobutane reacts with potassium hydroxide, some of the products are (2*S*,3*R*)-3-bromo-2-butanol and its enantiomer and *trans*-2-bromo-2-butene. Give mechanisms to account for these products.

Fischer projections: CH_3 (top), H–C–OH, H–C–Br, CH_3 (bottom) (2*S*,3*R*) | CH_3 (top), HO–C–H, Br–C–H, CH_3 (bottom) (2*R*,3*S*)

3-bromo-2-butanol

$H_3C(H)C{=}C(Br)CH_3$

trans-2-bromo-2-butene

6-58 A solution of pure (*S*)-2-iodobutane ($[\alpha] = +15.90°$) in acetone is allowed to react with radioactive iodide, ${}^{131}I^-$, until 1.0% of the iodobutane contains radioactive iodine. The specific rotation of this recovered iodobutane is found to be $+15.58°$.

(a) Determine the percentages of (*R*)- and (*S*)-2-iodobutane in the product mixture.

(b) What does this result suggest about the mechanism of the reaction of 2-iodobutane with iodide ion?

6-59 **(a)** Optically active 2-bromobutane undergoes racemization on treatment with a solution of KBr. Give a mechanism for this racemization.

(b) In contrast, optically active 2-butanol does not racemize on treatment with a solution of KOH. Explain why a reaction like that in part (a) does not occur.

(c) Optically active 2-butanol racemizes in dilute acid. Propose a mechanism for this racemization.

6-60 Predict the products of E1 elimination of the following compounds. Label the major products.

(a) cyclohexane with CH_3 (wedge) and adjacent carbon bearing Br and CH_3 (hashed)

(b) cyclohexyl–CH(Br)–CH_3

(c) $(CH_3)_3C$—CH(Br)—CH_3

6-61 When 1-bromomethylcyclohexene undergoes solvolysis in ethanol, three major products are formed. Give mechanisms to account for these three products.

1-bromomethylcyclohexene (CH_2Br) $\xrightarrow[\text{heat}]{\text{ethanol}}$ methylenecyclohexene + 2-ethoxy-1-methylenecyclohexane (OC_2H_5) + 1-($CH_2OC_2H_5$)cyclohexene

***6-62** Protonation converts the hydroxyl group of an alcohol to a good leaving group. Suggest a mechanism for each reaction.

(a) cyclohexanol (OH) $\xrightarrow[\text{(E1)}]{\text{H}_2\text{SO}_4\text{, heat}}$ cyclohexene + H_2O

(b) cyclohexanol (OH) $\xrightarrow[(S_N2 \text{ or } S_N1)]{\text{HBr, heat}}$ bromocyclohexane (Br) + H_2O

6-63 Give a mechanism to explain the two products formed in the following reaction.

3-methyl-1-butene $\xrightarrow{\text{NBS, } h\nu}$ not rearranged + rearranged

$(H)_2C{=}CH{-}CH(H)(CH_3)_2$ → $(H)_2C{=}CH{-}CBr(CH_3)_2$ + $Br{-}CH_2{-}CH{=}C(CH_3)_2$

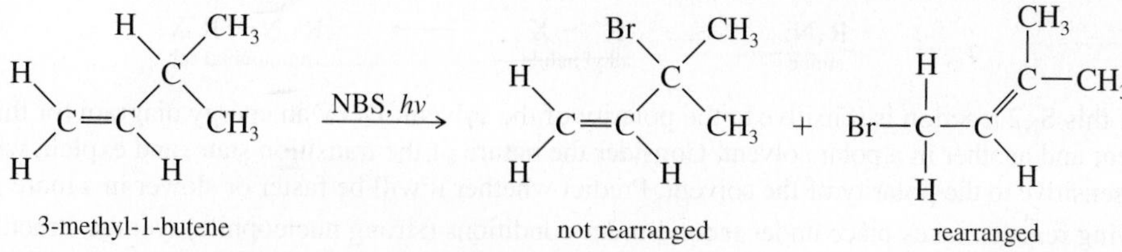

6-64 Predict the major product of the following reaction, and give a mechanism to support your prediction.

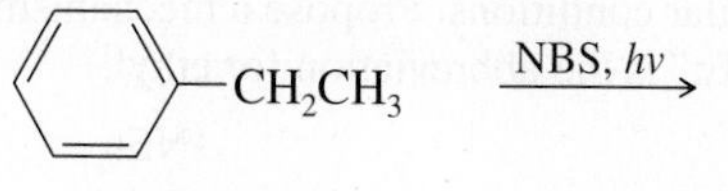

ethylbenzene ($C_6H_5{-}CH_2CH_3$) $\xrightarrow{\text{NBS, } h\nu}$

6-65 Because the S_N1 reaction goes through a flat carbocation, we might expect an optically active starting material to give a completely racemized product. In most cases, however, S_N1 reactions actually give more of the *inversion* product. In general, as the stability of the carbocation increases, the excess inversion product decreases. Extremely stable carbocations give completely racemic products. Explain these observations.

6-66 When 1-bromo-2-methylcyclohexane undergoes solvolysis in methanol, five major products are formed. Give mechanisms to account for these products.

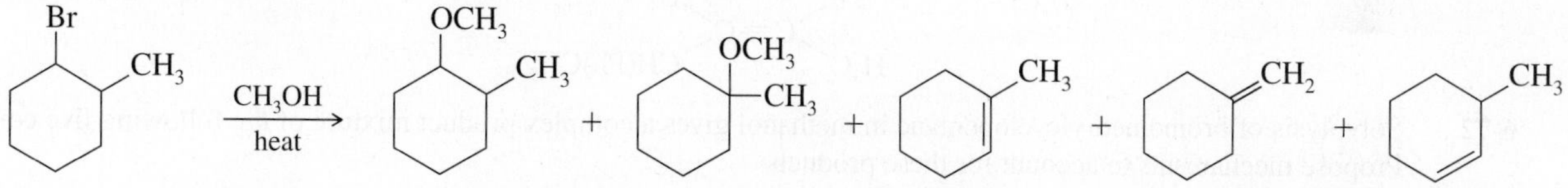

1-bromo-2-methylcyclohexane (Br, CH_3) $\xrightarrow[\text{heat}]{CH_3OH}$ 1-methoxy-2-methylcyclohexane (OCH_3, CH_3) + 1-methoxy-1-methylcyclohexane (OCH_3, CH_3) + 1-methylcyclohexene (CH_3) + methylenecyclohexane (CH_2) + 3-methylcyclohexene (CH_3)

***6-67** Deuterium (D) is the isotope of hydrogen of mass number 2, with a proton and a neutron in its nucleus. The chemistry of deuterium is nearly identical to the chemistry of hydrogen, except that the C—D bond is slightly (5.0 kJ/mol, or 1.2 kcal/mol) stronger than the C—H bond. Reaction rates tend to be slower if a C—D bond (as opposed to a C—H bond) is broken in a rate-limiting step. This effect on the rate is called a *kinetic isotope effect*. (Review Problem 4-56.)

(a) Propose a mechanism to explain each product in the following reaction.

$CH_3{-}CHBr{-}CH_3 \xrightarrow{\text{KOH, alcohol}} CH_2{=}CH{-}CH_3 + CH_3{-}CH(OH){-}CH_3$

elimination product; substitution product

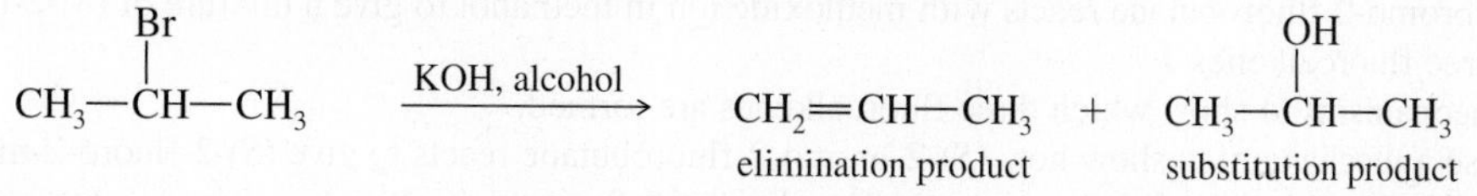

(b) When the following deuterated compound reacts under the same conditions, the rate of formation of the substitution product is unchanged, while the rate of formation of the elimination product is slowed by a factor of 7.

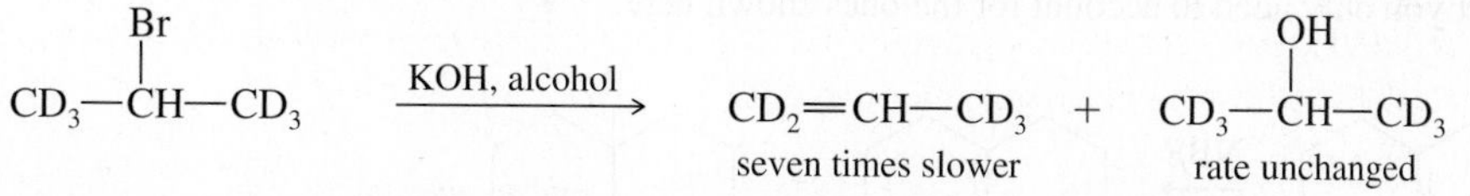

$CD_3{-}CHBr{-}CD_3 \xrightarrow{\text{KOH, alcohol}} CD_2{=}CH{-}CD_3 + CD_3{-}CH(OH){-}CD_3$

seven times slower; rate unchanged

Explain why the elimination rate is slower, but the substitution rate is unchanged.

(c) A similar reaction takes place on heating the alkyl halide in an acetone/water mixture.

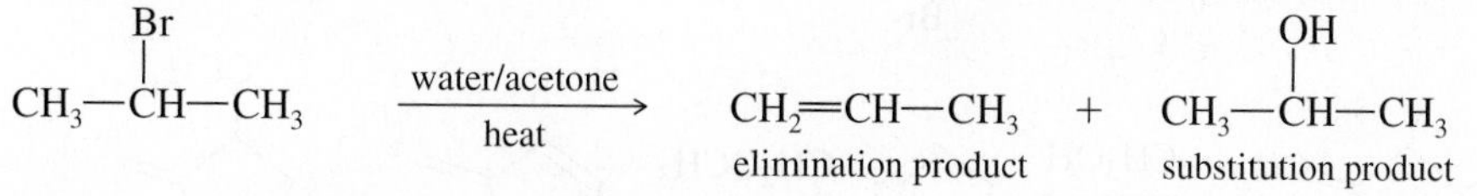

$CH_3{-}CHBr{-}CH_3 \xrightarrow[\text{heat}]{\text{water/acetone}} CH_2{=}CH{-}CH_3 + CH_3{-}CH(OH){-}CH_3$

elimination product; substitution product

Give a mechanism for the formation of each product under these conditions, and predict how the rate of formation of each product will change when the deuterated halide reacts. Explain your prediction.

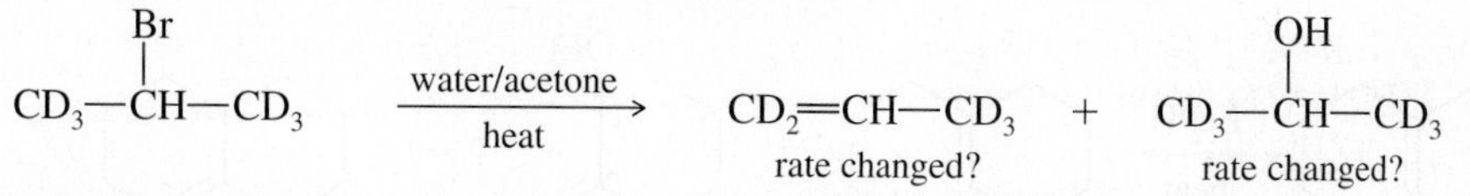

$CD_3{-}CHBr{-}CD_3 \xrightarrow[\text{heat}]{\text{water/acetone}} CD_2{=}CH{-}CD_3 + CD_3{-}CH(OH){-}CD_3$

rate changed?; rate changed?

***6-68** When the following compound is treated with sodium methoxide in methanol, two elimination products are possible. Explain why the deuterated product predominates by about a 7:1 ratio (refer to Problem 6-67).

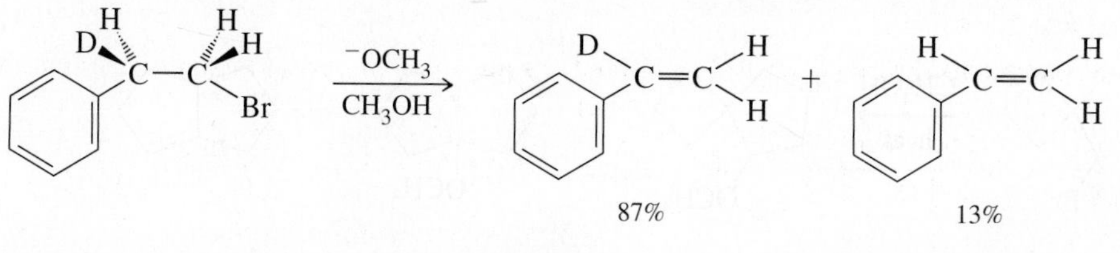

$C_6H_5{-}CHD{-}CH_2Br \xrightarrow[CH_3OH]{^-OCH_3} C_6H_5(D)C{=}CH_2$ (87%) + $C_6H_5(H)C{=}CH_2$ (13%)

***6-69** The reaction of an amine with an alkyl halide gives an ammonium salt.

$$\underset{\text{amine}}{R_3N:} \quad + \quad \underset{\text{alkyl halide}}{R'-X} \quad \longrightarrow \quad \underset{\text{ammonium salt}}{R_3\overset{+}{N}-R'X^-}$$

The rate of this S_N2 reaction is sensitive to the polarity of the solvent. Draw an energy diagram for this reaction in a nonpolar solvent and another in a polar solvent. Consider the nature of the transition state, and explain why this reaction should be sensitive to the polarity of the solvent. Predict whether it will be faster or slower in a more polar solvent.

***6-70** The following reaction takes place under second-order conditions (strong nucleophile), yet the structure of the product shows rearrangement. Also, the rate of this reaction is several thousand times faster than the rate of substitution of hydroxide ion on 2-chlorobutane under similar conditions. Propose a mechanism to explain the enhanced rate and rearrangement observed in this unusual reaction. ("Et" is the abbreviation for ethyl.)

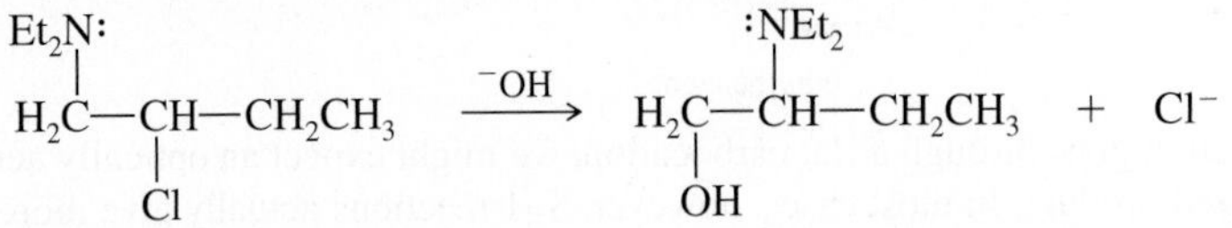

***6-71** **(a)** Design an alkyl halide that will give *only* 2,4-diphenyl-2-pentene upon treatment with potassium *tert*-butoxide (a bulky base that promotes E2 elimination).
(b) What stereochemistry is required in your alkyl halide so that *only* the following stereoisomer of the product is formed?

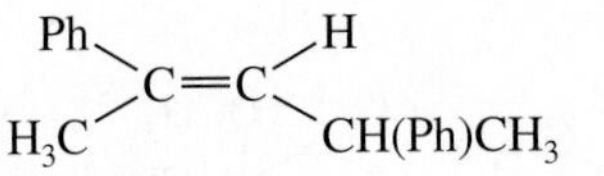

***6-72** Solvolysis of bromomethylcyclopentane in methanol gives a complex product mixture of the following five compounds. Propose mechanisms to account for these products.

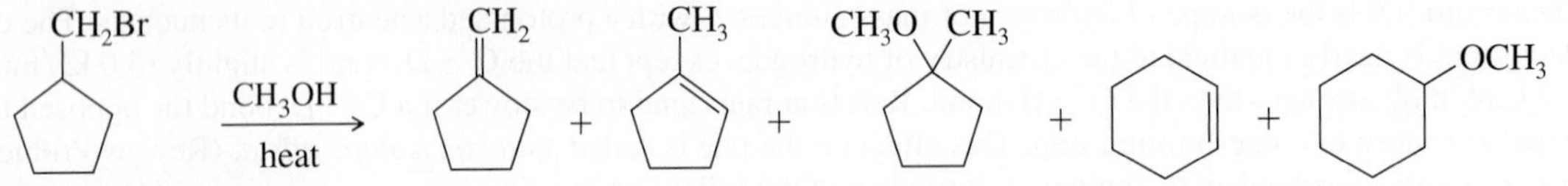

***6-73** Pure (*S*)-2-bromo-2-fluorobutane reacts with methoxide ion in methanol to give a mixture of (*S*)-2-fluoro-2-methoxybutane and three fluoroalkenes.
(a) Use mechanisms to show which three fluoroalkenes are formed.
(b) Propose a mechanism to show how (*S*)-2-bromo-2-fluorobutane reacts to give (*S*)-2-fluoro-2-methoxybutane. Has this reaction gone with retention or inversion of configuration?

***6-74** Propose mechanisms to account for the observed products in the following reactions. In some cases more products are formed, but you only need to account for the ones shown here.

(a)

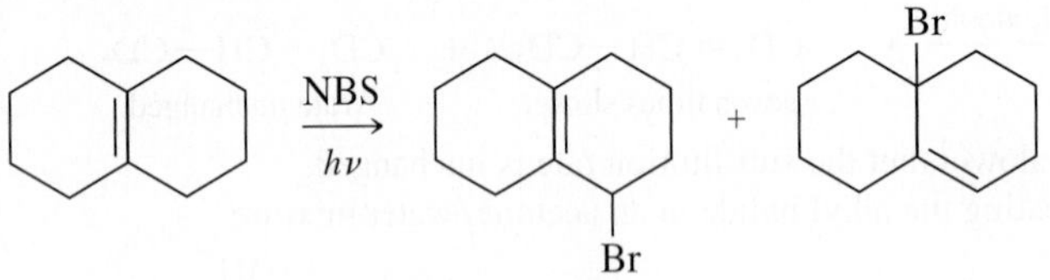

(b)

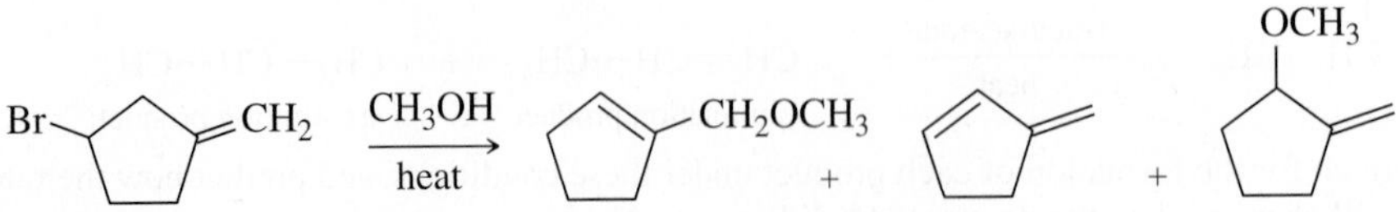

(c)

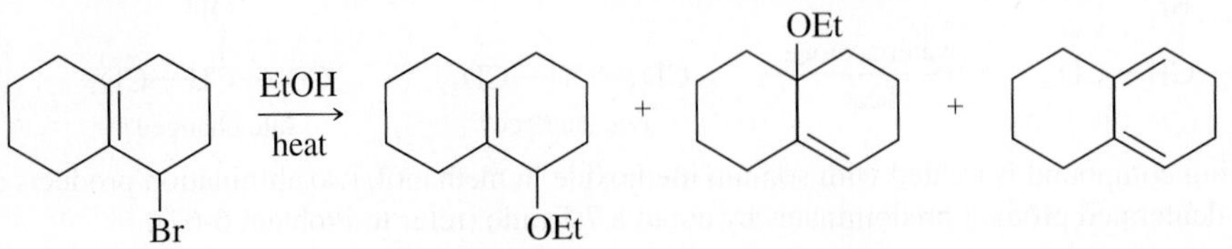

(d)

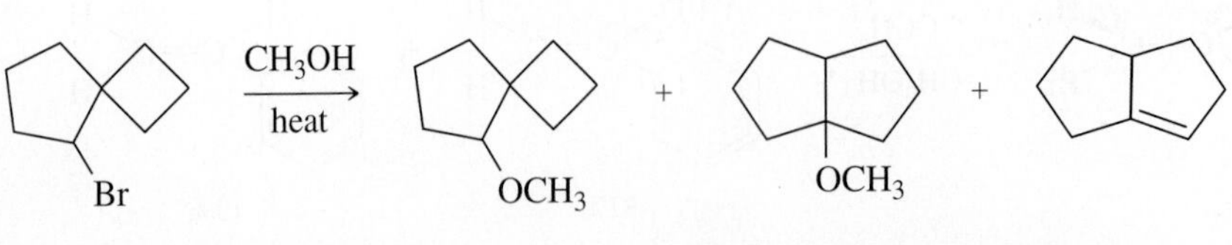

C H A P T E R

STRUCTURE AND SYNTHESIS OF ALKENES

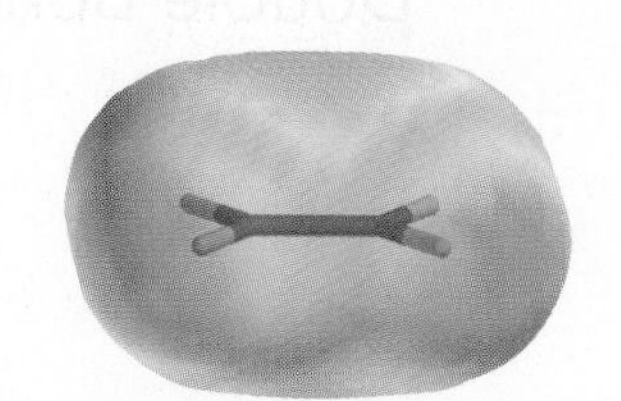

7-1 Introduction

Alkenes are hydrocarbons with carbon–carbon double bonds. Alkenes are sometimes called **olefins**, a term derived from *olefiant gas*, meaning "oil-forming gas." This term originated with early experimentalists who noticed the oily appearance of alkene derivatives. Alkenes are among the most important industrial compounds (see Section 7-6), and many alkenes are also found in plants and animals. *Ethylene* is the largest-volume industrial organic compound, used to make polyethylene and a variety of other industrial and consumer chemicals. *Pinene* is a major component of *turpentine*, the paint solvent distilled from extracts of evergreen trees. *Muscalure* (*cis*-9-tricosene) is the sex attractant of the common housefly.

$H_2C{=}CH_2$ — ethylene (ethene)

H_3C, CH_3, CH_3 — α-pinene

$CH_3(CH_2)_7$(H)C=C(H)$(CH_2)_{12}CH_3$ — *cis*-9-tricosene, "muscalure"

The bond energy of a carbon–carbon double bond is about 611 kJ/mol (146 kcal/mol), compared with the single-bond energy of about 347 kJ/mol (83 kcal/mol). From these energies, we can calculate the approximate energy of a pi bond:

double-bond dissociation energy	611 kJ/mol	(146 kcal/mol)
subtract sigma bond dissociation energy	(−)347 kJ/mol	(−)(83 kcal/mol)
pi bond dissociation energy	264 kJ/mol	(63 kcal/mol)

This value of 264 kJ/mol is much less than the sigma bond energy of 347 kJ/mol, showing that pi bonds should be more reactive than sigma bonds.

Because a carbon–carbon double bond is relatively reactive, it is considered to be a *functional group*, and alkenes are characterized by the reactions of their double bonds. In previous chapters, we saw alkene synthesis by elimination reactions and we encountered a few reactions of alkenes. In this chapter, we study alkenes in more detail, concentrating on their properties and the ways they are synthesized.

7-2 The Orbital Description of the Alkene Double Bond

In a Lewis structure, the double bond of an alkene is represented by two pairs of electrons between the carbon atoms. The Pauli exclusion principle tells us that two pairs of electrons can go into the region of space between the carbon nuclei only if each pair has its own molecular orbital. Using ethylene as an example, let's consider how the electrons are distributed in the double bond.

7-2A The Sigma Bond Framework

In Section 2-4, we saw how we can visualize the sigma bonds of organic molecules using hybrid atomic orbitals. In ethylene, each carbon atom is bonded to three other atoms (one carbon and two hydrogens), and there are no nonbonding electrons. Three hybrid orbitals are needed, implying sp^2 hybridization. Recall from Section 2-4 that sp^2 hybridization corresponds to bond angles of about 120°, giving optimum separation of three atoms bonded to the carbon atom.

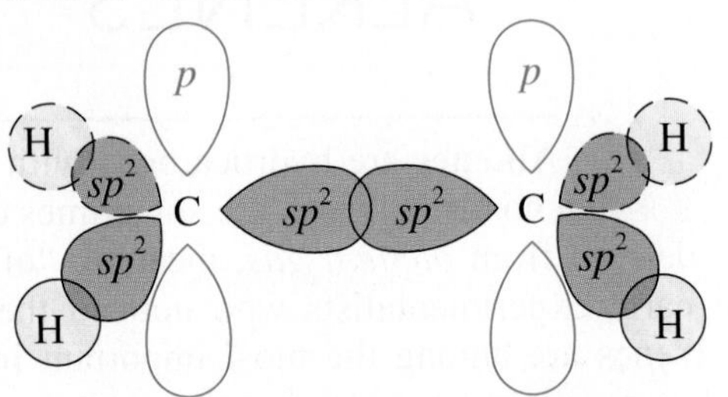

sigma bonding orbitals of ethylene

Each of the carbon–hydrogen sigma bonds is formed by overlap of an sp^2 hybrid orbital on carbon with the 1*s* orbital of a hydrogen atom. The C—H bond length in ethylene (1.08 Å) is slightly shorter than the C—H bond in ethane (1.09 Å) because the sp^2 orbital in ethylene has more *s* character (one-third *s*) than an sp^3 orbital (one-fourth *s*). The *s* orbital is closer to the nucleus than the *p* orbital, contributing to shorter bonds.

H, H, C=C, H, H; 1.33 Å; 116.6°; 121.7°; 1.08 Å

ethylene

H, H, H, C—C, H, H, H; 1.54 Å; 1.09 Å

ethane

The remaining sp^2 orbitals overlap in the region between the carbon nuclei, providing a bonding orbital. The pair of electrons in this bonding orbital forms one of the bonds between the carbon atoms. This bond is a sigma bond because its electron density is centered along the line joining the nuclei. The C=C bond in ethylene (1.33 Å) is much shorter than the C—C bond (1.54 Å) in ethane, partly because the sigma bond of ethylene is formed from sp^2 orbitals (with more *s* character) and partly because there are two bonds drawing the atoms together. The second carbon–carbon bond is a pi bond.

7-2B The Pi Bond

Two more electrons must go into the carbon–carbon bonding region to form the double bond in ethylene. Each carbon atom still has an unhybridized *p* orbital, and these overlap to form a pi-bonding molecular orbital. The two electrons in this orbital form the second bond between the double-bonded carbon atoms. For pi overlap to occur, these *p* orbitals must be parallel, which requires that the two carbon atoms be oriented with all their C—H bonds in a single plane (Figure 7-1). Half of the pi-bonding

electrostatic potential map

■ **FIGURE 7-1**
Parallel *p* orbitals in ethylene. The pi bond in ethylene is formed by overlap of the unhybridized *p* orbitals on the sp^2 hybrid carbon atoms. This overlap requires the two ends of the molecule to be coplanar.

orbital is above the C—C sigma bond, and the other half is below the sigma bond. The pi-bonding electrons give rise to regions of high electron density (red) in the electrostatic potential map of ethylene shown in Figure 7-1.

Figure 7-2 shows that the two ends of the ethylene molecule cannot be twisted with respect to each other without disrupting the pi bond. Unlike single bonds, a carbon–carbon double bond does not permit rotation. Six atoms, including the double-bonded carbon atoms and the four atoms bonded to them, must remain in the same plane. This is the origin of cis-trans isomerism. If two groups are on the same side of a double bond (cis), they cannot rotate to opposite sides (trans) without breaking the pi bond. Figure 7-2 shows that there are two distinct isomers of 2-butene: *cis*-2-butene and *trans*-2-butene.

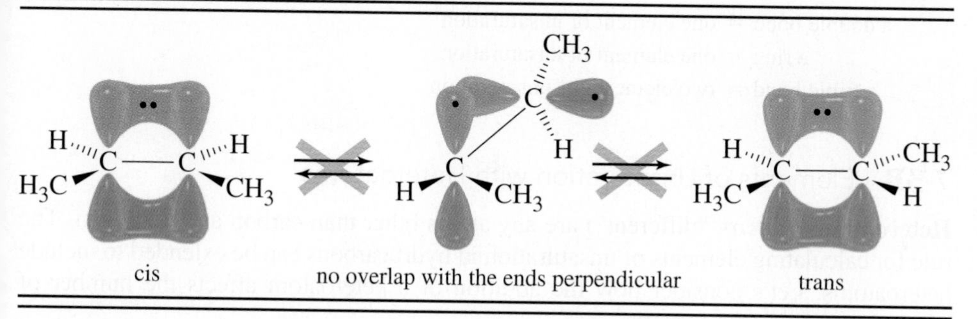

■ **FIGURE 7-2**
Distinct isomers resulting from C—C double bonds. The two isomers of 2-butene cannot interconvert by rotation about the carbon–carbon double bond without breaking the pi bond.

7-3 Elements of Unsaturation

7-3A Elements of Unsaturation in Hydrocarbons

Alkenes are said to be **unsaturated** because they are capable of adding hydrogen in the presence of a catalyst. The product, an alkane, is called **saturated** because it cannot react with any more hydrogen. The presence of a pi bond of an alkene (or an alkyne) or the ring of a cyclic compound decreases the number of hydrogen atoms in a molecular formula. These structural features are called **elements of unsaturation.*** Each element of unsaturation corresponds to two fewer hydrogen atoms than in the "saturated" formula.

$CH_3—CH_2—CH_3$	$CH_3—CH{=}CH_2$	CH_2 (ring) / $CH_2—CH_2$	$CH_3—C{\equiv}C—H$
propane, C_3H_8	propene, C_3H_6	cyclopropane, C_3H_6	propyne, C_3H_4
saturated	one element of unsaturation	one element of unsaturation	two elements of unsaturation

Consider, for example, the formula C_4H_8. A saturated alkane would have a $C_nH_{(2n+2)}$ formula, or C_4H_{10}. The formula C_4H_8 is missing two hydrogen atoms, so it has one

**Degree of unsaturation* and *index of hydrogen deficiency* are equivalent terms.

element of unsaturation, either a pi bond or a ring. There are five constitutional isomers of formula C_4H_8:

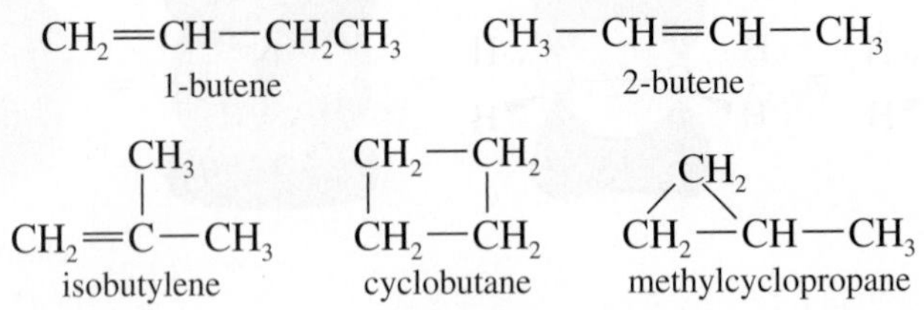

$CH_2{=}CH{-}CH_2CH_3$ (1-butene) $CH_3{-}CH{=}CH{-}CH_3$ (2-butene)

$CH_2{=}C(CH_3){-}CH_3$ (isobutylene) cyclobutane ($CH_2{-}CH_2$ / $CH_2{-}CH_2$ ring) methylcyclopropane (CH_2 ring with $CH_2{-}CH{-}CH_3$)

1-butene 2-butene

isobutylene cyclobutane methylcyclopropane

problem-solving Hint

If you prefer to use a formula, elements of unsaturation

$= \frac{1}{2}(2C + 2 - H)$

C = number of carbons
H = number of hydrogens

When you need a structure for a particular molecular formula, it helps to find the number of elements of unsaturation. Calculate the maximum number of hydrogen atoms from the saturated formula, $C_nH_{(2n+2)}$, and see how many are missing. The number of elements of unsaturation is simply half the number of missing hydrogens. This simple calculation allows you to consider possible structures quickly, without always having to check for the correct molecular formula.

PROBLEM 7-1

(a) Calculate the number of elements of unsaturation implied by the molecular formula C_6H_{12}.
(b) Give five examples of structures with this formula (C_6H_{12}). At least one should contain a ring, and at least one a double bond.

PROBLEM 7-2

Determine the number of elements of unsaturation in the molecular formula C_4H_6. Give all nine possible structures having this formula. Remember that

a double bond = one element of unsaturation
a ring = one element of unsaturation
a triple bond = two elements of unsaturation

7-3B Elements of Unsaturation with Heteroatoms

Heteroatoms (*hetero*, "different") are any atoms other than carbon and hydrogen. The rule for calculating elements of unsaturation in hydrocarbons can be extended to include heteroatoms. Let's consider how the addition of a heteroatom affects the number of hydrogen atoms in the formula.

Halogens Halogens simply substitute for hydrogen atoms in the molecular formula. The formula C_2H_6 is saturated, so the formula $C_2H_4F_2$ is also saturated. C_4H_8 has one element of unsaturation, and $C_4H_5Br_3$ also has one element of unsaturation. In calculating the number of elements of unsaturation, simply *count halogens as hydrogen atoms.*

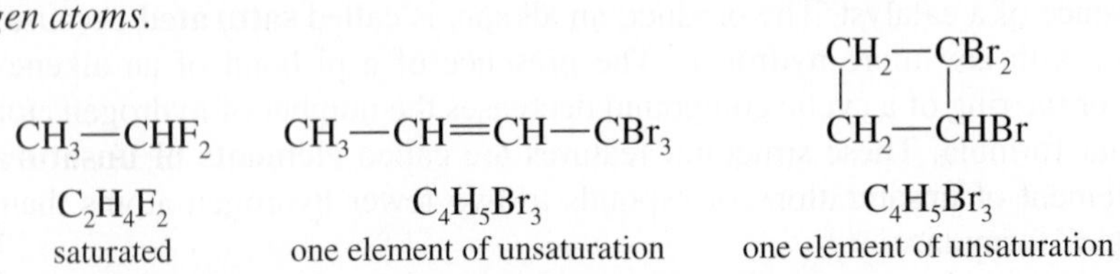

$CH_3{-}CHF_2$	$CH_3{-}CH{=}CH{-}CBr_3$	$CH_2{-}CBr_2$ / $CH_2{-}CHBr$ (ring)
$C_2H_4F_2$	$C_4H_5Br_3$	$C_4H_5Br_3$
saturated	one element of unsaturation	one element of unsaturation

Oxygen An oxygen atom can be added to the chain (or added to a C—H bond to make a C—OH group) without changing the number of hydrogen atoms or carbon atoms. In calculating the number of elements of unsaturation, *ignore the oxygen atoms.*

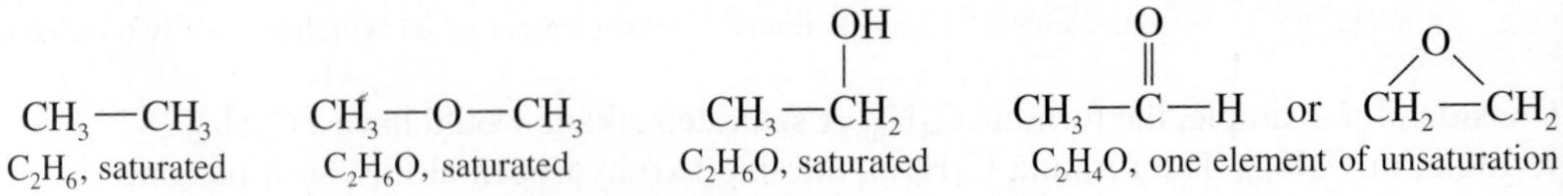

$CH_3{-}CH_3$	$CH_3{-}O{-}CH_3$	$CH_3{-}CH_2{-}OH$	$CH_3{-}C({=}O){-}H$ or $CH_2{-}CH_2$ (ring with O)
C_2H_6, saturated	C_2H_6O, saturated	C_2H_6O, saturated	C_2H_4O, one element of unsaturation

Nitrogen A nitrogen atom can take the place of a carbon atom in the chain, but nitrogen is trivalent, having only one additional hydrogen atom, compared with two hydrogens for each additional carbon atom. In computing the elements of unsaturation, *count nitrogen as half a carbon atom.*

```
      H   H   H       H
      |   |   |  ..   |
  H — C — C — C — N — C — H
      |   |   |   |   |
      H   H   H   H   H
```

carbon + 2 H   nitrogen + 1 H

The formula C_4H_9N is like a formula with $4\frac{1}{2}$ carbon atoms, with saturated formula $C_{4.5}H_{9+2}$. The formula C_4H_9N has one element of unsaturation, because it is two hydrogen atoms short of the saturated formula.

$CH_3—CH_2$ / :N—H / $H_2C{=}CH$ (pyrrolidine, N—H) $H_2C{=}CH—CH_2—CH_2—\ddot{N}H_2$

examples of formula C_4H_9N, one element of unsaturation

SOLVED PROBLEM 7-1

Draw at least four compounds of formula C_4H_6NOCl.

SOLUTION

Counting the nitrogen as $\frac{1}{2}$ carbon, ignoring the oxygen, and counting chlorine as a hydrogen shows the formula is equivalent to $C_{4.5}H_7$. The saturated formula for 4.5 carbon atoms is $C_{4.5}H_{11}$, so C_4H_6NOCl has two elements of unsaturation. These could be two double bonds, two rings, one triple bond, or a ring and a double bond. There are many possibilities, four of which are listed here.

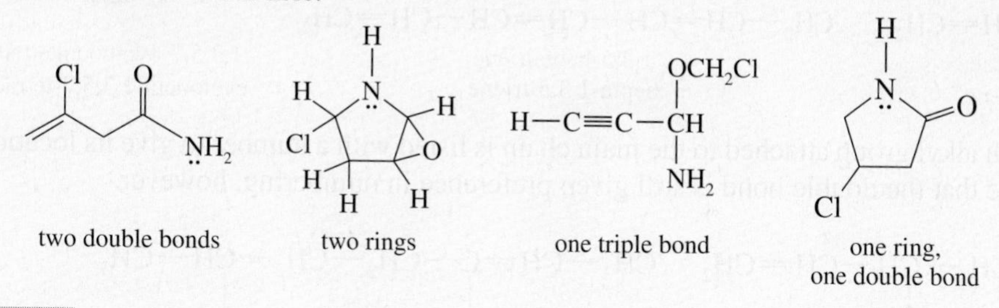

two double bonds   two rings   one triple bond   one ring, one double bond

> **problem solving — Hint**
>
> In figuring elements of unsaturation:
>
> Count halogens as hydrogens.
> Ignore oxygen.
> Count nitrogen as half a carbon.

PROBLEM 7-3

Draw five more compounds of formula C_4H_6NOCl.

PROBLEM 7-4

For each of the following molecular formulas, determine the number of elements of unsaturation, and give three examples.

(a) $C_4H_4Cl_2$ **(b)** C_4H_8O **(c)** $C_6H_8O_2$ **(d)** $C_5H_5NO_2$ **(e)** C_6H_3NClBr

7-4 Nomenclature of Alkenes

Simple alkenes are named much like alkanes, using the root name of the longest chain containing the double bond. The ending is changed from *-ane* to *-ene*. For example, "ethane" becomes "ethene," "propane" becomes "propene," and "cyclohexane" becomes "cyclohexene."

	$CH_2{=}CH_2$	$CH_2{=}CH—CH_3$	(cyclohexene ring)
IUPAC names:	ethene	propene	cyclohexene
Common names:	ethylene	propylene	

When the chain contains more than three carbon atoms, a number is used to give the location of the double bond. The chain is numbered starting from the end closest to the double bond, and the double bond is given the *lower* number of its two double-bonded carbon atoms. Cycloalkenes are assumed to have the double bond in the number 1 position.

$$\overset{1}{C}H_2{=}\overset{2}{C}H{-}\overset{3}{C}H_2{-}\overset{4}{C}H_3 \qquad \overset{1}{C}H_2{=}\overset{2}{C}H{-}\overset{3}{C}H_2{-}\overset{4}{C}H_2{-}\overset{5}{C}H_3$$

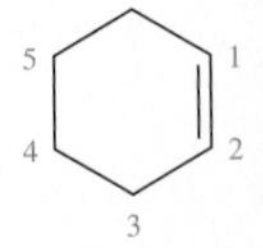

IUPAC names:	1-butene	1-pentene	cyclohexene
new IUPAC names:	but-1-ene	pent-1-ene	

$$\overset{1}{C}H_3{-}\overset{2}{C}H{=}\overset{3}{C}H{-}\overset{4}{C}H_3 \qquad \overset{1}{C}H_3{-}\overset{2}{C}H{=}\overset{3}{C}H{-}\overset{4}{C}H_2{-}\overset{5}{C}H_3$$

IUPAC names:	2-butene	2-pentene
new IUPAC names:	but-2-ene	pent-2-ene

In 1993, the IUPAC recommended a logical change in the positions of the numbers used in names. Instead of placing the numbers before the root name (1-butene), they recommended placing them immediately before the part of the name they locate (but-1-ene). The new placement is helpful for clarifying the names of compounds containing multiple functional groups. You should be prepared to recognize names using either placement of the numbers, because both are widely used. In this section, names using the new number placement are printed in green. Throughout this book, we will use the new number placement whenever it helps to clarify a name.

A compound with two double bonds is a **diene**. A **triene** has three double bonds, and a **tetraene** has four. Numbers are used to specify the locations of the double bonds.

$$\overset{1}{C}H_2{=}\overset{2}{C}H{-}\overset{3}{C}H{=}\overset{4}{C}H_2 \qquad \overset{7}{C}H_3{-}\overset{6}{C}H{=}\overset{5}{C}H{-}\overset{4}{C}H{=}\overset{3}{C}H{-}\overset{2}{C}H{=}\overset{1}{C}H_2$$

			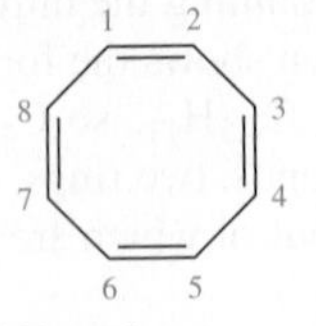
IUPAC names:	1,3-butadiene	1,3,5-heptatriene	1,3,5,7-cyclooctatetraene
new IUPAC names:	buta-1,3-diene	hepta-1,3,5-triene	cycloocta-1,3,5,7-tetraene

Each alkyl group attached to the main chain is listed with a number to give its location. Note that the double bond is still given preference in numbering, however.

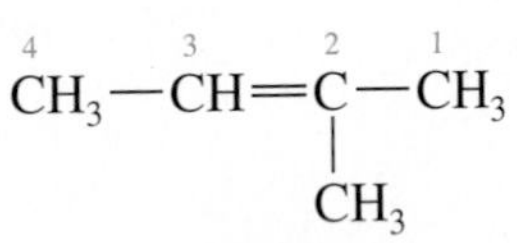

$$\overset{4}{C}H_3{-}\overset{3}{C}H{=}\overset{2}{C}(CH_3){-}\overset{1}{C}H_3 \qquad \overset{4}{C}H_3{-}\overset{3}{C}H(CH_3){-}\overset{2}{C}H{=}\overset{1}{C}H_2 \qquad \overset{1}{C}H_3{-}\overset{2}{C}H{=}\overset{3}{C}(CH_3){-}\overset{4}{C}H_2{-}\overset{5}{C}H_2{-}\overset{6}{C}H(CH_3){-}\overset{7}{C}H_3$$

2-methyl-2-butene
2-methylbut-2-ene

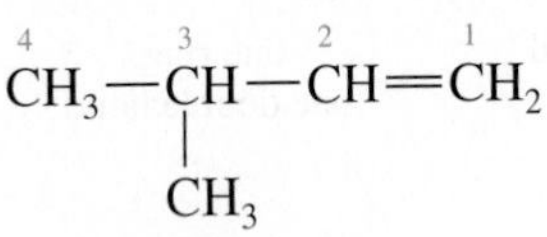

3-methyl-1-butene
3-methylbut-1-ene

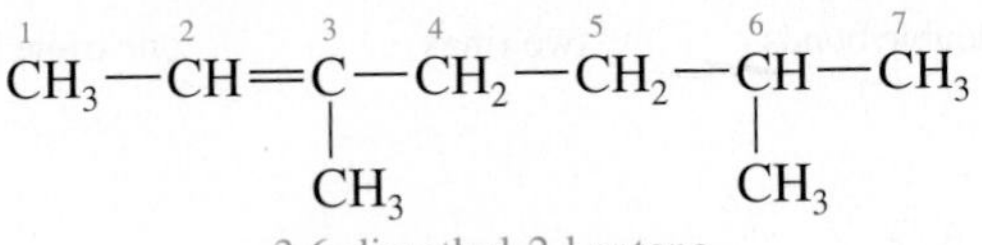

3,6-dimethyl-2-heptene
3,6-dimethylhept-2-ene

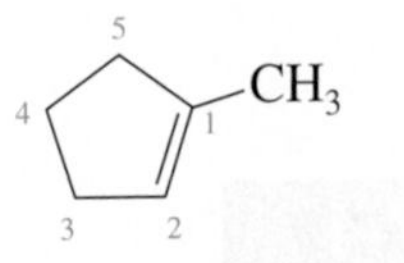

1-methylcyclopentene

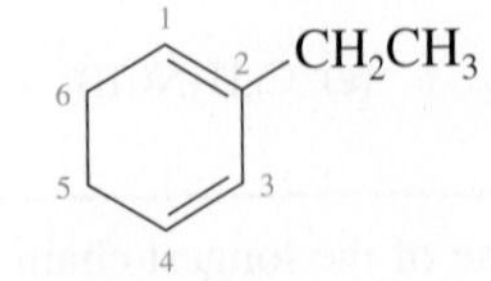

2-ethyl-1,3-cyclohexadiene
2-ethylcyclohexa-1,3-diene

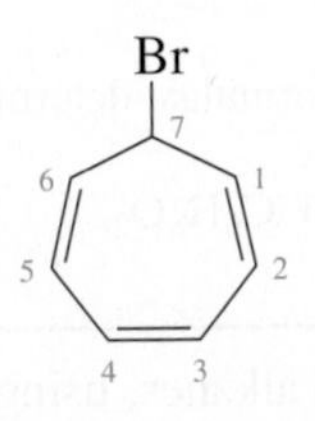

7-bromo-1,3,5-cycloheptatriene
7-bromocyclohepta-1,3,5-triene

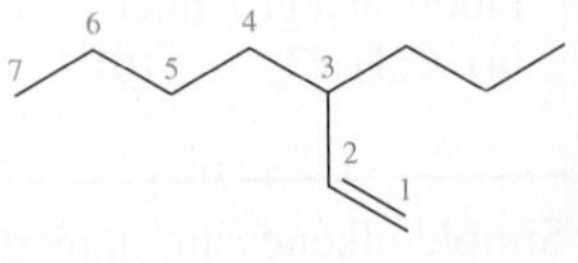

3-propyl-1-heptene
3-propylhept-1-ene

Alkenes as Substituents Alkenes named as substituents are called *alkenyl groups*. They can be named systematically (ethenyl, propenyl, etc.), or by common names. Common alkenyl substituents are the vinyl, allyl, methylene, and phenyl groups. The phenyl group (Ph) is different from the others because it is aromatic (see Chapter 16) and does not undergo the typical reactions of alkenes.

$\}=CH_2$
methylene group
(methylidene group)

$\}-CH=CH_2$
vinyl group
(ethenyl group)

3-methylenecyclohexene

$CH_2=CHCHCH_2CH=CH_2$ (with $CH=CH_2$ on C-3)
3-vinyl-1,5-hexadiene
3-vinylhexa-1,5-diene

$\}-CH_2-CH=CH_2$
allyl group
2-propenyl group

phenyl group
(Ph)

$CH_2=CH-CH_2-Cl$
allyl chloride
3-chloropropene

2-phenyl-1,3-cyclopentadiene
2-phenylcyclopenta-1,3-diene

Common Names Most alkenes are conveniently named by the IUPAC system, but common names are sometimes used for the simplest compounds.

The polyene antifungals are a group of drugs with a nonpolar region consisting of 4–7 sets of alternating single and double bonds. They insert themselves in the cell membranes of fungi, causing disruption and leakiness that results in fungal cell death.

The best-known polyene antifungal drug is Amphotericin B, whose structure is shown below.

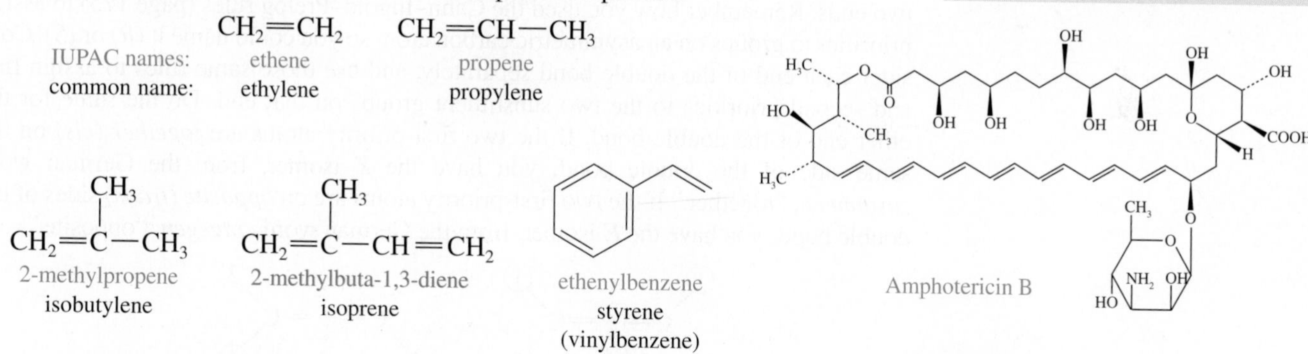

7-5 Nomenclature of Cis-Trans Isomers

7-5A Cis-Trans Nomenclature

In Chapters 2 and 5, we saw how the rigidity and lack of rotation of carbon–carbon double bonds give rise to **cis-trans isomerism**, also called **geometric isomerism**. If two similar groups bonded to the carbons of the double bond are on the same side of the bond, the alkene is the **cis** isomer. If the similar groups are on opposite sides of the bond, the alkene is **trans**. Not all alkenes are capable of showing cis-trans isomerism. If either carbon of the double bond holds two identical groups, the molecule cannot have cis and trans forms. Following are some cis and trans alkenes and some alkenes that cannot show cis-trans isomerism.

$(H_3C)(H)C=C(CH_2CH_3)(H)$
cis-2-pentene
cis-pent-2-ene

$(H_3C)(H)C=C(H)(CH_2CH_3)$
trans-2-pentene
trans-pent-2-ene

$(H_3C)(H_3C)C=C(H)(CH_2CH_3)$
2-methyl-2-pentene
2-methylpent-2-ene

$(H)(H)C=C(CH_2CH_2CH_3)(H)$
1-pentene
pent-1-ene

(neither cis nor trans)

Trans cycloalkenes are unstable unless the ring is large enough (at least eight carbon atoms) to accommodate the trans double bond (Section 7-7D). Therefore, all cycloalkenes are assumed to be cis unless they are specifically named trans. The cis name is rarely used with cycloalkenes, except to distinguish a large cycloalkene from its trans isomer.

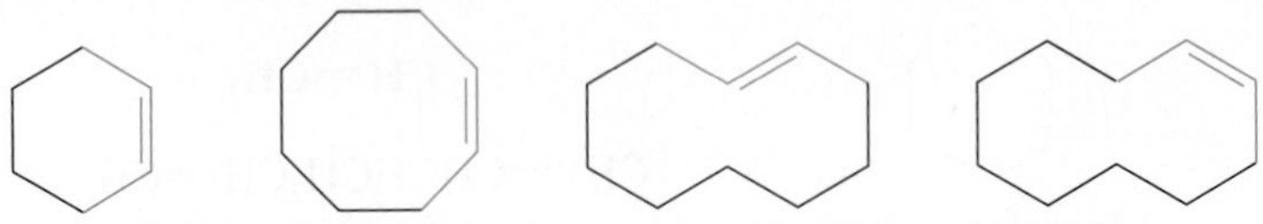

cyclohexene   cyclooctene   *trans*-cyclodecene   *cis*-cyclodecene

7-5B *E-Z* Nomenclature

The cis-trans nomenclature for geometric isomers sometimes gives an ambiguous name. For example, the isomers of 1-bromo-1-chloropropene are not clearly cis or trans because it is not obvious which substituents are referred to as being cis or trans.

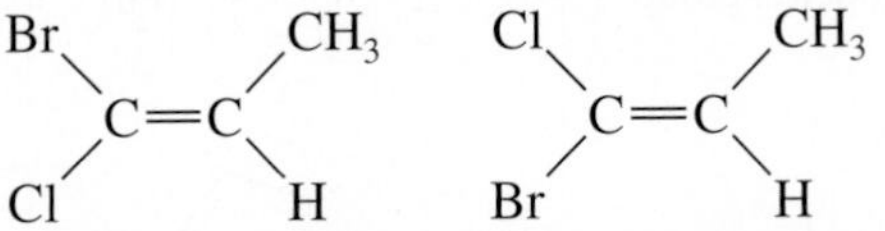

geometric isomers of 1-bromo-1-chloropropene

To deal with this problem, we use the ***E-Z* system** of nomenclature (pun intended) for cis-trans isomers, which is patterned after the Cahn–Ingold–Prelog convention for asymmetric carbon atoms (Section 5-3). It assigns a unique configuration of either *E* or *Z* to any double bond capable of geometric isomerism.

To name an alkene by the *E-Z* system, mentally separate the double bond into its two ends. Remember how you used the Cahn–Ingold–Prelog rules (page 175) to assign priorities to groups on an asymmetric carbon atom so you could name it (*R*) or (*S*). Consider each end of the double bond separately, and use those same rules to assign first and second priorities to the two substituent groups on that end. Do the same for the other end of the double bond. If the two first-priority atoms are *together (cis)* on the same side of the double bond, you have the ***Z*** isomer, from the German word *zusammen*, "together." If the two first-priority atoms are on *opposite (trans)* sides of the double bond, you have the ***E*** isomer, from the German word *entgegen*, "opposite."

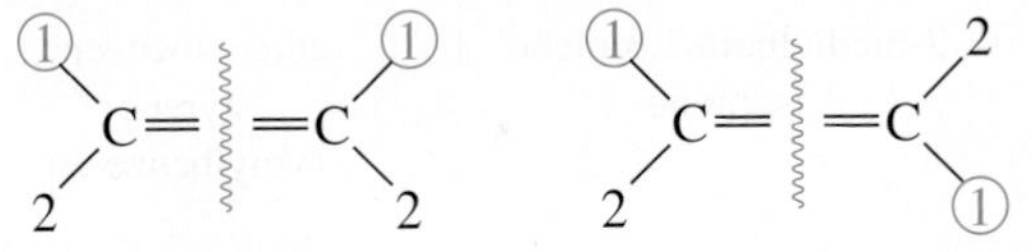

Zusammen   *Entgegen*

For example,

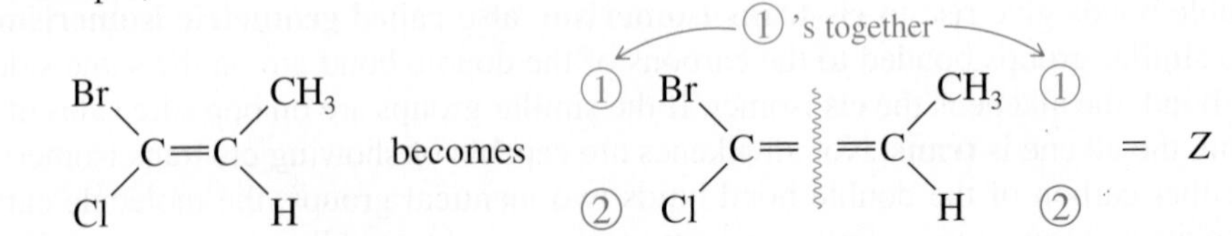

becomes   ① 's together   = *Z*

(*Z*)-1-bromo-1-chloropropene

The other isomer is named similarly:

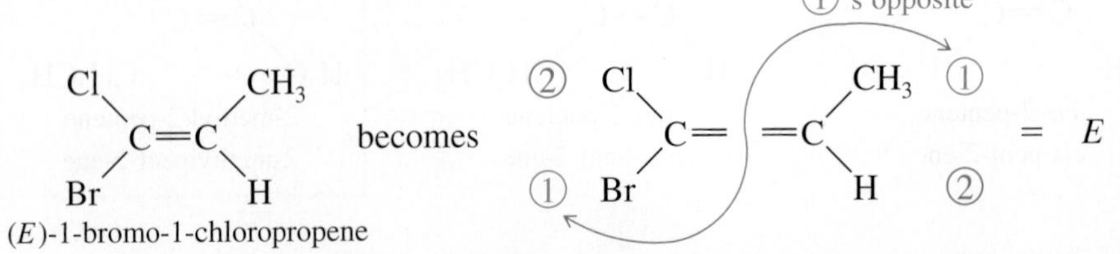

becomes   ①'s opposite   = *E*

(*E*)-1-bromo-1-chloropropene

The following example shows the use of the *E-Z* nomenclature with cyclic stereoisomers that are not clearly cis or trans.

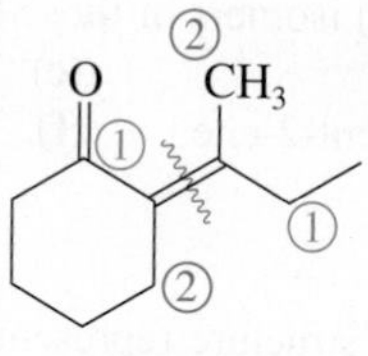

(*E*) isomer 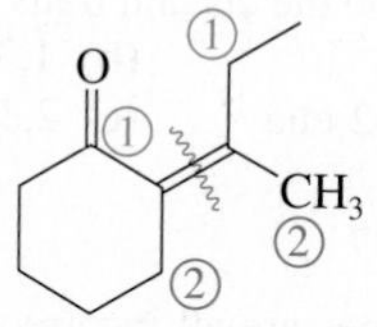 (*Z*) isomer

If the alkene has more than one double bond, the stereochemistry about each double bond should be specified. The following compound is properly named 3-bromo-(3*Z*,5*E*)-octadiene:

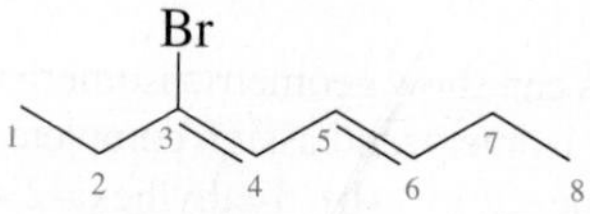

3-bromo-(3*Z*,5*E*)-octadiene

(3*Z*,5*E*)-3-bromoocta-3,5-diene

The use of *E-Z* names (rather than cis and trans) is always an option, but it is required whenever a double bond is not clearly cis or trans. Most trisubstituted and tetrasubstituted double bonds are more clearly named *E* or *Z* rather than cis or trans.

SUMMARY Rules for Naming Alkenes

The following rules summarize the IUPAC system for naming alkenes:

1. Select the longest chain or largest ring that contains the *largest possible number of double bonds*, and name it with the *-ene* suffix. If there are two double bonds, the suffix is *-diene*; for three, *-triene*; for four, *-tetraene*; and so on.
2. Number the chain from the end closest to the double bonds. Number a ring so that the double bond is between carbons 1 and 2. Place the numbers giving the locations of the double bonds in front of the root name (old system) or in front of the suffix *-ene*, *-diene*, etc. (new system).
3. Name substituent groups as in alkanes, indicating their locations by the number of the main-chain carbon to which they are attached. The ethenyl group and the propenyl group are usually called the *vinyl* group and the *allyl* group, respectively.
4. For compounds that show geometric isomerism, add the appropriate prefix: *cis-* or *trans-*, or *E-* or *Z-*. Cycloalkenes are assumed to be cis unless named otherwise.

PROBLEM 7-5

Give the systematic (IUPAC) names of the following alkenes.

(a) $CH_2{=}CH{-}CH_2{-}CH(CH_3)_2$ **(b)** $CH_3(CH_2)_3{-}C({=}CH_2){-}CH_2CH_3$

(c) $CH_2{=}CH{-}CH_2{-}CH{=}CH_2$ **(d)** $CH_2{=}C{=}CH{-}CH{=}CH_2$

(e) 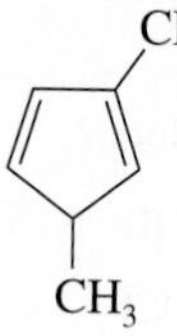 **(f)** 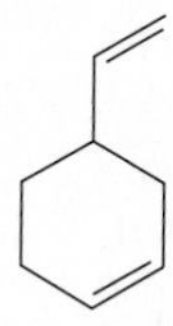 **(g)**

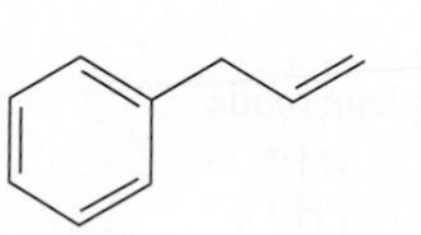

(h) 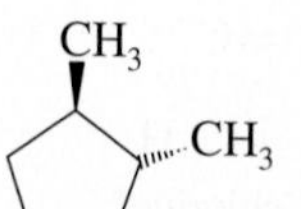 **(i)** 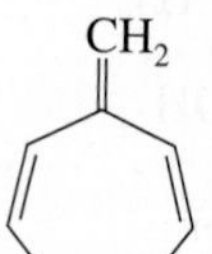 **(j)**

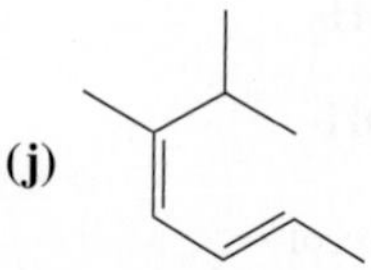

problem-solving Hint

To see whether a compound can have cis and trans isomers, draw the structure, then draw it again with the groups on one end of the double bond reversed. See if you can describe a difference between the two.

PROBLEM 7-6

1. Determine which of the following compounds show cis-trans isomerism.
2. Draw and name the cis and trans (or *Z* and *E*) isomers of those that do.
(a) 3-hexene **(b)** 1,3-butadiene **(c)** 2,4-hexadiene
(d) 3-methylpent-2-ene **(e)** 2,3-dimethylpent-2-ene **(f)** 3,4-dibromocyclopentene

PROBLEM 7-7

The following names are all incorrect. Draw the structure represented by the incorrect name (or a consistent structure if the name is ambiguous), and give your drawing the correct name.
(a) *cis*-2,3-dimethyl-2-pentene **(b)** 3-vinylhex-4-ene
(c) 2-methylcyclopentene **(d)** 6-chlorocyclohexadiene
(e) 2,5-dimethylcyclohexene **(f)** *cis*-2,5-dibromo-3-ethylpent-2-ene

PROBLEM 7-8

Some of the following examples can show geometric isomerism, and some cannot. For the ones that can, draw all the geometric isomers, and assign complete names using the *E-Z* system.
(a) 3-bromo-2-chloro-2-pentene **(b)** 3-ethylhexa-2,4-diene
(c) 3-bromo-2-methyl-3-hexene **(d)** 1,3-pentadiene
(e) 3-ethyl-5-methyl-3-octene **(f)** 3,7-dichloroocta-2,5-diene

(g) 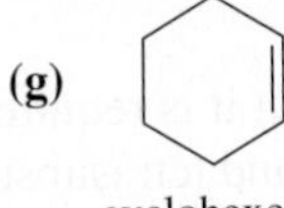
cyclohexene

(h) 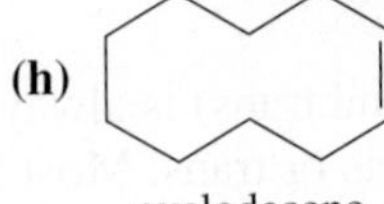
cyclodecene

(i) 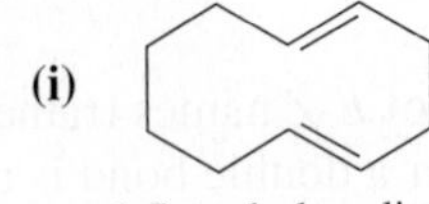
1,5-cyclodecadiene

7-6 Commercial Importance of Alkenes

Because the carbon–carbon double bond is readily converted to other functional groups, alkenes are important intermediates in the synthesis of polymers, drugs, pesticides, and other valuable chemicals.

Ethylene is the organic compound produced in the largest volume, at around 160 billion pounds per year worldwide. Most of this ethylene is polymerized to form about 90 billion pounds of polyethylene per year. The remainder is used to synthesize a wide variety of organic chemicals including ethanol, acetic acid, ethylene glycol, and vinyl chloride (Figure 7-3). Ethylene also serves as a plant hormone, accelerating the ripening of fruit.

polyethylene; acetaldehyde; oxidize; acetic acid
polymerize; oxidize
ethylene oxide; O_2, Ag catalyst; ethylene; Cl_2; ethylene dichloride
H^+, H_2O; H_2O, catalyst; NaOH
ethylene glycol; ethanol; vinyl chloride

■ **FIGURE 7-3**
Uses of ethylene. Ethylene is the largest-volume industrial organic chemical. Most of the 160 billion pounds produced each year is polymerized to make polyethylene. Much of the rest is used to produce a variety of useful two-carbon compounds.

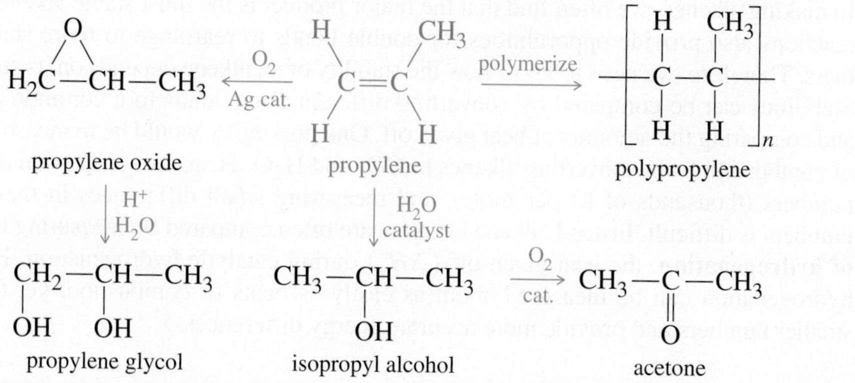

$$\text{propylene oxide} \xleftarrow[\text{Ag cat.}]{O_2} \text{propylene } (CH_3CH{=}CH_2) \xrightarrow{\text{polymerize}} \text{polypropylene } \left[-CH_2-CH(CH_3)-\right]_n$$

propylene oxide $\xrightarrow{H^+,\ H_2O}$ propylene glycol ($CH_2(OH)-CH(OH)-CH_3$)

propylene $\xrightarrow{H_2O,\ \text{catalyst}}$ isopropyl alcohol ($CH_3-CH(OH)-CH_3$) $\xrightarrow[\text{cat.}]{O_2}$ acetone ($CH_3-C(=O)-CH_3$)

■ **FIGURE 7-4**
Uses of propylene. Most propylene is polymerized to make polypropylene. It is also used to make several important three-carbon compounds.

For example, tomatoes are harvested and shipped while green, then treated with ethylene to make them ripen and turn red just before they are placed on display.

Propylene is produced at the rate of about 90 billion pounds per year worldwide, with much of that going to make about 40 billion pounds of polypropylene. The rest is used to make propylene glycol, acetone, isopropyl alcohol, and a variety of other useful organic chemicals (Figure 7-4).

Many common polymers are made by polymerizing alkenes. These polymers are used in consumer products from shoes to plastic bags to car bumpers. A **polymer** (Greek, *poly*, "many," and *meros*, "parts") is a large molecule made up of many **monomer** (Greek, *mono*, "one") molecules. An alkene monomer can **polymerize** by a chain reaction where additional alkene molecules add to the end of the growing polymer chain. Because these polymers result from addition of many individual alkene units, they are called **addition polymers. Polyolefins** are polymers made from monofunctional (single functional group) alkenes such as ethylene and propylene. Figure 7-5 shows some addition polymers made from simple alkenes and haloalkenes. We discuss polymerization reactions in Chapters 8 and 26.

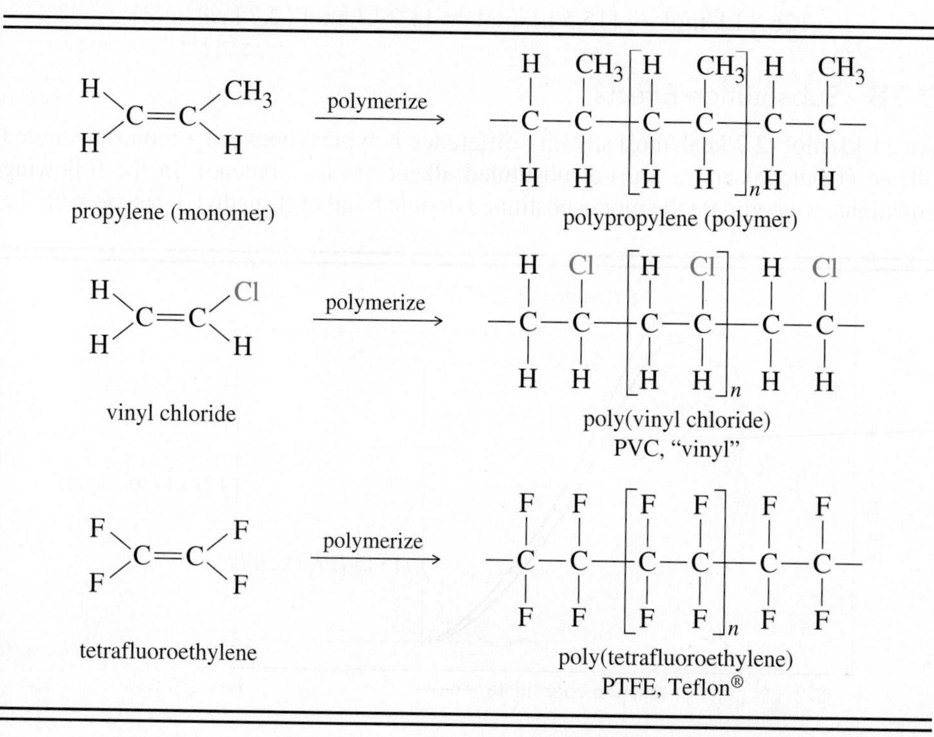

■ **FIGURE 7-5**
Addition polymers. Alkenes polymerize to form addition polymers. Many common polymers are produced this way.

7-7 Stability of Alkenes

In making alkenes, we often find that the major product is the most stable alkene. Many reactions also provide opportunities for double bonds to rearrange to more stable isomers. Therefore, we need to know how the stability of an alkene depends on its structure. Stabilities can be compared by converting different compounds to a common product and comparing the amounts of heat given off. One possibility would be to measure heats of combustion from converting alkenes to CO_2 and H_2O. Heats of combustion are large numbers (thousands of kJ per mole), and measuring small differences in these large numbers is difficult. Instead, alkene energies are often compared by measuring the **heat of hydrogenation**: the heat given off ($\Delta H°$) during catalytic hydrogenation. Heats of hydrogenation can be measured about as easily as heats of combustion, yet they are smaller numbers and provide more accurate energy differences.

7-7A Heats of Hydrogenation

When an alkene is treated with hydrogen in the presence of a platinum catalyst, hydrogen adds to the double bond, reducing the alkene to an alkane. Hydrogenation is mildly exothermic, evolving about 80 to 120 kJ (20 to 30 kcal) of heat per mole of hydrogen consumed. Consider the hydrogenation of 1-butene and *trans*-2-butene:

$$H_2C{=}CH{-}CH_2{-}CH_3 + H_2 \xrightarrow{Pt} CH_2(H){-}CH(H){-}CH_2{-}CH_3 \qquad \Delta H° = -127\ \text{kJ/mol}\ (-30.3\ \text{kcal/mol})$$

1-butene (monosubstituted) → butane

$$(H_3C)(H)C{=}C(H)(CH_3) + H_2 \xrightarrow{Pt} CH_3{-}CH(H){-}CH(H){-}CH_3 \qquad \Delta H° = -115\ \text{kJ/mol}\ (-27.6\ \text{kcal/mol})$$

trans-2-butene → butane

Figure 7-6 shows these heats of hydrogenation on a reaction-energy diagram. The difference in the stabilities of 1-butene and *trans*-2-butene is the difference in their heats of hydrogenation. *trans*-2-Butene is more stable by

$$126.8\ \text{kJ/mol} - 115.5\ \text{kJ/mol} = 11.3\ \text{kJ/mol}\ (2.7\ \text{kcal/mol})$$

7-7B Substitution Effects

An 11 kJ/mol (2.7 kcal/mol) stability difference is typical between a monosubstituted alkene (1-butene) and a trans-disubstituted alkene (*trans*-2-butene). In the following equations, we compare the monosubstituted double bond of 3-methyl-1-butene with the

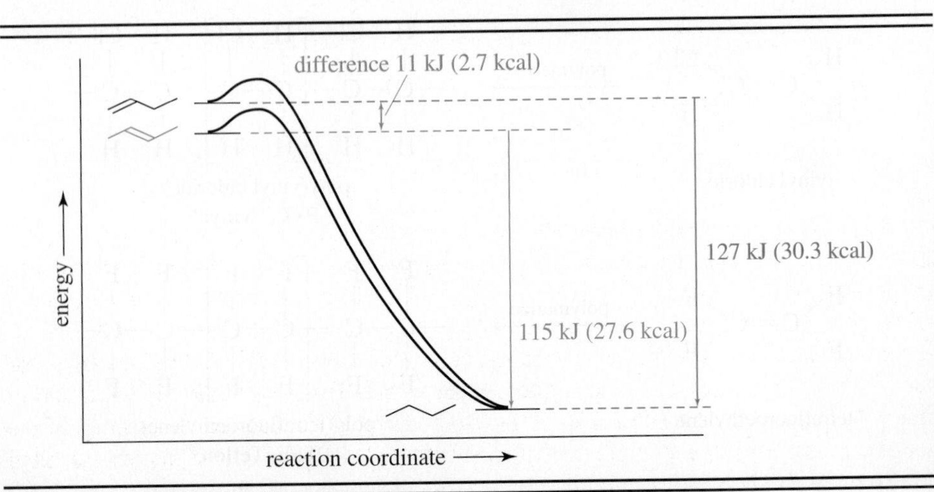

■ FIGURE 7-6
Relative heats of hydrogenation. *trans*-2-Butene is more stable than 1-butene by 11 kJ/mol (2.7 kcal/mol).

trisubstituted double bond of 2-methyl-2-butene. The trisubstituted alkene is more stable by 14 kJ/mol (3.4 kcal/mol).

$$\underset{\substack{\text{3-methyl-1-butene}\\ \text{(monosubstituted)}}}{CH_2{=}CH{-}CH(CH_3){-}CH_3} \xrightarrow{H_2,\ Pt} \underset{\text{2-methylbutane}}{CH_3{-}CH_2{-}CH(CH_3){-}CH_3} \qquad \Delta H^\circ = -127\ \text{kJ}\ (-30.3\ \text{kcal})$$

$$\underset{\substack{\text{2-methyl-2-butene}\\ \text{(trisubstituted)}}}{CH_3{-}CH{=}C(CH_3){-}CH_3} \xrightarrow{H_2,\ Pt} \underset{\text{2-methylbutane}}{CH_3{-}CH_2{-}CH(CH_3){-}CH_3} \qquad \Delta H^\circ = -113\ \text{kJ}\ (-26.9\ \text{kcal})$$

To be completely correct, we should compare heats of hydrogenation only for compounds that give the same alkane, as 3-methyl-1-butene and 2-methyl-2-butene do. However, most alkenes with similar substitution patterns give similar heats of hydrogenation. For example, 3,3-dimethyl-1-butene (below) hydrogenates to give a different alkane than does 3-methyl-1-butene or 1-butene (above); yet these three monosubstituted alkenes have similar heats of hydrogenation because the alkanes formed have similar energies. In effect, the heat of hydrogenation is a measure of the energy content of the pi bond.

$$\underset{\substack{\text{3,3-dimethyl-1-butene}\\ \text{(monosubstituted)}}}{CH_2{=}CH{-}C(CH_3)_2{-}CH_3} \xrightarrow{H_2,\ Pt} \underset{\text{2,2-dimethylbutane}}{CH_3{-}CH_2{-}C(CH_3)_2{-}CH_3} \qquad \Delta H^\circ = -127\ \text{kJ}\ (-30.3\ \text{kcal})$$

In practice, we can use heats of hydrogenation to compare the stabilities of different alkenes as long as they hydrogenate to give alkanes of similar energies. Most acyclic alkanes and unstrained cycloalkanes have similar energies, and we can use this approximation. Table 7-1 shows the heats of hydrogenation of a variety of alkenes with different substitution. The compounds are ranked in decreasing order of their heats of hydrogenation, that is, from the least stable double bonds to the most stable. Note that the values are similar for alkenes with similar substitution patterns.

The most stable double bonds are those with the most alkyl groups attached. For example, hydrogenation of ethylene (no alkyl groups attached) evolves 137 kJ/mol, while propene and 1-pentene (one alkyl group for each) give off 126 kJ/mol. Double bonds with two alkyl groups hydrogenate to produce about 116–120 kJ/mol. Three or four alkyl substituents further stabilize the double bond, as with 2-methyl-2-butene (trisubstituted, 113 kJ/mol) and 2,3-dimethyl-2-butene (tetrasubstituted, 111 kJ/mol).

The values in Table 7-1 confirm **Zaitsev's rule (Saytzeff's rule)**:

More substituted double bonds are usually more stable.

In other words, the alkyl groups attached to the double-bonded carbons stabilize the alkene.

Two factors are probably responsible for the stabilizing effect of alkyl groups on a double bond. Alkyl groups are electron-donating, and they contribute electron density to the pi bond. In addition, bulky substituents like alkyl groups are best situated as far apart as possible. In an alkane, they are separated by the tetrahedral bond angle, about 109.5°. A double bond increases this separation to about 120°. In general, alkyl groups are separated best by the most highly substituted double bond. This steric effect is illustrated in Figure 7-7 for two **double-bond isomers** (isomers that differ only in the position of the double bond). The isomer with the monosubstituted double bond separates the alkyl groups by only 109.5°, while the trisubstituted double bond separates them by about 120°.

TABLE 7-1

Molar Heats of Hydrogenation of Alkenes

Name	Structure	Molar Heat of Hydrogenation ($-\Delta H°$) kJ	kcal	General Structure
ethene (ethylene)	$H_2C{=}CH_2$	137	32.8	unsubstituted
propene (propylene)	$CH_3{-}CH{=}CH_2$	126	30.1	monosubstituted $R{-}CH{=}CH_2$
1-butene	$CH_3{-}CH_2{-}CH{=}CH_2$	127	30.3	
1-pentene	$CH_3{-}CH_2{-}CH_2{-}CH{=}CH_2$	126	30.1	
1-hexene	$CH_3{-}(CH_2)_3{-}CH{=}CH_2$	126	30.1	
3-methyl-1-butene	$(CH_3)_2CH{-}CH{=}CH_2$	127	30.3	
3,3-dimethyl-1-butene	$(CH_3)_3C{-}CH{=}CH_2$	127	30.3	
cis-2-butene	$CH_3(H)C{=}C(H)CH_3$ (cis)	120	28.6	disubstituted (cis) $RHC{=}CHR$ (cis)
cis-2-pentene	$CH_3{-}CH_2(H)C{=}C(H)CH_3$ (cis)	120	28.6	
2-methylpropene (isobutylene)	$(CH_3)_2C{=}CH_2$	117	28.0	disubstituted (geminal) $R_2C{=}CH_2$
2-methyl-1-butene	$CH_3{-}CH_2{-}C(CH_3){=}CH_2$	119	28.5	
2,3-dimethyl-1-butene	$(CH_3)_2CH{-}C(CH_3){=}CH_2$	117	28.0	
trans-2-butene	$CH_3(H)C{=}C(H)CH_3$ (trans)	116	27.6	disubstituted (trans) $RHC{=}CHR$ (trans)
trans-2-pentene	$CH_3{-}CH_2(H)C{=}C(H)CH_3$ (trans)	116	27.6	
2-methyl-2-butene	$CH_3{-}C(CH_3){=}CH{-}CH_3$	113	26.9	trisubstituted $R_2C{=}CHR$
2,3-dimethyl-2-butene	$(CH_3)_2C{=}C(CH_3)_2$	111	26.6	tetrasubstituted $R_2C{=}CR_2$

Note: A lower heat of hydrogenation corresponds to lower energy and greater stability of the alkene.

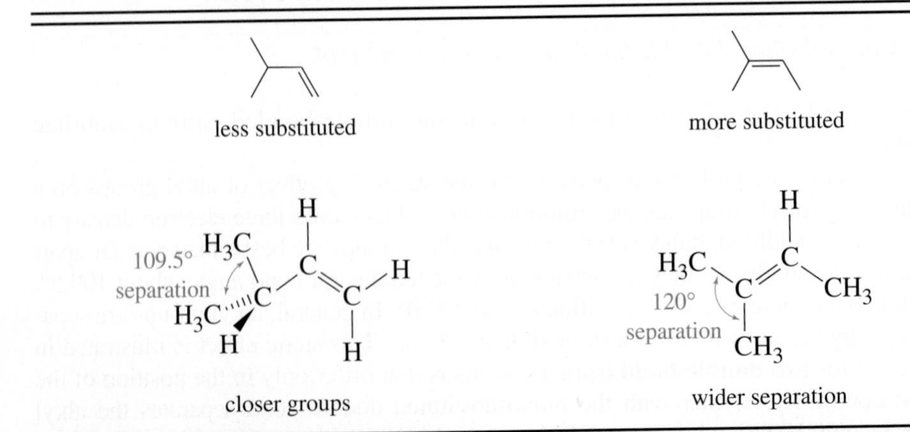

■ **FIGURE 7-7** Bond angles in double-bond isomers. The isomer with the more substituted double bond has a larger angular separation between the bulky alkyl groups.

PROBLEM 7-9

Use the data in Table 7-1 to predict the energy difference between 2,3-dimethyl-1-butene and 2,3-dimethyl-2-butene. Which of these double-bond isomers is more stable?

problem-solving Hint

Heats of hydrogenation are always exothermic. A larger amount of heat given off implies a less stable alkene, because the less stable alkene starts from a higher potential energy.

7-7C Energy Differences in cis-trans Isomers

The heats of hydrogenation in Table 7-1 show that trans isomers are generally more stable than the corresponding cis isomers. This trend seems reasonable because the alkyl substituents are separated farther in trans isomers than they are in cis isomers. The greater stability of the trans isomer is evident in the 2-pentenes, which show a 4 kJ/mol (1.0 kcal/mol) difference between the cis and trans isomers.

$$\underset{\text{cis}}{H_3C(H)C{=}C(H)CH_2CH_3} + H_2 \xrightarrow{Pt} CH_3{-}CH_2{-}CH_2{-}CH_2CH_3 \qquad \Delta H^\circ = -120\ \text{kJ/mol}\ (-28.6\ \text{kcal/mol})$$

$$\underset{\text{trans}}{H_3C(H)C{=}C(H)CH_2CH_3} + H_2 \xrightarrow{Pt} CH_3{-}CH_2{-}CH_2{-}CH_2CH_3 \qquad \Delta H^\circ = -116\ \text{kJ/mol}\ (-27.6\ \text{kcal/mol})$$

A 4 kJ/mol difference between cis and trans isomers is typical for disubstituted alkenes. Figure 7-8 summarizes the relative stabilities of alkenes, comparing them with ethylene, the least stable of the simple alkenes.

PROBLEM 7-10

Using Table 7-1 as a guide, predict which member of each pair is more stable, and by about how many kJ/mol or kcal/mol.

(a) *cis,cis*-2,4-hexadiene or *trans,trans*-2,4-hexadiene
(b) 2-methyl-1-butene or 3-methyl-1-butene
(c) 2-methyl-1-butene or 2-methyl-2-butene
(d) 2,3-dimethyl-1-butene or 2,3-dimethyl-2-butene

7-7D Stability of Cycloalkenes

Most cycloalkenes react like acyclic (noncyclic) alkenes. The presence of a ring makes a major difference only if there is ring strain, either because of a small ring or because of a trans double bond. Rings that are five-membered or larger can easily accommodate double bonds, and these cycloalkenes react much like straight-chain alkenes. Three- and four-membered rings show evidence of ring strain, however.

Cyclobutene Cyclobutene has a heat of hydrogenation of −128 kJ/mol (−30.7 kcal/mol), compared with −111 kJ/mol (−26.6 kcal/mol) for cyclopentene.

$$\text{cyclobutene} + H_2 \xrightarrow{Pt} \text{cyclobutane} \qquad \Delta H^\circ = -128\ \text{kJ/mol}\ (-30.7\ \text{kcal/mol})$$

$$\text{cyclopentene} + H_2 \xrightarrow{Pt} \text{cyclopentane} \qquad \Delta H^\circ = -111\ \text{kJ/mol}\ (-26.6\ \text{kcal/mol})$$

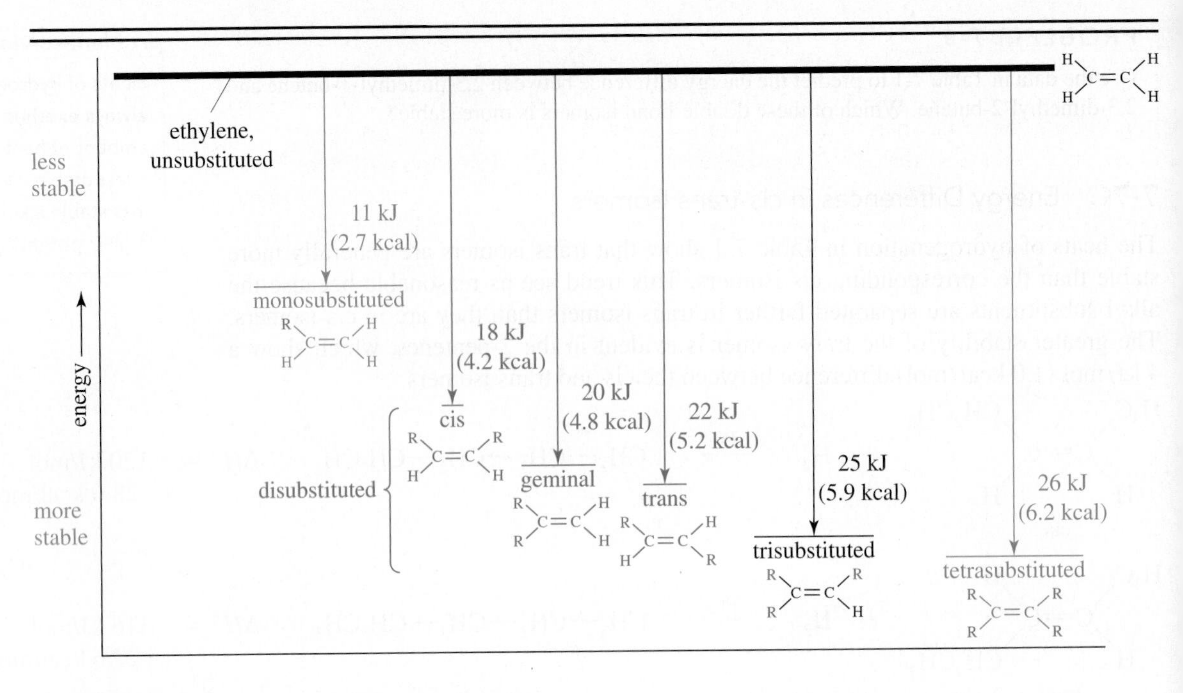

FIGURE 7-8
Relative energies of typical π bonds compared with ethylene. (The numbers are approximate.)

The double bond in cyclobutene has about 17 kJ/mol of *extra* ring strain (in addition to the ring strain in cyclobutane) by virtue of the small ring. The 90° bond angles in cyclobutene compress the angles of the sp^2 hybrid carbons (normally 120°) more than they compress the sp^3 hybrid angles (normally 109.5°) in cyclobutane. The extra ring strain in cyclobutene makes its double bond more reactive than a typical double bond.

Cyclopropene Cyclopropene has bond angles of about 60°, compressing the bond angles of the carbon–carbon double bond to half their usual value of 120°. The double bond in cyclopropene is highly strained.

unstrained angle 120°

$H_3C(H)C=CH_2$

propene

angle 60° (60° strain)

cyclopropene

Many chemists once believed that a cyclopropene could never be made because it would snap open (or polymerize) immediately from the large ring strain. Cyclopropene was eventually synthesized, however, and it can be stored in the cold. Cyclopropenes were still considered to be strange, highly unusual compounds. Natural-product chemists were surprised when they found that the kernel oil of *Sterculia foelida*, a tropical tree, contains *sterculic acid*, a carboxylic acid with a cyclopropene ring.

Sterculic acid is a potent inhibitor of several desaturases, which are the enzymes responsible for the formation of double bonds in long-chain acids used as fuels, membrane components, and other critical biological molecules. Consequently, vegetable oils containing sterculic acid must be hydrogenated or processed at high temperatures to reduce or destroy the cyclopropene ring.

$CH_3-(CH_2)_7-C=C-(CH_2)_7-COOH$ (with CH_2 bridging the two alkene carbons)

sterculic acid

Trans Cycloalkenes Another difference between cyclic and acyclic alkenes is the relationship between cis and trans isomers. In acyclic alkenes, the trans isomers are usually more stable; but the trans isomers of small cycloalkenes are rare, and those with fewer than eight carbon atoms are unstable at room temperature. The problem with making a trans cycloalkene lies in the geometry of the trans double bond. The two alkyl groups on a trans double bond are so far apart that several carbon atoms are needed to complete the ring.

Try to make a model of *trans*-cyclohexene, being careful that the large amount of ring strain does not break your models. *trans*-Cyclohexene is too strained to be isolated, but *trans*-cycloheptene can be isolated at low temperatures. *trans*-Cyclooctene is stable at room temperature, although its cis isomer is still more stable.

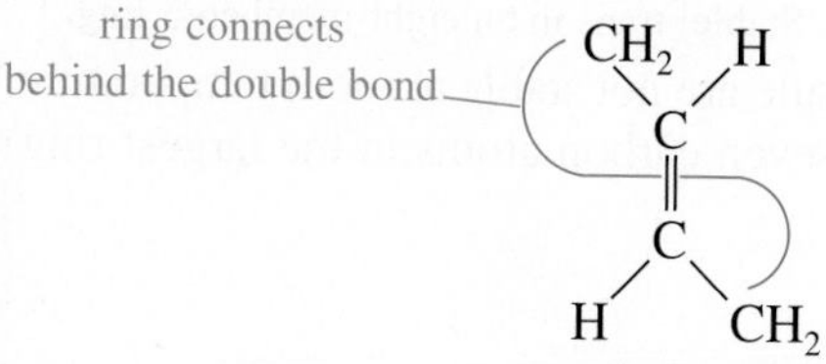

ring connects behind the double bond

trans cyclic system

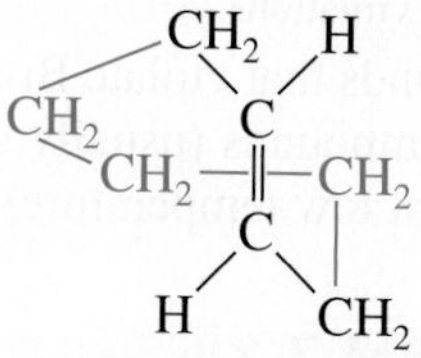

trans-cycloheptene
marginally stable

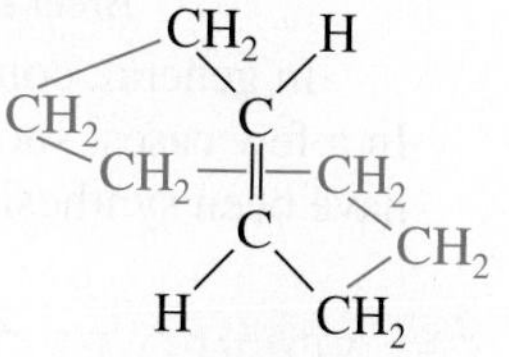

trans-cyclooctene
stable

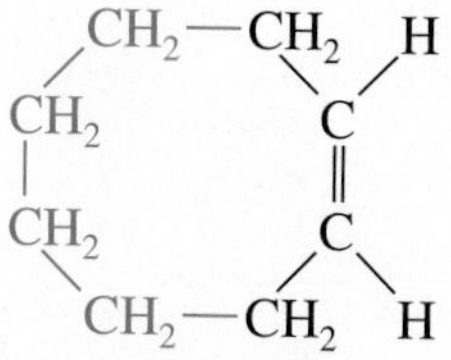

cis-cyclooctene
more stable

Once a cycloalkene contains at least ten or more carbon atoms, it can easily accommodate a trans double bond. For cyclodecene and larger cycloalkenes, the trans isomer is nearly as stable as the cis isomer.

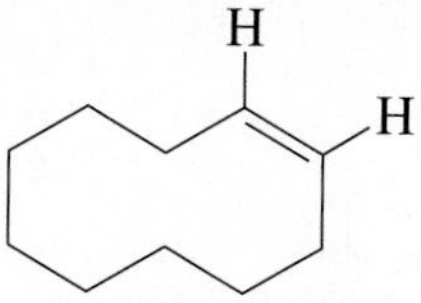

cis-cyclodecene

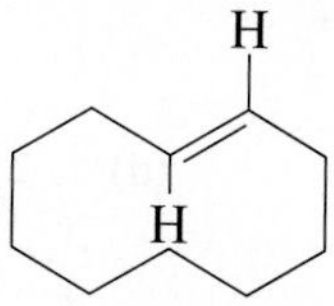

trans-cyclodecene

7-7E Bredt's Rule

We have seen that a trans cycloalkene is not stable unless there are at least eight carbon atoms in the ring. An interesting extension of this principle is called **Bredt's rule**.

> BREDT'S RULE: A bridged bicyclic compound cannot have a double bond at a bridgehead position unless one of the rings contains at least eight carbon atoms.

Let's review exactly what Bredt's rule means. A **bicyclic** compound is one that contains two rings. The **bridgehead carbon atoms** are part of both rings, with three links connecting them. A **bridged bicyclic** compound has at least one carbon atom in each of the three links between the bridgehead carbons. In the following examples, the bridgehead carbon atoms are circled in red.

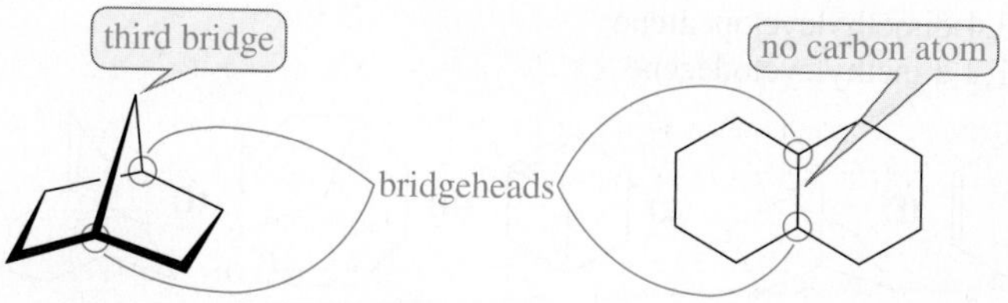

third bridge

bridgeheads

no carbon atom

norbornane
a bridged bicyclic compound

decalin
a fused bicyclic compound

If there is a double bond at the bridgehead carbon of a bridged bicyclic system, one of the two rings contains a cis double bond and the other must contain a trans double bond. For example, the following structures show that norbornane contains a five-membered ring and a six-membered ring. If there is a double bond at the bridgehead carbon atom, the five-membered ring contains a cis double bond and the six-membered ring contains a trans double bond. This unstable arrangement is called a "Bredt's rule violation." If the larger ring contains at least eight carbon atoms, then it can contain a trans double bond and the bridgehead double bond is stable.

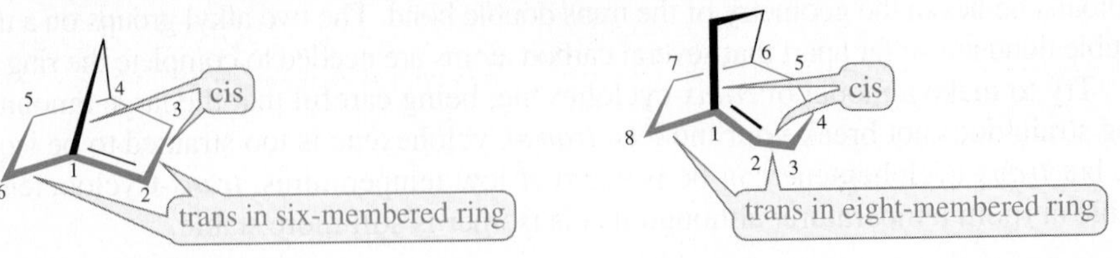

Bredt's rule violation

Stable: trans in an eight-membered ring

In general, compounds that violate Bredt's rule are not stable at room temperature. In a few cases, such compounds (usually with seven carbon atoms in the largest ring) have been synthesized at low temperatures.

SOLVED PROBLEM 7-2

Which of the following alkenes are stable?

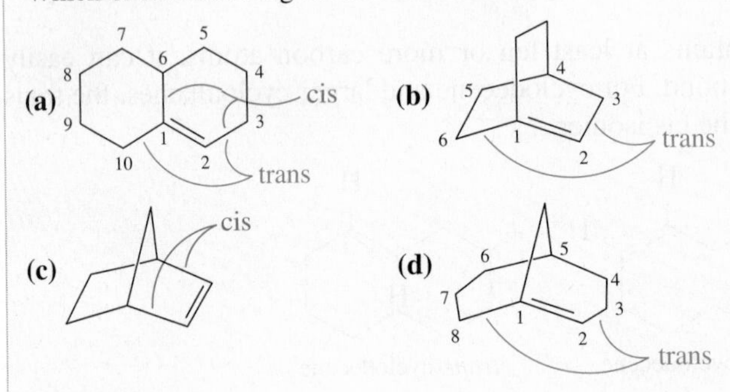

SOLUTION

Compound (a) is stable. Although the double bond is at a bridgehead, it is not a bridged bicyclic system. The trans double bond is in a 10-membered ring. Compound (b) is a Bredt's rule violation and is not stable. The largest ring contains six carbon atoms, and the trans double bond cannot be stable in this bridgehead position.

Compound (c) (norbornene) is stable. The (cis) double bond is not at a bridgehead carbon.

Compound (d) is stable. Although the double bond is at the bridgehead of a bridged bicyclic system, there is an eight-membered ring to accommodate the trans double bond.

PROBLEM 7-11

Explain why each of the following alkenes is stable or unstable.

(a) 1,2-dimethylcyclopentene
(b) *trans*-1,2-dimethylcyclopentene
(c) *trans*-3,4-dimethylcyclopentene
(d) *trans*-1,2-dimethylcyclodecene

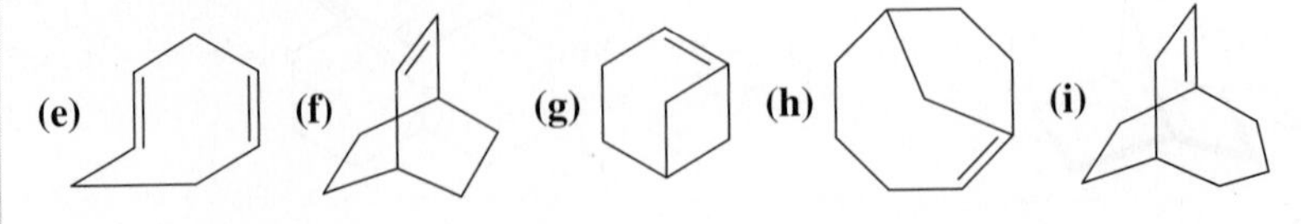

7-8 Physical Properties of Alkenes

7-8A Boiling Points and Densities

Most physical properties of alkenes are similar to those of the corresponding alkanes. For example, the boiling points of 1-butene, *cis*-2-butene, *trans*-2-butene, and *n*-butane are all close to 0 °C. Also like the alkanes, alkenes have densities around 0.6 or 0.7 g/cm^3. The boiling points and densities of some representative alkenes are listed in Table 7-2. The table shows that boiling points of alkenes increase smoothly with molecular weight. As with alkanes, increased branching leads to greater volatility and

TABLE 7-2

Physical Properties of Some Representative Alkenes

Name	Structure	Carbons	Boiling Point (°C)	Density (g/cm³)
ethene (ethylene)	$CH_2{=}CH_2$	2	−104	
propene (propylene)	$CH_3CH{=}CH_2$	3	−47	0.52
2-methylpropene (isobutylene)	$(CH_3)_2C{=}CH_2$	4	−7	0.59
1-butene	$CH_3CH_2CH{=}CH_2$	4	−6	0.59
trans-2-butene	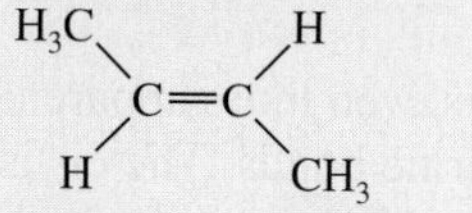 $H_3C(H)C{=}C(H)CH_3$ (trans)	4	1	0.60
cis-2-butene	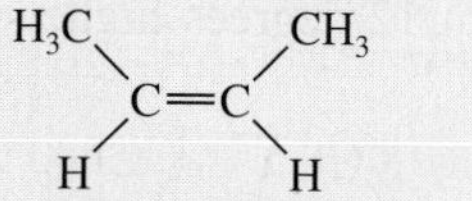 $H_3C(H)C{=}C(H)CH_3$ (cis)	4	4	0.62
3-methyl-1-butene	$(CH_3)_2CH{-}CH{=}CH_2$	5	25	0.65
1-pentene	$CH_3CH_2CH_2{-}CH{=}CH_2$	5	30	0.64
trans-2-pentene	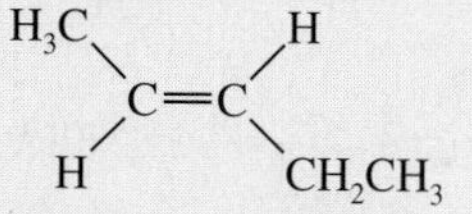 $H_3C(H)C{=}C(H)CH_2CH_3$ (trans)	5	36	0.65
cis-2-pentene	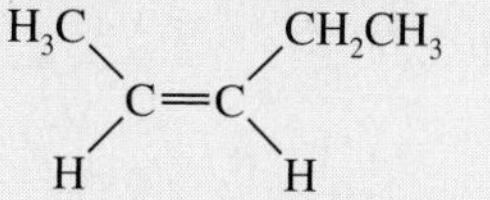 $H_3C(H)C{=}C(H)CH_2CH_3$ (cis)	5	37	0.66
2-methyl-2-butene	$(CH_3)_2C{=}CH{-}CH_3$	5	39	0.66
1-hexene	$CH_3(CH_2)_3{-}CH{=}CH_2$	6	64	0.68
2,3-dimethyl-2-butene	$(CH_3)_2C{=}C(CH_3)_2$	6	73	0.71
1-heptene	$CH_3(CH_2)_4{-}CH{=}CH_2$	7	93	0.70
1-octene	$CH_3(CH_2)_5{-}CH{=}CH_2$	8	122	0.72
1-nonene	$CH_3(CH_2)_6{-}CH{=}CH_2$	9	146	0.73
1-decene	$CH_3(CH_2)_7{-}CH{=}CH_2$	10	171	0.74

lower boiling points. For example, 2-methylpropene (isobutylene) has a boiling point of −7 °C, which is lower than the boiling point of any of the unbranched butenes.

7-8B Polarity

Like alkanes, alkenes are relatively nonpolar. They are insoluble in water but soluble in nonpolar solvents such as hexane, gasoline, halogenated solvents, and ethers. Alkenes tend to be slightly more polar than alkanes, however, for two reasons: The more weakly held electrons in the pi bond are more polarizable (contributing to instantaneous dipole moments), and the vinylic bonds tend to be slightly polar (contributing to a permanent dipole moment).

Alkyl groups are slightly electron-donating toward a double bond, helping to stabilize it. This donation slightly polarizes the vinylic bond, with a small partial positive charge on the alkyl group and a small negative charge on the double-bond carbon atom. For example, propene has a small dipole moment of 0.35 D.

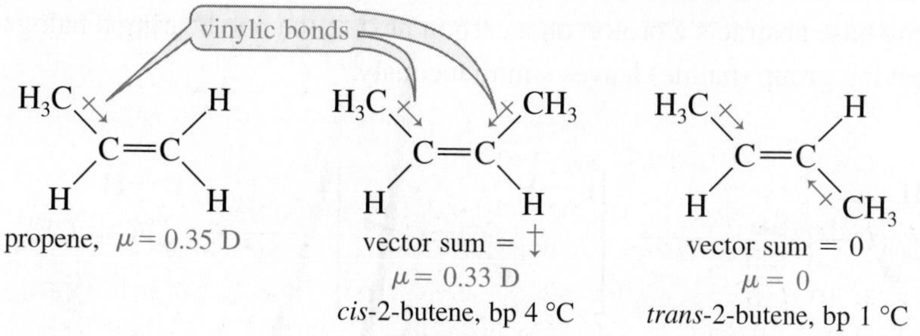

vinylic bonds

propene, $\mu = 0.35$ D

vector sum = ↕, $\mu = 0.33$ D
cis-2-butene, bp 4 °C

vector sum = 0, $\mu = 0$
trans-2-butene, bp 1 °C

In a cis-disubstituted alkene, the vector sum of the two dipole moments is directed perpendicular to the double bond. In a trans-disubstituted alkene, the two dipole moments tend to cancel out. If an alkene is symmetrically trans disubstituted, the dipole moment is zero. For example, *cis*-2-butene has a nonzero dipole moment, but *trans*-2-butene has no measurable dipole moment.

Compounds with permanent dipole moments engage in dipole–dipole attractions, while those without permanent dipole moments engage only in van der Waals attractions. *Cis*-2-butene and *trans*-2-butene have similar van der Waals attractions, but only the cis isomer has dipole–dipole attractions. Because of its increased intermolecular attractions, *cis*-2-butene must be heated to a slightly higher temperature (4 °C versus 1 °C) before it begins to boil.

The effect of bond polarity is even more apparent in the 1,2-dichloroethenes, with their strongly polar carbon–chlorine bonds. The cis isomer has a large dipole moment (2.4 D), giving it a boiling point 12 degrees higher than the trans isomer, with zero dipole moment.

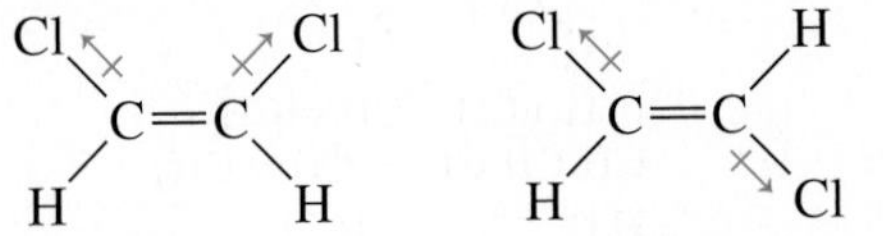

cis
vector sum = ↕
$\mu = 2.4$ D
bp = 60 °C

trans
vector sum = 0
$\mu = 0$
bp = 48 °C

PROBLEM 7-12

For each pair of compounds, predict the one with a higher boiling point. Which compounds have zero dipole moments?

(a) *cis*-1,2-dichloroethene or *cis*-1,2-dibromoethene
(b) *cis*- or *trans*-2,3-dichloro-2-butene
(c) cyclohexene or 1,2-dichlorocyclohexene

7-9 Alkene Synthesis by Elimination of Alkyl Halides

Dehydrohalogenation is the elimination of a hydrogen and a halogen from an alkyl halide to form an alkene. In Sections 6-17 through 6-21 we saw how dehydrohalogenation can take place by the E1 and E2 mechanisms. The second-order elimination (E2) is usually better for synthetic purposes because the E1 has more competing reactions.

7-9A Dehydrohalogenation by the E2 Mechanism

Second-order elimination is a reliable synthetic reaction, especially if the alkyl halide is a poor S_N2 substrate. E2 dehydrohalogenation takes place in one step, in which a strong base abstracts a proton from one carbon atom as the leaving group leaves the adjacent carbon.

MECHANISM 7-1 Dehydrohalogenation by the E2 Mechanism

E2 elimination takes place by a concerted one-step reaction.
A strong base abstracts a proton on a carbon next to the one bearing a halogen.
The leaving group (halide) leaves simultaneously.

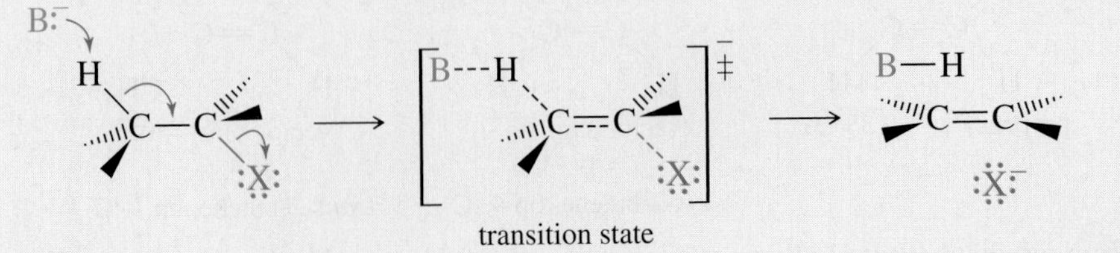

transition state

EXAMPLE: E2 elimination of tert-butyl bromide with sodium hydroxide.

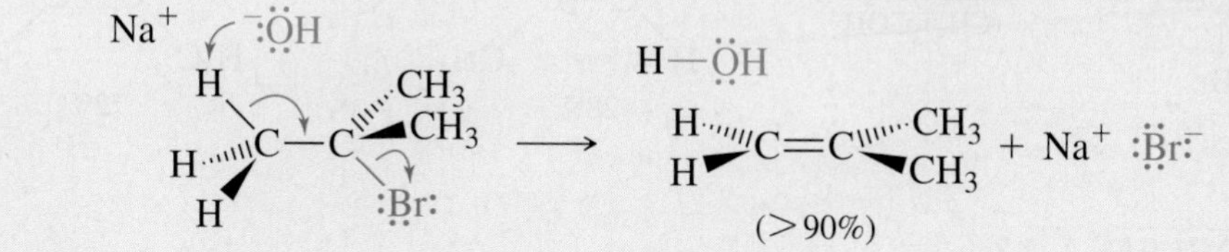

$$Na^+ \; {}^-\ddot{O}H + (H)_2HC{-}C(CH_3)_2Br \longrightarrow H{-}\ddot{O}H + H_2C{=}C(CH_3)_2 \; (>90\%) + Na^+ \; :\ddot{B}r:^-$$

The E2 dehydrohalogenation gives excellent yields with bulky secondary and tertiary alkyl halides, such as *tert*-butyl bromide in the preceding example. A strong base forces second-order elimination (E2) by abstracting a proton. The molecule's bulkiness hinders second-order substitution (S_N2), and a relatively pure elimination product results. Tertiary halides are the best E2 substrates because they are prone to elimination and cannot undergo S_N2 substitution.

Use of a Bulky Base If the substrate is prone to substitution, a bulky base can minimize the amount of substitution. Large alkyl groups on a bulky base hinder its approach to attack a carbon atom (substitution), yet it can easily abstract a proton (elimination). Some of the bulky strong bases commonly used for elimination are *tert*-butoxide ion, diisopropylamine, triethylamine, and 2,6-dimethylpyridine.

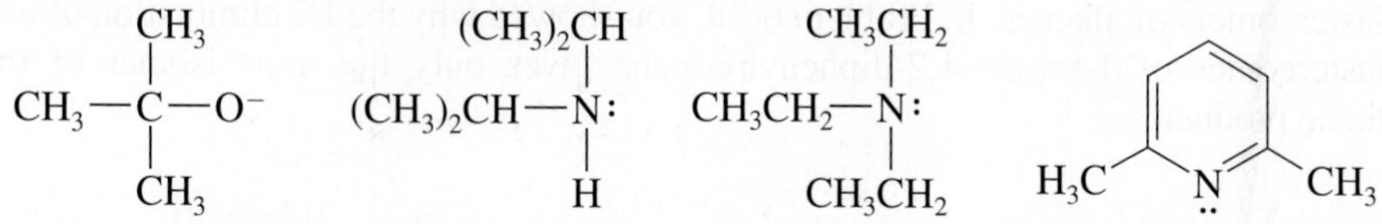

$(CH_3)_3C{-}O^-$ *tert*-butoxide; $[(CH_3)_2CH]_2N{-}H$ diisopropylamine; $(CH_3CH_2)_3N:$ triethylamine; 2,6-dimethylpyridine

The dehydrohalogenation of bromocyclohexane illustrates the use of a bulky base for elimination. Bromocyclohexane, a secondary alkyl halide, can undergo both substitution and elimination. Elimination (E2) is favored over substitution (S_N2) by using a bulky base such as diisopropylamine. Diisopropylamine is too bulky to be a good nucleophile, but it acts as a strong base to abstract a proton.

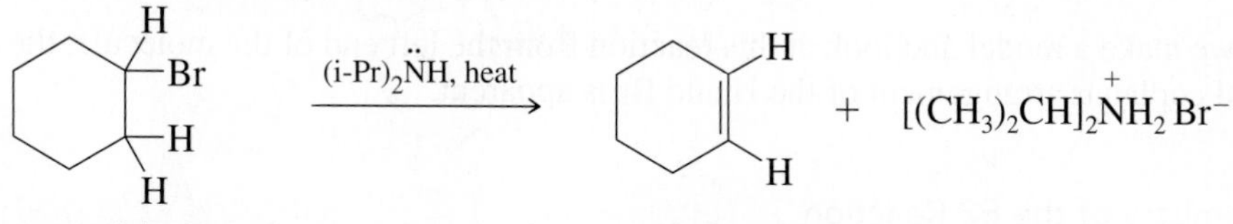

$$\text{bromocyclohexane} \xrightarrow{(i\text{-Pr})_2\ddot{N}H,\ \text{heat}} \text{cyclohexene (93\%)} + [(CH_3)_2CH]_2\overset{+}{N}H_2\ Br^-$$

Formation of the Hofmann Product Bulky bases can also accomplish dehydrohalogenations that do not follow the Zaitsev rule. Steric hindrance often prevents a bulky base from abstracting the proton that leads to the most highly substituted alkene. In these cases, it abstracts a less hindered proton, often the one that leads to formation of the least highly substituted product, called the **Hofmann product**. The following reaction gives mostly the **Zaitsev product** with the relatively unhindered ethoxide ion, but mostly the Hofmann product with the bulky *tert*-butoxide ion.

$$CH_3{-}CH_2{-}CBr(CH_3){-}CH_3 \xrightarrow[CH_3CH_2OH]{^-OCH_2CH_3} \underset{\text{Zaitsev product, 71\%}}{(H_3C)HC{=}C(CH_3)_2} + \underset{\text{Hofmann product, 29\%}}{CH_3{-}CH_2(H_3C)C{=}CH_2}$$

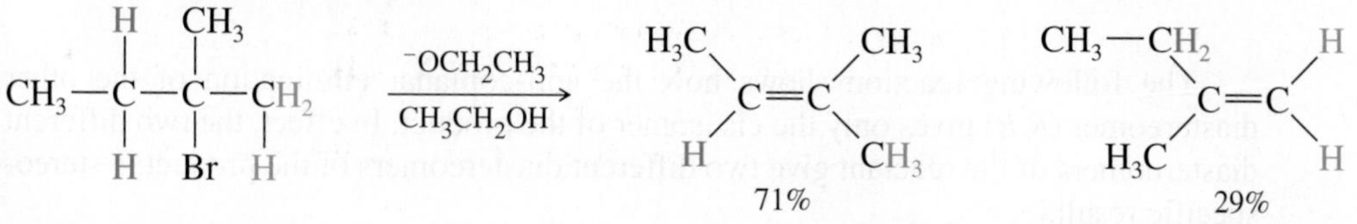

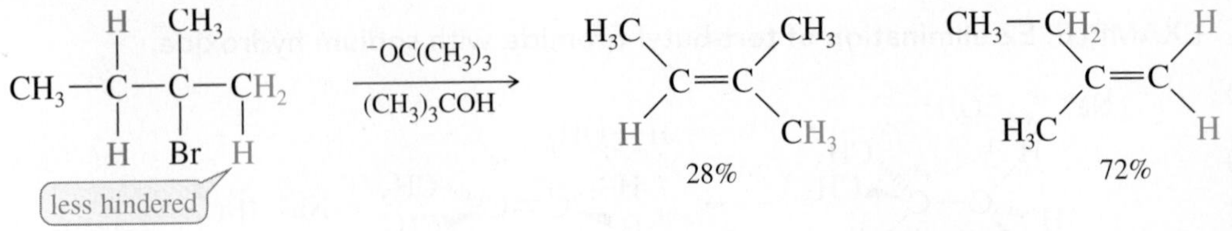

$$CH_3-\underset{H}{\overset{H}{C}}-\underset{Br}{\overset{CH_3}{C}}-\underset{H}{CH_2} \xrightarrow[(CH_3)_3COH]{^-OC(CH_3)_3} (H_3C)(H)C=C(CH_3)_2 + (CH_3-CH_2)(H_3C)C=CH_2$$

less hindered

28% 72%

PROBLEM 7-13

For each reaction, decide whether substitution or elimination (or both) is possible, and predict the products you expect. Label the major products.

(a) 1-bromo-1-methylcyclohexane + NaOH in acetone
(b) 1-bromo-1-methylcyclohexane + triethylamine (Et_3N:)
(c) chlorocyclohexane + $NaOCH_3$ in CH_3OH
(d) chlorocyclohexane + $NaOC(CH_3)_3$ in $(CH_3)_3COH$

7-9B Stereospecific E2 Reactions

Like the S_N2 reaction (Section 6-12), the E2 is **stereospecific**: Different stereoisomers of the reactant give different stereoisomers of the product. The E2 is stereospecific because it normally goes through an anti and coplanar transition state. The products are alkenes, and different diastereomers of starting materials commonly give different diastereomers of alkenes. In Problem 6-38, you showed why the E2 elimination of one diastereomer of 1-bromo-1,2-diphenylpropane gives only the trans isomer of the alkene product.

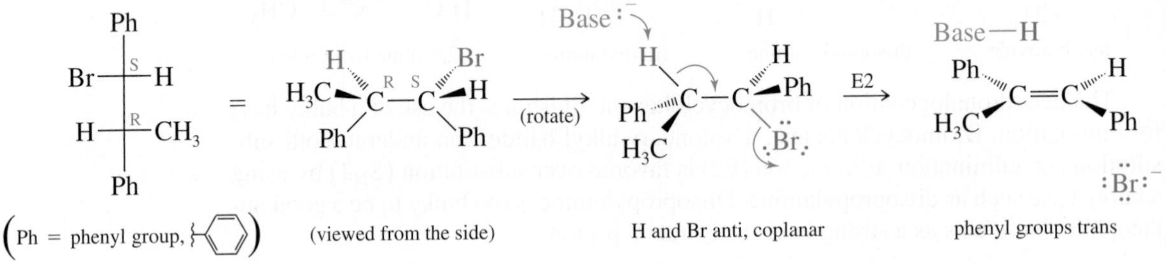

Ph, Br, S, H, H, R, CH₃, Ph = H, Br, R, S, H_3C, H, Ph, Ph (rotate) Base:⁻ H, H, Ph, Ph, H_3C, :Br: E2 Base—H, Ph, H, H_3C, Ph, :Br:⁻

(Ph = phenyl group) (viewed from the side) H and Br anti, coplanar phenyl groups trans

If we make a model and look at this reaction from the left end of the molecule, the anti and coplanar arrangement of the H and Br is apparent.

MECHANISM 7-2 Stereochemistry of the E2 Reaction

Most E2 reactions go through an anti-coplanar transition state. This geometry is most apparent if we view the reaction sighting down the carbon–carbon bond between the hydrogen and leaving group. Viewed from the left:

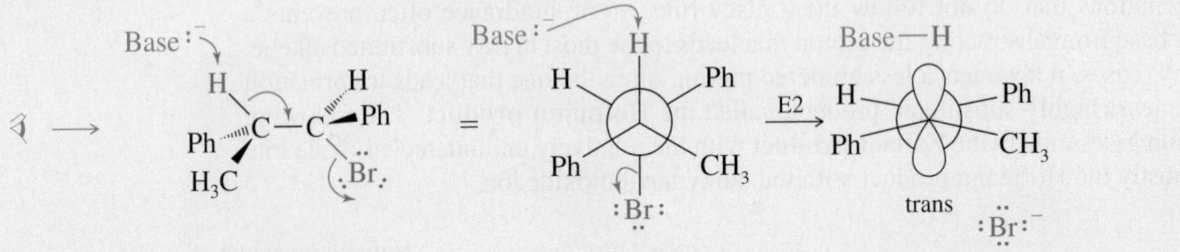

Base:⁻ H, H, Ph, Ph, H_3C, :Br: = Base:⁻ H, H, Ph, Ph, CH_3, :Br: E2 Base—H, H, Ph, Ph, CH_3, trans, :Br:⁻

The following reaction shows how the anti-coplanar elimination of the other diastereomer (*R,R*) gives only the cis isomer of the product. In effect, the two different diastereomers of the reactant give two different diastereomers of the product: a stereospecific result.

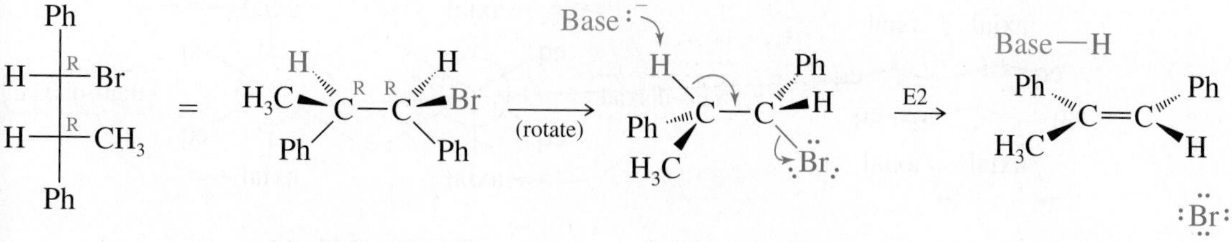

(viewed from the side)

H and Br anti, coplanar

phenyl groups cis

Viewed from the left end of the molecule:

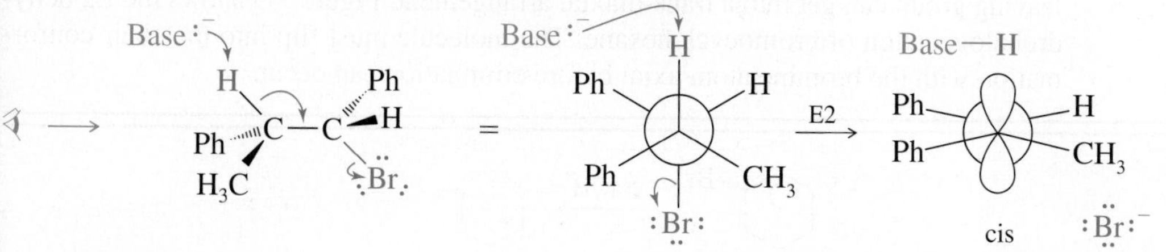

cis

PROBLEM 7-14

Show that the (*S,S*) enantiomer of this second (*R,R*) diastereomer of 1-bromo-1,2-diphenylpropane also undergoes E2 elimination to give the cis diastereomer of the product. (We do not expect these achiral reagents to distinguish between enantiomers.)

problem-solving Hint

Don't try to memorize your way through these reactions. Look at each one, and consider what it might do. Use your models for the ones that involve stereochemistry.

PROBLEM 7-15

Make models of the following compounds, and predict the products formed when they react with the strong bases shown.

(a) 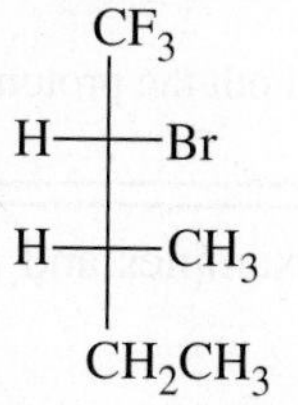 + KOH ⟶ (substitution and elimination)

(b) *meso*-1,2-dibromo-1,2-diphenylethane + $(CH_3CH_2)_3N$:

(c) (*d,l*)-1,2-dibromo-1,2-diphenylethane + $(CH_3CH_2)_3N$:

(d) 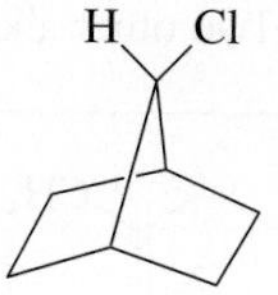 + NaOH in acetone

(e) 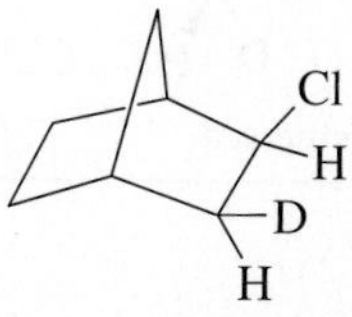 + $(CH_3)_3CO^-$

(f) 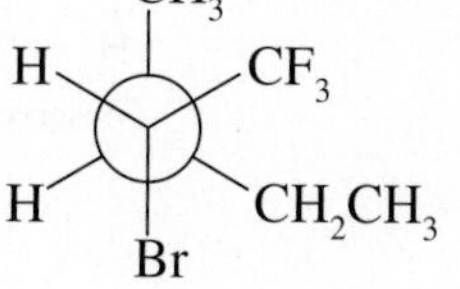 + $NaOCH(CH_3)_2$

7-9C E2 Reactions in Cyclohexane Systems

Nearly all cyclohexanes are most stable in chair conformations. In the chair, all the carbon–carbon bonds are staggered, and any two adjacent carbon atoms have axial bonds in an anti-coplanar conformation, ideally oriented for the E2 reaction. (As drawn in the following figure, the axial bonds are vertical.) On any two adjacent carbon atoms, one has its axial bond pointing up and the other has its axial bond pointing down. These two bonds are trans to each other, and we refer to their geometry as **trans-diaxial**.

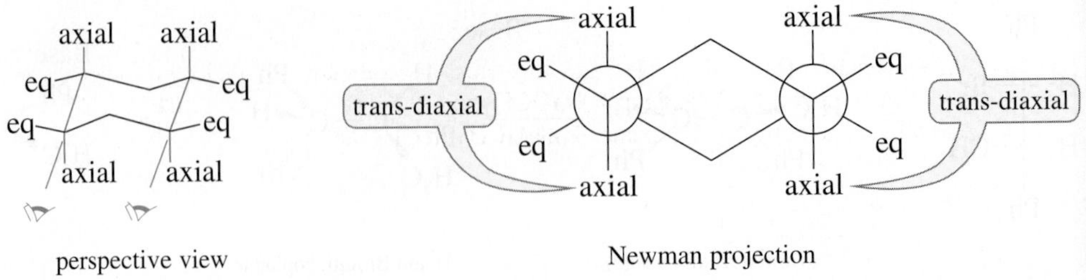

axial axial
eq eq
eq eq
axial axial

perspective view

axial axial
eq eq
trans-diaxial trans-diaxial
eq eq
axial axial

Newman projection

An E2 elimination can take place on this chair conformation only if the proton and the leaving group can get into a trans-diaxial arrangement. Figure 7-9 shows the E2 dehydrohalogenation of bromocyclohexane. The molecule must flip into the chair conformation with the bromine atom axial before elimination can occur.

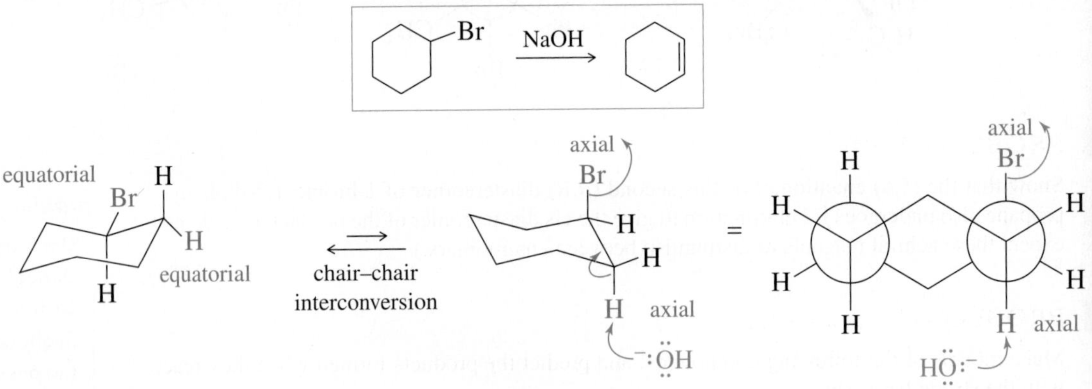

Br NaOH →

equatorial Br H H equatorial H chair–chair interconversion axial Br H H H axial :ÖH = H H H H H axial Br H H axial HÖ:⁻

■ FIGURE 7-9
E2 eliminations on cyclohexane rings. E2 elimination of bromocyclohexane requires that both the proton and the leaving group be trans and both be axial.

(You should make models of the structures in the following examples and problems so you can follow along more easily.)

problem-solving **Hint**

In a chair conformation of a cyclohexane ring, a trans-diaxial arrangement places the two groups anti and coplanar.

SOLVED PROBLEM 7-3

Explain why the following deuterated 1-bromo-2-methylcyclohexane undergoes dehydrohalogenation by the E2 mechanism, to give only the indicated product. Two other alkenes are not observed.

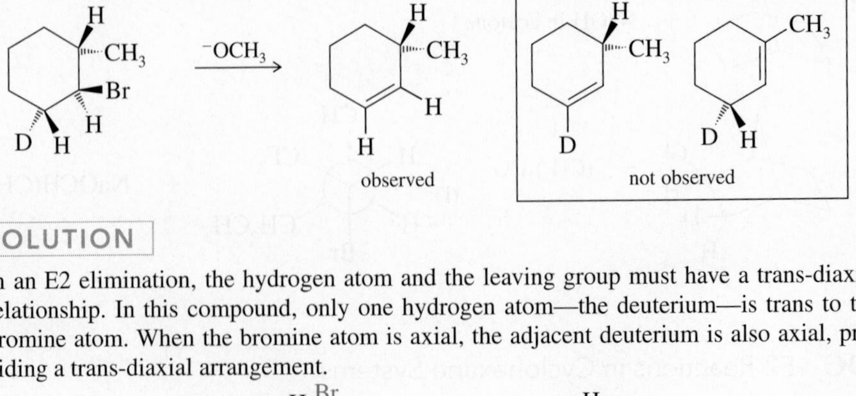

H CH_3 Br H D H $\xrightarrow{^-OCH_3}$ H CH_3 H H observed

H CH_3 D CH_3 D H not observed

SOLUTION

In an E2 elimination, the hydrogen atom and the leaving group must have a trans-diaxial relationship. In this compound, only one hydrogen atom—the deuterium—is trans to the bromine atom. When the bromine atom is axial, the adjacent deuterium is also axial, providing a trans-diaxial arrangement.

H Br H H H_3C D $CH_3\ddot{O}:^-$ $\xrightarrow{E2}$ H H H H_3C

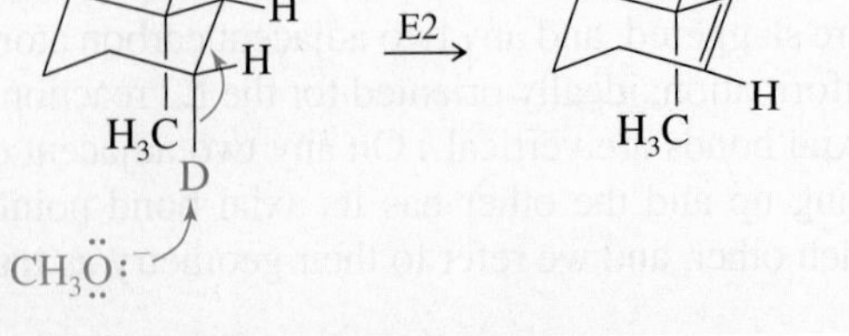

PROBLEM 7-16

Predict the elimination products of the following reactions, and label the major products.
(a) *cis*-1-bromo-2-methylcyclohexane + $NaOCH_3$ in CH_3OH
(b) *trans*-1-bromo-2-methylcyclohexane + $NaOCH_3$ in CH_3OH

PROBLEM 7-17

When the following stereoisomer of 2-bromo-1,3-dimethylcyclohexane is treated with sodium methoxide, no E2 reaction is observed. Explain why this compound cannot undergo the E2 reaction in the chair conformation.

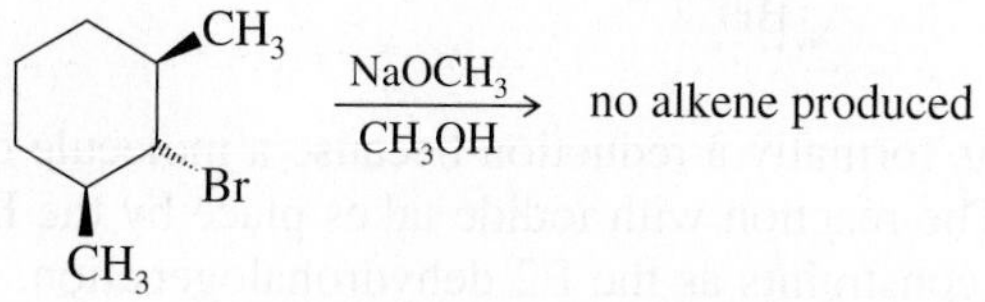

CH_3, Br, CH_3 — $\xrightarrow[CH_3OH]{NaOCH_3}$ no alkene produced

problem-solving Hint

Look for a hydrogen trans to the leaving group; then see if the hydrogen and the leaving group can become diaxial.

PROBLEM 7-18

(a) Two stereoisomers of a bromodecalin are shown. Although the difference between these stereoisomers may seem trivial, one isomer undergoes elimination with KOH much faster than the other. Predict the products of these eliminations, and explain the large difference in the ease of elimination.

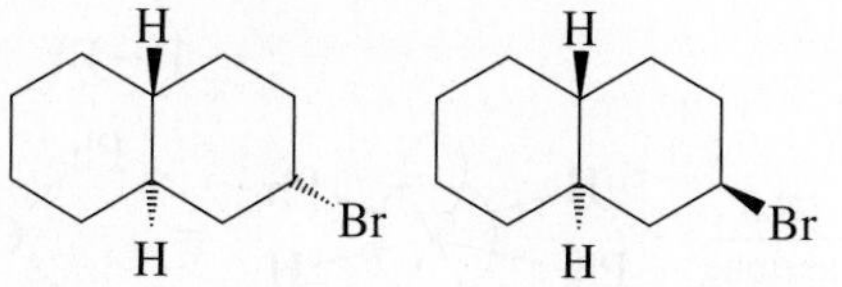

H, H, Br   H, H, Br

(b) Predict which of the following compounds will undergo elimination with KOH faster, and explain why. Predict the major product that will be formed.

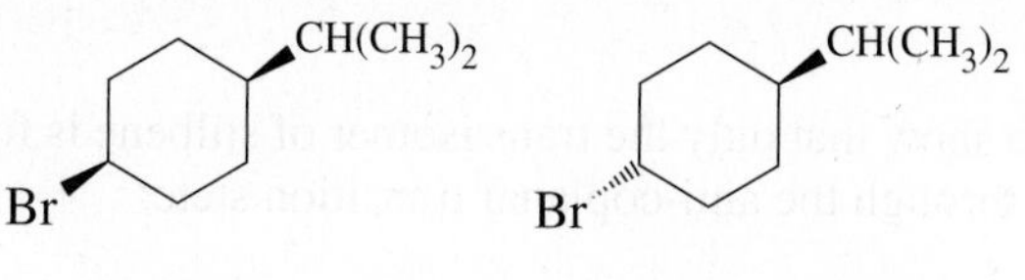

$CH(CH_3)_2$, Br $CH(CH_3)_2$, Br

PROBLEM 7-19

Give the expected product(s) of E2 elimination for each reaction. (*Hint*: Use models!)

(a) CH_3, H, Br, H, H_3C, H $\xrightarrow{NaOCH_3}$ one product

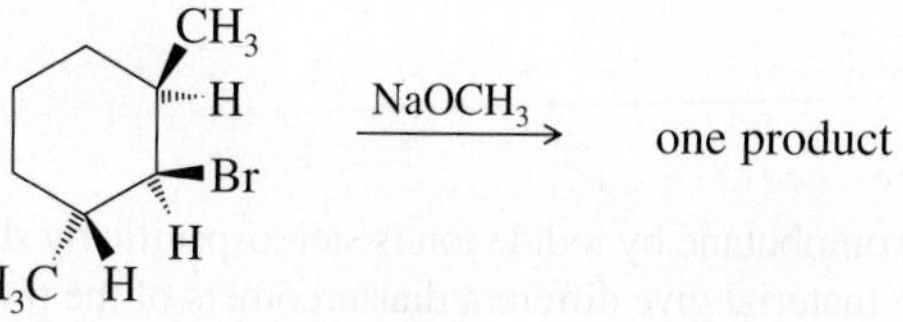

(b) H, H, H, Br, H, D $\xrightarrow{NaOCH_3}$ two products

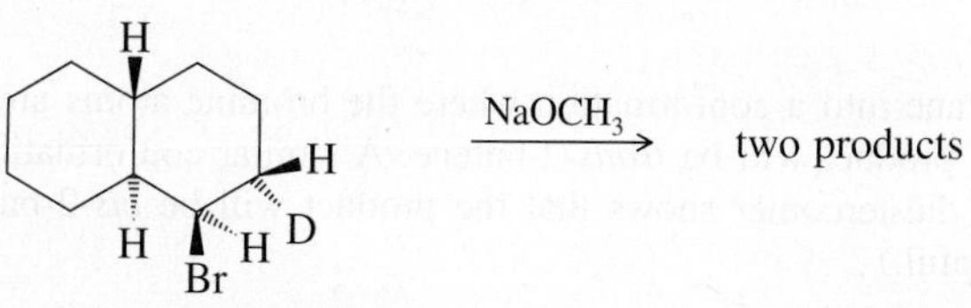

7-9D Debromination of Vicinal Dibromides

Vicinal dibromides (two bromines on adjacent carbon atoms) are converted to alkenes by reduction with iodide ion in acetone. This **debromination** is rarely an important synthetic reaction, because the most likely origin of a vicinal dibromide is from bromination of an alkene (Section 8-10). We discuss this reaction with dehydrohalogenation because the mechanisms are similar.

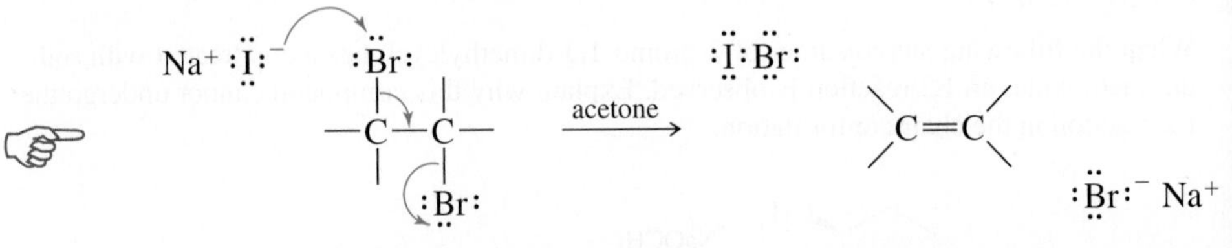

Na⁺ :I:⁻ + —C(Br)—C(Br)— —acetone→ C=C + I—Br + :Br:⁻ Na⁺

Debromination is formally a reduction because a molecule of Br_2 (an oxidizing agent) is removed. The reaction with iodide takes place by the E2 mechanism, with the same geometric constraints as the E2 dehydrohalogenation. Elimination usually takes place through an anti-coplanar arrangement, as shown in Mechanism 7-3. Acetone serves as a convenient solvent that dissolves most alkyl halides and sodium iodide.

MECHANISM 7-3 E2 Debromination of a Vicinal Dibromide

E2 debromination takes place by a concerted, stereospecific mechanism. Iodide ion removes one bromine atom, and the other bromine leaves as bromide ion.

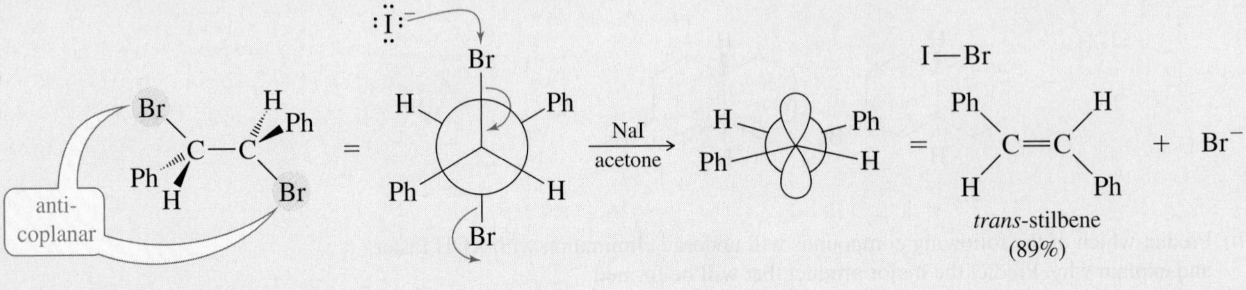

anti-coplanar

meso-1,2-dibromo-1,2-diphenylethane —NaI, acetone→ *trans*-stilbene (89%) + I—Br + Br^-

Use your models to show that only the trans isomer of stilbene is formed in this example by elimination through the anti-coplanar transition state.

PROBLEM 7-20

The preceding example shows *meso*-1,2-dibromo-1,2-diphenylethane reacting with iodide ion to give *trans*-stilbene. Show how the other diastereomer of the starting material gives a different stereoisomer of the product.

SOLVED PROBLEM 7-4

Show that the dehalogenation of 2,3-dibromobutane by iodide ion is stereospecific by showing that the two diastereomers of the starting material give different diastereomers of the product.

SOLUTION

Rotating *meso*-2,3-dibromobutane into a conformation where the bromine atoms are anti and coplanar, we find that the product will be *trans*-2-butene. A similar conformation of either enantiomer of the (±) diastereomer shows that the product will be *cis*-2-butene. (*Hint*: Your models will be helpful.)

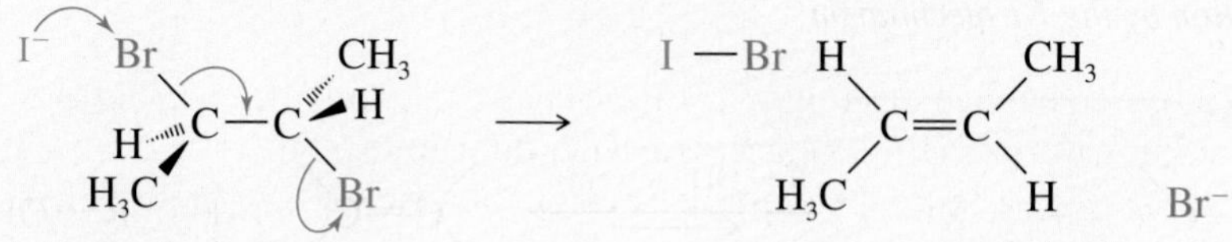

meso-2,3-dibromobutane → trans-2-butene

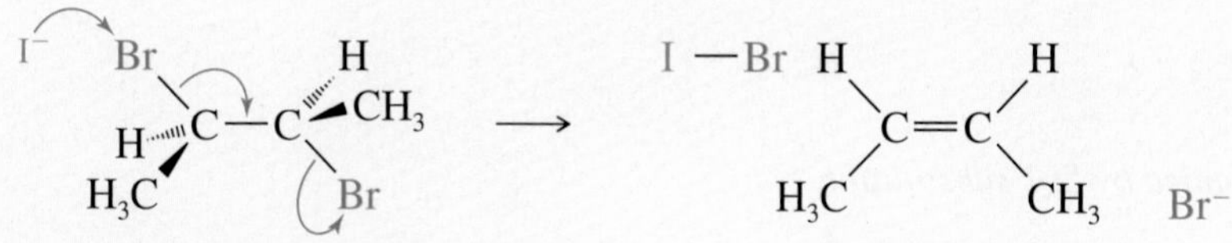

(R,R)-2,3-dibromobutane → cis-2-butene

PROBLEM 7-21

Solved Problem 7-4 showed that the debromination of (*R*,*R*)-2,3-dibromobutane gives *cis*-2-butene. Draw the same reaction using the (*S*,*S*) enantiomer and show that it gives the same diastereomer of the product.

PROBLEM 7-22

Predict the elimination products formed by debromination of the following compounds with iodide ion in acetone. Include stereochemistry, and give a correct name for each product.

(a) *trans*-1,2-dibromocyclohexane

(b) (3*R*,4*R*)-3,4-dibromoheptane

(c)

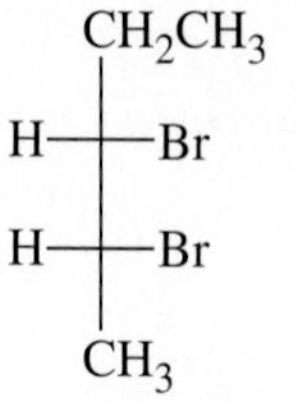

(d)

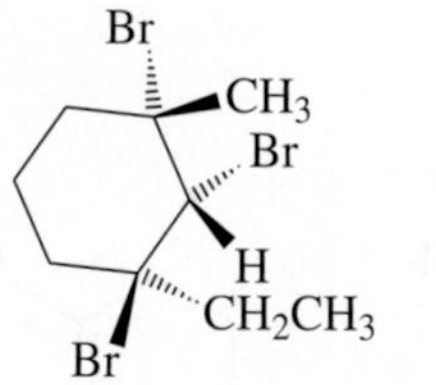

(e)

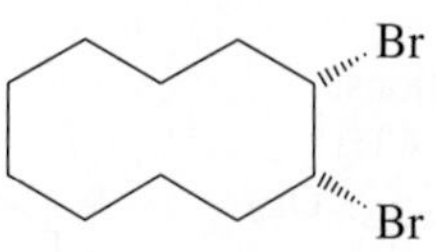

problem-solving Hint

Make a model of each compound, and place it in the conformation where the groups to be eliminated are anti and coplanar. The positions of the other groups will be near their positions in the alkene product.

PROBLEM 7-23

The following compounds show different rates of debromination. One reacts quite fast, and the other seems not to react at all. Explain this surprising difference in rates.

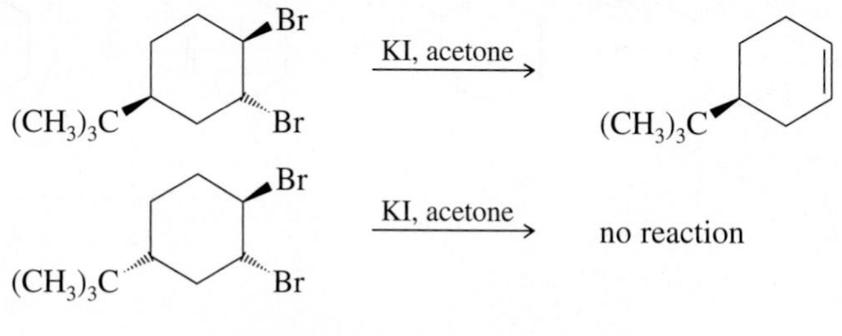

KI, acetone

KI, acetone → no reaction

A derivative of *trans*-stilbene known as diethylstilbestrol, or DES, was once taken by women during pregnancy to prevent miscarriages. The use of DES was discontinued because studies showed that DES increases the risk of cervical cancer in the children of women who take it.

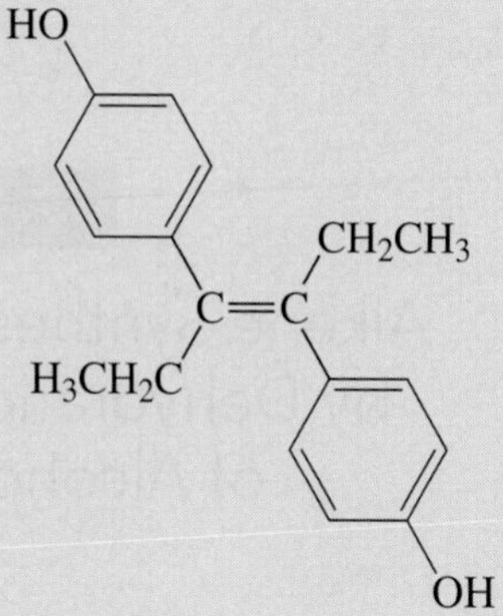

diethylstilbestrol (DES)

7-9E Dehydrohalogenation by the E1 Mechanism

First-order dehydrohalogenation usually takes place in a good ionizing solvent (such as an alcohol or water), without a strong nucleophile or base to force second-order kinetics. The substrate is usually a secondary or tertiary alkyl halide. First-order elimination requires ionization to form a carbocation, which loses a proton to a weak base (usually the solvent). El dehydrohalogenation is generally accompanied by S_N1 substitution, because the nucleophilic solvent can also attack the carbocation directly to form the substitution product.

Elimination by the E1 mechanism

formation of the carbocation — proton abstraction — R—ÖH (solvent) — elimination products

$$-\overset{H}{C}-\overset{X}{C}- \rightleftarrows -\overset{H}{C}-C^{+} + X^{-} \xrightleftharpoons{R-\ddot{O}H\ (\text{solvent})} C{=}C + R-\overset{+}{O}H_2\ X^{-}$$

Accompanied by S_N1 substitution

formation of the carbocation — nucleophilic attack — R—ÖH (solvent) — $-H^+$ — substitution products

$$-\overset{H}{C}-\overset{X}{C}- \rightleftarrows -\overset{H}{C}-C^{+} + X^{-} \xrightleftharpoons{R-\ddot{O}H\ (\text{solvent})} \xrightleftharpoons{-H^+} -\overset{H}{C}-\overset{O-R}{C}- + H-X$$

Like all reactions involving carbocation intermediates, E1 dehydrohalogenations are prone to rearrangement, as shown in Problem 7-24.

PROBLEM 7-24

Propose mechanisms for the following reactions.

(a) 1-bromo-1-methylcyclohexane $\xrightarrow{\text{EtOH, heat}}$ 1-ethoxy-1-methylcyclohexane + methylenecyclohexane + 1-methylcyclohexene

(b) 1-bromo-2-methylcyclohexane $\xrightarrow{\text{EtOH, heat}}$ 1-ethoxy-2-methylcyclohexane + 1-ethoxy-1-methylcyclohexane + 3-methylcyclohexene + 1-methylcyclohexene + methylenecyclohexane

7-10 Alkene Synthesis by Dehydration of Alcohols

Dehydration of alcohols is a common method for making alkenes. The word *dehydration* literally means "removal of water."

$$-\overset{|}{\underset{H}{C}}-\overset{|}{\underset{OH}{C}}- \xrightleftharpoons{\text{acidic catalyst, heat}} C{=}C + H_2O$$

Dehydration is reversible, and in most cases the equilibrium constant is not large. In fact, the reverse reaction (hydration) is a method for converting alkenes to alcohols (see Section 8-4). Dehydration can be forced to completion by removing the products from the reaction mixture as they form. The alkene boils at a lower temperature than the alcohol because the alcohol is hydrogen bonded. A carefully controlled distillation removes the alkene while leaving the alcohol in the reaction mixture.

Concentrated sulfuric acid and/or concentrated phosphoric acid are often used as reagents for dehydration because these acids act both as acidic catalysts and as dehydrating agents. Hydration of these acids is strongly exothermic. The overall reaction (using sulfuric acid) is

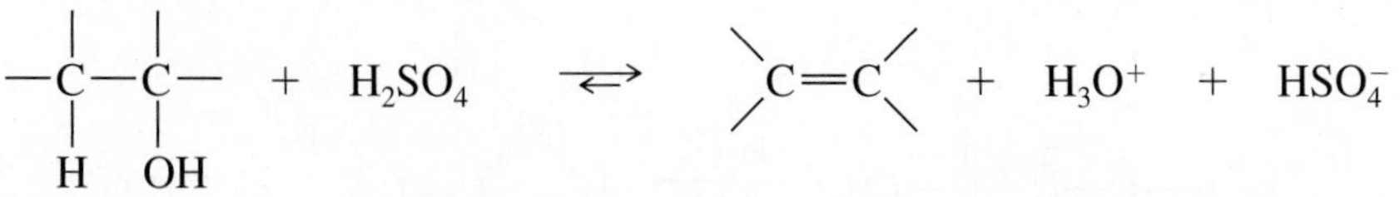

$$\underset{\quad H\quad\ OH}{-\overset{|}{\underset{|}{C}}-\overset{|}{\underset{|}{C}}-} + H_2SO_4 \rightleftharpoons \;\rangle C{=}C\langle\; + H_3O^+ + HSO_4^-$$

Hydration and dehydration reactions are common in biological pathways. The enzyme fumarase catalyzes the reversible addition of water to the double bond of fumarate to form malate. In contrast to the harsh conditions used in the chemical reaction, the enzymatic reaction takes place at neutral pH and at 37 °C.

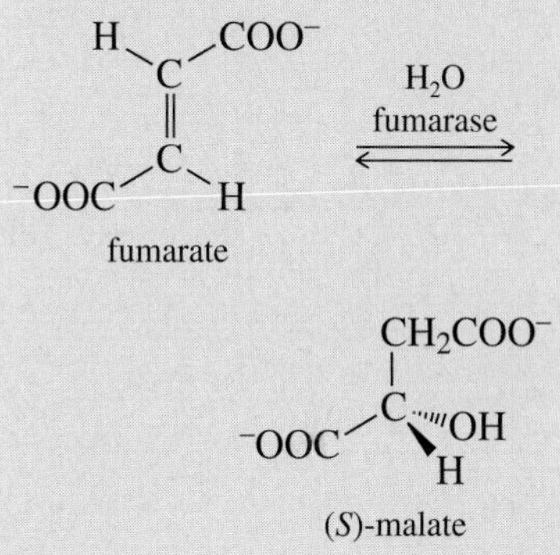

$$\text{fumarate: } (H)(^-OOC)C{=}C(H)(COO^-) \xrightleftharpoons[\text{fumarase}]{H_2O} \text{(S)-malate: } ^-OOC{-}C(H)(OH){-}CH_2COO^-$$

The mechanism of dehydration resembles the E1 mechanism introduced in Chapter 6 (Mechanism 6-8, p. 252). The hydroxyl group of the alcohol is a poor leaving group (^-OH), but protonation by the acidic catalyst converts it to a good leaving group (H_2O). In the second step, loss of water from the protonated alcohol gives a carbocation. The carbocation is a very strong acid: Any weak base such as H_2O or HSO_4^- can abstract the proton in the final step to give the alkene.

KEY MECHANISM 7-4 Acid-Catalyzed Dehydration of an Alcohol

Alcohol dehydrations usually involve E1 elimination of the protonated alcohol.

Step 1: Protonation of the hydroxyl group (fast equilibrium).

$$-\overset{H}{\underset{|}{C}}-\overset{:\ddot{O}-H}{\underset{|}{C}}- \;+\; H{-}O{-}\overset{O}{\underset{O}{S}}{-}O{-}H \;\rightleftharpoons\; -\overset{H}{\underset{|}{C}}-\overset{:\overset{H}{O^+}-H}{\underset{|}{C}}- \;\; HSO_4^-$$

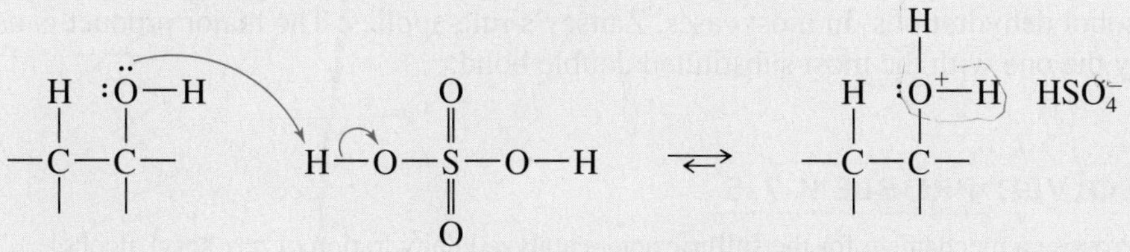

Step 2: Ionization to a carbocation (slow; rate limiting).

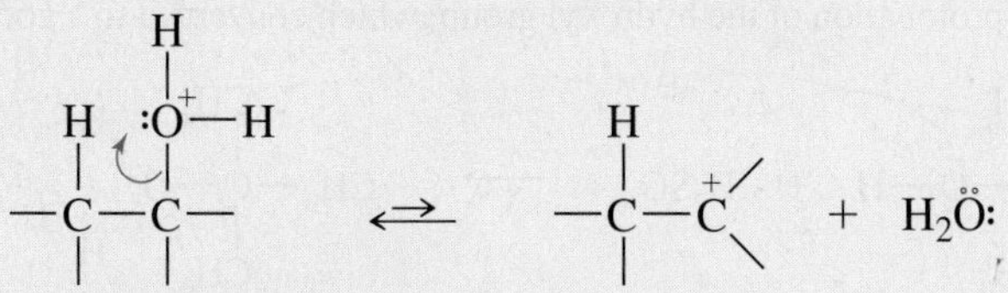

$$-\overset{H}{\underset{|}{C}}-\overset{:\overset{H}{O^+}-H}{\underset{|}{C}}- \;\rightleftharpoons\; -\overset{H}{\underset{|}{C}}-\overset{+}{C}\langle \;+\; H_2\ddot{O}:$$

Step 3: Deprotonation to give the alkene (fast).

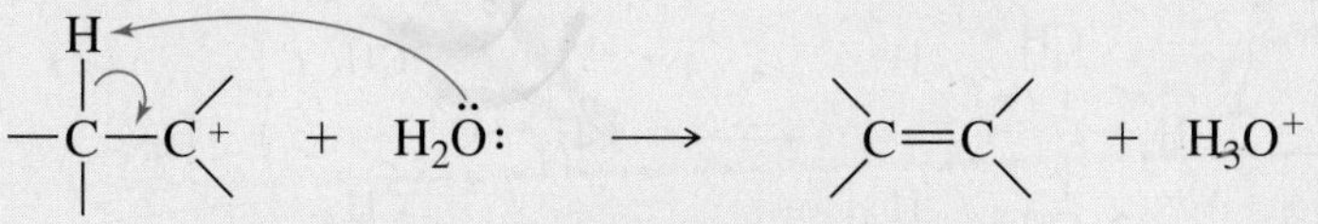

$$-\overset{H}{\underset{|}{C}}-C^+\langle \;+\; H_2\ddot{O}: \longrightarrow \;\rangle C{=}C\langle\; + H_3O^+$$

EXAMPLE: Acid-catalyzed dehydration of 2-butanol

Step 1: Protonation of the hydroxyl group (fast equilibrium).

$$CH_3-\overset{:\ddot{O}H}{CH}-CH_2CH_3 \xrightleftharpoons{H_2SO_4} CH_3-\overset{H-\ddot{O}^+-H}{CH}-CH_2CH_3$$

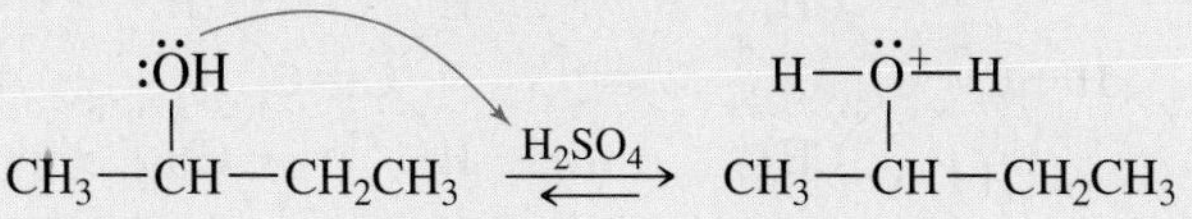

problem-solving Hint

In acid-catalyzed mechanisms, the first step is often addition of H^+, and the last step is often loss of H^+.

Step 2: Ionization to a carbocation (slow; rate limiting).

$$CH_3-\underset{|}{CH}(\overset{+}{\ddot{O}}H_2)-CH_2CH_3 \rightleftharpoons CH_3-\overset{+}{C}H-CH_2CH_3 + H-\ddot{O}-H$$

Step 3: Deprotonation to give the alkene (fast).

$$H-CH_2-\overset{+}{C}H-CH_2-CH_3 \xrightarrow{H_2\ddot{O}:} H(CH_3)C=C(H)CH_3 + H_3O^+$$

major product (cis and trans)

$$\text{or} \quad H-CH_2-\overset{+}{C}H-CH_2-CH_3 \xrightarrow{H_2\ddot{O}:} H_2C=CH-CH_2CH_3 + H_3O^+$$

minor product

Like other E1 reactions, alcohol dehydration follows an order of reactivity that reflects carbocation stability: 3° alcohols react faster than 2° alcohols, and 1° alcohols are the least reactive. Rearrangements of the carbocation intermediates are common in alcohol dehydrations. In most cases, Zaitsev's rule applies: The major product is usually the one with the most substituted double bond.

problem-solving Hint

Alcohol dehydrations usually go through E1 elimination of the protonated alcohol.

Reactivity is: 3° > 2° ≫ 1°

Rearrangements are common.

SOLVED PROBLEM 7-5

Propose a mechanism for the sulfuric acid–catalyzed dehydration of *tert*-butyl alcohol.

SOLUTION

The first step is protonation of the hydroxyl group, which converts it to a good leaving group.

$$(CH_3)_3C-\ddot{O}-H + H_2SO_4 \rightleftharpoons (CH_3)_3C-\overset{+}{\ddot{O}}H_2 + HSO_4^-$$

The second step is ionization of the protonated alcohol to give a carbocation.

$$(CH_3)_3C-\overset{+}{\ddot{O}}H_2 \rightleftharpoons (CH_3)_3C^+ + H_2\ddot{O}:$$

Abstraction of a proton completes the mechanism.

$$H_2\ddot{O}: \quad H-CH_2-C^+(CH_3)_2 \rightleftharpoons H_2C=C(CH_3)_2 + H_3O^+$$

PROBLEM 7-25

Propose mechanisms for the following reactions.

(a) cyclopentanol $\xrightarrow[\text{heat}]{H_2SO_4}$ cyclopentene

(b) 2-pentanol $\xrightarrow[\text{heat}]{H_2SO_4}$ 1-pentene + 2-pentene (cis + trans)

(c) 2-methylcyclohexanol $\xrightarrow[\text{heat}]{H_2SO_4}$ 1-methylcyclohexene + 3-methylcyclohexene + methylenecyclohexane

(d) $\xrightarrow[\text{heat}]{H_2SO_4/H_2O}$ (a minor product)

7-11 Alkene Synthesis by High-Temperature Industrial Methods

7-11A Catalytic Cracking of Alkanes

The least expensive way to make alkenes on a large scale is by the **catalytic cracking** of petroleum: heating a mixture of alkanes in the presence of a catalyst (usually aluminosilicates). Alkenes are formed by bond cleavage to give an alkene and a shortened alkane.

$$\underset{\text{long-chain alkane}}{H{-}(CH_2)_8{-}H} \xrightarrow[\text{catalyst}]{\text{heat}} \underset{\text{shorter alkane}}{H{-}(CH_2)_5{-}H} + \underset{\text{alkene}}{H_2C{=}CH{-}CH_2{-}H}$$

Cracking is used primarily to make small alkenes, up to about six carbon atoms. Its value depends on having a market for all the different alkenes and alkanes produced. The average molecular weight and the relative amounts of alkanes and alkenes can be controlled by varying the temperature, catalyst, and concentration of hydrogen in the cracking process. A careful distillation on a huge column separates the mixture into its pure components, ready to be packaged and sold.

Because the products are always mixtures, catalytic cracking is unsuitable for laboratory synthesis of alkenes. Better methods are available for synthesizing relatively pure alkenes from a variety of other functional groups. Several of these methods are discussed in Sections 7-9, 7-10, and later sections listed in the summary on page 314.

7-11B Dehydrogenation of Alkanes

Dehydrogenation is the removal of H_2 from a molecule, just the reverse of hydrogenation. Dehydrogenation of an alkane gives an alkene. This reaction has an unfavorable enthalpy change but a favorable entropy change.

$$-\overset{H}{\underset{|}{C}}-\overset{H}{\underset{|}{C}}- \xrightarrow[\text{catalyst}]{\text{heat}} \;>C{=}C< \; + \; H_2$$

$\Delta H° = +80$ to $+120$ kJ/mol ($+20$ to $+30$ kcal/mol) $\quad \Delta S° = +125$ J/kelvin-mol

This plant in Tokuyama, Japan, passes ethane rapidly over a hot catalyst. The products are ethylene and hydrogen.

$$CH_3CH_2CH_2CH_3 \xrightarrow{\text{Pt, 500 °C}} \left\{ \begin{array}{l} \text{cis-}CH_3CH{=}CHCH_3 + \text{trans-}CH_3CH{=}CHCH_3 \\ + \; H_2C{=}CH{-}CH_2CH_3 \; + \; H_2C{=}CH{-}CH{=}CH_2 \; + \; H_2 \end{array} \right.$$

The hydrogenation of alkenes (Section 7-7) is exothermic, with values of $\Delta H°$ around -80 to -120 kJ/mol (-20 to -30 kcal/mol). Therefore, dehydrogenation is endothermic and has an unfavorable (positive) value of $\Delta H°$. The entropy change for dehydrogenation is strongly favorable ($\Delta S° = +120$ J/kelvin-mol), however, because one alkane molecule is converted into two molecules (the alkene and hydrogen), and two molecules are more disordered than one.

The equilibrium constant for the hydrogenation–dehydrogenation equilibrium depends on the change in free energy, $\Delta G = \Delta H - T\Delta S$. At room temperature, the enthalpy term predominates and hydrogenation is favored. When the temperature is raised, however, the entropy term ($-T\Delta S$) becomes larger and eventually dominates the expression. At a sufficiently high temperature, dehydrogenation is favored.

PROBLEM 7-26

The dehydrogenation of butane to *trans*-2-butene has $\Delta H° = +116$ kJ/mol ($+27.6$ kcal/mol) and $\Delta S° = +117$ J/kelvin-mol ($+28.0$ cal/kelvin-mol).

(a) Compute the value of $\Delta G°$ for dehydrogenation at room temperature (25 °C or 298 °K). Is dehydrogenation favored or disfavored?

(b) Compute the value of ΔG for dehydrogenation at 1000 °C, assuming ΔS and ΔH are constant. Is dehydrogenation favored or disfavored?

In many ways, dehydrogenation is similar to catalytic cracking. In both cases, a catalyst lowers the activation energy, and both reactions use high temperatures to increase a favorable entropy term ($-T\Delta S$) and overcome an unfavorable enthalpy term (ΔH). Unfortunately, dehydrogenation and catalytic cracking also share a tendency to produce mixtures of products, and neither reaction is well suited for the laboratory synthesis of alkenes.

PROBLEM-SOLVING STRATEGY

PROPOSING REACTION MECHANISMS

At this point, we have seen examples of three major classes of reaction mechanisms:

- Those involving strong bases and strong nucleophiles
- Those involving strong acids and strong electrophiles
- Those involving free radicals

Many students have difficulty proposing mechanisms. We can use some general principles to approach this process, however, by breaking it down into a series of logical steps. Using a systematic approach, we can usually come up with a mechanism that is at least possible and that explains the products, without requiring any unusual steps. Appendix 4 contains more complete methods for approaching mechanism problems.

First, Classify the Reaction

Before you begin to propose a mechanism, you must determine what kind of reaction you are dealing with. Examine what you know about the reactants and the reaction conditions:

A free-radical initiator such as chlorine, bromine, or a peroxide (with heat or light) suggests that a free-radical chain reaction is most likely. Free-radical reactions were discussed in detail in Chapter 4.

Strong acids or strong electrophiles (or a reactant that can dissociate to give a strong electrophile) suggest mechanisms such as the S_N1, E1, alcohol dehydration, etc. that involve carbocations and other strongly acidic intermediates.

Strong bases or strong nucleophiles suggest mechanisms such as the S_N2 or E2, involving attack by the strong base or nucleophile on a substrate.

General Principles for Drawing Mechanisms

Once you have decided which type of mechanism is most likely (acidic, basic, or free-radical), some general principles can guide you in proposing the mechanism. Some principles for free-radical reactions were discussed in Chapter 4. Now we consider reactions that involve either strong nucleophiles or strong electrophiles as intermediates. In later chapters, we will apply these principles to more complex mechanisms.

Whenever you start to work out a mechanism, **draw all the bonds** and all the substituents of each carbon atom affected throughout the mechanism. Three-bonded carbon atoms are likely to be the reactive intermediates. If you attempt to draw condensed formulas or line–angle formulas, you will likely misplace a hydrogen atom and show the wrong carbon atom as a radical, cation, or anion.

Show only one step at a time; never combine steps, unless two or more bonds really do change position in one step (as in the E2 reaction, for example). Protonation of an alcohol and loss of water to give a carbocation, for example, must be shown as two steps. You must not simply circle the hydroxyl and the proton to show water falling off.

Use curved arrows to show the movement of electrons in each step of the reaction. This movement is always *from* the nucleophile (electron donor) to the electrophile (electron acceptor). For example, protonation of an alcohol must show the arrow going from the electrons of the hydroxyl oxygen to the proton—never from the proton to the hydroxyl group. *Don't* use curved arrows to try to "point out" where the proton (or other reagent) goes.

Reactions Involving Strong Nucleophiles

When a strong base or nucleophile is present, we expect to see intermediates that are also strong bases and strong nucleophiles; anionic intermediates are common. Acids and electrophiles in such a reaction are generally weak. Avoid drawing carbocations, H_3O^+, and other strong acids. They are unlikely to coexist with strong bases and strong nucleophiles.

Functional groups are often converted to alkoxides, carbanions, or other strong nucleophiles by deprotonation or reaction with a strong nucleophile. Then the carbanion or other strong nucleophile reacts with a weak electrophile such as a carbonyl group or an alkyl halide.

Consider, for example, the mechanism for the dehydrohalogenation of 3-bromopentane.

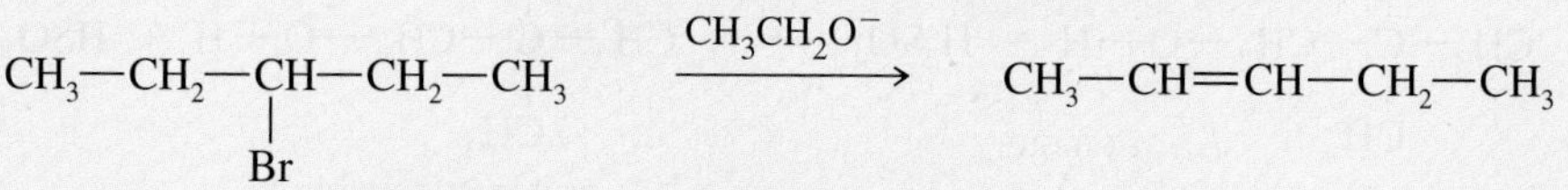

$$CH_3-CH_2-\underset{\underset{Br}{|}}{CH}-CH_2-CH_3 \xrightarrow{CH_3CH_2O^-} CH_3-CH{=}CH-CH_2-CH_3$$

Someone who has not read Chapter 6 or these guidelines for classifying mechanisms might propose an ionization, followed by loss of a proton:

Incorrect mechanism

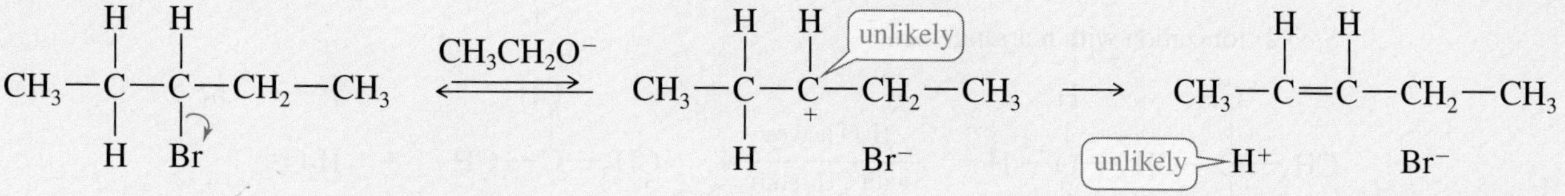

$$CH_3-\overset{H}{\underset{H}{C}}-\overset{H}{\underset{Br}{C}}-CH_2-CH_3 \xrightleftharpoons{CH_3CH_2O^-} CH_3-\overset{H}{\underset{H}{C}}-\overset{H}{\underset{+}{C}}-CH_2-CH_3 \;\; Br^- \longrightarrow CH_3-\overset{H}{C}{=}\overset{H}{C}-CH_2-CH_3 \;\; H^+ \;\; Br^-$$

(unlikely) (unlikely)

This mechanism would violate several general principles of proposing mechanisms. First, in the presence of ethoxide ion (a strong base), both the carbocation and the H^+ ion are unlikely. Second, the mechanism fails to explain why the strong base is required; the rate of ionization would be unaffected by the presence of ethoxide ion. Also, H^+ doesn't just fall off (even in an acidic reaction); it must be removed by a base.

The presence of ethoxide ion (a strong base and a strong nucleophile) in the reaction suggests that the mechanism involves only strong bases and nucleophiles and not any strongly acidic intermediates. As shown in Section 7-9A, the reaction occurs by the E2 mechanism, an example of a reaction involving a strong nucleophile. In this concerted reaction, ethoxide ion removes a proton as the electron pair left behind forms a pi bond and expels bromide ion.

Correct mechanism

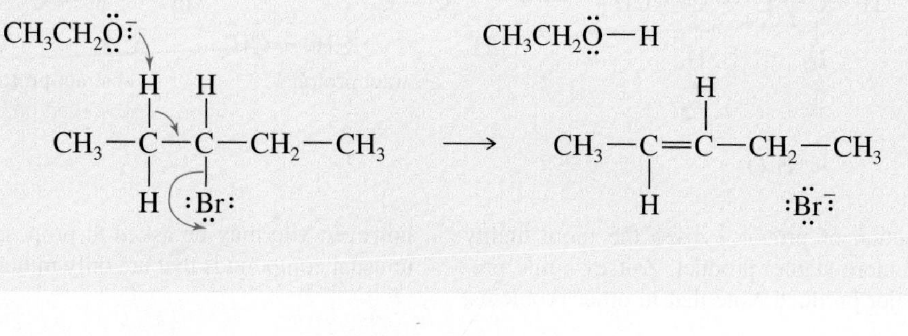

$$CH_3CH_2\ddot{O}:^- \quad CH_3-\overset{H}{\underset{H}{C}}-\overset{H}{\underset{:Br:}{C}}-CH_2-CH_3 \longrightarrow CH_3CH_2\ddot{O}-H \quad CH_3-\overset{H}{\underset{H}{C}}{=}C-CH_2-CH_3 \quad :\ddot{Br}:^-$$

(Continued)

Reactions Involving Strong Electrophiles

When a strong acid or electrophile is present, expect to see intermediates that are also strong acids and strong electrophiles. Cationic intermediates are common, but avoid drawing any species with more than one + charge. Bases and nucleophiles in such a reaction are generally weak. Avoid drawing carbanions, alkoxide ions, and other strong bases. They are unlikely to coexist with strong acids and strong electrophiles.

Functional groups are often converted to carbocations or other strong electrophiles by protonation or by reaction with a strong electrophile; then the carbocation or other strong electrophile reacts with a weak nucleophile such as an alkene or the solvent.

For example, consider the dehydration of 2,2-dimethyl-1-propanol:

$$CH_3-C(CH_3)_2-CH_2-OH \xrightarrow{H_2SO_4,\ 150\ °C} (CH_3)_2C{=}CH-CH_3$$

The presence of sulfuric acid indicates that the reaction is acidic and should involve strong electrophiles. The carbon skeleton of the product is different from the reactant. Under these acidic conditions, formation and rearrangement of a carbocation would be likely. The hydroxyl group is a poor leaving group; it certainly cannot ionize to give a carbocation and ^-OH (and we do not expect to see a strong base like ^-OH in this acidic reaction). The hydroxyl group is weakly basic, however, and it can become protonated in the presence of a strong acid. The protonated OH group becomes a good leaving group.

Step 1: Protonation of the hydroxyl group

$$CH_3-C(CH_3)_2-CH_2-\ddot{O}-H + H_2SO_4 \longrightarrow CH_3-C(CH_3)_2-CH_2-\overset{+}{\ddot{O}}(H)-H + HSO_4^-$$

starting alcohol → protonated alcohol

The protonated hydroxyl group $-\overset{+}{O}H_2$ is a good leaving group. A simple ionization to a carbocation would form a primary carbocation. Primary carbocations, however, are very unstable. Thus, a methyl shift occurs as water leaves, so a primary carbocation is never formed. A tertiary carbocation results. (You can visualize this as two steps if you prefer.)

Step 2: Ionization with rearrangement

$$CH_3-C(CH_3)_2-CH_2-\overset{+}{O}(H)-H \xrightarrow[\text{with } CH_3 \text{ shift } (\sim CH_3)]{H_2O \text{ leaves}} CH_3-\overset{+}{C}(CH_3)-CH_2-CH_3 + H_2\ddot{O}:$$

protonated alcohol → tertiary carbocation

The final step is loss of a proton to a weak base, such as HSO_4^- or H_2O (but *not* ^-OH, which is incompatible with the acidic solution). Either of two types of protons, labeled 1 and 2 in the following figure, could be lost to give alkenes. Loss of proton 2 gives the required product.

Step 3: Abstraction of a proton to form the required product

$$H-CH_2-\overset{+}{C}(CH_3)-CH(H)-CH_3 \xrightarrow{H_2\ddot{O}:} H_2C{=}C(CH_2-CH_3)(CH_3) \text{ or } (CH_3)_2C{=}CH(CH_3)$$

abstract proton 1 / abstract proton 2 (observed product)

Because abstraction of proton 2 gives the more highly substituted (therefore more stable) product, Zaitsev's rule predicts it will be the major product. Note that in other problems, however, you may be asked to propose mechanisms to explain unusual compounds that are only minor products.

PROBLEM 7-27

For practice in recognizing mechanisms, classify each reaction according to the type of mechanism you expect:

1. Free-radical chain reaction
2. Reaction involving strong bases and strong nucleophiles
3. Reaction involving strong acids and strong electrophiles

(a) 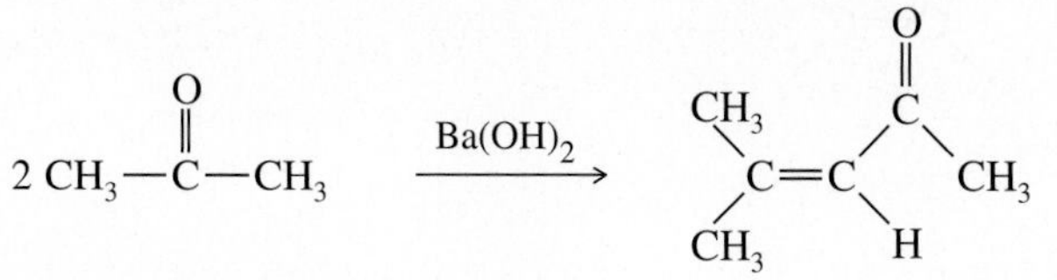 $2\ CH_3-C(=O)-CH_3 \xrightarrow{Ba(OH)_2} (CH_3)_2C{=}CH-C(=O)-CH_3$

(b) (epoxide-containing alkene) $\xrightarrow[H_2O]{H^+}$ (cyclopentane product with CH_2OH, CH_3, OH)

(c) styrene $\xrightarrow[\text{heat}]{Ph-C(=O)-O-O-C(=O)-Ph}$ polystyrene

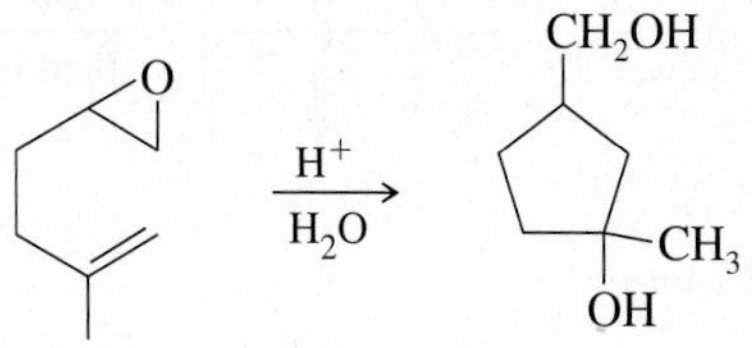

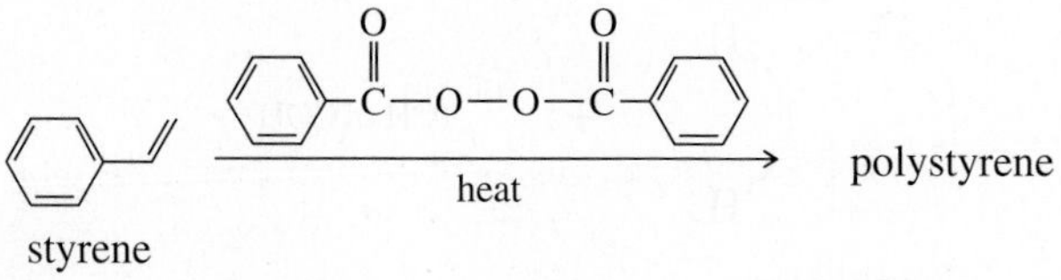

(d) ethylene $\xrightarrow{BF_3}$ polyethylene

PROBLEM 7-28

Propose mechanisms for the following reactions. Additional products may be formed, but your mechanism only needs to explain the products shown.

(a) $CH_3-CH_2-CH_2-CH_2-OH \xrightarrow{H_2SO_4\ 140\,°C} CH_3-CH{=}CH-CH_3 + CH_2{=}CH-CH_2CH_3$

(*Hint*: Hydride shift)

(b) 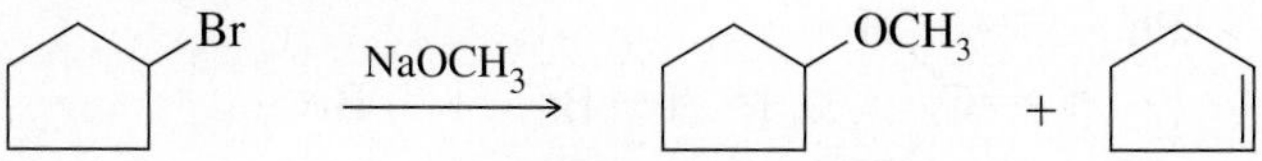 (Br) $\xrightarrow{NaOCH_3}$ (OCH_3) + (cyclopentene)

(c) 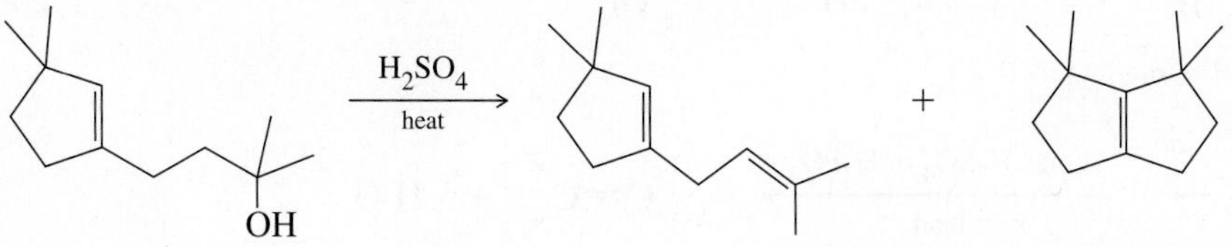 (OH) $\xrightarrow[\text{heat}]{H_2SO_4}$ (product) + (product)

PROBLEM 7-29

Propose mechanisms for the following reactions.

(a) (OH) $\xrightarrow[\text{heat}]{H_3PO_4}$ (cyclohexene)

(b) (CH_2OH) $\xrightarrow[\text{heat}]{H_2SO_4}$ (CH_2) + (CH_3) + (cycloheptene)

(c) (OH) $\xrightarrow[\text{heat}]{H_2SO_4}$ (product) + (product) + (product)

(d) (OH) $\xrightarrow[\text{heat}]{H_2SO_4}$ (product) + (product) + (product)

problem-solving Hint

Alcohol dehydrations usually go through E1 elimination of the protonated alcohol, with a carbocation intermediate. Rearrangements are common.

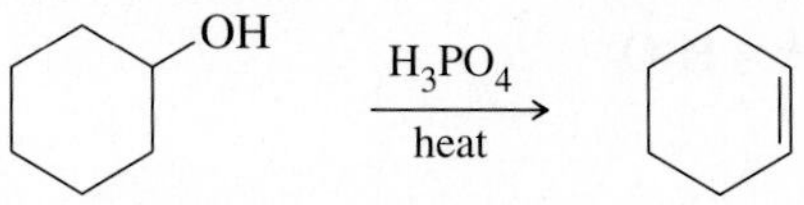

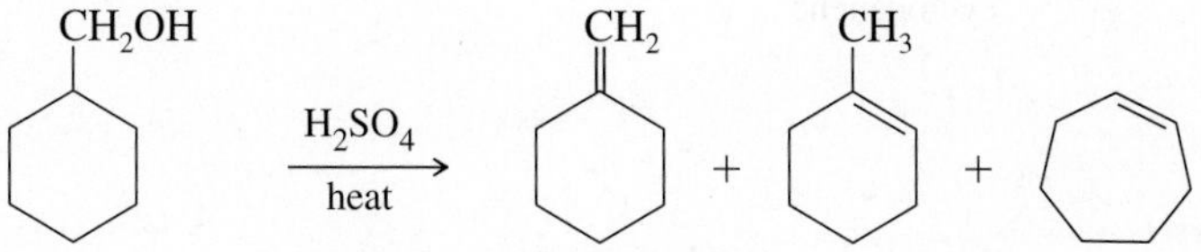

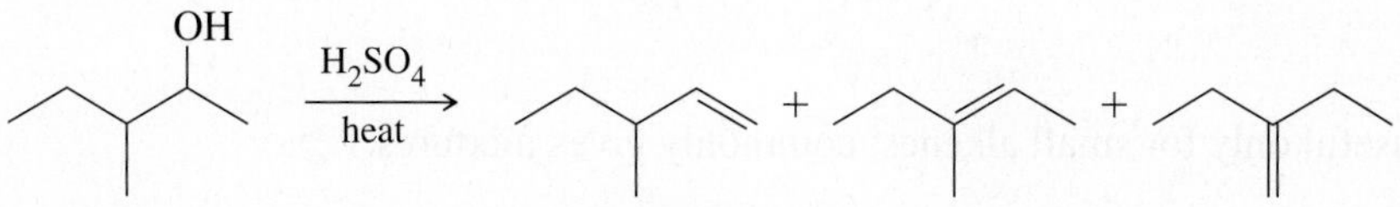

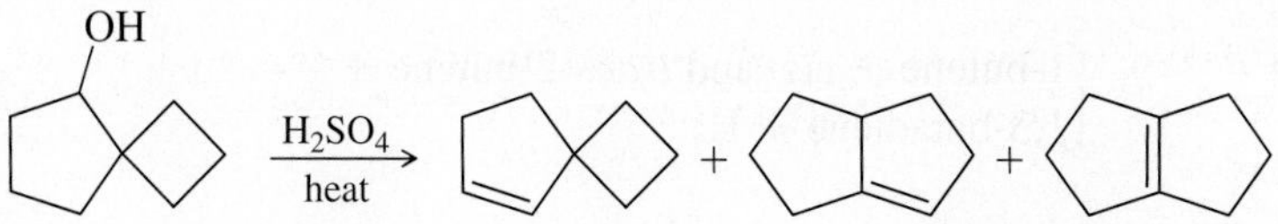

SUMMARY Methods for Synthesis of Alkenes

1. *Dehydrohalogenation of alkyl halides* (Section 7-9)

$$-\overset{H}{\underset{|}{\overset{|}{C}}}-\underset{X}{\underset{|}{\overset{|}{C}}}- \xrightarrow[\text{(loss of HX)}]{\text{base, heat}} \gt C=C \lt$$

Example

$$\text{chlorocyclooctane} \xrightarrow{(CH_3)_3CO^-K^+} \text{cyclooctene} + (CH_3)_3COH$$

2. *Dehalogenation of vicinal dibromides* (Section 7-9D)

$$-\overset{Br}{\underset{|}{\overset{|}{C}}}-\underset{Br}{\underset{|}{\overset{|}{C}}}- \xrightarrow[\text{acetone}]{\text{NaI}} \gt C=C \lt$$

Example

$$(Br)(Ph)(H)C-C(H)(Ph)(Br) \xrightarrow[\text{acetone}]{\text{NaI}} (Ph)(H)C=C(H)(Ph) + I-Br + Br^-$$

3. *Dehydration of alcohols* (Section 7-10)

$$-\underset{H}{\underset{|}{\overset{|}{C}}}-\underset{OH}{\underset{|}{\overset{|}{C}}}- \xrightarrow[\text{heat}]{\text{conc. } H_2SO_4 \text{ or } H_3PO_4} \gt C=C \lt + H_2O$$

Example

$$\text{cyclohexanol} \xrightarrow[150\ °C]{H_2SO_4} \text{cyclohexene} + H_2O$$

4. *Dehydrogenation of alkanes* (Section 7-11B)

$$-\underset{H}{\underset{|}{\overset{|}{C}}}-\underset{H}{\underset{|}{\overset{|}{C}}}- \xrightarrow{\text{heat, catalyst}} \gt C=C \lt + H_2$$

(Industrial prep, useful only for small alkenes; commonly gives mixtures.)

Example

$$CH_3CH_2CH_2CH_3 \xrightarrow{\text{Pt, 500 °C}} \begin{cases} \text{1-butene} + \textit{cis-} \text{ and } \textit{trans-}\text{2-butene} + \\ \text{1,3-butadiene} + H_2 \end{cases}$$

5. *Hofmann and Cope eliminations* (Sections 19-15 and 19-16)

$$\text{H}-\overset{|}{\underset{|}{\text{C}}}-\overset{|}{\underset{|}{\text{C}}}-{}^{+}\text{N(CH}_3)_3 \quad \text{I}^- \xrightarrow{\text{Ag}_2\text{O, heat}} \text{C}=\text{C} + :\text{N(CH}_3)_3$$

(Usually gives the least substituted alkene.)

Example

$$\text{CH}_3-\text{CH}_2-\underset{{}^{+}\text{N(CH}_3)_3}{\text{CH}}-\text{CH}_3 \quad \text{I}^- \xrightarrow{\text{Ag}_2\text{O, heat}} \text{CH}_3-\text{CH}_2-\text{CH}=\text{CH}_2 + :\text{N(CH}_3)_3$$

6. *Reduction of alkynes* (Section 9-9)

$$\text{R}-\text{C}\equiv\text{C}-\text{R}' \xrightarrow[\text{quinoline}]{\text{H}_2\text{, Pd/BaSO}_4} (\text{R})(\text{H})\text{C}=\text{C}(\text{R}')(\text{H}) \quad \text{cis alkene}$$

$$\text{R}-\text{C}\equiv\text{C}-\text{R}' \xrightarrow{\text{Na, NH}_3} (\text{R})(\text{H})\text{C}=\text{C}(\text{H})(\text{R}') \quad \text{trans alkene}$$

Examples

$$\text{CH}_3\text{CH}_2-\text{C}\equiv\text{C}-\text{CH}_2\text{CH}_3 \xrightarrow[\text{quinoline}]{\text{H}_2\text{, Pd/BaSO}_4} (\text{CH}_3\text{CH}_2)(\text{H})\text{C}=\text{C}(\text{CH}_2\text{CH}_3)(\text{H})$$

$$\text{CH}_3\text{CH}_2-\text{C}\equiv\text{C}-\text{CH}_2\text{CH}_3 \xrightarrow{\text{Na, NH}_3} (\text{CH}_3\text{CH}_2)(\text{H})\text{C}=\text{C}(\text{H})(\text{CH}_2\text{CH}_3)$$

7. *Wittig reaction* (Section 18-13)

$$(\text{R}')(\text{R})\text{C}=\text{O} + \text{Ph}_3\text{P}=\text{CHR}'' \longrightarrow (\text{R}')(\text{R})\text{C}=\text{CHR}'' + \text{Ph}_3\text{P}=\text{O}$$

Example

$$\text{cyclopentanone (C}=\text{O)} + \text{Ph}_3\text{P}=\text{CHCH}_3 \longrightarrow \text{cyclopentylidene C}=\text{C(H)(CH}_3) + \text{Ph}_3\text{P}=\text{O}$$

cyclopentanone

Glossary 7

alkene (olefin) A hydrocarbon with one or more carbon–carbon double bonds. (p. 281)

diene: A compound with two carbon–carbon double bonds. (p. 286)

triene: A compound with three carbon–carbon double bonds. (p. 286)

tetraene: A compound with four carbon–carbon double bonds. (p. 286)

allyl group A vinyl group plus a methylene group: $CH_2=CH-CH_2-$ (p. 287)

Bredt's rule A stable bridged bicyclic compound cannot have a double bond at a bridgehead position unless one of the rings contains at least eight carbon atoms. (p. 297)

bicyclic: Containing two rings.

bridged bicyclic: Having at least one carbon atom in each of the three links connecting the bridgehead carbons. (p. 297)

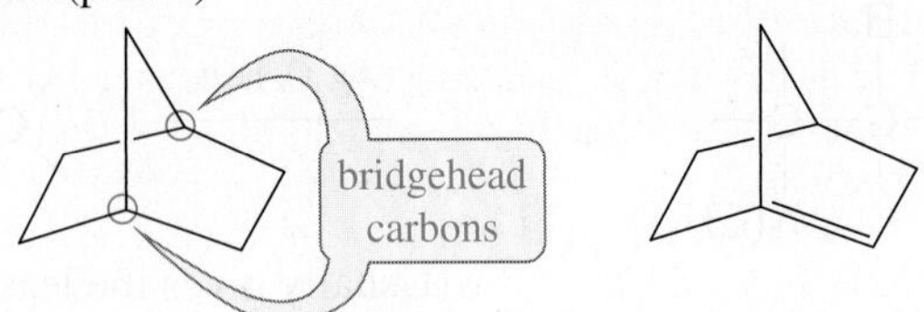

a bridged bicyclic compound   a Bredt's rule violation

bridgehead carbons: Those carbon atoms that are part of both rings, with three bridges of bonds connecting them.

catalytic cracking The heating of petroleum products in the presence of a catalyst (usually an aluminosilicate mineral), causing bond cleavage to form alkenes and alkanes of lower molecular weight. (p. 311)

cis-trans isomers **(geometric isomers)** Isomers that differ in their cis-trans arrangement on a ring or double bond. Cis-trans isomers are a subclass of diastereomers. (p. 287)

cis: Having similar groups on the same side of a double bond or a ring.

trans: Having similar groups on opposite sides of a double bond or a ring.

***Z*:** Having the higher-priority groups on the same side of a double bond.

***E*:** Having the higher-priority groups on opposite sides of a double bond.

dehalogenation The elimination of a halogen (X_2) from a compound. Dehalogenation is formally a reduction. An example is **debromination**. (p. 305)

$$\text{—C(Br)—C(Br)—} \xrightarrow{\text{NaI in acetone}} \text{>C=C<} + \text{I—Br} + \text{Br}^-$$

dehydration The elimination of water from a compound; usually acid-catalyzed. (p. 308)

$$\text{—C(H)—C(OH)—} \overset{\text{H}^+}{\rightleftharpoons} \text{>C=C<} + \text{H}_2\text{O}$$

dehydrogenation The elimination of hydrogen (H_2) from a compound; usually done in the presence of a catalyst. (p. 311)

$$\text{—C(H)—C(H)—} \overset{\text{Pt, high temperature}}{\rightleftharpoons} \text{>C=C<} + \text{H}_2$$

dehydrohalogenation The elimination of a hydrogen halide (HX) from a compound; usually base-promoted. (p. 300)

$$\text{—C(H)—C(X)—} \xrightarrow{\text{KOH}} \text{>C=C<} + \text{H}_2\text{O} + \text{K}^+\text{X}^-$$

double-bond isomers Constitutional isomers that differ only in the position of a double bond. Double-bond isomers hydrogenate to give the same alkane. (p. 293)

element of unsaturation A structural feature that results in two fewer hydrogen atoms in the molecular formula. A double bond or a ring is one element of unsaturation; a triple bond is two elements of unsaturation. (p. 283)

geminal dihalide A compound with two halogen atoms on the same carbon atom.

geometric isomers See **cis-trans isomers**. (p. 287)

heteroatom Any atom other than carbon or hydrogen. (p. 284)

Hofmann product The least highly substituted alkene product. (p. 301)

hydrogenation Addition of hydrogen to a molecule. The most common hydrogenation is the addition of H_2 across a double bond in the presence of a catalyst (*catalytic hydrogenation*). The value of $(-\Delta H°)$ for this reaction is called the **heat of hydrogenation**. (p. 292)

$$\text{>C=C<} + \text{H}_2 \xrightarrow{\text{Pt}} \text{—C(H)—C(H)—} \qquad -\Delta H° = \text{heat of hydrogenation}$$

olefin An alkene (p. 281)

polymer A substance of high molecular weight made by linking many small molecules, called **monomers**. (p. 291)

addition polymer: A polymer formed by simple addition of monomer units.

polyolefin: A type of addition polymer with an olefin (alkene) serving as the monomer.

saturated Having only single bonds; incapable of undergoing addition reactions. (p. 283)

Saytzeff Alternate spelling of Zaitsev.

stereospecific reaction A reaction in which different stereoisomers react to give different stereoisomers of the product. (p. 302).

trans-diaxial An anti and coplanar arrangement allowing E2 elimination of two adjacent substituents on a cyclohexane ring. The substituents must be trans to each other, and both must be in axial positions on the ring. (p. 303)

unsaturated Having multiple bonds that can undergo addition reactions. (p. 283)

vicinal dihalide A compound with two halogens on adjacent carbon atoms. (p. 305)

vinyl group An ethenyl group, $CH_2{=}CH{-}$. (p. 287)

Zaitsev's rule (Saytzeff's rule): An elimination usually gives the most stable alkene product, commonly the most substituted alkene. Zaitsev's rule does not always apply, especially with a bulky base or a bulky leaving group. (pp. 293, 301)

Zaitsev elimination: An elimination that gives the Zaitsev product.

Zaitsev product: The most substituted alkene product.

Essential Problem-Solving Skills in Chapter 7

1. Draw and name all alkenes with a given molecular formula.
2. Use the *E-Z* and cis-trans systems to name geometric isomers.
3. Use heats of hydrogenation to compare stabilities of alkenes.
4. Predict relative stabilities of alkenes and cycloalkenes, based on structure and stereochemistry.
5. Predict the products of dehydrohalogenation of alkyl halides, dehalogenation of dibromides, and dehydration of alcohols, including major and minor products.
6. Propose logical mechanisms for dehydrohalogenation, dehalogenation, and dehydration reactions.
7. Predict and explain the stereochemistry of E2 eliminations to form alkenes. Predict E2 reactions on cyclohexane systems.
8. Propose effective single-step and multistep syntheses of alkenes.

Study Problems

7-30 Define each term and give an example.

(a) double-bond isomers
(b) Zaitsev elimination
(c) element of unsaturation
(d) Hofmann product
(e) Bredt's rule violation
(f) hydrogenation
(g) dehydrogenation
(h) dehydrohalogenation
(i) dehydration
(j) dehalogenation
(k) geminal dihalide
(l) vicinal dihalide
(m) heteroatom
(n) polymer
(o) *E* and *Z* isomers

7-31 Draw a structure for each compound.

(a) 3-methyl-1-pentene
(b) *cis*-3-methyl-3-hexene
(c) 3,4-dibromobut-1-ene
(d) 1,3-cyclohexadiene
(e) cycloocta-1,4-diene
(f) (*Z*)-3-methyl-2-octene
(g) vinylcyclopropane
(h) (*Z*)-2-bromo-2-pentene
(i) (3*Z*,6*E*)-1,3,6-octatriene

7-32 Give a correct name for each compound.

(a) $CH_3{-}CH_2{-}\underset{\underset{CH_2}{\|}}{C}{-}CH_2{-}CH_2{-}CH_3$

(b) $(CH_3CH_2)_2C{=}CHCH_3$

(c)

(d)

(e)

(f) Cl CH2Cl

7-33 Label each structure as *Z*, *E*, or neither.

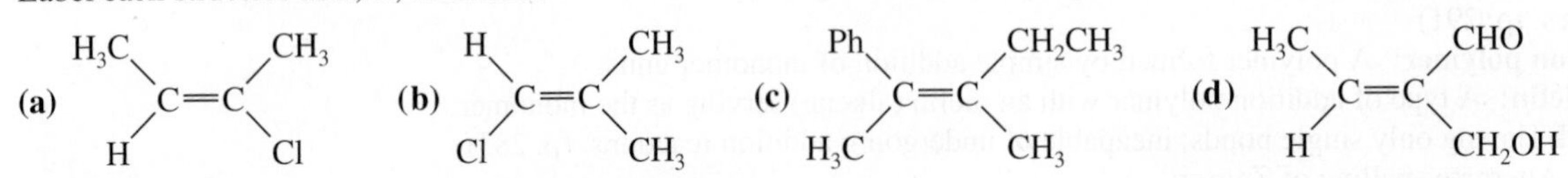

7-34 **(a)** Draw and name all five isomers of formula C_3H_5F.
(b) Draw all 12 acyclic (no rings) isomers of formula C_4H_7Br. Include stereoisomers.
(c) Cholesterol, $C_{27}H_{46}O$, has only one pi bond. With no additional information, what else can you say about its structure?

7-35 Draw and name all stereoisomers of 3-chlorohepta-2,4-diene
(a) Using the cis-trans nomenclature.
(b) Using the *E-Z* nomenclature.

7-36 Determine which compounds show cis-trans isomerism. Draw and label the isomers, using both the cis-trans and *E-Z* nomenclatures where applicable.
(a) 1-pentene **(b)** 2-pentene **(c)** 3-hexene
(d) 1,1-dibromopropene **(e)** 1,2-dibromopropene **(f)** 1-bromo-1-chlorohexa-1,3-diene

7-37 For each alkene, indicate the direction of the dipole moment. For each pair, determine which compound has the larger dipole moment.
(a) *cis*-1,2-difluoroethene or *trans*-1,2-difluoroethene
(b) *cis*-1,2-dibromoethene or *trans*-2,3-dibromo-2-butene
(c) *cis*-1,2-dibromo-1,2-dichloroethene or *cis*-1,2-dichloroethene

7-38 Predict the products of the following reactions. When more than one product is expected, predict which will be the major product.

(a) 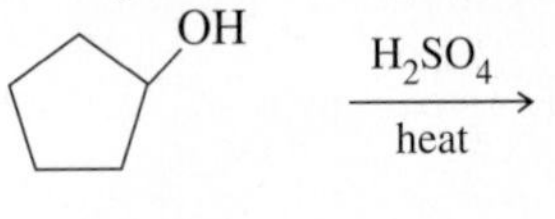 OH (cyclopentane ring) $\xrightarrow[\text{heat}]{H_2SO_4}$ **(b)** 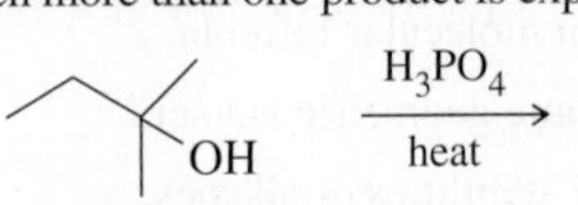 OH $\xrightarrow[\text{heat}]{H_3PO_4}$

(c) 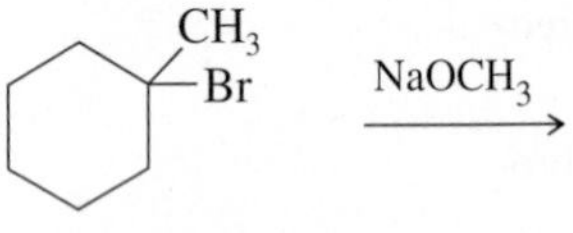 CH_3, Br (cyclohexane ring) $\xrightarrow{NaOCH_3}$ **(d)** 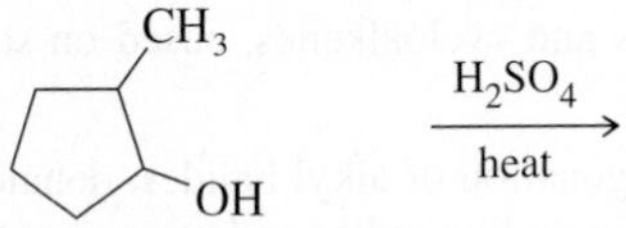 CH_3, OH (cyclopentane ring) $\xrightarrow[\text{heat}]{H_2SO_4}$

7-39 Write a balanced equation for each reaction.

(a) $CH_3{-}CH_2{-}CH(OH){-}CH_3 \xrightarrow{H_2SO_4,\ \text{heat}}$ **(b)** 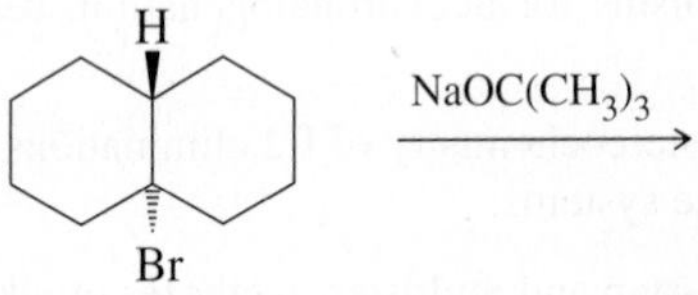 H, Br (bicyclic) $\xrightarrow{NaOC(CH_3)_3}$

(c) $CH_3{-}CH(Br){-}CH(Br){-}CH_3 \xrightarrow[\text{acetone}]{NaI}$ **(d)** $CH_3{-}CH(CH_3){-}C(CH_3)(Br){-}CH_3 \xrightarrow{NaOH,\ \text{heat}}$

7-40 Show how you would prepare cyclopentene from each compound.
(a) *trans*-1,2-dibromocyclopentane **(b)** cyclopentanol
(c) cyclopentyl bromide **(d)** cyclopentane (not by dehydrogenation)

7-41 Predict the products formed by sodium hydroxide-promoted dehydrohalogenation of the following compounds. In each case, predict which will be the major product.
(a) 1-bromobutane **(b)** 2-chlorobutane **(c)** 3-bromopentane
(d) *cis*-1-bromo-2-methylcyclohexane **(e)** *trans*-1-bromo-2-methylcyclohexane

7-42 What halides would undergo dehydrohalogenation to give the following pure alkenes?
(a) 1-hexene **(b)** isobutylene **(c)** 2-pentene
(d) methylenecyclohexane **(e)** 4-methylcyclohexene

7-43 In the dehydrohalogenation of alkyl halides, a strong base such as *tert*-butoxide usually gives the best results via the E2 mechanism.
(a) Explain why a strong base such as *tert*-butoxide cannot dehydrate an alcohol through the E2 mechanism.
(b) Explain why strong acid, used in the dehydration of an alcohol, is not effective in the dehydrohalogenation of an alkyl halide.

7-44 Predict the major products of acid-catalyzed dehydration of the following alcohols.
(a) 2-pentanol **(b)** 1-methylcyclopentanol
(c) 2-methylcyclohexanol **(d)** 2,2-dimethyl-1-propanol

7-45 Propose mechanisms for the following reactions. Additional products may be formed, but your mechanism only needs to explain the products shown.

(a) 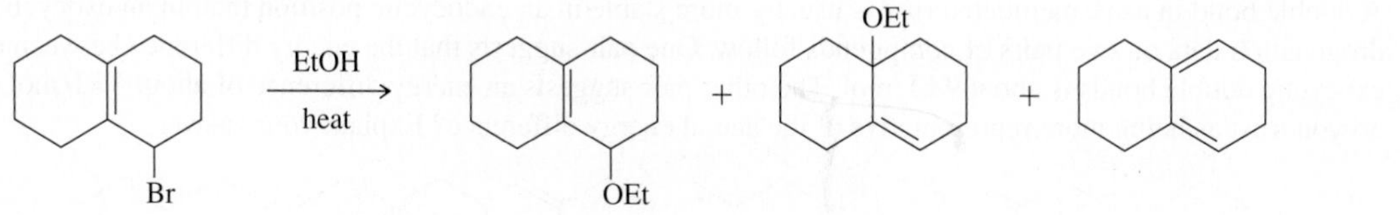 EtOH, heat

(b) 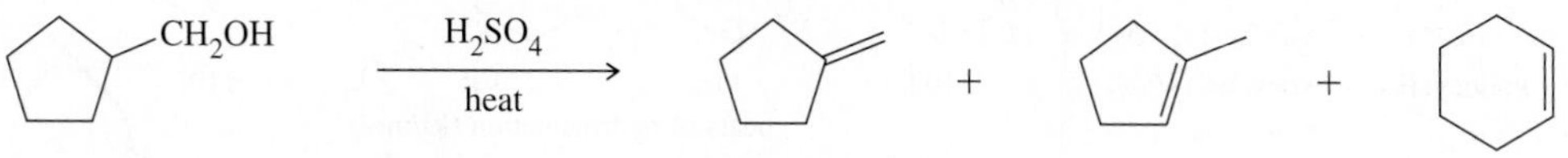 CH_2OH — H_2SO_4, heat

(c) 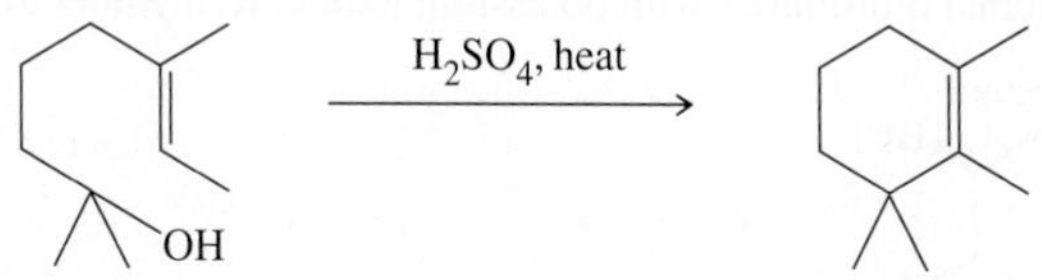 OH — H_2SO_4, heat

(d) 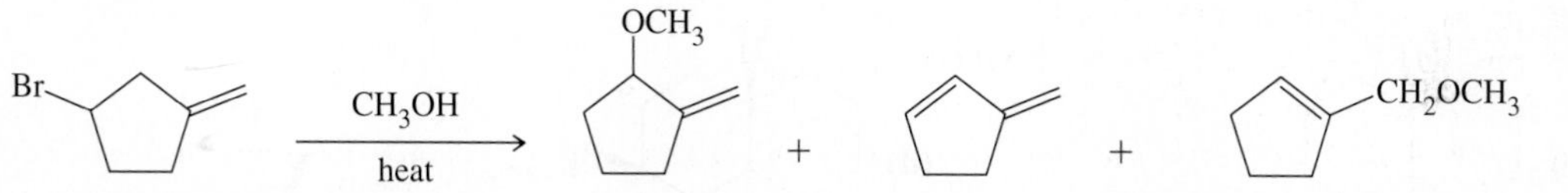 Br — CH_3OH, heat — OCH_3 + + CH_2OCH_3

7-46 Predict the dehydrohalogenation product(s) that result when the following alkyl halides are heated in alcoholic KOH. When more than one product is formed, predict the major and minor products.

(a) $(CH_3)_2CH-C(CH_3)_2$ with Br

(b) $(CH_3)_2CH-CH-CH_3$ with Br

(c) $(CH_3)_2C-CH_2-CH_3$ with Br

(d) CH_3, Cl, H D

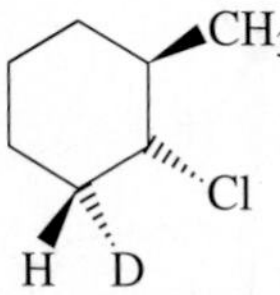

(e) 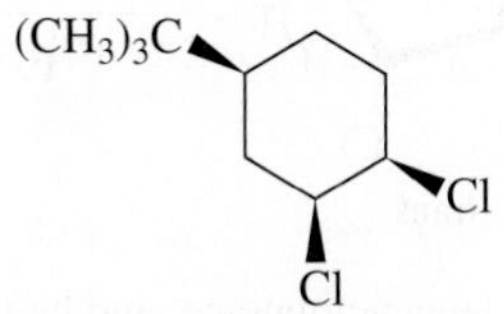 $(CH_3)_3C$, Cl, Cl

(f) 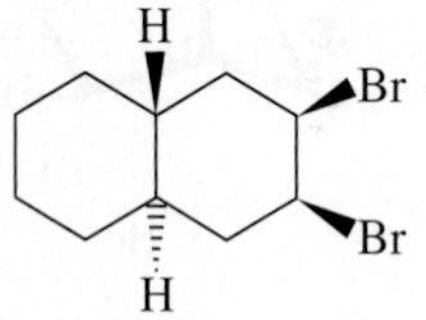 H, Br, Br, H

7-47 E1 eliminations of alkyl halides are rarely useful for synthetic purposes because they give mixtures of substitution and elimination products. Explain why the sulfuric acid-catalyzed dehydration of cyclohexanol gives a good yield of cyclohexene even though the reaction goes by an E1 mechanism. (*Hint*: What are the nucleophiles in the reaction mixture? What products are formed if these nucleophiles attack the carbocation? What further reactions can these substitution products undergo?)

***7-48** The following reaction is called the *pinacol rearrangement*. The reaction begins with an acid-promoted ionization to give a carbocation. This carbocation undergoes a methyl shift to give a more stable, resonance-stabilized cation. Loss of a proton gives the observed product. Propose a mechanism for the pinacol rearrangement.

$$CH_3-\underset{HO}{\overset{H_3C}{C}}-\underset{OH}{\overset{CH_3}{C}}-CH_3 \xrightarrow{H_2SO_4,\ heat} CH_3-\overset{O}{\overset{\|}{C}}-\underset{CH_3}{\overset{CH_3}{C}}-CH_3$$

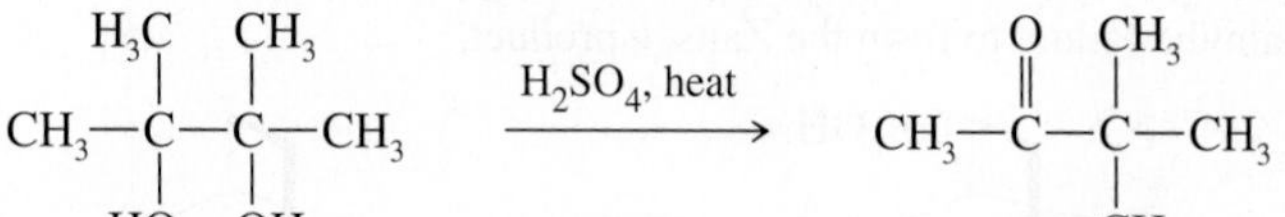

pinacol — pinacolone

7-49 Propose a mechanism to explain the formation of two products in the following reaction.

NBS, $h\nu$ — Br + CH_2Br

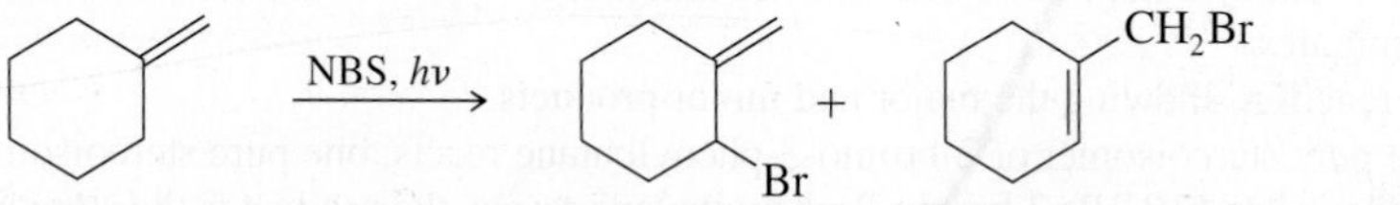

7-50 A chemist allows some pure (2*S*,3*R*)-3-bromo-2,3-diphenylpentane to react with a solution of sodium ethoxide ($NaOCH_2CH_3$) in ethanol. The products are two alkenes: **A** (cis-trans mixture) and **B**, a single pure isomer. Under the same conditions, the reaction of (2*S*,3*S*)-3-bromo-2,3-diphenylpentane gives two alkenes, **A** (cis-trans mixture) and **C**. Upon catalytic hydrogenation, all three of these alkenes (**A**, **B**, and **C**) give 2,3-diphenylpentane. Determine the structures of **A**, **B**, and **C**, give equations for their formation, and explain the stereospecificity of these reactions.

7-51 The energy difference between *cis*- and *trans*-2-butene is about 4 kJ/mol; however, the trans isomer of 4,4-dimethyl-2-pentene is nearly 16 kJ/mol more stable than the cis isomer. Explain this large difference.

7-52 A double bond in a six-membered ring is usually more stable in an endocyclic position than in an exocyclic position. Hydrogenation data on two pairs of compounds follow. One pair suggests that the energy difference between endocyclic and exocyclic double bonds is about 9 kJ/mol. The other pair suggests an energy difference of about 5 kJ/mol. Which number do you trust as being more representative of the actual energy difference? Explain your answer.

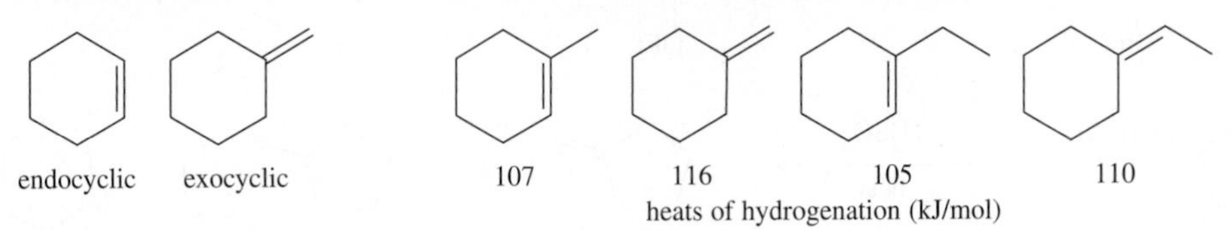

7-53 Predict the products of the following eliminations of vicinal dibromides with potassium iodide. Remember to consider the geometric constraints of the E2 reaction.

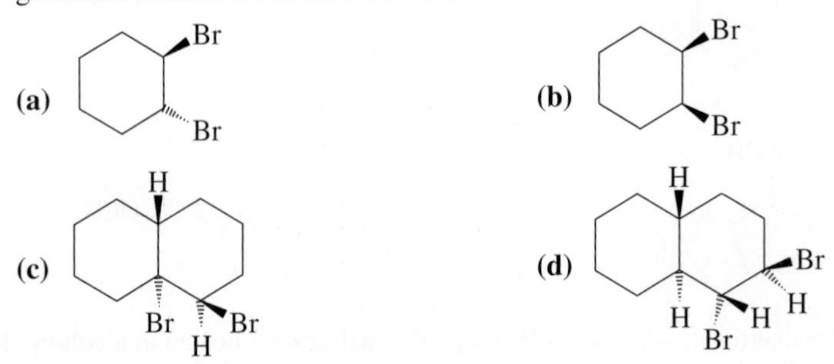

***7-54** One of the following dichloronorbornanes undergoes elimination much faster than the other. Determine which one reacts faster, and explain the large difference in rates.

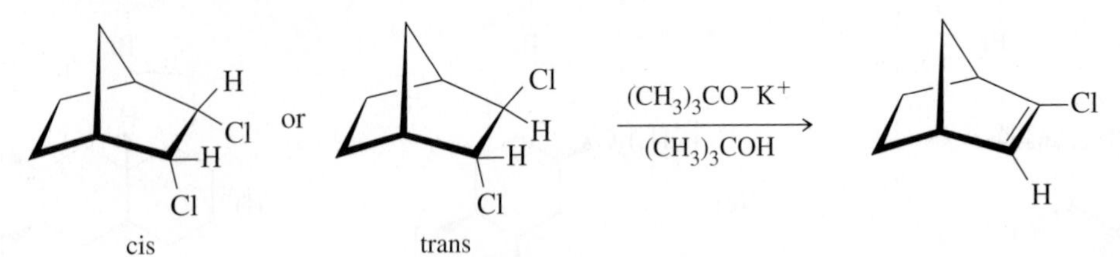

***7-55** A graduate student wanted to make methylenecyclobutane, and he tried the following reaction. Propose structures for the other products, and give mechanisms to account for their formation.

$$\text{cyclobutyl}-CH_2OH \xrightarrow[\text{heat}]{H_2SO_4} \text{methylenecyclobutane (minor)} + \text{other product}$$

***7-56** Write a mechanism that explains the formation of the following product. In your mechanism, explain the cause of the rearrangement, and explain the failure to form the Zaitsev product.

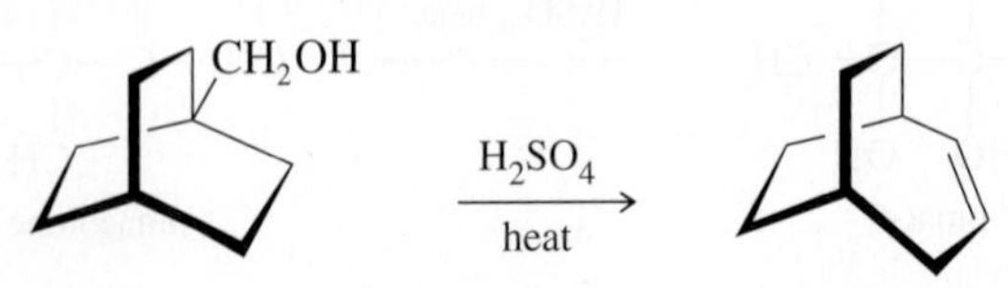

***7-57** When 2-bromo-3-phenylbutane is treated with sodium methoxide, two alkenes result (by E2 elimination). The Zaitsev product predominates.

(a) Draw the reaction, showing the major and minor products.

(b) When one pure stereoisomer of 2-bromo-3-phenylbutane reacts, one pure stereoisomer of the major product results. For example, when (2*R*,3*R*)-2-bromo-3-phenylbutane reacts, the product is the stereoisomer with the methyl groups cis. Use your models to draw a Newman projection of the transition state to show why this stereospecificity is observed.

(c) Use a Newman projection of the transition state to predict the major product of elimination of (2*R*,3*R*)-2-bromo-3-phenylbutane.

(d) Predict the major product from elimination of (2*R*,3*R*)-2-bromo-3-phenylbutane. This prediction can be made without drawing any structures, by considering the results in part (b).

CHAPTER

REACTIONS OF ALKENES

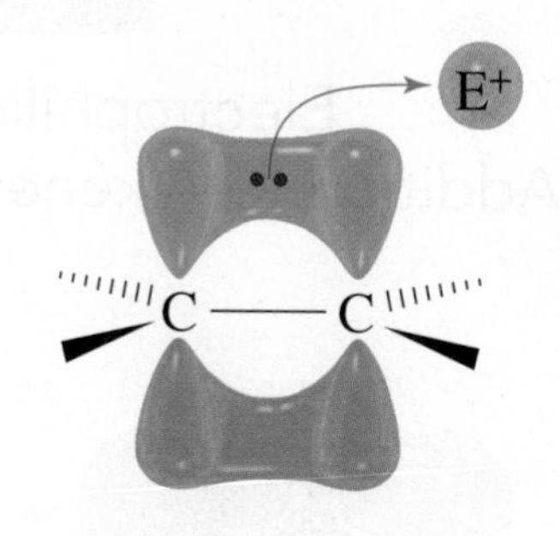

All alkenes have a common feature: a carbon–carbon double bond. The reactions of alkenes arise from the reactivity of the carbon–carbon double bond. Once again, the concept of the functional group helps to organize and simplify the study of chemical reactions. By studying the characteristic reactions of the double bond, we can predict the reactions of alkenes we have never seen before.

8-1 Reactivity of the Carbon–Carbon Double Bond

Because single bonds (sigma bonds) are more stable than pi bonds, the most common reactions of double bonds transform the pi bond into a sigma bond. For example, catalytic hydrogenation converts the C=C pi bond and the H—H sigma bond into two C—H sigma bonds (Section 7-7). The reaction is exothermic (ΔH° = about -80 to -120 kJ/mol or about -20 to -30 kcal/mol), showing that the product is more stable than the reactants.

$$\text{>C=C<} \;+\; \text{H—H} \xrightarrow{\text{catalyst}} \text{—}\overset{|}{\underset{\text{H}}{\text{C}}}\text{—}\overset{|}{\underset{\text{H}}{\text{C}}}\text{—} \;+\; \text{energy}$$

Hydrogenation of an alkene is an example of an **addition**, one of the three major reaction types we have studied: addition, elimination, and substitution. In an addition, two molecules combine to form one product molecule. When an alkene undergoes addition, two groups add to the carbon atoms of the double bond and the carbons become saturated. In many ways, addition is the reverse of **elimination**, in which one molecule splits into two fragment molecules. In a **substitution**, one fragment replaces another fragment in a molecule.

Addition

$$\text{>C=C<} \;+\; \text{X—Y} \longrightarrow \text{—}\overset{|}{\underset{\text{X}}{\text{C}}}\text{—}\overset{|}{\underset{\text{Y}}{\text{C}}}\text{—}$$

Elimination

$$\text{—}\overset{|}{\underset{\text{X}}{\text{C}}}\text{—}\overset{|}{\underset{\text{Y}}{\text{C}}}\text{—} \longrightarrow \text{>C=C<} \;+\; \text{X—Y}$$

Substitution

$$\text{—}\overset{|}{\underset{|}{\text{C}}}\text{—X} \;+\; \text{Y}^- \longrightarrow \text{—}\overset{|}{\underset{|}{\text{C}}}\text{—Y} \;+\; \text{X}^-$$

Addition is the most common reaction of alkenes, and in this chapter we consider additions to alkenes in detail. A wide variety of functional groups can be formed by adding suitable reagents to the double bonds of alkenes.

8-2 Electrophilic Addition to Alkenes

In principle, many different reagents could add to a double bond to form more stable products; that is, the reactions are energetically favorable. Not all of these reactions have convenient rates, however. For example, the reaction of ethylene with hydrogen (to give ethane) is strongly exothermic, but the rate is very slow. A mixture of ethylene and hydrogen can remain for years without appreciable reaction. Adding a catalyst such as platinum, palladium, or nickel allows the reaction to take place at a rapid rate.

Some reagents react with carbon–carbon double bonds without the aid of a catalyst. To understand what types of reagents react with double bonds, consider the structure of the pi bond. Although the electrons in the sigma bond framework are tightly held, the pi bond is delocalized above and below the sigma bond (Figure 8-1). The pi-bonding electrons are spread farther from the carbon nuclei, and they are more loosely held. A strong electrophile has an affinity for these loosely held electrons. It can pull them away to form a new bond (Figure 8-2), leaving one of the carbon atoms with only three bonds and a positive charge: a carbocation. In effect, the double bond has reacted as a nucleophile, donating a pair of electrons to the electrophile.

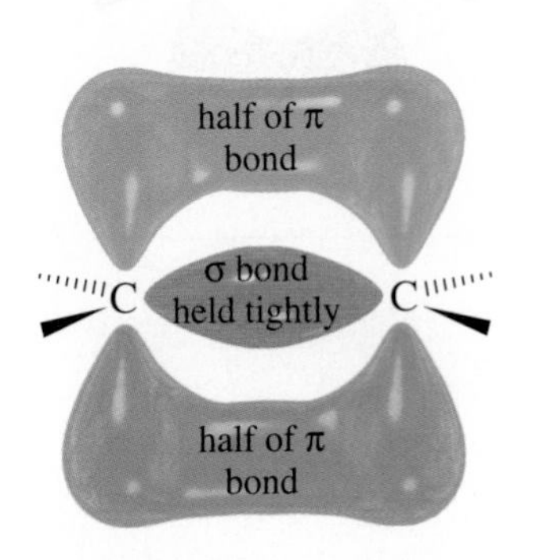

■ **FIGURE 8-1**
The electrons in the pi bond are spread farther from the carbon nuclei and are more loosely held than the sigma electrons.

Most addition reactions involve a second step in which a nucleophile attacks the carbocation (as in the second step of the S_N1 reaction), forming a stable addition product. In the product, both the electrophile and the nucleophile are bonded to the carbon atoms that were connected by the double bond. This reaction is outlined in Key Mechanism 8-1, identifying the electrophile as E^+ and the nucleophile as $Nuc:^-$. This type of reaction requires a strong electrophile to attract the electrons of the pi bond and generate a carbocation in the rate-limiting step. Most alkene reactions fall into this large class of **electrophilic additions** to alkenes.

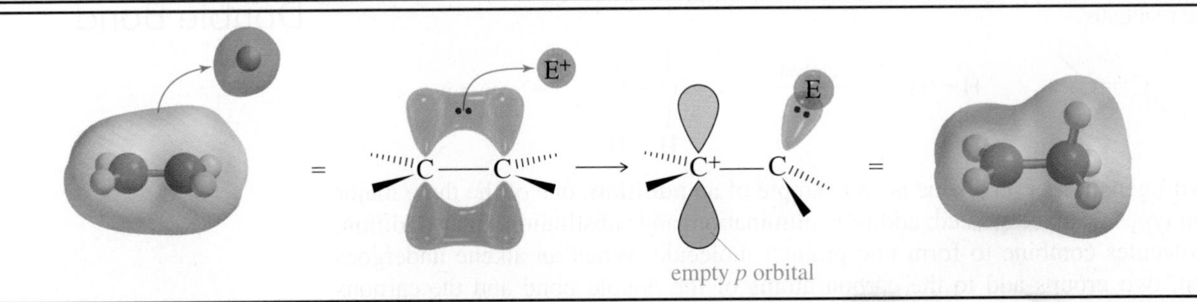

■ **FIGURE 8-2**
The pi bond as a nucleophile. A strong electrophile attracts the electrons out of the pi bond to form a new sigma bond, generating a carbocation. The (red) curved arrow shows the movement of electrons, from the electron-rich pi bond to the electron-poor electrophile.

KEY MECHANISM 8-1 Electrophilic Addition to Alkenes

A wide variety of electrophilic additions involve similar mechanisms. First, a strong electrophile attracts the loosely held electrons from the pi bond of an alkene. The electrophile forms a sigma bond to one of the carbons of the (former) double bond, while the other carbon becomes a carbocation. The carbocation (a strong electrophile) reacts with a nucleophile (often a weak nucleophile) to form another sigma bond.

Step 1: Attack of the pi bond on the electrophile forms a carbocation.

$$\text{>C=C<} \; + \; E^+ \; \longrightarrow \; -\underset{E}{\underset{|}{\overset{|}{C}}}-C^+<$$

+ on the more substituted carbon

Step 2: Attack by a nucleophile gives the addition product.

$$-\underset{E}{\overset{|}{C}}-\overset{|}{C^+}\!\!\diagdown + \text{Nuc:}^- \longrightarrow -\underset{E}{\overset{|}{C}}-\underset{\text{Nuc}}{\overset{|}{C}}-$$

EXAMPLE: Ionic addition of HBr to 2-butene

This example shows what happens when gaseous HBr adds to 2-butene. The proton in HBr is electrophilic; it reacts with the alkene to form a carbocation. Bromide ion reacts rapidly with the carbocation to give a stable product in which the elements of HBr have added to the ends of the double bond.

Step 1: Protonation of the double bond forms a carbocation.

$$CH_3-\overset{H}{C}=\overset{H}{C}-CH_3 \quad \text{H—}\ddot{Br}: \quad \rightleftarrows \quad CH_3-\underset{H}{\overset{H}{C}}-\overset{H}{\underset{+}{C}}-CH_3 \; + \; :\ddot{Br}:^-$$

Step 2: Bromide ion attacks the carbocation.

$$CH_3-\underset{H}{\overset{H}{C}}-\overset{H}{\underset{+}{C}}-CH_3 \; + \; :\ddot{Br}:^- \quad \rightleftarrows \quad CH_3-\underset{H}{\overset{H}{C}}-\underset{:Br:}{\overset{H}{C}}-CH_3$$

PROBLEM: Explain why the + charge of the carbocation always appears at the carbon of the (former) double bond that has NOT bonded to the electrophile.

We will consider several types of additions to alkenes, using a wide variety of reagents: water, borane, hydrogen, carbenes, halogens, oxidizing agents, and even other alkenes. Most, but not all, of these will be electrophilic additions. Table 8-1 summarizes

TABLE 8-1

Types of Additions to Alkenes

$\diagdown C=C \diagup$ Type of Addition [Elements Added][a]	Product	Type of Addition [Elements Added][a]	Product
hydration $[H_2O]$	$-\overset{H}{C}-\overset{OH}{C}-$	halogenation $[X_2]$, an oxidation	$-\overset{X}{C}-\overset{X}{C}-$
hydrogenation $[H_2]$, a reduction	$-\overset{H}{C}-\overset{H}{C}-$	halohydrin formation [HOX], an oxidation	$-\overset{X}{C}-\overset{OH}{C}-$
hydroxylation [HOOH], an oxidation	$-\overset{OH}{C}-\overset{OH}{C}-$	HX addition [HX] (hydrohalogenation)	$-\overset{H}{C}-\overset{X}{C}-$
oxidative cleavage $[O_2]$, an oxidation	$\diagdown C=O \quad O=C \diagup$	cyclopropanation $[CH_2]$	$-C-C-$ bridged by CH_2 (cyclopropane)
epoxidation [O], an oxidation	$-C-C-$ bridged by O (epoxide)		

[a]These are not the reagents used but simply the groups that appear in the product.

the classes of additions we will cover. Note that the table shows what elements have added across the double bond in the final product, but it says nothing about reagents or mechanisms. As we study these reactions, you should note the *regiochemistry* of each reaction, also called the *orientation of addition*, meaning which part of the reagent adds to which end of the double bond. Also note the *stereochemistry* if the reaction is stereospecific.

8-3 Addition of Hydrogen Halides to Alkenes

8-3A Orientation of Addition: Markovnikov's Rule

The simple mechanism shown for addition of HBr to 2-butene applies to a large number of electrophilic additions. We can use this mechanism to predict the outcome of some fairly complicated reactions. For example, the addition of HBr to 2-methyl-2-butene could lead to either of two products, yet only one is observed.

$$CH_3-C(CH_3)=CH-CH_3 + H-Br \longrightarrow CH_3-C(CH_3)(Br)-CH(H)-CH_3 \text{ (observed)} \quad \text{or} \quad CH_3-C(CH_3)(H)-CH(Br)-CH_3 \text{ (not observed)}$$

The first step is protonation of the double bond. If the proton adds to the secondary carbon, the product will be different from the one formed if the proton adds to the tertiary carbon.

$$CH_3-C(CH_3)=CH-CH_3 + H-Br \xrightarrow{\text{add } H^+ \text{ to secondary carbon}} CH_3-\overset{+}{C}(CH_3)-CH(H)-CH_3 \quad Br^-$$

tertiary carbocation

$$CH_3-C(CH_3)=CH-CH_3 + H-Br \xrightarrow{\text{add } H^+ \text{ to tertiary carbon}} CH_3-C(CH_3)(H)-\overset{+}{C}H-CH_3 \quad Br^-$$

secondary carbocation

problem-solving Hint

Stability of carbocations:
$3° > 2° > 1° > {}^+CH_3$
An electrophile adds to a double bond to give the most stable carbocation in the intermediate.

When the proton adds to the secondary carbon, a tertiary carbocation results. When the proton adds to the tertiary carbon atom, a secondary carbocation results. The tertiary carbocation is more stable (see Section 4-16A), so the first reaction is favored.

The second half of the mechanism produces the final product of the addition of HBr to 2-methyl-2-butene.

$$CH_3-\overset{+}{C}(CH_3)-CH(H)-CH_3 + Br:^- \longrightarrow CH_3-C(CH_3)(Br)-CH(H)-CH_3$$

Note that protonation of one carbon atom of a double bond gives a carbocation on the carbon atom that was *not* protonated. Therefore, the proton adds to the end of the double bond that is *less* substituted to give the *more substituted carbocation* (the more stable carbocation).

MECHANISM 8-2 Ionic Addition of HX to an Alkene

Step 1: Protonation of the pi bond forms a carbocation.

+ on the more substituted carbon

Step 2: Attack by the halide ion gives the addition product.

EXAMPLE:

The ionic addition of HBr to propene shows protonation of the less substituted carbon to give the more substituted carbocation. Reaction with bromide ion completes the addition.

less substituted

product

Positive charge on less substituted carbon. Less stable; *not formed.*

There are many examples of reactions where the proton adds to the less substituted carbon atom of the double bond in order to produce the more substituted carbocation. The addition of HBr (and other hydrogen halides) is said to be **regioselective** because in each case, one of the two possible orientations of addition results preferentially over the other.

Markovnikov's Rule A Russian chemist, Vladimir Markovnikov, first showed the orientation of addition of HBr to alkenes in 1869. Markovnikov stated:

> MARKOVNIKOV'S RULE: The addition of a proton acid to the double bond of an alkene results in a product with the acid proton bonded to the carbon atom that already holds the greater number of hydrogen atoms.

This is the original statement of **Markovnikov's rule**. Reactions that follow this rule are said to follow **Markovnikov orientation** and give the **Markovnikov product**. We are often interested in adding electrophiles other than proton acids to the double bonds of alkenes. Markovnikov's rule can be extended to include a wide variety of other additions, based on the addition of the electrophile in such a way as to produce the most stable carbocation.

> MARKOVNIKOV'S RULE (extended): In an electrophilic addition to an alkene, the electrophile adds in such a way as to generate the most stable intermediate.

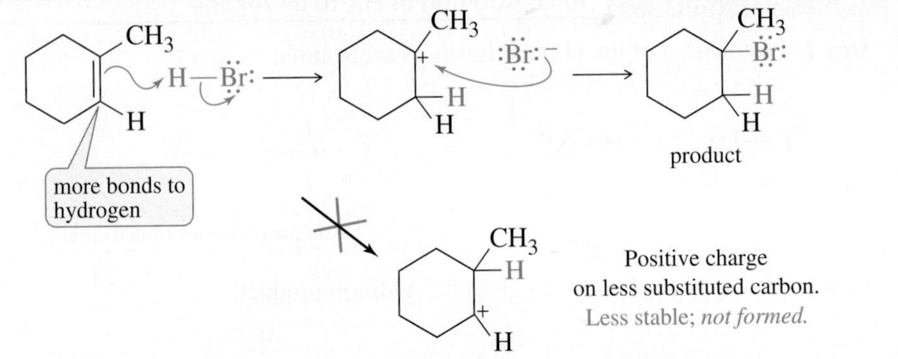

more bonds to hydrogen

product

Positive charge on less substituted carbon. Less stable; *not formed.*

■ **FIGURE 8-3**
An electrophile adds to the less substituted end of the double bond to give the more substituted (and therefore more stable) carbocation.

Figure 8-3 shows how HBr adds to 1-methylcyclohexene to give the product with an additional hydrogen bonded to the carbon that already had the most bonds to hydrogen (one) in the alkene. Note that this orientation results from addition of the proton in the way that generates the more stable carbocation.

Like HBr, both HCl and HI add to the double bonds of alkenes, and they also follow Markovnikov's rule; for example,

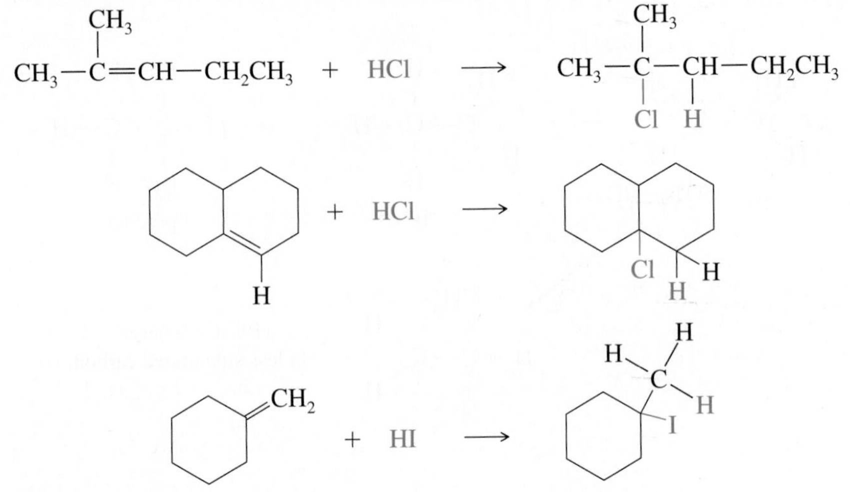

$$CH_3-C(CH_3)=CH-CH_2CH_3 + HCl \longrightarrow CH_3-C(CH_3)(Cl)-CH(H)-CH_2CH_3$$

$$+ \ HCl \longrightarrow$$

$$+ \ HI \longrightarrow$$

PROBLEM 8-1

Predict the major products of the following reactions, and propose mechanisms to support your predictions.

(a) 1-pentene + HBr
(b) 2-methylpropene + HCl
(c) 1-methylcyclohexene + HI
(d) 4-methylcyclohexene + HBr

PROBLEM 8-2

When 1,3-butadiene reacts with 1 mol of HBr, both 3-bromo-1-butene and 1-bromo-2-butene are formed. Propose a mechanism to account for this mixture of products.

8-3B Free-Radical Addition of HBr: Anti-Markovnikov Addition

In 1933, M. S. Kharasch and F. W. Mayo found that some additions of HBr (but not HCl or HI) to alkenes gave products that were opposite to those expected from Markovnikov's rule. These **anti-Markovnikov** reactions were most likely when the reagents or solvents came from old supplies that had accumulated peroxides from exposure to the air. Peroxides give rise to free radicals that initiate the addition, causing it to occur by a radical mechanism. The oxygen–oxygen bond in peroxides is rather weak, so it can break to give two alkoxy radicals.

$$R-\ddot{O}-\ddot{O}-R \xrightarrow{\text{heat}} R-\ddot{O}\cdot + \cdot\ddot{O}-R \qquad \Delta H^\circ = +150 \text{ kJ } (+36 \text{ kcal})$$

Alkoxy radicals (R—O·) initiate the anti-Markovnikov addition of HBr. The mechanism of this free-radical chain reaction is shown in Mechanism 8-3.

MECHANISM 8-3 Free-Radical Addition of HBr to Alkenes

Initiation: Formation of radicals.

$$\text{R—O—O—R} \xrightarrow{\text{heat}} \text{R—O}\cdot + \cdot\text{O—R}$$

$$\text{R—O}\cdot + \text{H—Br} \longrightarrow \text{R—O—H} + \text{Br}\cdot$$

Propagation: A radical reacts to generate another radical.

Step 1: A bromine radical adds to the double bond to generate an alkyl radical on the more substituted carbon atom.

$$\text{C=C} + \text{Br}\cdot \longrightarrow \text{—C(Br)—C}\cdot$$

radical on the more substituted carbon

Step 2: The alkyl radical abstracts a hydrogen atom from HBr to generate the product and a bromine radical.

$$\text{—C(Br)—C}\cdot + \text{H—Br} \longrightarrow \text{—C(Br)—C(H)—} + \text{Br}\cdot$$

The bromine radical generated in Step 2 goes on to react with another molecule of alkene in Step 1, continuing the chain.

EXAMPLE: Free-radical addition of HBr to propene.

Initiation: Radicals are formed.

$$\text{R—O—O—R} \xrightarrow{\text{heat}} \text{R—O}\cdot + \cdot\text{O—R}$$

$$\text{R—O}\cdot + \text{H—Br} \longrightarrow \text{R—O—H} + \text{Br}\cdot$$

Propagation: A radical reacts to generate another radical.

Step 1: A bromine radical adds to the double bond to generate an alkyl radical on the secondary carbon atom.

$$\text{(H}_3\text{C)(H)C=CH}_2 + \text{Br}\cdot \longrightarrow \text{(H}_3\text{C)(H)}\dot{\text{C}}\text{—C(Br)(H)—H}$$

· on the 2° carbon

Step 2: The alkyl radical abstracts a hydrogen atom from HBr to generate the product and a bromine radical.

$$\text{(H}_3\text{C)(H)}\dot{\text{C}}\text{—C(Br)(H)—H} + \text{H—Br} \longrightarrow \text{H—C(H)(CH}_3\text{)—C(Br)(H)—H} + \text{Br}\cdot$$

The bromine radical generated in Step 2 goes on to react in Step 1, continuing the chain.

Let's consider the individual steps. In the initiation step, free radicals generated from the peroxide react with HBr to form bromine radicals.

$$\mathrm{R{-}\ddot{O}\cdot + H{-}\ddot{B}r: \longrightarrow R{-}\ddot{O}{-}H + :\ddot{B}r\cdot} \qquad \Delta H^\circ = -63\ \text{kJ}\ (-15\ \text{kcal})$$

The bromine radical lacks an octet of electrons in its valence shell, making it electron-deficient and electrophilic. It adds to a double bond, forming a new free radical with the odd electron on a carbon atom.

$$\mathrm{:\ddot{B}r\cdot + \;>C{=}C<\; \longrightarrow -\underset{:\ddot{B}r:}{\overset{|}{C}}-\dot{C}<} \qquad \Delta H^\circ = -12\ \text{kJ}\ (-3\ \text{kcal})$$

This free radical reacts with an HBr molecule to form a C—H bond and generate another bromine radical.

$$\mathrm{-\underset{Br}{\overset{|}{C}}-\dot{C}< + H{-}\ddot{B}r: \longrightarrow -\underset{Br}{\overset{|}{C}}-\underset{H}{\overset{|}{C}}- + :\ddot{B}r\cdot} \qquad \Delta H^\circ = -25\ \text{kJ}\ (-6\ \text{kcal})$$

The regenerated bromine radical reacts with another molecule of the alkene, continuing the chain reaction. Both of the propagation steps are moderately exothermic, allowing them to proceed faster than the termination steps. Note that each propagation step starts with one free radical and ends with another free radical. The number of free radicals is constant, until the reactants are consumed, and free radicals come together and terminate the chain reaction.

Radical Addition of HBr to Unsymmetrical Alkenes Now we must explain the anti-Markovnikov orientation found in the products of the peroxide-catalyzed reaction. With an unsymmetrical alkene like 2-methyl-2-butene, adding the bromine radical to the secondary end of the double bond forms a tertiary radical.

$$\mathrm{CH_3{-}\overset{CH_3}{\overset{|}{C}}{=}CH{-}CH_3 + Br\cdot \longrightarrow CH_3{-}\overset{CH_3}{\overset{|}{\dot{C}}}{-}\underset{Br}{\underset{|}{CH}}{-}CH_3 \quad \text{but not} \quad CH_3{-}\overset{CH_3}{\overset{|}{\underset{Br}{\underset{|}{C}}}}{-}\dot{C}H{-}CH_3}$$

tertiary radical (more stable) — secondary radical (less stable)

As we saw in the protonation of an alkene, the electrophile (in this case, Br·) adds to the less substituted end of the double bond, and the unpaired electron appears on the more substituted carbon to give the more stable free radical. This intermediate reacts with HBr to give the anti-Markovnikov product, in which H has added to the more substituted end of the double bond: the end that started with *fewer* hydrogens.

$$\mathrm{CH_3{-}\overset{CH_3}{\overset{|}{\dot{C}}}{-}\underset{Br}{\underset{|}{CH}}{-}CH_3 + H{-}Br \longrightarrow CH_3{-}\overset{CH_3}{\overset{|}{\underset{H}{\underset{|}{C}}}}{-}\underset{Br}{\underset{|}{CH}}{-}CH_3 + Br\cdot}$$

anti-Markovnikov product

Note that *both* mechanisms for the addition of HBr to an alkene (with and without peroxides) follow our extended statement of Markovnikov's rule: In both cases, the electrophile adds to the less substituted end of the double bond to give the more stable intermediate, either a carbocation or a free radical. In the ionic reaction, the electrophile is H^+. In the peroxide-catalyzed free-radical reaction, Br· is the electrophile.

Many students wonder why the reaction with Markovnikov orientation does not take place in the presence of peroxides, together with the free-radical chain reaction. It actually does take place, but the peroxide-catalyzed reaction is faster. If just a tiny

problem-solving Hint

Stability of radicals:

3° > 2° > 1° > ·CH_3

A radical adds to a double bond to give the most stable radical in the intermediate.

bit of peroxide is present, a mixture of Markovnikov and anti-Markovnikov products results. If an appreciable amount of peroxide is present, the radical chain reaction is so much faster than the uncatalyzed ionic reaction that only the anti-Markovnikov product is observed.

The reversal of orientation in the presence of peroxides is called the **peroxide effect**. It occurs only with the addition of HBr to alkenes. The peroxide effect is not seen with HCl because the reaction of an alkyl radical with HCl is strongly endothermic.

$$\text{Cl—C—C}\cdot + \text{H—Cl} \longrightarrow \text{Cl—C—C—H} + \text{Cl}\cdot \qquad \Delta H° = +42 \text{ kJ } (+10 \text{ kcal})$$

Similarly, the peroxide effect is not observed with HI because the reaction of an iodine atom with an alkene is strongly endothermic. Only HBr has just the right reactivity for each step of the free-radical chain reaction to take place.

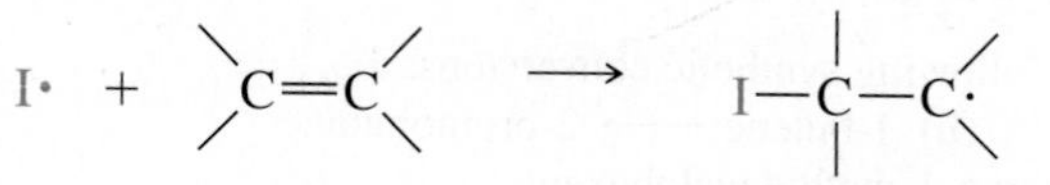

$$\text{I}\cdot + \text{C=C} \longrightarrow \text{I—C—C}\cdot \qquad \Delta H° = +54 \text{ kJ } (+13 \text{ kcal})$$

PROBLEM 8-3

Predict the major products of the following reactions, and propose mechanisms to support your predictions.

(a) 1-methylcyclopentene + HBr + $CH_3\text{—C(=O)—O—O—C(=O)—}CH_3$

(b) 1-phenylpropene + HBr + di-*tert*-butyl peroxide (phenyl = Ph = C_6H_5—)

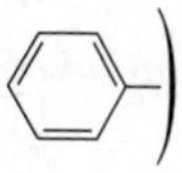

problem-solving Hint

Remember to write out complete structures, including all bonds and charges, when writing a mechanism or determining the course of a reaction.

SOLVED PROBLEM 8-1

Show how you would accomplish the following synthetic conversions.

(a) Convert 1-methylcyclohexene to 1-bromo-1-methylcyclohexane.

SOLUTION

This synthesis requires the addition of HBr to an alkene with Markovnikov orientation. Ionic addition of HBr gives the correct product.

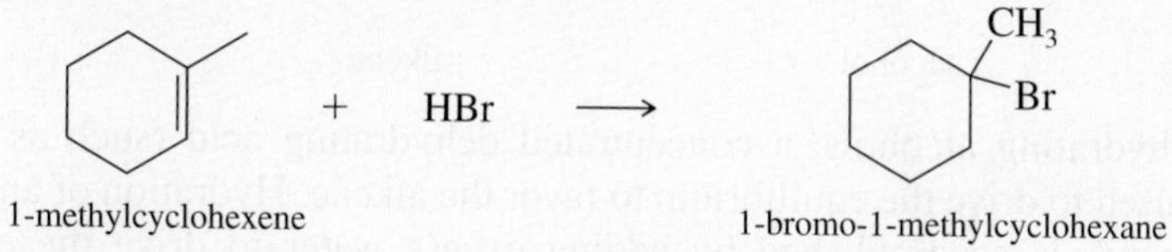

1-methylcyclohexene + HBr ⟶ 1-bromo-1-methylcyclohexane

(b) Convert 1-methylcyclohexanol to 1-bromo-2-methylcyclohexane.

SOLUTION

This synthesis requires the conversion of an alcohol to an alkyl bromide with the bromine atom at the neighboring carbon atom. This is the anti-Markovnikov product, which could be formed by the radical-catalyzed addition of HBr to 1-methylcyclohexene.

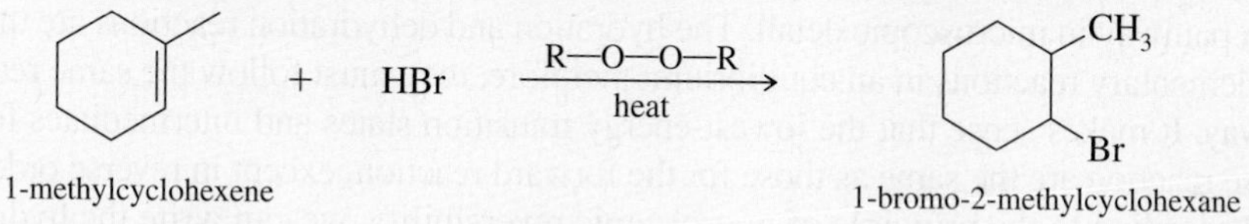

1-methylcyclohexene + HBr —(R—O—O—R, heat)⟶ 1-bromo-2-methylcyclohexane

(Continued)

1-Methylcyclohexene is easily synthesized by the dehydration of 1-methylcyclohexanol. The most substituted alkene is the desired product.

$$\text{1-methylcyclohexanol} \xrightarrow[\text{heat}]{H_2SO_4} \text{1-methylcyclohexene} + H_2O$$

The two-step synthesis is summarized as follows:

$$\text{1-methylcyclohexanol} \xrightarrow[\text{heat}]{H_2SO_4} \text{1-methylcyclohexene} \xrightarrow[\text{ROOR}]{HBr} \text{1-bromo-2-methylcyclohexane}$$

PROBLEM 8-4

Show how you would accomplish the following synthetic conversions.
(a) 1-butene ⟶ 1-bromobutane **(b)** 1-butene ⟶ 2-bromobutane
(c) 2-methylcyclohexanol ⟶ 1-bromo-1-methylcyclohexane
(d) 2-methyl-2-butanol ⟶ 2-bromo-3-methylbutane

8-4 Addition of Water: Hydration of Alkenes

An alkene may react with water in the presence of a strongly acidic catalyst to form an alcohol. Formally, this reaction is a **hydration** (the addition of water), with a hydrogen atom adding to one carbon and a hydroxyl group adding to the other. Hydration of an alkene is the reverse of the dehydration of alcohols we studied in Section 7-10.

Hydration of an alkene

$$\underset{\text{alkene}}{>C=C<} + H_2O \underset{}{\overset{H^+}{\rightleftarrows}} \underset{\substack{\text{alcohol} \\ \text{(Markovnikov orientation)}}}{-\overset{H}{\underset{|}{\overset{|}{C}}}-\overset{OH}{\underset{|}{\overset{|}{C}}}-}$$

Dehydration of an alcohol

$$\underset{\text{alcohol}}{-\overset{H}{\underset{|}{\overset{|}{C}}}-\overset{OH}{\underset{|}{\overset{|}{C}}}-} \overset{H^+}{\rightleftarrows} \underset{\text{alkene}}{>C=C<} + H_2O$$

For dehydrating alcohols, a concentrated dehydrating acid (such as H_2SO_4 or H_3PO_4) is used to drive the equilibrium to favor the alkene. Hydration of an alkene, on the other hand, is accomplished by adding excess water to drive the equilibrium toward the alcohol.

8-4A Mechanism of Hydration

The *principle of microscopic reversibility* states that a forward reaction and a reverse reaction taking place under the same conditions (as in an equilibrium) must follow the same reaction pathway in microscopic detail. The hydration and dehydration reactions are the two complementary reactions in an equilibrium; therefore, they must follow the same reaction pathway. It makes sense that the lowest-energy transition states and intermediates for the reverse reaction are the same as those for the forward reaction, except in reverse order.

According to the principle of microscopic reversibility, we can write the hydration mechanism by reversing the order of the steps of the dehydration (Section 7-10).

Protonation of the double bond forms a carbocation. Nucleophilic attack by water, followed by loss of a proton, gives the alcohol.

MECHANISM 8-4 Acid-Catalyzed Hydration of an Alkene

Step 1: Protonation of the double bond forms a carbocation.

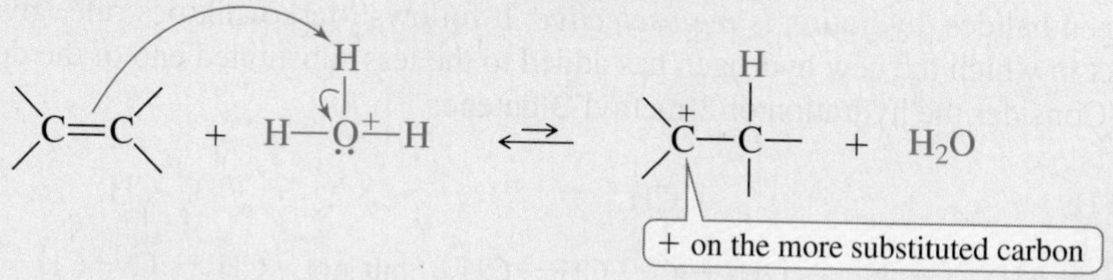

+ on the more substituted carbon

Step 2: Nucleophilic attack by water gives a protonated alcohol.

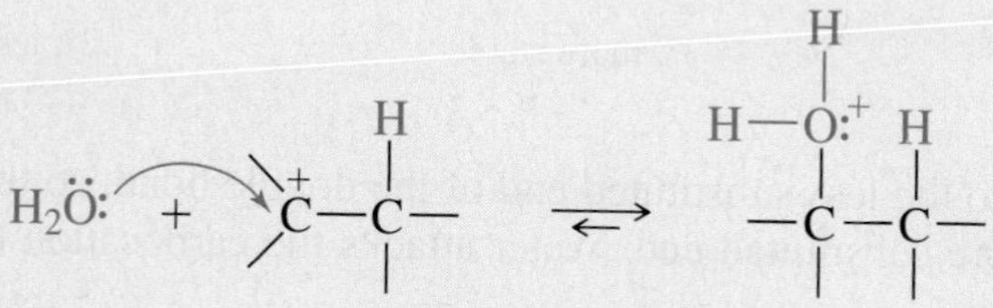

Step 3: Deprotonation gives the alcohol.

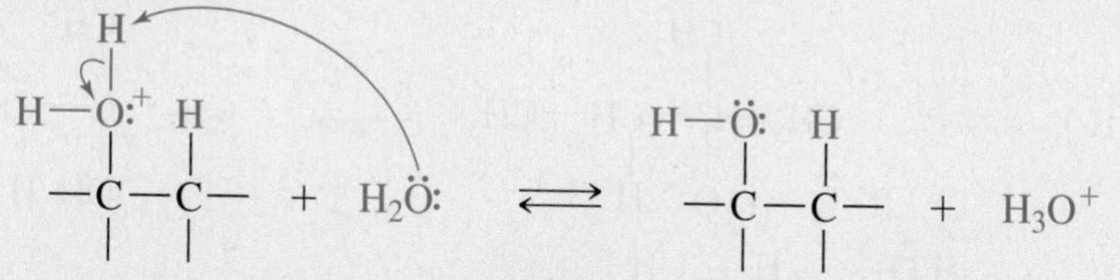

EXAMPLE: Acid-catalyzed hydration of propene.

Step 1: Protonation of the double bond forms a secondary carbocation.

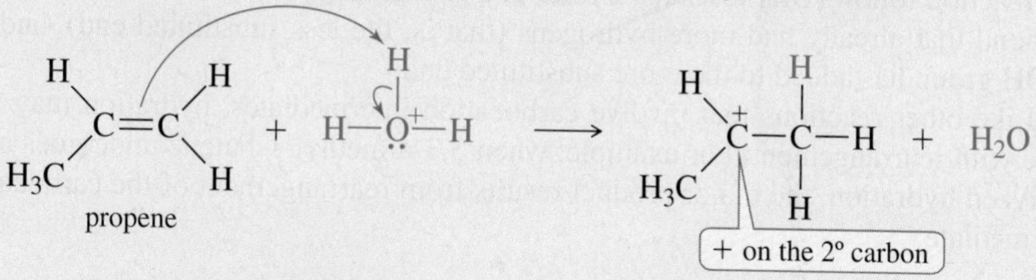

propene

+ on the 2° carbon

Step 2: Nucleophilic attack by water gives a protonated alcohol.

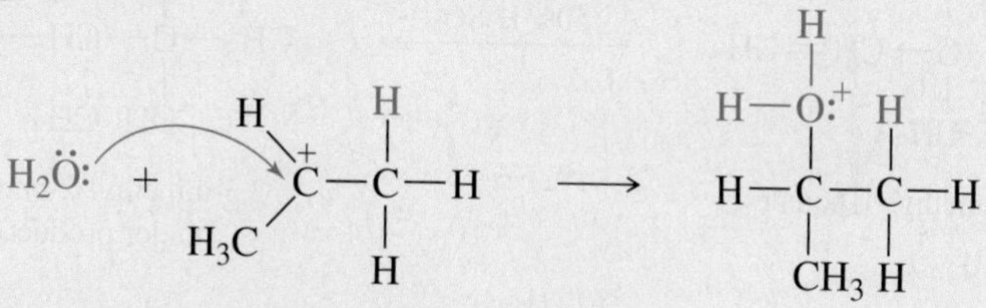

Step 3: Deprotonation gives the alcohol.

2-propanol

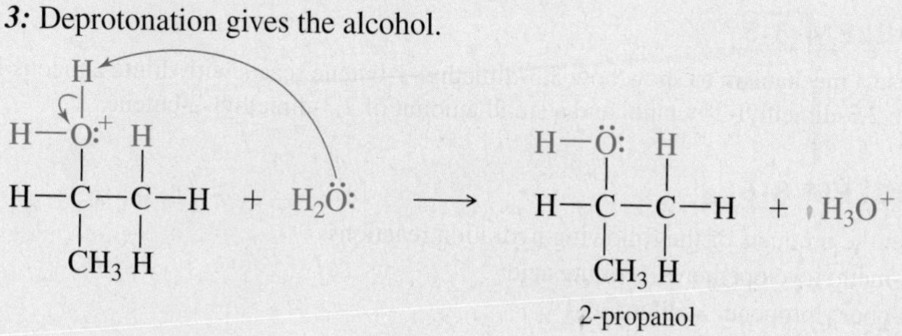

8-4B Orientation of Hydration

Step 1 of the hydration mechanism is similar to the first step in the addition of HBr. The proton adds to the *less* substituted end of the double bond to form the *more* substituted carbocation. Water attacks the carbocation to give (after loss of a proton) the alcohol with the —OH group on the more substituted carbon. Like the addition of hydrogen halides, hydration is *regioselective*: It follows Markovnikov's rule, giving a product in which the new hydrogen has added to the less substituted end of the double bond. Consider the hydration of 2-methyl-2-butene:

$$CH_3-\overset{CH_3}{\overset{|}{C}}=CH-CH_3 + H-\overset{+}{\underset{..}{O}}(H)-H \rightleftharpoons CH_3-\overset{CH_3}{\overset{|}{\underset{+}{C}}}-\underset{H}{\underset{|}{CH}}-CH_3 \text{ but not } CH_3-\overset{CH_3}{\overset{|}{\underset{H}{\underset{|}{C}}}}-\overset{+}{CH}-CH_3$$

3°, more stable — 2°, less stable

The proton adds to the less substituted end of the double bond, so the positive charge appears at the more substituted end. Water attacks the carbocation to give the protonated alcohol.

$$CH_3-\overset{CH_3}{\overset{|}{\underset{+}{C}}}-\underset{H}{\underset{|}{CH}}-CH_3 \;(H_2\ddot{O}:) \rightleftharpoons CH_3-\overset{CH_3}{\overset{|}{C}}(-\overset{+}{O}H_2)-\underset{H}{\underset{|}{CH}}-CH_3 \;(H_2\ddot{O}:) \rightleftharpoons CH_3-\overset{CH_3}{\overset{|}{\underset{OH}{\underset{|}{C}}}}-\underset{H}{\underset{|}{CH}}-CH_3 + H_3O^+$$

The reaction follows Markovnikov's rule. The proton has added to the end of the double bond that already had more hydrogens (that is, the less substituted end), and the —OH group has added to the more substituted end.

Like other reactions that involve carbocation intermediates, hydration may take place with rearrangement. For example, when 3,3-dimethyl-1-butene undergoes acid-catalyzed hydration, the major product results from rearrangement of the carbocation intermediate.

$$CH_3-\overset{CH_3}{\overset{|}{\underset{CH_3}{\underset{|}{C}}}}-CH=CH_2 \xrightarrow{50\%\ H_2SO_4} CH_3-\overset{CH_3}{\overset{|}{\underset{OH}{\underset{|}{C}}}}-\underset{CH_3}{\underset{|}{CH}}-CH_3$$

3,3-dimethyl-1-butene — 2,3-dimethyl-2-butanol (major product)

PROBLEM 8-5

Propose a mechanism to show how 3,3-dimethyl-1-butene reacts with dilute aqueous H_2SO_4 to give 2,3-dimethyl-2-butanol and a small amount of 2,3-dimethyl-2-butene.

problem-solving **Hint**

When predicting products for electrophilic additions, first draw the structure of the carbocation (or other intermediate) that results from electrophilic attack.

PROBLEM 8-6

Predict the products of the following hydration reactions.

(a) 1-methylcyclopentene + dilute acid
(b) 2-phenylpropene + dilute acid
(c) 1-phenylcyclohexene + dilute acid

8-5 Hydration by Oxymercuration–Demercuration

Many alkenes do not easily undergo hydration in aqueous acid. Some alkenes are nearly insoluble in aqueous acid, and others undergo side reactions such as rearrangement, polymerization, or charring under these strongly acidic conditions. In some cases, the overall equilibrium favors the alkene rather than the alcohol. No amount of catalysis can cause a reaction to occur if the energetics are unfavorable.

Oxymercuration–demercuration is another method for converting alkenes to alcohols with Markovnikov orientation. Oxymercuration–demercuration works with many alkenes that do not easily undergo direct hydration, and it takes place under milder conditions. No free carbocation is formed, so there is no opportunity for rearrangements or polymerization.

Oxymercuration–Demercuration

$$>C{=}C< \; + \; Hg(OAc)_2 \xrightarrow{H_2O} -\underset{HO}{\overset{|}{C}}-\underset{HgOAc}{\overset{|}{C}}- \xrightarrow{NaBH_4} -\underset{HO}{\overset{|}{C}}-\underset{H}{\overset{|}{C}}-$$

(Markovnikov orientation)

The reagent for mercuration is mercuric acetate, $Hg(OCOCH_3)_2$, abbreviated $Hg(OAc)_2$. There are several theories as to how this reagent acts as an electrophile; the simplest one is that mercuric acetate dissociates slightly to form a positively charged mercury species, $^{+}Hg(OAc)$.

$$\underset{Hg(OAc)_2}{CH_3-\overset{O}{\overset{\|}{C}}-O-Hg-O-\overset{O}{\overset{\|}{C}}-CH_3} \rightleftarrows \underset{^{+}Hg(OAc)}{CH_3-\overset{O}{\overset{\|}{C}}-O-Hg^{+}} + \underset{^{-}OAc}{CH_3-\overset{O}{\overset{\|}{C}}-O^{-}}$$

Oxymercuration involves an electrophilic attack on the double bond by the positively charged mercury species. The product is a *mercurinium ion*, an organometallic cation containing a three-membered ring. In the second step, water from the solvent attacks the mercurinium ion to give (after deprotonation) an organomercurial alcohol. A subsequent reaction is **demercuration**, to remove the mercury. Sodium borohydride ($NaBH_4$, a reducing agent) replaces the mercuric acetate fragment with a hydrogen atom.

MECHANISM 8-5 Oxymercuration of an Alkene

Step 1: Electrophilic attack forms a mercurinium ion.

$$>C{=}C< \; + \; ^{+}Hg(OAc) \longrightarrow -C-C- \text{ bridged by } Hg^{+}\text{–OAc}$$

mercurinium ion

Step 2: Water opens the ring to give an organomercurial alcohol.

$$\text{mercurinium ion} + H_2\ddot{O}: \longrightarrow -\underset{H-\overset{+}{O}:-H}{\overset{|}{C}}-\overset{Hg(OAc)}{\overset{|}{C}}- \xrightarrow{H_2\ddot{O}:} -\underset{:\ddot{O}H}{\overset{|}{C}}-\overset{Hg(OAc)}{\overset{|}{C}}- + H_3O^{+}$$

organomercurial alcohol

(Continued)

Demercuration replaces the mercuric fragment with hydrogen to give the alcohol.

$$4\ -\overset{\displaystyle Hg(OAc)}{\underset{}{C}}-\underset{\displaystyle OH}{C}- \ +\ NaBH_4\ +\ 4\ {}^-OH \longrightarrow 4\ -\overset{\displaystyle H}{C}-\underset{\displaystyle OH}{C}- \ +\ NaB(OH)_4\ +\ 4\ Hg\downarrow\ +\ 4\ {}^-OAc$$

organomercurial alcohol — alcohol

EXAMPLE: Oxymercuration–demercuration of propene.

Step 1: Electrophilic attack forms a mercurinium ion.

$$\text{propene } (H_3C)HC{=}CH_2 \ +\ {}^+Hg(OAc) \longrightarrow \text{mercurinium ion}$$

propene

mercurinium ion

Step 2: Water opens the ring to give an organomercurial alcohol.

$$\text{mercurinium ion} \xrightarrow{H_2\ddot{O}:} H_3C-\underset{H-\overset{+}{O}:-H}{\overset{H}{C}}-\overset{Hg(OAc)}{\underset{H}{C}}-H \longrightarrow H_3C-\underset{OH}{\overset{H}{C}}-\underset{H}{\overset{Hg(OAc)}{C}}-H + H_3O^+$$

Water attacks the more substituted carbon.

Demercuration replaces the mercuric fragment with hydrogen to give the alcohol.

$$H_3C-\underset{OH}{\overset{H}{C}}-\underset{H}{\overset{Hg(OAc)}{C}}-H \xrightarrow{NaBH_4} H_3C-\underset{OH}{\overset{H}{C}}-\underset{H}{\overset{H}{C}}-H$$

2-propanol

Oxymercuration–demercuration of an unsymmetrical alkene generally gives Markovnikov orientation of addition, as shown by the oxymercuration of propene in the preceding example. The mercurinium ion has a considerable amount of positive charge on both of its carbon atoms, but there is more of a positive charge on the more substituted carbon atom, where it is more stable. Attack by water occurs on this more electrophilic carbon, giving Markovnikov orientation. The electrophile, ${}^+Hg(OAc)$, remains bonded to the less substituted end of the double bond. Reduction of the organomercurial alcohol gives the Markovnikov alcohol: 2-propanol.

Similarly, oxymercuration–demercuration of 3,3-dimethyl-1-butene gives the Markovnikov product, 3,3-dimethyl-2-butanol, in excellent yield. Contrast this unrearranged product with the rearranged product formed in the acid-catalyzed hydration of the same alkene in Section 8-4B. Oxymercuration–demercuration reliably adds water across the double bond of an alkene with Markovnikov orientation and without rearrangement.

$$\underset{\text{3,3-dimethyl-1-butene}}{(CH_3)_3C(H)C{=}CH_2} \xrightarrow[H_2O]{Hg(OAc)_2} \underset{\text{mercurinium ion}}{(CH_3)_3C-\overset{\delta+}{C}H-CH_2-\overset{\delta+}{Hg}(OAc)} \xrightarrow{-H^+} \underset{\text{Markovnikov product}}{(CH_3)_3C-CH(OH)-CH_2-Hg(OAc)}$$

$$\underset{\text{Markovnikov product}}{(CH_3)_3C-CH(OH)-CH_2-Hg(OAc)} \xrightarrow{NaBH_4} \underset{\substack{\text{3,3-dimethyl-2-butanol} \\ \text{(94\% overall)}}}{(CH_3)_3C-CH(OH)-CH_3}$$

Of the methods we have seen for Markovnikov hydration of alkenes, oxymercuration–demercuration is most commonly used in the laboratory. It gives better yields than direct acid-catalyzed hydration, it avoids the possibility of rearrangements, and it does not involve harsh conditions. There are also disadvantages, however. Organomercurial compounds are highly toxic. They must be used with great care and then must be disposed of properly.

8-6 Alkoxymercuration–Demercuration

When mercuration takes place in an alcohol solvent, the alcohol serves as a nucleophile to attack the mercurinium ion. The resulting product contains an alkoxy (—O—R) group. In effect, **alkoxymercuration**–demercuration converts alkenes to ethers by adding an alcohol across the double bond of the alkene.

$$>C{=}C< \; + \; Hg(OAc)_2 \xrightarrow{ROH} -\underset{RO}{C}-\underset{HgOAc}{C}-$$

$$-\underset{RO}{C}-\underset{HgOAc}{C}- \xrightarrow{NaBH_4} \underset{\text{(Markovnikov orientation)}}{-\underset{RO}{C}-\underset{H}{C}-}$$

Mercury and its compounds were used for centuries as ingredients in antibacterial drugs, skin creams, and antiseptics. Mercury compounds are quite toxic, however. In the body, mercury combines with the thiol groups of critical enzymes, inactivating them. Mercury poisoning causes brain and kidney damage, often leading to death.

As we have seen, an alkene reacts to form a mercurinium ion that is attacked by the nucleophilic solvent. Attack by an alcohol solvent gives an organomercurial ether that can be reduced to the ether.

$$\text{mercurinium ion } (^+Hg(OAc)) + R-\ddot{O}-H \longrightarrow -\underset{R-O^+-H}{C}-\underset{}{C}(Hg(OAc))- \xrightarrow{H-\ddot{O}-R} \underset{\text{organomercurial ether}}{-\underset{R-\ddot{O}:}{C}-C(Hg(OAc))-} \xrightarrow{NaBH_4} \underset{\text{an ether}}{-\underset{R-O}{C}-\overset{H}{C}-}$$

The solvent attacks the mercurinium ion at the *more* substituted end of the double bond (where there is more δ^+ charge), giving Markovnikov orientation of addition. The Hg(OAc) group appears at the *less* substituted end of the double bond. Reduction gives the Markovnikov product, with hydrogen at the less substituted end of the double bond.

SOLVED PROBLEM 8-2

Show the intermediates and products that result from alkoxymercuration–demercuration of 1-methylcyclopentene, using methanol as the solvent.

SOLUTION

Mercuric acetate adds to 1-methylcyclopentene to give the cyclic mercurinium ion. This ion has a considerable amount of positive charge on the more substituted tertiary carbon atom. Methanol attacks this carbon from the opposite side, leading to ***anti* addition**: The reagents (HgOAc and OCH_3) have added to opposite faces of the double bond.

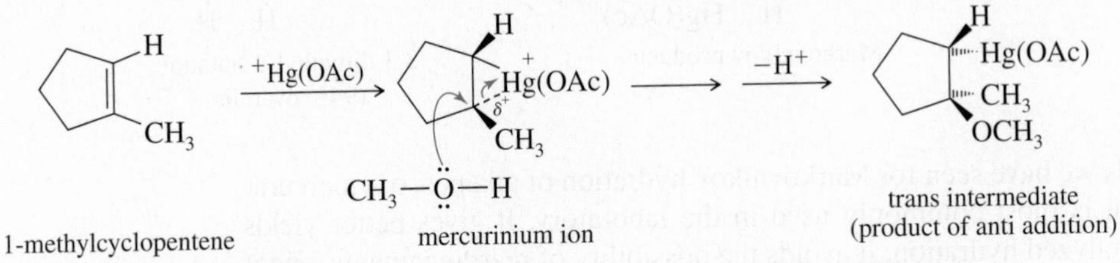

1-methylcyclopentene $\xrightarrow{^{+}Hg(OAc)}$ mercurinium ion (attacked by $CH_3—\ddot{O}—H$) $\longrightarrow \xrightarrow{-H^+}$ trans intermediate (product of anti addition)

Reduction of the intermediate gives the Markovnikov product, 1-methoxy-1-methylcyclopentane.

intermediate $\xrightarrow{NaBH_4}$ 1-methoxy-1-methylcyclopentane

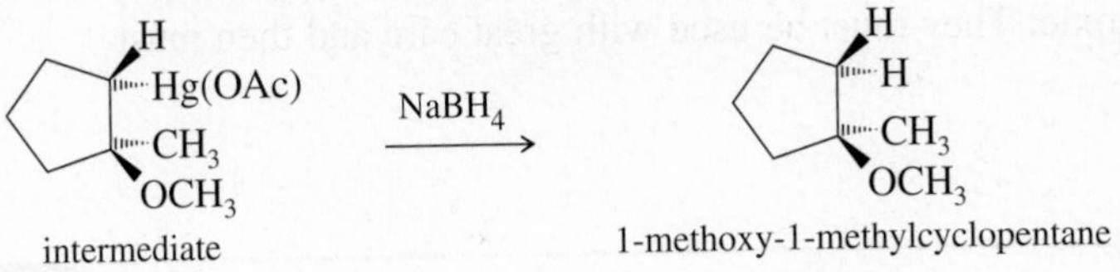

PROBLEM 8-7

(a) Propose a mechanism for the following reaction.

$$CH_3—\underset{CH_3}{C}{=}CH—CH_3 \xrightarrow{Hg(OAc)_2,\ CH_3CH_2OH} CH_3—\overset{CH_3}{\underset{CH_3CH_2O}{C}}—\underset{Hg(OAc)}{CH}—CH_3 \quad (90\%)$$

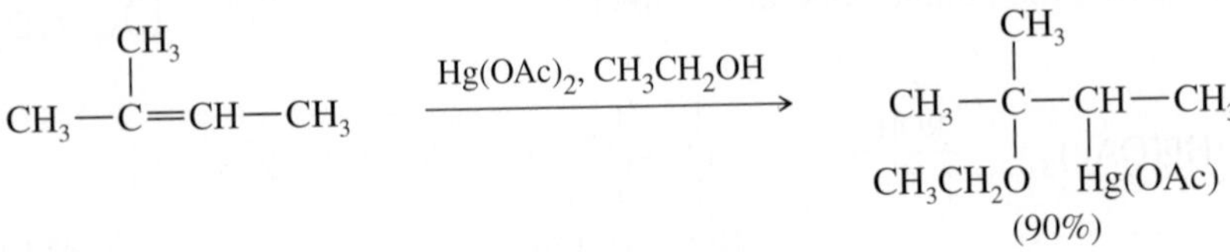

(b) Give the structure of the product that results when this intermediate is reduced by sodium borohydride.

PROBLEM 8-8

Predict the major products of the following reactions.

(a) 1-methylcyclohexene + aqueous $Hg(OAc)_2$

(b) the product from part (a), treated with $NaBH_4$

(c) 4-chlorocycloheptene + $Hg(OAc)_2$ in CH_3OH

(d) the product from part (c), treated with $NaBH_4$

PROBLEM 8-9

Show how you would accomplish the following synthetic conversions.

(a) 1-butene → 2-methoxybutane

(b) 1-iodo-2-methylcyclopentane → 1-methylcyclopentanol

(c) 3-methyl-1-pentene → 3-methyl-2-pentanol

Explain why acid-catalyzed hydration would be a poor choice for the reaction in (c).

8-7 Hydroboration of Alkenes

We have seen two methods for hydrating an alkene with Markovnikov orientation. What if we need to convert an alkene to the anti-Markovnikov alcohol? For example, the following transformation cannot be accomplished using the hydration procedures covered thus far.

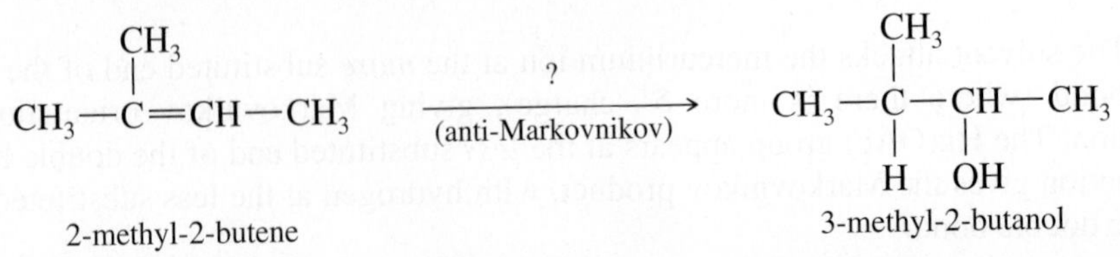

$$\underset{\text{2-methyl-2-butene}}{CH_3—\overset{CH_3}{C}{=}CH—CH_3} \xrightarrow[\text{(anti-Markovnikov)}]{?} \underset{\text{3-methyl-2-butanol}}{CH_3—\overset{CH_3}{\underset{H}{C}}—\underset{OH}{CH}—CH_3}$$

Such an anti-Markovnikov hydration was impossible until H. C. Brown, of Purdue University, discovered that diborane (B_2H_6) adds to alkenes with anti-Markovnikov orientation to form alkylboranes, which can be oxidized to give anti-Markovnikov alcohols. This discovery led to the development of a large field of borane chemistry, for which Brown received the Nobel Prize in Chemistry in 1979.

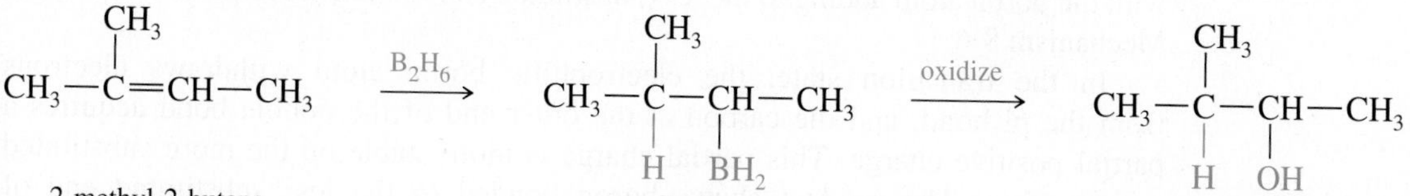

$$CH_3-\overset{\overset{CH_3}{|}}{C}=CH-CH_3 \xrightarrow{B_2H_6} CH_3-\underset{\underset{H}{|}}{\overset{\overset{CH_3}{|}}{C}}-\underset{\underset{BH_2}{|}}{CH}-CH_3 \xrightarrow{\text{oxidize}} CH_3-\underset{\underset{H}{|}}{\overset{\overset{CH_3}{|}}{C}}-\underset{\underset{OH}{|}}{CH}-CH_3$$

2-methyl-2-butene — an alkylborane — 3-methyl-2-butanol (>90%)

Diborane (B_2H_6) is a dimer composed of two molecules of borane (BH_3). The bonding in diborane is unconventional, using three-centered (banana-shaped) bonds with protons in the middle of them. Diborane is in equilibrium with a small amount of borane (BH_3), a strong Lewis acid with only six valence electrons.

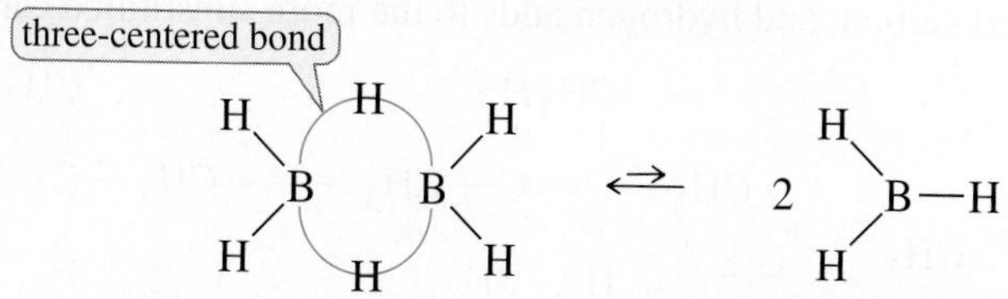

$$B_2H_6 \rightleftarrows 2\ BH_3$$

three-centered bond

diborane — borane

Diborane is an inconvenient reagent. It is a toxic, flammable, and explosive gas. It is more easily used as a complex with tetrahydrofuran (THF), a cyclic ether. This complex reacts like diborane, yet the solution is easily measured and transferred.

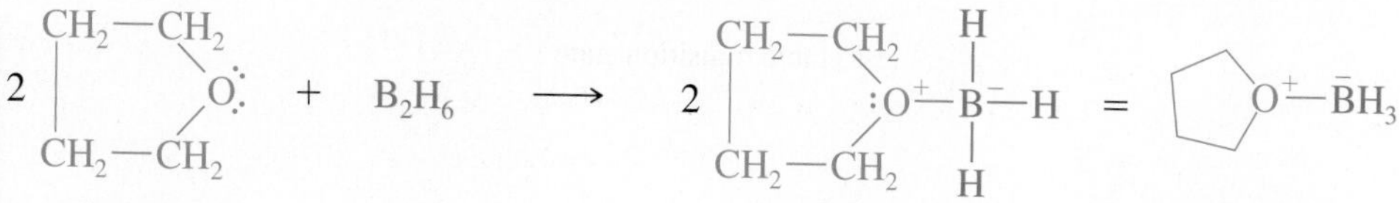

$$2\ \text{THF} + B_2H_6 \longrightarrow 2\ \text{THF}{:}\overset{+}{O}-\overset{-}{B}H_3 = BH_3 \cdot THF$$

tetrahydrofuran (THF) — diborane — borane–THF complex = $BH_3 \cdot THF$

The $BH_3 \cdot THF$ reagent is the form of borane commonly used in organic reactions. BH_3 adds to the double bond of an alkene to give an alkylborane. Basic hydrogen peroxide oxidizes the alkylborane to an alcohol. In effect, hydroboration–oxidation converts alkenes to alcohols by adding water across the double bond, with anti-Markovnikov orientation.

Hydroboration–oxidation:

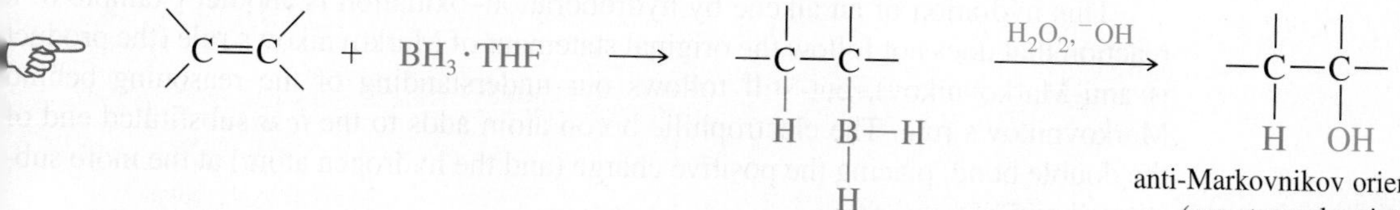

$$\rangle C=C\langle + BH_3 \cdot THF \longrightarrow -\underset{\underset{H}{|}}{C}-\underset{\underset{BH_2}{|}}{C}- \xrightarrow{H_2O_2,\ ^-OH} -\underset{\underset{H}{|}}{C}-\underset{\underset{OH}{|}}{C}-$$

anti-Markovnikov orientation (syn stereochemistry)

8-7A Mechanism of Hydroboration

Borane is an electron-deficient compound. It has only six valence electrons, so the boron atom in BH_3 cannot have an octet. Acquiring an octet is the driving force for the unusual bonding structures ("banana" bonds, for example) found in boron compounds. As an electron-deficient compound, BH_3 is a strong electrophile, capable of adding to a double bond. This **hydroboration** of the double bond is thought to occur in one step, with the boron atom adding to the less substituted end of the double bond, as shown in Mechanism 8-6.

In the transition state, the electrophilic boron atom withdraws electrons from the pi bond, and the carbon at the other end of the double bond acquires a partial positive charge. This partial charge is more stable on the more substituted carbon atom. The product shows boron bonded to the less substituted end of the double bond and hydrogen bonded to the more substituted end. Also, steric hindrance favors boron adding to the less hindered, less substituted end of the double bond.

MECHANISM 8-6 Hydroboration of an Alkene

Borane adds to the double bond in a single step. Boron adds to the less hindered, less substituted carbon, and hydrogen adds to the more substituted carbon.

$$(CH_3)_2C{=}CHCH_3 + H{-}BH_2 \longrightarrow \left[CH_3{-}\overset{\delta+}{C}(CH_3)\cdots CH(CH_3)\ \ H\cdots BH_2^{\delta-}\right] \longrightarrow CH_3{-}C(CH_3)(H){-}CH(BH_2){-}CH_3$$

more stable transition state

(not formed) $CH_3{-}C(CH_3)\cdots\overset{\delta+}{C}H{-}CH_3$ with $\overset{\delta-}{H_2B}\cdots H$

less stable transition state

The boron atom is removed by oxidation, using aqueous sodium hydroxide and hydrogen peroxide (HOOH or H_2O_2) to replace the boron atom with a hydroxyl (—OH) group.

$$CH_3{-}C(CH_3)(H){-}CH(BH_2){-}CH_3 \xrightarrow[H_2O]{H_2O_2,\ NaOH} CH_3{-}C(CH_3)(H){-}CH(OH){-}CH_3$$

This hydration of an alkene by hydroboration–oxidation is another example of a reaction that does not follow the original statement of Markovnikov's rule (the product is anti-Markovnikov), but still follows our understanding of the reasoning behind Markovnikov's rule. The electrophilic boron atom adds to the *less* substituted end of the double bond, placing the positive charge (and the hydrogen atom) at the more substituted end.

problem-solving Hint

Work backward on multistep syntheses.

SOLVED PROBLEM 8-3

Show how you would convert 1-methylcyclopentanol to 2-methylcyclopentanol.

SOLUTION

Working backward, use hydroboration–oxidation to form 2-methyl-cyclopentanol from 1-methylcyclopentene. The use of (1) and (2) above and below the reaction arrow indicates individual steps in a two-step sequence.

1-methylcyclopentene $\xrightarrow[(2)\ H_2O_2,\ ^-OH]{(1)\ BH_3 \cdot THF}$ *trans*-2-methylcyclopentanol

The 2-methylcyclopentanol that results from this synthesis is the pure trans isomer. This stereochemical result is discussed in Section 8-7C.

1-Methylcyclopentene is the most substituted alkene that results from dehydration of 1-methylcyclopentanol. Dehydration of the alcohol would give the correct alkene.

1-methylcyclopentanol $\xrightarrow{H_2SO_4}$ 1-methylcyclopentene + H_2O

PROBLEM 8-10

Predict the major products of the following reactions.

(a) propene + $BH_3 \cdot THF$

(b) the product from part (a) + H_2O_2/OH^-

(c) 2-methyl-2-pentene + $BH_3 \cdot THF$

(d) the product from part (c) + H_2O_2/OH^-

(e) 1-methylcyclohexene + $BH_3 \cdot THF$

(f) the product from part (e) + H_2O_2/OH^-

PROBLEM 8-11

Show how you would accomplish the following synthetic conversions.

(a) 1-butene → 1-butanol

(b) 1-butene → 2-butanol

(c) 2-bromo-2,4-dimethylpentane → 2,4-dimethyl-3-pentanol

8-7B Stoichiometry of Hydroboration

For simplicity, we have neglected the fact that 3 moles of an alkene can react with each mole of BH_3. Each B—H bond in BH_3 can add across the double bond of an alkene. The first addition forms an alkylborane, the second a dialkylborane, and the third a trialkylborane.

$$H-BH_2 \xrightarrow{C=C} \underset{\text{alkylborane}}{H-C-C-BH_2} \xrightarrow{C=C} \underset{\text{dialkylborane}}{(H-C-C)_2B-H} \xrightarrow{C=C} \underset{\text{trialkylborane}}{(H-C-C)_3B}$$

Summary

$$C=C + BH_3 \longrightarrow (H-C-C)_3B \xrightarrow{H_2O_2,\ ^-OH} 3\ H-C-C-OH$$

Trialkylboranes react exactly as we have discussed, and they oxidize to give anti-Markovnikov alcohols. Trialkylboranes are quite bulky, further reinforcing the preference for boron to add to the less hindered carbon atom of the double bond. Boranes are often drawn as the 1:1 monoalkylboranes to simplify their structure and emphasize the organic part of the molecule.

8-7C Stereochemistry of Hydroboration

The simultaneous addition of boron and hydrogen to the double bond (as shown in Mechanism 8-7) leads to a **syn addition**: Boron and hydrogen add across the double bond on the *same side* of the molecule. (If they added to opposite sides of the molecule, the process would be an **anti addition**.)

The stereochemistry of the hydroboration–oxidation of 1-methylcyclopentene is shown next. Boron and hydrogen add to the same face of the double bond (syn) to form a trialkylborane. Oxidation of the trialkylborane replaces boron with a hydroxyl group in the same stereochemical position. The product is *trans*-2-methylcyclopentanol. A racemic mixture is expected because a chiral product is formed from achiral reagents.

H CH$_3$ H B H H → [H CH$_3$ δ^+ H B H H δ^-] → H CH$_3$ H_2B H

transition state

H CH$_3$ H_2B H $\xrightarrow[^-OH]{H_2O_2}$ H CH$_3$ HO H

trans-2-methylcyclopentanol
(85% overall)
(racemic mixture of enantiomers)

The second step (oxidation of the borane to the alcohol) takes place with retention of configuration. Hydroperoxide ion adds to the borane, causing the alkyl group to migrate from boron to oxygen. The alkyl group migrates with retention of configuration because it moves with its electron pair and does not alter the tetrahedral structure of the migrating carbon atom. Hydrolysis of the borate ester gives the alcohol.

Formation of hydroperoxide ion

$$H{-}\ddot{O}{-}\ddot{O}{-}H + :^-\ddot{O}H \rightleftharpoons H{-}\ddot{O}{-}\ddot{O}:^- + H_2\ddot{O}:$$

Addition of hydroperoxide and migration of the alkyl group

$$R_3B + {}^-:\ddot{O}{-}\ddot{O}{-}H \longrightarrow R_3B^-{-}\ddot{O}{-}\ddot{O}{-}H \longrightarrow R_2B{-}\ddot{O}{-}R + {}^-:\ddot{O}H$$

hydroperoxide — R migrates — borate ester

Twice more to oxidize the other two alkyl groups

$$R_2B{-}OR \xrightarrow{^-OOH} \xrightarrow{^-OOH} B(OR)_3$$

trialkyl borate ester

Hydrolysis of the borate ester

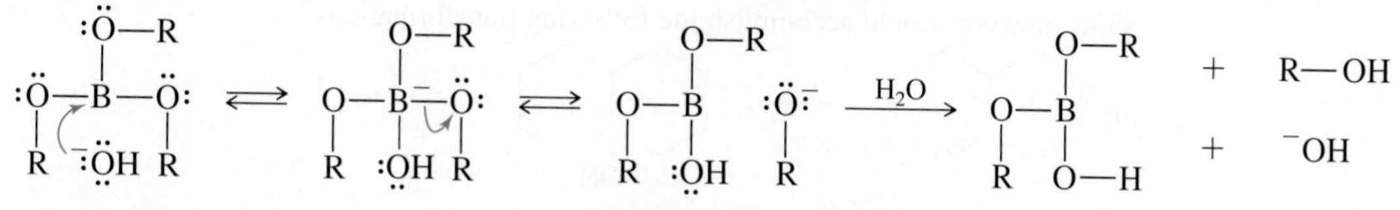

(The other two OR groups hydrolyze similarly)

Hydroboration of alkenes is another example of a **stereospecific reaction**, in which different stereoisomers of the starting compound react to give different stereoisomers of the product. Problem 8-14 considers the different products formed by the hydroboration–oxidation of two acyclic diastereomers.

SOLVED PROBLEM 8-4

A norbornene molecule labeled with deuterium is subjected to hydroboration–oxidation. Give the structures of the intermediates and products.

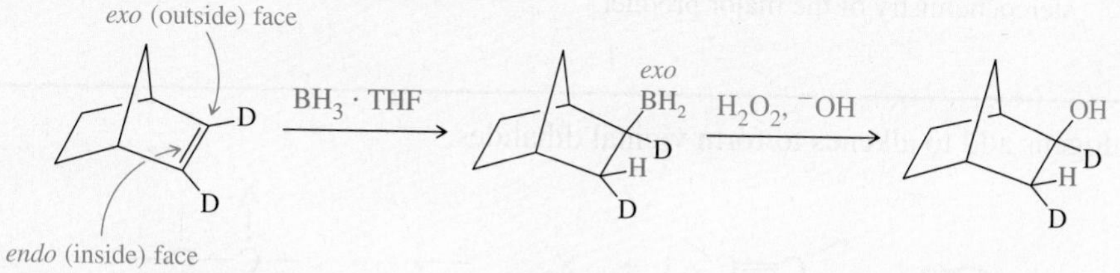

exo (outside) face

$BH_3 \cdot THF$

exo

BH_2 H_2O_2, ^-OH

endo (inside) face

deuterium-labeled norbornene

alkylborane

alcohol (racemic mixture)

SOLUTION

The syn addition of BH_3 across the double bond of norbornene takes place mostly from the more accessible outside (exo) face of the double bond. Oxidation gives a product with both the hydrogen atom and the hydroxyl group in exo positions. (The less accessible inner face of the double bond is called the endo face.)

PROBLEM 8-12

In the hydroboration of 1-methylcyclopentene shown in Solved Problem 8-3, the reagents are achiral, and the products are chiral. The product is a racemic mixture of *trans*-2-methylcyclopentanol, but only one enantiomer is shown. Show how the other enantiomer is formed.

PROBLEM 8-13

Predict the major products of the following reactions. Include stereochemistry where applicable.

(a) 1-methylcycloheptene + $BH_3 \cdot THF$, then H_2O_2, OH^-

(b) *trans*-4,4-dimethyl-2-pentene + $BH_3 \cdot THF$, then H_2O_2, OH^-

(c) + $BH_3 \cdot THF$, then H_2O_2, OH^-

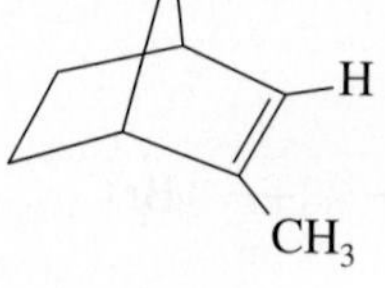

PROBLEM 8-14

(a) When (*Z*)-3-methyl-3-hexene undergoes hydroboration–oxidation, two isomeric products are formed. Give their structures, and label each asymmetric carbon atom as (*R*) or (*S*). What is the relationship between these isomers?

(b) Repeat part (a) for (*E*)-3-methyl-3-hexene. What is the relationship between the products formed from (*Z*)-3-methyl-3-hexene and those formed from (*E*)-3-methyl-3-hexene?

PROBLEM 8-15

Show how you would accomplish the following transformations.

(a) 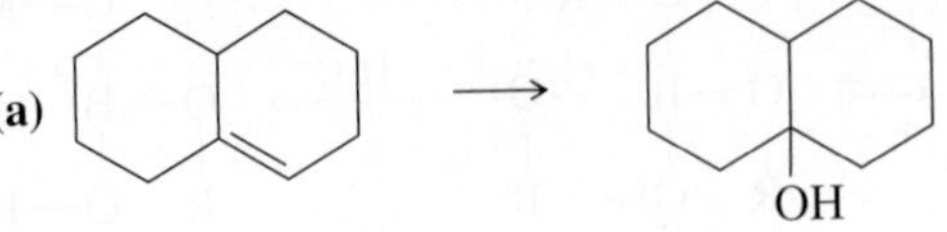 [octahydronaphthalene with ring-fusion double bond] → [decalin with OH at ring fusion carbon]

(b) 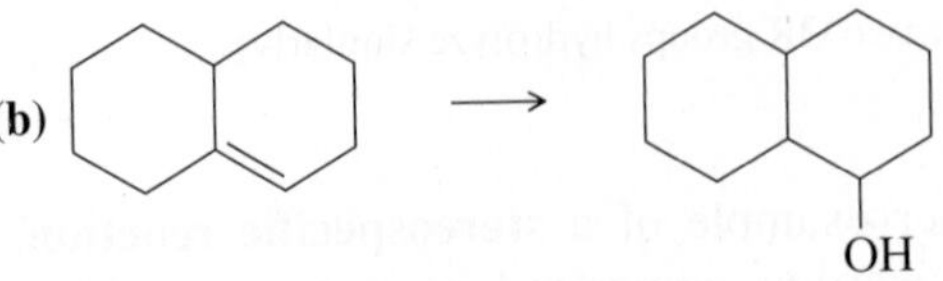 [octahydronaphthalene] → [decalin with OH]

(c) 1-methylcycloheptanol → 2-methylcycloheptanol

PROBLEM 8-16

(a) When HBr adds across the double bond of 1,2-dimethylcyclopentene, the product is a mixture of the cis and trans isomers. Show why this addition is not stereospecific.

(b) When 1,2-dimethylcyclopentene undergoes hydroboration–oxidation, one diastereomer of the product predominates. Show why this addition is stereospecific, and predict the stereochemistry of the major product.

8-8 Addition of Halogens to Alkenes

Halogens add to alkenes to form vicinal dihalides.

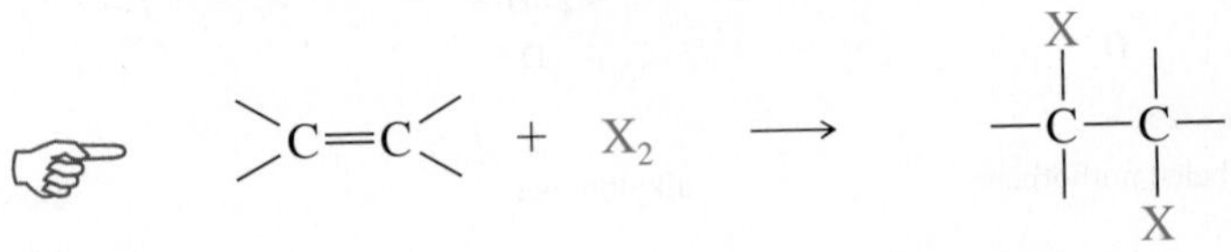

$$\text{>C=C<} + X_2 \longrightarrow -\overset{X}{\underset{|}{C}}-\underset{X}{C}-$$

(X_2 = Cl_2, Br_2, sometimes I_2) usually anti addition

8-8A Mechanism of Halogen Addition

A halogen molecule (Br_2, Cl_2, or I_2) is electrophilic; a nucleophile can react with a halogen, displacing a halide ion:

$$\text{Nuc:}^- + \text{:Br—Br:} \longrightarrow \text{Nuc—Br:} + \text{:Br:}^-$$

In this example, the nucleophile attacks the electrophilic nucleus of one bromine atom, and the other bromine serves as the leaving group, departing as bromide ion. Many reactions fit this general pattern; for example:

$$\text{HO:}^- + \text{:Br—Br:} \longrightarrow \text{HO—Br:} + \text{:Br:}^-$$

$$H_3N\text{:} + \text{:Cl—Cl:} \longrightarrow H_3\overset{+}{N}\text{—Cl:} + \text{:Cl:}^-$$

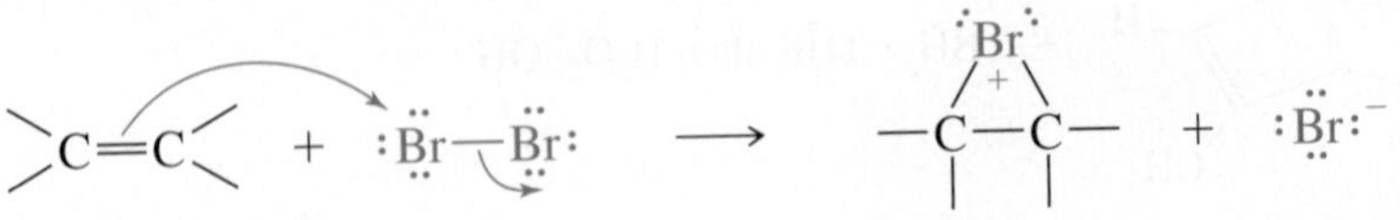

$$\text{>C=C<} + \text{:Br—Br:} \longrightarrow -\overset{Br^+}{C—C}- + \text{:Br:}^-$$

bromonium ion

In the last reaction, the pi electrons of an alkene attack the bromine molecule, expelling bromide ion. A **bromonium ion** results, containing a three-membered ring with a positive charge on the bromine atom. This bromonium ion is similar in structure to the mercurinium ion discussed in Section 8-5. Similar reactions with other halogens form other **halonium ions**. The structures of a **chloronium ion**, a **bromonium ion** and an **iodonium ion** are shown next.

Examples

chloronium ion   bromonium ion   iodonium ion

Unlike a normal carbocation, all the atoms in a halonium ion have filled octets. The three-membered ring has considerable ring strain, however, which, combined with a positive charge on an electronegative halogen atom, makes the halonium ion strongly electrophilic. Attack by a nucleophile, such as a halide ion, opens the halonium ion to give a stable product.

MECHANISM 8-7 Addition of Halogens to Alkenes

Step 1: Electrophilic attack forms a halonium ion.

halonium ion

Step 2: The halide ion opens the halonium ion.

X^- attacks from the back side

EXAMPLE: Addition of Br_2 to propene.

Step 1: Electrophilic attack forms a bromonium ion.

propene   bromonium ion

Step 2: Bromide ion opens the bromonium ion.

1,2-dibromopropane

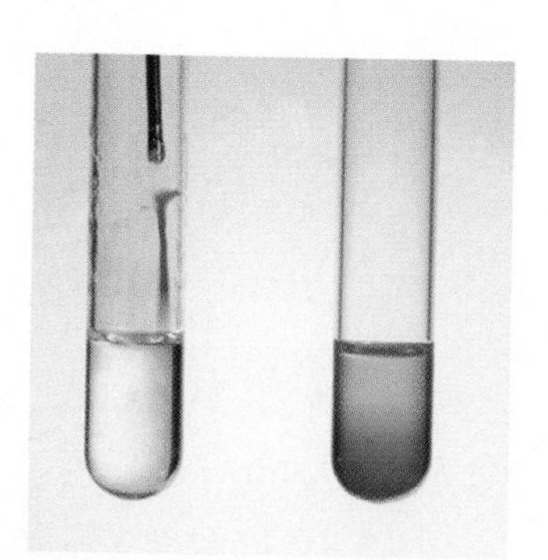

When a solution of bromine (red-brown) is added to cyclohexene, the bromine color quickly disappears because bromine adds across the double bond. When bromine is added to cyclohexane (at right), the color persists because no reaction occurs.

Chlorine and bromine commonly add to alkenes by the halonium ion mechanism. Iodination is used less frequently because diiodide products decompose easily. Any solvents used must be inert to the halogens; methylene chloride (CH_2Cl_2), chloroform ($CHCl_3$), and carbon tetrachloride (CCl_4) are the most frequent choices.

The addition of bromine has been used as a simple chemical test for the presence of olefinic double bonds. A solution of bromine in carbon tetrachloride is a clear, deep red color. When this red solution is added to an alkene, the red bromine color disappears (we say it is "decolorized"), and the solution becomes clear and colorless. (Although there are other functional groups that decolorize bromine, few do it as quickly as alkenes.)

8-8B Stereochemistry of Halogen Addition

The addition of bromine to cyclopentene is a stereospecific **anti addition.**

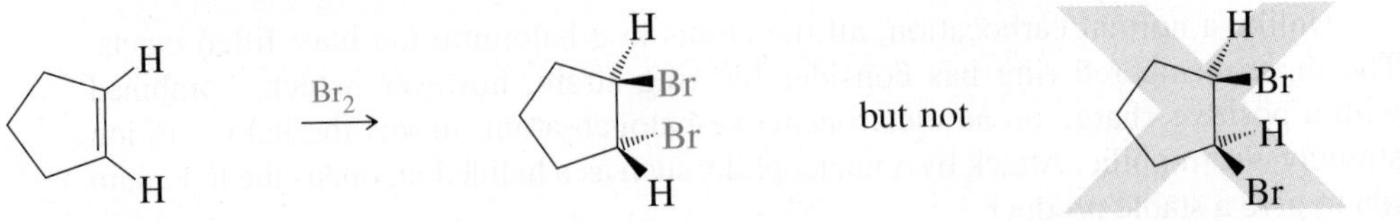

cyclopentene $\xrightarrow{Br_2}$ *trans*-1,2-dibromocyclopentane (92%) but not *cis*-1,2-dibromocyclopentane (not formed)

Anti stereochemistry results from the bromonium ion mechanism. When a nucleophile attacks a halonium ion, it must do so from the back side, in a manner similar to the S_N2 displacement. This back-side attack assures anti stereochemistry of addition.

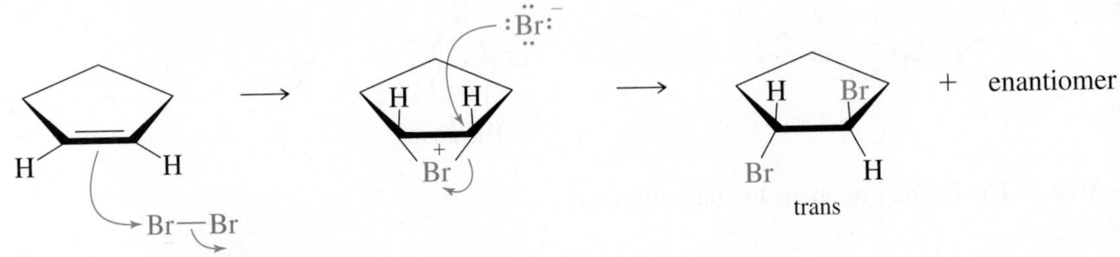

trans + enantiomer

Halogen addition is another example of a stereospecific reaction, in which different stereoisomers of the starting material give different stereoisomers of the product. Figure 8-4 shows additional examples of the anti addition of halogens to alkenes.

cyclohexene + Cl_2 ⟶ racemic *trans*-1,2-dichlorocyclohexane

cis-2-butene + Br_2 ⟶ (+ enantiomer) = (±)-2,3-dibromobutane

trans-2-butene + Br_2 ⟶ = *meso*-2,3-dibromobutane

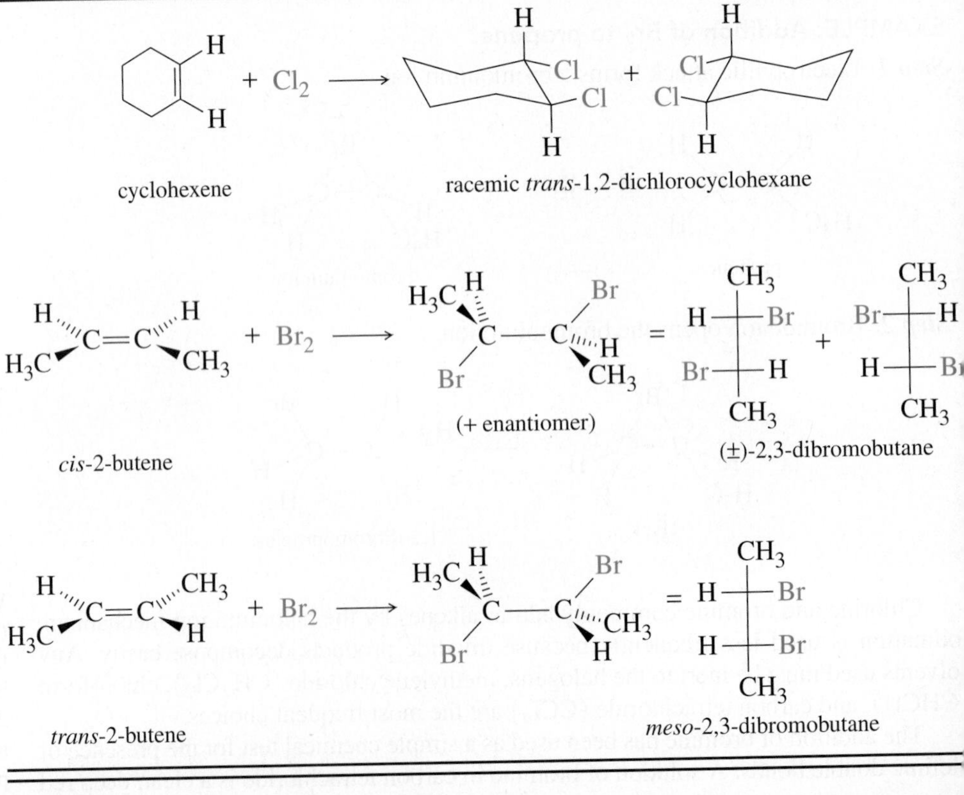

■ **FIGURE 8-4**
Examples of the anti addition of halogens to alkenes. The stereospecific anti addition gives predictable stereoisomers of the products.

PROBLEM 8-17

Give mechanisms to account for the stereochemistry of the products observed from the addition of bromine to *cis*- and *trans*-2-butene (Figure 8-4). Why are two products formed from the cis isomer but only one from the trans? (Making models will be helpful.)

PROBLEM 8-18

Propose mechanisms and predict the major products of the following reactions. Include stereochemistry where appropriate.

(a) cycloheptene + Br_2 in CH_2Cl_2 **(b)** 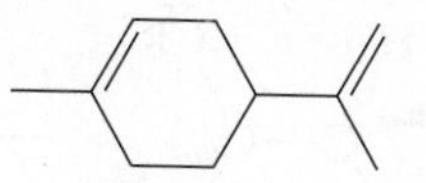 [structure] + 2 Cl_2 in CCl_4

(c) (*E*)-3-decene + Br_2 in CCl_4 **(d)** (*Z*)-3-decene + Br_2 in CCl_4

problem-solving Hint

Models may be helpful whenever stereochemistry is involved. Write complete structures, including all bonds and charges, when writing mechanisms.

8-9 Formation of Halohydrins

A **halohydrin** is an alcohol with a halogen on the adjacent carbon atom. In the presence of water, halogens add to alkenes to form halohydrins. The electrophilic halogen adds to the alkene to give a halonium ion, which is also electrophilic. Water acts as a nucleophile to open the halonium ion and form the halohydrin.

MECHANISM 8-8 Formation of Halohydrins

Step 1: Electrophilic attack forms a halonium ion.

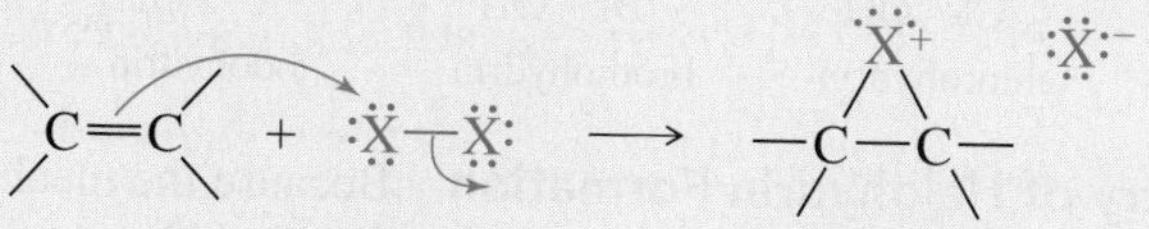

$$C{=}C \; + \; :\ddot{X}{-}\ddot{X}: \;\longrightarrow\; -C{-}C- \text{ (bridged by } X^+) \;\; :\ddot{X}:^-$$

(X = Cl, Br, or I) halonium ion

Step 2: Water opens the halonium ion; deprotonation gives the halohydrin.

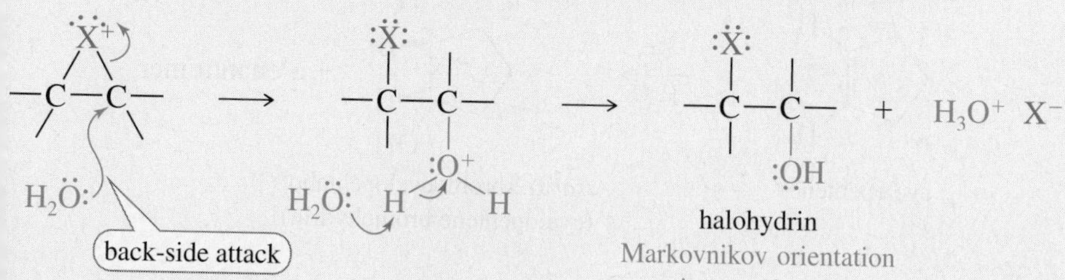

$H_2\ddot{O}:$ (back-side attack) → $-C-C-$ with $:\ddot{X}:$ and $:O^+$ (H, H) ; $H_2\ddot{O}:$ → halohydrin $-C-C-$ with $:\ddot{X}:$ and $:\ddot{O}H$ + H_3O^+ X^-

back-side attack

halohydrin
Markovnikov orientation
anti stereochemistry

EXAMPLE: Addition of Cl_2 to propene in water.

Step 1: Electrophilic attack forms a chloronium ion.

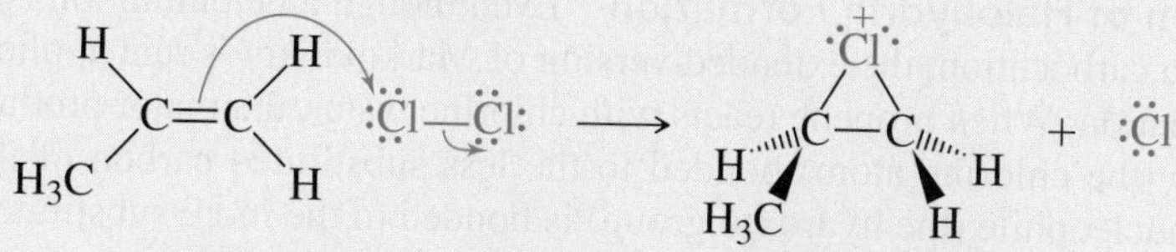

propene + $:\ddot{Cl}{-}\ddot{Cl}:$ → chloronium ion + $:\ddot{Cl}:^-$

propene chloronium ion

(Continued)

Step 2: Back-side attack by water opens the chloronium ion.

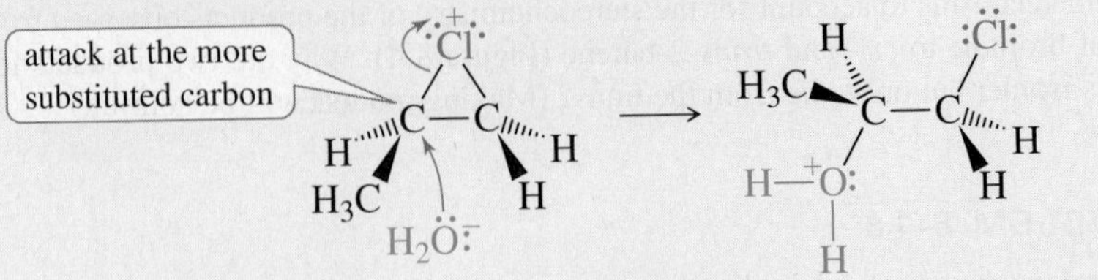

attack at the more substituted carbon

$H_2\ddot{O}:$ → H_3C, H, $H-\overset{+}{O}$:, H

Step 3: Water removes a proton to give the chlorohydrin.

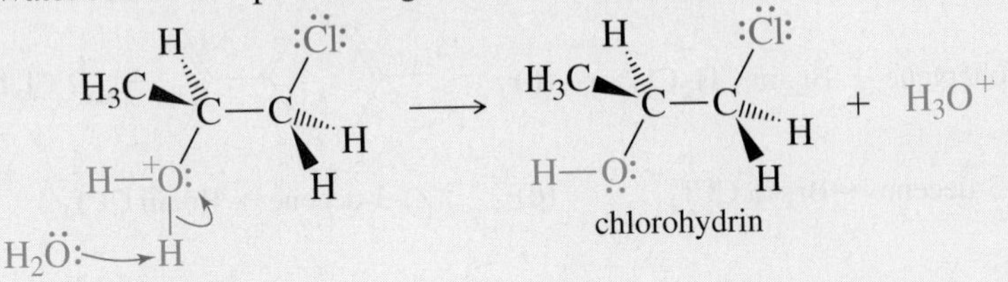

$H_2\ddot{O}:$ → ... + H_3O^+

chlorohydrin

When halogenation takes place with no solvent or with an inert solvent such as carbon tetrachloride (CCl_4) or chloroform ($CHCl_3$), only the halide ion is available as a nucleophile to attack the halonium ion. A dihalide results. But when an alkene reacts with a halogen in the presence of a nucleophilic solvent such as water, a solvent molecule is the most likely nucleophile to attack the halonium ion. When a water molecule attacks the halonium ion, the final product is a halohydrin, with a halogen on one carbon atom and a hydroxyl group on the adjacent carbon. The product may be a *chlorohydrin*, a *bromohydrin*, or an *iodohydrin*, depending on the halogen.

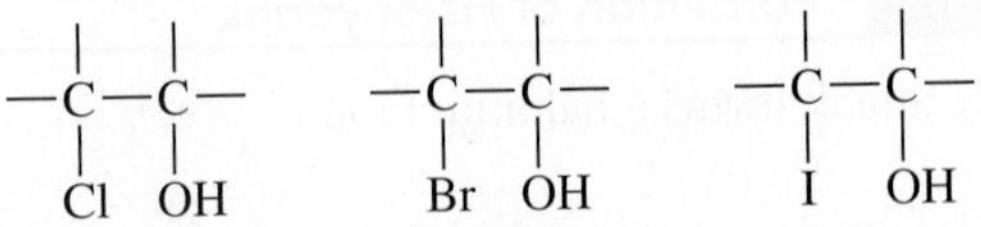

—C—C— (Cl, OH)	—C—C— (Br, OH)	—C—C— (I, OH)
chlorohydrin	bromohydrin	iodohydrin

Stereochemistry of Halohydrin Formation Because the mechanism involves a halonium ion, the stereochemistry of addition is anti, as in halogenation. For example, the addition of bromine water to cyclopentene gives *trans*-2-bromocyclopentanol, the product of anti addition across the double bond.

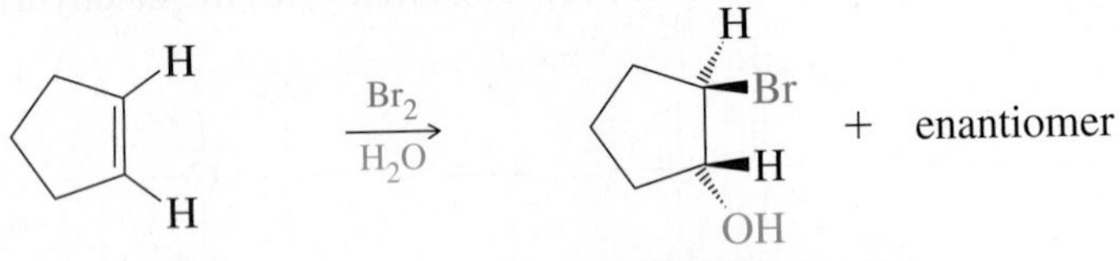

$$\text{cyclopentene} \xrightarrow[H_2O]{Br_2} \textit{trans}\text{-2-bromocyclopentanol} + \text{enantiomer}$$

cyclopentene

trans-2-bromocyclopentanol (cyclopentene bromohydrin)

PROBLEM 8-19

Propose a mechanism for the addition of bromine water to cyclopentene, being careful to show why the trans product results and how both enantiomers are formed.

Orientation of Halohydrin Formation Even though a halonium ion is involved rather than a carbocation, the extended version of Markovnikov's rule applies to halohydrin formation. When propene reacts with chlorine water, the major product has the electrophile (the chlorine atom) bonded to the less substituted carbon of the double bond. The nucleophile (the hydroxyl group) is bonded to the more substituted carbon.

$$H_2C{=}CH{-}CH_3 + Cl_2 + H_2O \longrightarrow \underset{Cl}{H_2C}{-}\underset{OH}{CH}{-}CH_3 + HCl$$

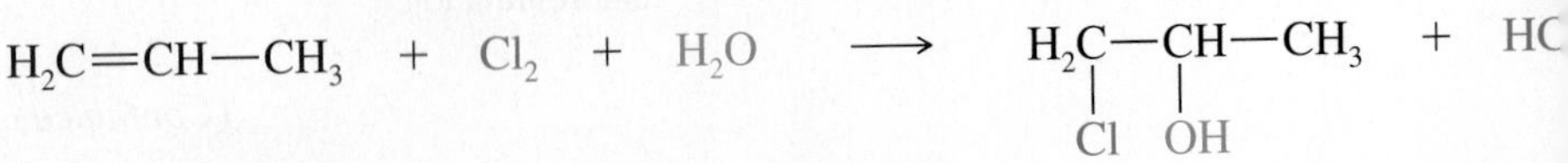

The Markovnikov orientation observed in halohydrin formation is explained by the structure of the halonium ion intermediate. The two carbon atoms bonded to the halogen have partial positive charges, with a larger charge (and a weaker bond to the halogen) on the more substituted carbon atom (Figure 8-5). The nucleophile (water) attacks this more substituted, more electrophilic carbon atom. The result is both anti stereochemistry and Markovnikov orientation.

larger δ+ on the more substituted carbon

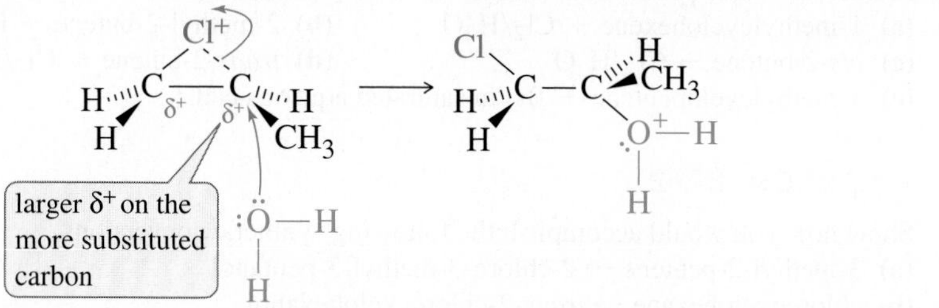

■ **FIGURE 8-5**
Orientation of halohydrin formation. The more substituted carbon of the chloronium ion bears more positive charge than the less substituted carbon. Attack by water occurs on the more substituted carbon to give the Markovnikov product.

This halonium ion mechanism can be used to explain and predict a wide variety of reactions in both nucleophilic and non-nucleophilic solvents. The halonium ion mechanism is similar to the mercurinium ion mechanism for oxymercuration of an alkene, and both give Markovnikov orientation (Section 8-5).

SOLVED PROBLEM 8-5

Propose a mechanism for the reaction of 1-methylcyclopentene with bromine water.

SOLUTION

1-Methylcyclopentene reacts with bromine to give a bromonium ion. Attack by water could occur at either the secondary carbon or the tertiary carbon of the bromonium ion. Attack actually occurs at the more substituted carbon, which bears more of the positive charge. The product is formed as a racemic mixture.

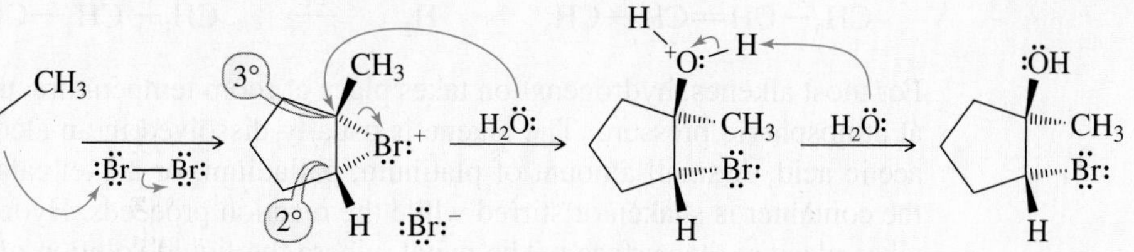

+ enantiomer

SOLVED PROBLEM 8-6

When cyclohexene is treated with bromine in saturated aqueous sodium chloride, a mixture of *trans*-2-bromocyclohexanol and *trans*-1-bromo-2-chlorocyclohexane results. Propose a mechanism to account for these two products.

SOLUTION

Cyclohexene reacts with bromine to give a bromonium ion, which will react with any available nucleophile. The most abundant nucleophiles in saturated aqueous sodium chloride solution are water and chloride ions. Attack by water gives the bromohydrin, and attack by chloride gives the dihalide. Either of these attacks gives anti stereochemistry.

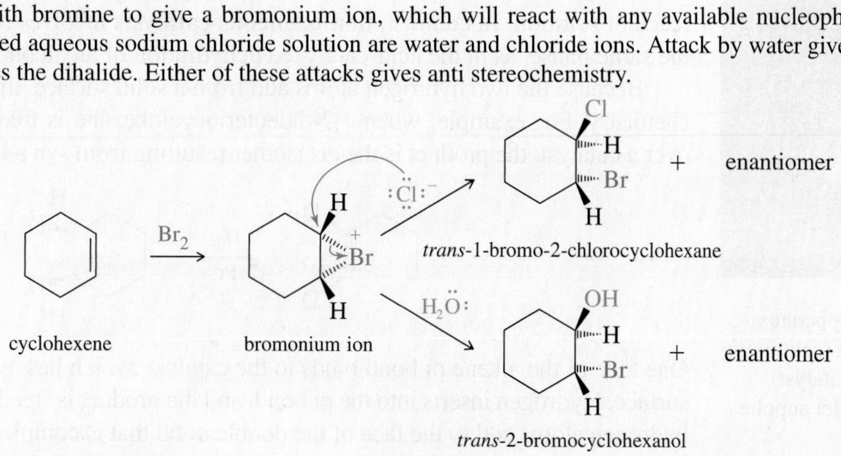

+ enantiomer

cyclohexene

bromonium ion

trans-1-bromo-2-chlorocyclohexane

+ enantiomer

trans-2-bromocyclohexanol

PROBLEM 8-20

The solutions to Solved Problem 8-5 and Solved Problem 8-6 showed only how one enantiomer of the product is formed. For each product, show how an equally probable reaction forms the other enantiomer.

PROBLEM 8-21

Predict the major product(s) for each reaction. Include stereochemistry where appropriate.
(a) 1-methylcyclohexene + Cl_2/H_2O
(b) 2-methyl-2-butene + Br_2/H_2O
(c) *cis*-2-butene + Cl_2/H_2O
(d) *trans*-2-butene + Cl_2/H_2O
(e) 1-methylcyclopentene + Br_2 in saturated aqueous NaCl

problem-solving **Hint**

The opening of a halonium ion is driven by its electrophilic nature. The weak nucleophile attacks the carbon bearing more positive charge.

PROBLEM 8-22

Show how you would accomplish the following synthetic conversions.
(a) 3-methyl-2-pentene → 2-chloro-3-methyl-3-pentanol
(b) chlorocyclohexane → *trans*-2-chlorocyclohexanol
(c) 1-methylcyclopentanol → 2-chloro-1-methylcyclopentanol

8-10 Catalytic Hydrogenation of Alkenes

Although we have mentioned **catalytic hydrogenation** before (Sections 7-7 and 8-1), we now consider the mechanism and stereochemistry in more detail. Hydrogenation of an alkene is formally a reduction, with H_2 adding across the double bond to give an alkane. The process usually requires a catalyst containing Pt, Pd, or Ni.

$$\mathrm{>C{=}C<} + H_2 \xrightarrow[\text{(Pt, Pd, Ni)}]{\text{catalyst}} \mathrm{-\overset{|}{\underset{H}{C}}-\overset{|}{\underset{H}{C}}-}$$

Example

$$CH_3-CH{=}CH-CH_3 + H_2 \xrightarrow{Pt} CH_3-CH_2-CH_2-CH_3$$

For most alkenes, hydrogenation takes place at room temperature, using hydrogen gas at atmospheric pressure. The alkene is usually dissolved in an alcohol, an alkane, or acetic acid. A small amount of platinum, palladium, or nickel catalyst is added, and the container is shaken or stirred while the reaction proceeds. Hydrogenation actually takes place at the surface of the metal, where the liquid solution of the alkene comes into contact with hydrogen and the catalyst.

Hydrogen gas is adsorbed onto the surface of these metal catalysts, and the catalyst weakens the H—H bond. In fact, if H_2 and D_2 are mixed in the presence of a platinum catalyst, the two isotopes quickly scramble to produce a random mixture of HD, H_2, and D_2. (No scrambling occurs in the absence of the catalyst.) Hydrogenation is an example of **heterogeneous catalysis**, because the (solid) catalyst is in a different phase from the reactant solution. In contrast, **homogeneous catalysis** involves reactants and catalyst in the same phase, as in the acid-catalyzed dehydration of an alcohol.

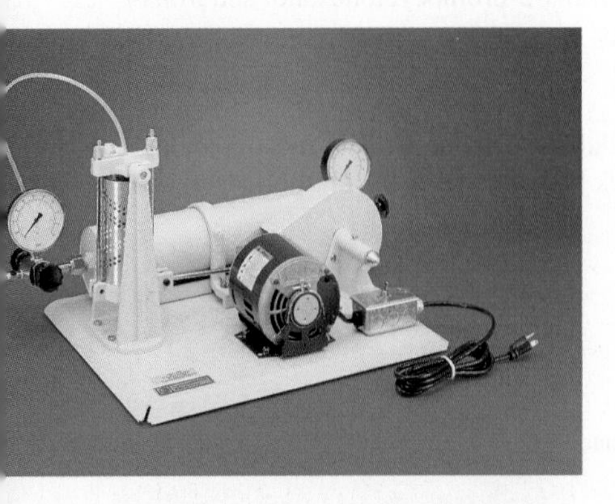

The Parr hydrogenation apparatus shakes the reaction vessel (containing the alkene and the solid catalyst), while a pressurized cylinder supplies hydrogen.

Because the two hydrogen atoms add from a solid surface, they add with **syn** stereochemistry. For example, when 1,2-dideuteriocyclohexene is treated with hydrogen gas over a catalyst, the product is the cis isomer resulting from syn addition (Figure 8-6).

[1,2-dideuteriocyclohexene $\xrightarrow[Pt]{H_2}$ *cis*-1,2-dideuteriocyclohexane (H and D on each carbon, both H's on the same face)]

One face of the alkene pi bond binds to the catalyst, which has hydrogen adsorbed on its surface. Hydrogen inserts into the pi bond, and the product is freed from the catalyst. Both hydrogen atoms add to the face of the double bond that is complexed with the catalyst.

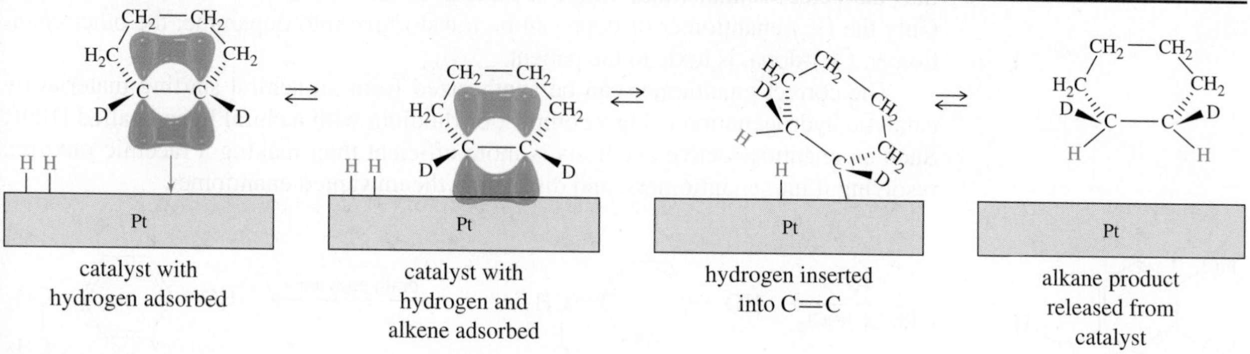

catalyst with hydrogen adsorbed ⇄ catalyst with hydrogen and alkene adsorbed ⇄ hydrogen inserted into C=C ⇄ alkane product released from catalyst

■ **FIGURE 8-6**
Syn stereochemistry in catalytic hydrogenation. A solid heterogeneous catalyst adds two hydrogen atoms to the same face of the pi bond (syn stereochemistry).

Soluble homogeneous catalysts, such as *Wilkinson's catalyst*, also catalyze the hydrogenation of carbon–carbon double bonds.

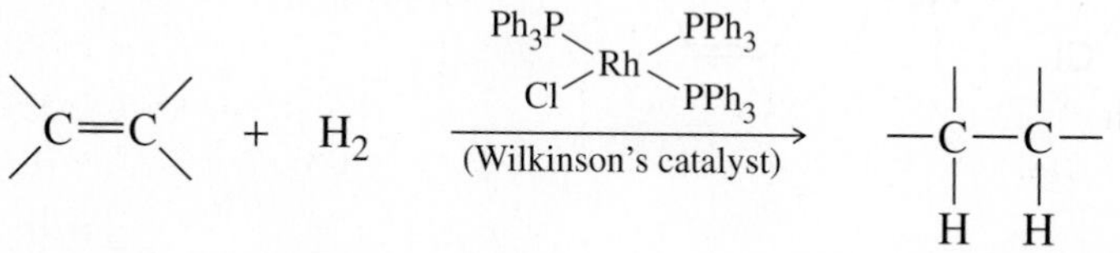

$$\mathrm{C{=}C} + H_2 \xrightarrow[\text{(Wilkinson's catalyst)}]{(Ph_3P)_3RhCl} \mathrm{H{-}C{-}C{-}H}$$

Wilkinson's catalyst is not chiral, but its triphenylphosphine (PPh_3) ligands can be replaced by chiral ligands to give chiral catalysts that are capable of converting optically inactive starting materials to optically active products. Such a process is called **asymmetric induction** or **enantioselective synthesis**. For example, Figure 8-7 shows a chiral ruthenium complex catalyzing an enantioselective hydrogenation of a carbon–carbon double bond to give a large excess of one enantiomer. Because the catalyst is chiral, the transition states leading to the two enantiomers of product are diastereomeric. They have different energies, and the transition state leading to the (*R*) enantiomer is favored. Ryoji Noyori and William Knowles shared the 2001 Nobel Prize in Chemistry for their work on chirally catalyzed hydrogenation reactions.

Enantioselective synthesis is particularly important in the pharmaceutical industry, because only one enantiomer of a chiral drug is likely to have the desired effect. For example, levodopa [(−)-dopa or *l*-dopa] is used in patients with Parkinson's disease to counteract a deficiency of dopamine, one of the neurotransmitters in the brain. Dopamine itself is useless as a drug because it cannot cross the "blood–brain barrier"; that is, it cannot get into the cerebrospinal fluid from the bloodstream. (−)-Dopa, on the other hand, is an amino acid related to tyrosine. It crosses the blood–brain barrier

$$\xrightarrow[\text{Ru (BINAP) Cl}_2]{H_2}$$

96% e.e. (*R*)

$Ru(BINAP)Cl_2$ =

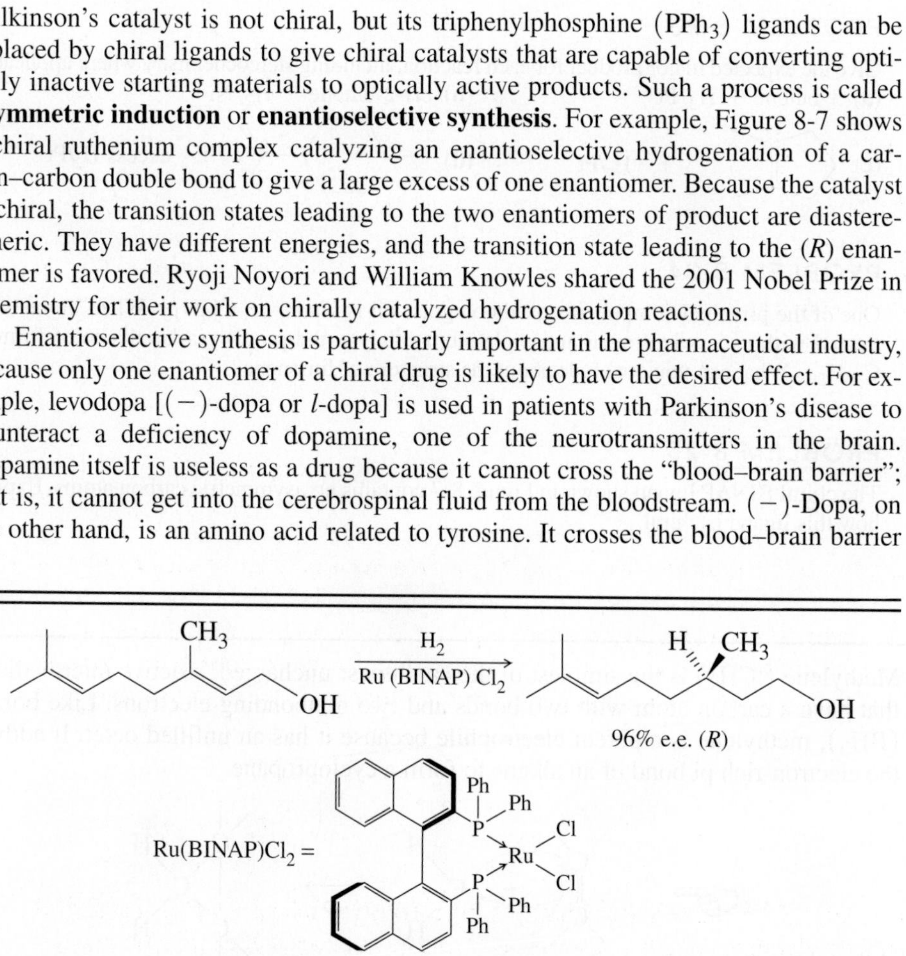

■ **FIGURE 8-7**
Chiral hydrogenation catalysts. Rhodium and ruthenium phosphines are effective homogeneous catalysts for hydrogenation. Chiral ligands can be attached to accomplish asymmetric induction, the creation of a new asymmetric carbon as mostly one enantiomer.

into the cerebrospinal fluid, where it undergoes enzymatic conversion to dopamine. Only the (−) enantiomer of dopa can be transformed into dopamine; the other enantiomer, (+)-dopa, is toxic to the patient.

The correct enantiomer can be synthesized from an achiral starting material by catalytic hydrogenation using a complex of rhodium with a chiral ligand called DIOP. Such an enantioselective synthesis is more efficient than making a racemic mixture, resolving it into enantiomers, and discarding the unwanted enantiomer.

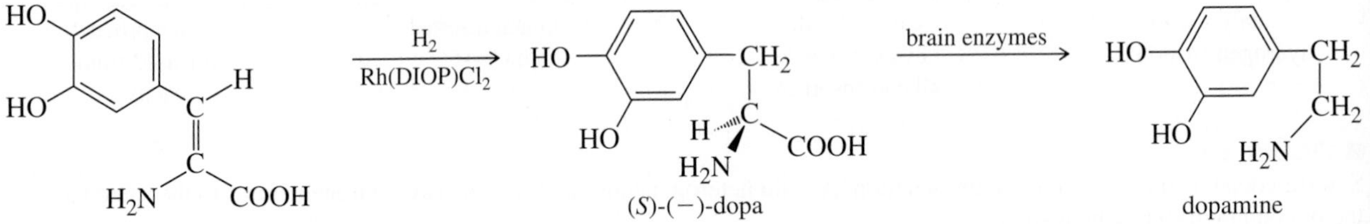

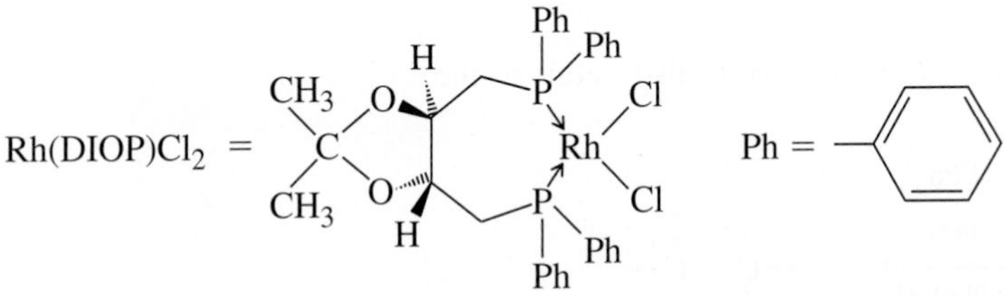

HO, HO, H, C, C, H_2N, COOH → (H_2, $Rh(DIOP)Cl_2$) → HO, HO, CH_2, H, C, COOH, H_2N (*S*)-(−)-dopa → (brain enzymes) → HO, HO, CH_2, CH_2, H_2N dopamine

$Rh(DIOP)Cl_2$ = CH3, CH3, C, O, O, H, H, P, P, Ph, Ph, Ph, Ph, Rh, Cl, Cl; Ph =

The enzymatic reduction of a double bond is a key step in the formation of a fatty acid that is ultimately incorporated into the cell wall of the bacterium that causes tuberculosis. The antituberculosis drug isoniazid blocks this enzyme, preventing reduction of the double bond. Without an intact cell wall, the bacteria die.

O, C, $NHNH_2$, N

isoniazid

PROBLEM 8-23

Give the expected major product for each reaction, including stereochemistry where applicable.

(a) 1-butene + H_2/Pt **(b)** *cis*-2-butene + H_2/Ni

(c) 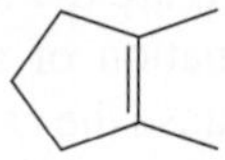 + H_2/Pt **(d)** 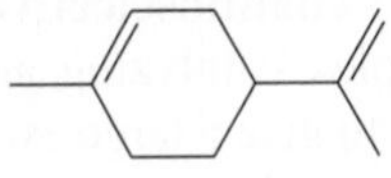 + excess H_2/Pt

PROBLEM 8-24

One of the principal components of lemon grass oil is *limonene*, $C_{10}H_{16}$. When limonene is treated with excess hydrogen and a platinum catalyst, the product is an alkane of formula $C_{10}H_{20}$. What can you conclude about the structure of limonene?

PROBLEM 8-25

The chiral BINAP ligand shown in Figure 8-7 contains no asymmetric carbon atoms. Explain how this ligand is chiral.

8-11 Addition of Carbenes to Alkenes

Methylene (:CH_2) is the simplest of the **carbenes:** uncharged, reactive intermediates that have a carbon atom with two bonds and two nonbonding electrons. Like borane (BH_3), methylene is a potent electrophile because it has an unfilled octet. It adds to the electron-rich pi bond of an alkene to form a cyclopropane.

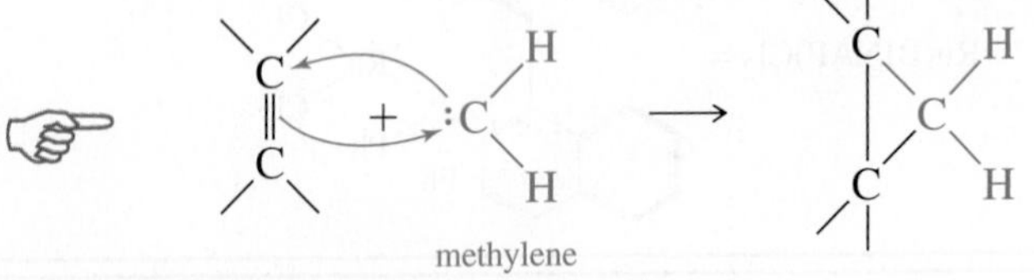

C=C + :C(H)(H) → cyclopropane (C, C, C, H, H)

methylene

Heating or photolysis of diazomethane gives nitrogen gas and methylene:

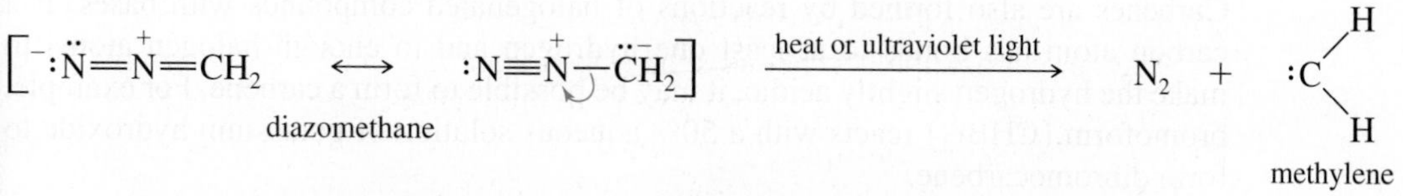

$$\left[{}^{-}\!:\ddot{N}=\overset{+}{N}=CH_2 \longleftrightarrow :N\equiv\overset{+}{N}-\ddot{C}H_2^{-} \right] \xrightarrow{\text{heat or ultraviolet light}} N_2 + :CH_2$$

diazomethane — methylene

Two difficulties arise when adding diazomethane to double bonds. First, it is extremely toxic and explosive. A safer reagent would be more convenient for routine use. Second, methylene generated from diazomethane is so reactive that it inserts into C—H bonds as well as C=C bonds. In the reaction of propene with diazomethane-generated methylene, several side products are formed.

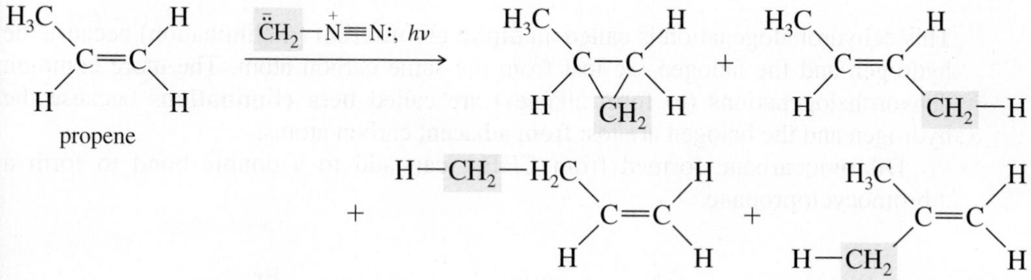

$$\underset{\text{propene}}{H_3C(H)C=CH_2} \xrightarrow{\ddot{C}H_2-\overset{+}{N}\equiv N:,\ h\nu} \text{methylcyclopropane} + H_3C(H)C=C(H)(CH_2-H) + H-CH_2-H_2C(H)C=CH_2 + H_3C(H-CH_2)C=CH_2$$

PROBLEM 8-26

Show how the insertion of methylene into a bond of cyclohexene can produce the following.

(a) norcarane,

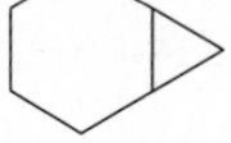

(b) 3-methylcyclohexene

(c) 1-methylcyclohexene

8-11A The Simmons–Smith Reaction

$$>C=C< + ICH_2ZnI \longrightarrow -C(CH_2)C- + ZnI_2$$

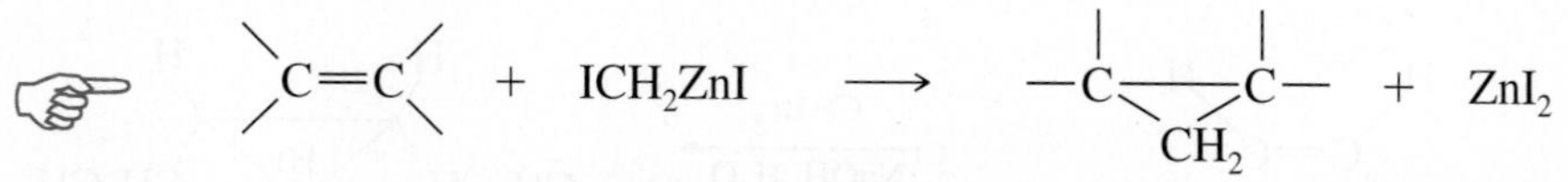

Two DuPont chemists discovered a reagent that converts alkenes to cyclopropanes in better yields than diazomethane, with fewer side reactions. The **Simmons–Smith reaction**, named in their honor, is one of the best ways of making cyclopropanes.

The Simmons–Smith reagent is made by adding methylene iodide to the "zinc–copper couple" (zinc dust that has been activated with an impurity of copper). The reagent probably resembles iodomethyl zinc iodide, ICH_2ZnI. This kind of reagent is called a *carbenoid* because it reacts much like a carbene, but it does not actually contain a divalent carbon atom.

$$CH_2I_2 + Zn(Cu) \longrightarrow \underset{\text{Simmons–Smith reagent (a carbenoid)}}{ICH_2ZnI}$$

$$\text{cyclohexene} \xrightarrow[\text{Zn, CuCl}]{CH_2I_2} \text{norcarane (59\%)}$$

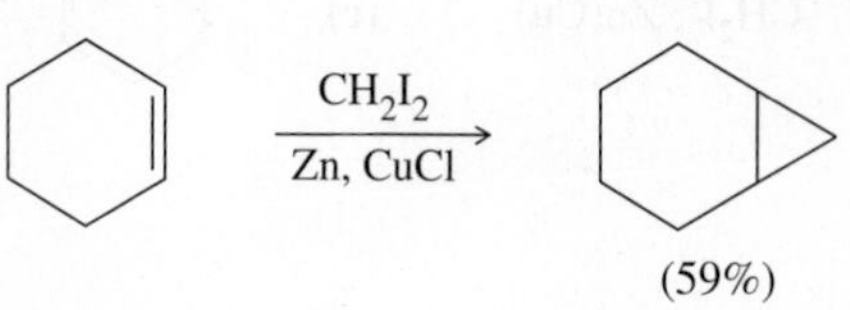

8-11B Formation of Carbenes by Alpha Elimination

Carbenes are also formed by reactions of halogenated compounds with bases. If a carbon atom has bonds to at least one hydrogen and to enough halogen atoms to make the hydrogen slightly acidic, it may be possible to form a carbene. For example, bromoform ($CHBr_3$) reacts with a 50% aqueous solution of potassium hydroxide to form dibromocarbene.

$$\underset{\text{bromoform}}{CHBr_3} + K^+ \ ^-OH \rightleftarrows \ ^-{:}CBr_3 \quad K^+ + H_2O$$

$$Br{-}\ddot{C}^-{-}Br \ (\text{with } Br \text{ below}) \rightleftarrows \underset{\text{dibromocarbene}}{:CBr_2} + :Br^-$$

This dehydrohalogenation is called an **alpha elimination** (α elimination) because the hydrogen and the halogen are lost from the same carbon atom. The more common dehydrohalogenations (to form alkenes) are called **beta eliminations** because the hydrogen and the halogen are lost from adjacent carbon atoms.

Dibromocarbene formed from $CHBr_3$ can add to a double bond to form a dibromocyclopropane.

$$\text{cyclopentene} \xrightarrow[KOH/H_2O]{CHBr_3} \text{6,6-dibromobicyclo[3.1.0]hexane (Br, Br)}$$

The products of these cyclopropanations retain any cis or trans stereochemistry of the reactants.

$$\text{trans-PhCH=CHPh (H, Ph / Ph, H)} \xrightarrow[NaOH,\ H_2O]{CHCl_3} \text{trans-1,1-dichloro-2,3-diphenylcyclopropane (H, Ph, Ph, H, Cl, Cl)}$$

$$\text{cis-}CH_3CH_2CH{=}CHCH_2CH_3 \text{ (H, H / } CH_3CH_2, CH_2CH_3) \xrightarrow[NaOH,\ H_2O]{CHBr_3} \text{cis-1,1-dibromo-2,3-diethylcyclopropane (H, H, } CH_3CH_2, CH_2CH_3, Br, Br)$$

PROBLEM 8-27

Predict the carbene addition products of the following reactions.

(a) cyclohexene + $CHCl_3$, 50% NaOH/H_2O

(b) 7-methylbicyclo[2.2.1]hept-2-en-7-ol (H_3C, OH) + CH_2I_2, Zn(Cu)

(c) 4-($CHBr_2$-methyl)cyclohexene ($CHBr_2$) + 50% NaOH/H_2O

PROBLEM 8-28

Show how you would accomplish each of the following synthetic conversions.

(a) *trans*-2-butene ⟶ *trans*-1,2-dimethylcyclopropane

(b) cyclopentene ⟶ (bicyclic product with H and Br)

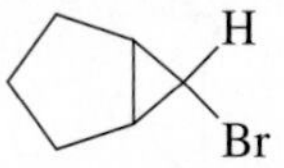

(c) cyclohexanol ⟶ (bicyclic product with Cl and Cl)

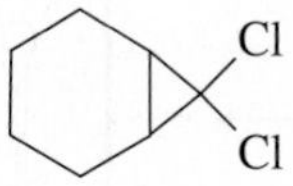

8-12 Epoxidation of Alkenes

Some of the most important reactions of alkenes involve oxidation. When we speak of oxidation, we usually mean reactions that form carbon–oxygen bonds. (Halogens are oxidizing agents, and the addition of a halogen molecule across a double bond is formally an oxidation as well.) Oxidations are particularly important because many common functional groups contain oxygen, and alkene oxidations are some of the best methods for introducing oxygen into organic molecules. We will consider methods for epoxidation, hydroxylation, and oxidative cleavage of alkene double bonds.

An **epoxide** is a three-membered cyclic ether, also called an **oxirane**. Epoxides are valuable synthetic intermediates used for converting alkenes to a variety of other functional groups. An alkene is converted to an epoxide by a **peroxyacid**, a carboxylic acid that has an extra oxygen atom in a —O—O— (peroxy) linkage.

$$>C=C< \; + \; R-\overset{O}{\overset{\|}{C}}-O-O-H \longrightarrow >C\overset{O}{-}C< \; + \; R-\overset{O}{\overset{\|}{C}}-O-H$$

alkene — peroxyacid — epoxide (oxirane) — acid

The **epoxidation** of an alkene is clearly an oxidation, since an oxygen atom is added. Peroxyacids are highly selective oxidizing agents. Some simple peroxyacids (sometimes called *peracids*) and their corresponding carboxylic acids are shown next.

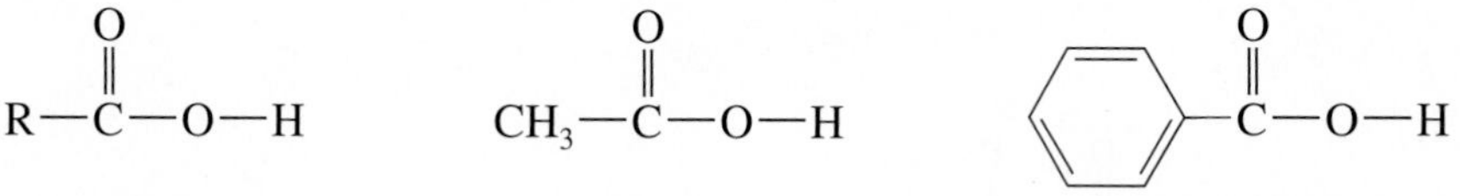

$R-\overset{O}{\overset{\|}{C}}-O-H$ a carboxylic acid; $CH_3-\overset{O}{\overset{\|}{C}}-O-H$ acetic acid; $C_6H_5-\overset{O}{\overset{\|}{C}}-O-H$ benzoic acid, $PhCO_2H$

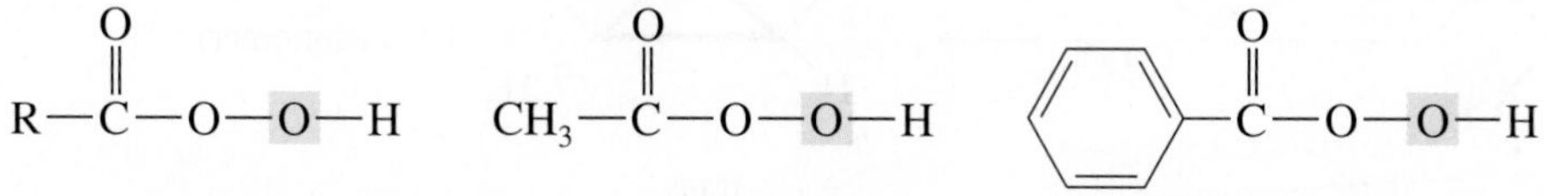

$R-\overset{O}{\overset{\|}{C}}-O-O-H$ a peroxyacid; $CH_3-\overset{O}{\overset{\|}{C}}-O-O-H$ peroxyacetic acid; $C_6H_5-\overset{O}{\overset{\|}{C}}-O-O-H$ peroxybenzoic acid, $PhCO_3H$

Epoxides are often found as components of natural products that plants use as defense mechanisms against insects. Typically, the epoxide reacts with critical cellular enzymes or DNA, preventing them from carrying out their normal functions. As a result, the insect is killed.

A peroxyacid epoxidizes an alkene by a concerted electrophilic reaction where several bonds are broken and several are formed at the same time. Starting with the alkene and the peroxyacid, a one-step reaction gives the epoxide and the acid directly, without any intermediates.

MECHANISM 8-9 Epoxidation of Alkenes

Peroxyacids epoxidize alkenes in a one-step (concerted) process.

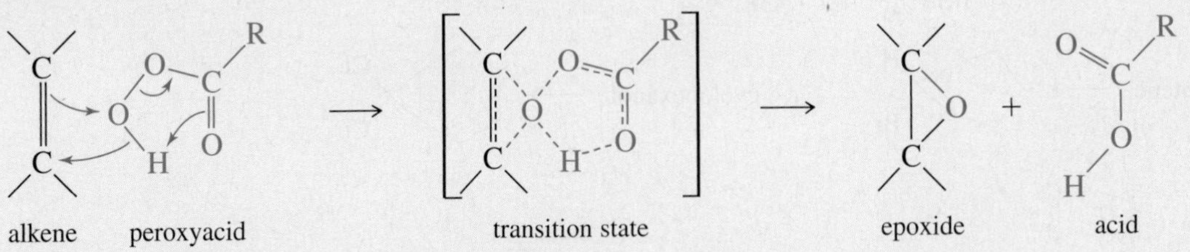

alkene peroxyacid → [transition state] → epoxide + acid

EXAMPLE: Epoxidation of propene by peroxyacetic acid.

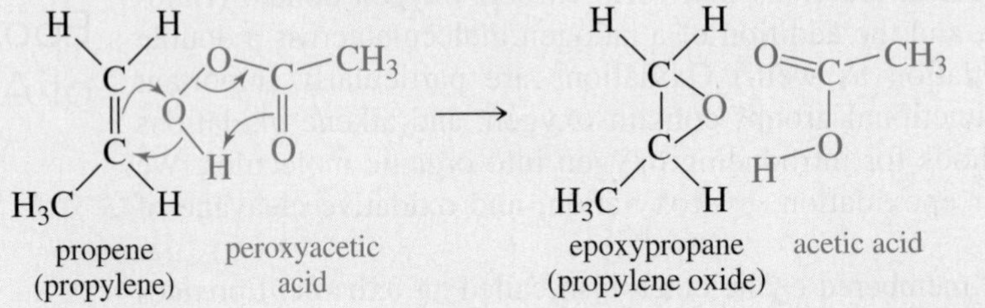

propene (propylene) + peroxyacetic acid → epoxypropane (propylene oxide) + acetic acid

Because the epoxidation takes place in one step, there is no opportunity for the alkene molecule to rotate and change its cis or trans geometry. The epoxide retains whatever stereochemistry is present in the alkene.

The following examples use *m*-chloroperoxybenzoic acid (MCPBA), a common epoxidizing reagent, to convert alkenes to epoxides having the same cis or trans stereochemistry. MCPBA is used for its desirable solubility properties: The peroxyacid dissolves, then the spent acid precipitates out of solution.

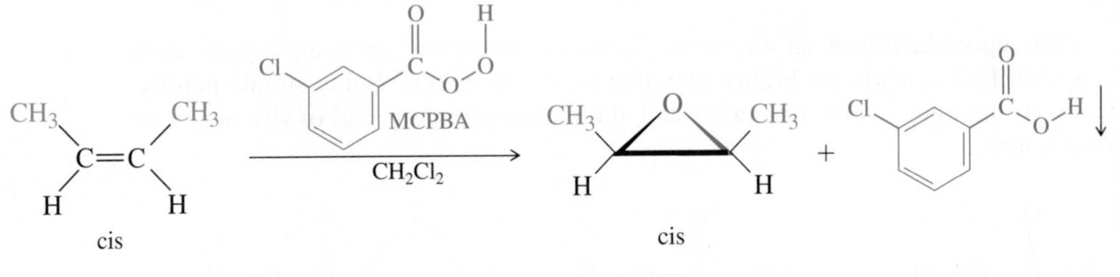

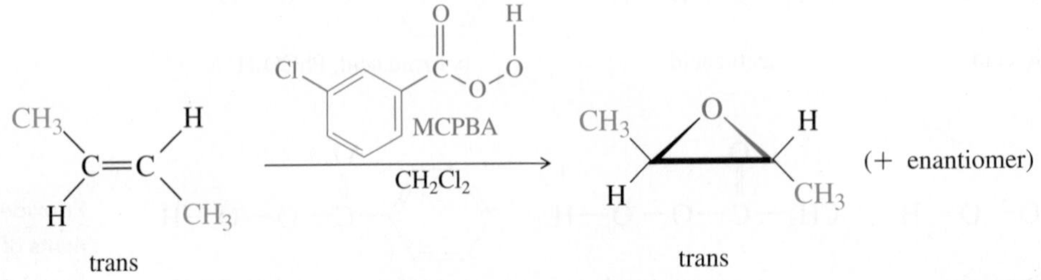

cis → (MCPBA, CH_2Cl_2) → cis + (m-chlorobenzoic acid ↓)

trans → (MCPBA, CH_2Cl_2) → trans (+ enantiomer)

PROBLEM 8-29

Predict the products, including stereochemistry where appropriate, for the *m*-chloroperoxybenzoic acid epoxidations of the following alkenes.

(a) *cis*-2-hexene
(b) *trans*-2-hexene
(c) *cis*-cyclodecene
(d) *trans*-cyclodecene

8-13 Acid-Catalyzed Opening of Epoxides

Most epoxides are easily isolated as stable products if the solution is not too acidic. Any moderately strong acid protonates the epoxide, however. Water attacks the protonated epoxide, opening the ring and forming a 1,2-diol, commonly called a **glycol**.

MECHANISM 8-10 Acid-Catalyzed Opening of Epoxides

The crucial step is a back-side attack by the solvent on the protonated epoxide.

Step 1: Protonation of the epoxide activates it toward nucleophilic attack.

epoxide $\xrightleftharpoons{H_3O^+}$ protonated epoxide

Step 2: Back-side attack by the solvent (water) opens the ring.

protonated epoxide + $H_2\ddot{O}$: (back-side attack) $\longrightarrow$

Step 3: Deprotonation gives the diol product.

$\rightleftharpoons$ + H_3O^+

a glycol
(anti orientation)

EXAMPLE: Acid-catalyzed hydrolysis of propylene oxide (epoxypropane).

Step 1: Protonation of the epoxide.

epoxypropane
(propylene oxide) $\xrightleftharpoons{H_3O^+}$ protonated epoxide

(Continued)

The body oxidizes the alkene components of drugs and other substances to epoxides, which are then hydrolyzed to diols by an epoxide hydrolase enzyme. The more reactive epoxides are rapidly converted to water-soluble diols and eliminated in the urine. Epoxide hydrolase enzymes are sometimes used in organic synthesis to produce chiral diols.

Steps 2 and 3: Back-side attack by water, then deprotonation of the product.

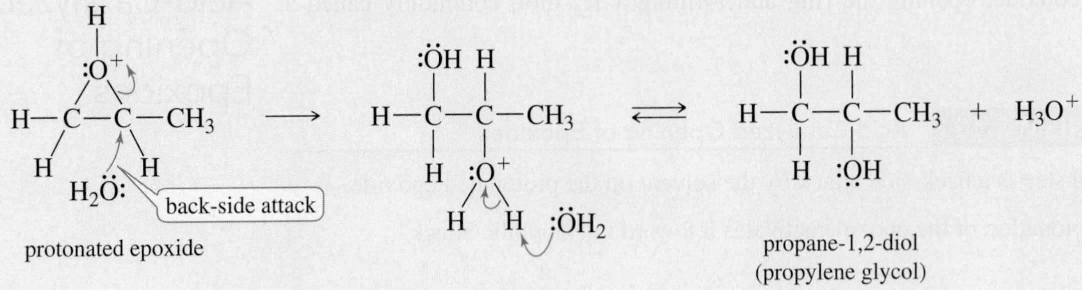

protonated epoxide — back-side attack — propane-1,2-diol (propylene glycol)

Because glycol formation involves a back-side attack on a protonated epoxide, the result is anti orientation of the hydroxyl groups on the double bond. For example, when 1,2-epoxycyclopentane ("cyclopentene oxide") is treated with dilute mineral acid, the product is pure *trans*-1,2-cyclopentanediol.

cyclopentene oxide — H_3O^+ — H_2O: — *trans*-1,2-cyclopentanediol (both enantiomers)

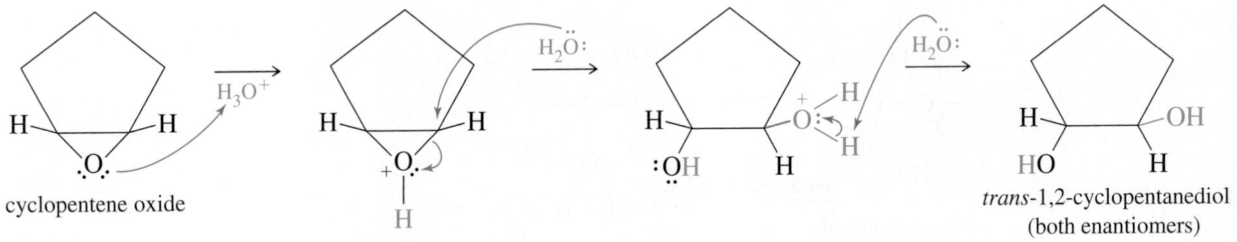

PROBLEM 8-30

(a) Propose a mechanism for the conversion of *cis*-3-hexene to the epoxide (3,4-epoxyhexane) and the ring-opening reaction to give the glycol, 3,4-hexanediol. In your mechanism, pay particular attention to the stereochemistry of the intermediates and products.

(b) Repeat part (a) for *trans*-3-hexene. Compare the products obtained from *cis*- and *trans*-3-hexene. Is this reaction sequence stereospecific?

Epoxidation reagents can be chosen to favor either the epoxide or the glycol. Peroxyacetic acid is used in strongly acidic water solutions. The acidic solution protonates the epoxide and converts it to the glycol. Peroxybenzoic acids are weak acids that can be used in nonnucleophilic solvents such as carbon tetrachloride. *m*-Chloroperoxybenzoic acid in CCl_4 generally gives good yields of epoxides. Figure 8-8 compares the uses of these reagents.

PROBLEM 8-31

Magnesium monoperoxyphthalate (MMPP) epoxidizes alkenes much like MCPBA. MMPP is more stable, however, and it may be safer to use for large-scale and industrial reactions. Propose a mechanism for the reaction of *trans*-2-methyl-3-heptene with MMPP, and predict the structure of the product(s).

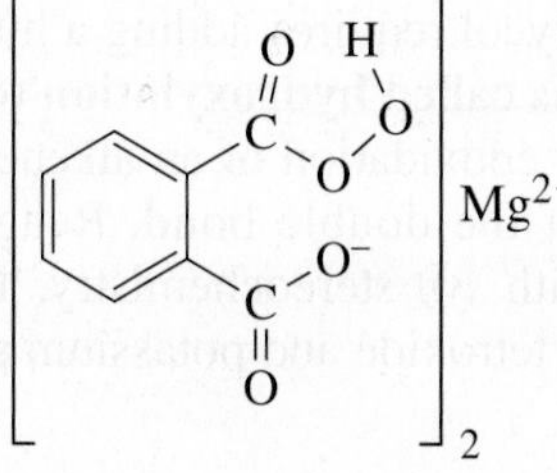

Magnesium monoperoxyphthalate, *MMPP*

PROBLEM 8-32

Predict the major products of the following reactions.

(a) *cis*-2-hexene + MCPBA in chloroform
(b) *trans*-3-hexene + peroxyacetic acid (CH_3CO_3H) in water
(c) 1-methylcyclohexene + MMPP in ethanol
(d) *trans*-cyclodecene + peroxyacetic acid in acidic water
(e) *cis*-cyclodecene + MCPBA in CH_2Cl_2, then dilute aqueous acid

PROBLEM 8-33

When 1,2-epoxycyclohexane (cyclohexene oxide) is treated with anhydrous HCl in methanol, the principal product is *trans*-2-methoxycyclohexanol. Propose a mechanism to account for the formation of this product.

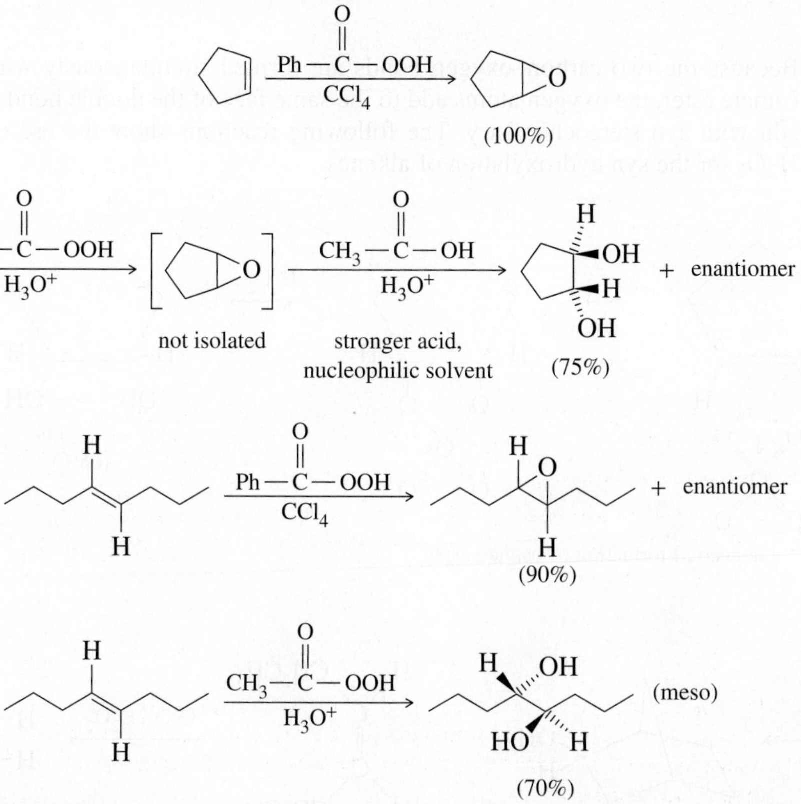

Ph—C(=O)—OOH, CCl_4 (100%)

CH_3—C(=O)—OOH, H_3O^+ → not isolated → CH_3—C(=O)—OH, H_3O^+ (stronger acid, nucleophilic solvent) → + enantiomer (75%)

Ph—C(=O)—OOH, CCl_4 → + enantiomer (90%)

CH_3—C(=O)—OOH, H_3O^+ → (meso) (70%)

■ **FIGURE 8-8**
Reagents for epoxidation. Peroxyacetic acid is used in strongly acidic aqueous solutions. Alkenes are epoxidized, then opened to glycols in one step. Weakly acidic peroxyacids, such as peroxybenzoic acid, can be used in nonaqueous solutions to give good yields of epoxides.

8-14 Syn Hydroxylation of Alkenes

Converting an alkene to a glycol requires adding a hydroxyl group to each end of the double bond. This addition is called **hydroxylation** (or **dihydroxylation**) of the double bond. We have seen that epoxidation of an alkene, followed by acidic hydrolysis, gives *anti* hydroxylation of the double bond. Reagents are also available for the hydroxylation of alkenes with *syn* stereochemistry. The two most common reagents for this purpose are osmium tetroxide and potassium permanganate.

$$C{=}C + OsO_4 + H_2O_2 \longrightarrow -\underset{OH}{C}-\underset{OH}{C}-$$

(*or* $KMnO_4$, ^-OH) syn addition

8-14A Osmium Tetroxide Hydroxylation

Osmium tetroxide (OsO_4, sometimes called *osmic acid*) reacts with alkenes in a concerted step to form a cyclic osmate ester. Oxidizing agents such as hydrogen peroxide (H_2O_2) or tertiary amine oxides ($R_3N^+{-}O^-$) are used to hydrolyze the osmate ester and reoxidize osmium to osmium tetroxide. The regenerated osmium tetroxide catalyst continues to hydroxylate more molecules of the alkene.

alkene + osmic acid $\longrightarrow$ osmate ester $\xrightarrow[\text{or } R_3N^+-O^-]{H_2O_2}$ glycol + OsO_4

Because the two carbon–oxygen bonds are formed simultaneously with the cyclic osmate ester, the oxygen atoms add to the same face of the double bond; that is, they add with syn stereochemistry. The following reactions show the use of OsO_4 and H_2O_2 for the syn hydroxylation of alkenes.

concerted formation of osmate ester $\xrightarrow{H_2O_2}$ *cis*-glycol (65%) + OsO_4

$\xrightarrow{OsO_4,\ H_2O_2}$

cis-3-hexene $\xrightarrow{OsO_4,\ H_2O_2}$ *meso*-3,4-hexanediol

8-14B Permanganate Hydroxylation

Osmium tetroxide is expensive, highly toxic, and volatile. A cold, dilute solution of potassium permanganate ($KMnO_4$) also hydroxylates alkenes with syn stereochemistry, with slightly reduced yields in most cases. Like osmium tetroxide, permanganate adds to the alkene double bond to form a cyclic ester: a manganate ester in this case. The basic solution hydrolyzes the manganate ester, liberating the glycol and producing a brown precipitate of manganese dioxide, MnO_2.

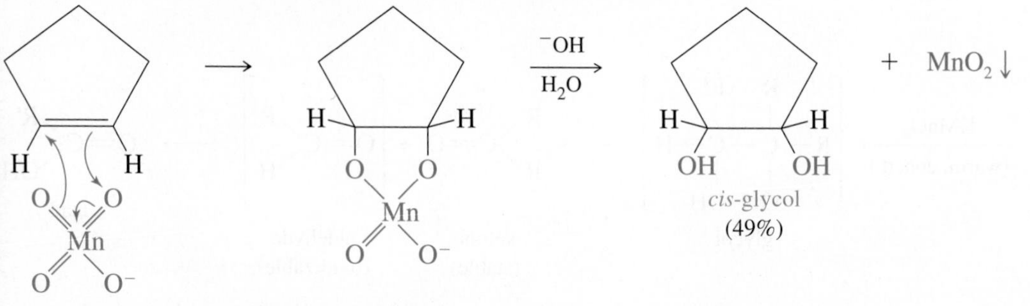

$\xrightarrow{}$ $\xrightarrow[H_2O]{^-OH}$ *cis*-glycol (49%) + $MnO_2\downarrow$

concerted formation of manganate ester

In addition to its synthetic value, the permanganate oxidation of alkenes provides a simple chemical test for the presence of an alkene. When an alkene is added to a clear, deep purple aqueous solution of potassium permanganate, the solution loses its purple color and becomes the murky, opaque brown color of MnO_2. (Although there are other functional groups that decolorize permanganate, few do it as quickly as alkenes.)

8-14C Choosing a Reagent

To hydroxylate an alkene with syn stereochemistry, which is the better reagent: osmium tetroxide or potassium permanganate? Osmium tetroxide gives better yields, but permanganate is cheaper and safer to use. The answer depends on the circumstances.

If the starting material is only 2 mg of a compound 15 steps along in a difficult synthesis, we use osmium tetroxide. The better yield is crucial because the starting material is precious and expensive, and little osmic acid is needed. If the hydroxylation is the first step in a synthesis and involves 5 kg of the starting material, we use potassium permanganate. The cost of buying enough osmium tetroxide would be prohibitive, and dealing with such a large amount of a volatile, toxic reagent would be inconvenient. On such a large scale, we can accept the lower yield of the permanganate oxidation.

PROBLEM 8-34

Predict the major products of the following reactions, including stereochemistry.
(a) cyclohexene + $KMnO_4/H_2O$ (cold, dilute)
(b) cyclohexene + peroxyacetic acid in water
(c) *cis*-2-pentene + OsO_4/H_2O_2
(d) *cis*-2-pentene + peroxyacetic acid in water
(e) *trans*-2-pentene + OsO_4/H_2O_2
(f) *trans*-2-pentene + peroxyacetic acid in water

PROBLEM 8-35

Show how you would accomplish the following conversions.
(a) *cis*-3-hexene to *meso*-3,4-hexanediol
(b) *cis*-3-hexene to (*d,l*)-3,4-hexanediol
(c) *trans*-3-hexene to *meso*-3,4-hexanediol
(d) *trans*-3-hexene to (*d,l*)-3,4-hexanediol

8-15 Oxidative Cleavage of Alkenes

8-15A Cleavage by Permanganate

In a potassium permanganate hydroxylation, if the solution is warm or acidic or too concentrated, **oxidative cleavage** of the glycol may occur. In effect, the double bond is cleaved to two carbonyl groups. The products are initially ketones and aldehydes, but aldehydes are oxidized to carboxylic acids under these strong oxidizing conditions. If the molecule contains a terminal $=CH_2$ group, that group is oxidized all the way to CO_2 and water.

$R_2C{=}CHR' \xrightarrow[\text{(warm, concd.)}]{KMnO_4}$ [R–C(R)(OH)–C(R')(OH)–H] glycol $\longrightarrow$ $R_2C{=}O$ ketone (stable) + [O=C(R')H] aldehyde (oxidizable) $\longrightarrow$ O=C(R')OH acid

Examples

butylidenecyclohexane $\xrightarrow[\text{(warm, concd.)}]{KMnO_4}$ cyclohexanone + butanoic acid

limonene $\xrightarrow[\text{(warm, concd.)}]{KMnO_4}$ keto diacid (COOH, COOH) + CO_2

8-15B Ozonolysis

Like permanganate, ozone cleaves double bonds to give ketones and aldehydes. However, ozonolysis is milder, and both ketones and aldehydes can be recovered without further oxidation.

$R_2C{=}CHR' + O_3 \longrightarrow$ ozonide $\xrightarrow{(CH_3)_2S}$ $R_2C{=}O$ ketone + O=C(R')H aldehyde

Ozone is a powerful lung irritant, causing a cough, sore throat, and tiredness. It can also increase a person's sensitivity to allergens. The mechanism may involve oxidation of the double bonds of the fatty acids that make up the surfactants and the membranes of the cells lining the bronchial airways and lungs.

Ozone (O_3) is a high-energy form of oxygen produced when ultraviolet light or an electrical discharge passes through oxygen gas. Ultraviolet light from the sun converts oxygen to ozone in the upper atmosphere. This "ozone layer" shields the earth from some of the high-energy ultraviolet radiation it would otherwise receive.

$$\tfrac{3}{2}O_2 + 142\text{ kJ (34 kcal)} \longrightarrow O_3$$

Ozone has 142 kJ/mol of excess energy over oxygen, and it is much more reactive. A Lewis structure of ozone shows that the central oxygen atom bears a positive charge, and each of the outer oxygen atoms bears half a negative charge.

$$O_3 = [\,{}^{-}\!:\ddot{O}-\overset{+}{O}=\ddot{O}: \longleftrightarrow :\ddot{O}=\overset{+}{O}-\ddot{O}:^{-}\,]$$

Ozone reacts with an alkene to form a cyclic compound called a *primary ozonide* or *molozonide* (because 1 mole of ozone has been added). The molozonide has two peroxy (—O—O—) linkages, so it is quite unstable. It rearranges rapidly, even at low temperatures, to form an ozonide.

molozonide (primary ozonide)

ozonide

Ozonides are not very stable, and they are rarely isolated. In most cases, they are immediately reduced by a mild reducing agent such as zinc or (more recently) dimethyl sulfide. The products of this reduction are ketones and aldehydes.

$CH_3—S—CH_3$ dimethyl sulfide

ozonide → ketones, aldehydes + $CH_3—\overset{O}{\overset{\|}{S}}—CH_3$ dimethyl sulfoxide (DMSO)

$$R_2C{=}CHR' \xrightarrow[(2)\ (CH_3)_2S]{(1)\ O_3} R_2C{=}O \quad O{=}CHR' \quad + \quad (CH_3)_2S{=}O$$

The following reactions show the products obtained from ozonolysis of some representative alkenes. Note how (1) and (2) are used with a single reaction arrow to denote the steps in a two-step sequence.

3-nonene $\xrightarrow[(2)\ (CH_3)_2S]{(1)\ O_3}$ $CH_3CH_2CHO + CH_3(CH_2)_4CHO$ (65%)

$\xrightarrow[(2)\ (CH_3)_2S]{(1)\ O_3}$ (dialdehyde, CHO, CHO) =

$\xrightarrow[(2)\ (CH_3)_2S]{(1)\ O_3}$ CHO CHO + $H_2C{=}O$

One of the most common uses of ozonolysis has been for determining the positions of double bonds in alkenes. For example, if we were uncertain of the position of the methyl group in a methylcyclopentene, the products of ozonolysis–reduction would confirm the structure of the original alkene.

1-methylcyclopentene $\xrightarrow[(2)\ (CH_3)_2S]{(1)\ O_3}$ (keto aldehyde: CH_3, O, O, H)

3-methylcyclopentene $\xrightarrow[(2)\ (CH_3)_2S]{(1)\ O_3}$ (dialdehyde: H–C=O, O=C–H)

problem-solving Hint

To predict the products from ozonolysis of an alkene, erase the double bond and add two oxygen atoms as carbonyl (C=O) groups where the double bond used to be.

SOLVED PROBLEM 8-7

Ozonolysis–reduction of an unknown alkene gives an equimolar mixture of cyclohexanecarbaldehyde and 2-butanone. Determine the structure of the original alkene.

cyclohexanecarbaldehyde (cyclohexyl–CH=O) 2-butanone ($CH_3-\overset{O}{\overset{\|}{C}}-CH_2-CH_3$)

SOLUTION

We can reconstruct the alkene by removing the two oxygen atoms of the carbonyl groups (C=O) and connecting the remaining carbon atoms with a double bond. One uncertainty remains, however: The original alkene might be either of two possible geometric isomers.

cyclohexyl(H)C=O O=C(CH_2CH_3)(CH_3) ← came from — cyclohexyl(H)C=C(CH_2CH_3)(CH_3) or cyclohexyl(H)C=C(CH_3)(CH_2CH_3)

remove oxygen atoms and reconnect the double bond

PROBLEM 8-36

Give structures of the alkenes that would give the following products upon ozonolysis–reduction.

(a) $CH_3-\overset{O}{\overset{\|}{C}}-CH_2-CH_2-CH_2-\overset{O}{\overset{\|}{C}}-CH_2-CH_3$

(b) cyclohexanone and $CH_3-CH_2-CH_2-\overset{O}{\overset{\|}{C}}-H$

(c) $CH_3-CH_2-\overset{O}{\overset{\|}{C}}-CH_2-CH_2-CH_2-CH_3$ and $CH_3-CH_2-\overset{O}{\overset{\|}{C}}-H$

Ozone is a strong oxidizing agent that can be used instead of chlorine to disinfect the water in swimming pools. Ozone oxidizes organic matter, and it kills bacteria and algae. Ozone is used instead of chlorine because it can be generated on-site (rather than storing and using toxic chemicals such as chlorine gas or sodium hypochlorite) and because it doesn't produce as many harmful by-products.

8-15C Comparison of Permanganate Cleavage and Ozonolysis

Both permanganate and ozonolysis break the carbon–carbon double bond and replace it with carbonyl (C=O) groups. In the permanganate cleavage, any aldehyde products are further oxidized to carboxylic acids. In the ozonolysis–reduction procedure, the aldehyde products are generated in the dimethyl sulfide reduction step (and not in the presence of ozone), and they are not oxidized.

concd. $KMnO_4$, ^-OH → (not isolated) →

(1) O_3 (2) $(CH_3)_2S$

PROBLEM 8-37

Predict the major products of the following reactions.

(a) (E)-3-methyl-3-octene + ozone, then $(CH_3)_2S$

(b) (Z)-3-methyl-3-octene + warm, concentrated $KMnO_4$

(c) (cyclohexylidenecyclopentane) + O_3, then $(CH_3)_2S$

(d) 1-ethylcycloheptene + ozone, then $(CH_3)_2S$

(e) 1-ethylcycloheptene + warm, concentrated $KMnO_4$

(f) 1-ethylcycloheptene + cold, dilute $KMnO_4$

problem-solving **Hint**

Osmium tetroxide, cold, dilute $KMnO_4$, and epoxidation oxidize the pi bond of an alkene but leave the sigma bond intact. Ozone and warm, concentrated $KMnO_4$ break the double bond entirely to give carbonyl compounds.

8-16 Polymerization of Alkenes

A **polymer** is a large molecule composed of many smaller repeating units (the **monomers**) bonded together. Alkenes serve as monomers for some of the most common polymers, such as polyethylene, polypropylene, polystyrene, poly(vinyl chloride), and many others. Alkenes generally undergo **addition polymerization**, the rapid addition of one molecule at a time to a growing polymer chain. There is generally a reactive intermediate (cation, anion, or radical) at the growing end of the chain; for that reason, addition polymers are also called **chain-growth polymers**.

Many alkenes undergo addition polymerization under the right conditions. The chain-growth mechanism involves addition of the reactive end of the growing chain across the double bond of the alkene monomer. Depending on the structure of the monomer, the reactive intermediates may be carbocations, free radicals, or carbanions.

8-16A Cationic Polymerization

Alkenes that easily form carbocations are good candidates for **cationic polymerization**, which is just another example of electrophilic addition to an alkene. Consider what happens when pure isobutylene is treated with a trace of concentrated sulfuric acid. Protonation of the alkene forms a carbocation. If a large concentration of isobutylene is available, another molecule of the alkene may act as the nucleophile and attack the carbocation to form the *dimer* (two monomers joined together) and give another carbocation. If the conditions are right, the growing cationic end of the chain will keep adding across more molecules of the monomer. The polymer of isobutylene is *polyisobutylene*, one of the constituents of *butyl rubber* used in inner tubes and other synthetic rubber products.

Protonation *Attack by the second molecule of isobutylene*

$$H_2SO_4 + H_2C{=}C(CH_3)_2 \longrightarrow CH_3{-}\overset{+}{C}(CH_3)_2 \quad H_2C{=}C(CH_3)_2 \longrightarrow CH_3{-}C(CH_3)_2{-}CH_2{-}\overset{+}{C}(CH_3)_2$$

isobutylene dimer

Attack by a third molecule to give a trimer

$$CH_3{-}C(CH_3)_2{-}CH_2{-}\overset{+}{C}(CH_3)_2 \quad H_2C{=}C(CH_3)_2 \longrightarrow CH_3{-}C(CH_3)_2{-}CH_2{-}C(CH_3)_2{-}CH_2{-}\overset{+}{C}(CH_3)_2 \longrightarrow \longrightarrow \text{polymer}$$

dimer third monomer trimer

Loss of a proton is the most common side reaction that terminates chain growth:

$$HSO_4^- \quad CH_3{-}C(CH_3)_2{-}CH_2{-}C(CH_3)_2{-}CH_2{-}\overset{+}{C}(CH_3)_2 \xrightarrow{-H^+} CH_3{-}C(CH_3)_2{-}CH_2{-}C(CH_3)_2{-}CH{=}C(CH_3)_2$$

Boron trifluoride (BF_3) is an excellent catalyst for cationic polymerization because it leaves no good nucleophile that might attack a carbocation intermediate and end the polymerization. Boron trifluoride is electron-deficient and a strong Lewis acid. It usually contains a trace of water that acts as a co-catalyst by adding to BF_3 and then protonating the monomer. Protonation occurs at the less substituted end of an alkene double bond to give the more stable carbocation. Each additional monomer molecule adds with the same orientation, always giving the more stable carbocation. The following reaction shows the polymerization of styrene (vinylbenzene) using BF_3 as the catalyst.

$$BF_3 + :\ddot{O}H_2 \longrightarrow F_3\overset{-}{B}{-}\overset{+}{O}H_2 \quad H_2C{=}CH(Ph) \longrightarrow F_3\overset{-}{B}{-}\ddot{O}H + H{-}CH_2{-}\overset{+}{C}H(Ph)$$

styrene

First chain-lengthening step

$$CH_3{-}\overset{+}{C}H(Ph) \quad H_2C{=}CH(Ph) \longrightarrow CH_3{-}CH(Ph){-}CH_2{-}\overset{+}{C}H(Ph)$$

After many steps the polymerization continues

$$Ⓟ{-}CH_2{-}CH(Ph){-}CH_2{-}\overset{+}{C}H(Ph) \quad H_2C{=}CH(Ph) \longrightarrow Ⓟ{-}CH_2{-}CH(Ph){-}CH_2{-}CH(Ph){-}CH_2{-}\overset{+}{C}H(Ph)$$

Ⓟ— = growing polymer chain

The most likely ending of this BF_3-catalyzed polymerization is the loss of a proton from the carbocation at the end of the chain. This side reaction terminates one chain, but it also protonates another molecule of styrene, initiating a new chain.

Termination of a polymer chain

Ⓟ$-CH_2-CH(Ph)-CH(H)-C^+(H)(Ph)$ + $H_2C=C(H)(Ph)$ ⟶ Ⓟ$-CH_2-CH(Ph)-CH=C(H)(Ph)$ + $H_3C-C^+(H)(Ph)$

polystyrene — starts another chain

The product of this polymerization is polystyrene: a clear, brittle plastic that is often used for inexpensive lenses, transparent containers, and styrofoam insulation. Polystyrene is also the major component of the resin beads that are used to make synthetic proteins. (See Section 24-11.)

PROBLEM 8-38

(a) Propose a mechanism for the following reaction.

$$2\ (CH_3)_2C{=}CH{-}CH_3 + \text{cat. } H^+ \longrightarrow \text{2,3,4,4-tetramethyl-2-hexene}$$

(b) Show the first three steps (as far as the tetramer) in the BF_3-catalyzed polymerization of propylene to form polypropylene.

PROBLEM 8-39

When cyclohexanol is dehydrated to cyclohexene, a gummy green substance forms on the bottom of the flask. Suggest what this residue might be, and propose a mechanism for its formation (as far as the dimer).

8-16B Free-Radical Polymerization

Many alkenes undergo **free-radical polymerization** when they are heated with radical initiators. For example, styrene polymerizes to polystyrene when it is heated to 100 °C with a peroxide initiator. A radical adds to styrene to give a resonance-stabilized radical, which then attacks another molecule of styrene to give an elongated radical.

Initiation step $\quad ROOR \xrightarrow{\text{heat}} 2\ RO\cdot$

Propagation step

$RO\cdot$ + $H_2C=CH(Ph)$ ⟶ $RO-CH_2-\dot{C}H(Ph)$ + $H_2C=CH(Ph)$ ⟶ $RO-CH_2-CH(Ph)-CH_2-\dot{C}H(Ph)$

styrene — stabilized radical — styrene — growing chain

Each propagation step adds another molecule of styrene to the radical end of the growing chain. This addition always takes place with the orientation that gives another resonance-stabilized benzylic (next to a benzene ring) radical.

Propagation step

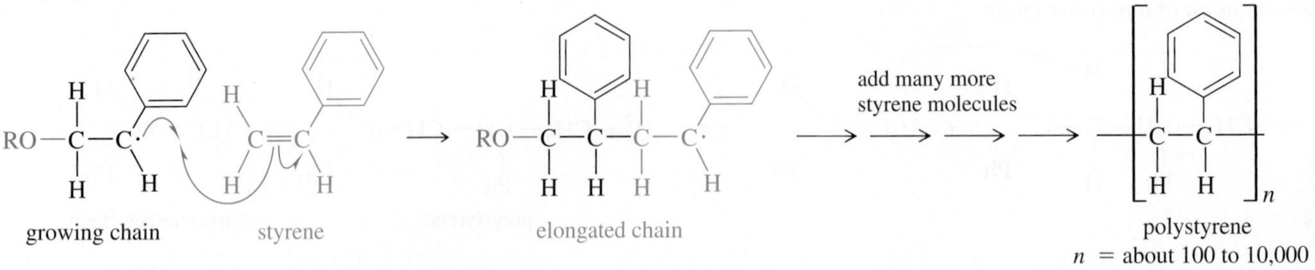

growing chain + styrene → elongated chain → add many more styrene molecules → polystyrene

n = about 100 to 10,000

Chain growth may continue with addition of several hundred or several thousand styrene units. Eventually, the chain reaction stops, either by the coupling of two chains or by reaction with an impurity (such as oxygen) or simply by running out of monomer.

PROBLEM 8-40

Show the intermediate that would result if the growing chain added to the other end of the styrene double bond. Explain why the final polymer has phenyl groups substituted on alternate carbon atoms rather than randomly distributed.

Ethylene is also polymerized by free-radical chain-growth polymerization. With ethylene, the free-radical intermediates are less stable, so stronger reaction conditions are required. Ethylene is commonly polymerized by free-radical initiators at pressures around 3000 atm and temperatures of about 200 °C. The product, called *low-density polyethylene*, is the material commonly used in polyethylene bags.

PROBLEM 8-41

Propose a mechanism for reaction of the first three ethylene units in the polymerization of ethylene in the presence of a peroxide.

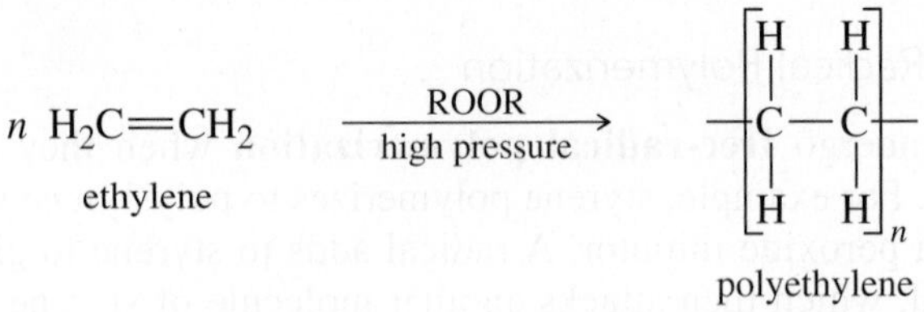

$$n\ H_2C{=}CH_2 \xrightarrow[\text{high pressure}]{\text{ROOR}} \left[-CH_2-CH_2- \right]_n$$

ethylene → polyethylene

8-16C Anionic Polymerization

Like cationic polymerization, **anionic polymerization** depends on the presence of a stabilizing group. To stabilize anions, the double bond should have a strong electron-withdrawing group such as a carbonyl group, a cyano group, or a nitro group. Methyl α-cyanoacrylate contains two powerful electron-withdrawing groups, and it undergoes nucleophilic additions very easily. If this liquid monomer is spread in a thin film between two surfaces, traces of basic impurities (metal oxides, etc.) can catalyze its rapid polymerization. The solidified polymer joins the two surfaces. The chemists who first made this monomer noticed how easily it polymerizes and realized that it could serve as a fast-setting glue. Methyl α-cyanoacrylate is sold commercially as Super Glue.

Initiation step

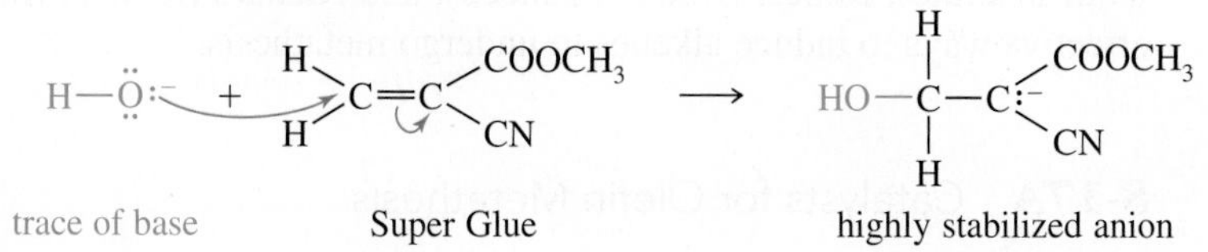

$$H-\ddot{O}:^- + H_2C=C(COOCH_3)(CN) \longrightarrow HO-CH_2-\ddot{C}^-(COOCH_3)(CN)$$

trace of base — Super Glue — highly stabilized anion

Chain lengthening step

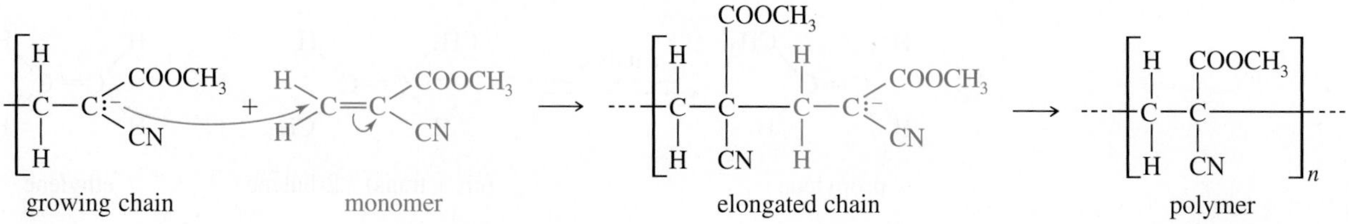

$$\text{---}[CH_2-\ddot{C}^-(COOCH_3)(CN)] + H_2C=C(COOCH_3)(CN) \longrightarrow \text{---}[CH_2-C(COOCH_3)(CN)]-CH_2-\ddot{C}^-(COOCH_3)(CN) \longrightarrow \text{---}[CH_2-C(COOCH_3)(CN)]_n\text{---}$$

growing chain — monomer — elongated chain — polymer

PROBLEM 8-42

Draw a mechanism for a base-catalyzed polymerization of methyl α-methacrylate to give the Plexiglas® polymer.

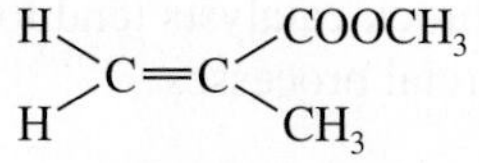

$$H_2C=C(COOCH_3)(CH_3)$$

methyl α-methacrylate

8-17 Olefin Metathesis

The double bond is the strongest bond in an alkene, yet it is also the most reactive bond. Imagine how useful it would be if we could break molecules at their double bonds and reassemble them as we please. That is the goal of olefin metathesis. We can think of an alkene as two alkylidene groups (=CHR) held together by the double bond, and mentally divide it up just like we divide the molecule when we go to name it as *E* or *Z* (Section 7-5B). **Olefin metathesis** is any reaction that trades and interchanges these alkylidene groups. The word *metathesis* comes from the Greek words *meta* (change) and *thesis* (position), meaning that the alkylidene groups change their positions in the products. Figure 8-9 shows the trading of alkylidene groups that takes place during olefin metathesis.

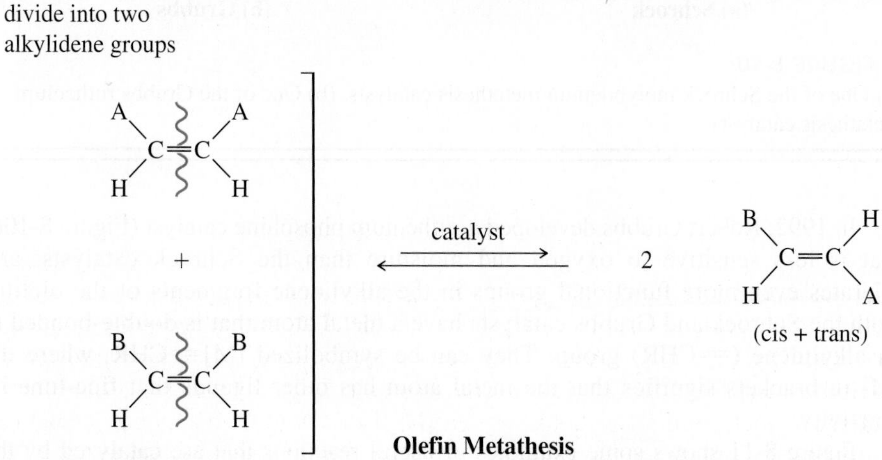

divide into two alkylidene groups

$$\text{AHC=CHA} + \text{BHC=CHB} \underset{}{\overset{\text{catalyst}}{\rightleftharpoons}} 2\ \text{BHC=CHA}$$

(cis + trans)

Olefin Metathesis

■ FIGURE 8-9
Olefin metathesis. During metathesis, the alkylidene groups of the reactant olefins trade partners and rearrange to give new combinations of alkenes in the products.

The 2005 Nobel Prize in Chemistry was awarded to Yves Chauvin (French Petroleum Institute), Robert Grubbs (Caltech), and Richard Schrock (MIT) for developing effective ways to induce alkenes to undergo metathesis.

8-17A Catalysts for Olefin Metathesis

Olefin metathesis was first observed in the 1950s, and was used in industry to convert propylene to a mixture of 2-butene and ethylene. This *Phillips Triolefin Process* used an aluminum/molybdenum catalyst whose exact structure was unknown.

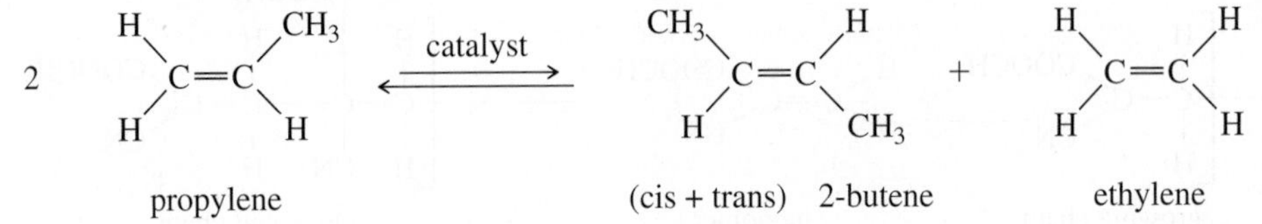

$$2\ H_2C{=}CH{-}CH_3 \underset{}{\overset{\text{catalyst}}{\rightleftharpoons}} CH_3CH{=}CHCH_3 + H_2C{=}CH_2$$

propylene → (cis + trans) 2-butene + ethylene

Around 1990, Richard Schrock developed versatile molybdenum and tungsten catalysts for olefin metathesis that tolerate a wide range of functional groups in the alkylidene fragments of the olefins. The Schrock catalyst shown in Figure 8-10a is now commercially available. The Schrock catalysts tend to be air- and moisture-sensitive, which limits their use in commercial processes.

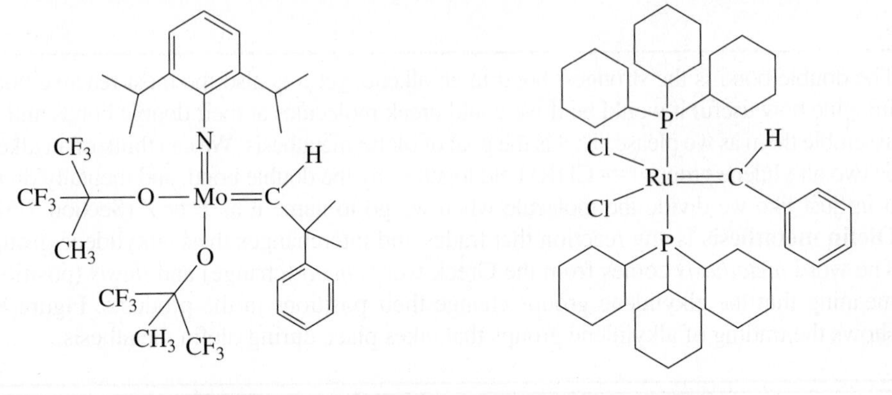

(a) Schrock (b) Grubbs

FIGURE 8-10
(a) One of the Schrock molybdenum metathesis catalysts. (b) One of the Grubbs ruthenium metathesis catalysts.

In 1992, Robert Grubbs developed a ruthenium phosphine catalyst (Figure 8-10b) that is less sensitive to oxygen and moisture than the Schrock catalysts, and tolerates even more functional groups in the alkylidene fragments of the olefins. Both the Schrock and Grubbs catalysts have a metal atom that is double-bonded to an alkylidene (=CHR) group. They can be symbolized [M]=CHR, where the [M] in brackets signifies that the metal atom has other ligands that fine-tune its reactivity.

Figure 8-11 shows some examples of useful reactions that are catalyzed by the Schrock and Grubbs catalysts. One important aspect of these metathesis reactions is that they are all reversible, so they form equilibrium mixtures of the reactants and all possible products unless something is done to drive the reaction toward the desired

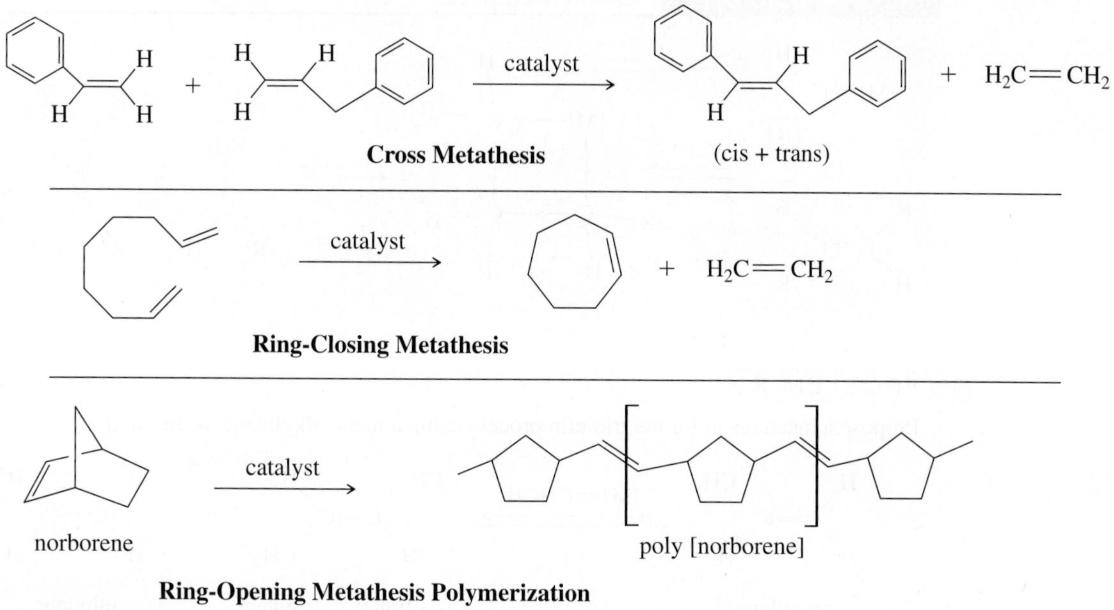

Cross Metathesis

catalyst

(cis + trans)

$+ H_2C{=}CH_2$

Ring-Closing Metathesis

catalyst

$+ H_2C{=}CH_2$

Ring-Opening Metathesis Polymerization

norborene

catalyst

poly [norborene]

■ FIGURE 8-11
Useful examples of metathesis reactions.

products. The first two examples in Figure 8-11 use the most common method, formation of ethylene gas. Ethylene bubbles off as it forms, effectively driving the reaction to completion. The ring-opening metathesis polymerization is exothermic and naturally goes to products because the ring strain in the bicyclic norbornene is released when the ring opens to form the polymer.

8-17B Mechanism of Olefin Metathesis

Several mechanisms were proposed to explain the catalytic metathesis reactions, but the mechanism published by Yves Chauvin in 1971 has come to be accepted as correct. We can think of an alkene as two alkylidene groups bonded together. Similarly, the Schrock and Grubbs catalysts are like a metal atom bonded to one alkylidene group.

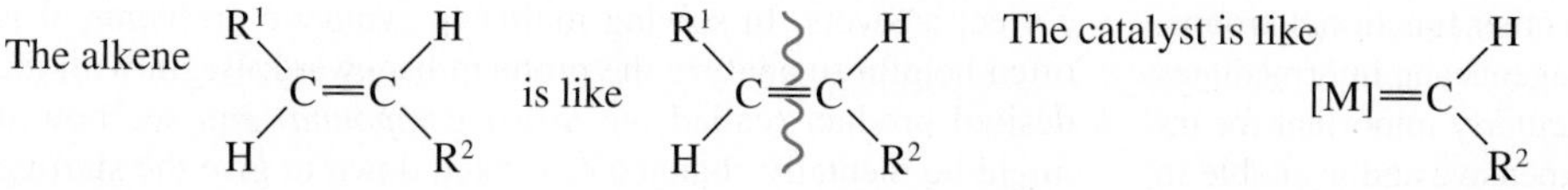

The alkene $R^1(H)C{=}C(H)R^2$ is like $R^1(H)C \wr\!\!= C(H)R^2$ The catalyst is like $[M]{=}C(H)R^2$

Chauvin proposed that the metal-alkylidene catalyst forms an intermediate four-membered ring with an alkene, as shown in Mechanism 8-11. Then the ring breaks apart, either to give the starting alkene and catalyst or to give a new alkene that has traded one alkylidene group with the catalyst.

This mechanism allows the alkylidene groups to change partners back and forth with the catalytic metal until a thermodynamic equilibrium is reached. As we saw earlier, good yields of products result if there is an effective driving force (such as formation of a gaseous by-product or release of ring strain) to push the equilibrium toward the desired products.

MECHANISM 8-11 Olefin Metathesis

$$[M]{=}CH(R) + R^1CH{=}CHR^2 \rightleftharpoons [M]{-}CH(R){-}CH(R^2){-}CH(R^1)\text{ (metallacyclobutane)} \rightleftharpoons [M]{=}CHR^1 + R^2CH{=}CHR$$

PROBLEM 8-43

Propose a mechanism for the triolefin process using a metal alkylidene as the catalyst.

$$2\ H_2C{=}CHCH_3 \xrightleftharpoons{[M]{=}CHCH_3} CH_3CH{=}CHCH_3 + H_2C{=}CH_2$$

propylene (cis + trans) 2-butene ethylene

PROBLEM 8-44

Show what reagents would be needed to synthesize the pheromone of the omnivorous leafroller (OLR) using olefin metathesis to assemble the molecule at the double bond.

OLR pheromone (cis + trans)

PROBLEM-SOLVING STRATEGY

ORGANIC SYNTHESIS

Alkyl halides and alkenes are readily made from other compounds, and they are easily converted to other functional groups. This flexibility makes them useful as reagents and intermediates for organic synthesis. Alkenes are particularly important for industrial syntheses because they are inexpensive and available in large quantities from cracking and dehydrogenation of petroleum fractions.

Organic synthesis is the preparation of desired compounds from readily available materials. Synthesis is one of the major areas of organic chemistry, and nearly every chapter of this book involves organic synthesis in some way. A synthesis may be a simple one-step reaction, or it may involve many steps and incorporate a subtle strategy for assembling the correct carbon skeleton with all the functional groups in the right positions.

Many of the problems in this book are synthesis problems. In some synthesis problems, you are asked to show how to convert a given starting material to the desired product. There are obvious one-step answers to some of these problems, but others may require several steps and there may be many correct answers. In solving multistep synthetic problems, it is often helpful to analyze the problem backward: Begin with the desired product (called the *target compound*) and see how it might be mentally changed or broken down to give the starting materials. This backward approach to synthesis is called a **retrosynthetic analysis.**

Some problems allow you to begin with any compounds that meet a certain restriction. For example, you might be allowed to use any alcohols containing no more than four carbon atoms. A retrosynthetic analysis can be used to break down the target compound into fragments no larger than four carbon atoms; then those fragments could be formed from the appropriate alcohols by functional group chemistry.

The following suggestions should help you solve synthesis problems:

1. Do not guess a starting material and try every possible reaction to convert it to the target compound. Rather, begin with the target compound and use a retrosynthetic analysis to simplify it.
2. Use simple equations, with reagents written above and below the arrows, to show the reactions. The equations do not have to be balanced, but they should include all the reagents and conditions that are important to the success of the reaction.

$$\mathrm{A} \xrightarrow{\mathrm{Br_2,\ light}} \mathrm{B} \xrightarrow[\mathrm{heat}]{\mathrm{NaOH,\ alcohol}} \mathrm{C} \xrightarrow{\mathrm{H^+,\ H_2O}} \mathrm{D}$$

3. Focus on the functional groups, since that is generally where reactions occur. Do not use any reagents that react with a functional group that you don't intend to modify.

In solving multistep synthesis problems, you will rarely be able to "see" the solution immediately. These problems are best approached systematically, working backward and considering alternative routes. To illustrate a systematic approach that can guide you in solving synthesis problems, we will work through the synthesis of a complex ether starting from alkenes. The problem-solving method described here will be extended in future chapters to multistep syntheses based on the reactions of additional functional groups.

A systematic retrosynthetic analysis begins with an examination of the structure of the product. We will consider the synthesis of the following compound from alkenes containing up to five carbon atoms.

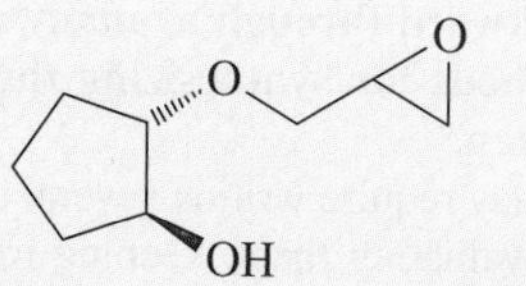

1. **Review the functional groups and carbon skeleton of the target compound.**
The target compound is an ether. One alkyl group is a five-carbon cyclopentane ring with two oxygen atoms situated trans. The other group has three carbons containing a reactive epoxide ring.
2. **Review the functional groups and carbon skeletons of the starting materials (if specified), and see how their skeletons might fit together in the target compound.**
The synthesis is to begin with alkenes containing up to five carbon atoms, so all the functional groups in the product must be derived from alkenes. Most likely, we will start with cyclopentene to give the five-carbon ring and propene to give the three-carbon chain.
3. **Compare methods for synthesizing the functional groups in the target compound, and select the reactions that are most likely to give the correct product.**

This step may require writing several possible reactions and evaluating them.

Ethers can be synthesized by nucleophilic reactions between alkyl halides and alkoxides (Section 6-9). The target compound might be formed by S_N2 attack of an alkoxide ion on an alkyl halide in either of two ways as shown below:

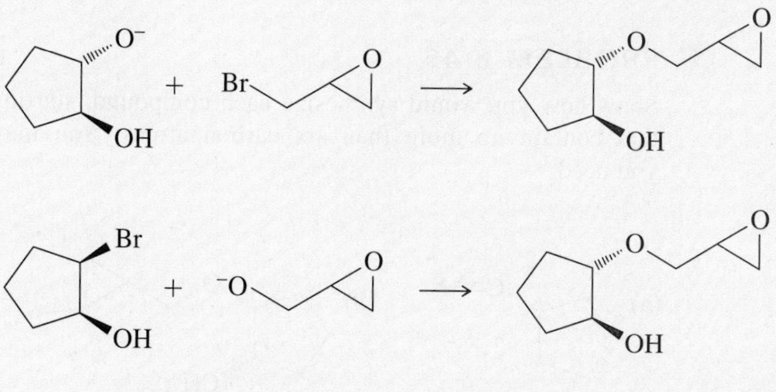

The first reaction is better because the S_N2 attack is on a primary alkyl halide, while the second is on a secondary halide. Also, in the second reaction the alkoxide might simply deprotonate the alcohol on the left and cause the reaction to fail.

4. **In general, reactive functional groups are best put into place toward the end of a synthesis.**

The target compound contains a reactive epoxide ring. Epoxides react with acids and bases, and the epoxide might not survive the crucial ether-forming reaction just shown. Perhaps the epoxide is best added after formation of the ether. That gives us the following final two steps in the synthesis:

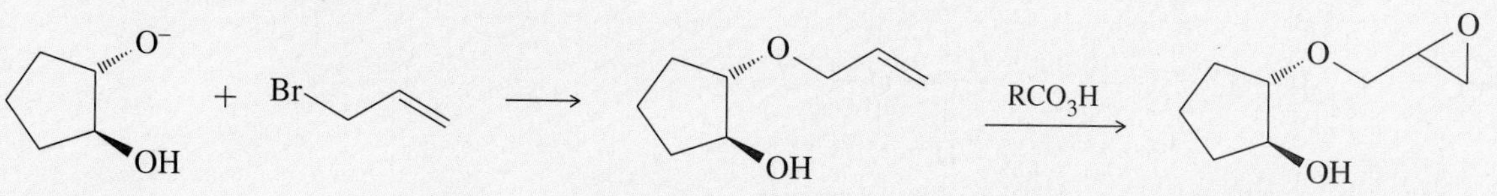

$\xrightarrow{RCO_3H}$

(Continued)

5. Working backward through as many steps as necessary, compare methods for synthesizing the reactants needed for the final step.
This process may require writing several possible reaction sequences and evaluating them, keeping in mind the specified starting materials.

Two reactants are needed to form the ether: an allylic halide and an alkoxide ion. Alkoxide ions are commonly formed by the reaction of an alcohol with sodium metal:

$$\text{R—O—H} + \text{Na} \longrightarrow \text{Na}^+ \ {}^-\text{O—R} + \tfrac{1}{2}\text{H}_2\uparrow$$

The alkoxide needed to make the ether is formed by adding sodium to a trans diol as shown below. Trans diols are formed by epoxidation and hydrolysis of alkenes (Section 8-13).

cyclopentene $\xrightarrow[H_3O^+]{RCO_3H}$ trans-cyclopentane-1,2-diol (OH, OH) $\xrightarrow{Na}$ alkoxide (O^- Na^+, OH) $+ \tfrac{1}{2}H_2\uparrow$

The other piece we need is an allylic bromide. Allylic bromides are formed by allylic bromination of alkenes (Section 6-6B).

propene (CH_3) $\xrightarrow[h\nu]{\text{NBS (trace } Br_2)}$ allyl bromide (Br)

6. Summarize the complete synthesis in the forward direction, including all steps and all reagents, and check it for errors and omissions.

This summary is left to you as a review of both the chemistry involved in the synthesis and the method used to develop multistep syntheses.

PROBLEM: Summarize the synthesis outlined in the problem-solving strategy. This summary should be in the synthetic (forward) direction, showing each step and all reagents.

Problem 8-45 requires devising several multistep syntheses. As practice in working such problems, we suggest that you proceed in order through the five steps just outlined.

PROBLEM 8-45

Show how you would synthesize each compound, starting with alkenes or cycloalkenes that contain no more than six carbon atoms. You may use any additional reagents you need.

(a) cyclopentenyl–C≡N

(b) trans-2-methylcyclopentyl ether, O–CH₂–(2,2-dimethylcyclopropyl) (CH_3)

(c) cyclopentenyl–O–CH₂–CH(OH)–CH(CH₃)₂ (OH)

SUMMARY Reactions of Alkenes

1. *Electrophilic Additions*

a. *Addition of hydrogen halides* (Section 8-3)

$$\rangle C{=}C\langle \; + \; \text{H—X} \longrightarrow \text{—}\underset{\text{H}}{\overset{|}{C}}\text{—}\underset{\text{X}}{\overset{|}{C}}\text{—}$$

(HX = HCl, HBr, or HI) Markovnikov orientation
(anti-Markovnikov with HBr and peroxides)

(Continued)

Example

$$CH_3-\underset{CH_3}{\overset{|}{C}}=CH_2 + HBr \xrightarrow{\text{no peroxides}} CH_3-\underset{Br}{\overset{CH_3}{C}}-CH_3$$

2-methylpropene → *tert*-butyl bromide (Markovnikov orientation)

$$CH_3-\overset{CH_3}{C}=CH_2 + HBr \xrightarrow{\text{peroxides}} CH_3-\overset{CH_3}{CH}-CH_2Br$$

isobutyl bromide (anti-Markovnikov orientation)

b. *Acid-catalyzed hydration* (Section 8-4)

$$\rangle C=C\langle + H_2O \xrightarrow{H^+} -\underset{H}{C}-\underset{OH}{C}-$$

(Markovnikov orientation)

Example

$$CH_3-CH=CH_2 + H_2O \xrightarrow{H_2SO_4} CH_3-\overset{OH}{CH}-CH_3$$

propene → 2-propanol

c. *Oxymercuration–demercuration* (Section 8-5)

$$\rangle C=C\langle + Hg(OAc)_2 \xrightarrow{H_2O} -\underset{HO}{C}-\underset{HgOAc}{C}- \xrightarrow{NaBH_4} -\underset{HO}{C}-\underset{H}{C}-$$

(Markovnikov orientation)

Example

$$H_2C=CHCH_2CH_3 \xrightarrow[H_2O]{Hg(OAc)_2} \overset{AcOHg}{CH_2}-\overset{OH}{CH}CH_2CH_3 \xrightarrow{NaBH_4} CH_3-\overset{OH}{CH}CH_2CH_3$$

2-butanol

d. *Alkoxymercuration–demercuration* (Section 8-6)

$$\rangle C=C\langle + Hg(OAc)_2 \xrightarrow{ROH} -\underset{RO}{C}-\underset{HgOAc}{C}- \xrightarrow{NaBH_4} -\underset{RO}{C}-\underset{H}{C}-$$

(Markovnikov orientation)

Example

$$H_2C=CH-CH_2-CH_3 \xrightarrow[(2)\ NaBH_4]{(1)\ Hg(OAc)_2,\ CH_3OH} H_3C-\underset{OCH_3}{CH}-CH_2-CH_3$$

1-butene → 2-methoxybutane

(*Continued*)

e. *Hydroboration–oxidation* (Section 8-7)

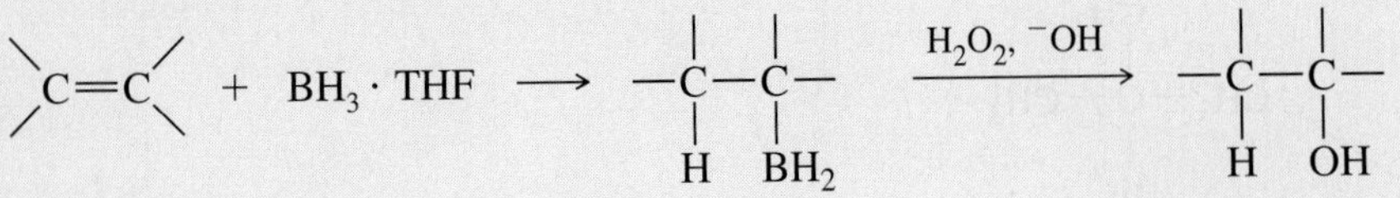

$$\text{>C=C<} + BH_3 \cdot THF \longrightarrow -\underset{H}{C}-\underset{BH_2}{C}- \xrightarrow{H_2O_2,\ ^{-}OH} -\underset{H}{C}-\underset{OH}{C}-$$

anti-Markovnikov orientation
(syn addition)

Example

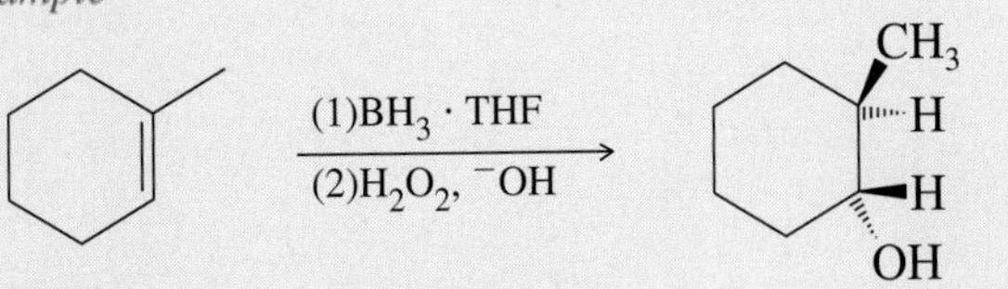

1-methylcyclohexene $\xrightarrow[(2) H_2O_2,\ ^{-}OH]{(1) BH_3 \cdot THF}$ (ring with CH_3, H, H, OH)

f. *Polymerization* (Section 8-16)

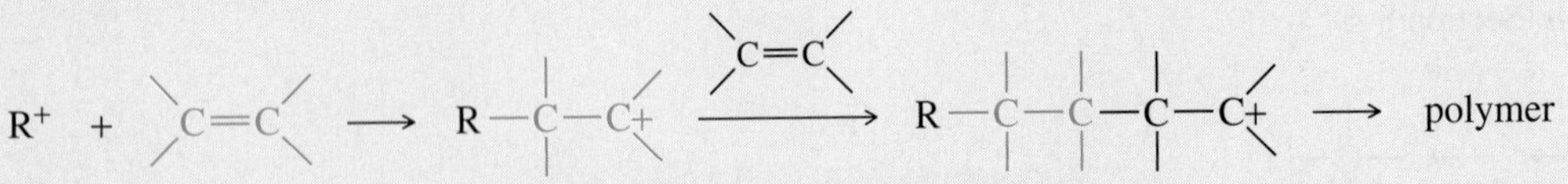

$$R^+ + \text{>C=C<} \longrightarrow R-\overset{|}{\underset{|}{C}}-C^+ \xrightarrow{\text{>C=C<}} R-C-C-C-C^+ \longrightarrow \text{polymer}$$

(also radical and anionic polymerization)

Example

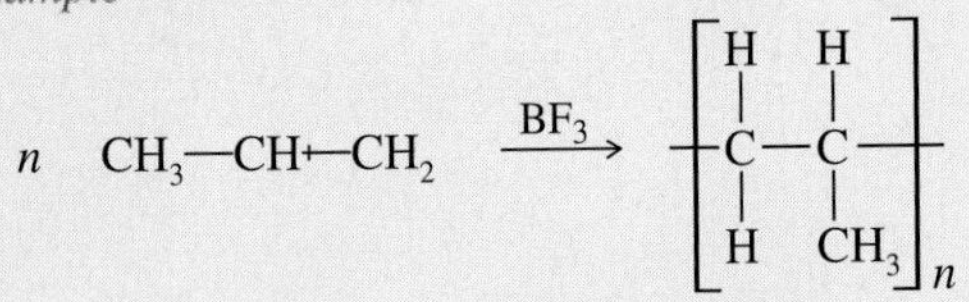

$$n\ CH_3-CH=CH_2 \xrightarrow{BF_3} \left[\begin{matrix} H & H \\ | & | \\ C & -C- \\ | & | \\ H & CH_3 \end{matrix}\right]_n$$

propylene — polypropylene

2. ***Reduction: Catalytic Hydrogenation*** (Section 8-10)

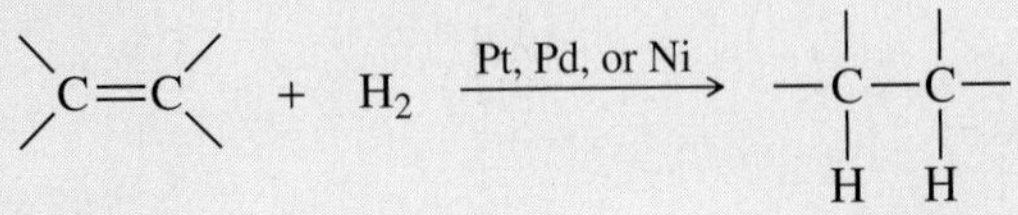

$$\text{>C=C<} + H_2 \xrightarrow{\text{Pt, Pd, or Ni}} -\underset{H}{C}-\underset{H}{C}-$$

(syn addition)

3. ***Addition of Carbenes: Cyclopropanation*** (Section 8-11)

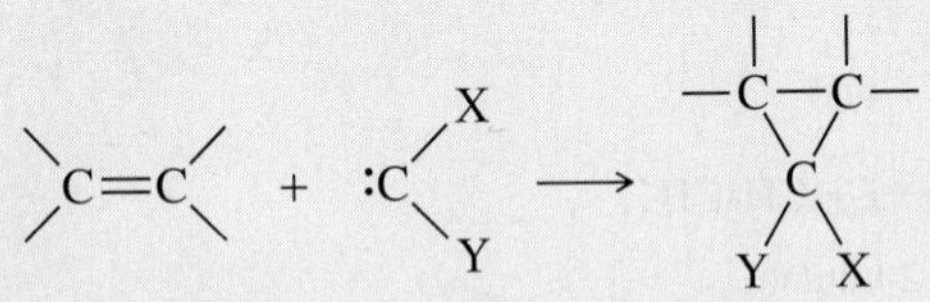

$$\text{>C=C<} + :C(X)(Y) \longrightarrow \text{cyclopropane } -C-C- \text{ bridged by } C(Y)(X)$$

(X,Y = H, Cl, Br, I, or —COOEt)

Example

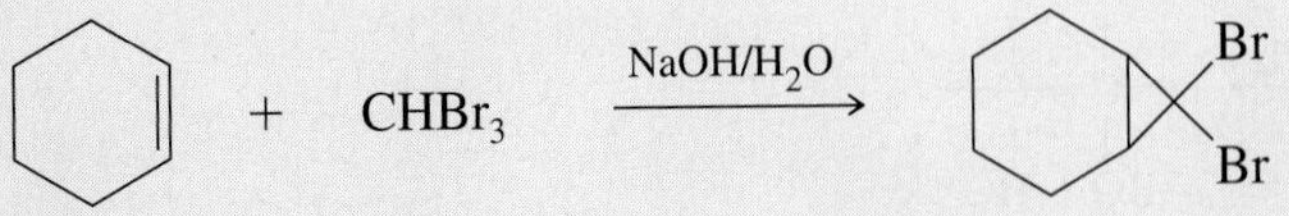

cyclohexene $+ CHBr_3 \xrightarrow{NaOH/H_2O}$ 7,7-dibromobicyclo[4.1.0]heptane (Br, Br)

4. ***Oxidative Additions***

a. *Addition of halogens* (Section 8-8)

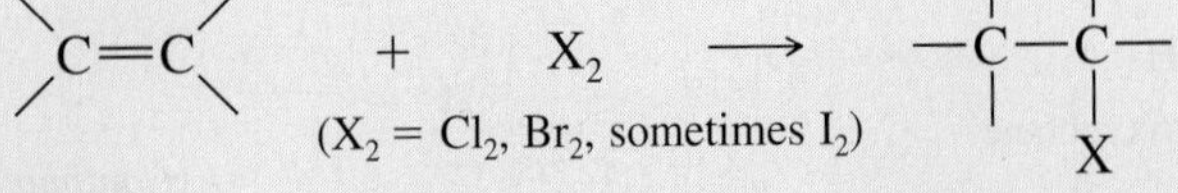

$$\text{>C=C<} + X_2 \longrightarrow -\overset{X}{C}-\underset{X}{C}-$$

($X_2 = Cl_2, Br_2$, sometimes I_2)

(anti addition)

(Continued)

Example

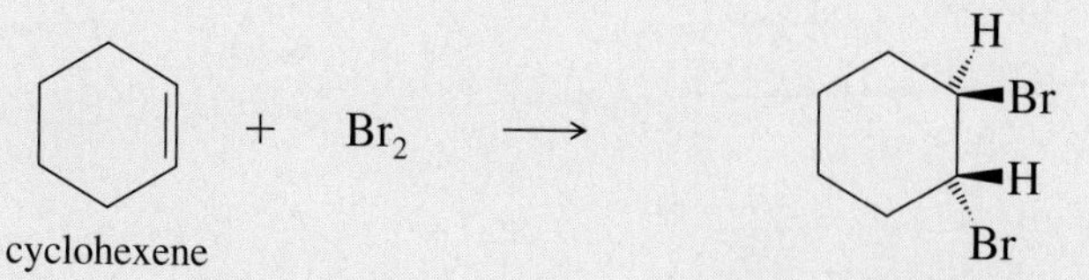

cyclohexene + Br_2 ⟶ *trans*-1,2-dibromocyclohexane

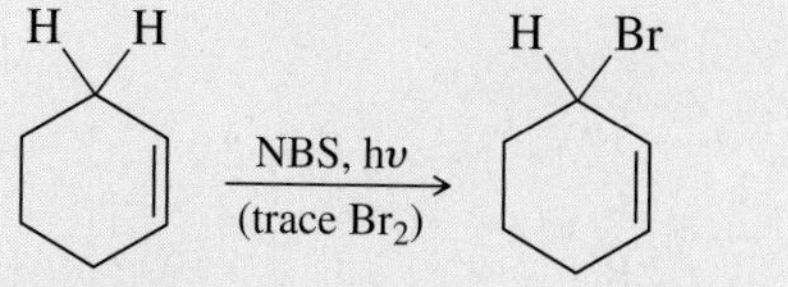

cyclohexene $\xrightarrow[\text{(trace } Br_2)]{\text{NBS, } h\nu}$ 3-bromocyclohexene

NBS provides a trace of Br_2 that (with light as initiator) allows radical substitution to proceed faster than the ionic addition. (Section 6-6B)

b. *Halohydrin formation* (Section 8-9)

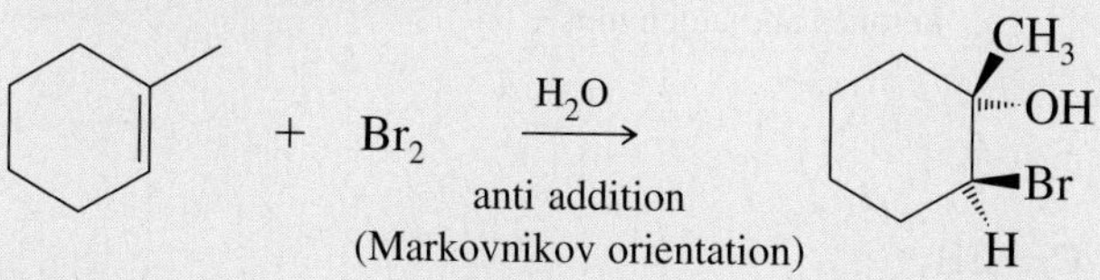

1-methylcyclohexene + Br_2 $\xrightarrow{H_2O}$ (anti addition; Markovnikov orientation) → 2-bromo-1-methylcyclohexanol (CH_3, OH, Br, H)

c. *Epoxidation* (Section 8-12)

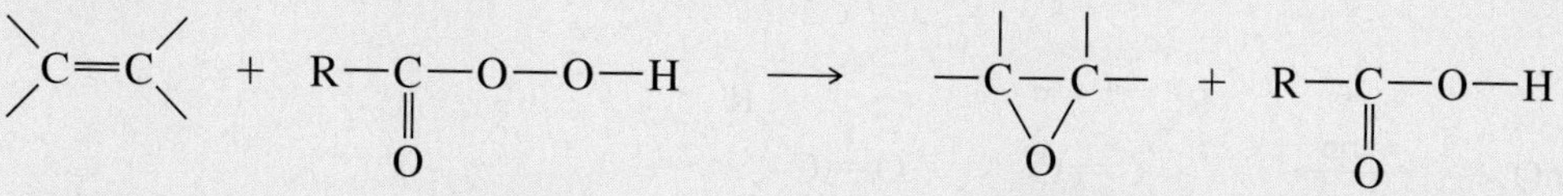

$$>C{=}C< \;+\; R{-}\overset{\displaystyle O}{\overset{\|}{C}}{-}O{-}O{-}H \;\longrightarrow\; -\overset{|}{C}{-}\overset{|}{C}-\text{ (bridged by O)} \;+\; R{-}\overset{\displaystyle O}{\overset{\|}{C}}{-}O{-}H$$

alkene — peroxyacid — syn addition

Example

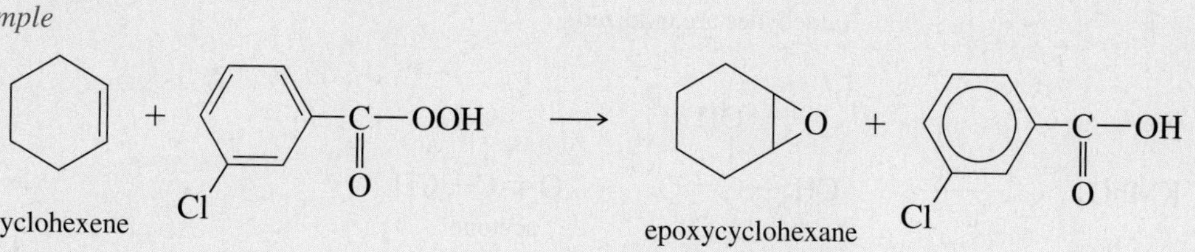

cyclohexene + 3-chlorophenyl–C(=O)–OOH ⟶ epoxycyclohexane (cyclohexene oxide) + 3-chlorophenyl–C(=O)–OH

d. *Anti hydroxylation* (Section 8-13)

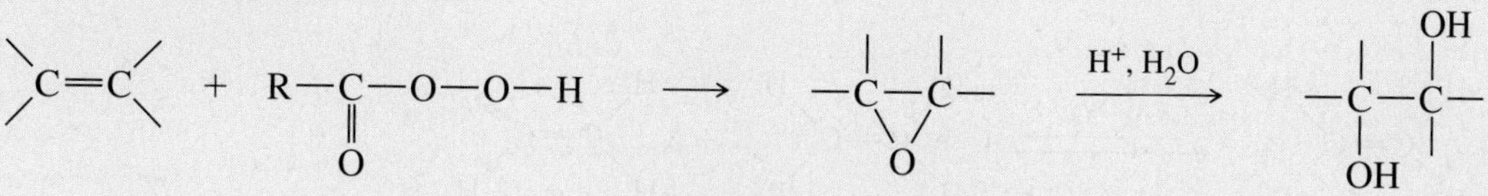

$$>C{=}C< \;+\; R{-}\overset{\displaystyle O}{\overset{\|}{C}}{-}O{-}O{-}H \;\longrightarrow\; -\overset{|}{C}{-}\overset{|}{C}-\text{ (bridged by O)} \;\xrightarrow{H^+,\, H_2O}\; -\overset{OH}{\overset{|}{C}}{-}\underset{OH}{\underset{|}{C}}-$$

Example

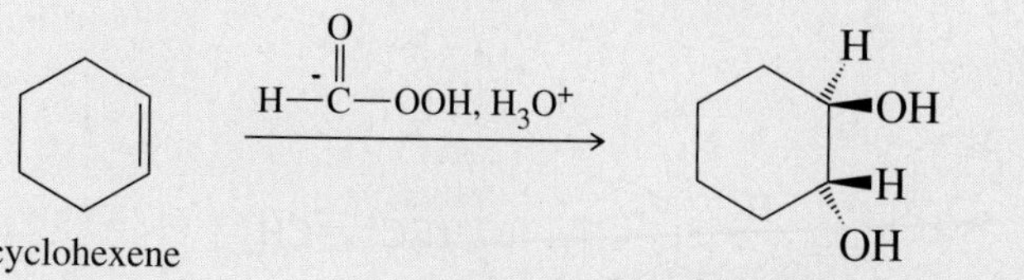

cyclohexene $\xrightarrow{H{-}\overset{O}{\overset{\|}{C}}{-}OOH,\ H_3O^+}$ *trans*-cyclohexane-1,2-diol

e. *Syn hydroxylation* (Section 8-14)

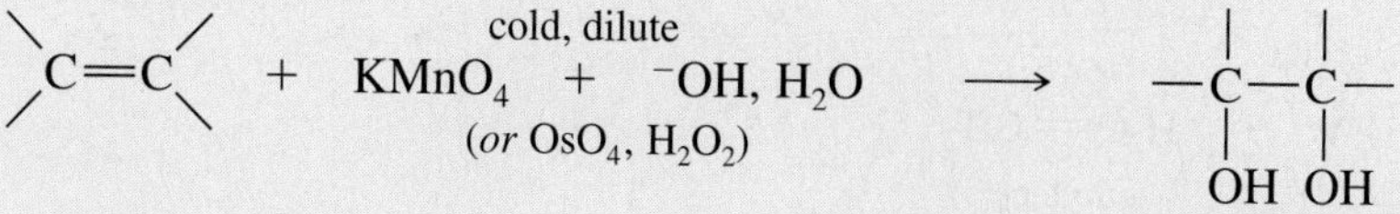

$$>C{=}C< \;+\; KMnO_4 \;+\; {}^-OH,\ H_2O \text{ (cold, dilute)} \text{ (or } OsO_4,\ H_2O_2) \;\longrightarrow\; -\underset{OH}{\underset{|}{C}}{-}\underset{OH}{\underset{|}{C}}-$$

(syn addition)

(*Continued*)

Example

cyclohexene $\xrightarrow{OsO_4,\ H_2O_2}$ *cis*-cyclohexane-1,2-diol

5. *Oxidative Cleavage of Alkenes* (Section 8-15)

a. *Ozonolysis*

$$R_2C{=}CHR' + O_3 \longrightarrow \text{ozonide} \xrightarrow{(CH_3)_2S} R_2C{=}O + O{=}CHR'$$

ozonide — ketones and aldehydes

Example

$$CH_3{-}CH{=}C(CH_3){-}CH_3 \xrightarrow[(2)\ (CH_3)_2S]{(1)\ O_3} CH_3{-}CH{=}O + O{=}C(CH_3){-}CH_3$$

2-methyl-2-butene — acetaldehyde — acetone

b. *Potassium permanganate*

$$R_2C{=}CHR' + KMnO_4 \xrightarrow{\text{warm}} R_2C{=}O + O{=}C(OH)R'$$

ketones and acids
(aldehydes are oxidized)

Example

$$CH_3{-}CH{=}C(CH_3){-}CH_3 + KMnO_4 \xrightarrow{\text{warm}} CH_3{-}C(OH){=}O + O{=}C(CH_3){-}CH_3$$

2-methyl-2-butene — acetic acid — acetone

6. *Olefin (Alkene) Metathesis* (Section 8-17)

$$R^1HC{=}CH_2 + H_2C{=}CHR^2 \overset{\text{catalyst}}{\rightleftharpoons} R^1HC{=}CHR^2 + H_2C{=}CH_2$$

(cis + trans) — ethylene

Example

$$PhCH{=}CH_2 + H_2C{=}CHCH_2Ph \xrightarrow{\text{catalyst}} PhCH{=}CHCH_2Ph + H_2C{=}CH_2$$

(cis + trans)

$$\text{1,8-nonadiene} \xrightarrow{\text{catalyst}} \text{cycloheptene} + H_2C{=}CH_2$$

1,8-nonadiene — cycloheptene — ethylene

Glossary 8

addition A reaction involving an increase in the number of groups attached to the alkene and a decrease in the number of elements of unsaturation. (p. 323)

anti addition: An addition in which two groups add to opposite faces of the double bond (as in addition of Br_2). (p. 346)

electrophilic addition: An addition in which the electrophile (electron-pair acceptor) bonds to one of the double-bonded carbons first, followed by the nucleophile. (p. 324)

syn addition: An addition in which two groups add to the same face of the double bond (as in osmium tetroxide hydroxylation). (pp. 342, 360)

addition polymer (chain-growth polymer) A polymer that results from rapid addition of one molecule at a time to a growing polymer chain, usually with a reactive intermediate (cation, radical, or anion) at the growing end of the chain. (p. 365)

alkoxy group (alkoxyl group) (—O—R) An alkyl group bonded through an oxygen atom, as in an ether. (p. 337)

alkoxymercuration The addition of mercuric acetate to an alkene in an alcohol solution, forming an alkoxymercurial intermediate. Demercuration gives an ether. (p. 337)

$$\mathrm{>C{=}C<} + \mathrm{Hg(OAc)_2} \xrightarrow{\mathrm{R{-}OH}} \mathrm{-C(OR)-C(HgOAc)-} \xrightarrow{\mathrm{NaBH_4}} \mathrm{-C(OR)-C(H)-}$$

alpha elimination (α elimination) The elimination of two atoms or groups from the same carbon atom. Alpha eliminations can be used to form carbenes. (p. 354)

$$\mathrm{CHBr_3 + KOH \longrightarrow :CBr_2 + H_2O + KBr}$$

anionic polymerization The process of forming an addition polymer by chain-growth polymerization involving an anion at the end of the growing chain. (p. 368)

asymmetric induction (enantioselective synthesis) The formation of an optically active product from an optically inactive starting material. Such a process requires the use of an optically active reagent or catalyst. (p. 351)

beta elimination (β elimination) The elimination of two atoms or groups from adjacent carbon atoms. This is the most common type of elimination. (p. 354)

$$\mathrm{-C(H)-C(Br)-} + \mathrm{KOH} \longrightarrow \mathrm{>C{=}C<} + \mathrm{H_2O} + \mathrm{KBr}$$

carbene A reactive intermediate with a neutral carbon atom having only two bonds and two nonbonding electrons. Methylene ($:CH_2$) is the simplest carbene. (p. 352)

cationic polymerization The process of forming an addition polymer by chain-growth polymerization involving a cation at the end of the growing chain. (p. 365)

chain-growth polymer See **addition polymer**. (p. 365)

demercuration The removal of a mercury species from a molecule. Demercuration of the products of oxymercuration and alkoxymercuration is usually accomplished using sodium borohydride. (p. 335)

epoxide (oxirane) A three-membered cyclic ether. (p. 355)

epoxidation: Formation of an epoxide, usually from an alkene. A peroxyacid is generally used for alkene epoxidations.

free-radical polymerization The process of forming an addition polymer by chain-growth polymerization involving a free radical at the end of the growing chain. (p. 367)

glycol A 1,2-diol. (p. 357)

halogenation The addition of a halogen (X_2) to a molecule, or the free-radical substitution of a halogen for a hydrogen. (p. 325)

halohydrin A beta-haloalcohol, with a halogen and a hydroxyl group on adjacent carbon atoms. (p. 347)

$$\mathrm{>C{=}C<} \xrightarrow[\mathrm{H_2O}]{\mathrm{Cl_2}} \mathrm{-C(Cl)-C(OH)-} + \mathrm{HCl}$$

a chlorohydrin

halonium ion A reactive, cationic intermediate with a three-membered ring containing a halogen atom; usually, a **chloronium ion**, a **bromonium ion**, or an **iodonium ion**. (p. 344)
heterogeneous catalysis Use of a catalyst that is in a separate phase from the reactants. For example, a platinum hydrogenation catalyst is a solid, a separate phase from the liquid alkene. (p. 350)
homogeneous catalysis Use of a catalyst that is in the same phase as the reactants. For example, the acid catalyst in hydration is in the liquid phase with the alkene. (p. 350)
hydration The addition of water to a molecule. Hydration of an alkene forms an alcohol. (p. 332)

$$\text{>C=C<} + H_2O \xrightarrow{H^+} -\underset{|}{\overset{H}{\overset{|}{C}}}-\underset{|}{\overset{OH}{\overset{|}{C}}}-$$

hydroboration The addition of borane (BH_3) or one of its derivatives ($BH_3 \cdot THF$, for example) to a molecule. (p. 338)
hydrogenation The addition of hydrogen to a molecule. The most common hydrogenation is the addition of H_2 across a double bond in the presence of a catalyst (**catalytic hydrogenation** or **catalytic reduction**). (p. 350)
hydroxylation (dihydroxylation) The addition of two hydroxyl groups, one at each carbon of the double bond; formally, an oxidation. (p. 360)

$$\text{>C=C<} + H_2O_2 \xrightarrow{OsO_4} -\underset{|}{\overset{HO}{\overset{|}{C}}}-\underset{|}{\overset{OH}{\overset{|}{C}}}-$$

Markovnikov's rule (*original statement*) When a proton acid adds to the double bond of an alkene, the proton bonds to the carbon atom that already has more hydrogen atoms. (p. 327)
Markovnikov's rule (*extended statement*) In an electrophilic addition to an alkene, the electrophile adds in such a way as to generate the most stable intermediate. (p. 327)

1-methylcyclohexene (CH_3, H) + HCl ⟶ product with CH_3 and Cl on the same carbon, H and H

Markovnikov product

Markovnikov orientation: An orientation of addition that obeys the original statement of Markovnikov's rule; one that gives the **Markovnikov product**. (p. 327)
anti-Markovnikov orientation: An orientation of addition that is the opposite of that predicted by the original statement of Markovnikov's rule; one that gives the **anti-Markovnikov product**. (p. 328)
MCPBA (*meta*-chloroperoxybenzoic acid) A common reagent for epoxidizing alkenes. MCPBA dissolves in common solvents such as dichloromethane. As the epoxidation takes place, the *m*-chlorobenzoic acid by-product precipitates out of solution. (p. 354)
metathesis (olefin metathesis) Any reaction that trades and interchanges the alkylidene groups of an alkene. (p. 369)

$$R^1(H)C{=}CH_2 + H_2C{=}CH(R^2) \xrightarrow{\text{catalyst}} R^1(H)C{=}CH(R^2) + H_2C{=}CH_2$$

olefin metathesis (cis + trans)

monomer One of the small molecules that bond together to form a polymer. (p. 365)
organic synthesis The preparation of desired organic compounds from readily available materials. (p. 372)
oxidative cleavage The cleavage of a carbon–carbon bond through oxidation. Carbon–carbon double bonds are commonly cleaved by ozonolysis/reduction or by warm, concentrated permanganate. (p. 362)

oxymercuration The addition of aqueous mercuric acetate to an alkene. (p. 335)

$$\ce{>C=C<} + \mathrm{Hg(OAc)_2} \xrightarrow{H_2O} \mathrm{-\overset{HO}{\underset{|}{\overset{|}{C}}}-\underset{HgOAc}{\overset{|}{\underset{|}{C}}}-} + \mathrm{HOAc}$$

ozonolysis The use of ozone, usually followed by reduction, to cleave a double bond. (p. 362)

peroxide effect The reversal of orientation of HBr addition to alkenes in the presence of peroxides. A free-radical mechanism is responsible for the peroxide effect. (p. 331)

peroxyacid (peracid) A carboxylic acid with an extra oxygen atom and a peroxy (—O—O—) linkage. The general formula is RCO_3H. (p. 355)

polymer A high-molecular-weight compound composed of many molecules of a smaller, simpler compound called the **monomer**. (p. 365)

polymerization: The reaction of monomer molecules to form a polymer.

regioselective reaction A reaction in which one direction of bond making or bond breaking occurs preferentially over all other directions. For example, the addition of HCl is regioselective, predicted by Markovnikov's rule. Hydroboration–oxidation is regioselective because it consistently gives anti-Markovnikov orientation. (p. 327)

retrosynthetic analysis A method of working backward to solve multistep synthetic problems. (p. 372)

Simmons–Smith reaction A cyclopropanation of an alkene using the carbenoid reagent generated from diiodomethane and the zinc–copper couple. (p. 353)

$$\text{cyclopentene} \xrightarrow{CH_2I_2,\ Zn(Cu)} \text{bicyclo[3.1.0]hexane}$$

Simmons-Smith reaction

stereospecific reaction A reaction that converts different stereoisomers of the starting material into different stereoisomers of the product. (p. 343)

Essential Problem-Solving Skills in Chapter 8

1. Predict the products of additions, oxidations, reductions, and cleavages of alkenes, including
   (a) orientation of reaction (regiochemistry),
   (b) stereochemistry.
2. Propose logical mechanisms to explain the observed products of alkene reactions, including regiochemistry and stereochemistry.
3. Use retrosynthetic analysis to solve multistep synthesis problems with alkenes as reagents, intermediates, or products.
4. When more than one method is usable for a chemical transformation, choose the better method and explain its advantages.
5. Use clues provided by products of reactions such as ozonolysis to determine the structure of an unknown alkene.

In studying these reaction-intensive chapters, students ask whether they should "memorize" all the reactions. Doing organic chemistry is like speaking a foreign language, and the reactions are our vocabulary. Without knowing the words, how can you construct sentences? Making flash cards often helps.

In organic chemistry, the mechanisms, regiochemistry, and stereochemistry are our grammar. You must develop *facility* with the reactions, as you develop facility with the words and grammar you use in speaking. Problems and multistep syntheses are the sentences of organic chemistry. You must *practice* combining all aspects of your vocabulary in solving these problems.

Students who fail exams often do so because they have memorized the vocabulary, but they have not practiced doing problems. Others fail because they think they can do problems, but they lack the vocabulary. If you understand the reactions and can do the end-of-chapter problems without looking back, you should do well on your exams.

Study Problems

8-46 Define each term, and give an example.

(a) electrophilic addition
(b) hydration
(c) asymmetric induction
(d) stereospecific addition
(e) syn addition
(f) anti addition
(g) Markovnikov addition
(h) hydroxylation
(i) peroxide effect
(j) hydrogenation
(k) polymerization
(l) monomer
(m) heterogeneous catalysis
(n) halogenation
(o) halohydrin
(p) homogeneous catalysis
(q) epoxidation
(r) oxidative cleavage
(s) hydroboration
(t) alpha elimination
(u) beta elimination
(v) oxymercuration–demercuration
(w) carbene addition
(x) cationic polymerization
(y) alkoxymercuration–demercuration
(z) addition polymer
(aa) olefin metathesis

8-47 Predict the major products of the following reactions, and give the structures of any intermediates. Include stereochemistry where appropriate.

(a) 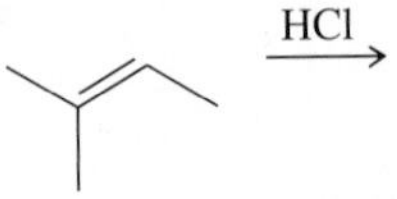 $\xrightarrow{HCl}$
(b) 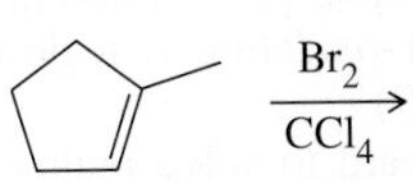 $\xrightarrow[CCl_4]{Br_2}$
(c) 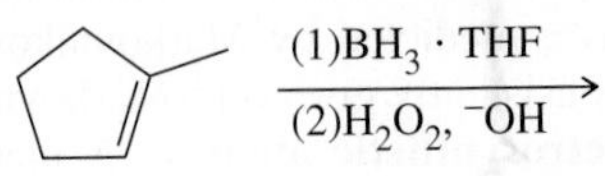 $\xrightarrow[(2)H_2O_2,\ ^-OH]{(1)BH_3 \cdot THF}$
(d) $\xrightarrow[(2)(CH_3)_2S]{(1)O_3}$
(e) $\xrightarrow[ROOR]{HBr}$
(f) $\xrightarrow[ROOR]{HCl}$
(g) $\xrightarrow{PhCO_3H}$
(h) $\xrightarrow[H_2O_2]{OsO_4}$
(i) $\xrightarrow[\text{(cold, dil)}]{KMnO_4,\ ^-OH}$
(j) $\xrightarrow[H^+,\ H_2O]{CH_3CO_3H}$
(k) $\xrightarrow[\text{(warm, concd.)}]{KMnO_4,\ ^-OH}$
(l) 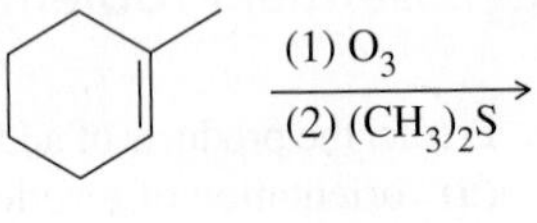 $\xrightarrow[(2)\ (CH_3)_2S]{(1)\ O_3}$
(m) 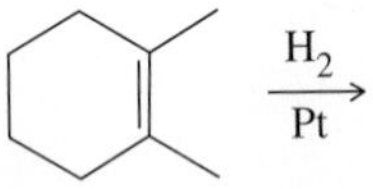 $\xrightarrow[Pt]{H_2}$
(n) $\xrightarrow{H^+,\ H_2O}$
(o) 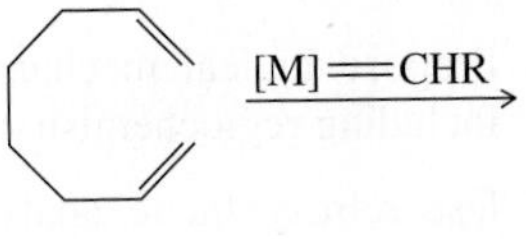 $\xrightarrow{[M]{=}CHR}$
(p) 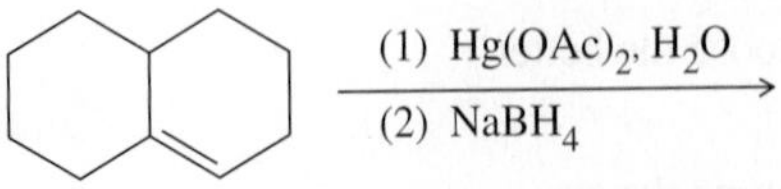 $\xrightarrow[(2)\ NaBH_4]{(1)\ Hg(OAc)_2,\ H_2O}$
(q) 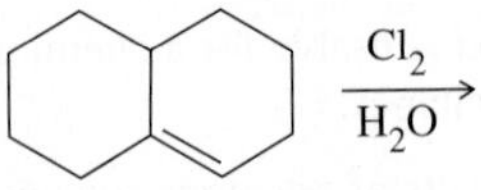 $\xrightarrow[H_2O]{Cl_2}$

8-48 Propose mechanisms consistent with the following reactions.

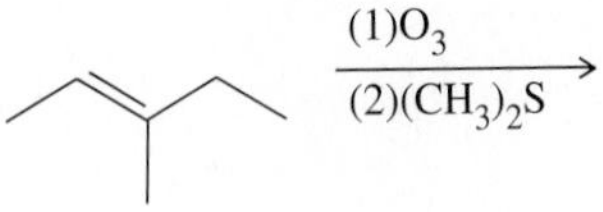

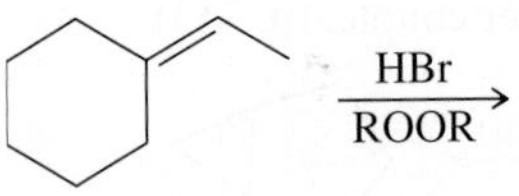

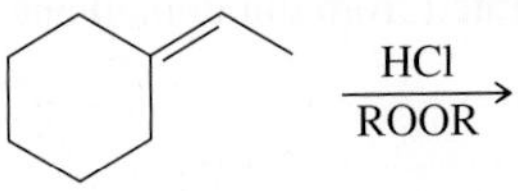

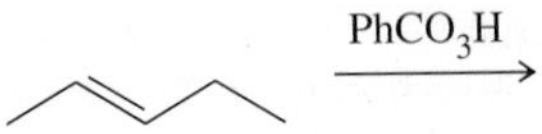

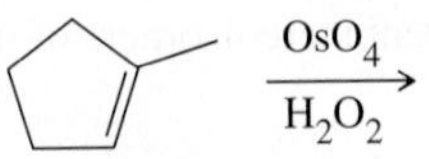

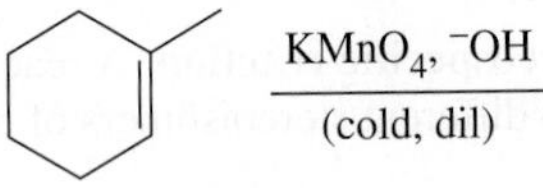

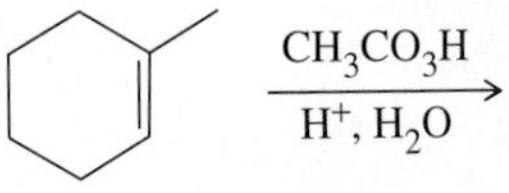

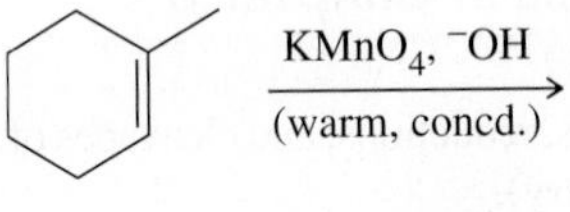

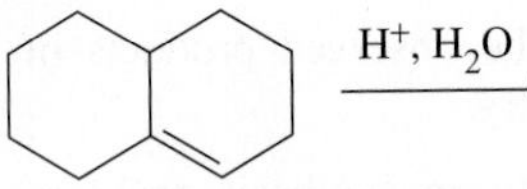

(a) 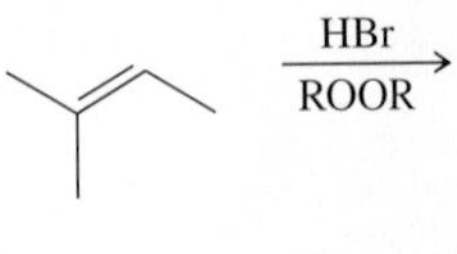 $\xrightarrow[ROOR]{HBr}$ Br
(b) 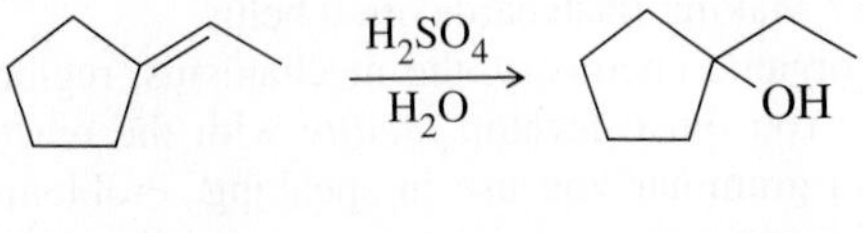 $\xrightarrow[H_2O]{H_2SO_4}$ OH
(c) 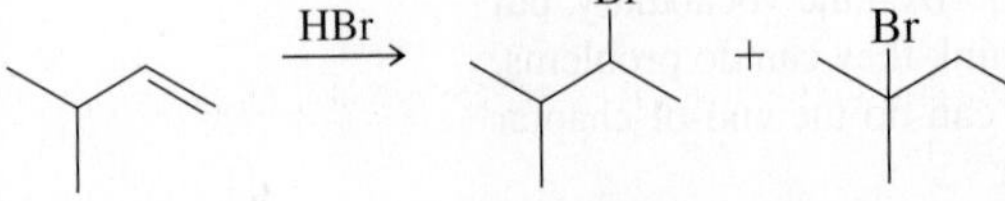 $\xrightarrow{HBr}$ Br + Br
(d) 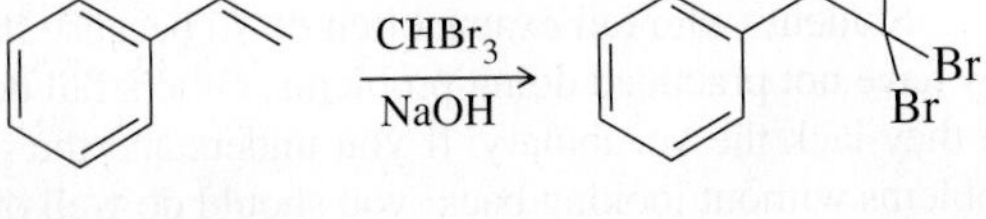 $\xrightarrow[NaOH]{CHBr_3}$ Br Br

(e) $\xrightarrow[CH_3OH]{HCl}$ + ... OCH_3 + ... Cl

(f) CH_3CH_2 ... O ... CH_2CH_3 $\xrightarrow{H^+, H_2O}$ CH_2CH_3, H—OH, H—OH, CH_2CH_3

(g) O $\xrightarrow[CH_3OH]{H^+}$ OH, OCH_3

(h) 2 H, H, C=C, H $\xrightarrow{H^+}$ CH_3—C—C, H, H, C, H

8-49 Show how you would synthesize each compound using methylenecyclohexane as your starting material.

methylenecyclohexane

(a) OH (b) Br (c) OH

(d) O (e) OCH_3 (f) OH, OH

(g) (h) Cl, OH (i) O

8-50 Limonene is one of the compounds that give lemons their tangy odor. Show the structures of the products expected when limonene reacts with an excess of each of these reagents.

limonene

(a) borane in tetrahydrofuran, followed by basic hydrogen peroxide
(b) *m*-chloroperoxybenzoic acid
(c) ozone, then dimethyl sulfide
(d) a mixture of osmic acid and hydrogen peroxide
(e) hot, concentrated potassium permanganate
(f) peroxyacetic acid in acidic water
(g) hydrogen and a platinum catalyst
(h) hydrogen bromide gas
(i) hydrogen bromide gas in a solution containing dimethyl peroxide
(j) bromine water
(k) chlorine gas
(l) mercuric acetate in methanol, followed by sodium borohydride
(m) $CHBr_3$ and 50% aq. NaOH

8-51 The structures of three monomers are shown. In each case, show the structure of the polymer that would result from polymerization of the monomer. Vinyl chloride is polymerized to "vinyl" plastics and PVC pipe. Tetrafluoroethylene polymerizes to Teflon®, used as non-stick coatings and PTFE valves and gaskets. Acrylonitrile is polymerized to Orlon®, used in sweaters and carpets.

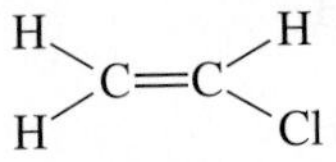

vinyl chloride 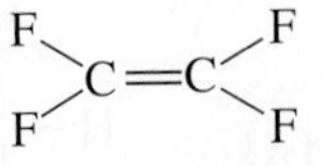   tetrafluoroethylene 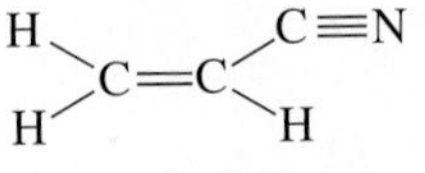   acrylonitrile

***8-52** When styrene (vinylbenzene) is commercially polymerized, about 1–3% of 1,4-divinylbenzene is often added to the styrene. The incorporation of some divinylbenzene gives a polymer with more strength and better resistance to organic solvents. Explain how a very small amount of divinylbenzene has a marked effect on the properties of the polymer.

8-53 The cationic polymerization of isobutylene (2-methylpropene) is shown in Section 8-16A. Isobutylene is often polymerized under free-radical conditions. Propose a mechanism for the free-radical polymerization of isobutylene.

8-54 Show what products you would expect from the following metathesis reactions, using the Schrock or Grubbs catalysts.

(a) 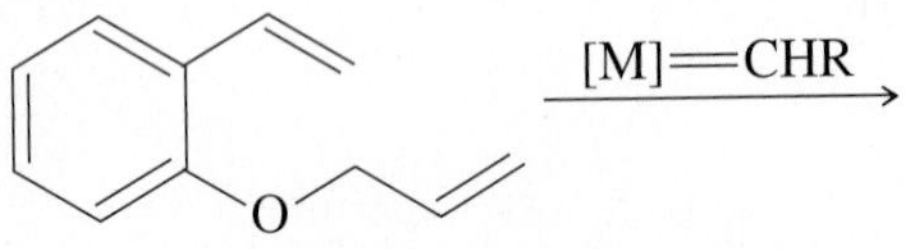 $\xrightarrow{[M]{=}CHR}$

(b) 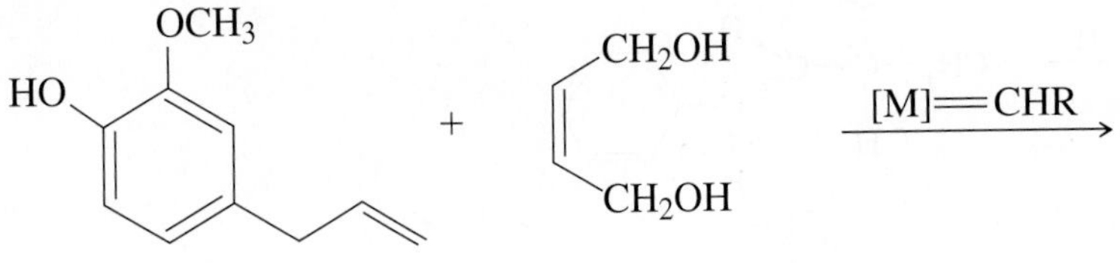 eugenol + $HOCH_2CH{=}CHCH_2OH$ $\xrightarrow{[M]{=}CHR}$

(c) 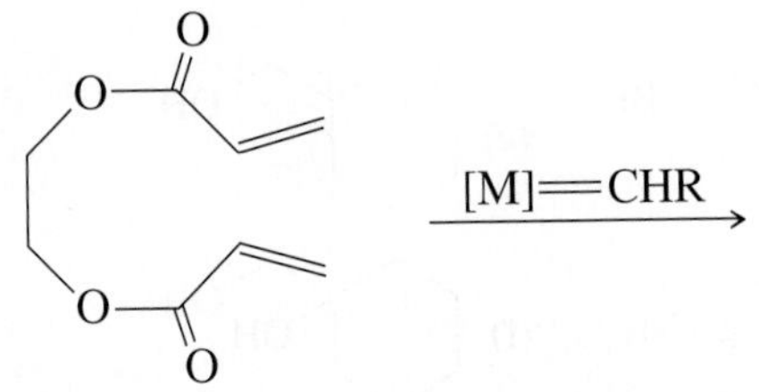 $\xrightarrow{[M]{=}CHR}$

8-55 Show how you might use olefin metathesis to assemble the following alkenes from smaller units:

(a)

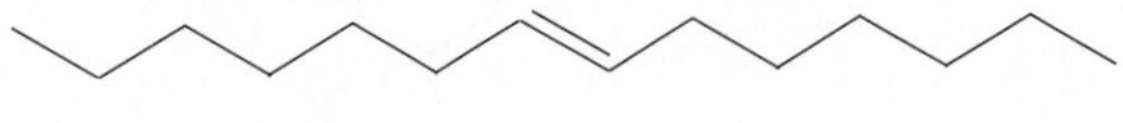

(b)

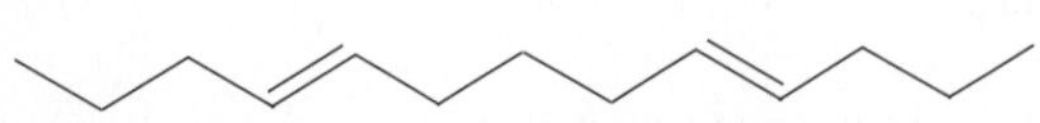

8-56 Cyclohexene is dissolved in a solution of lithium chloride in chloroform. To this solution is added one equivalent of bromine. The material isolated from this reaction contains primarily a mixture of *trans*-1,2-dibromocyclohexane and *trans*-1-bromo-2-chlorocyclohexane. Propose a mechanism to show how these compounds are formed.

8-57 Draw a reaction-energy diagram for the propagation steps of the free-radical addition of HBr to isobutylene. Draw curves representing the reactions leading to both the Markovnikov and the anti-Markovnikov products. Compare the values of ΔG° and E_a for the rate-limiting steps, and explain why only one of these products is observed.

8-58 Give the products expected when the following compounds are ozonized and reduced.

(a) 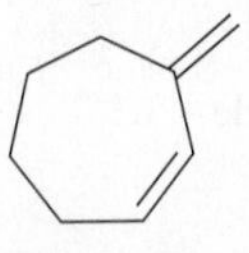   **(b)** 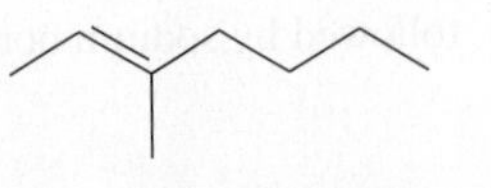   **(c)** 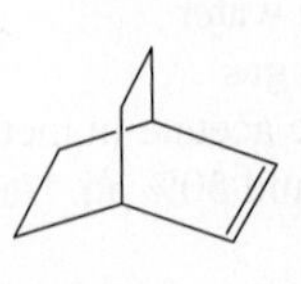   **(d)**

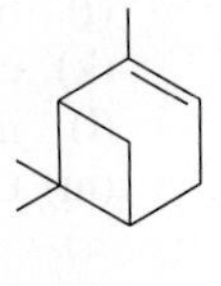

8-59 Show how you would make the following compounds from a suitable cyclic alkene.

(a) 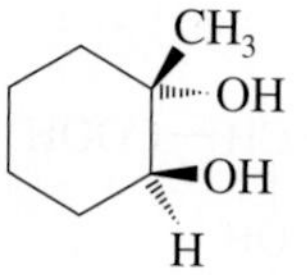 (b) 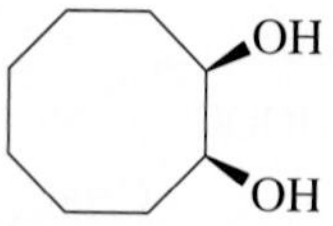 (c)

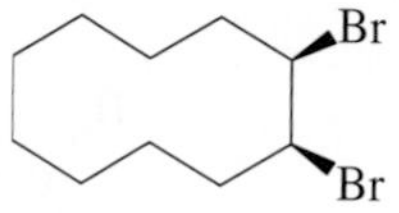

(d) 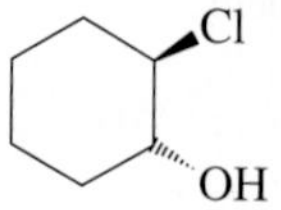 (e) 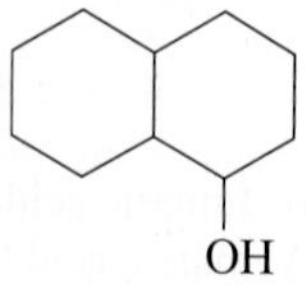 (f)

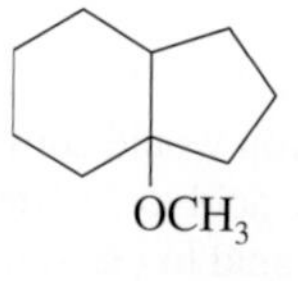

8-60 Unknown **X**, C_5H_9Br, does not react with bromine or with dilute $KMnO_4$. Upon treatment with potassium *tert*-butoxide, **X** gives only one product, **Y**, C_5H_8. Unlike **X**, **Y** decolorizes bromine and changes $KMnO_4$ from purple to brown. Catalytic hydrogenation of **Y** gives methylcyclobutane. Ozonolysis–reduction of **Y** gives dialdehyde **Z**, $C_5H_8O_2$. Propose consistent structures for **X, Y**, and **Z**. Is there any aspect of the structure of **X** that is still unknown?

8-61 One of the constituents of turpentine is α-pinene, formula $C_{10}H_{16}$. The following scheme (called a "road map") gives some reactions of α-pinene. Determine the structure of α-pinene and of the reaction products **A** through **E**.

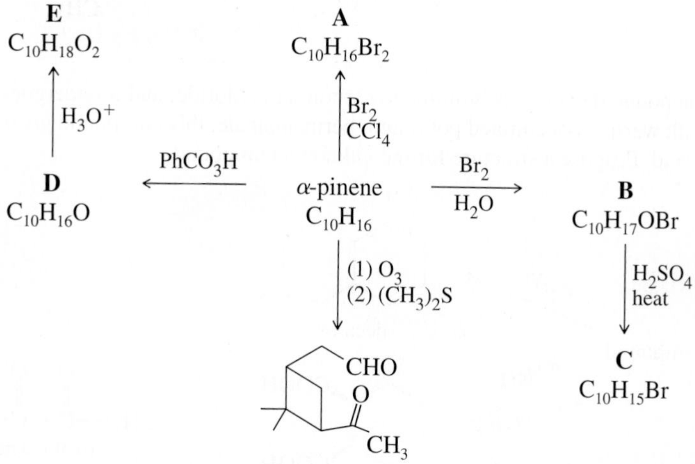

E $C_{10}H_{18}O_2$ ← H_3O^+ — **D** $C_{10}H_{16}O$ ← $PhCO_3H$ — α-pinene $C_{10}H_{16}$

α-pinene — Br_2, CCl_4 → **A** $C_{10}H_{16}Br_2$

α-pinene — Br_2, H_2O → **B** $C_{10}H_{17}OBr$ — H_2SO_4, heat → **C** $C_{10}H_{15}Br$

α-pinene — (1) O_3 (2) $(CH_3)_2S$ → CHO, O, CH_3

8-62 The sex attractant of the housefly has the formula $C_{23}H_{46}$. When treated with warm potassium permanganate, this pheromone gives two products: $CH_3(CH_2)_{12}COOH$ and $CH_3(CH_2)_7COOH$. Suggest a structure for this sex attractant. Explain which part of the structure is uncertain.

8-63 In contact with a platinum catalyst, an unknown alkene reacts with 3 equivalents of hydrogen gas to give 1-isopropyl-4-methylcyclohexane. When the unknown alkene is ozonized and reduced, the products are the following:

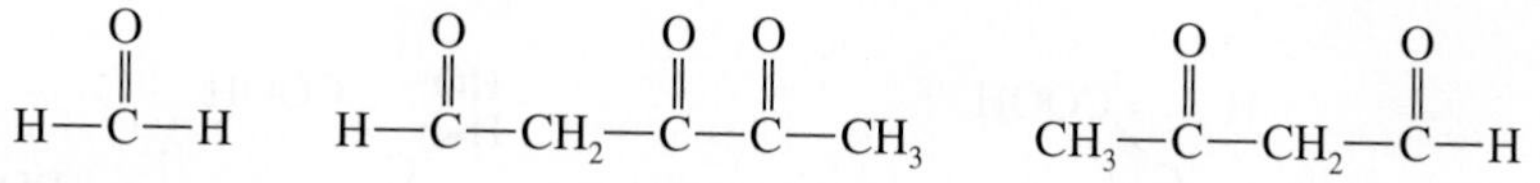

$$H-\overset{O}{\overset{\|}{C}}-H \qquad H-\overset{O}{\overset{\|}{C}}-CH_2-\overset{O}{\overset{\|}{C}}-\overset{O}{\overset{\|}{C}}-CH_3 \qquad CH_3-\overset{O}{\overset{\|}{C}}-CH_2-\overset{O}{\overset{\|}{C}}-H$$

Deduce the structure of the unknown alkene.

***8-64** Propose a mechanism for the following reaction.

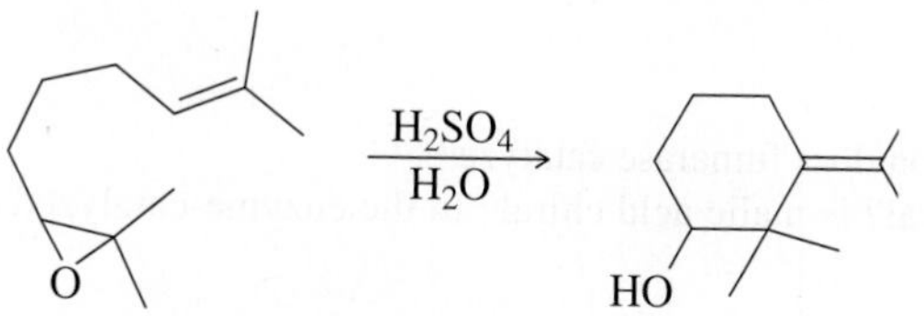

$\xrightarrow[H_2O]{H_2SO_4}$ HO

8-65 The two butenedioic acids are called *fumaric acid* (trans) and *maleic acid* (cis). 2,3-Dihydroxybutanedioic acid is called *tartaric acid*.

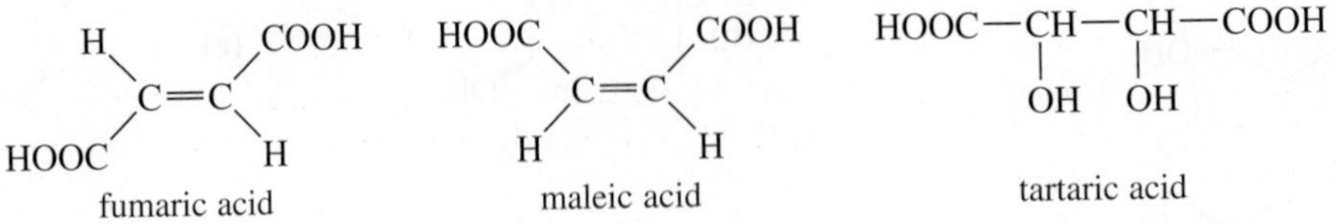

fumaric acid: H(HOOC)C=C(H)COOH (trans)

maleic acid: HOOC(H)C=C(H)COOH (cis)

tartaric acid: HOOC—CH(OH)—CH(OH)—COOH

Show how you would convert
(a) fumaric acid to (±)-tartaric acid.
(b) fumaric acid to *meso*-tartaric acid.
(c) maleic acid to (±)-tartaric acid.
(d) maleic acid to *meso*-tartaric acid.

8-66 The compound BD_3 is a deuterated form of borane. Predict the product formed when 1-methylcyclohexene reacts with $BD_3 \cdot THF$, followed by basic hydrogen peroxide.

8-67 A routine addition of HBr across the double bond of a vinylcyclopentane gave a small amount of an unexpected rearranged product. Propose a mechanism for the formation of this product, and explain why the rearrangement occurs.

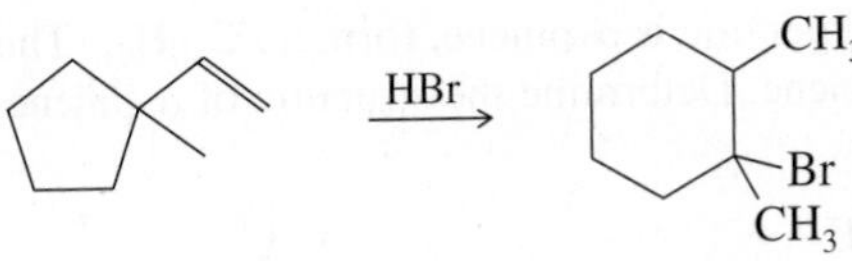

$$\xrightarrow{\text{HBr}}$$

Product labels: CH_3, Br, CH_3

8-68 An unknown compound decolorizes bromine in carbon tetrachloride, and it undergoes catalytic reduction to give decalin. When treated with warm, concentrated potassium permanganate, this compound gives *cis*-cyclohexane-1,2-dicarboxylic acid and oxalic acid. Propose a structure for the unknown compound.

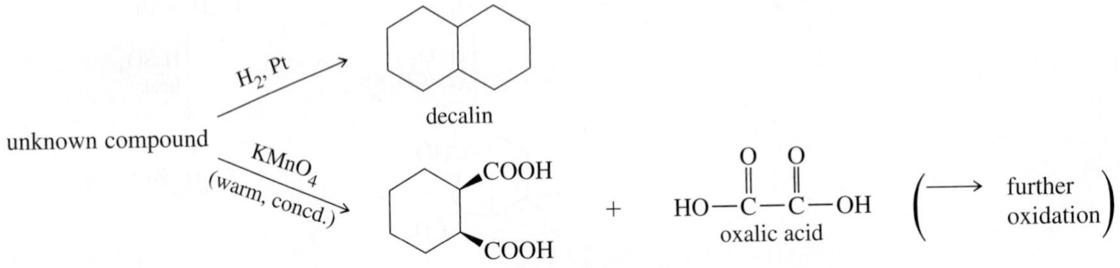

unknown compound $\xrightarrow{H_2, Pt}$ decalin

unknown compound $\xrightarrow[\text{(warm, concd.)}]{KMnO_4}$ *cis*-cyclohexane-1,2-dicarboxylic acid (COOH, COOH) + HO—C(=O)—C(=O)—OH oxalic acid (⟶ further oxidation)

***8-69** Many enzymes catalyze reactions that are similar to reactions we might use for organic synthesis. Enzymes tend to be stereospecific in their reactions, and asymmetric induction is common. The following reaction, part of the tricarboxylic acid cycle of cell respiration, resembles a reaction we might use in the laboratory; however, the enzyme-catalyzed reaction gives only the (*S*) enantiomer of the product, malic acid.

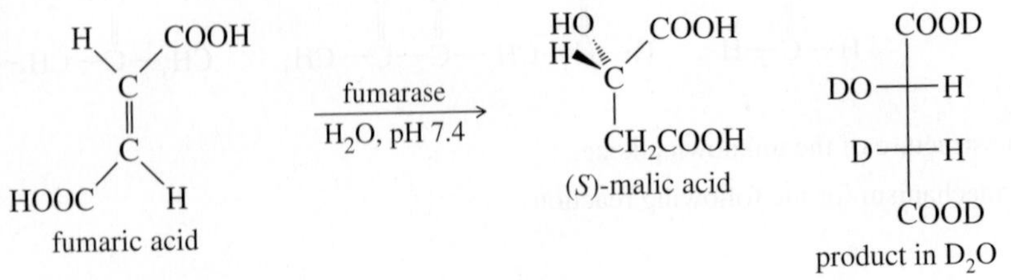

fumaric acid (H, COOH / HOOC, H) $\xrightarrow[H_2O,\ pH\ 7.4]{\text{fumarase}}$ (*S*)-malic acid (HO, COOH, H, CH_2COOH)

product in D_2O: COOD, DO—H, D—H, COOD

(a) What type of reaction does fumarase catalyze?
(b) Is fumaric acid chiral? Is malic acid chiral? In the enzyme-catalyzed reaction, is the product (malic acid) optically active?

(c) If we could run the preceding reaction in the laboratory using sulfuric acid as the catalyst, would the product (malic acid) be optically active?

(d) Do you expect the fumarase enzyme to be a chiral molecule?

(e) When the enzyme-catalyzed reaction takes place in D_2O, the *only* product is the stereoisomer just pictured. No enantiomer or diastereomer of this compound is formed. Is the enzyme-catalyzed reaction a syn or anti addition?

(f) Assume we found conditions to convert fumaric acid to deuterated malic acid using hydroboration with $BD_3 \cdot THF$, followed by oxidation with D_2O_2 and NaOD. Use Fischer projections to show the stereoisomer(s) of deuterated malic acid you would expect to be formed.

***8-70** **(a)** The following cyclization has been observed in the oxymercuration–demercuration of this unsaturated alcohol. Propose a mechanism for this reaction.

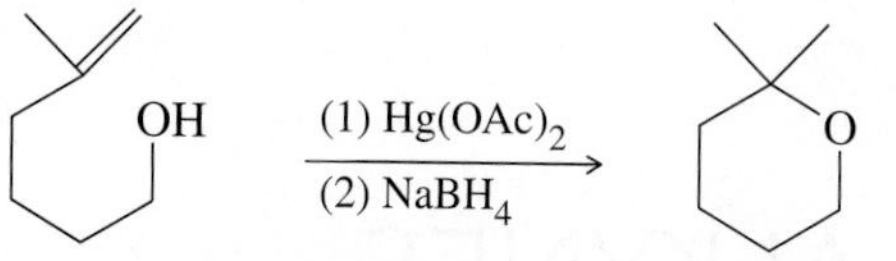

OH — (1) $Hg(OAc)_2$; (2) $NaBH_4$ → O

(b) Predict the product of formula $C_7H_{13}BrO$ from the reaction of this same unsaturated alcohol with bromine. Propose a mechanism to support your prediction.

***8-71** An inexperienced graduate student treated 5-decene with borane in THF, placed the flask in a refrigerator, and left for a party. When he returned from the party, he discovered that the refrigerator was broken, and it had gotten quite warm inside. Although all the THF had evaporated from the flask, he treated the residue with basic hydrogen peroxide. To his surprise, he recovered a fair yield of 1-decanol. Use a mechanism to show how this reaction might have occurred. (*Hint*: The addition of BH_3 is reversible.)

***8-72** We have seen many examples where halogens add to alkenes with anti stereochemistry via the halonium ion mechanism. However, when 1-phenylcyclohexene reacts with chlorine in carbon tetrachloride, a mixture of the cis and trans isomers of the product is recovered. Propose a mechanism, and explain this lack of stereospecificity.

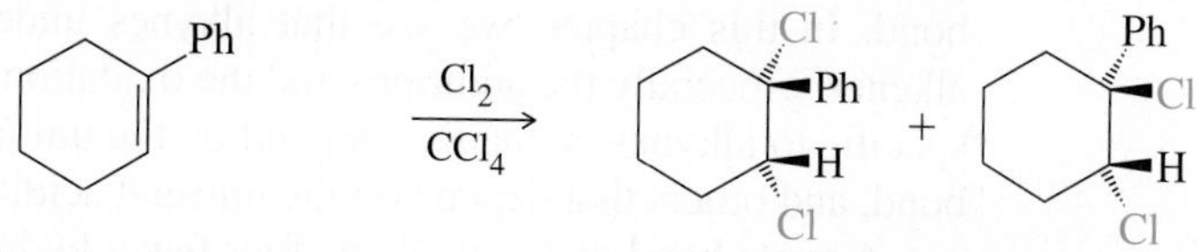

Ph — Cl_2, CCl_4 → Cl, Ph, H, Cl + Ph, Cl, H, Cl

1-phenylcyclohexene

cis- and *trans*-
1,2-dichloro-1-phenylcyclohexane

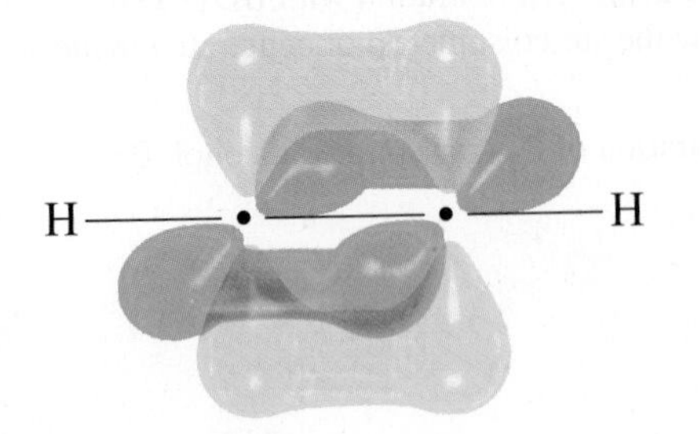

CHAPTER

9

ALKYNES

9-1 Introduction

Alkynes are hydrocarbons that contain carbon–carbon triple bonds. Alkynes are also called **acetylenes** because they are derivatives of acetylene, the simplest alkyne.

$H-C\equiv C-H$	$CH_3CH_2-C\equiv C-H$	$CH_3-C\equiv C-CH_3$
acetylene ethyne	ethylacetylene 1-butyne	dimethylacetylene 2-butyne

The chemistry of the carbon–carbon triple bond is similar to that of the double bond. In this chapter, we see that alkynes undergo most of the same reactions as alkenes, especially the additions and the oxidations. We also consider reactions that are specific to alkynes: some that depend on the unique characteristics of the $C\equiv C$ triple bond, and others that depend on the unusual acidity of the acetylenic $\equiv C-H$ bond.

A triple bond gives an alkyne four fewer hydrogens than the corresponding alkane. Its molecular formula is like that of a molecule with two double bonds: C_nH_{2n-2}. Therefore, the triple bond contributes two elements of unsaturation (eu) (Section 7-3).

H_3C-CH_3	$H_2C=CH_2$	$H-C\equiv C-H$
ethane, C_2H_6 0 eu, C_nH_{2n+2}	ethene, C_2H_4 1 eu, C_nH_{2n}	ethyne, C_2H_2 2 eu, C_nH_{2n-2}

Alkynes are not as common in nature as alkenes, but some plants do use alkynes tc protect themselves against disease or predators. Cicutoxin is a toxic compound found ir water hemlock, and capillin protects a plant against fungal diseases. The alkyne func tional group is uncommon in drugs, but parsalmide is used as an analgesic, and ethyny estradiol (a synthetic female hormone) is a common ingredient in birth control pills Dynemicin A is an antibacterial compound that is being tested as an antitumor agent.

$$HOCH_2CH_2CH_2-C\equiv C-C\equiv C-CH=CH-CH=CH-CH=CH-\underset{\displaystyle OH}{\underset{|}{C}}HCH_2CH_2CH$$

cicutoxin

$$CH_3-C\equiv C-C\equiv C-\overset{\displaystyle O}{\overset{\|}{C}}-C_6H_5$$

capillin

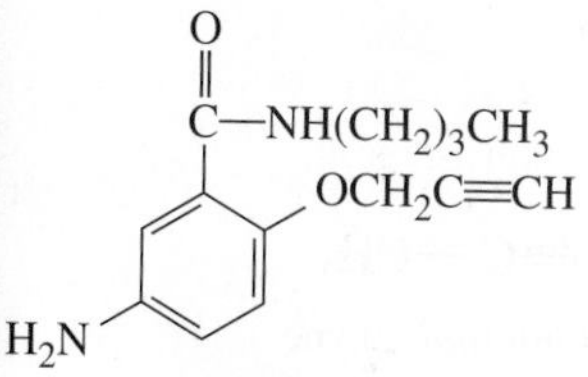

parsalmide 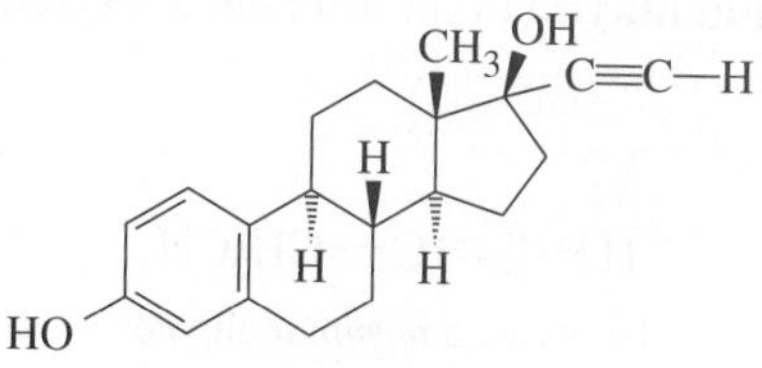 ethynyl estradiol 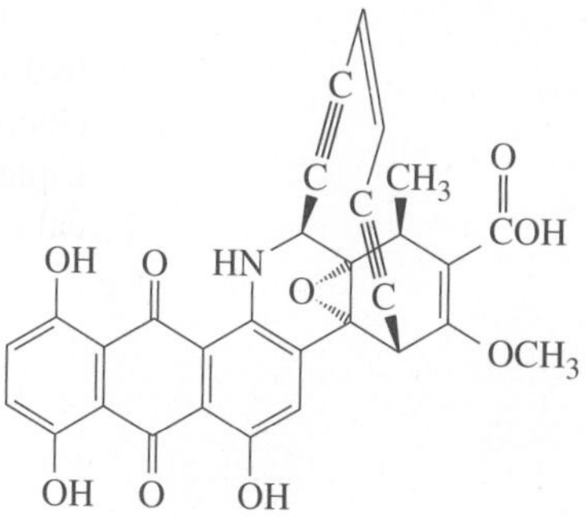 dynemicin A

PROBLEM 9-1

Draw structural formulas of at least two alkynes of each molecular formula.
(a) C_6H_{10} **(b)** C_8H_{12} **(c)** C_7H_8

9-2 Nomenclature of Alkynes

IUPAC Names The IUPAC nomenclature for alkynes is similar to that for alkenes. We find the longest continuous chain of carbon atoms that includes the triple bond and change the *-ane* ending of the parent alkane to *–yne*. The chain is numbered from the end closest to the triple bond, and the position of the triple bond is designated by its lower-numbered carbon atom. Substituents are given numbers to indicate their locations.

	$H-C\equiv C-H$	$CH_3-C\equiv C-H$	$CH_3-C\equiv C-CH_3$	$CH_3-CH(CH_3)-C\equiv C-CH_2-CH(Br)-CH_3$
IUPAC name:	ethyne (acetylene)	propyne	2-butyne but-2-yne	6-bromo-2-methyl-3-heptyne 6-bromo-2-methylhept-3-yne

When additional functional groups are present, the suffixes are combined to produce the compound names of the *alkenynes* (a double bond and a triple bond), *alkynols* (a triple bond and an alcohol), and so on. The new IUPAC system (placing the number right before the group) helps to clarify these names. The IUPAC rules give alcohols higher priority than alkenes or alkynes, so the numbering begins at the end closer to an alcohol. If the double bond and the triple bond are equidistant from the ends of the chain, number the chain so that the double bond receives a lower number than the triple bond (because "ene" comes before "yne" in the alphabet.

	$H_2C=C(CH_3)-C\equiv C-CH_3$	$CH_3-CH(OH)-C\equiv C-H$	$CH_3-C\equiv C-CH(OCH_3)-CH_2CH_3$
IUPAC name:	2-methyl-1-penten-3-yne	3-butyn-2-ol	4-methoxy-2-hexyne
new IUPAC name:	2-methylpent-1-en-3-yne	but-3-yn-2-ol	4-methoxyhex-2-yne

Common Names The common names of alkynes describe them as derivatives of acetylene. Most alkynes can be named as a molecule of acetylene with one or two alkyl substituents. This nomenclature is like the common nomenclature for ethers, where we name the two alkyl groups bonded to oxygen.

$H-C\equiv C-H$ acetylene	$R-C\equiv C-H$ an alkylacetylene	$R-C\equiv C-R'$ a dialkylacetylene
$CH_3-C\equiv C-H$ methylacetylene	$Ph-C\equiv C-H$ phenylacetylene	$CH_3-C\equiv C-CH_2CH_3$ ethylmethylacetylene
$(CH_3)_2CH-C\equiv C-CH(CH_3)_2$ diisopropylacetylene	$Ph-C\equiv C-Ph$ diphenylacetylene	$H-C\equiv C-CH_2OH$ hydroxymethylacetylene (propargyl alcohol)

Many of an alkyne's chemical properties depend on whether there is an acetylenic hydrogen ($H-C\equiv C$), that is, whether the triple bond comes at the end of a carbon chain. Such an alkyne is called a **terminal alkyne** or a **terminal acetylene**. If the triple bond is located somewhere other than the end of the carbon chain, the alkyne is called an **internal alkyne** or an **internal acetylene**.

acetylenic hydrogen

$H-C\equiv C-CH_2CH_3$

1-butyne, a *terminal* alkyne

(no acetylenic hydrogen)

$CH_3-C\equiv C-CH_3$

2-butyne, an *internal* alkyne

PROBLEM 9-2

For each molecular formula, draw all the isomeric alkynes, and give their IUPAC names. Circle the acetylenic hydrogen of each terminal alkyne.

(a) C_5H_8 (three isomers) **(b)** C_6H_{10} (seven isomers)

9-3 Physical Properties of Alkynes

The physical properties of alkynes (Table 9-1) are similar to those of alkanes and alkenes of similar molecular weights. Alkynes are relatively nonpolar and nearly insoluble in water. They are quite soluble in most organic solvents, including acetone, ether, methylene chloride, chloroform, and alcohols. Many alkynes have characteristic, mildly offensive odors. Acetylene, propyne, and the butynes are gases at room temperature, just like the corresponding alkanes and alkenes. In fact, the boiling points of alkynes are nearly the same as those of alkanes and alkenes with similar carbon skeletons.

TABLE 9-1
Physical Properties of Selected Alkynes

Name	Structure	mp (°C)	bp (°C)	Density (g/cm³)
ethyne (acetylene)	$H-C\equiv C-H$	−82	−84	0.62
propyne	$H-C\equiv C-CH_3$	−101	−23	0.67
1-butyne	$H-C\equiv C-CH_2CH_3$	−126	8	0.67
2-butyne	$CH_3-C\equiv C-CH_3$	−32	27	0.69
1-pentyne	$H-C\equiv C-CH_2CH_2CH_3$	−90	40	0.70
2-pentyne	$CH_3-C\equiv C-CH_2CH_3$	−101	55	0.71
3-methyl-1-butyne	$CH_3-CH(CH_3)-C\equiv C-H$		28	0.67
1-hexyne	$H-C\equiv C-(CH_2)_3-CH_3$	−132	71	0.72
2-hexyne	$CH_3-C\equiv C-CH_2CH_2CH_3$	−90	84	0.73
3-hexyne	$CH_3CH_2-C\equiv C-CH_2CH_3$	−101	82	0.73
3,3-dimethyl-1-butyne	$(CH_3)_3C-C\equiv C-H$	−81	38	0.67
1-heptyne	$H-C\equiv C-(CH_2)_4CH_3$	−81	100	0.73
1-octyne	$H-C\equiv C-(CH_2)_5CH_3$	−79	125	0.75
1-nonyne	$H-C\equiv C-(CH_2)_6CH_3$	−50	151	0.76
1-decyne	$H-C\equiv C-(CH_2)_7CH_3$	−36	174	0.77

9-4 Commercial Importance of Alkynes

9-4A Uses of Acetylene and Methylacetylene

Acetylene is by far the most important commercial alkyne. Acetylene is an importan industrial feedstock, but its largest use is as the fuel for the oxyacetylene welding torch. Acetylene is a colorless, foul-smelling gas that burns in air with a yellow, sooty flame. When the flame is supplied with pure oxygen, however, the color turns to ligh blue, and the flame temperature increases dramatically. A comparison of the heat o combustion for acetylene with those of ethene and ethane shows why this gas makes an excellent fuel for a high-temperature flame.

$$CH_3CH_3 + \frac{7}{2}\,O_2 \longrightarrow 2\,CO_2 + 3\,H_2O \qquad \Delta H^\circ = -1561\ \text{kJ}\ (-373\ \text{kcal})$$
$$-1561\ \text{kJ divided by 5 moles of products} = -312\ \text{kJ/mol of products}\ (-75\ \text{kcal/mol})$$

$$H_2C{=}CH_2 + 3\,O_2 \longrightarrow 2\,CO_2 + 2\,H_2O \qquad \Delta H^\circ = -1410\ \text{kJ}\ (-337\ \text{kcal})$$
$$-1410\ \text{kJ divided by 4 moles of products} = -352\ \text{kJ/mol of products}\ (-84\ \text{kcal/mol})$$

$$HC{\equiv}CH + \frac{5}{2}\,O_2 \longrightarrow 2\,CO_2 + 1\,H_2O \qquad \Delta H^\circ = -1326\ \text{kJ}\ (-317\ \text{kcal})$$
$$-1326\ \text{kJ divided by 3 moles of products} = -442\ \text{kJ/mol of products}\ (-106\ \text{kcal/mol})$$

If we were simply heating a house by burning one of these fuels, we might choose ethane as our fuel because it produces the most heat per mole of gas consumed. In the welding torch, we want the highest possible *temperature* of the gaseous products. The heat of reaction must raise the temperature of the products to the flame temperature. Roughly speaking, the increase in temperature of the products is proportional to the heat given off *per mole of products* formed. This rise in temperature is largest with acetylene, which gives off the most heat per mole of products. The oxyacetylene flame reaches temperatures as high as 2800 °C.

When acetylene was first used for welding, it was considered a dangerous, explosive gas. Acetylene is thermodynamically unstable. When the compressed gas is subjected to thermal or mechanical shock, it decomposes to its elements, releasing 234 kJ (56 kcal) of energy per mole. This initial decomposition often splits the container, allowing the products (hydrogen and finely divided carbon) to burn in the air.

An oxygen–acetylene flame is hot enough to melt steel for welding. A cutting torch uses an extra jet of oxygen to burn away hot steel.

$$H{-}C{\equiv}C{-}H \longrightarrow 2\,C + H_2 \qquad \Delta H^\circ = -234\ \text{kJ/mol}\ (-56\ \text{kcal/mol})$$

$$2\,C + H_2 \xrightarrow{\frac{5}{2}O_2} 2\,CO_2 + H_2O \qquad \Delta H^\circ = -1090\ \text{kJ/mol 2}\ (-261\ \text{kcal/mol})$$

Acetylene is safely stored and handled in cylinders that are filled with crushed firebrick wet with acetone. Acetylene dissolves freely in acetone, and the dissolved gas is not so prone to decomposition. Firebrick helps to control the decomposition by minimizing the free volume of the cylinder, cooling and controlling any decomposition before it gets out of control.

Methylacetylene also is used in welding torches. Methylacetylene does not decompose as easily as acetylene, and it burns better in air (as opposed to pure oxygen). Methylacetylene is well suited for household soldering and brazing that requires higher temperatures than propane torches can reach. The industrial synthesis of methylacetylene gives a mixture with its isomer, propadiene (allene). This mixture is sold commercially under the name MAPP® gas (*M*ethyl*A*cetylene-*P*ro*P*adiene).

$$\underset{\text{methylacetylene}}{CH_3{-}C{\equiv}C{-}H} \qquad \underset{\text{propadiene (allene)}}{H_2C{=}C{=}CH_2}$$

9-4B Manufacture of Acetylene

Acetylene, one of the cheapest organic chemicals, is made from coal or from natural gas. The synthesis from coal involves heating lime and coke (roasted coal) in an electric furnace to produce calcium carbide. Addition of water to calcium carbide produces acetylene and hydrated lime.

$$\underset{\text{coke}}{3\,C} + \underset{\text{lime}}{CaO} \xrightarrow{\text{electric furnace, 2500 °C}} \underset{\text{calcium carbide}}{CaC_2} + CO$$

$$CaC_2 + 2\,H_2O \longrightarrow \underset{\text{acetylene}}{H-C\equiv C-H} + \underset{\text{hydrated lime}}{Ca(OH)_2}$$

This second reaction once served as a light source in coal mines until battery-powered lights became available. A miner's lamp works by allowing water to drip slowly onto some calcium carbide. Acetylene is generated, feeding a small flame where the gas burns in air with a yellow flickering light. Unfortunately, this flame ignites the methane gas commonly found in coal seams, causing explosions. Battery-powered miner's lamps provide better light and reduce the danger of methane explosions.

A miner's carbide lamp. Water in the upper chamber slowly drips onto calcium carbide in the lower chamber, generating acetylene.

The synthesis of acetylene from natural gas is a simple process. Natural gas consists mostly of methane, which forms acetylene when it is heated for a very short period of time.

$$2\,CH_4 \xrightarrow[\text{0.01 sec}]{\text{1500 °C}} H-C\equiv C-H + 3\,H_2$$

Although this reaction is endothermic, there are twice as many moles of products as reactants. The increase in the number of moles results in an increase in entropy, and the $(-T\Delta S)$ term in the free energy $(\Delta G = \Delta H - T\Delta S)$ predominates at this high temperature.

PROBLEM 9-3

What reaction would acetylene likely undergo if it were kept at 1500 °C for too long?

9-5 Electronic Structure of Alkynes

In Section 2-4, we studied the electronic structure of a triple bond. Let's review this structure, using acetylene as the example. The Lewis structure of acetylene shows three pairs of electrons in the region between the carbon nuclei:

H:C:::C:H

Each carbon atom is bonded to two other atoms, and there are no nonbonding valence electrons. Each carbon atom needs two hybrid orbitals to form the sigma bond framework. Hybridization of the *s* orbital with one *p* orbital gives two hybrid orbitals, directed 180° apart, for each carbon atom. Overlap of these *sp* hybrid orbitals with each other and with the hydrogen *s* orbitals gives the sigma bond framework. Experimental results have confirmed this linear (180°) structure.

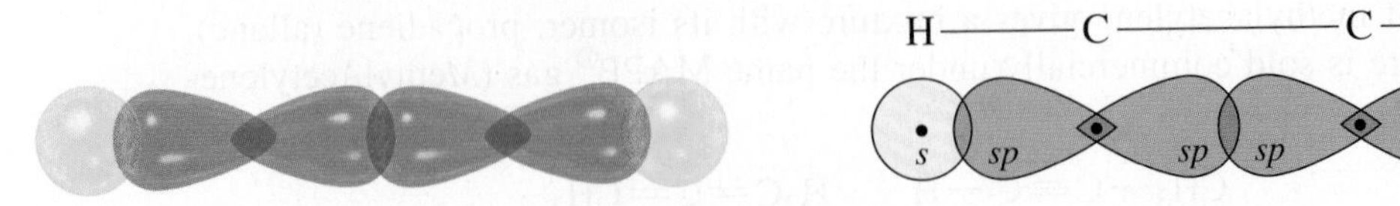

Two pi bonds result from overlap of the two remaining unhybridized *p* orbitals on each carbon atom. These orbitals overlap at right angles to each other, forming one pi bond with electron density above and below the C—C sigma bond, and the other with electron density in front and in back of the sigma bond. The shape of these pi bonds is such that they blend to form a cylinder of electron density encircling the sigma bond between the two carbon atoms.

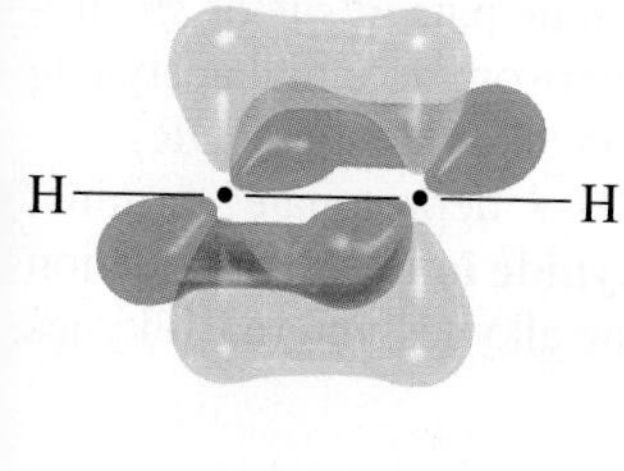

H σ bond C σ bond C σ bond H

overlap of p orbitals

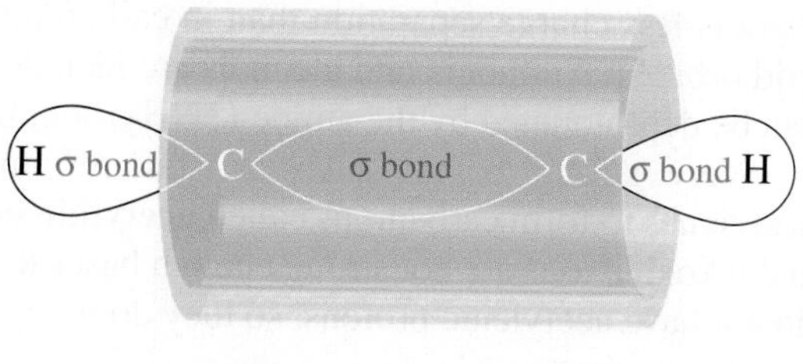

cylinder of electron density

EPM of acetylene

The carbon–carbon bond length in acetylene is 1.20 Å, and each carbon–hydrogen bond is 1.06 Å. Both bonds are shorter than the corresponding bonds in ethane and in ethene.

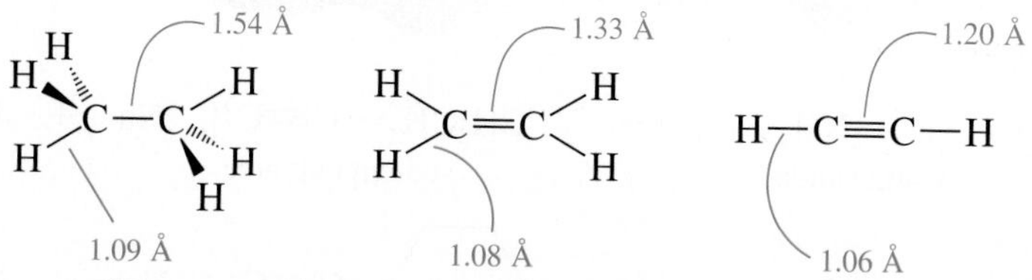

1.54 Å, 1.09 Å — ethane

1.33 Å, 1.08 Å — ethene

H—C≡C—H: 1.20 Å, 1.06 Å — ethyne

The triple bond is relatively short because of the attractive overlap of three bonding pairs of electrons and the high *s* **character** of the *sp* hybrid orbitals. The *sp* hybrid orbitals are about one-half *s* character (as opposed to one-third *s* character of sp^2 hybrids and one-fourth of sp^3 hybrids), using more of the closer, tightly held *s* orbital. The *sp* hybrid orbitals also account for the slightly shorter C—H bonds in acetylene compared with ethylene.

9-6 Acidity of Alkynes; Formation of Acetylide Ions

Terminal alkynes are much more acidic than other hydrocarbons. Removal of an acetylenic proton forms an acetylide ion, which plays a central role in alkyne chemistry.

The acidity of an acetylenic hydrogen stems from the nature of the *sp* hybrid ≡C—H bond. Table 9-2 shows how the acidity of a C—H bond varies with its hybridization, increasing with the increasing *s* character of the orbitals: $sp^3 < sp^2 < sp$. (Remember that a *smaller* value of pK_a corresponds to a stronger acid.) The acetylenic proton is about 10^{19} times as acidic as a vinyl proton.

Abstraction of an acetylenic proton gives a carbanion that has the lone pair of electrons in the *sp* hybrid orbital. Electrons in this orbital are close to the nucleus, and

TABLE 9-2

Compound	Conjugate Base	Hybridization	*s* Character	pK_a	
CH_3—CH_3	CH_3—CH_2^-	sp^3	25%	50	weakest acid
H_2C=CH_2	H_2C=CH^-	sp^2	33%	44	
$:NH_3$	$:\ddot{N}H_2^-$	(ammonia)		35	
H—C≡C—H	H—C≡C:$^-$	*sp*	50%	25	
R—OH	R—Ö:$^-$	(alcohols)		16–18	stronger acid

there is less charge separation than in carbanions with the lone pair in sp^2 or sp^3 hybrid orbitals. Ammonia and alcohols are included for comparison; note that acetylene can be deprotonated by the amide ($^-NH_2$) ion, but not by an alkoxide ion (^-OR).

Very strong bases (such as sodium amide, $NaNH_2$) deprotonate terminal acetylenes to form carbanions called **acetylide ions** (or **alkynide ions**). Hydroxide ion and alkoxide ions are not strong enough bases to deprotonate alkynes. Internal alkynes do not have acetylenic protons, so they do not react.

acidic proton

$$CH_3CH_2-C\equiv C-H + Na^+ \ ^-:\ddot{N}H_2 \longrightarrow CH_3CH_2-C\equiv C:^- \ ^+Na + NH_3$$

1-butyne, a terminal alkyne; sodium amide; sodium butynide

$$C_6H_{11}-C\equiv C-H + NaNH_2 \longrightarrow C_6H_{11}-C\equiv C:^- \ ^+Na + NH_3$$

cyclohexylacetylene; sodium amide; sodium cyclohexylacetylide

$$CH_3-C\equiv C-CH_3 \xrightarrow{NaNH_2} \text{no reaction}$$

(no acetylenic proton)
2-butyne, an internal alkyne

Sodium amide ($Na^+ \ ^-:\ddot{N}H_2$) is frequently used as the base in forming acetylide salts. The amide ion ($^-NH_2$) is the conjugate base of ammonia, a compound that is itself a base. Ammonia is also a very weak acid, however, with $K_a = 10^{-35}$ ($pK_a = 35$). One of its hydrogens can be reduced by sodium metal to give the sodium salt of the amide ion, a very strong conjugate base.

$$H-\ddot{N}(H)-H + Na \xrightarrow{Fe^{3+}\text{ catalyst}} Na^+ \ ^-:\ddot{N}(H)-H + \tfrac{1}{2}H_2\uparrow$$

ammonia; sodium amide ("sodamide")

$$R-C\equiv C-H + Na^+ \ ^-:\ddot{N}H_2 \longrightarrow R-C\equiv C:^- \ ^+Na + :NH_3$$

a sodium acetylide

Acetylide ions are strong nucleophiles. In fact, one of the best methods for synthesizing substituted alkynes is a nucleophilic attack by an acetylide ion on an unhindered alkyl halide. We consider this displacement reaction in detail in Section 9-7A.

$$CH_3CH_2-C\equiv C:^- \ ^+Na + H_3C-I \longrightarrow CH_3CH_2-C\equiv C-CH_3 + Na$$

PROBLEM 9-4

The boiling points of 1-hexene (64 °C) and 1-hexyne (71 °C) are sufficiently close that it i difficult to achieve a clean separation by distillation. Show how you might use the acidity c 1-hexyne to remove the last trace of it from a sample of 1-hexene.

PROBLEM 9-5

Predict the products of the following acid–base reactions, or indicate if no significant reaction would take place.

(a) $H-C\equiv C-H + NaNH_2$ **(b)** $H-C\equiv C-H + CH_3Li$

(c) $H-C\equiv C-H + NaOCH_3$ **(d)** $H-C\equiv C-H + NaOH$

(e) $H-C\equiv C:^{-}\ {}^{+}Na + CH_3OH$ **(f)** $H-C\equiv C:^{-}\ {}^{+}Na + H_2O$

(g) $H-C\equiv C:^{-}\ {}^{+}Na + H_2C=CH_2$ **(h)** $H_2C=CH_2 + NaNH_2$

(i) $CH_3OH + NaNH_2$

9-7 Synthesis of Alkynes from Acetylides

Two different approaches are commonly used for the synthesis of alkynes. In the first, an appropriate electrophile undergoes nucleophilic attack by an acetylide ion. The electrophile may be an unhindered primary alkyl halide (undergoes S_N2), or it may be a carbonyl compound (undergoes addition to give an alcohol). Either reaction joins two fragments and gives a product with a lengthened carbon skeleton. This approach is used in many laboratory syntheses of alkynes.

The second approach forms the triple bond by a double dehydrohalogenation of a dihalide. This reaction does not enlarge the carbon skeleton. Isomerization of the triple bond may occur (see Section 9-8), so dehydrohalogenation is useful only when the desired product has the triple bond in a thermodynamically favored position.

9-7A Alkylation of Acetylide Ions

An acetylide ion is a strong base and a powerful nucleophile. It can displace a halide ion from a suitable substrate, giving a substituted acetylene.

$$R-C\equiv C:^{-} + R'-X \xrightarrow{S_N2} R-C\equiv C-R' + X^{-}$$

(R′—X must be a primary alkyl halide)

If this S_N2 reaction is to produce a good yield, the alkyl halide must be an excellent S_N2 substrate: It must be primary, with no bulky substituents or branches close to the reaction center. In the following examples, acetylide ions displace primary halides to form elongated alkynes.

$$\underset{\text{sodium acetylide}}{H-C\equiv C:^{-}\ {}^{+}Na} + \underset{\text{1-bromobutane}}{CH_3CH_2CH_2CH_2-Br} \longrightarrow \underset{\substack{\text{1-hexyne}\\ \text{(butylacetylene)}\\ (75\%)}}{H-C\equiv C-CH_2CH_2CH_2CH_3} + NaBr$$

$$\underset{\substack{\text{ethynylcyclohexane}\\ \text{(cyclohexylacetylene)}}}{C_6H_{11}-C\equiv C-H} \xrightarrow[\text{(2) ethyl bromide}]{\text{(1) }NaNH_2} \underset{\substack{\text{1-cyclohexyl-1-butyne}\\ \text{(ethylcyclohexylacetylene)}\\ (70\%)}}{C_6H_{11}-C\equiv C-CH_2CH_3}$$

If the back-side approach is hindered, the acetylide ion may abstract a proton, giving elimination by the E2 mechanism.

$$\underset{\text{butynide ion}}{CH_3CH_2-C\equiv C:^{-}} + \underset{\text{isopropyl bromide}}{H_3C-CH(Br)-CH_3} \xrightarrow{E2} \underset{\text{butyne}}{CH_3CH_2-C\equiv C-H} + \underset{\text{propene}}{H_2C=CH-CH_3} + Br^{-}$$

problem-solving Hint

Alkylation of acetylide ions is an excellent way of lengthening a carbon chain. The triple bond can later be reduced (to an alkane or an alkene) if needed.

SOLVED PROBLEM 9-1

Show how to synthesize 3-decyne from acetylene and any necessary alkyl halides.

SOLUTION

Another name for 3-decyne is ethyl *n*-hexylacetylene. It can be made by adding an ethyl group and a hexyl group to acetylene. This can be done in either order. We begin by adding the hexyl group.

$$\underset{\text{acetylene}}{H{-}C{\equiv}C{-}H} \xrightarrow[\text{(2) } CH_3(CH_2)_5Br]{\text{(1) } NaNH_2} \underset{\text{1-octyne}}{CH_3(CH_2)_5{-}C{\equiv}C{-}H}$$

$$\underset{\text{1-octyne}}{CH_3(CH_2)_5{-}C{\equiv}C{-}H} \xrightarrow[\text{(2)} CH_3CH_2Br]{\text{(1)} NaNH_2} \underset{\text{3-decyne}}{CH_3(CH_2)_5{-}C{\equiv}C{-}CH_2CH_3}$$

PROBLEM 9-6

Show the reagents and intermediates involved in the other order of synthesis of 3-decyne, by adding the ethyl group first and the hexyl group last.

PROBLEM 9-7

Show how you might synthesize the following compounds, using acetylene and any suitable alkyl halides as your starting materials. If the compound given cannot be synthesized by this method, explain why.

(a) 1-hexyne
(b) 2-hexyne
(c) 3-hexyne
(d) 4-methyl-2-hexyne
(e) 5-methyl-2-hexyne
(f) cyclodecyne

9-7B Addition of Acetylide Ions to Carbonyl Groups

Like other carbanions, acetylide ions are strong nucleophiles and strong bases. In addition to displacing halide ions in S_N2 reactions, they can add to carbonyl (C=O) groups. Figure 9-1 shows the structure of the carbonyl group. Because oxygen is more

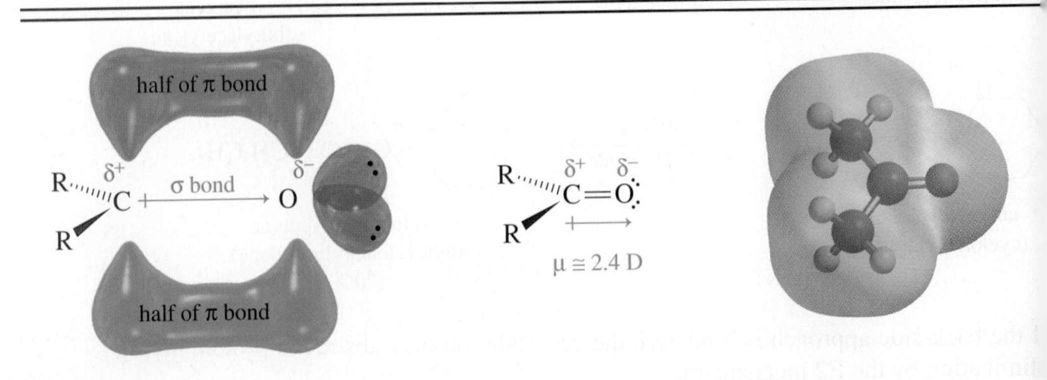

FIGURE 9-1
The C=O double bond of a carbonyl group resembles the C=C double bond of an alkene; however, the carbonyl double bond is strongly polarized. The oxygen atom bears a partial negative charge, and the carbon atom bears a partial positive charge.

electronegative than carbon, the C=O double bond is polarized. The oxygen atom has a partial negative charge balanced by an equal amount of positive charge on the carbon atom.

The positively charged carbon is electrophilic; attack by a nucleophile places a negative charge on the electronegative oxygen atom.

$$\text{Nuc:}^- + \overset{\delta+}{\text{C}}{=}\overset{\delta-}{\text{O}}\text{:} \longrightarrow \text{Nuc—C—}\ddot{\text{O}}\text{:}^-$$

alkoxide ion

The product of this nucleophilic attack is an alkoxide ion, a strong base. (An **alkoxide ion** is the conjugate base of an alcohol, a weak acid.) Addition of water or a dilute acid protonates the alkoxide to give the alcohol.

$$\text{Nuc—C—}\ddot{\text{O}}\text{:}^- \quad \text{H—}\ddot{\text{O}}\text{—H} \longrightarrow \text{Nuc—C—}\ddot{\text{O}}\text{H} + {}^-\text{:}\ddot{\text{O}}\text{H}$$

alkoxide (or H_3O^+)

An acetylide ion can serve as the nucleophile in this addition to a carbonyl group. The acetylide ion adds to the carbonyl group to form an alkoxide ion. Addition of dilute acid (in a separate step) protonates the alkoxide to give the alcohol.

$$\text{R}'\text{—C}\equiv\text{C:}^- + \text{R}_2\text{C}{=}\text{O} \longrightarrow \text{R}'\text{—C}\equiv\text{C—CR}_2\text{—}\ddot{\text{O}}\text{:}^- \xrightarrow{H_3O^+} \text{R}'\text{—C}\equiv\text{C—CR}_2\text{—OH}$$

acetylide; aldehyde or ketone; an acetylenic alcohol

An acetylide adds to formaldehyde ($H_2C{=}O$) to give (after the protonation step) a primary alcohol with one more carbon atom than there was in the acetylide.

$$\text{R}'\text{—C}\equiv\text{C:}^- + \text{H}_2\text{C}{=}\text{O} \longrightarrow \text{R}'\text{—C}\equiv\text{C—CH}_2\text{—}\ddot{\text{O}}\text{:}^- \xrightarrow{H_3O^+} \text{R}'\text{—C}\equiv\text{C—CH}_2\text{—OH}$$

formaldehyde; a 1° alcohol

Example

$$\underset{\text{propyne}}{CH_3\text{—C}\equiv\text{C—H}} \xrightarrow[\text{(3) } H_3O^+]{\text{(1) } NaNH_2 \text{ (2) } H_2C{=}O} \underset{\text{2-butyn-1-ol (1°)}}{CH_3\text{—C}\equiv\text{C—}CH_2\text{—OH}}$$

An acetylide adds to an aldehyde to give, after protonation, a secondary alcohol. The two groups of the secondary alcohol are the acetylide and the alkyl group that was bonded to the carbonyl group of the aldehyde.

The addition of an acetylide ion to a carbonyl group is used in the synthesis of ethchlorvynol, a drug used to cause drowsiness and induce sleep. Ethchlorvynol is relatively nonpolar, enhancing its distribution into the fatty tissue of the central nervous system.

$$CH_3CH_2\text{—C(OH)(CH=CHCl)—C}\equiv\text{CH}$$

ethchlorvynol

problem-solving Hint

Numbers (1), (2), (3), etc. are used to show a sequence of separate reactions over a single arrow. If the numbers were omitted, it would incorrectly imply mixing all these reagents together, rather than adding them in separate steps.

$$R'-C\equiv C:^- + \underset{H}{\overset{R}{\diagdown}}C=\ddot{O}: \longrightarrow R'-C\equiv C-\underset{H}{\overset{R}{|}}C-\ddot{O}:^- \xrightarrow{H_3O^+} R'-C\equiv C-\underset{H}{\overset{R}{|}}C-OH$$

an aldehyde — a 2° alcohol

Example

$$CH_3-\overset{CH_3}{\overset{|}{C}}H-C\equiv C-H \xrightarrow[(3)\ H_3O^+]{(1)\ NaNH_2\ (2)\ PhCHO} CH_3-\overset{CH_3}{\overset{|}{C}}H-C\equiv C-\overset{Ph}{\overset{|}{C}}H-OH$$

3-methyl-1-butyne — 4-methyl-1-phenyl-2-pentyn-1-ol (2°)

A ketone has two alkyl groups bonded to its carbonyl carbon atom. Addition of an acetylide, followed by protonation, gives a tertiary alcohol. The three alkyl groups bonded to the carbinol carbon atom (the carbon bearing the —OH group) are the acetylide and the two alkyl groups originally bonded to the carbonyl group in the ketone.

$$R'-C\equiv C:^- + \underset{R}{\overset{R}{\diagdown}}C=\ddot{O}: \longrightarrow R'-C\equiv C-\underset{R}{\overset{R}{|}}C-\ddot{O}:^- \xrightarrow{H_3O^+} R'-C\equiv C-\underset{R}{\overset{R}{|}}C-OH$$

a ketone — a 3° alcohol

Example

$$\text{cyclohexanone} \xrightarrow[(2)\ H_3O^+]{(1)\ Na^{+}\ ^{-}:C\equiv C-H} \text{1-ethynylcyclohexanol (C(OH)–C}\equiv\text{C–H on ring)}$$

cyclohexanone — 1-ethynylcyclohexanol (3°)

SOLVED PROBLEM 9-2

Show how you would synthesize the following compound, beginning with acetylene and any necessary additional reagents.

$$\text{cyclopentyl}-\overset{OH}{\overset{|}{C}}H-C\equiv C-CH_2CH_3$$

SOLUTION

We need to add two groups to acetylene: an ethyl group and a six-carbon aldehyde (to form the secondary alcohol). If we formed the alcohol group first, the weakly acidic —OH group would interfere with the alkylation by the ethyl group. Therefore, we should add the less reactive ethyl group first, and add the alcohol group later in the synthesis.

$$H-C\equiv C-H \xrightarrow[(2)\ CH_3CH_2Br]{(1)\ NaNH_2} H-C\equiv C-CH_2CH_3$$

The ethyl group is not acidic, and it does not interfere with the addition of the second group:

$$H-C\equiv C-CH_2CH_3 \xrightarrow{NaNH_2} Na^+ \ ^-{:}C\equiv C-CH_2CH_3 \xrightarrow[(2)\ H_3O^+]{(1)\ \text{cyclopentanecarbaldehyde}} \text{cyclopentyl}-CH(OH)-C\equiv C-CH_2CH_3$$

PROBLEM 9-8

Show how you would synthesize each compound, beginning with acetylene and any necessary additional reagents.

(a) 2-propyn-1-ol (propargyl alcohol)

$H-C\equiv C-CH_2OH$

(b) 2-heptyn-4-ol

$CH_3-C\equiv C-CH(OH)-CH_2CH_2CH_3$

(c) 2-phenyl-3-butyn-2-ol

$CH_3-C(OH)(Ph)-C\equiv C-H$

(d) 3-methyl-4-hexyn-3-ol

$CH_3CH_2-C(OH)(CH_3)-C\equiv C-CH_3$

problem-solving Hint

If a synthesis requires both alkylation of an acetylide and addition to a carbonyl, add the less reactive group first: alkylate, then add to a carbonyl. In general, you should add reactive functional groups late in a synthesis.

PROBLEM 9-9

Show how you would synthesize 2-phenylhex-3-yn-2-ol, starting with acetophenone ($PhCOCH_3$) and any other reagents you need. ("2-ol" means there is an OH group on C2.)

9-8 Synthesis of Alkynes by Elimination Reactions

In some cases, we can generate a carbon–carbon triple bond by eliminating two molecules of HX from a dihalide. Dehydrohalogenation of a *geminal* or *vicinal* dihalide gives a vinyl halide. Under strongly basic conditions, a second dehydrohalogenation may occur to form an alkyne.

$$\underset{\text{a vicinal dihalide}}{R-CHX-CHX-R'} \xrightarrow[\text{(fast)}]{\text{base, }-HX} \underset{\text{vinyl halide}}{(H)(R)C=C(R')(X)} \xrightarrow[\text{(slow)}]{\text{base, }-HX} \underset{\text{alkyne}}{R-C\equiv C-R'}$$

$$\underset{\text{a geminal dihalide}}{R-CH_2-CX_2-R'} \xrightarrow[\text{(fast)}]{\text{base, }-HX} \underset{\text{vinyl halide}}{(H)(R)C=C(R')(X)} \xrightarrow[\text{(slow)}]{\text{base, }-HX} \underset{\text{alkyne}}{R-C\equiv C-R'}$$

We have already seen (Section 7-9A) many examples of dehydrohalogenation of alkyl halides. The second step is new, however, because it involves dehydrohalogenation of a vinyl halide to give an alkyne. This second dehydrohalogenation occurs only under extremely basic conditions—for example, fused (molten) KOH or alcoholic KOH in a sealed tube, usually heated to temperatures close to 200 °C. Sodium amide is also used for the double dehydrohalogenation. Since the amide ion ($^{-}\!:\ddot{N}H_2$) is a much stronger base than hydroxide, the amide reaction takes place at a lower temperature. Using either KOH or sodium amide at these elevated temperatures implies brutal reaction conditions, encouraging side reactions and rearrangements. Yields are often poor. The following reactions are carefully chosen to form products that are not prone to side reactions. The KOH elimination tends to give the most stable internal alkyne. The sodium amide elimination tends to give a terminal alkyne (where possible) because the acetylenic hydrogen is deprotonated by the amide ion, giving an acetylide ion as the initial product.

$$CH_3-CH_2-CH(Br)-CH(Br)-CH_3 \xrightarrow[200\ °C]{KOH\ (fused)} CH_3-CH_2-C\equiv C-CH_3$$

2,3-dibromopentane → 2-pentyne (45%)

$$CH_3CH_2CH_2CH_2-CHCl_2 \xrightarrow[150\ °C]{NaNH_2} CH_3CH_2CH_2C\equiv C:^- \ Na^+ \xrightarrow{H_2O} CH_3CH_2CH_2C\equiv CH$$

1,1-dichloropentane → 1-pentyne (55%)

problem-solving Hint

R(H)C=C(X)R′

KOH, 200 °C → most stable internal alkyne

(1) $NaNH_2$, 150 °C (2) H_2O → terminal alkyne

PROBLEM 9-10

When 2,2-dibromo-1-phenylpropane is heated overnight in fused KOH at 200 °C, the major product is a foul-smelling compound of formula C_9H_8. Propose a structure for this product, and give a mechanism to account for its formation.

PROBLEM 9-11

When 2,2-dibromo-1-phenylpropane is heated overnight with sodium amide at 150 °C, the major product (after addition of water) is a different foul-smelling compound of formula C_9H_8. Propose a structure for this product, and give a mechanism to account for its formation.

SUMMARY Syntheses of Alkynes

1. *Alkylation of acetylide ions* (Section 9-7A)

$$R-C\equiv C:^- + R'-X \xrightarrow{S_N2} R-C\equiv C-R' + X^-$$

($R'-X$ must be an unhindered primary halide or tosylate)

Example

$$H_3C-C\equiv C:^-\ ^+Na + CH_3CH_2CH_2-Br \longrightarrow H_3C-C\equiv C-CH_2CH_2CH_3$$

sodium propynide + 1-bromopropane → 2-hexyne

2. *Additions to carbonyl groups* (Section 9-7B)

$$R-C\equiv C:^- + R'_2C=\ddot{O}: \longrightarrow R-C\equiv C-CR'_2-\ddot{O}:^- \xrightarrow[(or\ H_3O^+)]{H_2O} R-C\equiv C-CR'_2-OH$$

Example

$$\underset{\text{sodium acetylide}}{H{-}C{\equiv}C{:}^-\ Na^+} + \underset{\text{propanal}}{CH_3CH_2{-}\overset{O}{\overset{\|}{C}}{-}H} \longrightarrow H{-}C{\equiv}C{-}\underset{H}{\overset{CH_3CH_2}{C}}{-}O^-\ Na^+ \xrightarrow{H_2O} \underset{\text{1-pentyn-3-ol}}{H{-}C{\equiv}C{-}\overset{OH}{CH}{-}CH_2CH_3}$$

3. *Double dehydrohalogenation of alkyl dihalides* (Section 9-8)

$$R{-}\underset{H}{\overset{X}{C}}{-}\underset{H}{\overset{X}{C}}{-}R' \quad \text{or} \quad R{-}\underset{H}{\overset{H}{C}}{-}\underset{X}{\overset{X}{C}}{-}R' \xrightarrow[\text{or } NaNH_2]{\text{fused KOH}} R{-}C{\equiv}C{-}R'$$

(severe conditions)

(KOH forms internal alkynes; $NaNH_2$ forms terminal alkynes.)

Examples

$$\underset{\text{2,2-dichloropentane}}{CH_3CH_2{-}CH_2{-}CCl_2{-}CH_3} \xrightarrow{\text{KOH, 200 °C (fused)}} \underset{\text{2-pentyne}}{CH_3CH_2{-}C{\equiv}C{-}CH_3}$$

$$\underset{\text{2,2-dichloropentane}}{CH_3CH_2{-}CH_2{-}CCl_2{-}CH_3} \xrightarrow[\text{(2) } H_2O]{\text{(1) } NaNH_2\text{, 150 °C}} \underset{\text{1-pentyne}}{CH_3CH_2CH_2{-}C{\equiv}C{-}H}$$

9-9 Addition Reactions of Alkynes

We have already discussed some of the most important reactions of alkynes. The nucleophilic attack of acetylide ions on electrophiles, for example, is one of the best methods for making more complicated alkynes (Section 9-7). Now we consider reactions that involve transformations of the carbon–carbon triple bond itself.

Many of the reactions of alkynes are similar to the corresponding reactions of alkenes because both involve pi bonds between two carbon atoms. Like the pi bond of an alkene, the pi bonds of an alkyne are electron-rich, and they readily undergo addition reactions. Table 9-3 shows how the energy differences between the kinds of carbon–carbon bonds can be used to estimate how much energy it takes to break a particular bond. The bond energy of the alkyne triple bond is only about 226 kJ (54 kcal) more than the bond energy of an alkene double bond. This is the energy needed to break one of the pi bonds of an alkyne.

Reagents add across the triple bonds of alkynes just as they add across the double bonds of alkenes. In effect, this reaction converts a pi bond and a sigma bond into two sigma bonds. Since sigma bonds are generally stronger than pi bonds, the reaction is usually exothermic. Alkynes have two pi bonds, so up to two molecules can add across the triple bond, depending on the reagents and the conditions.

TABLE 9-3

Approximate Bond Energies of Carbon–Carbon Bonds

Bond	Total Energy	Class of Bond	Approximate Energy
C—C	347 kJ (83 kcal)	alkane sigma bond	347 kJ (83 kcal)
C=C	611 kJ (146 kcal)	alkene pi bond	264 kJ (63 kcal)
C≡C	837 kJ (200 kcal)	second alkyne pi bond	226 kJ (54 kcal)

$$\underset{\pi\text{ bond}}{R-C\equiv C-R'} + \underset{\sigma\text{ bond}}{A-B} \longrightarrow \underset{2\,\sigma\text{ bonds}}{\overset{A\qquad B}{\underset{R\qquad R'}{C=C}}} \xrightarrow{A-B} R-\overset{A}{\underset{A}{C}}-\overset{B}{\underset{B}{C}}-R'$$

We must consider the possibility of a double addition whenever a reagent adds across the triple bond of an alkyne. Some conditions may allow the reaction to stop after a single addition, while other conditions give double addition.

9-9A Catalytic Hydrogenation to Alkanes

In the presence of a suitable catalyst, hydrogen adds to an alkyne, reducing it to an alkane. For example, when either of the butyne isomers reacts with hydrogen and a platinum catalyst, the product is *n*-butane. Platinum, palladium, and nickel catalysts are commonly used in this reduction.

$$R-C\equiv C-R' + 2\,H_2 \xrightarrow{\text{Pt, Pd, or Ni}} R-\overset{H}{\underset{H}{C}}-\overset{H}{\underset{H}{C}}-R'$$

Examples

$$\underset{\text{1-butyne}}{H-C\equiv C-CH_2CH_3} + 2\,H_2 \xrightarrow{\text{Pt}} \underset{\text{butane (100\%)}}{H-CH_2-CH_2-CH_2CH_3}$$

$$\underset{\text{2-butyne}}{CH_3-C\equiv C-CH_3} + 2\,H_2 \xrightarrow{\text{Pt}} \underset{\text{butane (100\%)}}{CH_3-CH_2-CH_2-CH_3}$$

Catalytic hydrogenation takes place in two stages, with an alkene intermediate. With efficient catalysts such as platinum, palladium, or nickel, it is usually impossible to stop the reaction at the alkene stage.

$$R-C\equiv C-R' \xrightarrow{H_2,\ \text{Pt}} \left[\overset{R\qquad R'}{\underset{H\qquad H}{C=C}}\right] \xrightarrow{H_2,\ \text{Pt}} R-\overset{H}{\underset{H}{C}}-\overset{H}{\underset{H}{C}}-R'$$

9-9B Catalytic Hydrogenation to cis Alkenes

Hydrogenation of an alkyne can be stopped at the alkene stage by using a "poisoned" (partially deactivated) catalyst made by treating a good catalyst with a compound that makes the catalyst less effective. **Lindlar's catalyst**[1] is a poisoned palladium catalyst,

[1] Lindlar's catalyst was originally Pd on $CaCO_3$, deactivated by $Pb(OAc)_2$. Cram and Allinger modified the procedure to use Pd on $BaSO_4$, deactivated by quinoline.

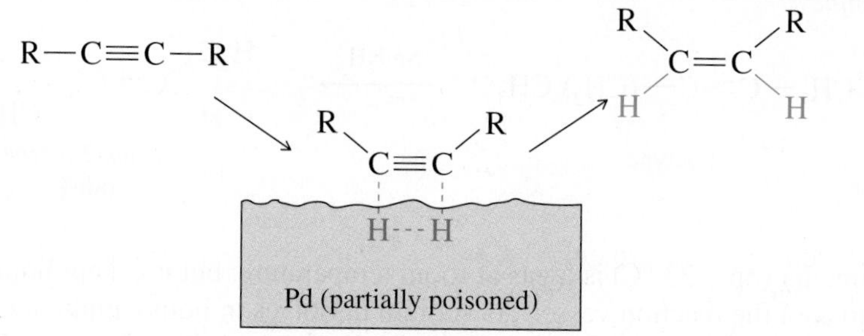

$$\text{R}-\text{C}\equiv\text{C}-\text{R} \rightarrow \text{R(C}\equiv\text{C)R on H---H, Pd (partially poisoned)} \rightarrow \text{RHC}=\text{CHR (cis)}$$

■ FIGURE 9-2
Catalytic hydrogenation of alkynes using Lindlar's catalyst.

composed of powdered barium sulfate coated with palladium, poisoned with quinoline. Nickel boride (Ni_2B) is a newer alternative to Lindlar's catalyst that is more easily made and often gives better yields.

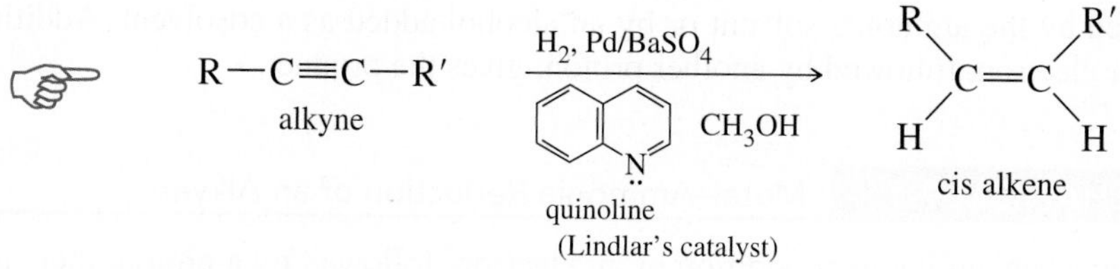

$$\underset{\text{alkyne}}{\text{R}-\text{C}\equiv\text{C}-\text{R}'} \xrightarrow[\text{quinoline (Lindlar's catalyst)} \quad \text{CH}_3\text{OH}]{\text{H}_2,\ \text{Pd/BaSO}_4} \underset{\text{cis alkene}}{\text{(R)(H)C}=\text{C(R}')\text{(H)}}$$

The catalytic hydrogenation of alkynes is similar to the hydrogenation of alkenes, and both proceed with syn stereochemistry. In catalytic hydrogenation, the face of a pi bond contacts the solid catalyst, and the catalyst weakens the pi bond, allowing two hydrogen atoms to add (Figure 9-2). This simultaneous (or nearly simultaneous) addition of two hydrogen atoms on the same face of the alkyne ensures syn stereochemistry.

In an internal alkyne, syn addition gives a cis product. For example, when 2-hexyne is hydrogenated using Lindlar's catalyst, the product is *cis*-2-hexene.

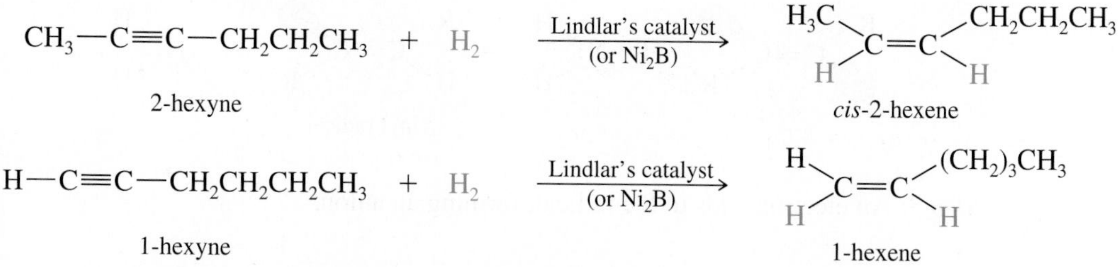

$$\underset{\text{2-hexyne}}{\text{CH}_3-\text{C}\equiv\text{C}-\text{CH}_2\text{CH}_2\text{CH}_3} + \text{H}_2 \xrightarrow[\text{(or Ni}_2\text{B)}]{\text{Lindlar's catalyst}} \underset{cis\text{-2-hexene}}{\text{(H}_3\text{C)(H)C}=\text{C(CH}_2\text{CH}_2\text{CH}_3\text{)(H)}}$$

$$\underset{\text{1-hexyne}}{\text{H}-\text{C}\equiv\text{C}-\text{CH}_2\text{CH}_2\text{CH}_2\text{CH}_3} + \text{H}_2 \xrightarrow[\text{(or Ni}_2\text{B)}]{\text{Lindlar's catalyst}} \underset{\text{1-hexene}}{\text{(H)(H)C}=\text{C((CH}_2)_3\text{CH}_3\text{)(H)}}$$

9-9C Metal–Ammonia Reduction to trans Alkenes

To form a trans alkene, two hydrogens must be added to the alkyne with anti stereochemistry. Sodium metal in liquid ammonia reduces alkynes with anti stereochemistry, so this reduction is used to convert alkynes to trans alkenes.

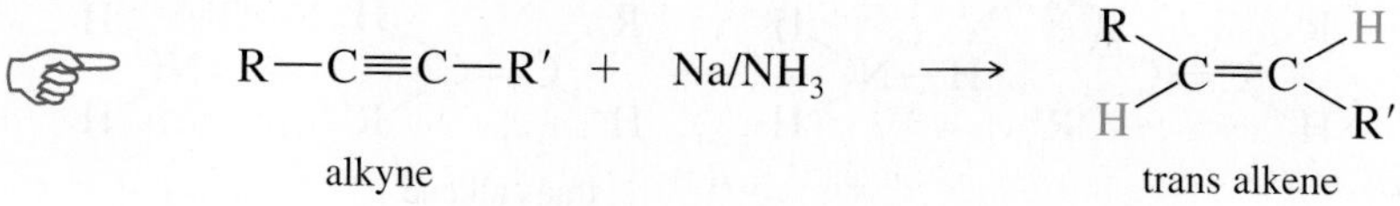

$$\underset{\text{alkyne}}{\text{R}-\text{C}\equiv\text{C}-\text{R}'} + \text{Na/NH}_3 \longrightarrow \underset{\text{trans alkene}}{\text{(R)(H)C}=\text{C(H)(R}')}$$

Example

$$CH_3-C\equiv C-(CH_2)_4CH_3 \xrightarrow{Na/NH_3} \text{trans-}H_3C(H)C=C(H)(CH_2)_4CH_3$$

2-octyne → *trans*-2-octene (80%)

Ammonia (bp −33 °C) is a gas at room temperature, but it is kept liquid by using dry ice to cool the reaction vessel. As sodium dissolves in liquid ammonia, it gives up electrons, which produce a deep blue color. It is these solvated electrons that actually reduce the alkyne.

$$NH_3 + Na \longrightarrow NH_3{\cdot}e^- \text{ (deep blue solution)} + Na^+$$

solvated electron

The metal–ammonia reduction proceeds by addition of an electron to the alkyne to form a radical anion, followed by protonation to give a neutral radical. Protons are provided by the ammonia solvent or by an alcohol added as a cosolvent. Addition of another electron, followed by another proton, gives the product.

MECHANISM 9-1 Metal–Ammonia Reduction of an Alkyne

This mechanism involves addition of an electron, followed by a proton, then addition of a second electron, followed by a second proton.

Step 1: An electron adds to the alkyne, forming a radical anion.

$$R-C\equiv C-R' \quad e^- \longrightarrow R(^-)C=C(\cdot)R'$$

alkyne → radical anion

Step 2: The radical anion is protonated to give a radical.

$$R(^-)C=C(\cdot)R' \quad H-\ddot{N}H_2 \longrightarrow R(H)C=C(\cdot)R' + :\ddot{N}H_2^-$$

vinyl radical

Step 3: An electron adds to the radical, forming an anion.

$$R(H)C=C(\cdot)R' \quad e^- \longrightarrow R(H)C=C(:^-)R'$$

most stable *trans*

vinyl anion

Step 4: Protonation of the anion gives an alkene.

$$R(H)C=C(:^-)R' \quad H-\ddot{N}H_2 \longrightarrow R(H)C=C(H)R' + :\ddot{N}H_2^-$$

trans alkene

The anti stereochemistry of the sodium–ammonia reduction appears to result from the greater stability of the vinyl radical in the trans configuration, where the alkyl groups are farther apart. An electron is added to the trans radical to give a trans vinyl anion, which is quickly protonated to the trans alkene.

PROBLEM 9-12

Show how you would convert

(a) 3-octyne to *cis*-3-octene
(b) 2-pentyne to *trans*-2-pentene
(c) *cis*-cyclodecene to *trans*-cyclodecene
(d) 1-butyne to *cis*-3-hexene

PROBLEM 9-13

The fragrance of Z-1-phenylhex-2-en-1-ol resembles that of roses, with a delicate citrus edge. Show how you would synthesize this compound from benzaldehyde (PhCHO) and any other reagents you need.

9-9D Addition of Halogens

Bromine and chlorine add to alkynes just as they add to alkenes. If 1 mole of halogen adds to 1 mole of an alkyne, the product is a dihaloalkene. The stereochemistry of addition may be either syn or anti, and the products are often mixtures of cis and trans isomers.

$$R-C\equiv C-R' + X_2 \xrightarrow{(X_2 = Cl_2 \text{ or } Br_2)} (R)(X)C=C(X)(R') + (R)(X)C=C(R')(X)$$

Example

$$CH_3(CH_2)_3-C\equiv C-H + Br_2 \longrightarrow \underset{(72\%)}{(CH_3(CH_2)_3)(Br)C=C(Br)(H)} + \underset{(28\%)}{(CH_3(CH_2)_3)(Br)C=C(H)(Br)}$$

If 2 moles of halogen add to 1 mole of an alkyne, a tetrahalide results. Sometimes it is difficult to keep the reaction from proceeding all the way to the tetrahalide even when we want it to stop at the dihalide.

$$R-C\equiv C-R' + 2\,X_2 \xrightarrow{(X_2 = Cl_2 \text{ or } Br_2)} R-CX_2-CX_2-R'$$

Example

$$CH_3(CH_2)_3-C\equiv C-H + 2\,Cl_2 \longrightarrow \underset{(100\%)}{CH_3(CH_2)_3-CCl_2-CCl_2-H}$$

PROBLEM 9-14

In the addition of just 1 mole of bromine to 1 mole of 1-hexyne, should the 1-hexyne be added to a bromine solution or should the bromine be added to the 1-hexyne? Explain your answer.

9-9E Addition of Hydrogen Halides

Hydrogen halides add across the triple bond of an alkyne in much the same way they add across the alkene double bond. The initial product is a vinyl halide. When a hydrogen halide adds to a terminal alkyne, the product has the orientation predicted by Markovnikov's rule. A second molecule of HX can add, usually with the same orientation as the first.

$$R-C\equiv C-H + H-X \longrightarrow (R)(X)C=C(H)(H) \xrightarrow{H-X} R-CX_2-CH_2-H$$

(HX = HCl, HBr, or HI)

For example, the reaction of 1-pentyne with HBr gives the Markovnikov product. In an internal alkyne such as 2-pentyne, however, the acetylenic carbon atoms are equally substituted, and a mixture of products results.

$$\underset{\text{1-pentyne}}{H-C\equiv C-CH_2CH_2CH_3} + HBr \longrightarrow \underset{\text{2-bromo-1-pentene (Markovnikov product)}}{(H)(H)C=C(CH_2CH_2CH_3)(Br)}$$

$$\underset{\text{2-pentyne}}{CH_3-C\equiv C-CH_2CH_3} + HBr \longrightarrow \underset{\text{2-bromo-2-pentene (E and Z isomers)}}{CH_3-C(Br)=C(H)-CH_2CH_3} + \underset{\text{3-bromo-2-pentene (E and Z isomers)}}{CH_3-C(H)=C(Br)-CH_2CH_3}$$

The mechanism is similar to the mechanism of hydrogen halide addition to alkenes. The **vinyl cation** formed in the first step is more stable with the positive charge on the more highly substituted carbon atom. Attack by halide ion completes the reaction.

$$\underset{\text{alkyne}}{R-C\equiv C-H} + H-X \longrightarrow \underset{\text{vinyl cation}}{R-\overset{+}{C}=C(H)(H)} + :\ddot{X}:^- \longrightarrow \underset{\text{Markovnikov orientation}}{(R)(X)C=C(H)(H)}$$

When 2 moles of a hydrogen halide add to an alkyne, the second mole usually adds with the same orientation as the first. This consistent orientation leads to a geminal dihalide. For example, a double Markovnikov addition of HBr to 1-pentyne gives 2,2-dibromopentane.

$$\underset{\text{1-pentyne}}{H-C\equiv C-CH_2CH_2CH_3} \xrightarrow{HBr} \underset{\text{2-bromo-1-pentene}}{(H)(H)C=C(CH_2CH_2CH_3)(Br)} \xrightarrow{HBr} \underset{\text{2,2-dibromopentane}}{H-CH_2-CBr_2-CH_2CH_2CH_3}$$

PROBLEM 9-15

Propose a mechanism for the entire reaction of 1-pentyne with 2 moles of HBr. Show why Markovnikov's rule should be observed in both the first and second additions of HBr.

PROBLEM 9-16

Predict the major product(s) of the following reactions:
(a) phenylacetylene + 2 HBr
(b) 1-hexyne + 2 HCl
(c) cyclooctyne + 2 HBr
*__(d)__ 2-hexyne + 2 HCl

In Section 8-3B, we saw the effect of peroxides on the addition of HBr to alkenes. Peroxides catalyze a free-radical chain reaction that adds HBr across the double bond of an alkene in the anti-Markovnikov sense. A similar reaction occurs with alkynes, with HBr adding with anti-Markovnikov orientation.

$$\underset{\text{1-pentyne}}{H-C\equiv C-CH_2CH_2CH_3} + \boxed{H}-Br \xrightarrow{\text{ROOR}} \underset{\text{1-bromo-1-pentene (mixture of } E \text{ and } Z \text{ isomers)}}{(H)(Br)C=C(CH_2CH_2CH_3)(\boxed{H})}$$

PROBLEM 9-17

Propose a mechanism for the reaction of 1-pentyne with HBr in the presence of peroxides. Show why anti-Markovnikov orientation results.

PROBLEM 9-18

Show how 1-hexyne might be converted to
(a) 1,2-dichloro-1-hexene
(b) 1-bromo-1-hexene
(c) 2-bromo-1-hexene
(d) 1,1,2,2-tetrabromohexane
(e) 2-bromohexane
(f) 2,2-dibromohexane

9-9F Hydration of Alkynes to Ketones and Aldehydes

Mercuric Ion-Catalyzed Hydration Alkynes undergo acid-catalyzed addition of water across the triple bond in the presence of mercuric ion as a catalyst. A mixture of mercuric sulfate in aqueous sulfuric acid is commonly used as the reagent. The hydration of alkynes is similar to the hydration of alkenes, and it also goes with Markovnikov orientation. The products are not the alcohols we might expect, however.

$$\underset{\text{alkyne}}{R-C\equiv C-H} + H_2O \xrightarrow[H_2SO_4]{HgSO_4} \underset{\text{a vinyl alcohol (enol)}}{\left[(R)(\boxed{H}-O)C=C(H)(H)\right]} \overset{H^+}{\rightleftarrows} \underset{\text{ketone}}{R-C(=O)-C(H)(\boxed{H})-H}$$

Electrophilic addition of mercuric ion gives a vinyl cation, which reacts with water and loses a proton to give an organomercurial alcohol.

$$\underset{\text{alkyne}}{R-C\equiv C-H} \xrightarrow{Hg^{2+}} \underset{\text{vinyl cation}}{R-\overset{+}{C}=C(H)(Hg^+)} \xrightarrow{H_2\ddot{O}:} H-\overset{+}{O}(H)-C(R)=C(H)(Hg^+) \quad H_2\ddot{O}: \longrightarrow \underset{\text{organomercurial alcohol}}{(HO)(R)C=C(H)(Hg^+)} + H_3O^+$$

Under the acidic reaction conditions, mercury is replaced by hydrogen to give a vinyl alcohol, called an **enol**.

organomercurial alcohol

resonance-stabilized intermediate

vinyl alcohol (enol)

$+ Hg^{2+}\ SO_4^{2-}$

A number of biological reactions involve the formation of an enol. Researchers are focusing on ways to use these reactions for therapeutic purposes. Several investigators have synthesized stable enols by placing bulky substituents around the double bond.

Enols tend to be unstable and isomerize to the ketone form. As shown next, this isomerization involves the shift of a proton and a double bond. The (boxed) hydroxyl proton is lost, and a proton is regained at the methyl position, while the pi bond shifts from the C=C position to the C=O position. This type of rapid equilibrium is called a **tautomerism**. The one shown is the **keto–enol tautomerism**, which is covered in more detail in Chapter 22. The keto form usually predominates.

enol

keto

keto–enol tautomerism

In acidic solution, the keto–enol tautomerism takes place by addition of a proton to the adjacent carbon atom, followed by loss of the hydroxyl proton from oxygen.

MECHANISM 9-2 Acid-Catalyzed Keto–Enol Tautomerism

Under acidic conditions, the proton first adds at its new position on the adjacent carbon atom, and then is removed from its old position in the hydroxyl group.

Step 1: Addition of a proton at the methylene group.

enol form

resonance-stabilized intermediate

Step 2: Loss of the hydroxyl proton.

resonance-stabilized intermediate

keto form

$+ H_3O^+$

problem-solving Hint

To move a proton (as in a tautomerism) under acidic conditions, try adding a proton in the new position, then removing it from the old position.

For example, the mercuric-catalyzed hydration of 1-butyne gives 1-buten-2-ol as an intermediate. In the acidic solution, the intermediate quickly equilibrates to its more stable keto tautomer, 2-butanone.

$$H-C\equiv C-CH_2CH_3 + H_2O \xrightarrow[H_2SO_4]{HgSO_4} \left[\begin{matrix} H \\ H \end{matrix} \!>\! C=C \!<\! \begin{matrix} CH_2CH_3 \\ O-H \end{matrix} \right] \overset{H^+}{\rightleftarrows} H-\underset{H}{\overset{H}{C}}-C(=O)CH_2CH_3$$

1-butyne — 1-buten-2-ol — 2-butanone

PROBLEM 9-19

When 2-pentyne reacts with mercuric sulfate in dilute sulfuric acid, the product is a mixture of two ketones. Give the structures of these products, and use mechanisms to show how they are formed.

Hydroboration–Oxidation In Section 8-7 we saw that hydroboration–oxidation adds water across the double bonds of alkenes with anti-Markovnikov orientation. A similar reaction takes place with alkynes, except that a hindered dialkylborane must be used to prevent addition of two molecules of borane across the triple bond. Di(secondary isoamyl)borane, called "disiamylborane," adds to the triple bond only once to give a vinylborane. (**Amyl** is an older common name for pentyl.) In a terminal alkyne, the boron atom bonds to the terminal carbon atom.

$$R-C\equiv C-H + Sia_2BH \longrightarrow \begin{matrix} R \\ H \end{matrix} \!>\! C=C \!<\! \begin{matrix} H \\ BSia_2 \end{matrix}$$

terminal alkyne — disiamylborane — a vinylborane

$$Sia = (H_3C)_2CH-CH(CH_3)-$$

"*sec*-isoamyl" or "**siamyl**"

Oxidation of the vinylborane (using basic hydrogen peroxide) gives a vinyl alcohol (enol), resulting from anti-Markovnikov addition of water across the triple bond. This enol quickly tautomerizes to its more stable carbonyl (keto) form. In the case of a terminal alkyne, the keto product is an aldehyde. This sequence is an excellent method for converting terminal alkynes to aldehydes.

$$\begin{matrix} R \\ H \end{matrix} \!>\! C=C \!<\! \begin{matrix} H \\ BSia_2 \end{matrix} \xrightarrow[NaOH]{H_2O_2} \left[\begin{matrix} R \\ H \end{matrix} \!>\! C=C \!<\! \begin{matrix} H \\ O-H \end{matrix} \right] \overset{^-OH}{\rightleftarrows} H-\underset{H}{\overset{R}{C}}-C(=O)H$$

vinylborane — unstable enol form — aldehyde

Under basic conditions, the keto–enol tautomerism operates by a different mechanism than it does in acid. In base, the proton is first removed from its old position in the OH group, and then replaced on carbon. In acid, the proton was first added on carbon, and then removed from the hydroxyl group.

MECHANISM 9-3 Base-Catalyzed Keto–Enol Tautomerism

Under basic conditions, the proton is first removed from its old position in the enol, and then replaced in its new position on the adjacent carbon atom of the ketone or aldehyde.

Step 1: Loss of the hydroxyl proton.

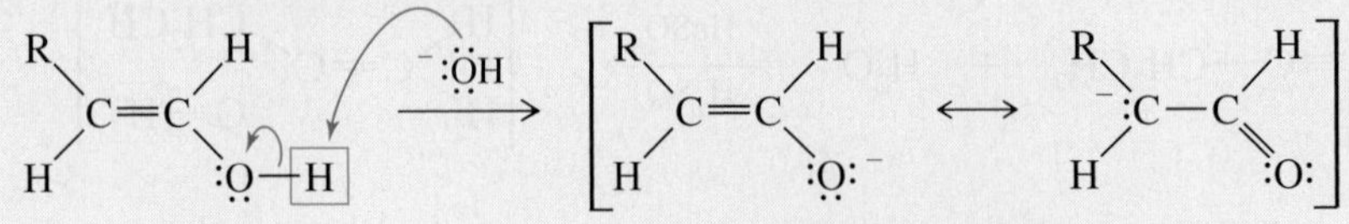

enol form

stabilized "enolate" ion

Step 2: Reprotonation on the adjacent carbon atom.

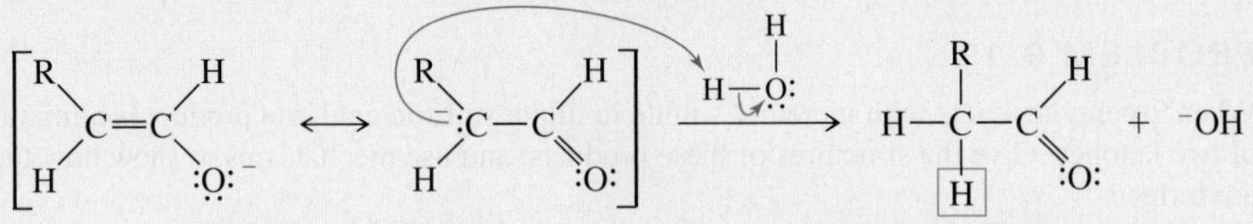

stabilized "enolate" ion

keto form

problem-solving Hint

To move a proton (as in a tautomerism) under basic conditions, try removing the proton from its old position, then adding it to the new position.

Hydroboration of 1-hexyne, for example, gives the vinylborane with boron on the less highly substituted carbon. Oxidation of this intermediate gives an enol that quickly tautomerizes to hexanal.

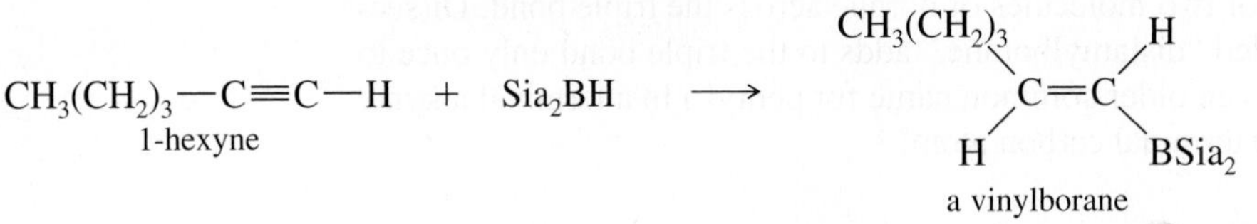

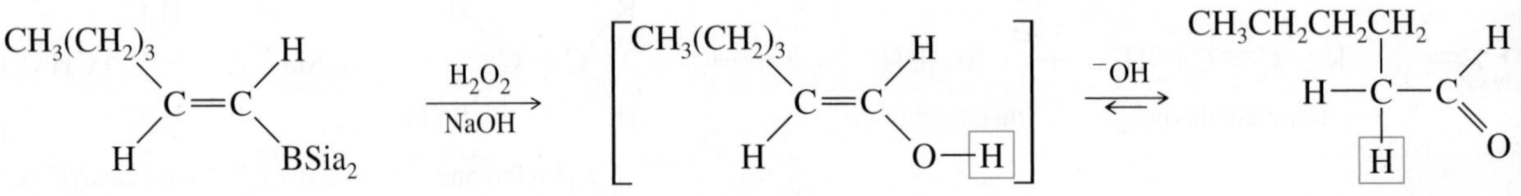

$$CH_3(CH_2)_3{-}C{\equiv}C{-}H + Sia_2BH \longrightarrow$$

1-hexyne

a vinylborane

$$\xrightarrow[\text{NaOH}]{H_2O_2}$$ $$\overset{^-OH}{\rightleftharpoons}$$

vinylborane

enol

hexanal (65%)

PROBLEM 9-20

The hydroboration–oxidation of internal alkynes produces ketones.

(a) When hydroboration–oxidation is applied to 2-butyne, a single pure product is obtained. Determine the structure of this product, and show the intermediates in its formation.

(b) When hydroboration–oxidation is applied to 2-pentyne, two products are obtained. Show why a mixture of products should be expected with any unsymmetrical internal alkyne.

PROBLEM 9-21

For each compound, give the product(s) expected from (1) $HgSO_4/H_2SO_4$-catalyzed hydration and (2) hydroboration–oxidation.

(a) 1-hexyne **(b)** 2-hexyne

(c) 3-hexyne **(d)** cyclodecyne

PROBLEM 9-22

Disiamylborane adds only once to alkynes by virtue of its two bulky secondary isoamyl groups. Disiamylborane is prepared by the reaction of $BH_3 \cdot THF$ with an alkene.

(a) Draw the structural formulas of the reagents and the products in the preparation of disiamylborane.

(b) Explain why the reaction in part (a) goes only as far as the dialkylborane. Why is Sia_3B not formed?

9-10 Oxidation of Alkynes

9-10A Permanganate Oxidations

Under mild conditions, potassium permanganate oxidizes alkenes to glycols, compounds with two —OH groups on adjacent carbon atoms (Section 8-14B). Recall that this oxidation involves adding a hydroxyl group to each end of the double bond (hydroxylation). A similar reaction occurs with alkynes. If an alkyne is treated with cold, aqueous potassium permanganate under nearly neutral conditions, an α-diketone results. This is conceptually the same as hydroxylating each of the two pi bonds of the alkyne, then losing two molecules of water to give the diketone.

$$R-C\equiv C-R' \xrightarrow[H_2O,\ \text{neutral}]{KMnO_4} \left[R-C(OH)_2-C(OH)_2-R' \right] \xrightarrow{(-2\,H_2O)} \underset{\text{diketone}}{R-C(=O)-C(=O)-R'}$$

For example, when 2-pentyne is treated with a cold, dilute solution of neutral permanganate, the product is 2,3-pentanedione.

$$\underset{\text{2-pentyne}}{CH_3-C\equiv C-CH_2CH_3} \xrightarrow[H_2O,\ \text{neutral}]{KMnO_4} \underset{\substack{\text{2,3-pentanedione} \\ (90\%)}}{CH_3-C(=O)-C(=O)-CH_2CH_3}$$

Terminal alkynes probably give a keto-aldehyde at first, but the aldehyde quickly oxidizes to an acid under these conditions.

$$\underset{\text{terminal alkyne}}{R-C\equiv C-H} \xrightarrow[H_2O,\ \text{neutral}]{KMnO_4} \underset{\text{keto-aldehyde}}{\left[R-C(=O)-C(=O)-H \right]} \xrightarrow{KMnO_4} \underset{\text{keto-acid}}{R-C(=O)-C(=O)-OH}$$

If the reaction mixture becomes warm or too basic, the diketone undergoes oxidative cleavage. The products are the carboxylate salts of carboxylic acids, which can be converted to the free acids by adding dilute acid.

$$R-C\equiv C-R' \xrightarrow[H_2O,\ \text{heat}]{KMnO_4,\ KOH} \underset{\text{carboxylate salts}}{R-C(=O)-O^- + {}^-O-C(=O)-R'} \xrightarrow[H_2O]{HCl} R-C(=O)-OH + HO-C(=O)-R'$$

For example, warm, basic permanganate cleaves the triple bond of 2-pentyne to give acetate and propionate ions. Acidification reprotonates these anions to acetic acid and propionic acid.

$$\underset{\text{2-pentyne}}{CH_3-C\equiv C-CH_2CH_3} \xrightarrow[H_2O,\ \text{heat}]{KMnO_4,\ KOH} \underset{\text{acetate}}{CH_3-C(=O)-O^-} + \underset{\text{propionate}}{{}^-O-C(=O)-CH_2CH_3}$$

$$\xrightarrow{H^+} \underset{\text{acetic acid}}{CH_3-C(=O)-OH} + \underset{\text{propionic acid}}{HO-C(=O)-CH_2CH_3}$$

Terminal alkynes are cleaved similarly to give a carboxylate ion and formate ion. Under these oxidizing conditions, formate oxidizes further to carbonate, which becomes CO_2 after protonation.

$$\underset{\text{1-hexyne}}{CH_3(CH_2)_3-C\equiv C-H} \xrightarrow[H_2O]{KMnO_4,\ KOH} \underset{\text{pentanoate}}{CH_3(CH_2)_3-\overset{O}{\overset{\|}{C}}-O^-} + \underset{\text{formate}}{\left[{}^-O-\overset{O}{\overset{\|}{C}}-H\right]}$$

$$\underset{\text{formate}}{\left[{}^-O-\overset{O}{\overset{\|}{C}}-H\right]} \xrightarrow[H_2O]{KMnO_4,\ KOH} \underset{\text{carbonate}}{{}^-O-\overset{O}{\overset{\|}{C}}-O^-} \xrightarrow{H^+} \underset{\text{carbonic acid}}{\left[HO-\overset{O}{\overset{\|}{C}}-OH\right]} \rightleftarrows CO_2 + H_2O$$

The overall reaction is:

$$\underset{\text{1-hexyne}}{CH_3(CH_2)_3-C\equiv C-H} \xrightarrow[(2)\ H^+,\ H_2O]{(1)\ KMnO_4,\ KOH,\ H_2O} \underset{\text{pentanoic acid}}{CH_3(CH_2)_3-\overset{O}{\overset{\|}{C}}-OH} + CO_2\uparrow$$

9-10B Ozonolysis

Ozonolysis of an alkyne, followed by hydrolysis, cleaves the triple bond and gives two carboxylic acids. Either permanganate cleavage or ozonolysis can be used to determine the position of the triple bond in an unknown alkyne (see Problem 9-24).

$$R-C\equiv C-R' \xrightarrow[(2)\ H_2O]{(1)\ O_3} R-COOH + R'-COOH$$

Examples

$$\underset{\text{2-pentyne}}{CH_3-C\equiv C-CH_2CH_3} \xrightarrow[(2)\ H_2O]{(1)\ O_3} \underset{\text{acetic acid}}{CH_3-COOH} + \underset{\text{propionic acid}}{CH_3CH_2-COOH}$$

$$\underset{\text{1-hexyne}}{CH_3(CH_2)_3-C\equiv C-H} \xrightarrow[(2)\ H_2O]{(1)\ O_3} \underset{\text{pentanoic acid}}{CH_3(CH_2)_3-\overset{O}{\overset{\|}{C}}-OH} + \underset{\text{formic acid}}{HO-\overset{O}{\overset{\|}{C}}-H}$$

PROBLEM 9-23

Predict the product(s) you would expect from treatment of each compound with (1) dilute, neutral $KMnO_4$ and (2) warm, basic $KMnO_4$, then dilute acid.

(a) 1-hexyne **(b)** 2-hexyne **(c)** 3-hexyne
(d) 2-methyl-3-hexyne **(e)** cyclodecyne

PROBLEM 9-24

Oxidative cleavages can help to determine the positions of the triple bonds in alkynes.

(a) An unknown alkyne undergoes oxidative cleavage to give adipic acid and two equivalents of acetic acid. Propose a structure for the alkyne.

$$\text{unknown alkyne} \xrightarrow[(2)\ H_2O]{(1)\ O_3} \underset{\text{adipic acid}}{HOOC-(CH_2)_4-COOH} + 2\,CH_3COOH$$

(b) An unknown alkyne undergoes oxidative cleavage to give the following triacid plus one equivalent of propionic acid. Propose a structure for the alkyne.

$$\text{unknown alkyne} \xrightarrow[(2)\ H_2O]{(1)\ O_3} \underset{\text{a triacid}}{HOOC-(CH_2)_7-\overset{COOH}{\overset{|}{C}H}-COOH} + \underset{\text{propionic acid}}{CH_3CH_2COOH}$$

PROBLEM-SOLVING STRATEGY

MULTISTEP SYNTHESIS

Multistep synthesis problems are useful for exercising your knowledge of organic reactions, and in Chapter 8 we illustrated a systematic approach to synthesis. Now we apply this approach to a fairly difficult problem emphasizing alkyne chemistry. The compound to be synthesized is *cis*-2-methylhex-4-en-3-ol. (The "3-ol" means there is an alcohol —OH group on C3.)

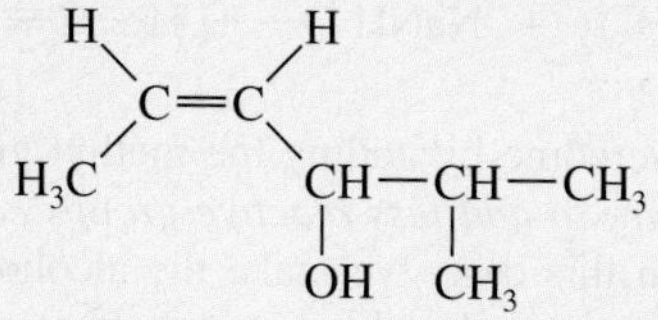

$$\underset{H_3C}{\overset{H}{}}\!\!>C{=}C<\!\!\underset{CH(OH)-CH(CH_3)-CH_3}{\overset{H}{}}$$

cis-2-methylhex-4-en-3-ol

The starting materials are acetylene and compounds containing no more than four carbon atoms. In this problem, it is necessary to consider not only how to assemble the carbon skeleton and how to introduce the functional groups, but also when it is best to put in the functional groups. We begin with an examination of the target compound, and then we examine possible intermediates and synthetic routes.

1. **Review the functional groups and carbon skeleton of the target compound.**
The target compound contains seven carbon atoms and two functional groups: a cis carbon–carbon double bond and an alcohol. The best method for generating a cis double bond is the catalytic hydrogenation of a triple bond (Section 9-9B).

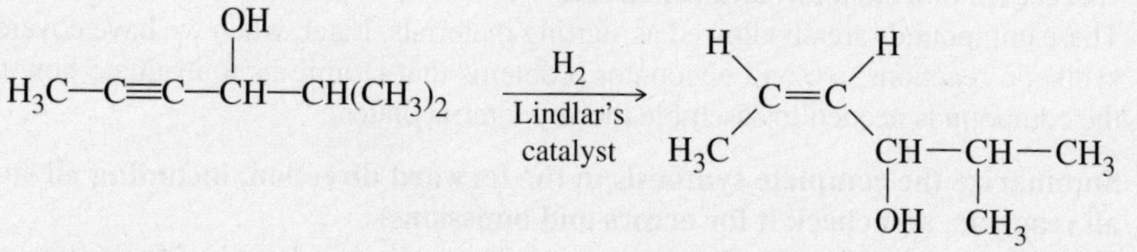

$$H_3C-C\equiv C-\underset{OH}{CH}-CH(CH_3)_2 \xrightarrow[\text{Lindlar's catalyst}]{H_2} \underset{H_3C}{\overset{H}{}}\!\!>C{=}C<\!\!\underset{\underset{OH}{CH}-\underset{CH_3}{CH}-CH_3}{\overset{H}{}}$$

Using this hydrogenation as the final step simplifies the problem to a synthesis of this acetylenic alcohol. We know how to form carbon–carbon bonds next to triple bonds, and we have seen the formation of acetylenic alcohols (Section 9-7B).

2. **Review the functional groups and carbon skeletons of the starting materials, and see how their skeletons might fit together in the target compound.**
Acetylene is listed as one of the starting materials, and we have good methods (Section 9-7) for making carbon–carbon bonds next to triple bonds, by using acetylide ions as nucleophiles. We can break the target structure into three pieces, each containing no more than four carbon atoms.

$$\underset{\text{1 carbon}}{H_3C-} \qquad \underset{\text{acetylene}}{-C\equiv C-} \qquad \underset{\text{4 carbons (functionalized)}}{-\underset{OH}{CH}-\underset{CH_3}{CH}-CH_3}$$

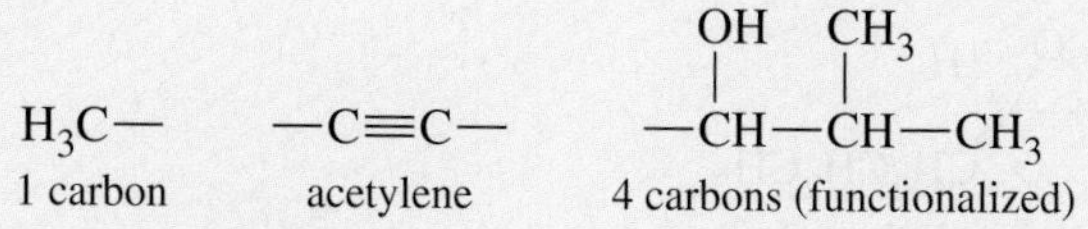

3. **Compare methods for assembling the carbon skeleton of the target compound. Which ones provide a key intermediate with the correct carbon skeleton and functional groups correctly positioned for conversion to the functionality in the target molecule?**
Acetylenic alcohols result when acetylides add to ketones and aldehydes (Section 9-7B). Reaction of the acetylide ion with 2-methylpropanal gives one of the groups needed on the triple bond.

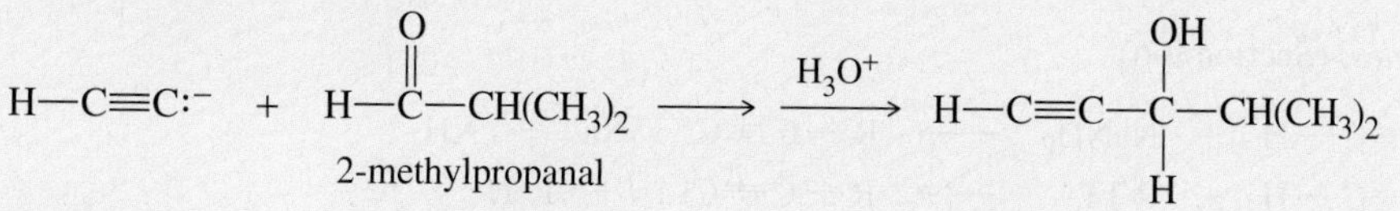

$$H-C\equiv C:^- \;+\; \underset{\text{2-methylpropanal}}{H-\overset{O}{\overset{\|}{C}}-CH(CH_3)_2} \longrightarrow \xrightarrow{H_3O^+} H-C\equiv C-\overset{OH}{\underset{H}{C}}-CH(CH_3)_2$$

(*Continued*)

A methyl group is needed on the other end of the double bond of the target compound. Methylation requires formation of an acetylide, however (Section 9-7A):

$$CH_3I \ + \ ^{-}{:}C{\equiv}C{-}R \longrightarrow H_3C{-}C{\equiv}C{-}R \ + \ I^-$$

Since the hydroxyl group in the acetylenic alcohol is much more acidic than the acetylenic proton, any attempt to form the acetylide would fail.

$$H{-}C{\equiv}C{-}CH(OH){-}CH(CH_3)_2 \ + \ NaNH_2 \longrightarrow H{-}C{\equiv}C{-}CH(O^-){-}CH(CH_3)_2 \ + \ NH_3$$

problem-solving Hint

Add less reactive groups earlier in a synthesis and more reactive groups later.

This problem can be overcome by adding the methyl group first and then the alcohol portion. *In general, we try to add less reactive groups earlier in a synthesis, and more reactive groups later.* In this case, we make the alcohol group after adding the alkyl group because the alkyl group is less likely to be affected by subsequent reactions.

$$H{-}C{\equiv}C{-}H \xrightarrow[(2)\ CH_3I]{(1)\ NaNH_2} H_3C{-}C{\equiv}C{-}H \xrightarrow{NaNH_2} H_3C{-}C{\equiv}C{:}^-\ Na^+$$

$$H_3C{-}C{\equiv}C{:}^- \ + \ H{-}C({=}O){-}CH(CH_3)_2 \longrightarrow \xrightarrow{H_3O^+} H_3C{-}C{\equiv}C{-}CH(OH){-}CH(CH_3)_2$$

4. **Working backward through as many steps as necessary, compare methods for synthesizing the reactants needed for assembly of the key intermediate with the correct carbon skeleton and functionality.**
These compounds are all allowed as starting materials. Later, when we have covered more synthetic reactions, we will encounter problems that require us to evaluate how to make the compounds needed to assemble the key intermediates.

5. **Summarize the complete synthesis in the forward direction, including all steps and all reagents, and check it for errors and omissions.**
This final step is left to you as an exercise. Try to do it without looking at this solution, reviewing each thought process as you summarize the synthesis.

Now practice using a systematic approach with the syntheses in Problem 9-25.

PROBLEM 9-25

Develop syntheses for the following compounds, using acetylene and compounds containing no more than four carbon atoms as your organic starting materials.

(a) 3-methylnon-4-yn-3-ol ("3-ol" means there is an OH group on C3.)
(b) *cis*-1-ethyl-2-methylcyclopropane
(c) epoxide: CH_3CH_2 and H on one carbon; H and $CH_2CH_2CH_3$ on the other carbon (O bridging)
(d) *meso*-hexane-3,4-diol

SUMMARY Reactions of Alkynes

I. ACETYLIDE CHEMISTRY

1. *Formation of acetylide anions (alkynides)* (Section 9-6)

$$R{-}C{\equiv}C{-}H \ + \ NaNH_2 \longrightarrow R{-}C{\equiv}C{:}^-\ {}^+Na \ + \ NH_3$$

$$R{-}C{\equiv}C{-}H \ + \ R'Li \longrightarrow R{-}C{\equiv}CLi \ + \ R'H$$

$$R{-}C{\equiv}C{-}H \ + \ R'MgX \longrightarrow R{-}C{\equiv}CMgX \ + \ R'{-}H$$

(Continued)

Example

$$\underset{\text{propyne}}{CH_3-C{\equiv}C-H} + \underset{\text{sodium amide}}{NaNH_2} \longrightarrow \underset{\substack{\text{sodium propynide}\\\text{(propynyl sodium)}}}{CH_3-C{\equiv}C{:}^{-}\ {}^{+}Na} + NH_3$$

2. *Alkylation of acetylide ions* (Section 9-7A)

$$R-C{\equiv}C{:}^{-} + R'-X \longrightarrow R-C{\equiv}C-R'$$

($R'-X$ must be an unhindered primary halide or tosylate.)

Example

$$\underset{\text{sodium butynide}}{CH_3CH_2-C{\equiv}C{:}^{-}\ {}^{+}Na} + \underset{\text{1-bromopropane}}{CH_3CH_2CH_2-Br} \longrightarrow \underset{\text{3-heptyne}}{CH_3CH_2-C{\equiv}C-CH_2CH_2CH_3}$$

3. *Reactions with carbonyl groups* (Section 9-7B)

$$R-C{\equiv}C{:}^{-} + R'_2C{=}\ddot{O}{:} \longrightarrow R-C{\equiv}C-CR'_2-\ddot{O}{:}^{-} \xrightarrow[\text{(or } H_3O^+)]{H_2O} R-C{\equiv}C-CR'_2-OH$$

Example

$$\underset{\text{sodium propynide}}{CH_3-C{\equiv}C{:}^{-}\ Na^{+}} \xrightarrow[(2)\ H_2O]{(1)\ CH_3CH_2-C(=O)-CH_3} \underset{\text{3-methyl-4-hexyn-3-ol}}{CH_3-C{\equiv}C-C(OH)(CH_3)-CH_2CH_3}$$

II. *ADDITIONS TO THE TRIPLE BOND*

1. *Reduction to alkanes* (Section 9-9A)

$$R-C{\equiv}C-R' + 2\,H_2 \xrightarrow{\text{Pt, Pd, or Ni}} R-CH_2-CH_2-R'$$

Example

$$\underset{\text{2-pentyn-1-ol}}{CH_3CH_2-C{\equiv}C-CH_2-OH} + 2\,H_2 \xrightarrow{Pt} \underset{\text{1-pentanol}}{CH_3CH_2-CH_2-CH_2-CH_2-OH}$$

2. *Reduction to alkenes* (Sections 9-9B and 9-9C)

$$R-C{\equiv}C-R' + H_2 \xrightarrow[\text{(Lindlar's catalyst)}]{Pd/BaSO_4,\ \text{quinoline}} \underset{cis}{(R)(H)C{=}C(R')(H)}$$

$$R-C{\equiv}C-R' \xrightarrow{Na,\ NH_3} \underset{trans}{(R)(H)C{=}C(H)(R')}$$

Examples

$$\underset{\text{3-hexyne}}{CH_3CH_2-C{\equiv}C-CH_2CH_3} \xrightarrow[\text{quinoline}]{H_2,\ Pd/BaSO_4} \underset{cis\text{-3-hexene}}{(CH_3CH_2)(H)C{=}C(CH_2CH_3)(H)}$$

(Continued)

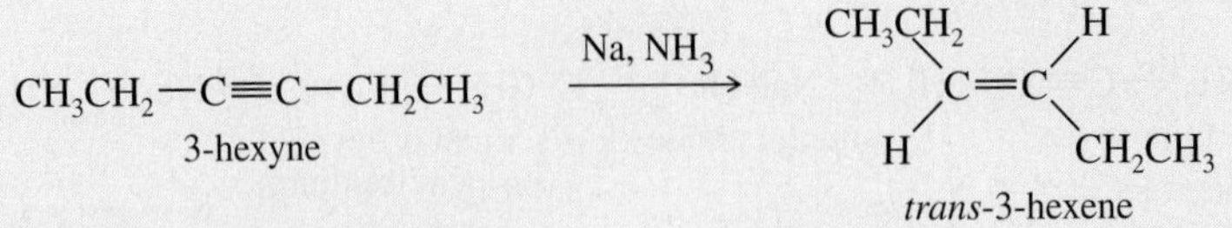

$$CH_3CH_2-C\equiv C-CH_2CH_3 \xrightarrow{Na,\ NH_3} \text{trans-3-hexene}$$

3-hexyne → *trans*-3-hexene ($CH_3CH_2(H)C=C(H)CH_2CH_3$)

3. *Addition of halogens* ($X_2 = Cl_2, Br_2$) (Section 9-9D)

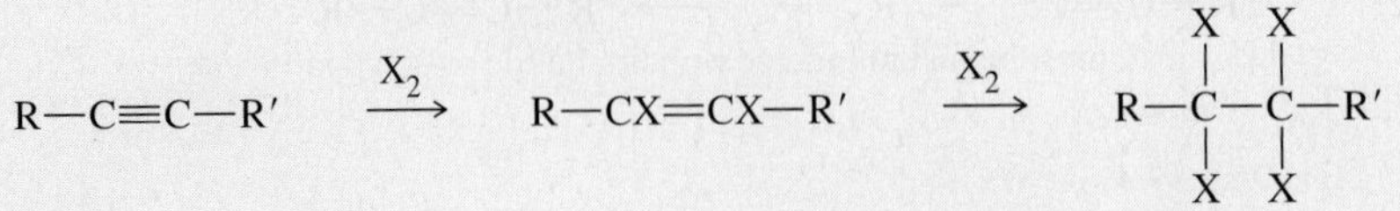

$$R-C\equiv C-R' \xrightarrow{X_2} R-CX=CX-R' \xrightarrow{X_2} R-CX_2-CX_2-R'$$

Example

$$CH_3C\equiv CCH_2CH_3 \xrightarrow{Br_2} CH_3CBr=CBrCH_2CH_3 \xrightarrow{Br_2} CH_3-CBr_2-CBr_2-CH_2CH_3$$

2-pentyne → *cis*- and *trans*-2,3-dibromo-2-pentene → 2,2,3,3-tetrabromopentane

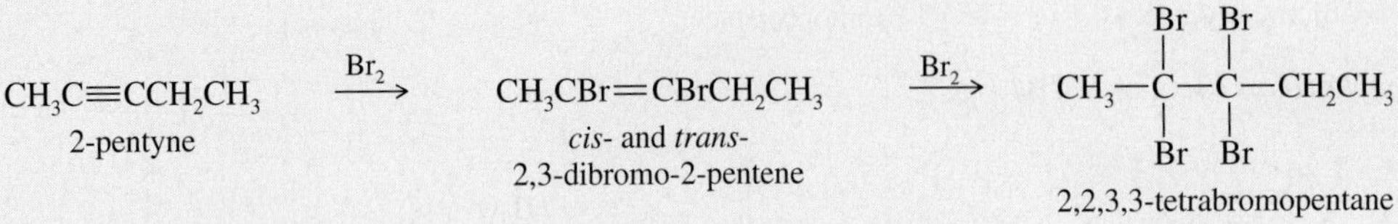

4. *Addition of hydrogen halides* (*where HX = HCl, HBr, or HI*) (Section 9-9E)

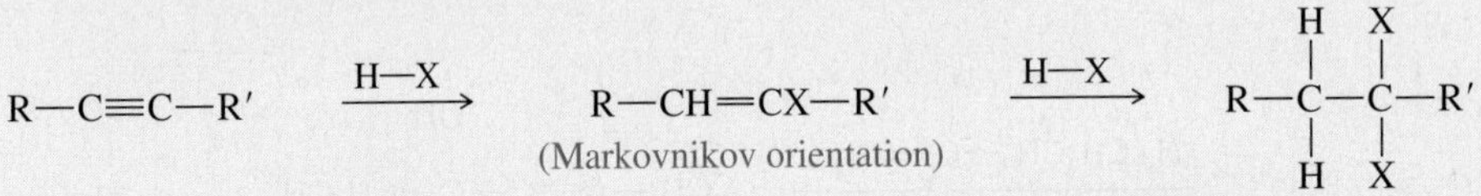

$$R-C\equiv C-R' \xrightarrow{H-X} R-CH=CX-R' \xrightarrow{H-X} R-CH_2-CX_2-R'$$

(Markovnikov orientation)

Example

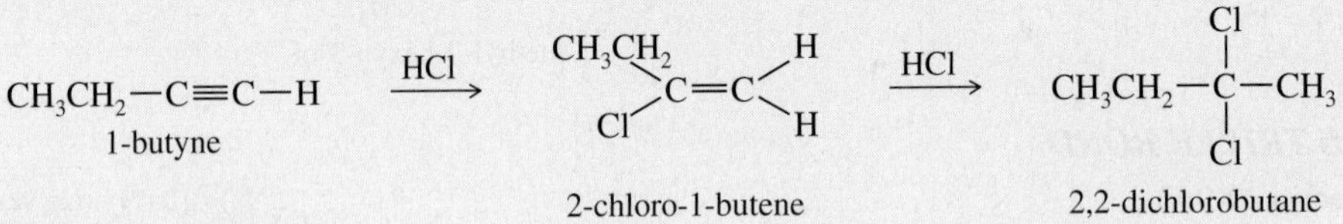

$$CH_3CH_2-C\equiv C-H \xrightarrow{HCl} CH_3CH_2(Cl)C=CH_2 \xrightarrow{HCl} CH_3CH_2-CCl_2-CH_3$$

1-butyne → 2-chloro-1-butene → 2,2-dichlorobutane

5. *Addition of water* (Section 9-9F)

a. *Catalyzed by* $HgSO_4/H_2SO_4$

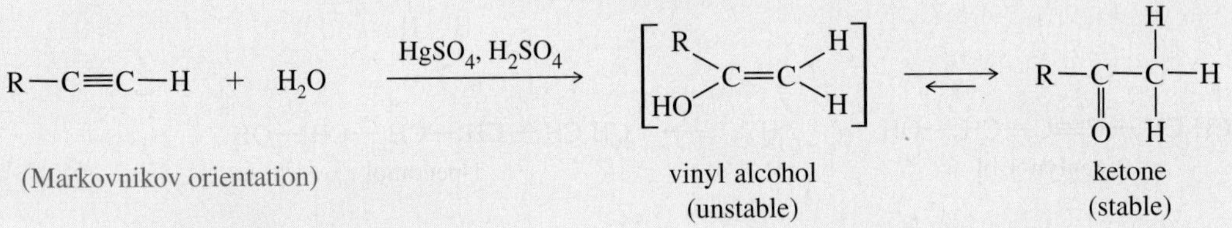

$$R-C\equiv C-H + H_2O \xrightarrow{HgSO_4,\ H_2SO_4} \left[\begin{array}{c} R \quad\quad H \\ C=C \\ HO \quad\quad H \end{array} \right] \rightleftharpoons R-C(=O)-CH_3$$

(Markovnikov orientation) — vinyl alcohol (unstable) — ketone (stable)

Example

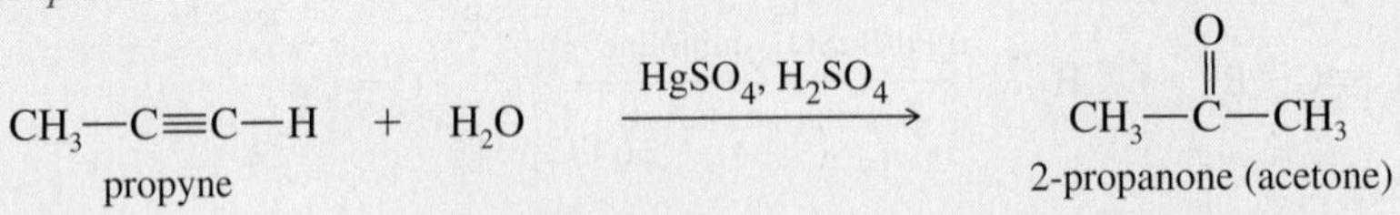

$$CH_3-C\equiv C-H + H_2O \xrightarrow{HgSO_4,\ H_2SO_4} CH_3-C(=O)-CH_3$$

propyne → 2-propanone (acetone)

b. *Hydroboration–oxidation*

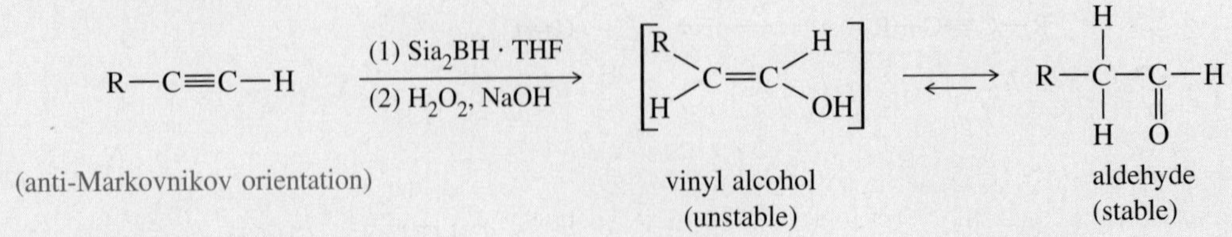

$$R-C\equiv C-H \xrightarrow[(2)\ H_2O_2,\ NaOH]{(1)\ Sia_2BH \cdot THF} \left[\begin{array}{c} R \quad\quad H \\ C=C \\ H \quad\quad OH \end{array} \right] \rightleftharpoons R-CH_2-C(=O)-H$$

(anti-Markovnikov orientation) — vinyl alcohol (unstable) — aldehyde (stable)

Example

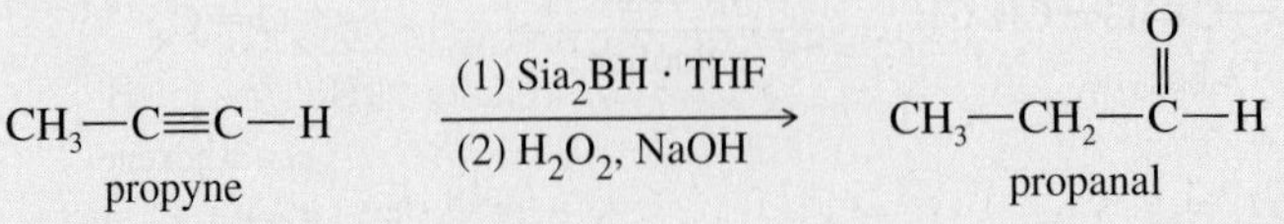

$$CH_3-C\equiv C-H \xrightarrow[(2)\ H_2O_2,\ NaOH]{(1)\ Sia_2BH \cdot THF} CH_3-CH_2-C(=O)-H$$

propyne → propanal

(*Continued*)

III. OXIDATION OF ALKYNES (SECTION 9-10)

1. *Oxidation to α-diketones* (Section 9-10A)

$$\mathrm{R{-}C{\equiv}C{-}R'} \xrightarrow[\mathrm{H_2O,\ neutral}]{\mathrm{KMnO_4}} \mathrm{R{-}C({=}O){-}C({=}O){-}R'}$$

Example

$$\underset{\text{2-pentyne}}{\mathrm{CH_3{-}C{\equiv}C{-}CH_2CH_3}} \xrightarrow[\mathrm{H_2O,\ neutral}]{\mathrm{KMnO_4}} \underset{\text{pentane-2,3-dione}}{\mathrm{CH_3{-}C({=}O){-}C({=}O){-}CH_2CH_3}}$$

2. *Oxidative cleavage* (Section 9-10B)

$$\mathrm{R{-}C{\equiv}C{-}R'} \xrightarrow[\text{(or } \mathrm{O_3}\text{, then } \mathrm{H_2O})]{(1)\ \mathrm{KMnO_4},\ ^-\mathrm{OH}\quad (2)\ \mathrm{H^+}} \mathrm{R{-}C({=}O){-}OH} + \mathrm{HO{-}C({=}O){-}R'}$$

Examples

$$\mathrm{CH_3{-}C{\equiv}C{-}CH_2CH_3} \xrightarrow[(2)\ \mathrm{H^+}]{(1)\ \mathrm{KMnO_4,\ NaOH}} \mathrm{CH_3{-}C({=}O){-}OH} + \mathrm{HO{-}C({=}O){-}CH_2CH_3}$$

$$\mathrm{CH_3CH_2CH_2{-}C{\equiv}C{-}H} \xrightarrow[(2)\ \mathrm{H^+}]{(1)\ \mathrm{KMnO_4,\ NaOH}} \mathrm{CH_3CH_2CH_2{-}C({=}O){-}OH} + \mathrm{CO_2}\uparrow$$

9 Glossary

acetylene The simplest alkyne, H—C≡C—H. Also used as a synonym for *alkyne*, a generic term for a compound containing a C≡C triple bond. (p. 388)

acetylide ion (alkynide ion) The anionic salt of a terminal alkyne. Metal acetylides are organometallic compounds with a metal atom in place of the weakly acidic acetylenic hydrogen of a terminal alkyne. (p. 394)

$$\mathrm{R{-}C{\equiv}C{-}H} + \mathrm{Na^+\ ^-{:}\ddot{N}H_2} \longrightarrow \underset{\text{a sodium acetylide}}{\mathrm{R{-}C{\equiv}C{:}^-\ ^+Na}} + \mathrm{{:}NH_3}$$

alkoxide ion R—O⁻, the conjugate base of an alcohol. (p. 397)

$$\underset{\text{alkoxide}}{\mathrm{R{-}\ddot{O}{:}^-}} + \mathrm{H_2O} \rightleftharpoons \underset{\text{alcohol}}{\mathrm{R{-}\ddot{O}{-}H}} + \mathrm{^-OH}$$

alkyne Any compound containing a carbon–carbon triple bond. (pp. 388, 390)
A **terminal alkyne** has a triple bond at the end of a chain, with an **acetylenic hydrogen**.
An **internal alkyne** has the triple bond somewhere other than at the end of the chain.

acetylenic hydrogen → $\boxed{\mathrm{H}}\mathrm{{-}C{\equiv}C{-}CH_2CH_3}$ 1-butyne, a terminal alkyne

(no acetylenic hydrogen) $\mathrm{CH_3{-}C{\equiv}C{-}CH_3}$ 2-butyne, an internal alkyne

amyl An older common name for pentyl. (p. 409)

enol An alcohol with the hydroxyl group bonded to a carbon atom of a carbon–carbon double bond. Most enols are unstable, spontaneously isomerizing to their carbonyl tautomers, called the **keto** form of the compound. See **tautomers**. (p. 408)

Lindlar's catalyst A heterogeneous catalyst for the hydrogenation of alkynes to cis alkenes. In its most common form, it consists of a thin coating of palladium on barium sulfate, with quinoline added to decrease the catalytic activity. (p. 402)

***s* character** The fraction of a hybrid orbital that corresponds to an *s* orbital; about one-half for *sp* hybrids, one-third for sp^2 hybrids, and one-fourth for sp^3 hybrids. (p. 393)

siamyl group A contraction for secondary isoamyl, abbreviated "Sia." This is the 1,2-dimethylpropyl group. Disiamylborane is used for hydroboration of terminal alkynes because this bulky borane adds only once to the triple bond. (p. 409)

Sia = $(H_3C)_2CH-CH(CH_3)-$ "*sec*-isoamyl" or "siamyl"

$R'-C\equiv C-H + Sia_2BH \longrightarrow$ R′(H)C=C(H)$BSia_2$

alkyne disiamylborane a vinylborane

tautomers Isomers that can quickly interconvert by the movement of a proton (and a double bond) from one site to another. An equilibrium between tautomers is called a **tautomerism**. (p. 408)

C=C–O–H (enol form) $\underset{}{\overset{H^+ \text{ or } ^-OH}{\rightleftharpoons}}$ H–C–C=O (keto form)

The keto–enol tautomerism is the equilibrium between these two tautomers.

vinyl cation A cation with a positive charge on one of the carbon atoms of a C=C double bond. The cationic carbon atom is usually *sp* hybridized. Vinyl cations are often generated by the addition of an electrophile to a carbon–carbon triple bond. (p. 406)

$R-C\equiv C-R' \xrightarrow{E^+}$ R(E)C=$\overset{+}{C}$–R′ (sp^2, sp) a vinyl cation

Essential Problem-Solving Skills in Chapter 9

1. Name alkynes, and draw the structures from their names.
2. Explain why alkynes are more acidic than alkanes and alkenes. Show how to generate nucleophilic acetylide ions and heavy-metal acetylides.
3. Propose effective single-step and multistep syntheses of alkynes.
4. Predict the products of additions, oxidations, reductions, and cleavages of alkynes, including orientation of reaction (regiochemistry) and stereochemistry.
5. Use alkynes as starting materials and intermediates in one-step and multistep syntheses.
6. Show how the reduction of an alkyne leads to an alkene or alkene derivative with the desired stereochemistry.

Study Problems

9-26 Briefly define each term, and give an example.
(a) alkyne **(b)** acetylide ion **(c)** enol
(d) tautomerism **(e)** Lindlar's catalyst **(f)** disiamylborane
(g) vinyl cation **(h)** oxidative cleavage of an alkyne
(i) hydration of an alkyne **(j)** hydroboration of an alkyne

9-27 Write structural formulas for the following compounds.
(a) 2-octyne **(b)** ethylisopentylacetylene **(c)** ethynylbenzene
(d) cyclohexylacetylene **(e)** 5-methyl-3-octyne **(f)** *trans*-3,5-dibromocyclodecyne
(g) 5,5-dibromo-4-phenylcyclooct-1-yne **(h)** (*E*)-6-ethyloct-2-en-4-yne **(i)** 1,4-heptadiyne
(j) vinylacetylene **(k)** (*S*)-3-methyl-1-penten-4-yne

9-28 Give common names for the following compounds.
(a) $CH_3-C\equiv C-CH_2CH_3$ **(b)** $Ph-C\equiv C-H$
(c) 3-methyl-4-octyne **(d)** $(CH_3)_3C-C\equiv C-CH(CH_3)CH_2CH_3$

9-29 Give IUPAC names for the following compounds.

(a) $CH_3-C\equiv C-CH(Ph)-CH_3$

(b) $CH_3-CBr_2-C\equiv C-CH_3$

(c) $(CH_3)_3C-C\equiv C-CH(CH_3)CH_2CH_3$

(d) $(H_3C)(H)C=C(CH_3)(C\equiv C-CH_2CH_3)$ (H₃C and CH₃ on the same side; H and $C\equiv C-CH_2CH_3$ on the same side)

(e) $CH_3-C\equiv C-C(CH_3)(CH_2CH_3)-OH$

(f) cyclopentyl$-CH_2-C\equiv C-CH_3$

9-30 **(a)** Draw and name the three alkynes of formula C_5H_8.
(b) Which compounds in part (a) will react with sodium amide? Show the products that result.

9-31 A marginal note on page 397 states, "The addition of an acetylide ion to a carbonyl group is used in the synthesis of ethchlorvynol, a drug used to cause drowsiness and induce sleep." Show how you would accomplish this synthesis from acetylene and a carbonyl compound.

$CH_3CH_2-C(OH)(CH=CHCl)-C\equiv CH$

ethchlorvynol

9-32 *Muscalure*, the sex attractant of the common housefly, is *cis*-9-tricosene. Most syntheses of alkenes give the more stable trans isomer as the major product. Devise a synthesis of muscalure from acetylene and other compounds of your choice. Your synthesis must give specifically the cis isomer of muscalure.

$CH_3(CH_2)_7(H)C=C(H)(CH_2)_{12}CH_3$ (both H on the same side)

cis-9-tricosene, "muscalure"

9-33 Predict the products of reaction of 1-pentyne with the following reagents.
(a) 1 equivalent of HCl
(b) 2 equivalents of HCl
(c) excess H_2, Ni
(d) H_2, $Pd/BaSO_4$, quinoline
(e) 1 equivalent of Br_2
(f) 2 equivalents of Br_2
(g) cold, dilute $KMnO_4$
(h) warm, concd. $KMnO_4$, NaOH
(i) Na, liquid ammonia
(j) $NaNH_2$
(k) $H_2SO_4/HgSO_4$, H_2O
(l) Sia_2BH, then H_2O_2, ^-OH

9-34 Show how you would accomplish the following synthetic transformations. Show all intermediates.
(a) 2,2-dibromobutane $\longrightarrow$ 1-butyne
(b) 2,2-dibromobutane $\longrightarrow$ 2-butyne
(c) 1-butyne $\longrightarrow$ 3-octyne
(d) *trans*-2-hexene $\longrightarrow$ 2-hexyne
(e) 2,2-dibromohexane $\longrightarrow$ 1-hexyne
(f) cyclodecyne $\longrightarrow$ *cis*-cyclodecene
(g) cyclodecyne $\longrightarrow$ *trans*-cyclodecene
(h) 1-hexyne $\longrightarrow$ 2-hexanone, $CH_3COCH_2CH_2CH_2CH_3$
(i) 1-hexyne $\longrightarrow$ hexanal, $CH_3(CH_2)_4CHO$
(j) *trans*-2-hexene $\longrightarrow$ *cis*-2-hexene

9-35 Show how you would synthesize the following compounds from acetylene and any other needed reagents:
(a) 6-phenylhex-1-en-4-yne
(b) *cis*-1-phenyl-2-pentene
(c) *trans*-1-phenyl-2-pentene
(d)

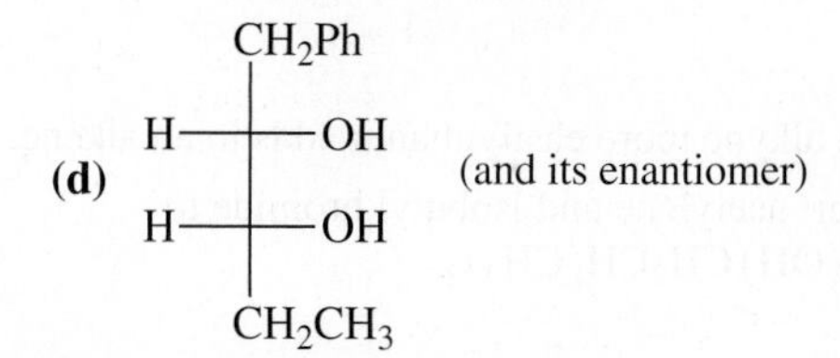

9-36 Predict the products formed when $CH_3CH_2-C\equiv C:^- Na^+$ reacts with the following compounds.
(a) ethyl bromide
(b) *tert*-butyl bromide
(c) formaldehyde
(d) cyclohexanone
(e) $CH_3CH_2CH_2CHO$
(f) cyclohexanol
(g) 2-butanone, $CH_3CH_2COCH_3$

9-37 Show how you would synthesize the following compounds, starting with acetylene and any compounds containing no more than four carbon atoms.
(a) 1-hexyne
(b) 2-hexyne
(c) *cis*-2-hexene
(d) *trans*-2-hexene
(e) 1,1-dibromohexane
(f) 2,2-dibromohexane
(g) pentanal, $CH_3CH_2CH_2CH_2CHO$
(h) 2-pentanone, $CH_3-CO-CH_2CH_2CH_3$
(i) $(\pm)$-3,4-dibromohexane
(j) *meso*-2,3-butanediol
(k) 2-methylhex-3-yn-2-ol

9-38 When treated with hydrogen and a platinum catalyst, an unknown compound (**X**) absorbs 5 equivalents of hydrogen to give *n*-butylcyclohexane. Treatment of **X** with an excess of ozone, followed by dimethyl sulfide and water, gives the following products:

$$H-\overset{O}{\overset{\|}{C}}-CH_2-CH_2-\overset{O}{\overset{\|}{C}}-\overset{O}{\overset{\|}{C}}-H$$

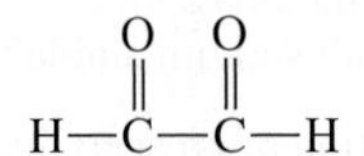

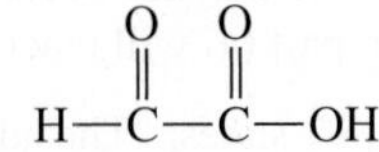

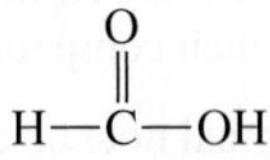

Propose a structure for the unknown compound (**X**). Is there any uncertainty in your structure?

9-39 When compound (**Z**) is treated with ozone, followed by dimethyl sulfide and washing with water, the products are formic acid, 3-oxobutanoic acid, and hexanal.

$$(\mathbf{Z}) \xrightarrow[(2)\ (CH_3)_2S,\ H_2O]{(1)\ O_3} \underset{\text{formic acid}}{H-\overset{O}{\overset{\|}{C}}-OH} + \underset{\text{3-oxobutanoic acid}}{CH_3-\overset{O}{\overset{\|}{C}}-CH_2-\overset{O}{\overset{\|}{C}}-OH} + \underset{\text{hexanal}}{CH_3(CH_2)_4-\overset{O}{\overset{\|}{C}}-H}$$

Propose a structure for compound (**Z**). What uncertainty is there in the structure you have proposed?

***9-40** Show how you would convert the following starting materials into the target compound. You may use any additional reagents you need.

Starting materials: $C_6H_5-CH_2Br$ (benzyl bromide); cyclopentanecarbaldehyde (cyclopentyl$-\overset{O}{\overset{\|}{C}}-H$); $HC\equiv CH$

$\xrightarrow{\text{other reagents as needed}}$ (epoxide: cyclopentane spiro-fused epoxide carbon bonded to O and to a carbon bearing H and $-C\equiv C-CH_2-C_6H_5$)

***9-41** The following functional-group interchange is a useful synthesis of aldehydes.

$$\underset{\text{terminal alkyne}}{R-C\equiv C-H} \longrightarrow \underset{\text{aldehyde}}{R-CH_2-\overset{O}{\overset{\|}{C}}-H}$$

(a) What reagents were used in this chapter for this transformation? Give an example to illustrate this method.
(b) This functional-group interchange can also be accomplished using the following sequence.

$$R-C\equiv C-H \xrightarrow[CH_3CH_2OH]{NaOCH_2CH_3} \overset{H}{\underset{R}{}}C{=}C\overset{OCH_2CH_3}{\underset{H}{}} \xrightarrow{H_3O^+} R-CH_2-\overset{O}{\overset{\|}{C}}-H$$

Propose mechanisms for these steps.
(c) Explain why a nucleophilic reagent such as ethoxide adds to an alkyne more easily than it adds to an alkene.

***9-42** Using any necessary inorganic reagents, show how you would convert acetylene and isobutyl bromide to
(a) *meso*-2,7-dimethyl-4,5-octanediol, $(CH_3)_2CHCH_2CH(OH)CH(OH)CH_2CH(CH_3)_2$
(b) $(\pm)$-2,7-dimethyl-4,5-octanediol

CHAPTER

10 STRUCTURE AND SYNTHESIS OF ALCOHOLS

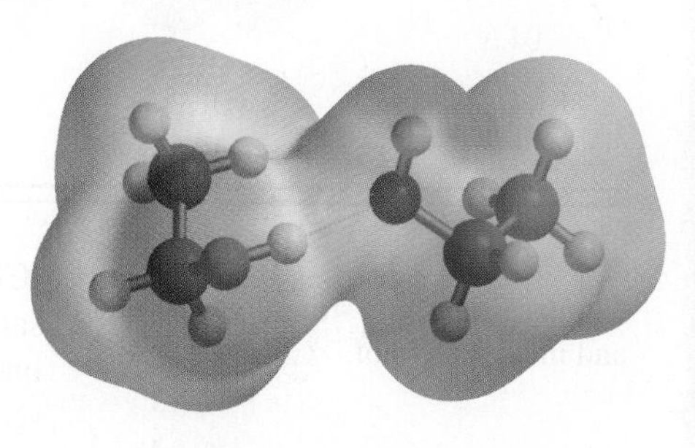
hydrogen bonding in ethanol

10-1 Introduction

Alcohols are organic compounds containing hydroxyl (—OH) groups. They are some of the most common and useful compounds in nature, in industry, and around the house. The word *alcohol* is one of the oldest chemical terms, derived from the early Arabic *al-kuhl*. Originally it meant "the powder," and later "the essence." Ethyl alcohol, distilled from wine, was considered to be "the essence" of wine. Ethyl alcohol (grain alcohol) is found in alcoholic beverages, cosmetics, and drug preparations. Methyl alcohol (wood alcohol) is used as a fuel and solvent. Isopropyl alcohol (rubbing alcohol) is used as a skin cleanser for injections and minor cuts.

$CH_3—CH_2—OH$	$CH_3—OH$	$CH_3—CH(OH)—CH_3$
ethyl alcohol	methyl alcohol	isopropyl alcohol
ethanol	methanol	2-propanol

Alcohols are synthesized by a wide variety of methods, and the hydroxyl group may be converted to most other functional groups. For these reasons, alcohols are versatile synthetic intermediates. In this chapter, we discuss the physical properties of alcohols and summarize the methods used to synthesize them. In Chapter 11 (Reactions of Alcohols), we continue our study of the central role that alcohols play in organic chemistry as reagents, solvents, and synthetic intermediates.

10-2 Structure and Classification of Alcohols

The structure of an alcohol resembles the structure of water, with an alkyl group replacing one of the hydrogen atoms of water. Figure 10-1 compares the structures of water and methanol. Both have sp^3-hybridized oxygen atoms, but the C—O—H bond angle in methanol (108.9°) is considerably larger than the H—O—H bond angle in water (104.5°) because the methyl group is much larger than a hydrogen atom. The bulky methyl group counteracts the bond angle compression caused by oxygen's nonbonding pairs of electrons. The O—H bond lengths are about the same in water and methanol (0.96 Å), but the C—O bond is considerably longer (1.4 Å), reflecting the larger covalent radius of carbon compared to hydrogen.

One way of organizing the alcohol family is to classify each alcohol according to the type of **carbinol carbon atom**: the one bonded to the —OH group. If this carbon atom is primary (bonded to one other carbon atom), the compound is a **primary alcohol**. A **secondary alcohol** has the —OH group attached to a secondary carbon atom, and a **tertiary alcohol** has it bonded to a tertiary carbon. When we studied alkyl halides

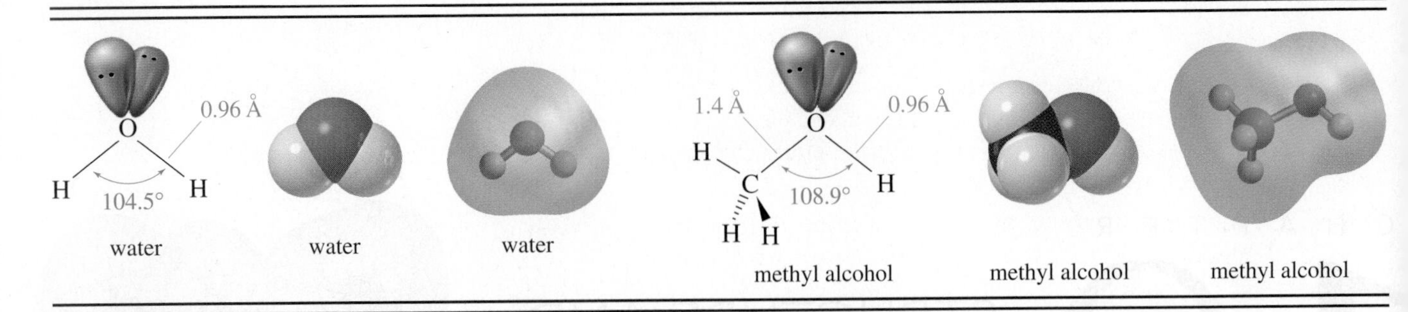

■ **FIGURE 10-1**
Comparison of the structures of water and methyl alcohol.

(Chapter 6), we saw that primary, secondary, and tertiary halides react differently. The same is true for alcohols. We need to learn how these classes of alcohols are similar and under what conditions they react differently. Figure 10-2 shows examples of primary, secondary, and tertiary alcohols.

Compounds with a hydroxyl group bonded directly to an aromatic (benzene) ring are called **phenols**. Phenols have many properties similar to those of alcohols, while other properties derive from their aromatic character. In this chapter, we consider the properties of phenols that are similar to those of alcohols and note some of the differences. In Chapter 16, we consider the aromatic nature of phenols and the reactions that result from their aromaticity.

Type	*Structure*	*Examples*		
Primary alcohol	$R-CH_2-OH$	CH_3CH_2-OH ethanol	$CH_3CH(CH_3)CH_2-OH$ 2-methyl-1-propanol	$C_6H_5-CH_2-OH$ benzyl alcohol
Secondary alcohol	$R-CHR'-OH$	$CH_3-CH(OH)-CH_2-CH_3$ 2-butanol	cyclohexanol	cholesterol
Tertiary alcohol	$R-CR'R''-OH$	$(CH_3)_3C-OH$ 2-methyl-2-propanol	Ph_3C-OH triphenylmethanol	1-methylcyclopentanol
Phenols	C_6H_5-OH	phenol	3-methylphenol	hydroquinone

■ **FIGURE 10-2**
Classification of alcohols. Alcohols are classified according to the type of carbon atom (primary, secondary, or tertiary) bonded to the hydroxyl group. Phenols have a hydroxyl group bonded to a carbon atom in a benzene ring.

10-3 Nomenclature of Alcohols and Phenols

10-3A IUPAC Names ("Alkanol" Names)

The IUPAC system provides unique names for alcohols, based on rules that are similar to those for other classes of compounds. In general, the name carries the *-ol* suffix, together with a number to give the location of the hydroxyl group. The formal rules are summarized in the following three steps:

1. Name the longest carbon chain that contains the carbon atom bearing the —OH group. Drop the final *-e* from the alkane name and add the suffix *-ol* to give the root name.
2. Number the longest carbon chain starting at the end nearest the hydroxyl group, and use the appropriate number to indicate the position of the —OH group. (The hydroxyl group takes precedence over double and triple bonds.)
3. Name all the substituents and give their numbers, as you would for an alkane or an alkene.

In the following example, the longest carbon chain has four carbons, so the root name is *butanol*. The —OH group is on the second carbon atom, so this is a 2-butanol. The complete IUPAC name is 1-bromo-3,3-dimethyl-2-butanol. The new IUPAC positioning of numbers would place the 2 next to the group it locates (-ol), giving the name 1-bromo-3,3-dimethylbutan-2-ol.

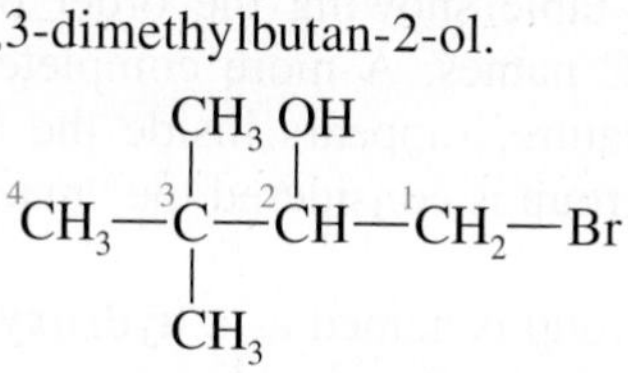

$$\overset{4}{CH_3}-\overset{3}{C}(CH_3)_2-\overset{2}{CH}(OH)-\overset{1}{CH_2}-Br$$

Cyclic alcohols are named using the prefix *cyclo-*; the hydroxyl group is assumed to be on C1.

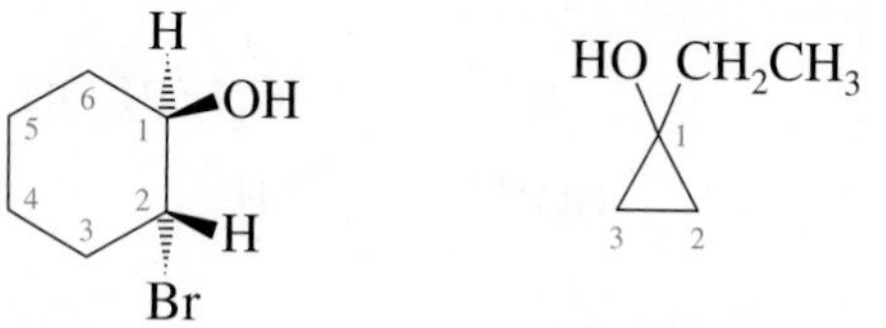

IUPAC name: *trans*-2-bromocyclohexanol 1-ethylcyclopropanol
new IUPAC name: *trans*-2-bromocyclohexan-1-ol 1-ethylcyclopropan-1-ol

SOLVED PROBLEM 10-1

Give the systematic (IUPAC) name for the following alcohol.

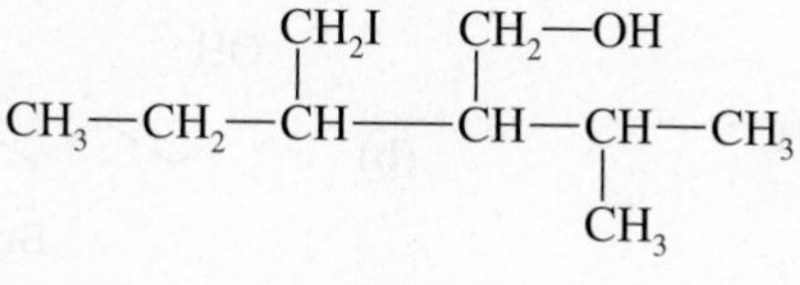

$$CH_3-CH_2-CH(CH_2I)-CH(CH_2-OH)-CH(CH_3)-CH_3$$

SOLUTION

The longest chain contains six carbon atoms, but it does not contain the carbon bonded to the hydroxyl group. The longest chain containing the carbon bonded to the —OH group is the one outlined by the green box, containing five carbon atoms. This chain is numbered from right to left in order to give the hydroxyl-bearing carbon atom the lowest possible number.

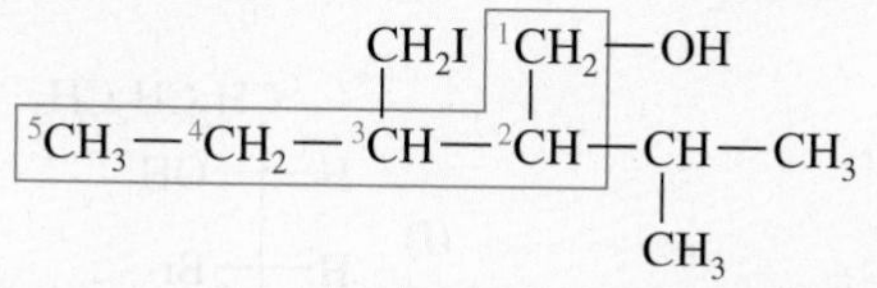

$$\overset{5}{CH_3}-\overset{4}{CH_2}-\overset{3}{CH}(CH_2I)-\overset{2}{CH}(\overset{1}{CH_2}-OH)-CH(CH_3)-CH_3$$

The correct name for this compound is 3-(iodomethyl)-2-isopropylpentan-1-ol.

In naming alcohols containing double and triple bonds, use the *-ol* suffix after the alkene or alkyne name. The alcohol functional group takes precedence over double and triple bonds, so the chain is numbered in order to give the lowest possible number to the carbon atom bonded to the hydroxyl group. The position of the —OH group is given by putting its number before the *-ol* suffix. Numbers for the multiple bonds were once given early in the name, but the 1997 revision of the IUPAC rules puts them next to the *-en* or *-yn* suffix they describe. Both the new and old placements of the numbers are shown in the following figure.

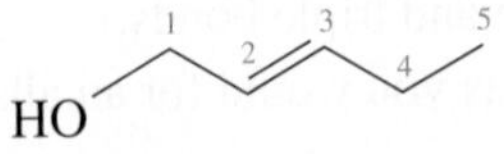

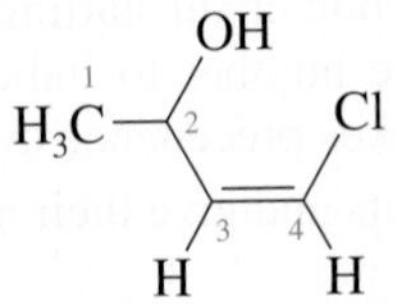

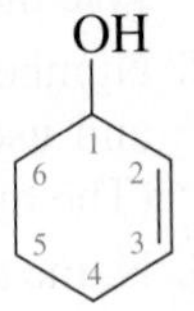

IUPAC name:	*trans*-2-penten-1-ol	(*Z*)-4-chloro-3-buten-2-ol	2-cyclohexen-1-ol
new IUPAC name:	*trans*-pent-2-en-1-ol	(*Z*)-4-chlorobut-3-en-2-ol	cyclohex-2-en-1-ol

Table 10-1 is a partial table showing the order of precedence of functional groups for assigning IUPAC names. A more complete table, titled "Summary of Functional Group Nomenclature," appears inside the back cover. In general, the highest-priority functional group is considered the "main" group, and the others are treated as substituents.

The —OH functional group is named as a **hydroxy** substituent when it appears on a structure with a higher-priority functional group or when the structure is too difficult to name as a simple alcohol.

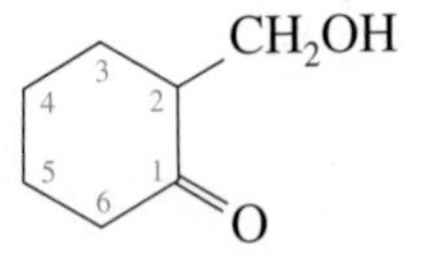

2-hydroxymethylcyclohexanone 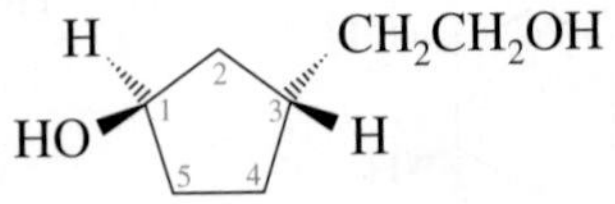 *trans*-3-(2-hydroxyethyl)cyclopentanol 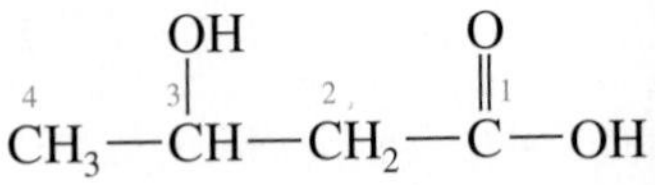 3-hydroxybutanoic acid

$CH_3-CH(OH)-CH_2-C(=O)-OH$

TABLE 10-1

Priority of Functional Groups in Naming Organic Compounds (decreasing priority)

- acids
- esters
- aldehydes
- ketones
- alcohols
- amines
- alkenes
- alkynes
- alkanes
- ethers
- halides

PROBLEM 10-1

Give the IUPAC names of the following alcohols.

(a) 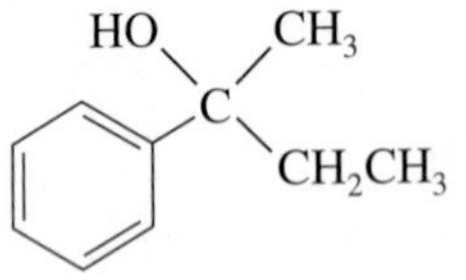 (b) 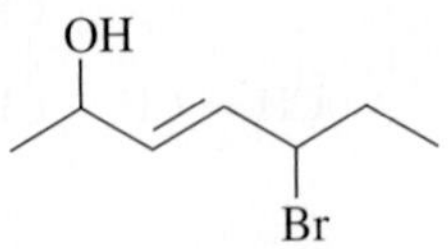 (c) 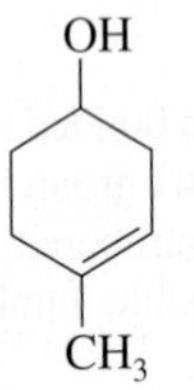 (d) 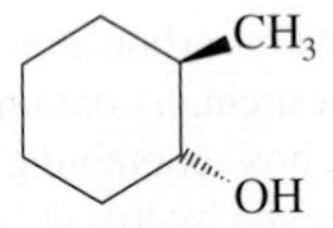 (e) 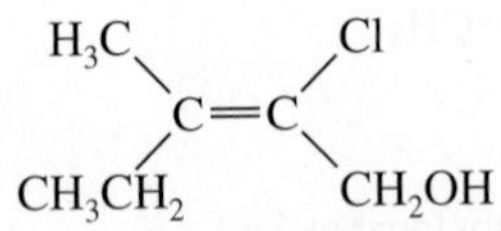 (f)

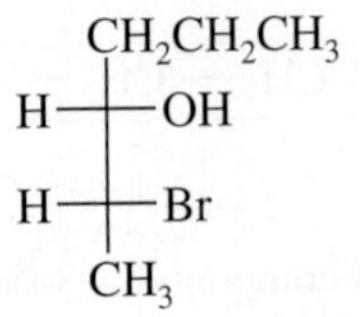

10-3B Common Names of Alcohols

The common name of an alcohol is derived from the common name of the alkyl group and the word *alcohol*. This system pictures an alcohol as a molecule of water with an alkyl group replacing one of the hydrogen atoms. If the structure is complex, the common nomenclature becomes awkward, and the IUPAC nomenclature should be used.

	$CH_3—OH$	$CH_3CH_2CH_2—OH$	$CH_3—CH(OH)—CH_3$	$H_2C=CH—CH_2—OH$
common name:	methyl alcohol	*n*-propyl alcohol	isopropyl alcohol	allyl alcohol
IUPAC name:	methanol	1-propanol	2-propanol	2-propen-1-ol

	$CH_3CH_2CH_2CH_2—OH$	$CH_3—CH(OH)—CH_2CH_3$	$CH_3—C(CH_3)_2—OH$	$CH_3—CH(CH_3)—CH_2—OH$
common name:	*n*-butyl alcohol	*sec*-butyl alcohol	*t*-butyl alcohol	isobutyl alcohol
IUPAC name:	1-butanol	2-butanol	2-methyl-2-propanol	2-methyl-1-propanol

PROBLEM 10-2

Give both the IUPAC name and the common name for each alcohol.

(a) $CH_3CH_2CH(OH)CH_3$ **(b)**  [cyclopropyl ring bearing OH] **(c)** 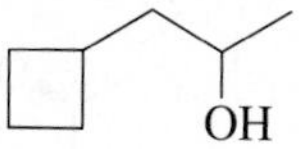 [cyclobutyl–CH₂–CH(OH)–CH₃ skeletal structure, OH]

(d) $(CH_3)_2CHCH_2CH_2OH$

PROBLEM 10-3

For each molecular formula, draw all the possible constitutional isomers of alcohols with that formula. Give the IUPAC name for each alcohol.

(a) C_3H_8O **(b)** $C_4H_{10}O$ **(c)** C_3H_6O **(d)** C_3H_4O

10-3C Names of Diols

Alcohols with two —OH groups are called **diols** or **glycols**. They are named like other alcohols except that the suffix *diol* is used and two numbers are needed to tell where the two hydroxyl groups are located. This is the preferred, systematic (IUPAC) method for naming diols.

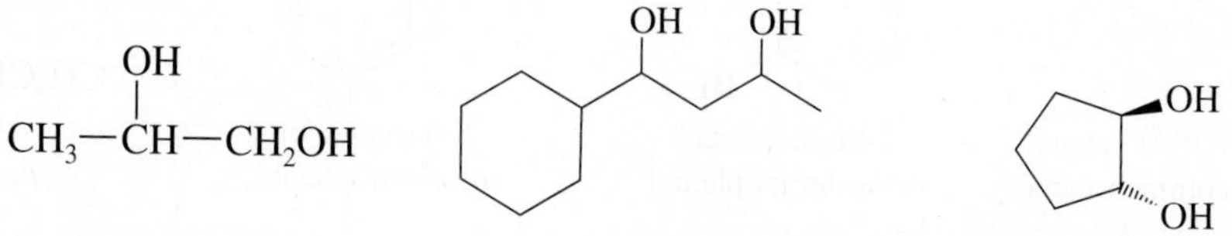

	$CH_3—CH(OH)—CH_2OH$	[cyclohexyl–CH₂–CH(OH)–CH₂–CH(OH)–CH₃; OH, OH]	[cyclopentane with OH (wedge) and OH (hash)]
IUPAC name:	propane-1,2-diol	1-cyclohexylbutane-1,3-diol	*trans*-cyclopentane-1,2-diol

The term *glycol* generally means a 1,2-diol, or **vicinal diol**, with its two hydroxyl groups on adjacent carbon atoms. Glycols are usually synthesized by the hydroxylation of alkenes, using peroxyacids, osmium tetroxide, or potassium permanganate (Section 8-14).

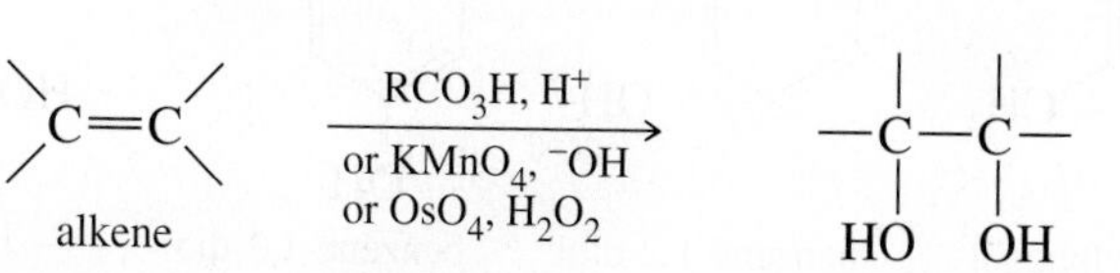

$$\underset{\text{alkene}}{>C=C<} \xrightarrow[\text{or } OsO_4,\ H_2O_2]{RCO_3H,\ H^+ \text{ or } KMnO_4,\ ^-OH} \underset{\text{vicinal diol (glycol)}}{—\underset{HO}{\overset{|}{C}}—\underset{OH}{\overset{|}{C}}—}$$

This synthesis of glycols is reflected in their common names. The glycol is named for the alkene from which it is synthesized:

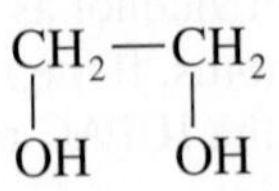

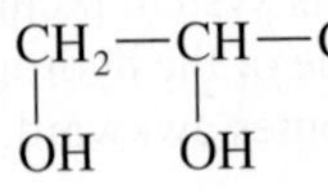

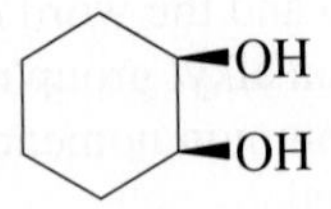

	CH_2-CH_2 (OH, OH)	$CH_2-CH-CH_3$ (OH, OH)	cyclohexane with two cis OH
IUPAC name:	ethane-1,2-diol	propane-1,2-diol	*cis*-cyclohexane-1,2-diol
common name:	ethylene glycol	propylene glycol	*cis*-cyclohexene glycol

The common names of glycols can be awkward and confusing because the *-ene* portion of the name implies the presence of an alkene double bond, but the glycol does not contain a double bond. We will generally use the IUPAC "diol" nomenclature for diols, but be aware that the names "ethylene glycol" (automotive antifreeze) and "propylene glycol" (used in medicines and foods) are universally accepted for these common diols.

PROBLEM 10-4

Give a systematic (IUPAC) name for each diol.

(a) $CH_3CH(OH)(CH_2)_4CH(OH)C(CH_3)_3$ **(b)** $HO-(CH_2)_8-OH$

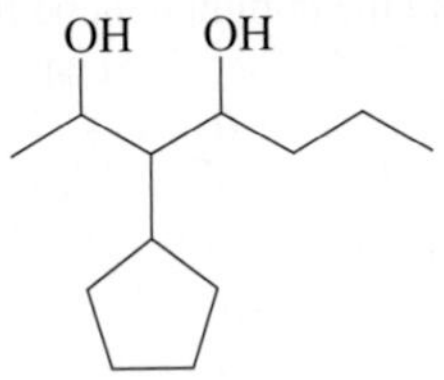

(c) HO, OH **(d)** OH OH **(e)** OH, HO

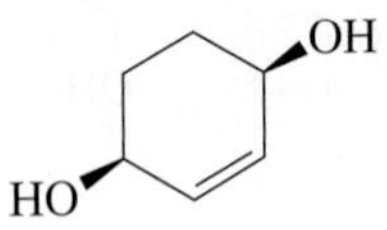

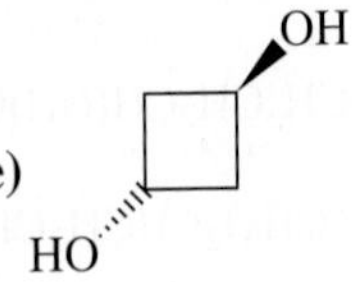

10-3D Names of Phenols

Phenol was given the common name "carbolic acid" because it was originally isolated from the acidic fraction of coal tar. Phenol is a potent neurotoxin, and skin exposure causes deep, painless burns. Weak aqueous solutions of phenol have been used as antiseptics.

Because the phenol structure involves a benzene ring, the terms *ortho* (1,2-disubstituted), *meta* (1,3-disubstituted), and *para* (1,4-disubstituted) are often used in the common names. The following examples illustrate the systematic names and the common names of some simple phenols.

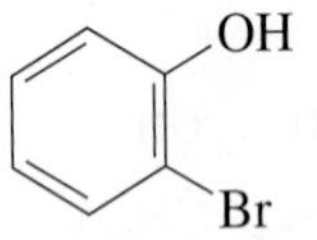

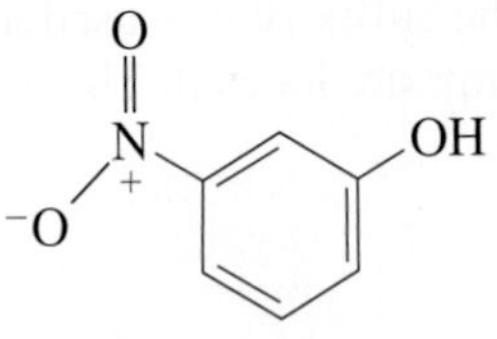

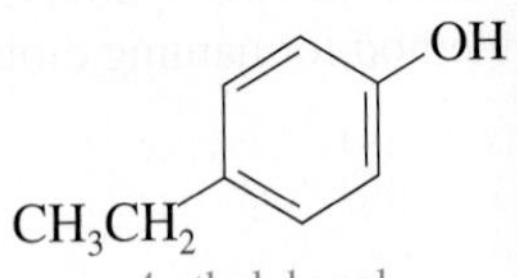

	OH, Br	O, N, +, $^-$O, OH	OH, CH_3CH_2
IUPAC name:	2-bromophenol	3-nitrophenol	4-ethylphenol
common name:	*ortho*-bromophenol	*meta*-nitrophenol	*para*-ethylphenol

Soil bacteria convert many aromatic compounds to catechol. Then they cleave the ring and degrade the products further to water and carbon dioxide. The soil around highways is often enriched in these bacteria feeding on the runoff of hydrocarbons that vehicles deposit on the road.

The methylphenols are called *cresols*, while the names of the benzenediols are based on their historical uses and sources rather than their structures. We will generally use the systematic names of phenolic compounds.

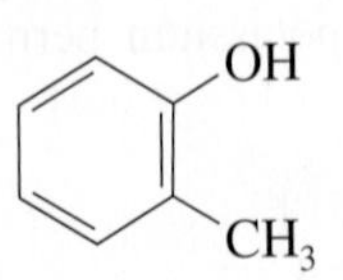

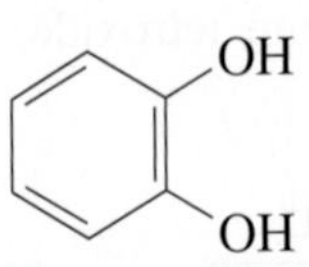

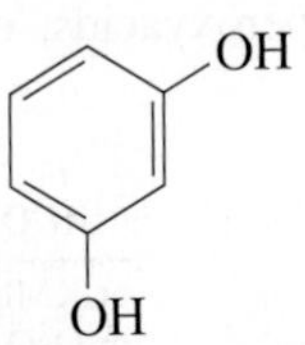

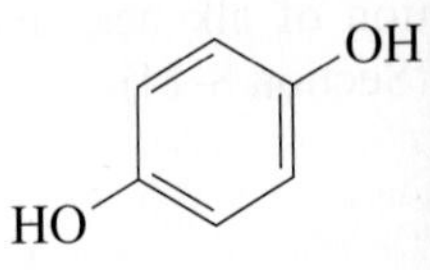

	OH, CH_3	OH, OH	OH, OH	OH, HO
IUPAC name:	2-methylphenol	benzene-1,2-diol	benzene-1,3-diol	benzene-1,4-diol
common name:	*ortho*-cresol	catechol	resorcinol	hydroquinone

10-4 Physical Properties of Alcohols

Most of the common alcohols, up to about 11 or 12 carbon atoms, are liquids at room temperature. Methanol and ethanol are free-flowing volatile liquids with characteristic fruity odors. The higher alcohols (the butanols through the decanols) are somewhat viscous, and some of the highly branched isomers are solids at room temperature. These higher alcohols have heavier but still fruity odors. 1-Propanol and 2-propanol fall in the middle, with a barely noticeable viscosity and a characteristic odor often associated with a physician's office. Table 10-2 lists the physical properties of some common alcohols.

10-4A Boiling Points of Alcohols

Because we often deal with liquid alcohols, we forget how surprising it *should* be that the lower-molecular-weight alcohols are liquids. For example, ethyl alcohol and propane have similar molecular weights, yet their boiling points differ by about 120 °C. Dimethyl ether has an intermediate boiling point.

H—O—CH_2CH_3 $\mu = 1.69$ D
ethanol, MW 46
bp 78 °C

H_3C—O—CH_3 $\mu = 1.30$ D
dimethyl ether, MW 46
bp −25 °C

H_3C—CH_2—CH_3 $\mu = 0.08$ D
propane, MW 44
bp −42 °C

Such a large difference in boiling points suggests that ethanol molecules are attracted to each other much more strongly than propane molecules. Two important intermolecular forces are responsible: hydrogen bonding and dipole–dipole attractions (Section 2-10).

Hydrogen bonding is the major intermolecular attraction responsible for ethanol's high boiling point. The hydroxyl hydrogen of ethanol is strongly polarized by its bond to oxygen, and it forms a hydrogen bond with a pair of nonbonding electrons from the oxygen atom of another alcohol molecule (Section 2-10C). Ethers have two alkyl groups bonded to their oxygen atoms, so they have no O—H hydrogen atoms to form hydrogen

TABLE 10-2
Physical Properties of Selected Alcohols

IUPAC Name	Common Name	Formula	mp (°C)	bp (°C)	Density (g/mL)
methanol	methyl alcohol	CH_3OH	−97	65	0.79
ethanol	ethyl alcohol	CH_3CH_2OH	−114	78	0.79
1-propanol	*n*-propyl alcohol	$CH_3CH_2CH_2OH$	−126	97	0.80
2-propanol	isopropyl alcohol	$(CH_3)_2CHOH$	−89	82	0.79
1-butanol	*n*-butyl alcohol	$CH_3(CH_2)_3OH$	−90	118	0.81
2-butanol	*sec*-butyl alcohol	$CH_3CH(OH)CH_2CH_3$	−114	100	0.81
2-methyl-1-propanol	isobutyl alcohol	$(CH_3)_2CHCH_2OH$	−108	108	0.80
2-methyl-2-propanol	*t*-butyl alcohol	$(CH_3)_3COH$	25	83	0.79
1-pentanol	*n*-pentyl alcohol	$CH_3(CH_2)_4OH$	−79	138	0.82
3-methyl-1-butanol	isopentyl alcohol	$(CH_3)_2CHCH_2CH_2OH$	−117	132	0.81
2,2-dimethyl-1-propanol	neopentyl alcohol	$(CH_3)_3CCH_2OH$	52	113	0.81
cyclopentanol	cyclopentyl alcohol	*cyclo*-C_5H_9OH	−19	141	0.95
1-hexanol	*n*-hexyl alcohol	$CH_3(CH_2)_5OH$	−52	156	0.82
cyclohexanol	cyclohexyl alcohol	*cyclo*-$C_6H_{11}OH$	25	162	0.96
1-heptanol	*n*-heptyl alcohol	$CH_3(CH_2)_6OH$	−34	176	0.82
1-octanol	*n*-octyl alcohol	$CH_3(CH_2)_7OH$	−16	194	0.83
1-nonanol	*n*-nonyl alcohol	$CH_3(CH_2)_8OH$	−6	214	0.83
1-decanol	*n*-decyl alcohol	$CH_3(CH_2)_9OH$	6	233	0.83
2-propen-1-ol	allyl alcohol	$H_2C{=}CH{-}CH_2OH$	−129	97	0.86
phenylmethanol	benzyl alcohol	Ph—CH_2OH	−15	205	1.05
diphenylmethanol	diphenylcarbinol	Ph_2CHOH	69	298	
triphenylmethanol	triphenylcarbinol	Ph_3COH	162	380	1.20
1,2-ethanediol	ethylene glycol	$HOCH_2CH_2OH$	−13	198	1.12
1,2-propanediol	propylene glycol	$CH_3CH(OH)CH_2OH$	−59	188	1.04
1,2,3-propanetriol	glycerol	$HOCH_2CH(OH)CH_2OH$	18	290	1.26

bonds. Hydrogen bonds have a strength of about 21 kJ (5 kcal) per mole: weaker than typical covalent bonds of 300 to 500 kJ, but much stronger than dipole–dipole attractions.

Dipole–dipole attractions also contribute to the relatively high boiling points of alcohols and ethers. The polarized C—O and H—O bonds and the nonbonding electrons add to produce a dipole moment of 1.69 D in ethanol, compared with a dipole moment of only 0.08 D in propane. In liquid ethanol, the positive and negative ends of these dipoles align to produce attractive interactions.

We can compare the effects of hydrogen bonding and dipole–dipole attractions by comparing ethanol with dimethyl ether. Like ethanol, dimethyl ether has a large dipole moment (1.30 D), but dimethyl ether cannot engage in hydrogen bonding because it has no —O—H hydrogens.

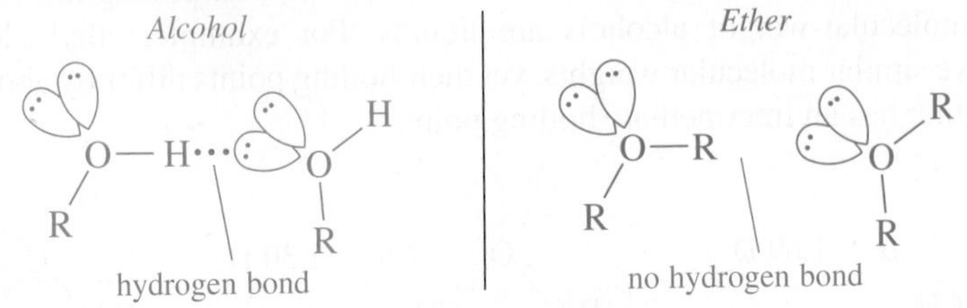

The boiling point of dimethyl ether is −25 °C, about 17° higher than that of propane, but still 103° lower than that of ethanol. Hydrogen bonds are clearly much stronger intermolecular attractions than dipole–dipole attractions.

10-4B Solubility Properties of Alcohols

Water and alcohols have similar properties because they all contain hydroxyl groups that can form hydrogen bonds. Alcohols form hydrogen bonds with water, and several of the lower-molecular-weight alcohols are **miscible** (soluble in any proportions) with water. Similarly, alcohols are much better solvents than hydrocarbons for polar substances. Significant amounts of ionic compounds such as sodium chloride can dissolve in some of the lower alcohols. We call the hydroxyl group **hydrophilic**, meaning "water loving," because of its affinity for water and other polar substances.

The alcohol's alkyl group is called **hydrophobic** ("water hating") because it acts like an alkane: It disrupts the network of hydrogen bonds and dipole–dipole attractions of a polar solvent such as water. The alkyl group makes the alcohol less hydrophilic, yet it lends solubility in nonpolar organic solvents. As a result, most alcohols are miscible with a wide range of nonpolar organic solvents.

Table 10-3 lists the solubility of some simple alcohols in water. The water solubility decreases as the alkyl group becomes larger. Alcohols with one-, two-, or three-carbon alkyl groups are miscible with water. A four-carbon alkyl group is large enough that some isomers are not miscible, yet *tert*-butyl alcohol, with a compact spherical shape, is miscible. In general, each hydroxyl group or other hydrogen-bonding group can carry about four carbon atoms into water. 1-Hexanol, with 6 carbon atoms, is only slightly soluble in water, but hexane-1,6-diol, with two hydrogen-bonding groups, is miscible with water. Phenol is unusually soluble for a six-carbon alcohol because of its compact shape and the particularly strong hydrogen bonds formed between phenolic —OH groups and water molecules.

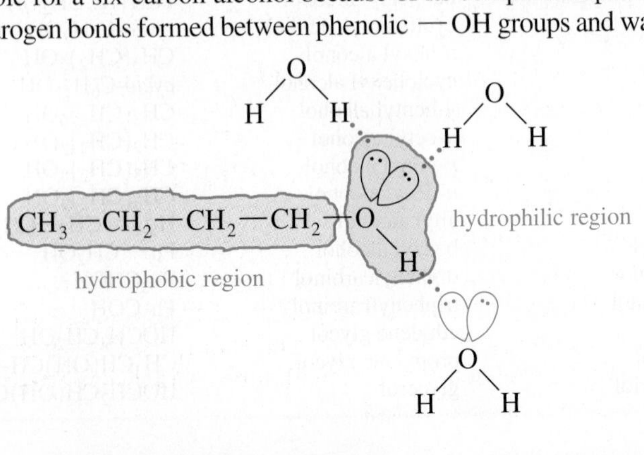

TABLE 10-3

Solubility of Alcohols in Water (at 25 °C)

Alcohol	Solubility in Water
methyl	miscible
ethyl	miscible
n-propyl	miscible
t-butyl	miscible
isobutyl	10.0%
n-butyl	9.1%
n-pentyl	2.7%
cyclohexyl	3.6%
n-hexyl	0.6%
phenol	9.3%
hexane-1,6-diol	miscible

PROBLEM 10-5

Predict which member of each pair will be more soluble in water. Explain the reasons for your answers.

(a) 1-hexanol or cyclohexanol
(b) 1-heptanol or 4-methylphenol
(c) 3-ethyl-3-hexanol or 2-octanol
(d) 2-hexanol or cyclooctane-1,4-diol
(e) (H, OH, OH, H structure) or (H, OH, OH, H structure)

PROBLEM 10-6

Dimethylamine, $(CH_3)_2NH$, has a molecular weight of 45 and a boiling point of 7.4 °C. Trimethylamine, $(CH_3)_3N$, has a higher molecular weight (59) but a *lower* boiling point (3.5 °C). Explain this apparent discrepancy.

10-5 Commercially Important Alcohols

10-5A Methanol

Methanol (methyl alcohol) was originally produced by the destructive distillation of wood chips in the absence of air. This source led to the name **wood alcohol**. During Prohibition (1919–1933), when the manufacture of alcoholic beverages was prohibited in the United States, anything called "alcohol" was often used for mixing drinks. Since methanol is more toxic than ethanol, this practice resulted in many cases of blindness and death.

Today, most methanol is synthesized by a catalytic reaction of carbon monoxide with hydrogen. This reaction uses high temperatures and pressures and requires large, complicated industrial reactors.

$$\underset{\text{synthesis gas}}{CO + 2\,H} \xrightarrow[\text{CuO}-\text{ZnO/Al}_2\text{O}_3]{300-400\ °\text{C},\ 200-300\ \text{atm H}_2} CH_3OH$$

Synthesis gas, containing the hydrogen and carbon monoxide needed to make methanol, can be generated by the partial burning of coal in the presence of water. Careful regulation of the amount of water added allows production of synthesis gas with the correct ratio of carbon monoxide to hydrogen.

$$3\,C + 4\,H_2O \xrightarrow{\text{high temperature}} \underbrace{CO_2 + 2\,CO + 4\,H_2}_{\text{synthesis gas}}$$

Methanol is one of the most common industrial solvents. It is cheap, relatively less toxic (compared with halogenated solvents), and it dissolves a wide variety of polar and nonpolar substances. Methanol is also a starting material for a wide variety of methyl ethers, methyl esters, and other compounds used in plastics, medicines, fuels, and solvents.

Methanol is a good fuel for internal combustion engines. From 1965–2006, all the cars at the Indianapolis 500 used methanol-fueled engines. The switch from gasoline to methanol was driven by a bad fire after a crash in 1964. Methanol is less flammable than gasoline, and water is effective against methanol fires (water mixes with and dilutes methanol). As with any alternative fuel, there are advantages and disadvantages to the use of methanol. Its high octane rating, low pollutant emissions, and lower flammability must be weighed against its lower energy content (smaller ΔH of combustion per gram), requiring 1.7 g of methanol to produce the same energy as 1 g of gasoline. Because of its excellent solvent properties, methanol is hard on rings, seals, and plastic fuel-system parts. Its tendency to burn with little or no visible flame can allow dangerous methanol fires to go undetected.

Experience at Indianapolis has proved that methanol (derived from coal) is an excellent fuel for automotive engines.

10-5B Ethanol

The prehistoric discovery of ethanol probably occurred when rotten fruit was consumed and found to have an intoxicating effect. This discovery presumably led to the intentional fermentation of fruit juices. The primitive wine that resulted could be stored (in a sealed container) without danger of decomposition, and it also served as a safe, unpolluted source of water to drink.

Ethanol can be produced by the fermentation of sugars and starches from many different sources. Grains such as corn, wheat, rye, and barley are common sources, resulting in the name **grain alcohol** for ethanol. Cooking the grain, followed by addition of sprouted barley, called *malt*, converts some of the starches to simpler sugars. Brewer's yeast is then added, and the solution is incubated while the yeast cells convert simple sugars such as glucose to ethanol and carbon dioxide.

$$\underset{\text{glucose}}{C_6H_{12}O_6} \xrightarrow{\text{yeast enzymes}} 2\ \underset{\text{ethanol}}{C_2H_5OH} + 2\ CO_2$$

The alcoholic solution that results from fermentation contains only 12–15% alcohol, because yeast cells cannot survive higher concentrations. Distillation increases the alcohol concentration to about 40–50% (80 to 100 "proof") for "hard" liquors. Distillation of ethanol–water solutions cannot increase the ethanol concentration above 95% because a solution of 95% ethanol and 5% water boils at a lower temperature (78.15 °C) than either pure water (100 °C) or pure ethanol (78.3 °C). Such a mixture of liquids that boils at a lower temperature than either of its components is called a minimum-boiling **azeotrope**.

The 95% alcohol produced by distillation is well suited for use as a solvent and a reagent when traces of water do not affect the reaction. When **absolute alcohol** (100% ethanol) is required, the 95% azeotrope is passed through a dehydrating agent such as anhydrous calcium oxide (CaO), which removes the final 5% of water.

Since World War II, most industrial ethanol has been synthesized directly by the catalyzed high-temperature, high-pressure, gas-phase reaction of water with ethylene. This process uses catalysts such as P_2O_5, tungsten oxide, or various specially treated clays.

$$H_2C{=}CH_2 + H_2O \xrightarrow[\text{catalyst}]{100-300\text{ atm, }300\ °C} CH_3{-}CH_2{-}OH$$

Like methanol, ethanol is an excellent solvent of low toxicity that is cheap to produce. Unfortunately, the liquor tax makes ethanol relatively expensive. Use of untaxed ethanol is possible, but it requires extensive record keeping and purchase of a special license. **Denatured alcohol** is ethanol that contains impurities that make it undrinkable. Denatured ethanol is untaxed, but the impurities (methanol, methyl isobutyl ketone, aviation gasoline, etc.) also make it unsuitable for many laboratory uses.

Like methanol, ethanol is a good motor fuel, with similar advantages and disadvantages. The race cars at the Indianapolis 500 have used ethanol as their primary fuel since 2006. A car's carburetor must be adjusted (for a richer mixture) and fitted with alcohol-resistant seals if it is to run on pure ethanol. Solutions of about 10% ethanol in gasoline ("gasohol") work well without any adjustments, however.

Many people imagine ethanol to be nontoxic, and methanol to be horribly toxic. Actually, methanol is about twice as toxic as ethanol: Typical fatal doses for adults are about 100 mL of methanol or about 200 mL of ethanol, although smaller doses of methanol may damage the optic nerve. Many people die each year from underestimating ethanol's toxicity. In the lab, we would never ingest even a tiny fraction of these amounts. Therefore, we consider these solvents to be relatively nontoxic compared with truly hazardous solvents such as benzene and chloroform.

Government subsidies have encouraged the fermentation of food grains (primarily corn) to produce ethanol for fuel. The major effect has been to increase the price of food grains, while having little or no impact on fuel supplies.

Fermentation is not the most efficient way to produce ethanol, and the growing of corn and converting it to ethanol consumes about as much fuel as it produces. In general, foods are more valuable commodities than fuels, and these "food to fuel" schemes are not viable unless they are subsidized.

Waste materials, available at little or no expense, can be converted to fuels economically in some cases. Brazil has become independent of foreign oil by converting its sugarcane waste to ethanol for use as a motor fuel.

Friendly Reminder

Everything is toxic in large enough amounts—even water.

10-5C 2-Propanol

2-Propanol (isopropyl alcohol) is made by the catalytic hydration of propylene. Isopropyl alcohol is commonly used as **rubbing alcohol** (rather than ethanol) because it has less of a drying effect on the skin, and it is not regulated and taxed by the government.

2-Propanol is about as toxic as methanol when taken orally, but it is safer for use on the skin because it does not pass through skin as easily as methanol.

$$CH_3{-}CH{=}CH_2 \;(\text{propylene}) + H_2O \xrightarrow[\text{catalyst}]{100\text{–}300\text{ atm, }300\text{ °C}} CH_3{-}CH(OH){-}CH_3 \;(\text{2-propanol})$$

Both ethanol and 2-propanol are effective topical antiseptics. Ethanol is also an ingredient in many mouthwashes. These alcohols kill the microorganisms on the wound surface and in the mouth, but their low toxicity does not kill the cells of the skin or mouth tissues.

10-6 Acidity of Alcohols and Phenols

Like the hydroxyl proton of water, the hydroxyl proton of an alcohol is weakly acidic. A strong base can remove the hydroxyl proton to give an **alkoxide ion**.

$$R{-}\ddot{O}{-}H \;(\text{alcohol}) + B{:}^- \rightleftharpoons R{-}\ddot{O}{:}^- \;(\text{alkoxide ion}) + B{-}H$$

Example

$$CH_3CH_2{-}\ddot{O}{-}H \;(\text{ethanol}) + B{:}^- \rightleftharpoons CH_3CH_2{-}\ddot{O}{:}^- \;(\text{ethoxide ion}) + B{-}H$$

The acidities of alcohols vary widely, from alcohols that are about as acidic as water to some that are much less acidic. The acid-dissociation constant, K_a, of an alcohol is defined by the equilibrium

$$R{-}O{-}H + H_2O \overset{K_a}{\rightleftharpoons} R{-}O^- + H_3O^+$$

$$K_a = \frac{[H_3O^+][RO^-]}{[ROH]} \qquad pK_a = -\log(K_a)$$

Table 10-4 compares the acid-dissociation constants of some alcohols with those of water and other acids.

10-6A Effects on Acidity

The acid-dissociation constants for alcohols vary according to their structure, from about 10^{-16} for methanol down to about 10^{-18} for most tertiary alcohols. The acidity decreases as the substitution on the alkyl group increases, because a more highly sub-

TABLE 10-4

Acid-Dissociation Constants of Representative Alcohols

Alcohol	Structure	K_a	pK_a
methanol	$CH_3{-}OH$	3.2×10^{-16}	15.5
ethanol	$CH_3CH_2{-}OH$	1.3×10^{-16}	15.9
2-chloroethanol	$Cl{-}CH_2CH_2{-}OH$	5.0×10^{-15}	14.3
2,2,2-trichloroethanol	$Cl_3C{-}CH_2{-}OH$	6.3×10^{-13}	12.2
isopropyl alcohol	$(CH_3)_2CH{-}OH$	3.2×10^{-17}	16.5
tert-butyl alcohol	$(CH_3)_3C{-}OH$	1.0×10^{-18}	18.0
cyclohexanol	$C_6H_{11}{-}OH$	1.0×10^{-18}	18.0
phenol	$C_6H_5{-}OH$	1.0×10^{-10}	10.0
	Comparison with Other Acids		
water	H_2O	1.8×10^{-16}	15.7
acetic acid	CH_3COOH	1.6×10^{-5}	4.8
hydrochloric acid	HCl	$1 \times 10^{+7}$	−7

stituted alkyl group inhibits solvation of the alkoxide ion, decreasing the stability of the alkoxide ion and driving the dissociation equilibrium toward the left.

Table 10-4 shows that substitution by electron-withdrawing halogen atoms enhances the acidity of alcohols. For example, 2-chloroethanol is more acidic than ethanol because the electron-withdrawing chlorine atom helps to stabilize the 2-chloroethoxide ion.

$$\underset{\text{ethanol}}{CH_3-CH_2-OH} + H_2O \rightleftharpoons \underset{\substack{\text{ethoxide ion} \\ \text{(less stable)}}}{CH_3-CH_2-O^-} + H_3O^+ \qquad K_a = 1.3 \times 10^{-16}$$

$$\underset{\text{2-chloroethanol}}{Cl-CH_2-CH_2-OH} + H_2O \rightleftharpoons \underset{\substack{\text{2-chloroethoxide ion} \\ \text{(stabilized by Cl)}}}{Cl-CH_2-CH_2-O^-} + H_3O^+ \qquad K_a = 5.0 \times 10^{-15}$$

PROBLEM 10-7

Predict which member of each pair will be more acidic. Explain your answers.
(a) methanol or *tert*-butyl alcohol
(b) 2-chloropropan-1-ol or 3-chloropropan-1-ol
(c) 2-chloroethanol or 2,2-dichloroethanol
(d) 2,2-dichloropropan-1-ol or 2,2-difluoropropan-1-ol

PROBLEM 10-8

Without looking them up, rank the following compounds in decreasing order of acidity. These examples represent large classes of compounds that differ widely in acidity.

water, ethanol, 2-chloroethanol, *tert*-butyl alcohol, ammonia, sulfuric acid, hexane, hexyne, acetic acid

10-6B Formation of Sodium and Potassium Alkoxides

Alkoxide ions are strong nucleophiles and strong bases, and we have already seen many of their useful reactions. When an alkoxide ion is needed in a synthesis, it is often formed by the reaction of sodium or potassium metal with the alcohol. This is an oxidation–reduction, with the metal being oxidized and the hydrogen ion reduced to form hydrogen gas. Hydrogen bubbles out of the solution, leaving the sodium or potassium salt of the alkoxide ion.

$$R-O-H + Na \longrightarrow R-O^-\,{}^+Na + \tfrac{1}{2}H_2\uparrow$$

Example

$$\underset{\text{ethanol}}{CH_3CH_2OH} + \underset{\text{sodium metal}}{Na} \longrightarrow \underset{\text{sodium ethoxide}}{CH_3CH_2O^-\,{}^+Na} + \underset{\text{hydrogen gas}}{\tfrac{1}{2}H_2\uparrow}$$

The more acidic alcohols, like methanol and ethanol, react rapidly with sodium to form sodium methoxide and sodium ethoxide. Secondary alcohols, such as 2-propanol, react more slowly. Tertiary alcohols, such as *tert*-butyl alcohol, react very slowly with sodium. Potassium is often used with secondary and tertiary alcohols because it is more reactive than sodium, and the reaction can be completed in a convenient amount of time.

$$\underset{\textit{tert}\text{-butyl alcohol}}{(CH_3)_3C-OH} + \underset{\text{potassium metal}}{K} \longrightarrow \underset{\text{potassium }\textit{tert}\text{-butoxide}}{(CH_3)_3C-O^-\,{}^+K} + \tfrac{1}{2}H_2\uparrow$$

Some alcohols react slowly with both sodium and potassium. In these cases, a useful alternative is sodium hydride, often in tetrahydrofuran (THF) solution. Sodium hydride reacts quickly to form the alkoxide, even with difficult compounds.

$$\underset{\text{alcohol}}{R-\ddot{O}-H} + \underset{\text{sodium hydride}}{NaH} \xrightarrow{THF} \underset{\text{sodium alkoxide}}{R-\ddot{O}:^{-}\,^{+}Na} + \underset{\text{hydrogen}}{H_2\uparrow}$$

10-6C Acidity of Phenols

We might expect that phenol would have about the same acidity as cyclohexanol, since their structures are similar. This prediction is wrong: Phenol is nearly 100 million (10^8) times more acidic than cyclohexanol.

The famous British surgeon Joseph Lister (1827–1912) used dilute solutions of phenol to kill germs in wounds. He found that antiseptic surgery using phenol reduced the mortality rate from amputations by nearly 50%. Within the next decade, Lister's phenol-based antiseptic techniques revolutionized surgery.

$$H_2O + \text{cyclohexanol} \underset{}{\overset{K_a = 10^{-18}}{\rightleftharpoons}} \text{alkoxide ion} + H_3O^+$$

$$H_2O + \text{phenol} \underset{}{\overset{K_a = 10^{-10}}{\rightleftharpoons}} \text{phenoxide ion (phenolate ion)} + H_3O^+$$

Cyclohexanol is a typical secondary alcohol, with a typical acid-dissociation constant for an alcohol. There must be something special about phenol that makes it unusually acidic. The phenoxide ion is more stable than a typical alkoxide ion because the negative charge is not confined to the oxygen atom but is delocalized over the oxygen and three carbon atoms of the ring.

[Resonance structures of the phenoxide ion: negative charge on O ↔ on ortho carbon ↔ on para carbon ↔ on other ortho carbon]

A large part of the negative charge in the resonance hybrid still resides on the oxygen atom, since it is the most electronegative of the four atoms sharing the charge. But the ability to spread the negative charge over four atoms rather than concentrating it on just one atom produces a more stable ion. The reaction of phenol with sodium hydroxide is exothermic, and the following equilibrium lies to the right.

$$\underset{\text{phenol, p}K_a = 10.0}{PhOH} + Na^+ \ ^{-}\!:\ddot{O}H \rightleftharpoons \underset{\text{sodium phenoxide}}{PhO^{-}\,^{+}Na} + \underset{\text{p}K_a = 15.7}{H_2O}$$

Phenoxide anions are prepared simply by adding the phenol to an aqueous solution of sodium hydroxide or potassium hydroxide. There is no need to use sodium or potassium metal. Phenol was once called *carbolic acid* because of its ability to neutralize common bases.

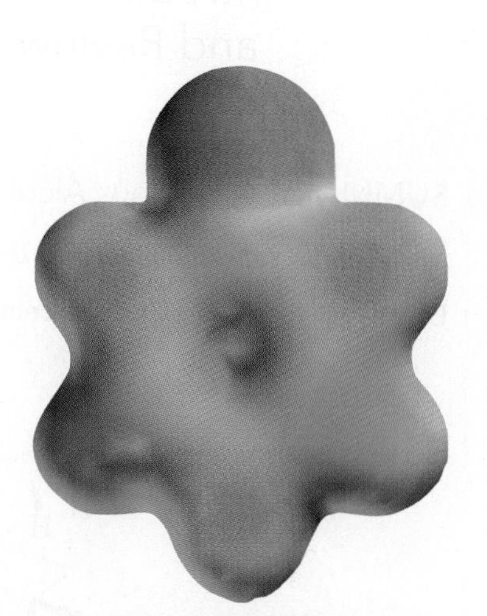
EPM of phenoxide ion

PROBLEM 10-9

A nitro group ($-NO_2$) effectively stabilizes a negative charge on an adjacent carbon atom through resonance:

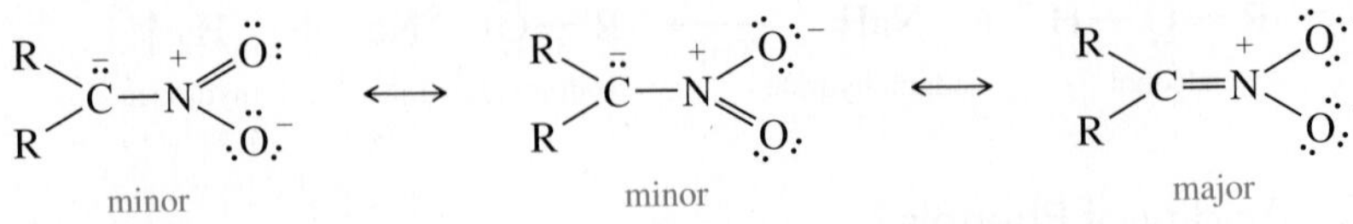

$R_2\ddot{C}^{-}-N^{+}(=O)O^{-}$ (minor) $\longleftrightarrow$ $R_2\ddot{C}^{-}-N^{+}(O^{-})=O$ (minor) $\longleftrightarrow$ $R_2C=N^{+}(O^{-})_2$ (major)

Two of the following nitrophenols are much more acidic than phenol itself. The third compound is only slightly more acidic than phenol. Use resonance structures of the appropriate phenoxide ions to show why two of these anions should be unusually stable.

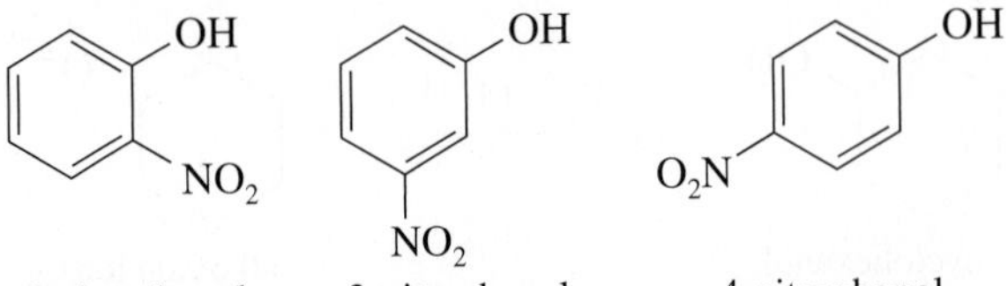

2-nitrophenol 3-nitrophenol 4-nitrophenol

Phenol is commonly used to separate cellular DNA from proteins, one step in the process that leads to the cloning of a gene. An aqueous phenol solution dissolves DNA, but it complexes with the proteins and causes them to precipitate. Centrifugation removes the precipitated proteins. Finally, addition of ethanol causes the purified DNA to precipitate so that it can be collected.

PROBLEM 10-10

The following compounds are only slightly soluble in water, but one of them is very soluble in a dilute aqueous solution of sodium hydroxide. The other is still only slightly soluble.

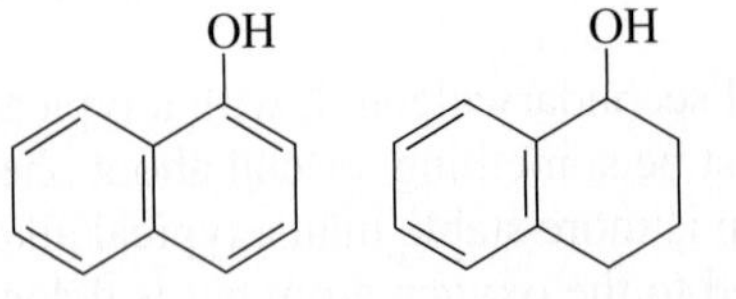

(a) Explain the difference in solubility of these compounds in dilute sodium hydroxide.
(b) Show how this difference might be exploited to separate a mixture of these two compounds using a separatory funnel.

10-7 Synthesis of Alcohols: Introduction and Review

One of the reasons alcohols are important synthetic intermediates is that they can be synthesized directly from a wide variety of other functional groups. In Chapters 6 and 8, we examined the conversion of alkyl halides to alcohols by substitution and the conversion of alkenes to alcohols by hydration, hydroboration, and hydroxylation. These reactions are summarized here, with references for review if needed.

Following this review, we will consider the largest and most versatile group of alcohol syntheses: nucleophilic additions to carbonyl compounds.

SUMMARY Previous Alcohol Syntheses

Nucleophilic Substitution on an Alkyl Halide **(Chapter 6)**

Usually via the S_N2 mechanism; competes with elimination.

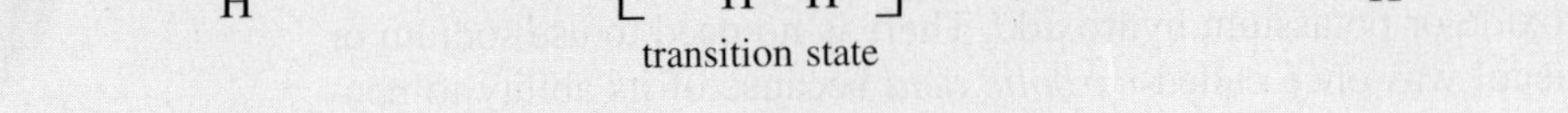

$HO^{-} + RCH_2-X \longrightarrow [HO\cdots C\cdots X]^{\ddagger}$ (transition state) $\longrightarrow HO-CH_2R + {}^{-}{:}X$

(Continued)

Example

(S)-2-bromobutane $\xrightarrow{KOH}$ (R)-2-butanol, 100% inverted configuration (plus elimination products)

Synthesis of Alcohols from Alkenes (Chapter 8)

1. *Acid-catalyzed hydration* (Section 8-4)

$$\text{C=C} + H_2O \xrightarrow{H^+} -\underset{H}{C}-\underset{OH}{C}-$$

Markovnikov orientation

2. *Oxymercuration–demercuration* (Section 8-5)

$$\text{C=C} + Hg(OAc)_2 \xrightarrow{H_2O} -\underset{(AcO)Hg}{C}-\overset{OH}{C}- \xrightarrow{NaBH_4} -\underset{H}{C}-\overset{OH}{C}-$$

Markovnikov orientation

Example

$$(H_3C)(H)C=C(CH_3)_2 \xrightarrow[H_2O]{Hg(OAc)_2} H-\underset{(AcO)Hg}{\overset{H_3C}{C}}-\underset{CH_3}{\overset{OH}{C}}-CH_3 \xrightarrow{NaBH_4} H-\underset{H}{\overset{H_3C}{C}}-\underset{CH_3}{\overset{OH}{C}}-CH_3$$

(90% overall)

3. *Hydroboration–oxidation* (Section 8-7)

$$\text{C=C} \xrightarrow[(2)\ H_2O_2,\ NaOH]{(1)\ BH_3 \cdot THF} -\underset{H}{C}-\underset{OH}{C}-$$

syn addition, anti-Markovnikov orientation

Example

1-methylcyclopentene $\xrightarrow{BH_3 \cdot THF}$ (CH$_3$, H, BH$_2$, H cyclopentane intermediate) $\xrightarrow{H_2O_2/NaOH}$ *trans*-2-methylcyclopentanol (85%)

4. *Hydroxylation: synthesis of 1,2-diols from alkenes* (Sections 8-13 and 8-14)

Syn Hydroxylation

$$\text{C=C} \xrightarrow[\text{or } KMnO_4,\ ^-OH \text{ (cold, dilute)}]{OsO_4,\ H_2O_2} -\underset{HO}{C}-\underset{OH}{C}-$$

syn hydroxylation

(*Continued*)

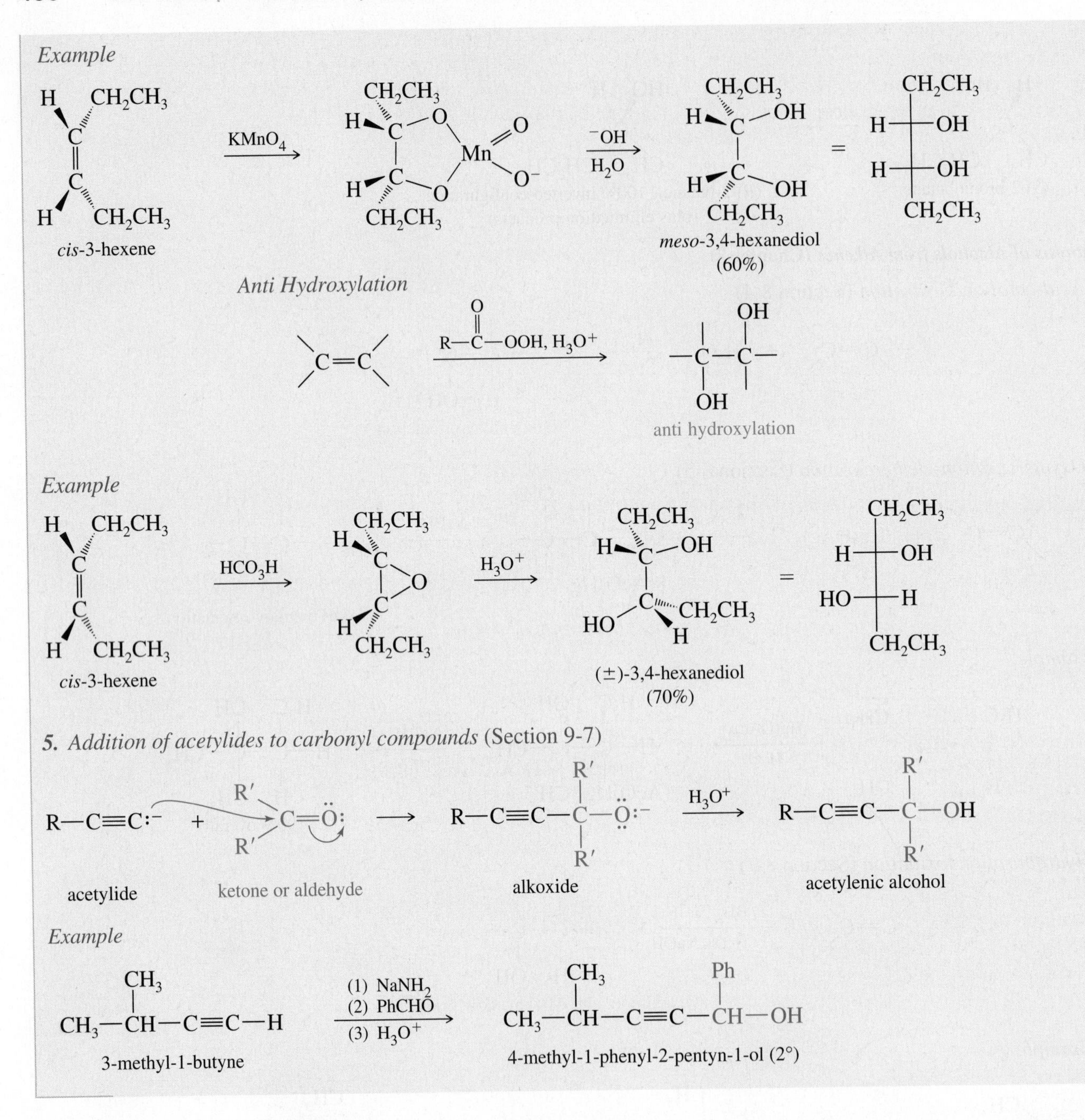

10-8 Organometallic Reagents for Alcohol Synthesis

Organometallic compounds contain covalent bonds between carbon atoms and metal atoms. Organometallic reagents are useful because they have nucleophilic carbon atoms, in contrast to the electrophilic carbon atoms of alkyl halides. Most metals (M) are more electropositive than carbon, and the C—M bond is polarized with a partial positive charge on the metal and a partial negative charge on carbon. The following partial periodic table shows the electronegativities of some metals used in making organometallic compounds.

Electronegativities

Li 1.0			C 2.5
Na 0.9	Mg 1.3	Al 1.6	
K 0.8			

C—M bond

$\overset{\delta^-}{C}\leftarrow\overset{\delta^+}{Li}$

$\overset{\delta^-}{C}\leftarrow\overset{\delta^+}{Mg}$

We have already encountered one type of organometallic compound with a negative charge on carbon: sodium acetylides, covered in Section 9-7. Terminal alkynes are weakly acidic, and they are converted to sodium acetylides by treatment with an unusually strong base, sodium amide. These sodium acetylides are useful nucleophiles, reacting with alkyl halides and carbonyl compounds to form new carbon–carbon bonds.

$$\underset{\text{terminal alkyne}}{R-C\equiv C-H} + \underset{\text{sodium amide}}{NaNH_2} \longrightarrow \underset{\text{a sodium acetylide}}{R-C\equiv C\!:^-\ Na^+} + \underset{\text{ammonia}}{NH_3}$$

$$\underset{\text{acetylide}}{R-C\equiv C\!:^-} + \underset{\text{alkyl halide}}{R'-CH_2-X} \longrightarrow \underset{\text{substituted alkyne}}{R-C\equiv C-CH_2-R'} + X^-$$

$$\underset{\text{acetylide}}{R-C\equiv C\!:^-} + \underset{\text{ketone or aldehyde}}{R'_2C=\ddot{O}\!:} \longrightarrow \underset{\text{alkoxide}}{R-C\equiv C-CR'_2-\ddot{O}\!:^-} \xrightarrow{H_3O^+} \underset{\text{acetylenic alcohol}}{R-C\equiv C-CR'_2-OH}$$

Most alkyl and alkenyl groups are not acidic enough to be deprotonated by sodium amide, but they can be made into Grignard reagents and organolithium reagents. These reagents are extremely versatile, providing some of our best ways of forming carbon–carbon bonds.

10-8A Grignard Reagents

Organometallic compounds of lithium and magnesium are frequently used for the synthesis of alcohols. The organomagnesium halides, of empirical formula R—Mg—X, are called **Grignard reagents** in honor of the French chemist Victor Grignard, who discovered their utility around 1905 and received the Nobel Prize in chemistry in 1912. Grignard reagents result from the reaction of an alkyl halide with magnesium metal. This reaction is always carried out in a dry (anhydrous) ether solvent, which is needed to solvate and stabilize the Grignard reagent as it forms. Although we write the Grignard reagent as R—Mg—X, the actual species in solution usually contains two, three, or four of these units associated together with several molecules of the ether solvent. Diethyl ether, $CH_3CH_2-O-CH_2CH_3$, is the most common solvent for these reactions, although other ethers are also used.

$$\underset{(X = Cl,\ Br,\ or\ I)}{R-X + Mg} \xrightarrow{CH_3CH_2OCH_2CH_3} \underset{\text{organomagnesium halide (Grignard reagent)}}{\overset{\delta^-}{R}-\overset{\delta^+}{Mg}-X} \quad \text{reacts like } R\!:^-\ \overset{+}{Mg}X$$

Grignard reagents may be made from primary, secondary, and tertiary alkyl halides, as well as from vinyl and aryl halides. Alkyl iodides are the most reactive halides, followed by bromides and chlorides. Alkyl fluorides generally do not react.

reactivity: $R-I > R-Br > R-Cl \gg R-F$

The following reactions show the formation of some typical Grignard reagents.

$$\underset{\text{iodomethane}}{CH_3-I} + Mg \xrightarrow{\text{ether}} \underset{\text{methylmagnesium iodide}}{CH_3-Mg-I}$$

$$\text{bromocyclohexane (C}_6\text{H}_{10}\text{(H)Br)} + Mg \xrightarrow{\text{ether}} \text{cyclohexylmagnesium bromide (C}_6\text{H}_{10}\text{(H)MgBr)}$$

$$\underset{\text{allyl bromide}}{H_2C{=}CH{-}CH_2{-}Br} + Mg \xrightarrow{\text{ether}} \underset{\text{allylmagnesium bromide}}{H_2C{=}CH{-}CH_2{-}MgBr}$$

10-8B Organolithium Reagents

Like magnesium, lithium reacts with alkyl halides, vinyl halides, and aryl halides to form organometallic compounds. Ether is not necessary for this reaction. **Organolithium reagents** are made and used in a wide variety of solvents, including alkanes.

$$\underset{(X = Cl, Br, \text{ or } I)}{R{-}X} + 2\,Li \longrightarrow Li^{+}\,{}^{-}X + \underset{\text{organolithium}}{R{-}Li} \quad \text{reacts like } R{:}^{-}\,Li^{+}$$

Examples

$$\underset{n\text{-butyl bromide}}{CH_3CH_2CH_2CH_2{-}Br} + 2\,Li \xrightarrow{\text{hexane}} \underset{n\text{-butyllithium}}{CH_3CH_2CH_2CH_2{-}Li} + LiBr$$

$$\underset{\text{vinyl chloride}}{H_2C{=}CH{-}Cl} + 2\,Li \xrightarrow{\text{pentane}} \underset{\text{vinyllithium}}{H_2C{=}CH{-}Li} + LiCl$$

$$\underset{\text{bromobenzene}}{C_6H_5{-}Br} + 2\,Li \xrightarrow{\text{ether}} \underset{\text{phenyllithium}}{C_6H_5{-}Li} + LiBr$$

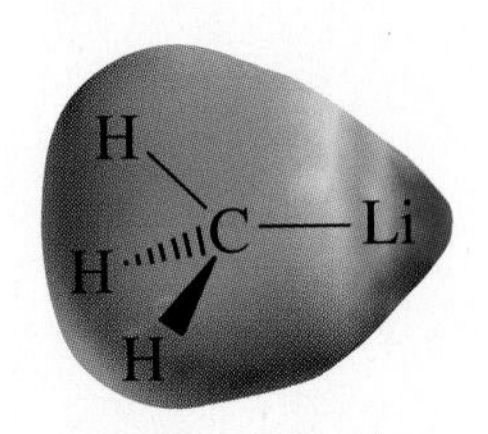

EPM of CH_3Li

The electrostatic potential map (EPM) of methyllithium is shown at left. The blue (electron-poor) color of the metal results from its partial positive charge, and the red (electron-rich) color of the methyl group shows its partial negative charge.

PROBLEM 10-11

Which of the following compounds are suitable solvents for Grignard reactions?

(a) *n*-hexane **(b)** $CH_3{-}O{-}CH_3$ **(c)** $CHCl_3$
(d) cyclohexane **(e)** benzene **(f)** $CH_3OCH_2CH_2OCH_3$

(g) 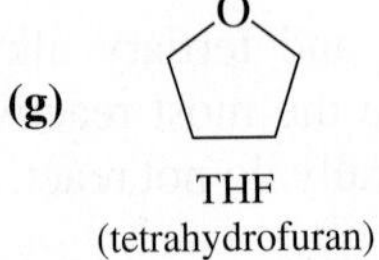

THF (tetrahydrofuran)

(h) 1,4-dioxane

PROBLEM 10-12

Predict the products of the following reactions.

(a) $CH_3CH_2Br + Mg \xrightarrow{\text{ether}}$

(b) isobutyl iodide $+ 2\,Li \xrightarrow{\text{hexane}}$

(c) 1-bromo-4-fluorocyclohexane $+ Mg \xrightarrow{\text{THF}}$

(d) $CH_2{=}CCl{-}CH_2CH_3 + 2\,Li \xrightarrow{\text{ether}}$

10-9 Addition of Organometallic Reagents to Carbonyl Compounds

Because they resemble carbanions, Grignard and organolithium reagents are strong nucleophiles and strong bases. Their most useful nucleophilic reactions are additions to carbonyl (C=O) groups, much like we saw with acetylide ions (Section 9-7B). The carbonyl group is polarized, with a partial positive charge on carbon and a partial negative charge on oxygen. The positively charged carbon is electrophilic; attack by a nucleophile places a negative charge on the electronegative oxygen atom.

$$R:^- + \overset{\delta+}{C}=\overset{\delta-}{\ddot{O}}: \longrightarrow R-C-\ddot{O}:^-$$

The product of this nucleophilic attack is an alkoxide ion, a strong base. Addition of water or a dilute acid in a second step protonates the alkoxide to give the alcohol.

$$\underset{\text{alkoxide}}{R-C-\ddot{O}:^-} \quad \underset{(\text{or } H_3O^+)}{H-\ddot{O}-H} \longrightarrow R-C-\ddot{O}H + {}^-:\ddot{O}H$$

Either a Grignard reagent or an organolithium reagent can serve as the nucleophile in this addition to a carbonyl group. The following discussions refer to Grignard reagents, but they also apply to organolithium reagents. Key Mechanism 10-1 shows that the Grignard reagent first adds to the carbonyl group to form an alkoxide ion. Addition of dilute acid (in a separate step) protonates the alkoxide to give the alcohol.

We are interested primarily in the reactions of Grignard reagents with ketones and aldehydes. **Ketones** are compounds with two alkyl groups bonded to a carbonyl group. **Aldehydes** have one alkyl group and one hydrogen atom bonded to the carbonyl group. **Formaldehyde** has two hydrogen atoms bonded to the carbonyl group.

$$\underset{\text{a ketone}}{R_2C=O} \qquad \underset{\text{an aldehyde}}{R(H)C=O} \qquad \underset{\text{formaldehyde}}{H_2C=O}$$

The electrostatic potential map (EPM) of formaldehyde shows the polarization of the carbonyl group, with an electron-rich (red) region around oxygen and an electron-poor (blue) region near carbon.

H, C=O, H

EPM of formaldehyde

KEY MECHANISM 10-1 Grignard Reactions

Grignard and organolithium reagents provide some of the best methods for assembling a carbon skeleton. These strong nucleophiles add to ketones and aldehydes to give alkoxide ions, which are protonated to give alcohols.

Formation of the Grignard reagent: Magnesium reacts with an alkyl halide in an anhydrous ether solution.

$$R'-X + Mg \xrightarrow{\text{ether}} R'-MgX$$

(Continued)

Reaction 1: The Grignard reagent attacks a carbonyl compound to form an alkoxide salt.

$$\overset{\delta-}{R'}-\overset{\delta+}{MgX} + R_2C=\ddot{O}: \xrightarrow{\text{ether}} R'-CR_2-\ddot{O}:^{-}\ {}^{+}MgX$$

magnesium alkoxide salt

Reaction 2: After the first reaction is complete, water or dilute acid is added to protonate the alkoxide and give the alcohol.

$$R'-CR_2-\ddot{O}:^{-}\ {}^{+}MgX \xrightarrow{H-\ddot{O}-H} R'-CR_2-\ddot{O}-H + XMgOH$$

magnesium alkoxide salt → alcohol

EXAMPLE: Addition of phenylmagnesium bromide to acetone.

Formation of the Grignard reagent: Magnesium reacts with bromobenzene in an ether solution to give phenylmagnesium bromide.

$$C_6H_5-Br + Mg \xrightarrow{\text{ether}} C_6H_5-MgBr$$

phenylmagnesium bromide

Reaction 1: The Grignard reagent attacks a carbonyl compound to form an alkoxide salt.

$$C_6H_5-MgBr + (H_3C)_2C=\ddot{O}: \xrightarrow{\text{ether}} C_6H_5-C(CH_3)_2-\ddot{O}:^{-}\ {}^{+}MgBr$$

magnesium alkoxide salt

Reaction 2: After the first reaction is complete, water or dilute acid is added to protonate the alkoxide and give the alcohol.

$$C_6H_5-C(CH_3)_2-\ddot{O}:^{-}\ {}^{+}MgBr \xrightarrow{H-\ddot{O}-H} C_6H_5-C(CH_3)_2-OH + BrMgOH$$

magnesium alkoxide salt → 2-phenyl-2-propanol

QUESTION: What would be the result if water were accidentally added in the first reaction with the Grignard reagent and the carbonyl compound?

10-9A Addition to Formaldehyde: Formation of Primary Alcohols

Addition of a Grignard reagent to formaldehyde, followed by protonation, gives a primary alcohol with one more carbon atom than in the Grignard reagent.

$$\underset{\text{Grignard reagent}}{\boxed{R}-MgX} + \underset{\text{formaldehyde}}{H_2C{=}O} \xrightarrow{\text{ether}} \boxed{R}-\overset{H}{\underset{H}{C}}-O^{-}\ {}^{+}MgX \xrightarrow{H_3O^+} \underset{\text{primary alcohol}}{\boxed{R}-CH_2-OH}$$

For example,

$$\underset{\text{butylmagnesium bromide}}{CH_3CH_2CH_2CH_2-MgBr} + \underset{\text{formaldehyde}}{H_2C{=}O} \xrightarrow[\text{(2) } H_3O^+]{\text{(1) ether solvent}} \underset{\text{1-pentanol (92\%)}}{CH_3CH_2CH_2CH_2-\overset{H}{\underset{H}{C}}-OH}$$

PROBLEM 10-13

Show how you would synthesize the following primary alcohols by adding an appropriate Grignard reagent to formaldehyde.

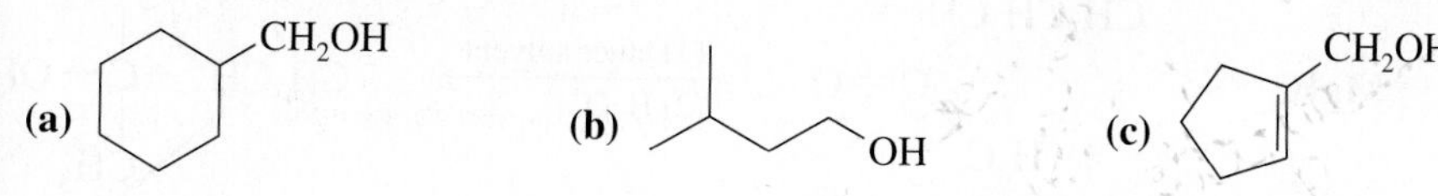

problem-solving Hint

Note the use of $\xrightarrow[(2)]{(1)}$ to show separate reactions with one reaction arrow.

10-9B Addition to Aldehydes: Formation of Secondary Alcohols

Grignard reagents add to aldehydes to give, after protonation, secondary alcohols.

$$\underset{\text{Grignard reagent}}{\boxed{R}-MgX} + \underset{\text{aldehyde}}{R'(H)C{=}O} \xrightarrow{\text{ether}} \boxed{R}-\overset{R'}{\underset{H}{C}}-O^{-}\ {}^{+}MgX \xrightarrow{H_3O^+} \underset{\text{secondary alcohol}}{\boxed{R}-\overset{R'}{\underset{H}{C}}-OH}$$

The two alkyl groups of the secondary alcohol are the alkyl group from the Grignard reagent and the alkyl group that was bonded to the carbonyl group of the aldehyde.

$$CH_3CH_2-MgBr + \underset{\text{acetaldehyde}}{H_3C(H)C{=}O} \xrightarrow{\text{ether}} CH_3-CH_2-\overset{CH_3}{\underset{H}{C}}-O^{-}\ {}^{+}MgBr \xrightarrow{H_3O^+} \underset{\text{2-butanol (85\%)}}{CH_3CH_2-\overset{CH_3}{\underset{H}{C}}-OH}$$

problem-solving Hint

A secondary alcohol has two groups on the carbinol carbon atom. Consider two possible reactions, with either group added as the Grignard reagent.

PROBLEM 10-14

Show two ways you could synthesize each of the following secondary alcohols by adding an appropriate Grignard reagent to an aldehyde.

(a) 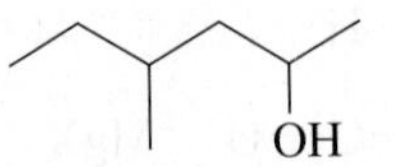 [skeletal structure with OH] (b) 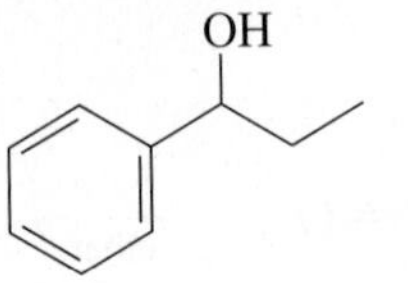 [phenyl–CH(OH)–CH₂CH₃] (c) 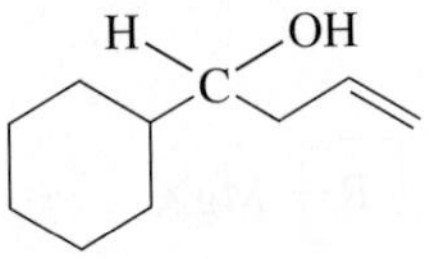 [cyclohexyl–C(H)(OH)–CH₂CH=CH₂]

10-9C Addition to Ketones: Formation of Tertiary Alcohols

A ketone has two alkyl groups bonded to its carbonyl carbon atom. Addition of a Grignard reagent, followed by protonation, gives a tertiary alcohol, with three alkyl groups bonded to the carbinol carbon atom.

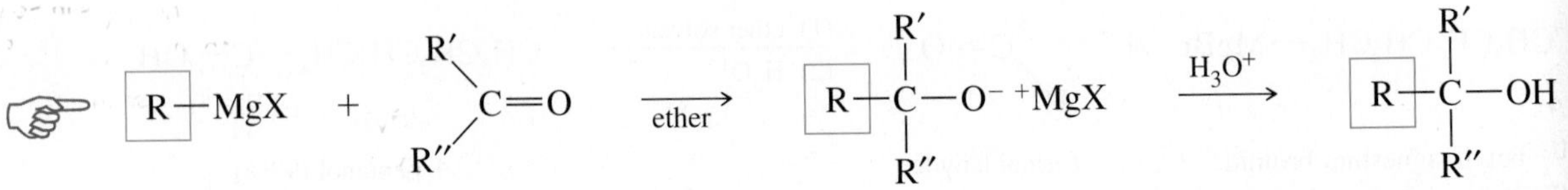

$$\underset{\text{Grignard reagent}}{R-MgX} + \underset{\text{ketone}}{R'R''C{=}O} \xrightarrow{\text{ether}} R-C(R')(R'')-O^{-}\ {}^{+}MgX \xrightarrow{H_3O^+} \underset{\text{tertiary alcohol}}{R-C(R')(R'')-OH}$$

Two of the alkyl groups are the two originally bonded to the ketone carbonyl group. The third alkyl group comes from the Grignard reagent.

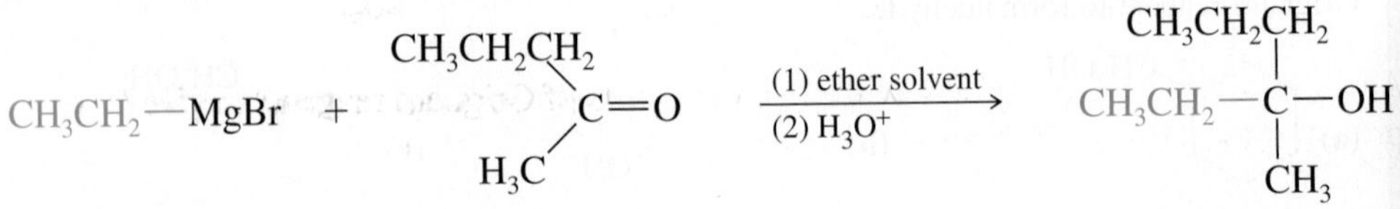

$$CH_3CH_2-MgBr + \underset{\text{2-pentanone}}{(CH_3CH_2CH_2)(H_3C)C{=}O} \xrightarrow[(2)\ H_3O^+]{(1)\ \text{ether solvent}} \underset{\text{3-methyl-3-hexanol (90\%)}}{CH_3CH_2-C(CH_2CH_2CH_3)(CH_3)-OH}$$

SOLVED PROBLEM 10-2

Show how you would synthesize the following alcohol from compounds containing no more than five carbon atoms.

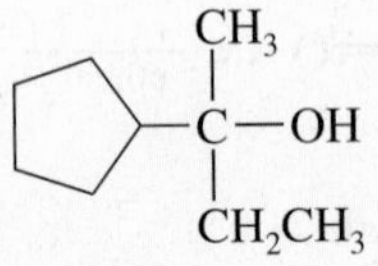

$$\text{cyclopentyl}-C(CH_3)(CH_2CH_3)-OH$$

SOLUTION

This is a tertiary alcohol; any one of the three alkyl groups might be added in the form of a Grignard reagent. We can propose three combinations of Grignard reagents with ketones:

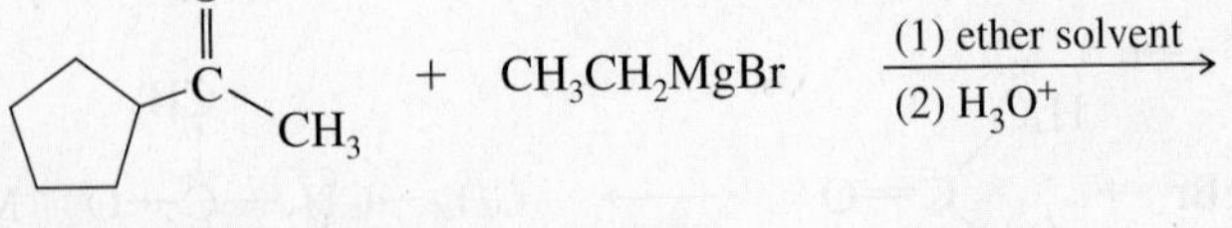

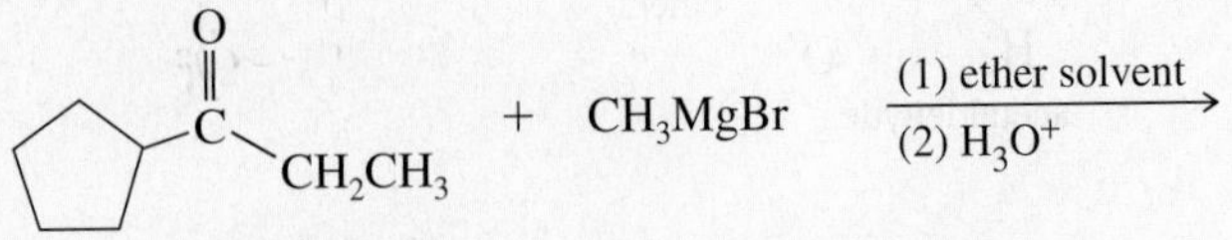

$$\text{cyclopentyl}-C({=}O)-CH_3 + CH_3CH_2MgBr \xrightarrow[(2)\ H_3O^+]{(1)\ \text{ether solvent}}$$

$$\text{cyclopentyl}-C({=}O)-CH_2CH_3 + CH_3MgBr \xrightarrow[(2)\ H_3O^+]{(1)\ \text{ether solvent}}$$

$$CH_3C(=O)CH_2CH_3 + \text{cyclopentyl}-MgBr \xrightarrow[(2)\ H_3O^+]{(1)\ \text{ether solvent}}$$

Any of these three syntheses would probably work, but only the third begins with fragments containing no more than five carbon atoms. The other two syntheses would require further steps to generate the ketones from compounds containing no more than five carbon atoms.

PROBLEM 10-15

Show how you would synthesize each tertiary alcohol by adding an appropriate Grignard reagent to a ketone.

(a) 3-phenylhexan-3-ol (3 ways) **(b)** Ph_3COH
(c) 1-ethylcyclopentanol **(d)** 2-cyclopentyl-2-pentanol

problem-solving **Hint**

A tertiary alcohol has three groups on the carbinol carbon atom. Consider three possible reactions (as in Solved Problem 10-2), with each of these groups added as the Grignard reagent.

10-9D Addition to Acid Chlorides and Esters

Acid chlorides and **esters** are derivatives of carboxylic acids. In such **acid derivatives,** the —OH group of a carboxylic acid is replaced by other electron-withdrawing groups. In acid chlorides, the hydroxyl group of the acid is replaced by a chlorine atom. In esters, the hydroxyl group is replaced by an alkoxyl (—O—R) group.

$$\underset{\text{carboxylic acid}}{R-C(=O)-OH} \qquad \underset{\text{acid chloride}}{R-C(=O)-Cl} \qquad \underset{\text{ester}}{R-C(=O)-O-R'}$$

Acid chlorides and esters react with two equivalents of Grignard reagents to give (after protonation) tertiary alcohols.

$$2\ R-MgX + \underset{\text{acid chloride}}{R'-C(=O)-Cl} \xrightarrow[(2)\ H_3O^+]{(1)\ \text{ether solvent}} \underset{\text{tertiary alcohol}}{R'-C(R)(R)-OH}$$

$$2\ R-MgX + \underset{\text{ester}}{R'-C(=O)-OR''} \xrightarrow[(2)\ H_3O^+]{(1)\ \text{ether solvent}} \underset{\text{tertiary alcohol}}{R'-C(R)(R)-OH}$$

Addition of the first equivalent of the Grignard reagent produces an unstable intermediate that expels a chloride ion (in the acid chloride) or an alkoxide ion (in the ester), to give a ketone. The alkoxide ion is a suitable leaving group in this reaction because its leaving stabilizes a negatively charged intermediate in a fast, strongly exothermic step.

Attack on an acid chloride

$$R-MgX + \underset{\text{acid chloride}}{R'(Cl)C=\ddot{O}:} \longrightarrow \underset{\text{intermediate}}{R-C(R')(:\ddot{Cl}:)-\ddot{O}:^-} \longrightarrow \underset{\text{ketone}}{R'(R)C=\ddot{O}:} \quad :\ddot{Cl}:^-$$

Attack on an ester

$$R-MgX + R'(R''-\ddot{O}-)C=\ddot{O}: \longrightarrow R-C(R')(-\ddot{O}:^-)(-\ddot{O}-R'') \longrightarrow R'(R)C=O \quad {}^-:\ddot{O}-R''$$

ester · intermediate · ketone

The ketone reacts with a second equivalent of the Grignard reagent, forming the magnesium salt of a tertiary alkoxide. Protonation gives a tertiary alcohol with one of its alkyl groups derived from the acid chloride or ester, and the other two derived from the Grignard reagent.

$$R-Mg-X + R'(R)C=\ddot{O}: \longrightarrow R-C(R')(R)-\ddot{O}:^- \ {}^+MgX \xrightarrow{H_3O^+} R-C(R')(R)-OH$$

Grignard (second equivalent) · ketone intermediate · alkoxide · tertiary alcohol

problem-solving Hint

When making a tertiary alcohol with two identical alkyl groups, consider using an acid chloride or ester.

Consider an example using an ester. When an excess of ethylmagnesium bromide is added to methyl benzoate, the first equivalent adds and methoxide is expelled, giving propiophenone. Addition of a second equivalent, followed by protonation, gives a tertiary alcohol: 3-phenyl-3-pentanol.

$$CH_3CH_2-MgBr + Ph-C(=\ddot{O}:)-OCH_3 \longrightarrow Ph-C(-\ddot{O}:^-)(-\ddot{O}CH_3)(CH_2CH_3) \longrightarrow Ph(CH_3CH_2)C=\ddot{O}: \quad {}^-:\ddot{O}CH_3$$

first equivalent · methyl benzoate · propiophenone

$$CH_3CH_2-MgBr + Ph(CH_3CH_2)C=\ddot{O}: \longrightarrow CH_3CH_2-C(Ph)(CH_2CH_3)-\ddot{O}:^- \ {}^+MgBr \xrightarrow{H_3O^+} CH_3CH_2-C(Ph)(CH_2CH_3)-OH$$

second equivalent · propiophenone · 3-phenyl-3-pentanol (82

PROBLEM 10-16

Propose a mechanism for the reaction of acetyl chloride with phenylmagnesium bromide to give 1,1-diphenylethanol.

$$CH_3-\overset{O}{\overset{\|}{C}}-Cl + 2\ C_6H_5-MgBr \xrightarrow[(2)\ H_3O^+]{(1)\ \text{ether solvent}} CH_3-\overset{OH}{\overset{|}{C}}(C_6H_5)_2$$

acetyl chloride — phenylmagnesium bromide — 1,1-diphenylethanol

PROBLEM 10-17

Show how you would add Grignard reagents to acid chlorides or esters to synthesize the following alcohols.

(a) Ph_3C-OH **(b)** 3-ethyl-2-methyl-3-pentanol
(c) dicyclohexylphenylmethanol

PROBLEM 10-18

A formate ester, such as ethyl formate, reacts with an excess of a Grignard reagent to give (after protonation) secondary alcohols with two identical alkyl groups.

$$2\ R-MgX + H-\overset{O}{\overset{\|}{C}}-O-CH_2CH_3 \xrightarrow[(2)\ H_3O^+]{(1)\ \text{ether solvent}} R-\overset{OH}{\overset{|}{CH}}-R$$

ethyl formate — secondary alcohol

problem-solving Hint

When making a secondary alcohol with identical alkyl groups, consider using a formate ester.

(a) Propose a mechanism to show how the reaction of ethyl formate with an excess of allylmagnesium bromide gives, after protonation, 1,6-heptadien-4-ol.

$$2\ H_2C=CH-CH_2MgBr + H-\overset{O}{\overset{\|}{C}}-OCH_2CH_3 \xrightarrow[(2)\ H_3O^+]{(1)\ \text{ether solvent}} (H_2C=CH-CH_2)_2CH-OH$$

allylmagnesium bromide — ethyl formate — 1,6-heptadien-4-ol (80%)

(b) Show how you would use reactions of Grignard reagents with ethyl formate to synthesize the following secondary alcohols.
(i) 3-pentanol **(ii)** diphenylmethanol **(iii)** *trans, trans*-2,7-nonadien-5-ol

10-9E Addition to Ethylene Oxide

Grignard reagents usually do not react with ethers, but **epoxides** are unusually reactive ethers because of their ring strain. Ethylene oxide reacts with Grignard reagents to give, after protonation, primary alcohols with *two* additional carbon atoms. Notice that the nucleophilic attack by the Grignard reagent opens the ring and relieves the ring strain.

$$R-MgX + \underset{\text{ethylene oxide}}{CH_2-CH_2(O)} \xrightarrow{\text{ether}} \underset{\text{alkoxide}}{R-CH_2-\overset{:\ddot{O}:^-\ ^+MgX}{\overset{|}{CH_2}}} \xrightarrow{H_3O^+} \underset{\text{primary alcohol}}{R-CH_2-\overset{OH}{\overset{|}{CH_2}}}$$

Example

$$CH_3(CH_2)_3-MgBr + CH_2-CH_2(O) \longrightarrow C_4H_9-CH_2-\overset{:\ddot{O}:^-\ ^+MgBr}{\overset{|}{CH_2}} \xrightarrow{H_3O^+} C_4H_9-CH_2-\overset{OH}{\overset{|}{CH_2}}$$

butylmagnesium bromide — ethylene oxide — 1-hexanol (61%)

problem-solving Hint

The reaction of a Grignard reagent with an epoxide is the only Grignard reaction we have seen where the new OH group is NOT on the same carbon atom where the Grignard formed a new bond. In this case, the new OH group appears on the second carbon from the new bond.

PROBLEM 10-19

Show how you would synthesize the following alcohols by adding Grignard reagents to ethylene oxide.

(a) 2-phenylethanol **(b)** 4-methyl-1-pentanol **(c)** (cyclohexane bearing CH_2CH_2OH and an adjacent CH_3)

PROBLEM 10-20

In Section 9-7B, we saw how acetylide ions add to carbonyl groups in much the same way as Grignard and organolithium reagents. Acetylide ions also add to ethylene oxide much like Grignard and organolithium reagents. Predict the products obtained by adding the following acetylide ions to ethylene oxide, followed by a dilute acid workup.

(a) $HC{\equiv}C:^-$ **(b)** $CH_3CH_2{-}C{\equiv}C:^-$

SUMMARY Grignard Reactions

1. Nucleophilic Additions to Carbonyl Compounds

$$R{-}MgX + H_2C{=}O \text{ (formaldehyde)} \xrightarrow[(2)\ H_3O^+]{(1)\ \text{ether solvent}} R{-}CH_2{-}OH \text{ (1° alcohol)}$$

$$R{-}MgX + R'HC{=}O \text{ (aldehyde)} \xrightarrow[(2)\ H_3O^+]{(1)\ \text{ether solvent}} R{-}CHR'{-}OH \text{ (2° alcohol)}$$

$$R{-}MgX + R'R''C{=}O \text{ (ketone)} \xrightarrow[(2)\ H_3O^+]{(1)\ \text{ether solvent}} R{-}CR'R''{-}OH \text{ (3° alcohol)}$$

$$2\ R{-}MgX + R'{-}C(=O){-}OR'' \text{ (ester or acid chloride)} \xrightarrow[(2)\ H_3O^+]{(1)\ \text{ether solvent}} R'{-}CR_2{-}OH$$

3° alcohol
two groups added

2. Nucleophilic Displacement of Epoxides

$$R{-}MgX + CH_2{-}CH_2 \text{ (ethylene oxide, O bridging)} \xrightarrow[(2)\ H_3O^+]{(1)\ \text{ether solvent}} R{-}CH_2CH_2{-}OH$$

1° alcohol
two carbons added

PROBLEM 10-21

Recall from Section 9-7 how acetylide ions are alkylated by displacing unhindered alkyl halides.

$$H{-}C{\equiv}C:^- \quad R{-}CH_2{-}Br \longrightarrow H{-}C{\equiv}C{-}CH_2{-}R + Br^-$$

Like acetylide ions, Grignard and organolithium reagents are strong bases and strong nucleophiles. Fortunately, they do not displace halides as easily as acetylide ions do. If they did displace alkyl halides, it would be impossible to form the reagents from alkyl halides because whenever a molecule of reagent formed, it would react with a molecule of the halide starting material. All that would be formed is a coupling product. In fact, coupling is a side reaction that hurts the yield of many Grignard reactions.

$$\text{R—Br} + \text{Mg} \xrightarrow{\text{ether}} \text{R—Mg—Br} \xrightarrow{\text{R—Br}} \text{R—R} + \text{MgBr}_2$$

undesirable coupling

If we *want* to couple two groups together efficiently, we can do it by using an organocopper reagent, a **lithium dialkylcuprate**, to couple with an alkyl halide.

$$\underset{\text{a lithium dialkylcuprate}}{\text{R}_2\text{CuLi}} + \text{R}'\text{—X} \longrightarrow \text{R—R}' + \text{R—Cu} + \text{LiX}$$

The lithium dialkylcuprate (also called a *Gilman reagent*) is formed by the reaction of two equivalents of the corresponding organolithium reagent (Section 10-8B) with cuprous iodide:

$$2\,\text{R—Li} + \text{CuI} \longrightarrow \text{R}_2\text{CuLi} + \text{LiI}$$

The coupling takes place as if a carbanion (R:^-) were present and the carbanion attacked the alkyl halide to display the halide ion. This is not necessarily the actual mechanism, however.

$$\text{R—}\underset{|}{\overset{}{\text{Cu}^-}}\ {}^+\text{Li} \;(\text{R}) \quad \text{—}\overset{|}{\underset{|}{\text{C}}}\text{—X} \longrightarrow \text{R—}\overset{|}{\underset{|}{\text{C}}}\text{—} \quad {}^-\text{:X}$$

(hypothetical mechanism)

Example

$$\underset{\text{2-chlorobutane}}{\text{CH}_3\text{CH}_2\underset{\text{CH}_3}{\underset{|}{\text{CH}}}\text{—Cl}} \xrightarrow[\text{(2) CuI}]{\text{(1) Li}} \underset{\text{lithium dialkylcuprate}}{\left(\text{CH}_3\text{CH}_2\underset{\text{CH}_3}{\underset{|}{\text{CH}}}\text{—}\right)_2\text{CuLi}}$$

$$\underset{\text{lithium dialkylcuprate}}{\left(\text{CH}_3\text{CH}_2\underset{\text{CH}_3}{\underset{|}{\text{CH}}}\text{—}\right)_2\text{CuLi}} \xrightarrow{\text{CH}_3\text{CH}_2\text{CH}_2\text{CH}_2\text{—Br}} \underset{\text{3-methylheptane (70\%)}}{\text{CH}_3\text{CH}_2\underset{\text{CH}_3}{\underset{|}{\text{CH}}}\text{—CH}_2\text{CH}_2\text{CH}_2\text{CH}_3}$$

Show how you would synthesize the following compounds from alkyl halides, vinyl halides, and aryl halides containing no more than six carbon atoms.

(a) *n*-octane
(b) vinylcyclohexane
(c) *n*-butylcyclohexane
(d) *trans*-3-octene

10-10 Side Reactions of Organometallic Reagents: Reduction of Alkyl Halides

Grignard and organolithium reagents are strong nucleophiles and strong bases. Besides their additions to carbonyl compounds, they react with other acidic or electrophilic compounds. In some cases, these are useful reactions, but they are often seen as annoying side reactions where a small impurity of water or an alcohol destroys the reagent.

10-10A Reactions with Acidic Compounds

Grignard and organolithium reagents react vigorously and irreversibly with water. Therefore, all reagents and solvents used in these reactions must be dry.

$$\overset{\delta^-}{R}\text{—}\overset{\delta^+}{MgX} \;+\; H\text{—}O\text{—}H \;\longrightarrow\; R\text{—}H \;+\; XMgOH$$

For example, consider the reaction of ethyllithium with water:

$$\underset{\text{ethyllithium}}{CH_3\text{—}\overset{\delta^-}{CH_2}\text{—}\overset{\delta^+}{Li}} \;+\; H\text{—}O\text{—}H \;\longrightarrow\; \underset{\text{ethane}}{CH_3\text{—}CH_2\text{—}H} \;+\; Li^+\ {}^-OH$$

The products are strongly favored in this reaction. Ethane is a *very* weak acid (K_a of about 10^{-50}), so the reverse reaction (abstraction of a proton from ethane by lithium hydroxide) is unlikely. When ethyllithium is added to water, ethane instantly bubbles to the surface.

Why would we ever want to add an organometallic reagent to water? This is a method for reducing an alkyl halide to an alkane:

$$R\text{—}X \;+\; Mg \xrightarrow{\text{ether}} R\text{—}MgX \xrightarrow{H_2O} R\text{—}H \;+\; XMgOH$$

$$R\text{—}X \;+\; 2\,Li \longrightarrow R\text{—}Li \;+\; LiX \xrightarrow{H_2O} R\text{—}H \;+\; LiOH$$

The overall reaction is a *reduction* because it replaces the electronegative halogen atom with a hydrogen atom. In particular, this reaction provides a way to "label" a compound with deuterium (^2H, a heavy isotope of hydrogen) at any position where a halogen is present.

$$CH_3\text{—}\underset{}{\overset{CH_3}{CH}}\text{—}\underset{Br}{CH}\text{—}CH_3 \xrightarrow[\text{ether}]{Mg} CH_3\text{—}\overset{CH_3}{CH}\text{—}\underset{MgBr}{CH}\text{—}CH_3 \xrightarrow{D\text{—}\ddot{O}\text{—}D} CH_3\text{—}\overset{CH_3}{CH}\text{—}\underset{D}{CH}\text{—}CH_3 \;+\; BrMgOD$$

In addition to O—H groups, the protons of N—H and S—H groups and the hydrogen atom of a terminal alkyne, —C≡C—H, are sufficiently acidic to protonate Grignard and organolithium reagents. Unless we want to protonate the reagent, compounds with these groups are considered incompatible with Grignard and organolithium reagents.

$$CH_3CH_2CH_2CH_2Li + (CH_3CH_2)_2NH \longrightarrow CH_3CH_2CH_2CH_3 + (CH_3CH_2CH)_2N^-\ Li^+$$

$$CH_3CH_2CH_2CH_2Li + CH_3(CH_2)_4\text{—}C{\equiv}C\text{—}H \longrightarrow CH_3CH_2CH_2CH_3 + CH_3(CH_2)_4\text{—}C{\equiv}C\text{—}Li$$

PROBLEM 10-22

Predict the products of the following reactions.

(a) *sec*-butylmagnesium iodide + D_2O ⟶

(b) *n*-butyllithium + CH_3CH_2OH ⟶

(c) isobutylmagnesium bromide + 1-butyne ⟶

(d) cyclohexyllithium + $CH_3\text{—}\overset{O}{\overset{\|}{C}}\text{—}OH$ (acetic acid) ⟶

(e) phenylmagnesium bromide + D_2O ⟶

10-10B Reactions with Electrophilic Multiple Bonds

Grignard reagents are useful because they add to the electrophilic double bonds of carbonyl groups. However, we must make sure that the *only* electrophilic double bond in the solution is the one we want the reagent to attack. There must be no electrophilic double (or triple) bonds in the solvent or in the Grignard reagent itself, or they will be attacked as well. Any multiple bond involving a strongly electronegative element is likely to be attacked, including C=O, S=O, C=N, N=O, and C≡N bonds.

In later chapters, we will encounter methods for *protecting* susceptible groups to prevent the reagent from attacking them. For now, simply remember that the following groups react with Grignard and organolithium reagents; avoid compounds containing these groups except for the one carbonyl group that gives the desired reaction.

Protonate the Grignard or organolithium: O—H, N—H, S—H, C≡C—H

Attacked by the Grignard or organolithium: C=O, C=N, C≡N, S=O, N=O

problem-solving Hint

Grignard reagents are incompatible with water or acid. Dilute acid is used *in a separate step* to hydrolyze the magnesium alkoxide.

correct: $\xrightarrow[(2)\ H_3O^+]{(1) RMgX}$

correct: $\xrightarrow[\text{ether}]{RMgX}$ $\xrightarrow{H_3O^+}$

incorrect: $\xrightarrow[H_3O^+]{RMgX}$

(The incorrect example means using a Grignard in aqueous acid.)

PROBLEM 10-23

Point out the flaws in the following incorrect Grignard syntheses.

(a) 3-bromopiperidine (N—H) $\xrightarrow{(1)\ Mg,\ ether;\ (2)\ Ph—CHO;\ (3)\ H_3O^+}$ piperidine (N—H) bearing CH(OH)—Ph ✗

(b) Br-substituted bicyclic lactone (O, =O) $\xrightarrow{(1)\ Mg,\ ether;\ (2)\ H_2C{=}O;\ (3)\ H_3O^+}$ $HOCH_2$-substituted bicyclic lactone ✗

(c) cyclohexyl-MgBr $\xrightarrow{CH_3\overset{O}{\overset{\|}{C}}CH_3,\ H_3O^+}$ cyclohexyl-C(CH_3)_2OH ✗

(d) 3-hydroxycyclohexanone (O, OH) $\xrightarrow{(1)\ CH_3CH_2MgBr;\ (2)\ H_3O^+}$ 1-ethylcyclohexane-1,3-diol (HO, CH_2CH_3, OH) ✗

10-11 Reduction of the Carbonyl Group: Synthesis of 1° and 2° Alcohols

Grignard reagents convert carbonyl compounds to alcohols by adding alkyl groups. **Hydride reagents** add a hydride ion ($H:^-$), reducing the carbonyl group to an alkoxide ion with no additional carbon atoms. Subsequent protonation gives the alcohol. Converting a ketone or an aldehyde to an alcohol involves adding two hydrogen atoms across the C=O bond: a reduction. Mechanism 10-2 shows the mechanism for this reduction.

The two most useful hydride reagents, sodium borohydride ($NaBH_4$) and lithium aluminum hydride ($LiAlH_4$), reduce carbonyl groups in excellent yields. These reagents are called *complex hydrides* because they do not have a simple hydride structure such as Na^+H^- or Li^+H^-. Instead, their hydrogen atoms, bearing partial negative charges, are

MECHANISM 10-2 Hydride Reduction of a Carbonyl Group

Sodium borohydride and lithium aluminum hydride reduce ketones and aldehydes to alcohols.

Reaction 1: Nucleophilic attack by the hydride ion forms an alkoxide ion.

$$H{:}^- + R_2C{=}\ddot{O}{:} \xrightarrow{\text{ether}} H{-}CR_2{-}\ddot{O}{:}^-$$

hydride ion → alkoxide ion

Reaction 2: After the first reaction is complete, water or dilute acid is added to protonate the alkoxide.

$$H{-}CR_2{-}\ddot{O}{:}^- \xrightarrow{H-\ddot{O}-H} H{-}CR_2{-}\ddot{O}H$$

alkoxide ion → alcohol

EXAMPLE: Hydride reduction of cyclopentanone to cyclopentanol.

Reaction 1: Nucleophilic attack by the hydride ion forms an alkoxide ion.

$$Na^+\ H{-}BH_2{-}H^- + \text{cyclopentanone} \xrightarrow{\text{ether}} \text{alkoxide ion}\ (H,\ {:}\ddot{O}{:}^-)\ Na^+ + BH_3$$

sodium borohydride, cyclopentanone, alkoxide ion

Reaction 2: After the first reaction is complete, water or dilute acid is added to protonate the alkoxide.

$$\text{alkoxide ion}\ (H,\ {:}\ddot{O}{:}^-) \xrightarrow{H-\ddot{O}-H} \text{cyclopentanol}\ (H,\ OH) + {}^-OH$$

alkoxide ion → cyclopentanol

covalently bonded to boron and aluminum atoms. This arrangement makes the hydride a better nucleophile while reducing its basicity.

$$Na^+\ H{-}\overset{H}{\underset{H}{B^-}}{-}H \qquad Li^+\ H{-}\overset{H}{\underset{H}{Al^-}}{-}H$$

sodium borohydride   lithium aluminum hydride

Aluminum is less electronegative than boron, so more of the negative charge in the AlH_4^- ion is borne by the hydrogen atoms. Therefore, lithium aluminum hydride (LAH) is a much stronger reducing agent, and it is much more difficult to work with than sodium borohydride. LAH reacts explosively with water and alcohols, liberating hydrogen gas and sometimes starting fires. Sodium borohydride reacts slowly with alcohols and with water as long as the pH is high (basic). Sodium borohydride is a convenient and highly selective reducing agent.

10-11A Uses of Sodium Borohydride

Sodium borohydride ($NaBH_4$) reduces aldehydes to primary alcohols, and ketones to secondary alcohols. The reactions take place in a wide variety of solvents, including alcohols, ethers, and water. The yields are generally excellent.

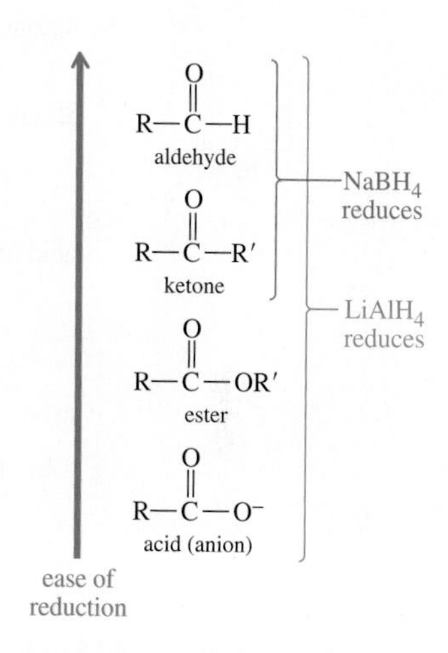

$$\text{C}_6\text{H}_{11}\text{—CHO} \xrightarrow{NaBH_4,\ CH_3CH_2OH} \text{C}_6\text{H}_{11}\text{—CH}_2\text{OH}$$

cyclohexane carbaldehyde → cyclohexyl methanol (95%)

$$CH_3\text{—}\overset{O}{\overset{\|}{C}}\text{—}CH_2CH_3 \xrightarrow{NaBH_4,\ CH_3OH} CH_3\text{—}\overset{OH}{\overset{|}{C}H}\text{—}CH_2CH_3$$

2-butanone → (±)-2-butanol (100%)

Sodium borohydride is selective; it usually does not react with carbonyl groups that are less reactive than ketones and aldehydes. For example, carboxylic acids and esters are unreactive toward borohydride reduction. Thus, sodium borohydride can reduce a ketone or an aldehyde in the presence of an acid or an ester.

$$O{=}\text{C}_6\text{H}_{10}\text{—}CH_2\text{—}\overset{O}{\overset{\|}{C}}\text{—}OCH_3 \xrightarrow{NaBH_4} \text{HO(H)C}_6\text{H}_{10}\text{—}CH_2\text{—}\overset{O}{\overset{\|}{C}}\text{—}OCH_3$$

10-11B Uses of Lithium Aluminum Hydride

Lithium aluminum hydride ($LiAlH_4$, abbreviated LAH) is a much stronger reagent than sodium borohydride. It easily reduces ketones and aldehydes and also the less-reactive carbonyl groups: those in acids, esters, and other acid derivatives (see Chapter 21). LAH reduces ketones to secondary alcohols, and it reduces aldehydes, acids, and esters to primary alcohols. The lithium salt of the alkoxide ion is initially formed, then the (cautious!) addition of dilute acid protonates the alkoxide. For example, LAH reduces both functional groups of the keto ester in the previous example.

problem-solving Hint

LAH and water are incompatible. Water is added in a *separate* hydrolysis step. An explosion and fire would result from the process indicated by $\xrightarrow[H_3O^+]{LiAlH_4}$.

$$O{=}\text{C}_6\text{H}_{10}\text{—}CH_2\text{—}\overset{O}{\overset{\|}{C}}\text{—}OCH_3 \xrightarrow[(2)\ H_3O^+]{(1)\ LiAlH_4} \text{HO(H)C}_6\text{H}_{10}\text{—}CH_2\text{—}CH_2OH$$

In summary, sodium borohydride is the best reagent for reduction of a simple ketone or aldehyde. Using $NaBH_4$, we can reduce a ketone or an aldehyde in the presence of an acid or an ester, but we do not have a method (so far) for reducing an acid or an ester in the presence of a ketone or an aldehyde. The sluggish acid or ester requires the use of $LiAlH_4$, and this reagent also reduces the ketone or aldehyde.

SUMMARY Reactions of $LiAlH_4$ and $NaBH_4$

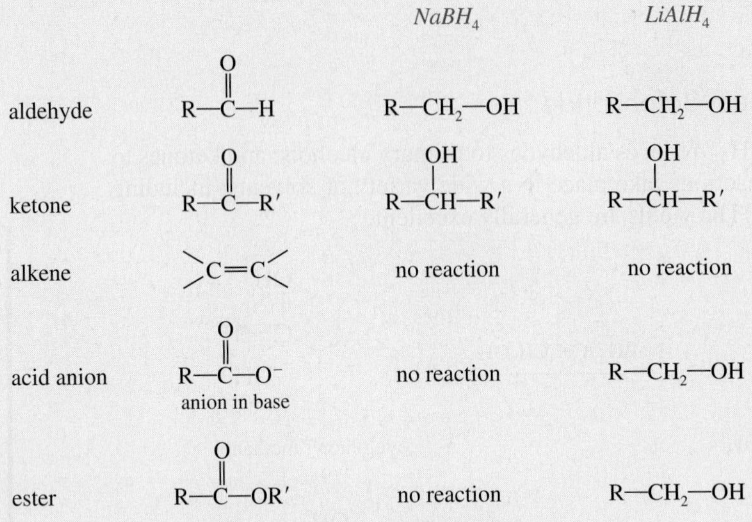

Note: The products shown are the final products, after hydrolysis of the alkoxide.

problem-solving Hint

When making a primary or secondary alcohol, you can consider adding an alkyl group last (as a Grignard reagent) or adding a hydrogen last (by reducing a ketone or aldehyde).

PROBLEM 10-24

Predict the products you would expect from the reaction of $NaBH_4$ with the following compounds.

(a) $CH_3—(CH_2)_8—CHO$ **(b)** $CH_3CH_2—C(=O)—OCH_3$ **(c)** Ph—COOH

(d) cyclohexanone **(e)** 3-formyl-5-oxocyclohexane with H—C(=O)— and —C(=O)—OCH$_3$ substituents **(f)** lactone ring (O, O) bearing —C(=O)—H

PROBLEM 10-25

Repeat Problem 10-24 using $LiAlH_4$ (followed by hydrolysis) as the reagent.

PROBLEM 10-26

Show how you would synthesize the following alcohols by reducing appropriate carbonyl compounds.

(a) 1-heptanol **(b)** 2-heptanol **(c)** 2-methyl-3-hexanol **(d)** bicyclic lactone (O, =O) bearing OH

10-11C Catalytic Hydrogenation of Ketones and Aldehydes

Reducing a ketone or an aldehyde to an alcohol involves adding two hydrogen atoms across the C=O bond. This addition can be accomplished by catalytic hydrogenation, commonly using Raney nickel as the catalyst.

$$-C(=O)- + H_2 \xrightarrow{\text{Raney Ni}} -CH(OH)-$$

Raney nickel is a finely divided hydrogen-bearing form of nickel made by treating a nickel–aluminum alloy with a strong sodium hydroxide solution. The aluminum in the alloy reacts to form hydrogen, leaving behind a finely divided nickel powder saturated with hydrogen. Raney nickel is an effective catalyst for the hydrogenation of ketones and aldehydes to alcohols. Carbon–carbon double bonds are also reduced under these conditions, however, so any alkene double bonds in the starting material will also be reduced. In most cases, sodium borohydride is more convenient for reducing simple ketones and aldehydes.

$$H_2C{=}CH{-}CH_2{-}C(CH_3)_2{-}CHO + 2\,H_2 \xrightarrow{\text{Raney Ni}} CH_3{-}CH_2{-}CH_2{-}C(CH_3)_2{-}CH_2OH$$

2,2-dimethyl-4-pentenal → 2,2-dimethyl-1-pentanol (94%)

$$H_2C{=}CH{-}CH_2{-}C(CH_3)_2{-}CHO \xrightarrow[\text{(for comparison)}]{NaBH_4} H_2C{=}CH{-}CH_2{-}C(CH_3)_2{-}CH_2OH$$

2,2-dimethylpent-4-en-1-ol

SUMMARY Alcohol Syntheses by Nucleophilic Additions to Carbonyl Groups

(Alcohol syntheses from alkenes and alkyl halides were summarized in Section 10-7.)

1. *Addition of a Grignard or organolithium reagent* (Section 10-9)

$$-C(=O)- + R{-}MgX \xrightarrow{\text{ether}} -C(R)(O^-\,{}^+MgX)- \xrightarrow{H_3O^+} -C(R)(OH)-$$

a. *Addition to formaldehyde gives a primary alcohol*

$$CH_3CH_2MgBr + H_2C{=}O \xrightarrow[(2)\ H_3O^+]{(1)\ \text{ether solvent}} CH_3CH_2{-}CH_2{-}OH$$

ethylmagnesium bromide → 1-propanol

b. *Addition to an aldehyde gives a secondary alcohol*

$$C_6H_5{-}MgBr + CH_3{-}C(=O){-}H \xrightarrow[(2)\ H_3O^+]{(1)\ \text{ether solvent}} C_6H_5{-}CH(CH_3){-}OH$$

phenylmagnesium bromide + acetaldehyde → 1-phenylethanol

(*Continued*)

c. *Addition to a ketone gives a tertiary alcohol*

$$CH_3CH_2MgCl + \text{cyclohexanone} \xrightarrow[\text{(2) } H_3O^+]{\text{(1) ether}} \text{1-ethylcyclohexanol (OH, } CH_2CH_3\text{)}$$

cyclohexanone — 1-ethylcyclohexanol

d. *Addition to an acid halide or an ester gives a tertiary alcohol*

$$CH_3-\overset{O}{\overset{\|}{C}}-Cl \text{ (acetyl chloride) or } CH_3-\overset{O}{\overset{\|}{C}}-OCH_3 \text{ (methyl acetate)} \xrightarrow[\text{(2) } H_3O^+]{\text{(1) 2 cyclohexyl-MgBr (cyclohexylmagnesium bromide)}} CH_3-\overset{OH}{\overset{|}{C}}(C_6H_{11})_2$$

acetyl chloride or methyl acetate — 1,1-dicyclohexylethanol

e. *Addition to ethylene oxide gives a primary alcohol (with two additional carbon atoms added)*

$$\text{cyclohexyl-MgBr} \xrightarrow[\text{(2) } H_3O^+]{\text{(1) } CH_2-CH_2 \text{ (O bridged)}} \text{cyclohexyl-}CH_2CH_2OH$$

cyclohexylmagnesium bromide — 2-cyclohexylethanol

2. *Reduction of carbonyl compounds* (Section 10-11)
   a. *Catalytic hydrogenation of aldehydes and ketones*

$$-\overset{O}{\overset{\|}{C}}- + H_2 \xrightarrow{\text{Raney Ni}} -\overset{OH}{\overset{|}{CH}}-$$

This method is usually not as selective or as effective as the use of hydride reagents.

b. *Use of hydride reagents*
   (1) Reduction of an aldehyde gives a primary alcohol

$$C_6H_5-\overset{O}{\overset{\|}{C}}-H \xrightarrow{NaBH_4} C_6H_5-CH_2OH$$

benzaldehyde — benzyl alcohol

   (2) Reduction of a ketone gives a secondary alcohol

$$\text{cyclohexanone} \xrightarrow{NaBH_4} \text{cyclohexanol (H, OH)}$$

cyclohexanone — cyclohexanol

(3) Reduction of an acid or ester gives a primary alcohol

$$\left.\begin{array}{c} CH_3-(CH_2)_8-\overset{O}{\overset{\|}{C}}-OH \\ \text{decanoic acid} \\ CH_3-(CH_2)_8-\overset{O}{\overset{\|}{C}}-OCH_3 \\ \text{methyl decanoate} \end{array}\right\} \xrightarrow[(2)\ H_3O^+]{(1)\ LiAlH_4} \underset{\text{1-decanol}}{CH_3-(CH_2)_8-CH_2-OH}$$

10-12 Thiols (Mercaptans)

Thiols are sulfur analogues of alcohols, with an $-SH$ group in place of the alcohol $-OH$ group. Oxygen and sulfur are in the same column of the periodic table (group VIA), with oxygen in the second row and sulfur in the third. IUPAC names for thiols are derived from the alkane names, using the suffix *-thiol*. Thiols are also called **mercaptans** ("captures mercury") because they form stable heavy-metal derivatives. Common names are formed like those of alcohols, using the name of the alkyl group with the word *mercaptan*. The $-SH$ group itself is called a *mercapto* group.

	CH_3-SH	$CH_3CH_2CH_2CH_2-SH$	$CH_3CH=CHCH_2-SH$	$HS-CH_2CH_2-OH$
IUPAC name:	methanethiol	1-butanethiol	2-butene-1-thiol	2-mercaptoethanol
common name:	methyl mercaptan	*n*-butyl mercaptan		

Thiols' ability to complex heavy metals has proved useful for making antidotes to heavy-metal poisoning. For example, in World War II the Allies were concerned that the Germans would use lewisite, a volatile arsenic compound, as a chemical warfare agent. Thiols complex strongly with arsenic, and British scientists developed dimercaprol (2,3-dimercapto-1-propanol) as an effective antidote. The Allies came to refer to this compound as "British anti-lewisite" (BAL), a name that is still used. Dimercaprol is useful against a variety of heavy metals, including arsenic, mercury, and gold.

$$\underset{\text{lewisite}}{(Cl)(H)C=C(H)(AsCl_2)} \qquad \underset{\substack{\text{dimercaprol} \\ \text{British anti-lewisite (BAL)}}}{\underset{SH\quad\ \ SH\quad\ \ OH}{CH_2-CH-CH_2}}$$

The odor of thiols is their strongest characteristic. **Skunk** scent is composed mainly of 3-methylbutane-1-thiol and 2-butene-1-thiol, with small amounts of other thiols. Ethanethiol is added to natural gas (odorless methane) to give it the characteristic "gassy" odor for detecting leaks.

Offensive use of thiols. Skunks spray thiols to protect themselves from people, dogs, and other animals.

Although oxygen is more electronegative than sulfur, thiols are more acidic than alcohols. Their enhanced acidity results from two effects: First, $S-H$ bonds are generally weaker than $O-H$ bonds, making $S-H$ bonds easier to break. Second, the

thiolate ion (R—S⁻) has its negative charge on sulfur, which allows the charge to be delocalized over a larger region than the negative charge of an alkoxide ion, borne on a smaller oxygen atom. Thiolate ions are easily formed by treating the thiol with aqueous sodium hydroxide.

Garlic has served throughout history as a remedy for numerous diseases. Movies have often depicted its power to repel werewolves and vampires. The characteristic garlic odor derives from the many sulfur compounds it contains. One of the major constituents is allicin, a compound with antibacterial properties.

allicin

$$CH_3{-}CH_2{-}SH \; + \; {}^{-}OH \; \rightleftharpoons \; CH_3{-}CH_2{-}S^{-} \; + \; H_2O$$

ethanethiol, $pK_a = 10.5$; ethanethiolate; H_2O $pK_a = 15.7$

$$C_6H_5{-}SH \; + \; {}^{-}OH \; \rightleftharpoons \; C_6H_5{-}S^{-} \; + \; H_2O$$

benzenethiol (thiophenol), $pK_a = 7.8$; benzenethiolate; H_2O $pK_a = 15.7$

For comparison

$$CH_3{-}CH_2{-}OH \; + \; {}^{-}OH \; \rightleftharpoons \; CH_3{-}CH_2{-}O^{-} \; + \; H_2O$$

ethanol, $pK_a = 15.9$; ethoxide; H_2O $pK_a = 15.7$

PROBLEM 10-27

Arrange the following compounds in order of decreasing acidity.

CH_3COOH CH_3OH CH_3CH_3 CH_3SO_3H CH_3NH_2 CH_3SH $CH_3C{\equiv}CH$

Thiols can be prepared by S_N2 reactions of sodium hydrosulfide with unhindered alkyl halides. The thiol product is still nucleophilic, so a large excess of hydrosulfide is used to prevent the product from undergoing a second alkylation to give a sulfide (R—S—R).

$$Na^{+} \; H{-}\ddot{S}{:}^{-} \; + \; R{-}X \; \longrightarrow \; R{-}SH \; + \; Na^{+}\,{}^{-}X$$

sodium hydrosulfide; alkyl halide; thiol

A protein can be made that withstands higher temperatures by the introduction of additional disulfide bonds. For example, laundry detergents frequently contain enzymes to remove protein and blood stains. By replacing strategically located amino acid residues with cysteines, a modified enzyme results that stays in its active conformation in hot water.

Unlike alcohols, thiols are easily oxidized to give a dimer called a **disulfide**. The reverse reaction, reduction of the disulfide to the thiol, takes place under reducing conditions. Formation and cleavage of disulfide linkages is an important aspect of protein chemistry (Chapter 24), where disulfide "bridges" between cysteine amino acid residues hold the protein chain in its active conformation.

$$R{-}SH \; + \; HS{-}R \; \underset{Zn,\ HCl}{\overset{Br_2}{\rightleftharpoons}} \; R{-}S{-}S{-}R \; + \; 2\,HBr$$

two molecules of thiol; disulfide

Example

$$2\; H_2N{-}CH(CH_2SH){-}C(=O){-}OH \; \underset{[H]\ (reduce)}{\overset{[O]\ (oxidize)}{\rightleftharpoons}} \; H_2N{-}CH(COOH){-}CH_2{-}S{-}S{-}CH_2{-}CH(COOH){-}NH_2 \; + \; H_2O$$

two cysteine residues; cystine disulfide bridge

More examples of disulfide bridges appear in Section 24-8C.

Just as mild oxidation converts thiols to disulfides, vigorous oxidation converts them to **sulfonic acids**. $KMnO_4$ or nitric acid (HNO_3), or even bleach (NaOCl), can be used as the oxidant for this reaction. Any Lewis structure of a sulfonic acid requires either separation of formal charges or more than 8 electrons around sulfur. Sulfur can have an expanded octet, as it does in SF_4 (10 electrons) and SF_6 (12 electrons). The three resonance forms shown here are most commonly used. Organic chemists tend to use the form with an expanded octet, and inorganic chemists tend to use the forms with charge separation.

R—S—H (thiol) $\xrightarrow[\text{(vigorous oxidation)}]{KMnO_4 \text{ or } HNO_3}$ [R—S(=O)(=O)—O—H (expanded octet) ⟷ R—S⁺(—O⁻)(=O)—O—H (both) ⟷ R—S²⁺(—O⁻)(—O⁻)—O—H (charge separation)]

sulfonic acid

Example

benzenethiol (C₆H₅—SH) $\xrightarrow[\text{(boil)}]{HNO_3}$ benzenesulfonic acid (C₆H₅—S(=O)(=O)—OH)

PROBLEM 10-28

Give IUPAC names for the following compounds.

(a) $CH_3CH(CH_3)CH_2CH(SH)CH_3$

(b) $(CH_3CH_2)(CH_3)C{=}C(CH_2SH)(CH_3)$

(c) cyclohexene ring bearing SH

PROBLEM 10-29

Authentic skunk spray has become valuable for use in scent-masking products. Show how you would synthesize the two major components of skunk spray (3-methylbutane-1-thiol and 2-butene-1-thiol) from any of the readily available butenes or from 1,3-butadiene.

Glutathione, a tripeptide containing a thiol group, serves as a mild reducing agent to detoxify peroxides and maintain the cysteine residues of hemoglobin in the reduced state. Glutathione can also detoxify alkylating agents. For example, the thiol of glutathione reacts with methyl iodide by an S_N2 reaction, rendering the methyl iodide harmless and preventing its reaction with other molecules in the body.

Glossary 10

acid derivatives Compounds that are related to carboxylic acids but have other electron-withdrawing groups in place of the —OH group of the acid. Three examples are **acid chlorides, esters**, and **amides**. (p. 443)

R—C(=O)—OH (carboxylic acid) R—C(=O)—Cl (acid chloride) R—C(=O)—O—R′ (ester) R—C(=O)—NH_2 (amide)

alcohol A compound in which a hydrogen atom of a hydrocarbon has been replaced by a hydroxyl group, —OH. (p. 421)

Alcohols are classified as **primary**, **secondary**, or **tertiary** depending on whether the hydroxyl group is bonded to a primary, secondary, or tertiary carbon atom. (p. 421)

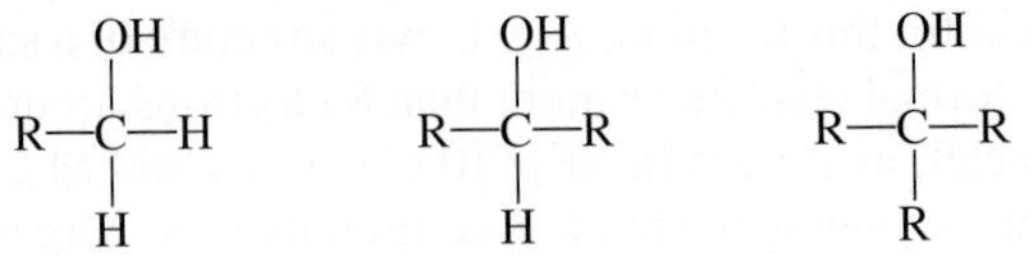

R—CH(OH)—H	R—C(OH)(H)—R	R—C(OH)(R)—R
primary alcohol	secondary alcohol	tertiary alcohol

aldehyde A carbonyl compound with one alkyl group and one hydrogen on the carbonyl group. **Formaldehyde** has two hydrogens on the carbonyl group. (p. 439)
alkoxide ion The anion ($R{-}\ddot{O}{:}^-$) formed by deprotonation of an alcohol. (p. 431)
azeotrope A mixture of two or more liquids that distills at a constant temperature and gives a distillate of definite composition. For example, a mixture of 95% ethanol and 5% water has a lower boiling point than pure ethanol or pure water. (p. 430)
carbinol carbon atom In an alcohol, the carbon atom bonded to the hydroxyl group. (p. 421)
denatured alcohol A form of ethanol containing toxic impurities, making it unfit for drinking. (p. 430)
diol A compound with two alcohol —OH groups. (p. 425)
disulfide The oxidized dimer of a thiol, R—S—S—R. (p. 456)
epoxides (oxiranes) Compounds containing oxygen in a three-membered ring. (p. 445)
glycol Synonymous with **diol**. The term *glycol* is most commonly applied to the 1,2-diols, also called **vicinal diols**. (p. 425)
grain alcohol Ethanol, ethyl alcohol. **Absolute alcohol** is 100% ethanol. (p. 430)
Grignard reagent An organomagnesium halide, written in the form R—Mg—X. The actual reagent is more complicated in structure, usually a dimer or trimer complexed with several molecules of ether. (p. 437)
hydride reagent A compound of hydrogen with a less-electronegative element, so the hydrogen can be donated with its pair of electrons to an organic compound. Hydride transfer reduces the organic compound. Hydride reagents include simple hydrides such as NaH and LiH as well as complex hydrides such as $NaBH_4$ and $LiAlH_4$. (p. 449)

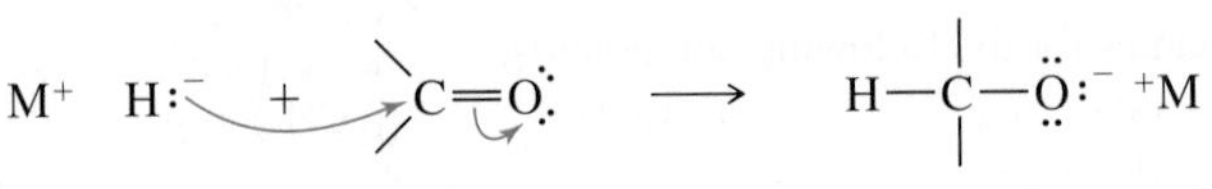

$$M^+ \ H{:}^- + \ \rangle C{=}\ddot{O}{:} \longrightarrow H{-}\overset{|}{\underset{|}{C}}{-}\ddot{\underset{..}{O}}{:}^- \ {}^+M$$

hydride reagent — reduced

hydrophilic ("water loving") Attracted to water, water-soluble. (p. 428)
hydrophobic ("water hating") Repelled by water, water-insoluble. (p. 428)
hydroxy group (hydroxyl group) The —OH group, as in an alcohol. (p. 424)
ketone A carbonyl compound with two alkyl groups bonded to the carbonyl group. (p. 439)
lithium dialkylcuprate (Gilman reagent) An organometallic reagent used to couple with an alkyl halide. (p. 447)

$$R_2CuLi + R'{-}X \longrightarrow R{-}R' + R{-}Cu + LiX$$

lithium dialkylcuprate

mercaptan (thiol) The sulfur analogue of an alcohol, R—SH. (p. 455)
miscible Mutually soluble in any proportions. (p. 428)
organolithium reagent An organometallic reagent of the form R—Li. (p. 438)
organometallic compounds (organometallic reagents) Compounds containing metal atoms directly bonded to carbon. (p. 436)
phenol A compound with a hydroxyl group bonded directly to an aromatic ring. (p. 422)
Raney nickel A finely divided nickel/aluminum alloy that has been treated with NaOH to dissolve out most of the aluminum. Used as a catalyst for the hydrogenation of ketones and aldehydes to alcohols. (p. 453)
rubbing alcohol 2-Propanol, isopropyl alcohol. (p. 430)

skunk (*noun*) A digitigrade omnivorous quadruped that effectively synthesizes thiols; (*verb*) to prevent from scoring in a game or contest. (p. 455)
sulfonic acid A strongly acidic compound of formula $R-SO_3H$, formed by vigorous oxidation of a thiol. (p. 457)
thiol (mercaptan) The sulfur analogue of an alcohol, $R-SH$. (p. 455)
thiolate ion (mercaptide) The $R-\ddot{\underset{..}{S}}:^-$ anion, formed by deprotonation of a thiol. (p. 456)
wood alcohol Methanol, methyl alcohol. (p. 429)

Essential Problem-Solving Skills in Chapter 10

1. Draw and name alcohols, phenols, diols, and thiols.
2. Predict relative boiling points, acidities, and solubilities of alcohols.
3. Show how to convert alkenes, alkyl halides, and carbonyl compounds to alcohols.
4. Predict the alcohol products of hydration, hydroboration, and hydroxylation of alkenes.
5. Use Grignard and organolithium reagents effectively for the synthesis of primary, secondary, and tertiary alcohols with the required carbon skeletons.
6. Propose syntheses and oxidation products of simple thiols.

Study Problems

10-30 Briefly define each term, and give an example.

(a) primary alcohol **(b)** secondary alcohol **(c)** tertiary alcohol
(d) phenol **(e)** diol **(f)** glycol
(g) alkoxide ion **(h)** epoxide **(i)** Grignard reagent
(j) organolithium reagent **(k)** ketone **(l)** aldehyde
(m) hydroxyl group **(n)** acid chloride **(o)** ester
(p) hydride reagents **(q)** thiol **(r)** disulfide
(s) wood alcohol **(t)** rubbing alcohol **(u)** grain alcohol

10-31 Give a systematic (IUPAC) name for each alcohol. Classify each as primary, secondary, or tertiary.

(a) OH

(b) $Br-CHCH_3$ OH

(c) OH Cl

(d)
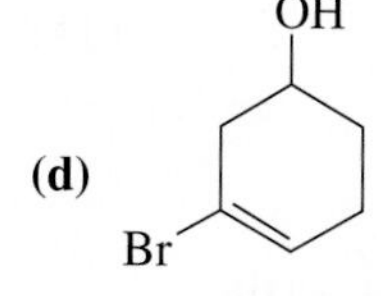

(e)
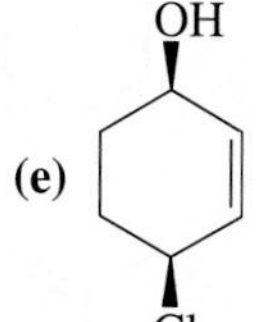

(f) OH

(g) CH_2OH

10-32 Give systematic (IUPAC) names for the following diols and phenols.

(a) OH OH Cl

(b) H OH OH H

(c) OH NO_2

(d) OH Cl Br

10-33 Draw the structures of the following compounds.

(a) triphenylmethanol **(b)** 4-(chloromethyl)heptan-3-ol **(c)** 2-cyclohexen-1-ol
(d) 3-cyclopentylhexan-3-ol **(e)** *meso*-2,4-pentanediol **(f)** cyclopentene glycol
(g) 3-(iodomethyl)phenol **(h)** (2*R*, 3*R*)-2,3-hexanediol **(i)** cyclopent-3-ene-1-thiol
(j) dimethyl disulfide **(k)** 3-methylhex-4-yn-2-ol

10-34 Predict which member of each pair has the higher boiling point, and explain the reasons for your predictions.

(a) 1-hexanol or 3,3-dimethyl-1-butanol **(b)** 2-hexanone or 2-hexanol
(c) 2-hexanol or 1,5-hexanediol **(d)** 2-pentanol or 2-hexanol

10-35 Predict which member of each pair is more acidic, and explain the reasons for your predictions.

(a) cyclopentanol or 3-chlorophenol **(b)** cyclohexanol or cyclohexanethiol
(c) cyclohexanol or cyclohexanecarboxylic acid **(d)** 2,2-dichloro-1-butanol or 1-butanol

10-36 Predict which member of each group is most soluble in water, and explain the reasons for your predictions.

(a) 1-butanol, 1-pentanol, or 2-propanol
(b) chlorocyclohexane, cyclohexanol, or 1,2-cyclohexanediol
(c) phenol, cyclohexanol, or 4-methylcyclohexanol

10-37 Show how you would synthesize the following alcohols from appropriate alkenes.

(a) 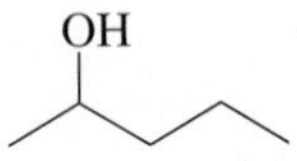 OH **(b)** 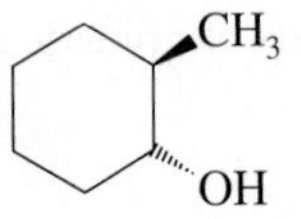 CH_3 OH **(c)** 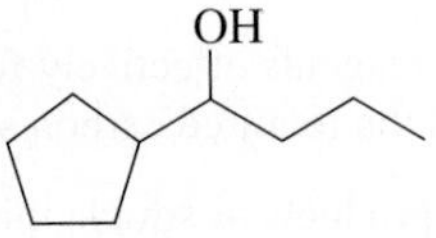 OH **(d)** 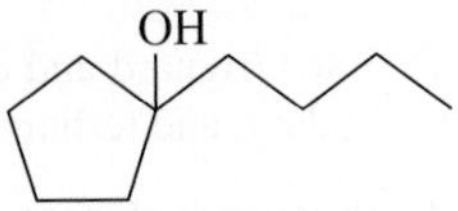 OH

10-38 Draw the organic products you would expect to isolate from the following reactions (after hydrolysis).

(a) 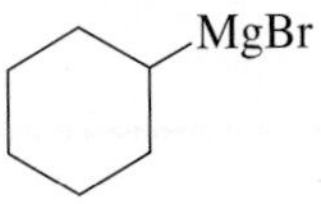 MgBr + $H_2C{=}O$ **(b)** 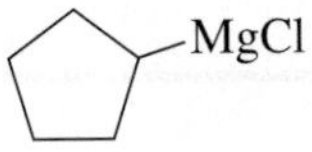 MgCl + 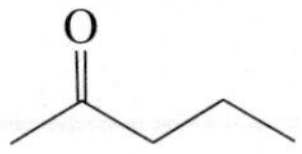 O **(c)** $CH_3{-}CH(MgI)(CH_3)$ + Ph—CHO

(d) CH_3MgI + 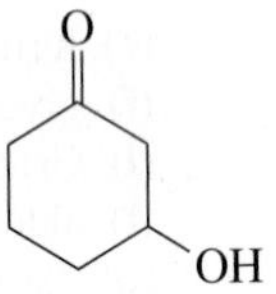 O OH **(e)** 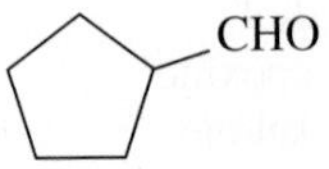 CHO + $NaBH_4$ **(f)** Ph—MgBr + O C Ph Ph

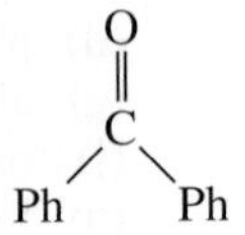

(g) 2 Ph—MgBr + 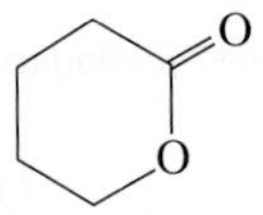 O O **(h)** 2 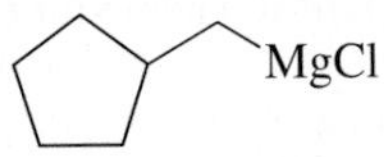 MgCl + Ph—C(=O)—Cl

(i) 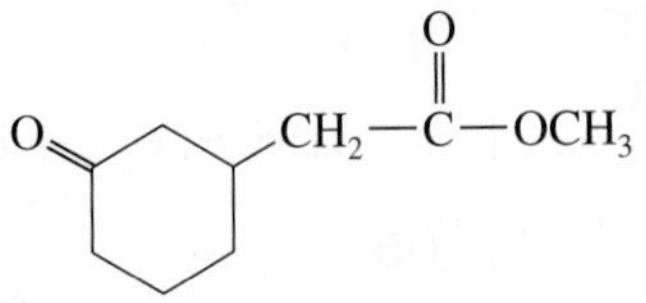 O CH_2—C(=O)—OCH_3 + $NaBH_4$ **(j)** 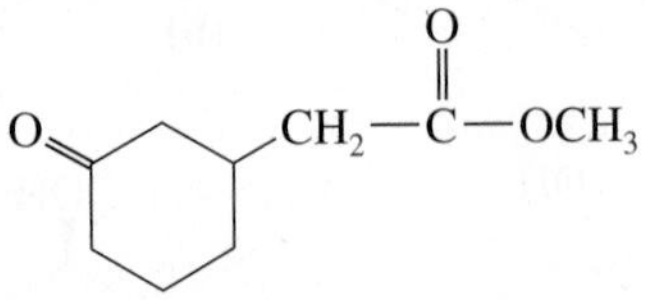 O CH_2—C(=O)—OCH_3 + $LiAlH_4$

(k) 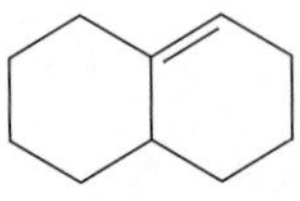 (1) $Hg(OAc)_2$, H_2O (2) $NaBH_4$ **(l)** 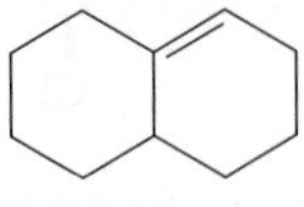 (1) $BH_3 \cdot THF$ (2) H_2O_2, ^{-}OH

(m) 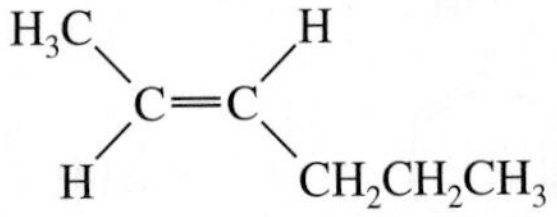 H_3C H C=C H $CH_2CH_2CH_3$ cold, dilute $KMnO_4$ ^{-}OH **(n)** 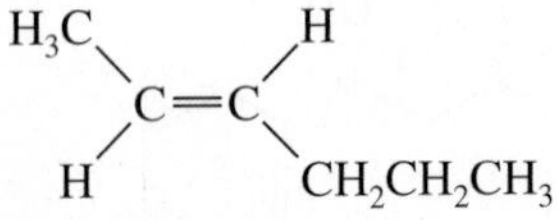 H_3C H C=C H $CH_2CH_2CH_3$ HCO_3H H_3O^+

(o) $(CH_2{=}CH)_2CuLi$ + $CH_3CH_2CH{=}CHCH_2Br$

10-39 Show how you would use Grignard syntheses to prepare the following alcohols from the indicated starting materials and any other necessary reagents.

(a) 3-octanol from hexanal, $CH_3(CH_2)_4CHO$
(b) 1-octanol from 1-bromoheptane
(c) 1-cyclohexylethanol from acetaldehyde, CH_3CHO
(d) 2-cyclohexylethanol from bromocyclohexane
(e) benzyl alcohol ($Ph—CH_2—OH$) from bromobenzene ($Ph—Br$)

(f) cyclohexyl–C(OH)(CH$_3$)–CH$_3$ from cyclohexyl–C(=O)–OCH_2CH_3

(g) cyclopentylphenylmethanol from benzaldehyde ($Ph—CHO$)

10-40 Show how you would accomplish the following transformations. You may use any additional reagents you need.

(a) 1-propylcyclopentene ⟶ cyclopentanol with $CH_2CH_2CH_3$ (H, OH trans arrangement)

(b) $Ph—CH_2CH_2Cl$ ⟶ $Ph—CH_2CH_2CH_2OH$

(c) cyclohex-2-en-1-one ⟶ cyclohex-2-en-1-ol

(d) cyclohex-2-en-1-one ⟶ cyclohexanone

(e) $CH_3—\overset{O}{\overset{\|}{C}}—CH_2CH_2—\overset{O}{\overset{\|}{C}}—OCH_2CH_3 \longrightarrow CH_3—\overset{OH}{\overset{|}{C}H}—CH_2CH_2—\overset{O}{\overset{\|}{C}}—OCH_2CH_3$

(f) $CH_3—\overset{O}{\overset{\|}{C}}—CH_2CH_2—\overset{O}{\overset{\|}{C}}—OCH_2CH_3 \longrightarrow CH_3—\overset{OH}{\overset{|}{C}H}—CH_2CH_2—\overset{OH}{\overset{|}{C}H_2}$

10-41 Show how you would synthesize

(a) 2-phenylethanol by the addition of formaldehyde to a suitable Grignard reagent
(b) 2-phenylethanol from a suitable alkene
(c) cyclohexylmethanol from an alkyl halide using an S_N2 reaction
(d) 3-cyclohexyl-1-propanol by the addition of ethylene oxide to a suitable Grignard reagent
(e) *cis*-pent-2-en-1-thiol from a suitable alkenyl halide
(f) 2,5-dimethylhexane from a four-carbon alkyl halide

10-42 Complete the following acid–base reactions. In each case, indicate whether the equilibrium favors the reactants or the products, and explain your reasoning.

(a) $CH_3CH_2—O^-$ + phenol (Ph–OH) $\rightleftarrows$

(b) KOH + 3,4-dichlorophenol (Cl–C$_6$H$_3$(Cl)–OH) $\rightleftarrows$

(c) 1-naphthol (OH) + CH_3O^- $\rightleftarrows$

(d) cyclopentanol (OH) + KOH $\rightleftarrows$

(e) $(CH_3)_3C—O^-$ + CH_3CH_2OH $\rightleftarrows$
(f) $(CH_3)_3C—O^-$ + H_2O $\rightleftarrows$
(g) KOH + CH_3CH_2OH $\rightleftarrows$

10-43 Suggest carbonyl compounds and reducing agents that might be used to form the following alcohols.

(a) *n*-octanol **(b)** 1-cyclohexyl-1-propanol **(c)** 1-phenyl-1-butanol

(d) 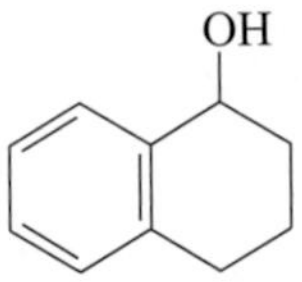 OH **(e)** 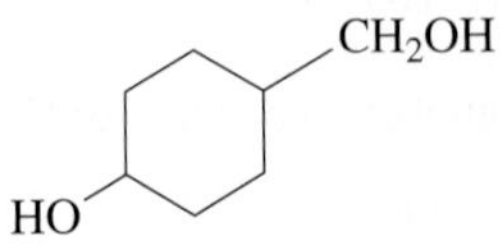 CH_2OH HO **(f)** 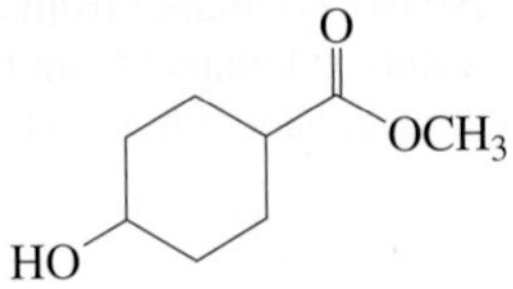 O OCH_3 HO

10-44 Show how you would synthesize the following compounds from any starting materials containing no more than six carbon atoms.

(a) 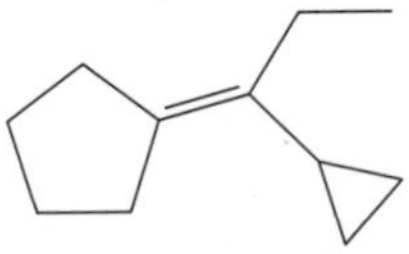 **(b)** 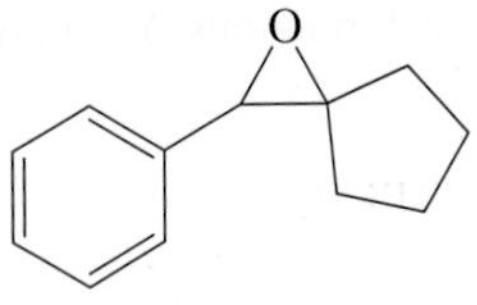 O **(c)** 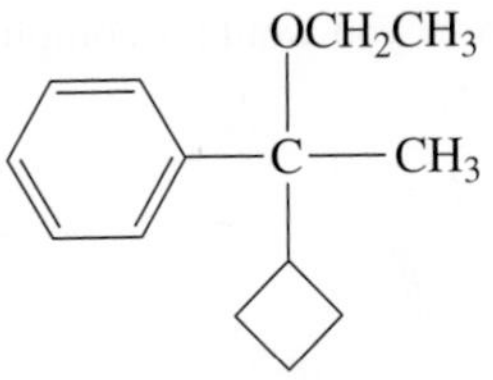 OCH_2CH_3 C — CH_3

***10-45** Geminal diols, or 1,1-diols, are usually unstable, spontaneously losing water to give carbonyl compounds. Therefore, geminal diols are regarded as hydrated forms of ketones and aldehydes. Propose a mechanism for the acid-catalyzed loss of water from propane-2,2-diol to give acetone.

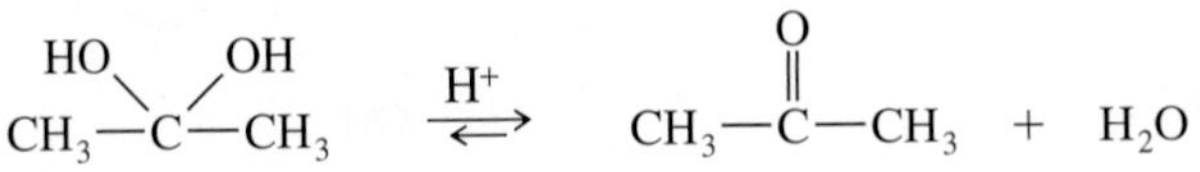

$$CH_3-C(OH)_2-CH_3 \xrightleftharpoons{H^+} CH_3-\overset{O}{\overset{\|}{C}}-CH_3 + H_2O$$

propane-2,2-diol acetone

10-46 Vinyl alcohols are generally unstable, quickly isomerizing to carbonyl compounds. Propose mechanisms for the following isomerizations.

(a) 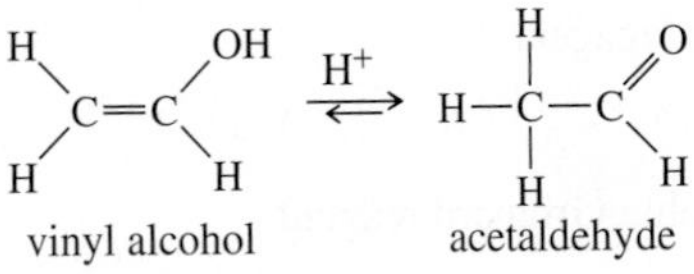 vinyl alcohol $\xrightleftharpoons{H^+}$ acetaldehyde (b) 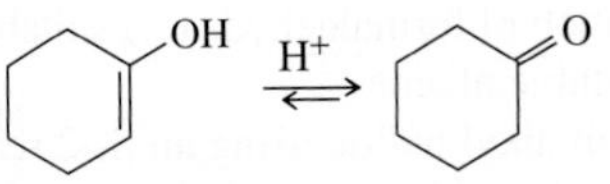 OH $\xrightleftharpoons{H^+}$ O (c) 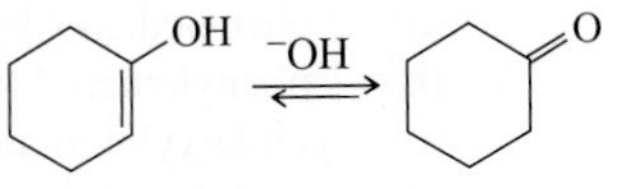 OH $\xrightleftharpoons{^-OH}$ O

***10-47** Compound **A** ($C_7H_{11}Br$) is treated with magnesium in ether to give **B** ($C_7H_{11}MgBr$), which reacts violently with D_2O to give 1-methylcyclohexene with a deuterium atom on the methyl group (**C**). Reaction of **B** with acetone (CH_3COCH_3) followed by hydrolysis gives **D** ($C_{10}H_{18}O$). Heating **D** with concentrated H_2SO_4 gives **E** ($C_{10}H_{16}$), which decolorizes two equivalents of Br_2 to give **F** ($C_{10}H_{16}Br_4$). **E** undergoes hydrogenation with excess H_2 and a Pt catalyst to give isobutylcyclohexane. Determine the structures of compounds **A** through **F**, and show your reasoning throughout.

***10-48** Grignard reagents react slowly with oxetane to produce primary alcohols. Propose a mechanism for this reaction, and suggest why oxetane reacts with Grignard reagents even though most ethers do not.

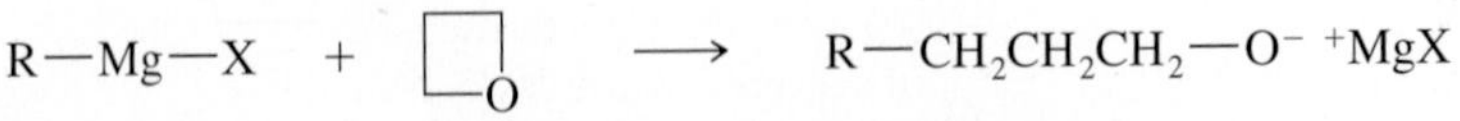

$$R-Mg-X + \text{oxetane} \longrightarrow R-CH_2CH_2CH_2-O^- \ {}^+MgX$$

Grignard reagent oxetane salt of 1° alcohol

***10-49** Determine the structures of compounds **A** through **G**, including stereochemistry where appropriate.

cyclopentanone $\xrightarrow[(2)\ H_3O^+]{(1)\ CH_3MgI}$ $C_6H_{12}O$ **A** $\xrightarrow[heat]{H_2SO_4}$ C_6H_{10} **B** $\xrightarrow{H_2,\ Pt}$ methylcyclopentane (CH_3)

$C_{10}H_{16}$ **G** $\xrightarrow[warm,\ concd.]{KMnO_4}$ cyclopentanone

$C_6H_{12}O$ **D** $\xrightarrow[heat]{H_2SO_4}$ C_6H_{10} **B**

$C_{10}H_{18}O$ **F** $\xrightarrow[heat]{H_2SO_4}$ $C_{10}H_{16}$ **G**

cyclopentene $\xrightarrow{PhCO_3H}$ C_5H_8O **C** $\xrightarrow[(2)\ H_3O^+]{(1)\ CH_3MgI}$ $C_6H_{12}O$ **D**

cyclopentene $\xrightarrow{HBr}$ C_5H_9Br **E** $\xrightarrow{(1)\ Mg,\ ether;\ (2)\ cyclopentanone;\ (3)\ H_3O^+}$ $C_{10}H_{18}O$ **F**

***10-50** Many hunting dogs enjoy standing nose-to-nose with a skunk while barking furiously, oblivious to the skunk spray directed toward them. One moderately effective way of lessening the amount of odor is to wash the dog in a bath containing dilute hydrogen peroxide, sodium bicarbonate, and some mild dish detergent. Use chemical reactions to describe how this mixture helps to remove the skunk spray from the dog. The two major components of skunk oil are 3-methylbutane-1-thiol and 2-butene-1-thiol.

10-51 Propose structures for intermediates and products (**A**) through (**L**).

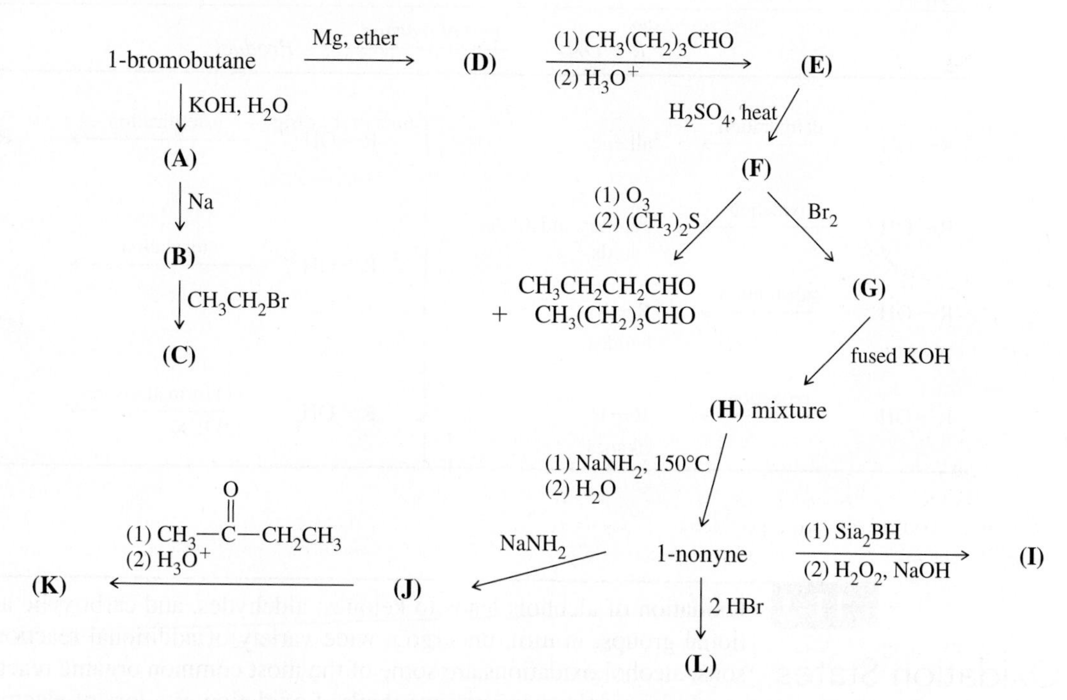

10-52 Devise a synthesis for each compound, starting with methylenecyclohexane and any other reagents you need.

(a) 1-methylcyclohexanol
(b) cyclohexylmethanol
(c) 1-(hydroxymethyl)cyclohexanol
(d) *trans*-2-methylcyclohexanol
(e) 2-chloro-1-methylcyclohexanol
(f) 1-(phenylmethyl)cyclohexanol

$$\begin{array}{c} CH_3CH_2CH_2 \\ \overset{\delta^-}{Br}\cdots C \cdots \ddot{O}^{\delta^+}(H)(H) \\ H\ H \end{array}$$

CHAPTER 11

REACTIONS OF ALCOHOLS

Alcohols are important organic compounds because the hydroxyl group is easily converted to almost any other functional group. In Chapter 10, we studied reactions that form alcohols. In this chapter, we seek to understand how alcohols react and which reagents are best for converting them to other kinds of compounds. Table 11-1 summarizes the types of reactions alcohols undergo and the products that result.

TABLE 11-1

Types of Reactions of Alcohols

R—OH $\xrightarrow{\text{type of reaction}}$ *Product*

R—OH	$\xrightarrow{\text{dehydration}}$	alkenes	R—OH	$\xrightarrow{\text{esterification}}$	R—O—C(=O)—R′ esters
R—OH	$\xrightarrow{\text{oxidation}}$	ketones, aldehydes, acids	R—OH	$\xrightarrow{\text{tosylation}}$	R—OTs tosylate esters (good leaving group)
R—OH	$\xrightarrow{\text{substitution}}$	R—X halides			
R—OH	$\xrightarrow{\text{reduction}}$	R—H alkanes	R—OH	$\xrightarrow[\text{(2) R′X}]{\text{(1) form alkoxide}}$	R—O—R′ ethers

11-1 Oxidation States of Alcohols and Related Functional Groups

Oxidation of alcohols leads to ketones, aldehydes, and carboxylic acids. These functional groups, in turn, undergo a wide variety of additional reactions. For these reasons, alcohol oxidations are some of the most common organic reactions.

In inorganic chemistry, we think of oxidation as a loss of electrons and reduction as a gain of electrons. This picture works well for inorganic ions, as when Cr^{6+} is reduced to Cr^{3+}. Most organic compounds are uncharged, however, and gain or loss of electrons is not obvious. Organic chemists tend to think of **oxidation** as the result of adding an oxidizing agent (O_2, Br_2, etc.), and **reduction** as the result of adding a reducing agent (H_2, $NaBH_4$, etc.). Most organic chemists habitually use the following simple rules, based on the change in the formula of the substance:

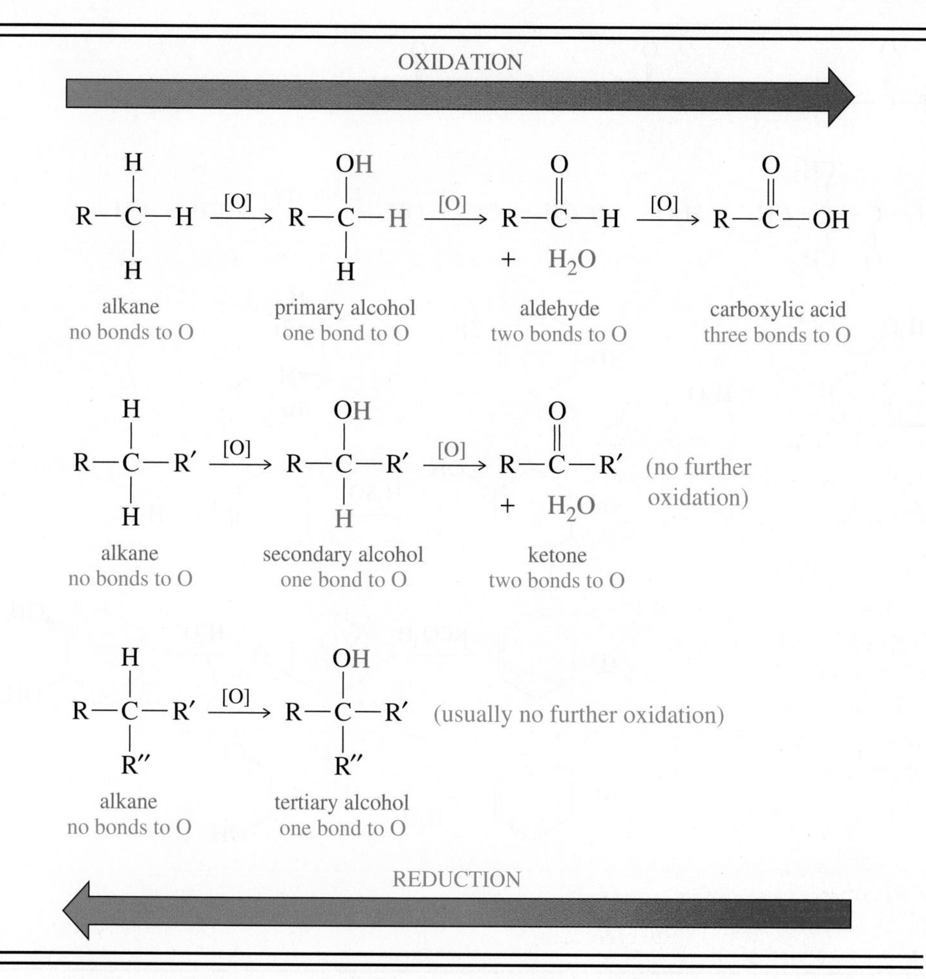

■ **FIGURE 11-1**
Oxidation states of alcohols. An alcohol is more oxidized than an alkane, yet less oxidized than carbonyl compounds such as ketones, aldehydes, and acids. Oxidation of a primary alcohol leads to an aldehyde, and further oxidation leads to an acid. Secondary alcohols are oxidized to ketones. Tertiary alcohols cannot be oxidized without breaking carbon–carbon bonds.

> **OXIDATION:** addition of O or O_2; addition of X_2 (halogens); loss of H_2.
> **REDUCTION:** addition of H_2 (or H^-); loss of O or O_2; loss of X_2.
> **NEITHER:** addition or loss of H^+, ^-OH, H_2O, HX, etc. is neither an oxidation nor a reduction.

We can tell that an oxidation or a reduction of an alcohol has taken place by counting the number of C—O bonds to the carbon atom. Oxidation usually converts C—H bonds to C—O bonds. The first row of structures in Figure 11-1 shows that a primary alcohol is more oxidized than an alkane because the carbinol (C—OH) carbon atom has one bond to oxygen, while the alkane has no bonds to oxygen. Oxidation of a primary alcohol gives an aldehyde, whose carbonyl carbon has two bonds to oxygen. Oxidation of the aldehyde to an acid adds another bond to oxygen, for a total of three. Further oxidation would require breaking a carbon–carbon bond to give four bonds to oxygen, the oxidation state of carbon dioxide.

Figure 11-1 compares the oxidation states of primary, secondary, and tertiary alcohols with those obtained by oxidation or reduction. The symbol [O] indicates an unspecified oxidizing agent. Notice that oxidation of a primary or secondary alcohol forms a carbonyl (C=O) group by the removal of two hydrogen atoms: one from the carbinol carbon and one from the hydroxyl group. A tertiary alcohol cannot easily oxidize because there is no hydrogen atom available on the carbinol carbon.

PROBLEM 11-1

Classify each reaction as an oxidation, a reduction, or neither.

(a) $CH_3{-}CH_2OH \xrightarrow{CrO_3\cdot\text{pyridine}} CH_3{-}\overset{\overset{\displaystyle O}{\|}}{C}{-}H \xrightarrow{H_2CrO_4} CH_3{-}\overset{\overset{\displaystyle O}{\|}}{C}{-}OH$

(b) $CH_4 \longrightarrow CH_3OH \longrightarrow H{-}C(=O){-}OH \longrightarrow H{-}C(=O){-}H \longrightarrow HO{-}C(=O){-}OH$

(c) $CH_3{-}C(CH_3)(OH){-}C(CH_3)(OH){-}CH_3 \xrightarrow{H^+} CH_3{-}C(=O){-}C(CH_3)_2{-}CH_3 + H_2O$

(d) $CH_3{-}CH_2{-}OH \xrightarrow{LiAlH_4/TiCl_4} CH_3{-}CH_3$

(e) cyclopentyl–CHO $\xrightarrow{H^+, CH_3OH}$ cyclopentyl–CH(OCH_3)$_2$ $+ H_2O$

(f) cyclohexene $\xrightarrow{Br_2}$ trans-1,2-dibromocyclohexane (H, Br; H, Br)

(g) cyclohexene $\xrightarrow{HBr}$ bromocyclohexane (H, H, H, Br)

(h) cyclohexanol $\xrightarrow{H_2SO_4}$ cyclohexene $+ H_2O$

(i) cyclohexene $\xrightarrow[H_2O_2]{OsO_4}$ cis-cyclohexane-1,2-diol (OH, OH)

(j) cyclohexene $\xrightarrow{RCO_3H}$ epoxide (O) $\xrightarrow{H_3O^+}$ trans-cyclohexane-1,2-diol (OH, OH)

(k) cyclohexene $\xrightarrow[(2)\ H_2O_2,\ ^-OH]{(1)\ BH_3 \cdot THF}$ cyclohexanol (OH)

(l) cyclohexene $\xrightarrow[H_2O]{Cl_2}$ trans-2-chlorocyclohexanol (Cl, OH)

11-2 Oxidation of Alcohols

Primary and secondary alcohols are easily oxidized by a variety of reagents, including chromium oxides, permanganate, nitric acid, and even household bleach (NaOCl, sodium hypochlorite). The choice of reagent depends on the amount and value of the alcohol. We use cheap oxidants for large-scale oxidations of simple, inexpensive alcohols. We use the most effective and selective reagents, regardless of cost, for delicate and valuable alcohols. In this chapter, we study only the oxidants that have the widest range of uses and the best selectivity. An understanding of the most common oxidants can later be extended to include additional reagents.

11-2A Oxidation of Secondary Alcohols

Secondary alcohols are easily oxidized to give excellent yields of ketones. The **chromic acid reagent** is often used for laboratory oxidations of secondary alcohols.

$$R{-}CH(OH){-}R' \xrightarrow{Na_2Cr_2O_7/H_2SO_4} R{-}C(=O){-}R'$$

secondary alcohol → ketone

Example

cyclohexanol $\xrightarrow[H_2SO_4]{Na_2Cr_2O_7}$ cyclohexanone (90%)

The chromic acid reagent is prepared by dissolving sodium dichromate ($Na_2Cr_2O_7$) in a mixture of sulfuric acid and water. The active species in the mixture is probably chromic acid, H_2CrO_4, or the acid chromate ion, $HCrO_4^-$. Adding chromium trioxide (CrO_3) to dilute sulfuric acid achieves the same result.

$$\underset{\text{sodium dichromate}}{Na_2Cr_2O_7} + H_2O + 2\,H_2SO_4 \longrightarrow \underset{\text{chromic acid }(H_2CrO_4)}{2\,HO{-}Cr({=}O)_2{-}OH} + 2\,Na^+ + 2\,HSO_4^-$$

$$\underset{\text{chromium trioxide}}{CrO_3} + H_2O \xrightarrow{H_2SO_4} \underset{\text{chromic acid}}{HO{-}Cr({=}O)_2{-}OH} \rightleftharpoons H^+ + \underset{\text{acid chromate ion}}{{}^-O{-}Cr({=}O)_2{-}OH}$$

The mechanism of chromic acid oxidation probably involves the formation of a chromate ester. Elimination of the chromate ester gives the ketone. In the elimination, the carbinol carbon retains its oxygen atom but loses its hydrogen and gains the second bond to oxygen.

Formation of the chromate ester

$$\underset{\text{alcohol}}{R{-}CHR'{-}O{-}H} + \underset{\text{chromic acid}}{H{-}O{-}Cr({=}O)_2{-}OH} \longrightarrow \underset{\text{chromate ester}}{R{-}CHR'{-}O{-}Cr({=}O)_2{-}OH} + H_2O$$

Elimination of the chromate ester and oxidation of the carbinol carbon

$$H_2\ddot{O}\!: + R{-}CHR'{-}\ddot{O}{-}\underset{\text{Cr (VI)}}{Cr({=}O)_2{-}OH} \longrightarrow R{-}CR'{=}\ddot{O}\!: + H_3O^+ + \underset{\text{Cr (IV)}}{O{=}Cr(O^-){-}OH}$$

The chromium(IV) species formed reacts further to give the stable reduced form, chromium(III). Both sodium dichromate and chromic acid are orange, but chromic ion (Cr^{3+}) is a deep blue. One can follow the progress of a chromic acid oxidation by observing the color change from orange through various shades of green to a greenish blue. In fact, the color change observed with chromic acid can be used as a test for the presence of an oxidizable alcohol.

11-2B Oxidation of Primary Alcohols

Oxidation of a primary alcohol initially forms an aldehyde. Unlike a ketone, however, an aldehyde is easily oxidized further to give a carboxylic acid.

$$\underset{\text{primary alcohol}}{R{-}CH(OH){-}H} \xrightarrow{[O]} \underset{\text{aldehyde}}{R{-}C({=}O){-}H} \xrightarrow{[O]} \underset{\text{carboxylic acid}}{R{-}C({=}O){-}OH}$$

Obtaining the aldehyde is often difficult, since most oxidizing agents strong enough to oxidize primary alcohols also oxidize aldehydes. Chromic acid generally oxidizes a primary alcohol all the way to the carboxylic acid.

$$\text{cyclohexyl methanol (C}_6\text{H}_{11}\text{–CH}_2\text{OH)} \xrightarrow[H_2SO_4]{Na_2Cr_2O_7} \text{cyclohexanecarboxylic acid (C}_6\text{H}_{11}\text{–COOH) (92\%)}$$

cyclohexyl methanol — cyclohexanecarboxylic acid (92%)

Pyridinium chlorochromate (PCC):

$C_5H_5N^+–H \quad CrO_3Cl^-$

$CrO_3 \cdot$ pyridine $\cdot HCl$
or $pyH^+ \, CrO_3Cl^-$

A better reagent for the limited oxidation of primary alcohols to aldehydes is **pyridinium chlorochromate (PCC)**, a complex of chromium trioxide with pyridine and HCl. PCC oxidizes most primary alcohols to aldehydes in excellent yields. Unlike most other oxidants, PCC is soluble in nonpolar solvents such as dichloromethane (CH_2Cl_2), which is an excellent solvent for most organic compounds. PCC can also serve as a mild reagent for oxidizing secondary alcohols to ketones.

$$R–CH(OH)–H \xrightarrow[CH_2Cl_2]{CrO_3 \cdot \text{pyridine} \cdot HCl \text{ (PCC)}} R–C(=O)–H$$

primary alcohol — aldehyde

Example

$$CH_3(CH_2)_5–CH_2OH \xrightarrow[CH_2Cl_2]{PCC} CH_3(CH_2)_5–C(=O)–H$$

1-heptanol — heptanal (78%)

11-2C Resistance of Tertiary Alcohols to Oxidation

Oxidation of tertiary alcohols is not an important reaction in organic chemistry. Tertiary alcohols have no hydrogen atoms on the carbinol carbon atom, so oxidation must take place by breaking carbon–carbon bonds. These oxidations require severe conditions and result in mixtures of products.

The **chromic acid test** for primary and secondary alcohols exploits the resistance of tertiary alcohols to oxidation. When a primary or secondary alcohol is added to the chromic acid reagent, the orange color changes to green or blue. When a nonoxidizable substance (such as a tertiary alcohol, a ketone, or an alkane) is added to the reagent, no immediate color change occurs.

Summary of Alcohol Oxidations

To Oxidize	Product	Reagent
2° alcohol	ketone	chromic acid (or PCC)
1° alcohol	aldehyde	PCC
1° alcohol	carboxylic acid	chromic acid

PROBLEM 11-2

Predict the products of the reactions of the following compounds with chromic acid and also with PCC.

(a) cyclohexanol
(b) 1-methylcyclohexanol
(c) cyclopentylmethanol
(d) cyclohexanone
(e) cyclohexane
(f) acetic acid, CH_3COOH
(g) ethanol
(h) acetaldehyde, CH_3CHO

11-3 Additional Methods for Oxidizing Alcohols

Many other reagents and procedures have been developed for oxidizing alcohols. Some are simply modifications of the procedures we have seen. For example, the **Collins reagent** is a complex of chromium trioxide and pyridine, the original version of PCC. The **Jones reagent** is a milder form of chromic acid: a solution of diluted chromic acid in acetone.

All of the chromium reagents produce by-products and washings that contain hazardous chromium salts and must be collected as hazardous waste. In many cases, simple oxidants such as household bleach (sodium hypochlorite, NaOCl) can accomplish the same oxidations as chromic acid without using heavy metals, and without generating hazardous waste. Oxidations using sodium hypochlorite involve mildly basic conditions that may be better than chromic acid for acid-sensitive compounds.

$$\text{cyclohexanol} \xrightarrow[H_2O]{NaOCl} \text{cyclohexanone (85\%)}$$

Two other strong oxidants are potassium permanganate and nitric acid. Both of these reagents are less expensive than the chromium reagents, and both of them give by-products that are less environmentally hazardous than spent chromium reagents. Both permanganate and nitric acid oxidize secondary alcohols to ketones and primary alcohols to carboxylic acids. If these strong oxidants are not carefully controlled, they will cleave carbon–carbon bonds.

$$\underset{\text{1-phenylethanol}}{Ph-CH(OH)-CH_3} \xrightarrow[H_2O]{KMnO_4} \underset{\text{acetophenone (72\%)}}{Ph-C(=O)-CH_3} + MnO_2$$

$$\underset{\text{1-hexanol}}{CH_3(CH_2)_4-CH_2OH} \xrightarrow[10\text{–}20\ °C]{71\%\ HNO_3} \underset{\text{hexanoic acid (80\%)}}{CH_3(CH_2)_4-C(=O)-OH}$$

Perhaps the least expensive method for oxidizing alcohols is dehydrogenation: literally the removal of two hydrogen atoms. This industrial reaction takes place at high temperature using a copper, zinc, or copper oxide catalyst. The hydrogen by-product may be sold or used for reductions elsewhere in the plant. The primary limitation of dehydrogenation is the inability of many organic compounds to survive the high-temperature reaction. *Dehydrogenation is not well suited for laboratory syntheses.*

$$R-C(OH)(H)-R' \xrightarrow{\text{heat, CuO}} R-C(=O)-R' + H_2\uparrow$$

Example

$$\underset{\text{2-butanol}}{CH_3-CH(OH)-CH_2CH_3} \xrightarrow[400\ °C]{Cu\text{-}Zn} \underset{\text{2-butanone}}{CH_3-C(=O)-CH_2CH_3} + H_2$$

The **Swern oxidation** uses dimethyl sulfoxide (DMSO) as the oxidizing agent to convert alcohols to ketones and aldehydes. DMSO and oxalyl chloride are added to the alcohol at low temperature, followed by a hindered base such as triethylamine. Secondary alcohols are oxidized to ketones, and primary alcohols are oxidized only as far as the aldehyde. The by-products of this reaction are all volatile and are easily separated from the organic products.

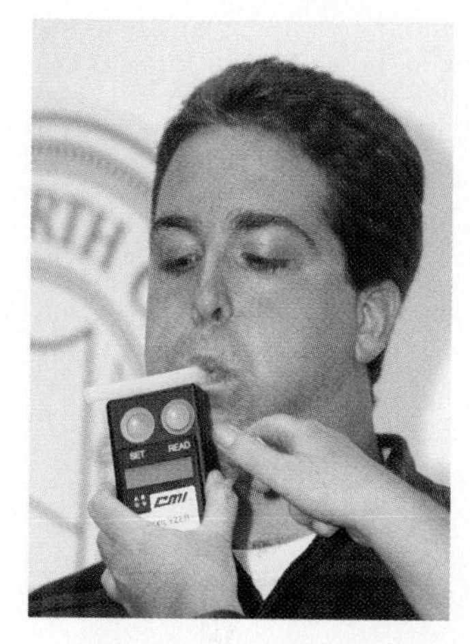

A small fuel cell in this portable breath tester catalyzes the oxidation of ethanol by oxygen in the air. The oxidation generates an electric current that is proportional to the concentration of ethanol in the sample.

$$\underset{\text{alcohol}}{-\overset{\text{OH}}{\underset{|}{\overset{|}{\text{C}}}}-\text{H}} + \underset{\substack{\text{DMSO}\\ \text{dimethyl sulfoxide}}}{H_3C-\overset{O}{\overset{\|}{S}}-CH_3} + \underset{\substack{(COCl)_2\\ \text{oxalyl chloride}}}{Cl-\overset{O}{\overset{\|}{C}}-\overset{O}{\overset{\|}{C}}-Cl} \xrightarrow[CH_2Cl_2]{(CH_3CH_2)_3N:} \underset{\substack{\text{ketone}\\ \text{or aldehyde}}}{>C=O} + \underset{\text{dimethyl sulfide}}{H_3C-S-CH_3} + CO_2 + CO + 2\,HCl$$

Examples

$$\underset{\text{cyclopentanol}}{\text{C}_5\text{H}_9\text{OH}} \xrightarrow[Et_3N,\ CH_2Cl_2,\ -60\ °C]{DMSO,\ (COCl)_2} \underset{\text{cyclopentanone (90\%)}}{\text{C}_5\text{H}_8\text{=O}}$$

$$\underset{\text{1-decanol}}{CH_3(CH_2)_8-\overset{OH}{\overset{|}{\underset{H}{\underset{|}{C}}}}-H} \xrightarrow[Et_3N,\ CH_2Cl_2,\ -60\ °C]{DMSO,\ (COCl)_2} \underset{\text{decanal (85\%)}}{CH_3(CH_2)_8-CHO}$$

PROBLEM 11-3

The Swern oxidation provides a useful alternative to PCC that avoids using chromium reagents as oxidants.

(a) Determine which species are oxidized and which are reduced in the Swern oxidation.
(b) In Section 8-15B, dimethyl sulfide was added to an ozonide after ozonolysis. What was its function there?

PROBLEM 11-4

What is it about dehydrogenation that enables it to take place at 300 °C but not at 25 °C?

(a) Would you expect the kinetics, thermodynamics, or both to be unfavorable at 25 °C? (*Hint*: Is the reverse reaction favorable at 25 °C?)
(b) Which of these factors (kinetics or thermodynamics) improves as the temperature is raised?
(c) Explain the changes in the kinetics and thermodynamics of this reaction as the temperature increases.

problem-solving **Hint**

The summary table on page 468 is worth reviewing. Remember that permanganate oxidizes alkenes as well as alcohols.

PROBLEM 11-5

Give the structure of the principal product(s) when each of the following alcohols reacts with (1) $Na_2Cr_2O_7/H_2SO_4$, (2) PCC, (3) $KMnO_4$, ^{-}OH.

(a) 1-octanol **(b)** 3-octanol
(c) 2-cyclohexen-1-ol **(d)** 1-methylcyclohexanol

SOLVED PROBLEM 11-1

Suggest the most appropriate method for each of the following laboratory syntheses.

(a) cyclopentanol ⟶ cyclopentanone

SOLUTION

Many reagents are available to oxidize a simple secondary alcohol to a ketone. Dehydrogenation is impractical for a synthesis in a laboratory, where the facilities and apparatus for reactions at high temperatures and pressures are rarely available. Most labs would have chromium trioxide or sodium dichromate available, and the chromic acid oxidation would be simple. Bleach (sodium hypochlorite) might be a cheaper and less polluting alternative to the chromium reagents. PCC and the Swern oxidation would also work, although these reagents are more complicated to prepare and use.

$$\underset{\text{cyclopentanol}}{\text{C}_5\text{H}_9\text{OH}} \xrightarrow[H_2SO_4]{Na_2Cr_2O_7} \underset{\text{cyclopentanone}}{\text{C}_5\text{H}_8\text{=O}}$$

(b) 2-octen-l-ol ⟶ 2-octenal (structure below)

SOLUTION

This synthesis requires more finesse. The aldehyde is easily over-oxidized to a carboxylic acid, and the double bond reacts with oxidants such as $KMnO_4$. Our choices are limited to PCC or the Swern oxidation.

$$\text{2-octen-1-ol } (CH_3(CH_2)_4CH{=}CHCH_2OH) \xrightarrow[\text{(or Swern)}]{PCC,\ CH_2Cl_2} \text{2-octenal } (CH_3(CH_2)_4CH{=}CH{-}CHO)$$

PROBLEM 11-6

Suggest the most appropriate method for each of the following *laboratory* syntheses.

(a) 1-butanol ⟶ butanal, $CH_3CH_2CH_2CHO$
(b) 2-buten-l-ol ⟶ 2-butenoic acid, $CH_3CH{=}CH{-}COOH$
(c) 2-butanol ⟶ 2-butanone, $CH_3COCH_2CH_3$
(d) cyclopentanol ⟶ 1-ethylcyclopentanol
(e) cyclopentylmethanol ⟶ 1-cyclopentylpropanol
(f) 1-methylcyclohexanol ⟶ 2-methylcyclohexanone (several steps)

11-4 Biological Oxidation of Alcohols

Although it is the least toxic alcohol, ethanol is still a poisonous substance. When someone is suffering from a mild case of ethanol poisoning, we say that he or she is in*toxic*ated. Animals often consume food that has fermented and contains alcohol. Their bodies must detoxify any alcohol in the food to keep it from building up in the blood and poisoning the brain. To detoxify ethanol, the liver produces an enzyme called **alcohol dehydrogenase (ADH)**.

Alcohol dehydrogenase catalyzes an oxidation: the removal of two hydrogen atoms from the alcohol molecule. The oxidizing agent is **nicotinamide adenine dinucleotide (NAD)**. NAD exists in two forms: the oxidized form, called NAD^+, and the reduced form, called NADH. The following equation shows that ethanol is oxidized to acetaldehyde, and NAD^+ is reduced to NADH.

$$\underset{\substack{\text{ethanol}\\\text{reduced form}}}{CH_3{-}CH(OH){-}H} + \underset{\substack{NAD^+\\\text{oxidized form}}}{NAD^+} \xrightarrow{ADH} \underset{\substack{\text{acetaldehyde}\\\text{oxidized form}}}{CH_3{-}C({=}O){-}H} + \underset{\substack{NADH\\\text{reduced form}}}{NADH} + H^+$$

ADH = alcohol dehydrogenase

A subsequent oxidation, catalyzed by **aldehyde dehydrogenase (ALDH)**, converts acetaldehyde to acetic acid, a normal metabolite.

$$CH_3{-}C({=}O){-}H + H_2O + NAD^+ \xrightarrow{ALDH} \underset{\text{acetic acid}}{CH_3{-}C({=}O){-}OH} + NADH + H^+$$

ALDH = aldehyde dehydrogenase

These oxidations take place with most small primary alcohols. Unfortunately, the oxidation products of some other alcohols are more toxic than acetic acid. Methanol is oxidized first to formaldehyde and then to formic acid. Both of these compounds are more toxic than methanol itself.

$$\underset{\text{methanol}}{H_3C{-}O{-}H} \xrightarrow[-2\,H]{[O]} \underset{\text{formaldehyde}}{H{-}CH{=}O} \xrightarrow{[O]} \underset{\text{formic acid}}{H{-}C(=O){-}O{-}H}$$

Ethylene glycol is a toxic diol. Its oxidation product is oxalic acid, the toxic compound found in the leaves of rhubarb and many other plants.

$$\underset{\text{ethylene glycol}}{HOCH_2{-}CH_2OH} \xrightarrow[-4\,H]{2[O]} H{-}C(=O){-}C(=O){-}H + 2\,H_2O \xrightarrow{2[O]} \underset{\text{oxalic acid}}{HO{-}C(=O){-}C(=O){-}OH}$$

Many poisonings by methanol and ethylene glycol occur each year. Alcoholics occasionally drink ethanol that has been denatured by the addition of methanol. Methanol is oxidized to formic acid, which may cause blindness and death. Dogs are often poisoned by sweet-tasting ethylene glycol when antifreeze is left in an open container. Once the glycol is metabolized to oxalic acid, the dog's kidneys fail, causing death.

The treatment for methanol or ethylene glycol poisoning is the same. The patient is given intravenous infusions of diluted ethanol. The ADH enzyme is swamped by all the ethanol, allowing time for the kidneys to excrete most of the methanol (or ethylene glycol) before it can be oxidized to formic acid (or oxalic acid). This is an example of *competitive inhibition* of an enzyme. The enzyme catalyzes oxidation of both ethanol and methanol, but a large quantity of ethanol ties up the enzyme, allowing time for excretion of most of the methanol before it is oxidized.

NAD^+ is derived from vitamin B_3, known as niacin. There is a misconception that taking large supplements of niacin before a night of drinking ethanol will lessen the severity of the "hangover" the next morning. Metabolism is more complex than this simple idea suggests.

One common effect of taking large amounts of niacin is flushing caused by dilation of the capillaries in the skin. This flushing looks like a severe sunburn and can be quite uncomfortable, but it usually subsides in a few hours.

nicotinic acid (niacin) [pyridine ring with COOH]

PROBLEM 11-7

A chronic alcoholic requires a much larger dose of ethanol as an antidote to methanol poisoning than does a nonalcoholic patient. Suggest a reason why a larger dose of the competitive inhibitor is required for an alcoholic.

PROBLEM 11-8

Unlike ethylene glycol, propylene glycol (propane-1,2-diol) is nontoxic because it oxidizes to a common metabolic intermediate. Give the structures of the biological oxidation products of propylene glycol.

11-5 Alcohols as Nucleophiles and Electrophiles; Formation of Tosylates

One reason alcohols are such versatile chemical intermediates is that they react as both nucleophiles and electrophiles. The following scheme shows an alcohol reacting as a weak nucleophile, bonding to a strong electrophile (in this case, a carbocation).

$$\underset{\text{weak nucleophile}}{R{-}\ddot{O}(H){:}} + \underset{\text{strong electrophile}}{C^+} \longrightarrow R{-}\overset{+}{O}(H){-}C \xrightarrow{R{-}\ddot{O}{-}H} R{-}\ddot{O}{-}C + R{-}\overset{+}{O}H_2$$

An alcohol is easily converted to a strong nucleophile by forming its alkoxide ion. The alkoxide ion can attack a weaker electrophile, such as an alkyl halide.

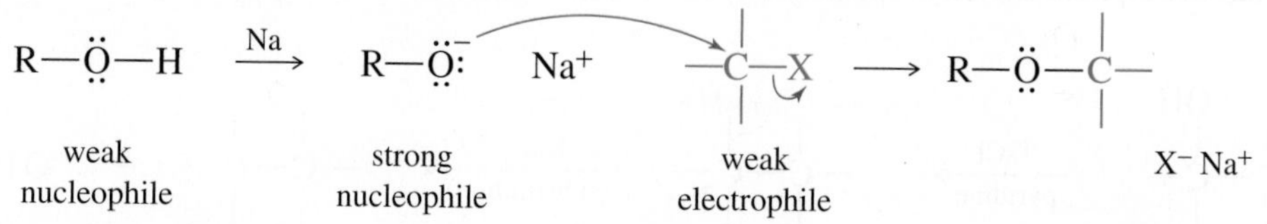

$$R{-}\ddot{O}{-}H \xrightarrow{Na} R{-}\ddot{O}{:}^{-} \quad Na^{+} \quad {-}C{-}X \longrightarrow R{-}\ddot{O}{-}C{-} \quad X^{-}\,Na^{+}$$

weak nucleophile — strong nucleophile — weak electrophile

The O—H bond is broken when alcohols react as nucleophiles, both when an alcohol reacts as a weak nucleophile, or when an alcohol is converted to its alkoxide that then reacts as a strong nucleophile. In contrast, when an alcohol reacts as an electrophile, the C—O bond is broken.

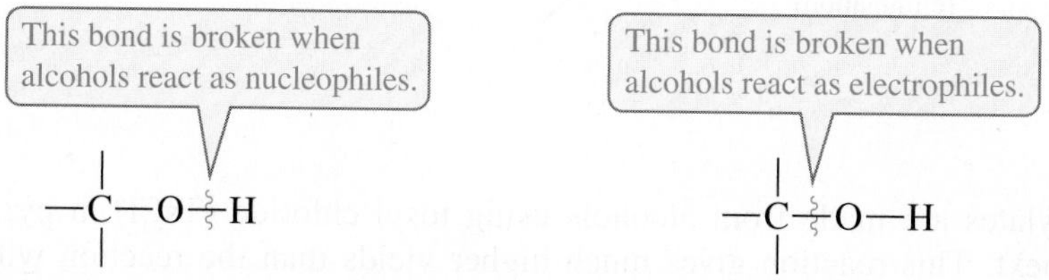

This bond is broken when alcohols react as nucleophiles.

$${-}C{-}O{\wr}H$$

This bond is broken when alcohols react as electrophiles.

$${-}C{\wr}O{-}H$$

An alcohol is a weak electrophile because the hydroxyl group is a poor leaving group. The hydroxyl group becomes a good leaving group (H_2O) when it is protonated. For example, HBr reacts with a primary alcohol by an S_N2 attack of bromide on the protonated alcohol. Note that the C—O bond is broken in this reaction.

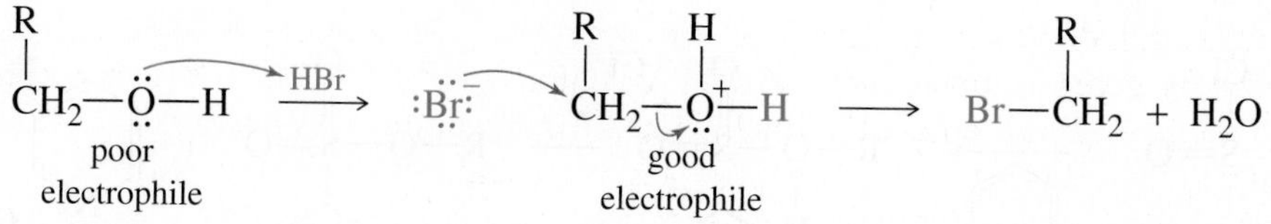

$$R{-}CH_2{-}\ddot{O}{-}H \xrightarrow{HBr} :\ddot{Br}:^{-} \quad R{-}CH_2{-}\overset{+}{\ddot{O}}(H){-}H \longrightarrow Br{-}CH_2{-}R + H_2O$$

poor electrophile — good electrophile

The disadvantage of using a protonated alcohol is that a strongly acidic solution is required to protonate the alcohol. Although halide ions are stable in acid, few other good nucleophiles are stable in strongly acidic solutions. Most strong nucleophiles are also basic and will abstract a proton in acid. Once protonated, the reagent is no longer nucleophilic. For example, an acetylide ion would instantly become protonated if it were added to a protonated alcohol.

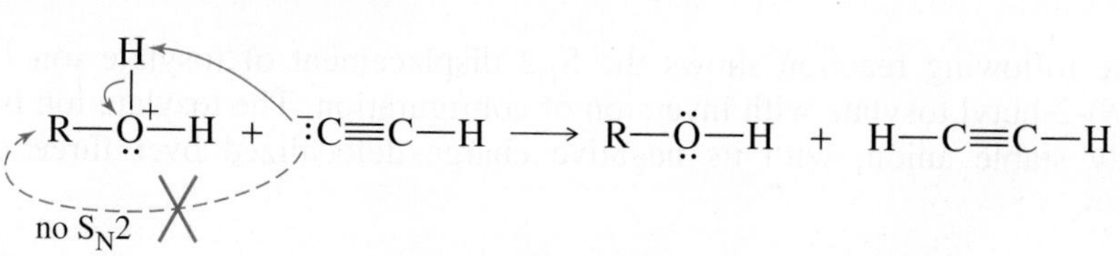

$$R{-}\overset{+}{O}(H){-}H + {}^{-}{:}C{\equiv}C{-}H \longrightarrow R{-}\ddot{O}{-}H + H{-}C{\equiv}C{-}H$$

no S_N2

How can we convert an alcohol to an electrophile that is compatible with basic nucleophiles? We can convert it to an alkyl halide, or we can simply make its tosylate ester. A **tosylate ester** (symbolized ROTs) is the product of condensation of an alcohol with *p*-toluenesulfonic acid (symbolized TsOH).

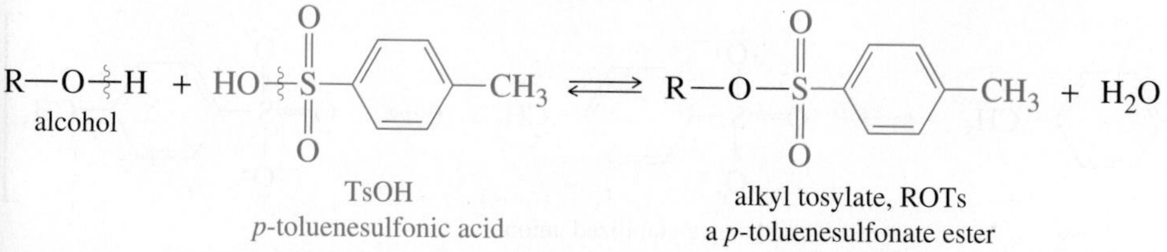

$$R{-}O{\wr}H + HO{\wr}SO_2{-}C_6H_4{-}CH_3 \rightleftharpoons R{-}O{-}SO_2{-}C_6H_4{-}CH_3 + H_2O$$

alcohol — TsOH, *p*-toluenesulfonic acid — alkyl tosylate, ROTs, a *p*-toluenesulfonate ester

problem-solving Hint

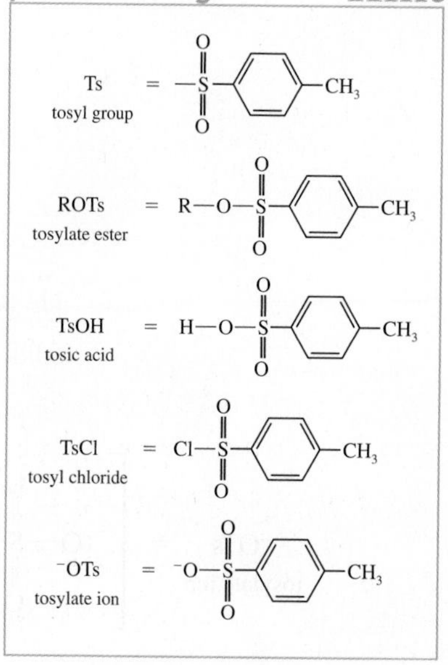

Ts (tosyl group)	=	$-SO_2-C_6H_4-CH_3$
ROTs (tosylate ester)	=	$R-O-SO_2-C_6H_4-CH_3$
TsOH (tosic acid)	=	$H-O-SO_2-C_6H_4-CH_3$
TsCl (tosyl chloride)	=	$Cl-SO_2-C_6H_4-CH_3$
$^{-}$OTs (tosylate ion)	=	$^{-}O-SO_2-C_6H_4-CH_3$

The tosylate group is an excellent leaving group, and alkyl tosylates undergo substitution and elimination much like alkyl halides. In many cases, a tosylate is more reactive than the equivalent alkyl halide.

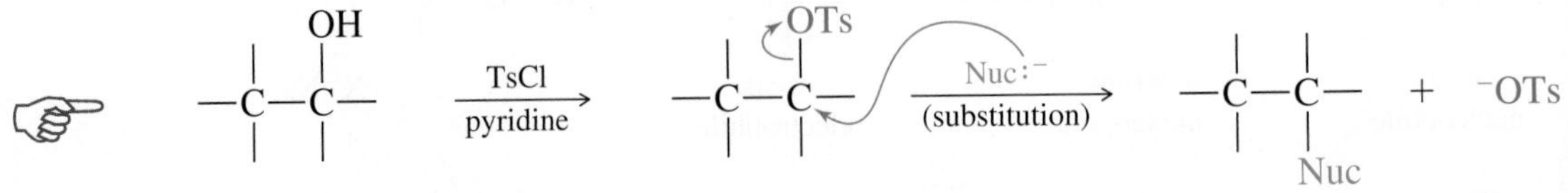
OH
TsCl
pyridine
OTs
Nuc:⁻
(substitution)
Nuc
⁻OTs

or elimination:

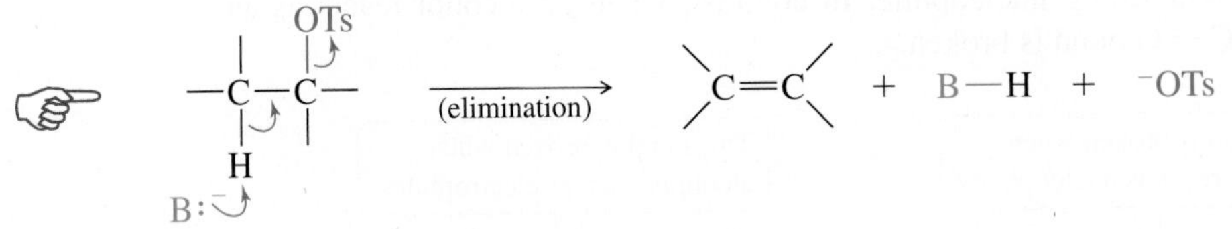
OTs
H
B:
(elimination)
C=C
B—H
⁻OTs

Tosylates are made from alcohols using tosyl chloride (TsCl) in pyridine, as shown next. This reaction gives much higher yields than the reaction with TsOH itself. The mechanism of tosylate formation shows that the C—O bond of the alcohol remains intact throughout the reaction, and the alcohol retains its stereochemical configuration. Pyridine serves as an organic base to remove the HCl formed in the reaction, preventing it from protonating the alcohol and causing side reactions.

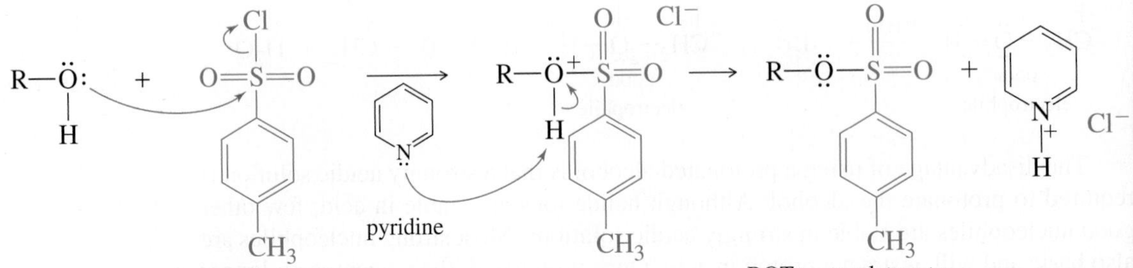
R—Ö:
H
Cl
O=S=O
CH₃
pyridine
Cl⁻
CH₃
Cl⁻
H
p-toluenesulfonyl chloride
TsCl, "tosyl chloride"
ROTs, a tosylate ester

The following reaction shows the S_N2 displacement of tosylate ion ($^-$OTs) from (*S*)-2-butyl tosylate with inversion of configuration. The tosylate ion is a particularly stable anion, with its negative charge delocalized over three oxygen atoms.

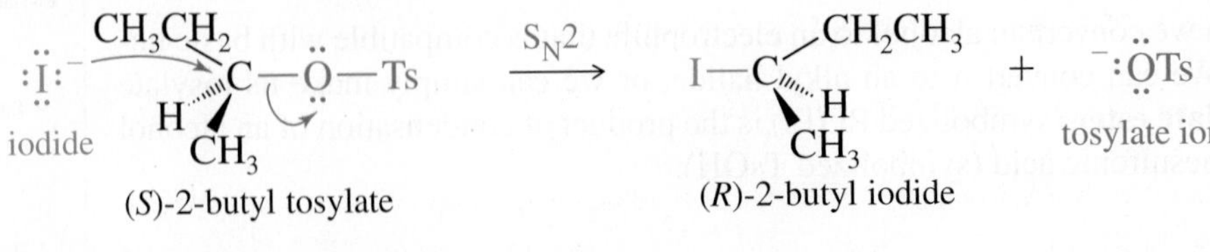
iodide
CH_3CH_2
Ts
H
CH_3
S_N2
(S)-2-butyl tosylate
CH_2CH_3
I
(R)-2-butyl iodide
tosylate ion

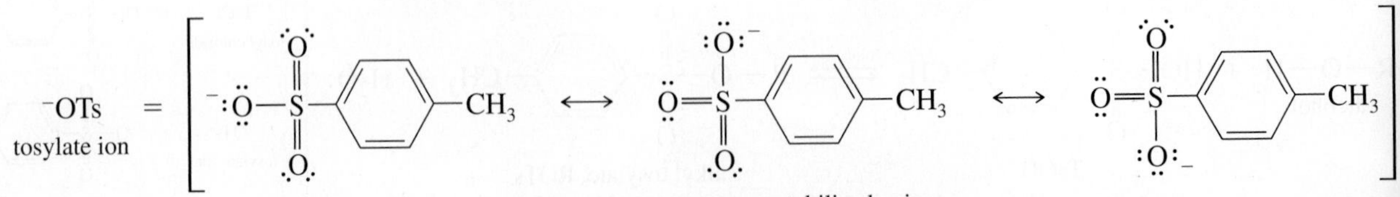
⁻OTs
tosylate ion
CH_3
resonance-stabilized anion

Like halides, the tosylate leaving group is displaced by a wide variety of nucleophiles. The S_N2 mechanism (strong nucleophile) is more commonly used in synthetic preparations than the S_N1. The following reactions show the generality of S_N2 displacements of tosylates. In each case, R must be an unhindered primary or secondary alkyl group if substitution is to predominate over elimination.

SUMMARY S_N2 Reactions of Tosylate Esters

$$R{-}OTs + {}^{-}OH \text{ (hydroxide)} \longrightarrow R{-}OH \text{ (alcohol)} + {}^{-}OTs$$

$$R{-}OTs + {}^{-}C{\equiv}N \text{ (cyanide)} \longrightarrow R{-}C{\equiv}N \text{ (nitrile)} + {}^{-}OTs$$

$$R{-}OTs + Br^{-} \text{ (halide)} \longrightarrow R{-}Br \text{ (alkyl halide)} + {}^{-}OTs$$

$$R{-}OTs + R'{-}O^{-} \text{ (alkoxide)} \longrightarrow R{-}O{-}R' \text{ (ether)} + {}^{-}OTs$$

$$R{-}OTs + {:}NH_3 \text{ (ammonia)} \longrightarrow R{-}NH_3^{+}\ {}^{-}OTs \text{ (amine salt)}$$

$$R{-}OTs + LiAlH_4 \text{ (LAH)} \longrightarrow R{-}H \text{ (alkane)} + {}^{-}OTs$$

PROBLEM 11-9

Predict the major products of the following reactions.
(a) ethyl tosylate + potassium *tert*-butoxide
(b) isobutyl tosylate + NaI
(c) (*R*)-2-hexyl tosylate + NaCN
(d) the tosylate of cyclohexylmethanol + excess NH_3
(e) *n*-butyl tosylate + sodium acetylide, $H{-}C{\equiv}C{:}^{-}\ {}^{+}Na$

problem-solving Hint

Tosylate esters are particularly useful: They are great leaving groups, often better than halides. Grignard reactions build alcohols, which are easily converted to tosylates for substitution or elimination.

PROBLEM 11-10

Show how you would convert 1-propanol to the following compounds using tosylate intermediates. You may use whatever additional reagents are needed.
(a) 1-bromopropane
(b) *n*-propylamine, $CH_3CH_2CH_2NH_2$
(c) $CH_3CH_2CH_2OCH_2CH_3$ ethyl propyl ether
(d) $CH_3CH_2CH_2CN$ butyronitrile

11-6 Reduction of Alcohols

The reduction of alcohols to alkanes is not a common reaction because it removes a functional group, leaving fewer options for further reactions.

$$R{-}OH \xrightarrow{\text{reduction}} R{-}H \quad \text{(rare)}$$

We can reduce an alcohol in two steps, by dehydrating it to an alkene, then hydrogenating the alkene.

$$\text{cyclopentanol} \xrightarrow[\text{heat}]{H_2SO_4} \text{cyclopentene} \xrightarrow[\text{Pt}]{H_2} \text{cyclopentane}$$

Another method for reducing an alcohol involves converting the alcohol to the tosylate ester, then using a hydride reducing agent to displace the tosylate leaving group. This reaction works with most primary and secondary alcohols.

cyclohexanol + tosyl chloride, TsCl $\xrightarrow{\text{pyridine}}$ cyclohexyl tosylate $\xrightarrow{LiAlH_4}$ cyclohexane (75%)

PROBLEM 11-11

Predict the products of the following reactions.

(a) cyclohexylmethanol + TsCl/pyridine
(b) product of (a) + $LiAlH_4$
(c) 1-methylcyclohexanol + H_2SO_4, heat
(d) product of (c) + H_2, Pt

11-7 Reactions of Alcohols with Hydrohalic Acids

Tosylation of an alcohol, followed by displacement of the tosylate by a halide ion, converts an alcohol to an alkyl halide. This is not the most common method for converting alcohols to alkyl halides, however, because simple, one-step reactions are available. A common method is to treat the alcohol with a hydrohalic acid, usually HCl or HBr.

In acidic solution, an alcohol is in equilibrium with its protonated form. Protonation converts the hydroxyl group from a poor leaving group (^-OH) to a good leaving group (H_2O). Once the alcohol is protonated, all the usual substitution and elimination reactions are feasible, depending on the structure (1°, 2°, 3°) of the alcohol.

$$R{-}\ddot{O}{-}H + H^+ \rightleftharpoons R{-}\overset{H}{\overset{|}{O^+}}{-}H \xrightarrow[S_N1 \text{ or } S_N2]{X^-} R{-}X$$

poor leaving group — good leaving group

Most good nucleophiles are basic, becoming protonated and losing their nucleophilicity in acidic solutions. Halide ions are exceptions, however. Halides are anions of strong acids, so they are weak bases. Solutions of HBr and HCl contain nucleophilic Br^- and Cl^- ions. These acids are commonly used to convert alcohols to the corresponding alkyl halides.

Reactions with Hydrobromic Acid

$$R{-}OH + HBr/H_2O \longrightarrow R{-}Br$$

Concentrated hydrobromic acid rapidly converts *tert*-butyl alcohol to *tert*-butyl bromide. The strong acid protonates the hydroxyl group, converting it to a good leaving group. The hindered tertiary carbon atom cannot undergo S_N2 displacement, but it can ionize to a tertiary carbocation. Attack by bromide gives the alkyl bromide. The mechanism is similar to other S_N1 mechanisms we have studied, except that water serves as the leaving group from the protonated alcohol.

MECHANISM 11-1 Reaction of a Tertiary Alcohol with HBr (S_N1)

A tertiary alcohol reacts with HBr by the S_N1 mechanism.

EXAMPLE: Conversion of *tert*-butyl alcohol to *tert*-butyl bromide.

Step 1: Protonation converts the hydroxyl group to a good leaving group.

$$(CH_3)_3C-\ddot{O}-H + H-\ddot{Br}: \rightleftharpoons (CH_3)_3C-\overset{+}{\ddot{O}}H_2 + :\ddot{Br}:^-$$

tert-butyl alcohol

Step 2: Water leaves, forming a carbocation.

$$(CH_3)_3C-\overset{+}{\ddot{O}}H_2 \rightleftharpoons (CH_3)_3C^+ + H_2O$$

Step 3: Bromide ion attacks the carbocation.

$$(CH_3)_3C^+ + :\ddot{Br}:^- \longrightarrow (CH_3)_3C-\ddot{Br}:$$

tert-butyl bromide

Many other alcohols react with HBr, with the reaction mechanism depending on the structure of the alcohol. For example, 1-butanol reacts with sodium bromide in concentrated sulfuric acid to give 1-bromobutane by an S_N2 displacement. The sodium bromide/sulfuric acid reagent generates HBr in the solution.

$$\underset{\text{1-butanol}}{CH_3(CH_2)_2-CH_2OH} \xrightarrow{NaBr,\ H_2SO_4} \underset{\text{1-bromobutane (90\%)}}{CH_3(CH_2)_2-CH_2Br}$$

Protonation converts the hydroxyl group to a good leaving group, but ionization to a primary carbocation is unfavorable. The protonated primary alcohol is well suited for the S_N2 displacement, however. Back-side attack by bromide ion gives 1-bromobutane.

MECHANISM 11-2 Reaction of a Primary Alcohol with HBr (S_N2)

A primary alcohol reacts with HBr by the S_N2 mechanism.

EXAMPLE: Conversion of 1-butanol to 1-bromobutane.

Step 1: Protonation converts the hydroxyl group to a good leaving group.

$$CH_3CH_2CH_2-CH_2-\ddot{O}-H + H-\ddot{Br}: \rightleftharpoons CH_3CH_2CH_2-CH_2-\overset{+}{\ddot{O}}H_2 + :\ddot{Br}:^-$$

1-butanol

(*Continued*)

Step 2: Bromide displaces water to give the alkylbromide.

$$:\ddot{Br}:^- + CH_3CH_2CH_2CH_2-\overset{+}{O}H_2 \rightleftharpoons :\ddot{Br}-CH_2CH_2CH_2CH_3 + H_2O$$

1-bromobutane

Secondary alcohols also react with HBr to form alkyl bromides, usually by the S_N1 mechanism. For example, cyclohexanol is converted to bromocyclohexane using HBr as the reagent.

$$\text{cyclohexanol} \xrightarrow{HBr} \text{bromocyclohexane (80\%)}$$

problem-solving Hint

Memorizing all these mechanisms is not the best way to study this material. Depending on the substrate, these reactions can go by more than one mechanism. Gain experience working problems, then consider each individual case to propose a likely mechanism.

PROBLEM 11-12

Propose a mechanism for the reaction of
(a) 1-methylcyclohexanol with HBr to form 1-bromo-1-methylcyclohexane.
(b) 2-cyclohexylethanol with HBr to form 1-bromo-2-cyclohexylethane.

Reactions with Hydrochloric Acid

$$R-OH + HCl/H_2O \xrightarrow{ZnCl_2} R-Cl$$

Hydrochloric acid (HCl) reacts with alcohols in much the same way that hydrobromic acid does. For example, concentrated aqueous HCl reacts with *tert*-butyl alcohol to give *tert*-butyl chloride.

$$(CH_3)_3C-OH + HCl/H_2O \longrightarrow (CH_3)_3C-Cl + H_2O$$

tert-butyl alcohol; *tert*-butyl chloride (98%)

PROBLEM 11-13

The reaction of *tert*-butyl alcohol with concentrated HCl goes by the S_N1 mechanism. Write a mechanism for this reaction.

Chloride ion is a weaker nucleophile than bromide ion because it is smaller and less polarizable. An additional Lewis acid, such as zinc chloride ($ZnCl_2$), is sometimes necessary to promote the reaction of HCl with primary and secondary alcohols. Zinc chloride coordinates with the oxygen of the alcohol in the same way a proton does—except that zinc chloride coordinates more strongly.

The reagent composed of HCl and $ZnCl_2$ is called the **Lucas reagent**. Secondary and tertiary alcohols react with the Lucas reagent by the S_N1 mechanism.

S_N1 reaction with the Lucas reagent (fast)

$$(CH_3)_2CH-\ddot{O}-H \underset{}{\overset{ZnCl_2}{\rightleftharpoons}} (CH_3)_2CH-\overset{+}{O}(H)-ZnCl_2^- \rightleftharpoons (CH_3)_2CH^+$$

alcohol–zinc chloride complex; carbocation

$$(CH_3)_2CH^+ \xrightarrow{Cl^-} (CH_3)_2CH-Cl + H\ddot{O}-ZnCl_2^-$$

When a primary alcohol reacts with the Lucas reagent, ionization is not possible—the primary carbocation is too unstable. Primary substrates react by an S_N2 mechanism, which is slower than the S_N1 reaction of secondary and tertiary substrates. For example, when 1-butanol reacts with the Lucas reagent, the chloride ion attacks the complex from the back, displacing the leaving group.

S_N2 reaction with the Lucas reagent (slow)

$$:\ddot{Cl}:^- + CH_3CH_2CH_2-CH_2-\overset{+}{O}(H)-\overset{-}{Zn}Cl_2 \longrightarrow \left[Cl\cdots C(H)(H)(CH_2CH_2CH_3)\cdots \overset{+}{O}(H)-\overset{-}{Zn}Cl_2 \right]^{\ddagger} \longrightarrow Cl-CH_2CH_2CH_2CH_3 + :\ddot{O}(H)-\overset{-}{Zn}Cl_2$$

transition state

The Lucas Test The Lucas reagent reacts with primary, secondary, and tertiary alcohols at predictable rates, and these rates can distinguish among the three types of alcohols. When the reagent is first added to the alcohol, the mixture forms a single homogeneous phase: The concentrated HCl solution is very polar, and the polar alcohol–zinc chloride complex dissolves. Once the alcohol has reacted to form the alkyl halide, the relatively nonpolar halide separates into a second phase. (R—OH dissolves, but R—Cl does not.)

The **Lucas test** involves adding the Lucas reagent to an unknown alcohol and watching for the second phase to separate (see Table 11-2). Tertiary alcohols react and show a second phase almost instantly because they form relatively stable tertiary carbocations. Secondary alcohols react in about 1 to 5 minutes because their secondary carbocations are less stable than tertiary ones. Primary alcohols react very slowly. Since the activated primary alcohol cannot form a carbocation, it simply remains in solution until it is attacked by the chloride ion. With a primary alcohol, the reaction may take from 10 minutes to several days.

TABLE 11-2

Reactions of Alcohols with the Lucas Reagent

Alcohol Type	Time to React (min)
primary	>6
secondary	1–5
tertiary	<1

PROBLEM 11-14

Show how you would use a simple chemical test to distinguish between the following pairs of compounds. Tell what you would observe with each compound.
(a) isopropyl alcohol and *tert*-butyl alcohol
(b) isopropyl alcohol and 2-butanone, $CH_3COCH_2CH_3$
(c) 1-hexanol and cyclohexanol
(d) allyl alcohol and 1-propanol
(e) 2-butanone and *tert*-butyl alcohol

Limitations on the Use of Hydrohalic Acids with Alcohols The reactions of alcohols with hydrohalic acids do not always give good yields of the expected alkyl halides. Four principal limitations restrict the generality of this technique.

1. *Poor yields of alkyl chlorides from primary and secondary alcohols.* Primary and secondary alcohols react with HCl much more slowly than tertiary alcohols, even with zinc chloride added. Under these conditions, side reactions may prevent good yields of the alkyl halides.
2. *Eliminations.* Heating an alcohol in a concentrated acid such as HCl or HBr often leads to elimination. Once the hydroxyl group of the alcohol has been protonated and converted to a good leaving group, it becomes a candidate for both substitution and elimination.
3. *Rearrangements.* Carbocation intermediates are always prone to rearrangements. We have seen (Section 6-15) that hydrogen atoms and alkyl groups can migrate from one carbon atom to another to form a more stable carbocation. This rearrangement may occur as the leaving group leaves, or it may occur once the cation has formed.

4. *Limited ability to make alkyl iodides.* Many alcohols do not react with HI to give acceptable yields of alkyl iodides. Alkyl iodides are valuable intermediates, however, because iodides are the most reactive of the alkyl halides. We will discuss another technique for making alkyl iodides in the next section.

SOLVED PROBLEM 11-2

When 3-methyl-2-butanol is treated with concentrated HBr, the major product is 2-bromo-2-methylbutane. Propose a mechanism for the formation of this product.

$$CH_3-C(H)(CH_3)-CH(OH)-CH_3 \xrightarrow{HBr} CH_3-C(Br)(CH_3)-CH_2-CH_3$$

3-methyl-2-butanol → 2-bromo-2-methylbutane

SOLUTION

The alcohol is protonated by the strong acid. This protonated secondary alcohol loses water to form a secondary carbocation.

$$CH_3-C(H)(CH_3)-CH(\ddot{O}H)-CH_3 \underset{}{\overset{H^+}{\rightleftharpoons}} CH_3-C(H)(CH_3)-CH(\overset{+}{O}H_2)-CH_3 \rightleftharpoons CH_3-C(H)(CH_3)-\overset{+}{C}H-CH_3 + H_2\ddot{O}:$$

protonated alcohol; secondary carbocation

A hydride shift transforms the secondary carbocation into a more stable tertiary cation. Attack by bromide leads to the observed product.

$$CH_3-C(H)(CH_3)-\overset{+}{C}H-CH_3 \longrightarrow CH_3-\overset{+}{C}(CH_3)-CH(H)-CH_3 \xrightarrow{:\ddot{Br}:^-} CH_3-C(Br)(CH_3)-CH(H)-CH_3$$

secondary carbocation; tertiary carbocation; observed product

Although rearrangements are usually seen as annoying side reactions, a clever chemist can use a rearrangement to accomplish a synthetic goal. Problem 11-15 shows how an alcohol substitution with rearrangement might be used in a synthesis.

PROBLEM 11-15

Neopentyl alcohol, $(CH_3)_3CCH_2OH$, reacts with concentrated HBr to give 2-bromo-2-methylbutane, a rearranged product. Propose a mechanism for the formation of this product.

PROBLEM 11-16

Explain the products observed in the following reaction of an alcohol with the Lucas reagent.

$$\text{1,2-dimethylcyclohexan-1-ol (H, CH}_3\text{; OH, CH}_3) \xrightarrow{HCl/ZnCl_2} \text{(H, CH}_3\text{; Cl, CH}_3) + \text{(H, CH}_3\text{; Cl, CH}_3)$$

PROBLEM 11-17

When *cis*-2-methylcyclohexanol reacts with the Lucas reagent, the major product is 1-chloro-1-methylcyclohexane. Propose a mechanism to explain the formation of this product.

11-8 Reactions of Alcohols with Phosphorus Halides

Several phosphorus halides are useful for converting alcohols to alkyl halides. Phosphorus tribromide, phosphorus trichloride, and phosphorus pentachloride work well and are commercially available.

$$3\,R{-}OH + PCl_3 \longrightarrow 3\,R{-}Cl + P(OH)_3$$
$$3\,R{-}OH + PBr_3 \longrightarrow 3\,R{-}Br + P(OH)_3$$
$$R{-}OH + PCl_5 \longrightarrow R{-}Cl + POCl_3 + HCl$$

Phosphorus triiodide is not sufficiently stable to be stored, but it can be generated in situ (in the reaction mixture) by the reaction of phosphorus with iodine.

$$2\,P + 3\,I_2 \rightleftharpoons 2\,PI_3$$
$$6\,R{-}OH + 2\,P + 3\,I_2 \longrightarrow 6\,R{-}I + 2\,P(OH)_3$$

Phosphorus halides produce good yields of most primary and secondary alkyl halides, but none works well with tertiary alcohols. The two phosphorus halides used most often are PBr_3 and the phosphorus/iodine combination. Phosphorus tribromide is often the best reagent for converting a primary or secondary alcohol to the alkyl bromide, especially if the alcohol might rearrange in strong acid. A phosphorus and iodine combination is one of the best reagents for converting a primary or secondary alcohol to the alkyl iodide. For the synthesis of alkyl chlorides, thionyl chloride (discussed in the next section) generally gives better yields than PCl_3 or PCl_5, especially with tertiary alcohols.

The following examples show the conversion of primary and secondary alcohols to bromides and iodides by treatment with PBr_3 and P/I_2.

$$(CH_3)_3C{-}CH_2OH + PBr_3 \longrightarrow (CH_3)_3C{-}CH_2Br$$

neopentyl alcohol → neopentyl bromide (60%)

$$CH_3(CH_2)_{14}{-}CH_2OH + P/I_2 \longrightarrow CH_3(CH_2)_{14}{-}CH_2I$$

(85%)

cyclopentanol $\xrightarrow{PBr_3}$ bromocyclopentane (OH → Br)

(90%)

PROBLEM 11-18

Write balanced equations for the three preceding reactions.

Mechanism of the Reaction with Phosphorus Trihalides The mechanism of the reaction of alcohols with phosphorus trihalides explains why rearrangements are uncommon and why phosphorus halides work poorly with tertiary alcohols. The mechanism is shown here using PBr_3 as the reagent; PCl_3 and PI_3 (generated from phosphorus and iodine) react in a similar manner.

MECHANISM 11-3 Reaction of Alcohols with PBr_3

Step 1: PBr_3 is a strong electrophile. An alcohol displaces bromide ion from PBr_3 to give an excellent leaving group.

$$R{-}\ddot{O}H + PBr_3 \longrightarrow R{-}\overset{+}{O}H{-}PBr_2 + :\ddot{Br}:^-$$

excellent leaving group

(*Continued*)

Step 2: Bromide displaces the leaving group to give the alkyl bromide.

$$:\ddot{Br}:^- + R-\ddot{O}^+(H)-PBr_2 \longrightarrow :\ddot{Br}-R + :\ddot{O}(H)-PBr_2$$

leaving group

EXAMPLE: Reaction of (*R*)-2-pentanol with PBr_3.

Step 1: Displacement of bromide and formation of a leaving group.

$$CH_3CH_2CH_2(H_3C)(H)C-\ddot{O}H + :PBr_3 \longrightarrow CH_3CH_2CH_2(H_3C)(H)C-\ddot{O}^+(H)-PBr_2 + :\ddot{Br}:^-$$

(*R*)-2-pentanol

Step 2: Bromide displaces the leaving group to give (*S*)-2-bromopentane.

$$:\ddot{Br}:^- + CH_3CH_2CH_2(H_3C)(H)C-\ddot{O}^+(H)-PBr_2 \longrightarrow :\ddot{Br}-C(H)(CH_3)CH_2CH_2CH_3 + :\ddot{O}(H)-PBr_2$$

(*S*)-2-bromopentane

Rearrangements are uncommon because no carbocation is involved, so there is no opportunity for rearrangement. This mechanism also explains the poor yields with tertiary alcohols. The final step is an S_N2 displacement where bromide attacks the back side of the alkyl group. This attack is hindered if the alkyl group is tertiary. In the case of a tertiary alcohol, an ionization to a carbocation is needed. This ionization is slow, and it invites side reactions.

11-9 Reactions of Alcohols with Thionyl Chloride

Thionyl chloride ($SOCl_2$) is often the best reagent for converting an alcohol to an alkyl chloride. The by-products (gaseous SO_2 and HCl) leave the reaction mixture and ensure there can be no reverse reaction.

$$R-OH + Cl-\overset{O}{\overset{\|}{S}}-Cl \xrightarrow{\text{heat}} R-Cl + SO_2 + HCl$$

Under the proper conditions, thionyl chloride reacts by the interesting mechanism summarized next. In the first step, the nonbonding electrons of the hydroxyl oxygen atom attack the electrophilic sulfur atom of thionyl chloride. A chloride ion is expelled, and a proton is lost to give a chlorosulfite ester. In the next step, the chlorosulfite ester ionizes (when R = 2° or 3°), and the sulfur atom quickly delivers chloride to the carbocation. When R is primary, chloride probably bonds to carbon at the same time that the C—O bond is breaking.

$$R-\ddot{O}H + Cl_2S{=}O \longrightarrow R-\ddot{O}^+(H)-S(Cl)_2-\ddot{O}:^- \longrightarrow R-\ddot{O}^+(H)-S(=\ddot{O})Cl + Cl^- \longrightarrow R-\ddot{O}-S(=\ddot{O})Cl + HCl$$

thionyl chloride; chlorosulfite ester

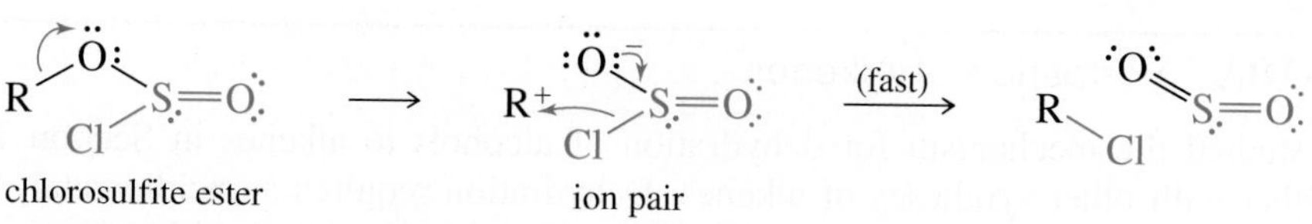

chlorosulfite ester → ion pair → (fast)

This mechanism resembles the S_N1, except that the nucleophile is delivered to the carbocation by the leaving group, usually giving retention of configuration as shown in the following example. (Under different conditions, retention of configuration might not be observed.)

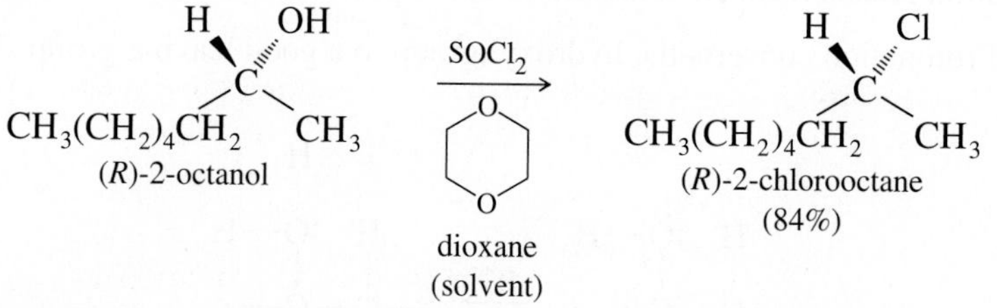

(R)-2-octanol $\xrightarrow{SOCl_2}$ (R)-2-chlorooctane (84%)

dioxane (solvent)

Summary of the Best Reagents for Converting Alcohols to Alkyl Halides			
Class of Alcohol	**Chloride**	**Bromide**	**Iodide**
primary	$SOCl_2$	PBr_3 or HBr*	P/I_2
secondary	$SOCl_2$	PBr_3	P/I_2^*
tertiary	HCl	HBr	HI*

*Works only in selected cases.

PROBLEM 11-19

Suggest how you would convert *trans*-4-methylcyclohexanol to
(a) *trans*-1-chloro-4-methylcyclohexane.
(b) *cis*-1-chloro-4-methylcyclohexane.

PROBLEM 11-20

Two products are observed in the following reaction.

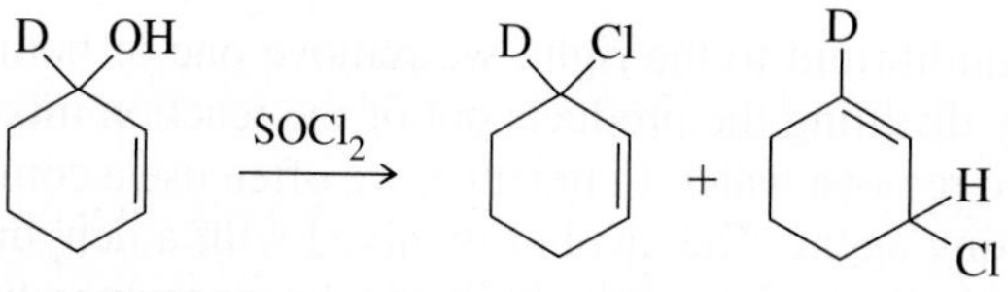

$\xrightarrow{SOCl_2}$ +

(a) Suggest a mechanism to explain how these two products are formed.
(b) Your mechanism for part (a) should be different from the usual mechanism of the reaction of $SOCl_2$ with alcohols. Explain why the reaction follows a different mechanism in this case.

problem-solving Hint

Thionyl chloride reacts with alcohols by various mechanisms that depend on the substrate, the solvent, and the temperature. Be cautious in predicting the structure and stereochemistry of a product unless you know the actual mechanism.

PROBLEM 11-21

Give the structures of the products you would expect when each alcohol reacts with (1) HCl, $ZnCl_2$; (2) HBr; (3) PBr_3; (4) P/I_2; (5) $SOCl_2$.
(a) 1-butanol **(b)** 2-methyl-2-butanol **(c)** 2,2-dimethyl-1-butanol
(d) *cis*-3-methylcyclopentanol

11-10 Dehydration Reactions of Alcohols

11-10A Formation of Alkenes

We studied the mechanism for dehydration of alcohols to alkenes in Section 7-10 together with other syntheses of alkenes. Dehydration requires an acidic catalyst to protonate the hydroxyl group of the alcohol and convert it to a good leaving group. Loss of water, followed by loss of a proton, gives the alkene. An equilibrium is established between reactants and products.

MECHANISM 11-4 (Review): Acid-Catalyzed Dehydration of an Alcohol

Dehydration results from E1 elimination of the protonated alcohol.

Step 1: Protonation converts the hydroxyl group to a good leaving group.

$$\text{H–C–C–}\ddot{\text{O}}\text{–H} \underset{}{\overset{H^+}{\rightleftharpoons}} \text{H–C–C–}\dot{\text{O}}^{+}\text{H}_2$$

Step 2: Water leaves, forming a carbocation.

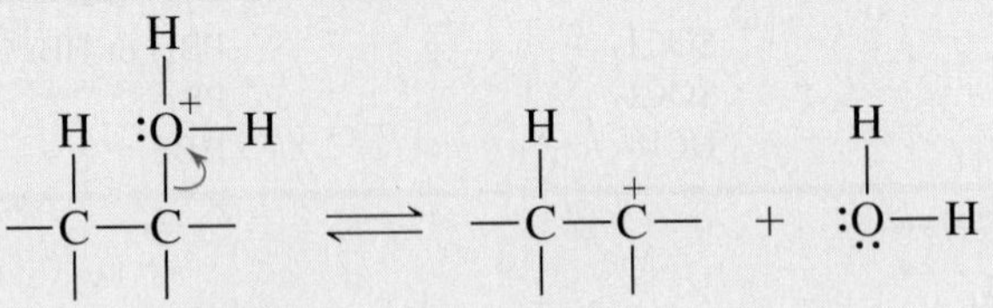

$$\text{H–C–C–}\text{O}^{+}\text{H}_2 \rightleftharpoons \text{H–C–C}^{+} + \text{H–}\ddot{\text{O}}\text{–H}$$

Step 3: Loss of a proton gives the alkene.

$$H_2\ddot{O}: + \text{H–C–C}^{+} \rightleftharpoons \text{C=C} + H_3O^+$$

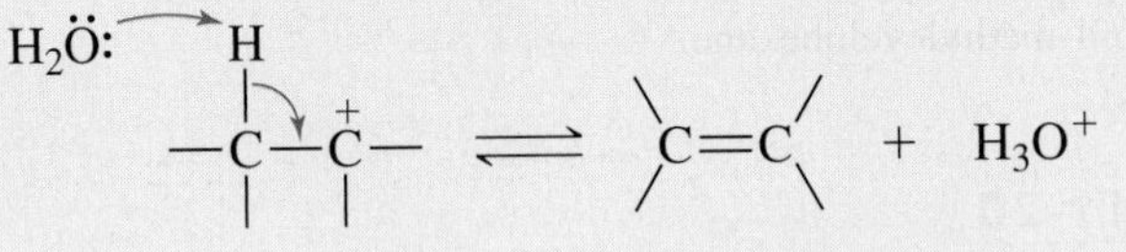

To drive this equilibrium to the right, we remove one or both of the products as they form, either by distilling the products out of the reaction mixture or by adding a dehydrating agent to remove water. In practice, we often use a combination of distillation and a dehydrating agent. The alcohol is mixed with a dehydrating acid, and the mixture is heated to boiling. The alkene boils at a lower temperature than the alcohol (because the alcohol is hydrogen-bonded), and the alkene distills out of the mixture. For example,

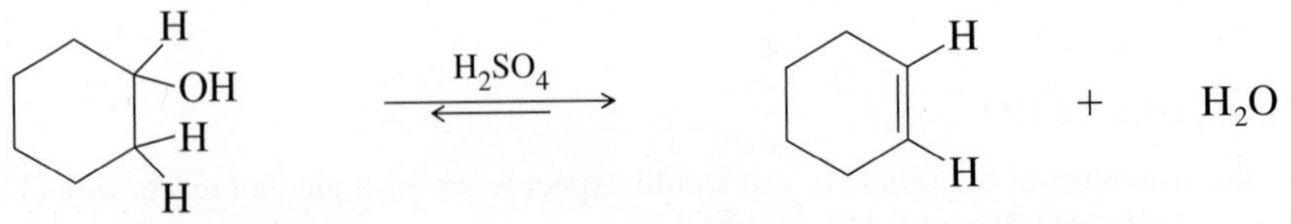

$$\text{cyclohexanol} \underset{}{\overset{H_2SO_4}{\rightleftharpoons}} \text{cyclohexene} + H_2O$$

cyclohexanol, bp 161 °C

cyclohexene, bp 83 °C (80%)
(distilled from the mixture)

Alcohol dehydrations generally take place through the E1 mechanism. Protonation of the hydroxyl group converts it to a good leaving group. Water leaves, forming a carbocation. Loss of a proton gives the alkene.

H_2SO_4 ⇌ HSO_4^- ⇌ $H_2\ddot{O}:$ ⇌ + H_3O^+

Figure 11-2 shows the reaction-energy diagram for the E1 dehydration of an alcohol. The first step is a mildly exothermic protonation, followed by an endothermic, rate-limiting ionization. A fast, strongly exothermic deprotonation gives the alkene. Because the rate-limiting step is formation of a carbocation, the ease of dehydration follows from the ease of formation of carbocations: 3° > 2° > 1°. As in other carbocation reactions, rearrangements are common.

With primary alcohols, rearrangement and isomerization of the products are so common that acid-catalyzed dehydration is rarely a good method for converting them to alkenes. The following mechanism shows how 1-butanol undergoes dehydration with rearrangement to give a mixture of 1-butene and 2-butene. The more highly substituted product, 2-butene, is the major product, in accordance with the Zaitsev rule (Section 6-18).

Ionization of the protonated alcohol, with rearrangement

H^+ ⟶ $\xrightarrow[H:^-\text{ migrates}]{H_2O\text{ leaves}}$

secondary carbocation

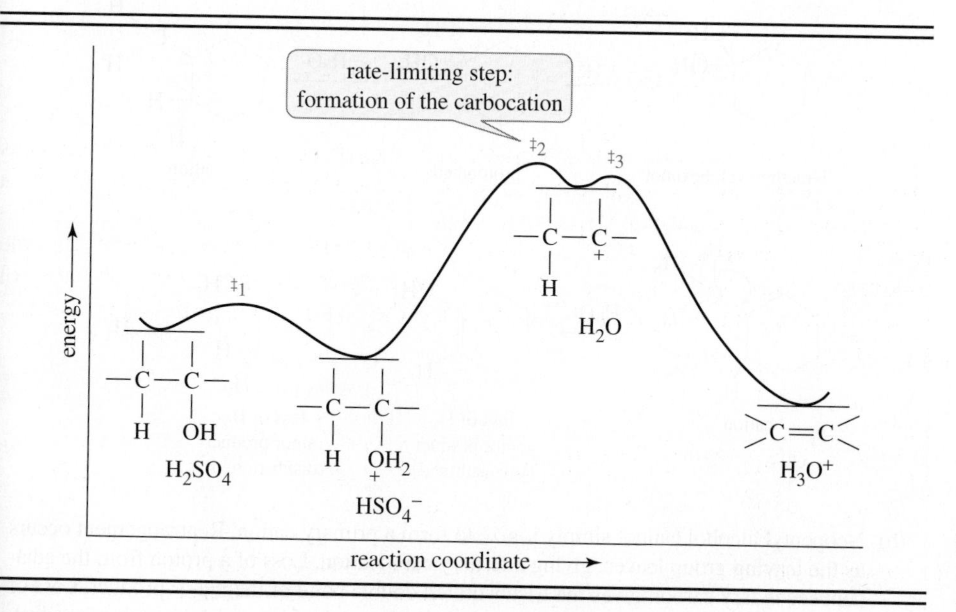

■ FIGURE 11-2
Reaction-energy diagram for dehydration of an alcohol.

Loss of either proton to give two products

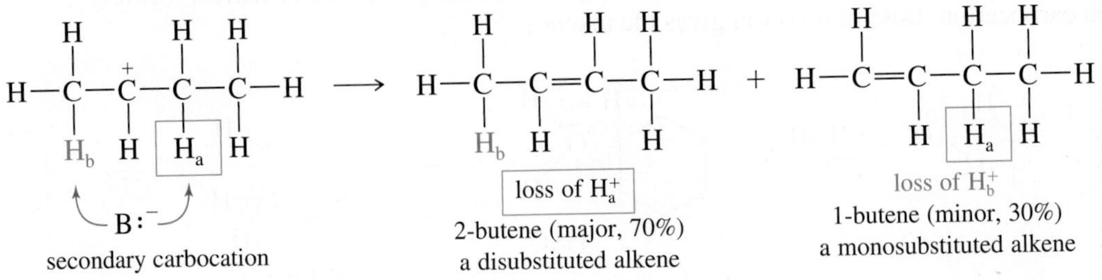

secondary carbocation

B:⁻

loss of H_a^+

2-butene (major, 70%)
a disubstituted alkene

loss of H_b^+

1-butene (minor, 30%)
a monosubstituted alkene

Let's review the utility of dehydration and give guidelines for predicting the products:

1. Dehydration usually goes by the E1 mechanism. Rearrangements may occur to form more stable carbocations.
2. Dehydration works best with tertiary alcohols and almost as well with secondary alcohols. Rearrangements and poor yields are common with primary alcohols.
3. (Zaitsev's rule) If two or more alkenes might be formed by deprotonation of the carbocation, the most substituted alkene usually predominates.

Solved Problem 11-3 shows how these rules are used to predict the products of dehydrations. The carbocations are drawn to show how rearrangements occur and how more than one product may result.

problem-solving Hint

Most alcohol dehydrations go by El mechanisms involving protonation of the OH group, followed by loss of water.

SOLVED PROBLEM 11-3

Predict the products of sulfuric acid-catalyzed dehydration of the following alcohols.
(a) 1-methylcyclohexanol (b) neopentyl alcohol

SOLUTION

(a) 1-Methylcyclohexanol reacts to form a tertiary carbocation. A proton may be abstracted from any one of three carbon atoms. The two secondary atoms are equivalent, and abstraction of a proton from one of them leads to the trisubstituted double bond of the major product. Abstraction of a methyl proton leads to the disubstituted double bond of the minor product.

1-methylcyclohexanol $\xrightarrow{H^+}$ protonated $\xrightarrow{-H_2O}$ cation

cation $\xrightarrow{H_2\ddot{O}:}$ loss of H_a, major product (trisubstituted) + loss of H_b, minor product (disubstituted) + H_3

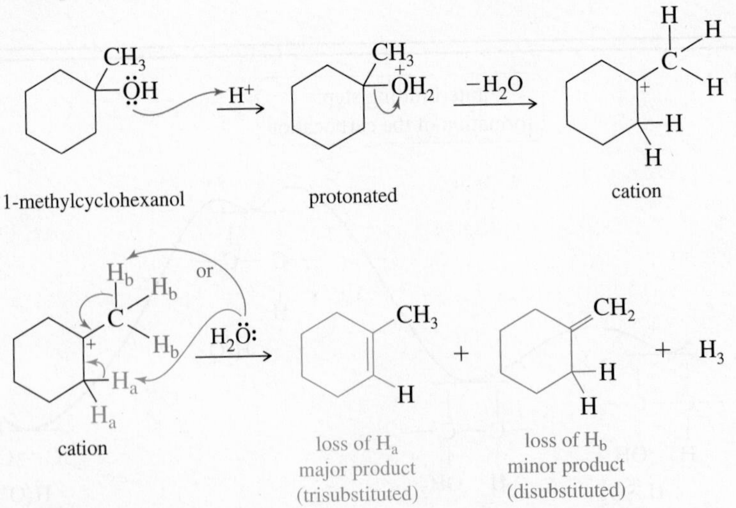

(b) Neopentyl alcohol cannot simply ionize to form a primary cation. Rearrangement occurs as the leaving group leaves, giving a tertiary carbocation. Loss of a proton from the adjacent secondary carbon gives the trisubstituted double bond of the major product. Loss of a proton from the methyl group gives the disubstituted double bond of the minor product.

$$CH_3-C(CH_3)_2-CH_2\ddot{O}H \xrightarrow{H^+} CH_3-C(CH_3)_2-CH_2-\overset{+}{O}H_2 \longrightarrow CH_3-\overset{+}{C}(CH_3)-CH_2 \quad :\ddot{O}H_2$$

neopentyl alcohol (2,2-dimethyl-1-propanol) — ionization with rearrangement — 3° cation

$$H_b-C(H_b)(H_b)-\overset{+}{C}(CH_3)-C(CH_3)(H_a)-H_a \xrightarrow{-H^+} (H_3C)_2C=C(CH_3)H + HC(H)=C(CH_2CH_3)CH_3$$

$H_2\ddot{O}:$

loss of H_a^+ — major product (trisubstituted)

loss of H_b^+ — minor product (disubstituted)

PROBLEM 11-22

Predict the products of the sulfuric acid-catalyzed dehydration of the following alcohols. When more than one product is expected, label the major and minor products.

(a) 2-methyl-2-butanol **(b)** 1-pentanol **(c)** 2-pentanol
(d) 1-isopropylcyclohexanol **(e)** 2-methylcyclohexanol

problem-solving **Hint**

Draw the carbocation, look for possible rearrangements, then consider all the ways that the original carbocation and any rearranged carbocation might lose protons to give alkenes. Zaitsev's rule usually predicts the major product.

PROBLEM 11-23

Some alcohols undergo rearrangement or other unwanted side reactions when they dehydrate in acid. Alcohols may be dehydrated under mildly *basic* conditions using phosphorus oxychloride ($POCl_3$) in pyridine. The alcohol reacts with phosphorus oxychloride much like it reacts with tosyl chloride (Section 11-5), displacing a chloride ion from phosphorus to give an alkyl dichlorophosphate ester. The dichlorophosphate group is an outstanding leaving group. Pyridine reacts as a base with the dichlorophosphate ester to give an E2 elimination. Propose a mechanism for the dehydration of cyclohexanol by $POCl_3$ in pyridine.

$O=PCl_3$ — phosphorus oxychloride

pyridine

11-10B Bimolecular Dehydration to Form Ethers (Industrial)

In some cases, a protonated primary alcohol may be attacked by another molecule of the alcohol and undergo an S_N2 displacement. The net reaction is a bimolecular dehydration to form an ether. For example, the attack by ethanol on a protonated molecule of ethanol gives diethyl ether.

$$CH_3CH_2-\ddot{O}H \;+\; CH_3CH_2-\overset{+}{O}H_2 \xrightarrow{S_N2} CH_3CH_2-\overset{+}{O}(H)-CH_2CH_3 \;\; :\ddot{O}(Et)H \longrightarrow CH_3CH_2-\ddot{O}-CH_2CH_3 + Et\overset{+}{O}H_2$$

nucleophilic — electrophilic — protonated ether — diethyl ether

Bimolecular dehydration can be used to synthesize symmetrical dialkyl ethers from simple, unhindered primary alcohols. This method is used for the industrial synthesis of diethyl ether ($CH_3CH_2—O—CH_2CH_3$) and dimethyl ether ($CH_3—O—CH_3$). Under the acidic dehydration conditions, two reactions compete: Elimination (to give an alkene) competes with substitution (to give an ether).

$$2\ CH_3CH_2OH \xrightarrow{H_2SO_4,\ 140\ °C} CH_3CH_2—O—CH_2CH_3 + H_2O$$

ethanol → diethyl ether

Elimination to give the alkene, a unimolecular dehydration

$$CH_3CH_2OH \xrightarrow{H_2SO_4,\ 180\ °C} CH_2=CH_2 + H_2O$$

ethanol → ethylene

PROBLEM 11-24

Contrast the mechanisms of the two preceding dehydrations of ethanol.

How can we control these two competing dehydrations? The ether synthesis (substitution) shows two molecules of alcohol giving two product molecules: one of diethyl ether and one of water. The elimination shows one molecule of alcohol giving two molecules: one of ethylene and one of water. The elimination results in an increase in the number of molecules and therefore an *increase* in the randomness (entropy) of the system. The elimination has a more positive change in entropy (ΔS) than the substitution, and the $-T\Delta S$ term in the Gibbs free energy becomes more favorable for the elimination as the temperature increases. Substitution (to give the ether) is favored around 140 °C and below, and elimination is favored around 180 °C and above. Diethyl ether is produced industrially by heating ethanol with an acidic catalyst at around 140 °C.

PROBLEM 11-25

Explain why the acid-catalyzed dehydration is a poor method for the synthesis of an unsymmetrical ether such as ethyl methyl ether, $CH_3CH_2—O—CH_3$.

PROBLEM-SOLVING STRATEGY

PROPOSING REACTION MECHANISMS

In view of the large number of reactions we've covered, proposing mechanisms for reactions you have never seen may seem nearly impossible. As you gain experience in working mechanism problems, you will start to see similarities to known reactions. Let's consider how an organic chemist systematically approaches a mechanism problem. (A more complete version of this method appears in Appendix 4.) Although this stepwise approach cannot solve all mechanism problems, it should provide a starting point to begin building your experience and confidence.

Determining the Type of Mechanism

First, determine what kinds of conditions and catalysts are involved. In general, reactions may be classified as involving (a) strong electrophiles (including acid-catalyzed reactions), (b) strong nucleophiles (including base-catalyzed reactions), or (c) free radicals. These three types of mechanisms are quite distinct, and you should first try to determine which type is involved.

(a) In the presence of a strong acid or a reactant that can dissociate to give a strong electrophile, the mechanism probably involves strong electrophiles as intermediates. Acid-catalyzed reactions and reactions involving carbocations (such as the S_N1, the E1, and most alcohol dehydrations) fall in this category.

(b) In the presence of a strong base or a strong nucleophile, the mechanism probably involves strong nucleophiles as intermediates. Base-catalyzed reactions and those depending on base strength (such as the S_N2 and the E2) generally fall in this category.

(c) Free-radical reactions usually require a free-radical initiator such as chlorine, bromine, NBS, or a peroxide. In most free-radical reactions, there is no need for a strong acid or base.

Once you have determined which type of mechanism you will write, use a systematic approach to the problem. At this point, we consider mostly the electrophilic reactions covered in recent chapters. Suggestions for drawing the mechanisms of reactions involving strong nucleophiles and free-radical reactions are collected in Appendix 4.

Reactions Involving Strong Electrophiles

When a strong acid or electrophile is present, expect to see intermediates that are strong acids and strong electrophiles. Cationic intermediates are common. Bases and nucleophiles in such a reaction are generally weak, however. Avoid drawing carbanions, hydroxide ions, alkoxide ions, and other strong bases. They are unlikely to co-exist with strong acids and strong electrophiles.

Functional groups are often converted to carbocations or other strong electrophiles by protonation or reaction with a strong electrophile. Then the carbocation or other strong electrophile reacts with a weak nucleophile such as an alkene or the solvent.

1. **Consider the carbon skeletons of the reactants and products, and decide which carbon atoms in the products are most likely derived from which carbon atoms in the reactants.**
2. **Consider whether any of the reactants is a strong enough electrophile to react without being activated. If not, consider how one of the reactants might be converted to a strong electrophile by protonation of a basic site, or complexation with a Lewis acid or ionization.**
   Protonation of an alcohol, for example, converts it to a strong electrophile, which can undergo attack or lose water to give a carbocation, an even stronger electrophile. Protonation of an alkene converts it to a carbocation.
3. **Consider how a nucleophilic site on another reactant (or, in a cyclization in another part of the same molecule) can attack the strong electrophile to form a bond needed in the product. Draw the product of this bond formation.**
   If the intermediate is a carbocation, consider whether it is likely to rearrange to form a bond in the product. If there isn't any possible nucleophilic attack that leads in the direction of the product, consider other ways of converting one of the reactants to a strong electrophile.
4. **Consider how the product of a nucleophilic attack might be converted to the final product (if it has the right carbon skeleton) or reactivated to form another bond needed in the product.**
   To move a proton from one atom to another under acidic conditions (as in an isomerization), try adding a proton to the new position, then removing it from the old position.
5. **Draw out all the steps of the mechanism using curved arrows to show the movement of electrons.**
   Be careful to show only one step at a time.

Common Mistakes to Avoid in Drawing Mechanisms

1. Do not use condensed or line–angle formulas for reaction sites. Draw all the bonds and all the substituents of each carbon atom affected throughout the mechanism. In reactions involving strong electrophiles and acidic conditions, three-bonded carbon atoms are likely to be carbocations. If you draw condensed formulas or line–angle formulas, you will likely misplace a hydrogen atom and show a reactive species on the wrong carbon.
2. Do not show more than one step occurring at once. Do not show two or three bonds changing position in one step unless the changes really are concerted (take place simultaneously). For example, protonation of an alcohol and loss of water to give a carbocation are two steps. You must not show the hydroxyl group "jumping" off the alcohol to join up with an anxiously waiting proton.
3. Remember that curved arrows show *movement of electrons*, always from the nucleophile (electron donor) to the electrophile (electron acceptor). For example, protonation of a double bond must show the arrow going from the electrons of the double bond to the proton—never from the proton to the double bond. Resist the urge to use an arrow to "point out" where the proton (or other reagent) goes.

SAMPLE PROBLEM

To illustrate the stepwise method for reactions involving strong electrophiles, we will develop a mechanism to account for the following cyclization:

$$\xrightarrow[\text{heat}]{H_2SO_4}$$

OH

The cyclized product is a minor product in this reaction. Note that a mechanism problem is different from a synthesis problem: In a mechanism problem, we are limited to the reagents given and are asked to explain how these reactants form these products under the conditions shown. Also, a mechanism problem may deal with how an unusual or unexpected minor product is formed.

In the presence of sulfuric acid, this is clearly an acid-catalyzed mechanism. We expect strong electrophiles, cationic intermediates (possibly carbocations), and strong acids. Carbanions, hydroxide ions, alkoxide ions, and other strong bases and strong nucleophiles are unlikely.

1. **Consider the carbon skeletons of the reactants and products, and decide which carbon atoms in the products are most likely derived from which carbon atoms in the reactants.**

(Continued)

Drawing the starting material and the product with all the substituents of the affected carbon atoms, we see the major changes shown here. A vinyl hydrogen must be lost, a =C—C bond must be formed, a methyl group must move over one carbon atom, and the hydroxyl group must be lost.

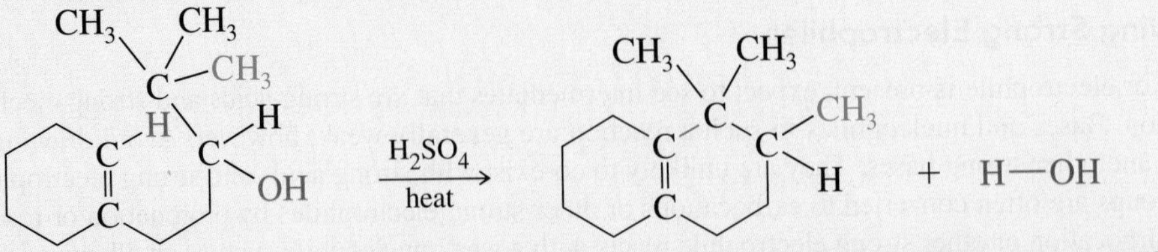

$\xrightarrow[\text{heat}]{H_2SO_4}$ + H—OH

2. Consider whether any of the reactants is a strong enough electrophile to react without being activated. If not, consider how one of the reactants might be converted to a strong electrophile by protonation of a basic site, or complexation with a Lewis acid, or ionization.

The starting material is not a strong electrophile, so it must be activated. Sulfuric acid could generate a strong electrophile either by protonating the double bond or by protonating the hydroxyl group. Protonating the double bond would form the tertiary carbocation, activating the wrong end of the double bond. Also, there is no good nucleophilic site on the side chain to attack this carbocation to form the correct ring. Protonating the double bond is a dead end.

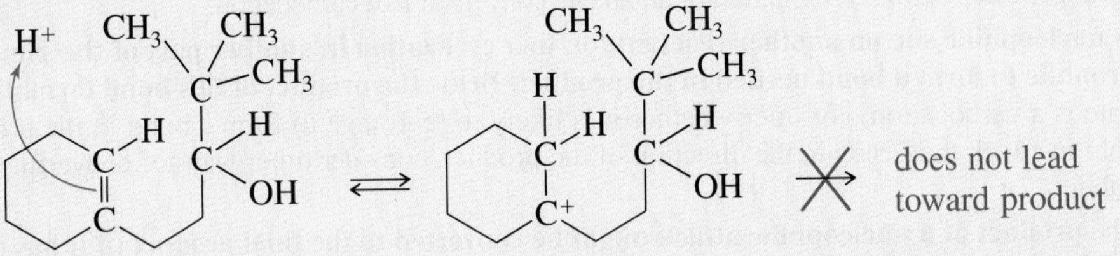

does not lead toward product

The other basic site is the hydroxyl group. An alcohol can protonate on the hydroxyl group and lose water to form a carbocation.

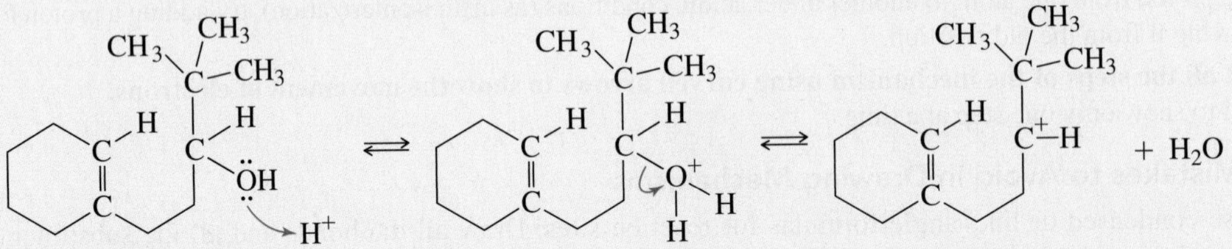

+ H_2O

3. Consider how a nucleophilic site on another reactant (or, in a cyclization, in another part of the same molecule) can attack the strong electrophile to form a bond needed in the product. Draw the product of this bond formation.

The carbocation can be attacked by the electrons in the double bond to form a ring; but the positive charge is on the wrong carbon atom to give a six-membered ring. A favorable rearrangement of the secondary carbocation to a tertiary one shifts the positive charge to the correct carbon atom and accomplishes the methyl shift we identified in step 1. Attack by the (weakly) nucleophilic electrons in the double bond gives the correct six-membered ring.

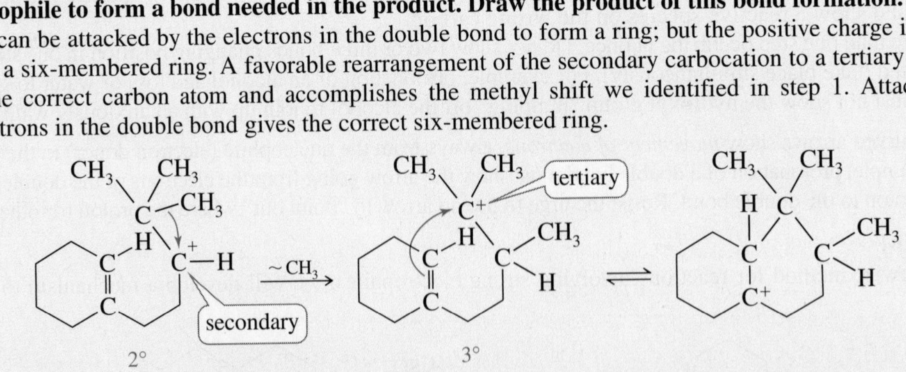

secondary $\xrightarrow{\sim CH_3}$ tertiary

2° 3°

4. Consider how the product of nucleophilic attack might be converted to the final product (if it has the right carbon skeleton) or reactivated to form another bond needed in the product.

Loss of a proton (to HSO_4^- or H_2O, but *not* to ^-OH, which is not compatible with acid) gives the observed product.

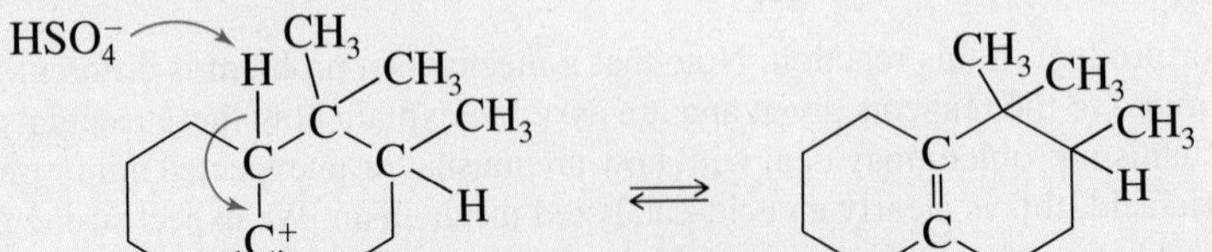

5. Draw out all the steps of the mechanism using curved arrows to show the movement of electrons.

Combining the equations written immediately above gives the complete mechanism for this reaction.

The following problems require proposing mechanisms for reactions involving strong electrophiles. Work each one by completing the five steps just described.

PROBLEM 11-26

Propose a mechanism for each reaction.

(a) 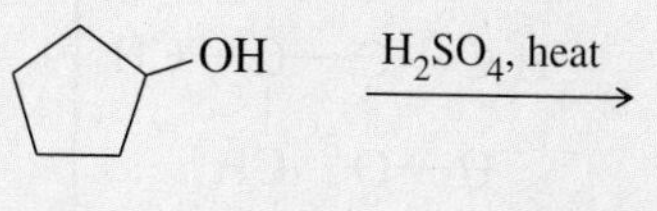 Cyclopentanol $\xrightarrow{H_2SO_4,\ heat}$ cyclopentene

(b) 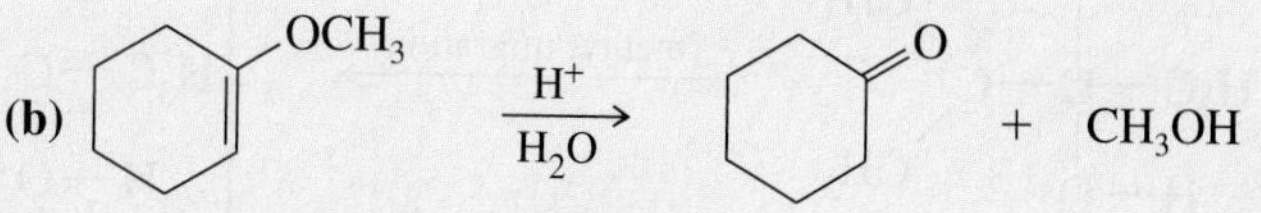 1-Methoxycyclohexene $\xrightarrow[H_2O]{H^+}$ cyclohexanone + CH_3OH

(c) 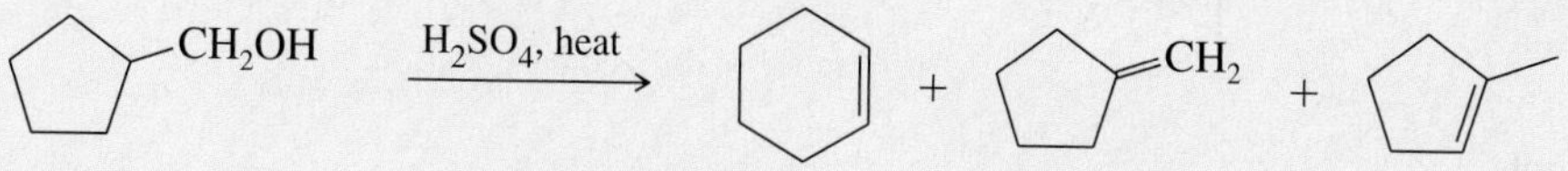 Cyclopentylmethanol $\xrightarrow{H_2SO_4,\ heat}$ cyclohexene + methylenecyclopentane + 1-methylcyclopentene

*(d) 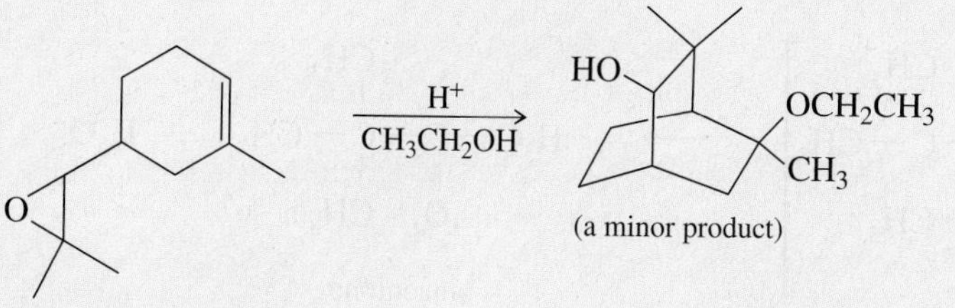 $\xrightarrow[CH_3CH_2OH]{H^+}$ HO, OCH_2CH_3, CH_3 (a minor product)

PROBLEM 11-27

When the following substituted cycloheptanol undergoes dehydration, one of the minor products has undergone a ring contraction. Propose a mechanism to show how this ring contraction occurs.

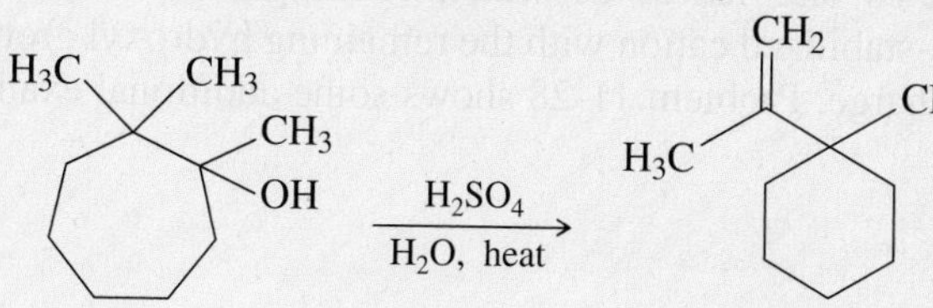

H_3C, CH_3, CH_3, OH (cycloheptanol) $\xrightarrow[H_2O,\ heat]{H_2SO_4}$ CH_2, CH_3, H_3C (cyclohexane) (minor)

11-11 Unique Reactions of Diols

11-11A The Pinacol Rearrangement

Using our knowledge of alcohol reactions, we can explain results that seem strange at first glance. The following dehydration is an example of the **pinacol rearrangement**:

$$(CH_3)_2C(OH)-C(OH)(CH_3)_2 \xrightarrow[100\ °C]{H_2SO_4} H_3C-C(=O)-C(CH_3)_3 + H_2O$$

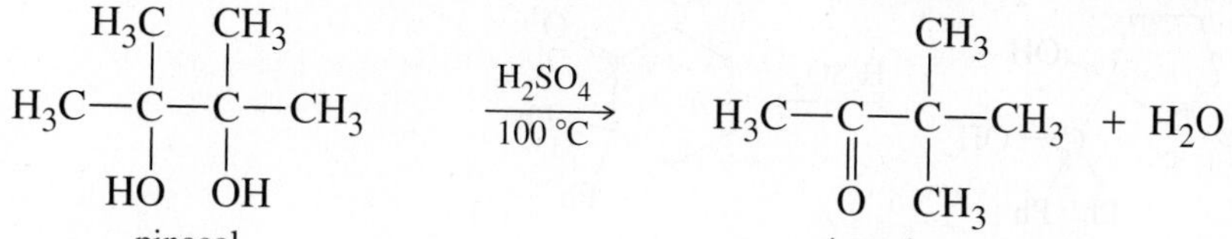

pinacol (2,3-dimethyl-2,3-butanediol) → pinacolone (3,3-dimethyl-2-butanone)

The pinacol rearrangement is formally a dehydration. The reaction is acid-catalyzed, and the first step is protonation of one of the hydroxyl oxygens. Loss of water gives a tertiary carbocation, as expected for any tertiary alcohol. Migration of a methyl group places the positive charge on the carbon atom bearing the second —OH group, where oxygen's nonbonding electrons help to stabilize the positive charge through resonance. This extra stability is the driving force for the rearrangement, which converts a relatively stable 3° carbocation into an even better resonance-stabilized carbocation. Deprotonation of the resonance-stabilized cation gives the product, pinacolone.

MECHANISM 11-5 The Pinacol Rearrangement

Step 1: Protonation of a hydroxyl group. *Step 2:* Loss of water gives a carbocation.

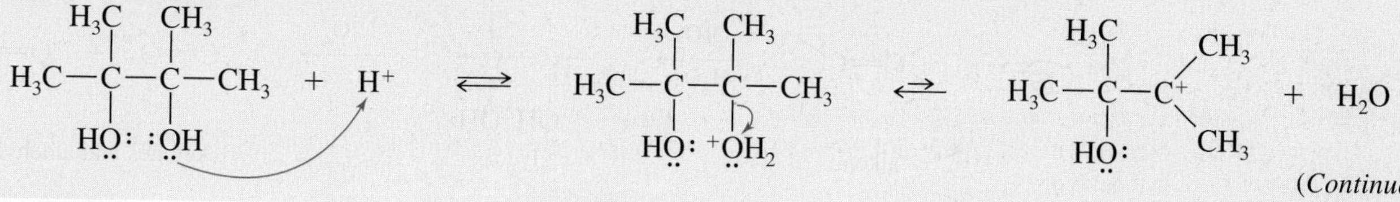

$$(CH_3)_2C(\ddot{O}H)-C(\ddot{O}H)(CH_3)_2 + H^+ \rightleftarrows (CH_3)_2C(\ddot{O}H)-C(\overset{+}{O}H_2)(CH_3)_2 \rightleftarrows (CH_3)_2C(\ddot{O}H)-C^+(CH_3)_2 + H_2O$$

(Continued)

Step 3: Methyl migration forms a resonance-stabilized carbocation.

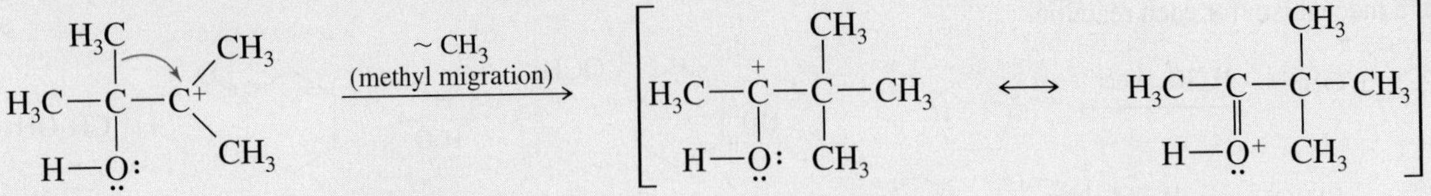

$$(CH_3)_2C(OH)\text{—}C^+(CH_3)_2 \xrightarrow[\text{(methyl migration)}]{\sim CH_3} \left[H_3C\text{—}\overset{+}{C}(OH)\text{—}C(CH_3)_3 \longleftrightarrow H_3C\text{—}C(=\overset{+}{O}H)\text{—}C(CH_3)_3 \right]$$

resonance-stabilized carbocation

Step 4: Deprotonation gives the product.

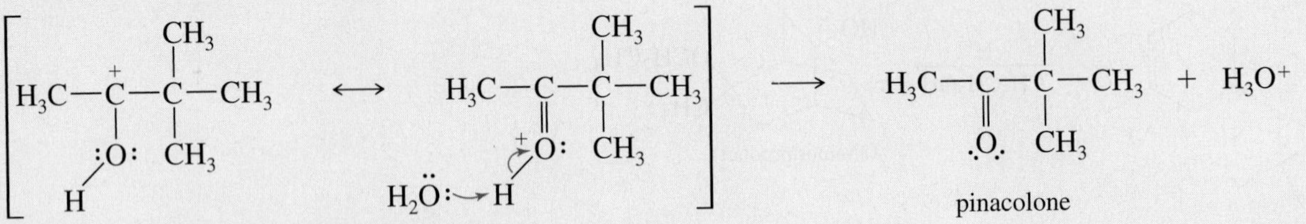

$$\left[H_3C\text{—}\overset{+}{C}(OH)\text{—}C(CH_3)_3 \longleftrightarrow H_3C\text{—}C(=\overset{+}{O}H)\text{—}C(CH_3)_3 \right] \xrightarrow{H_2\ddot{O}:} H_3C\text{—}C(=O)\text{—}C(CH_3)_3 + H_3O^+$$

resonance-stabilized carbocation

pinacolone

Pinacol-like rearrangements are common in acid-catalyzed reactions of diols. One of the hydroxyl groups protonates and leaves as water, forming a carbocation. Rearrangement gives a resonance-stabilized cation with the remaining hydroxyl group helping to stabilize the positive charge. Problem 11-28 shows some additional examples of pinacol rearrangements.

PROBLEM 11-28

Propose a mechanism for each reaction.

(a) 1,2-dimethylcyclohexane-1,2-diol (H_3C, CH_3, HO OH) $\xrightarrow{H^+}$ 1-acetyl-1-methylcyclopentane + 2,2-dimethylcyclohexanone

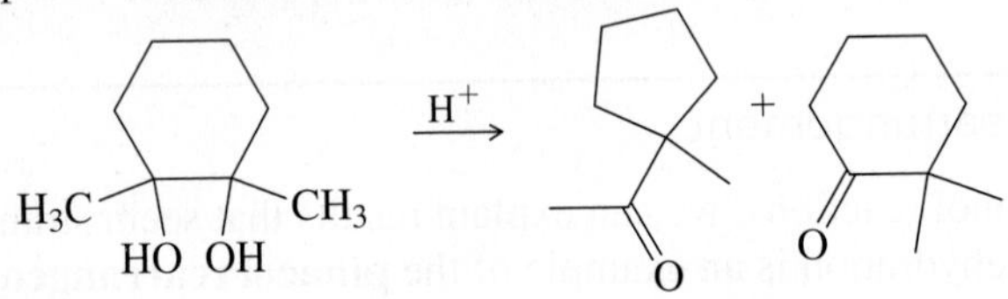

(b) 1-[hydroxy(diphenyl)methyl]cyclopentanol (OH; C—OH; Ph Ph) $\xrightarrow{H_2SO_4}$ 2,2-diphenylcyclohexanone (O; Ph; Ph)

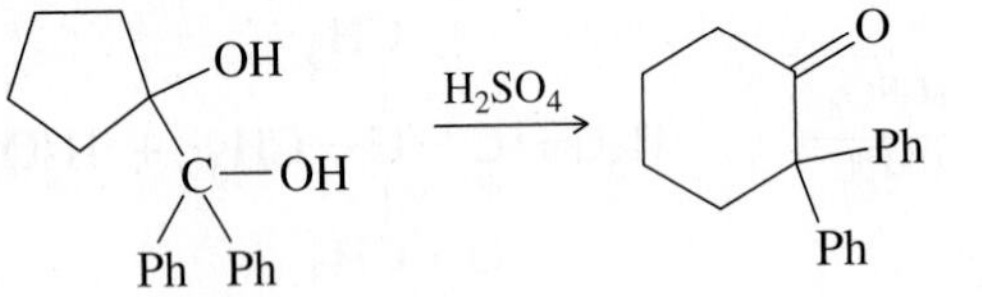

problem-solving Hint

By analogy with the pinacol rearrangement, watch for carbocation rearrangements that move the + charge to a carbinol carbon atom.

PROBLEM 11-29

The following reaction involves a starting material with a double bond and a hydroxyl group, yet its mechanism resembles a pinacol rearrangement. Propose a mechanism, and point out the part of your mechanism that resembles a pinacol rearrangement.

1-vinylcyclopropanol (OH; CH=CH$_2$) $\xrightarrow{H_2SO_4}$ 2-methylcyclobutanone (O; CH_3)

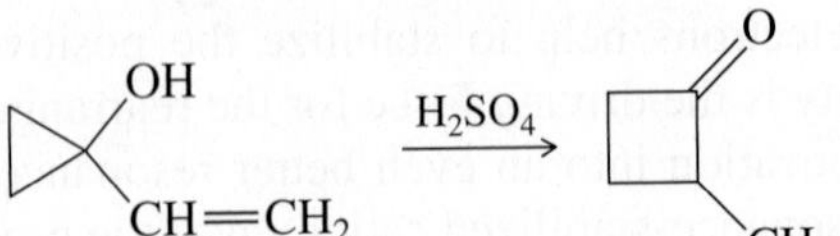

11-11B Periodic Acid Cleavage of Glycols

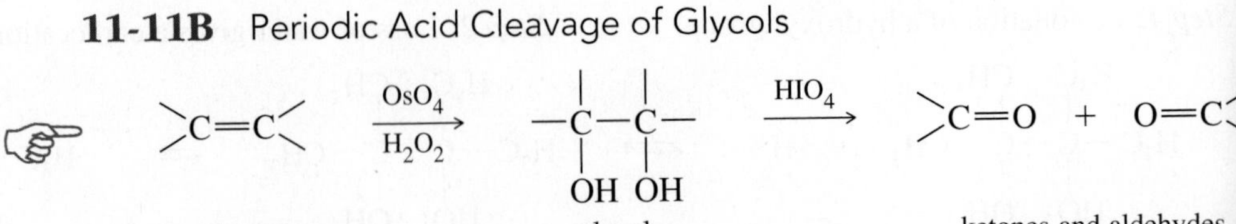

$$>C=C< \xrightarrow[H_2O_2]{OsO_4} \text{—}\underset{OH}{C}\text{—}\underset{OH}{C}\text{—} \xrightarrow{HIO_4} >C=O \;+\; O=C<$$

alkene glycol ketones and aldehydes

1,2-Diols (glycols), such as those formed by hydroxylation of alkenes, are cleaved by periodic acid (HIO_4). The products are the same ketones and aldehydes that would be formed by ozonolysis–reduction of the alkene. Hydroxylation followed by periodic acid cleavage serves as a useful alternative to ozonolysis, and the periodate cleavage by itself is useful for determining the structures of sugars (Chapter 23).

Periodic acid cleavage of a glycol probably involves a cyclic periodate intermediate like that shown here.

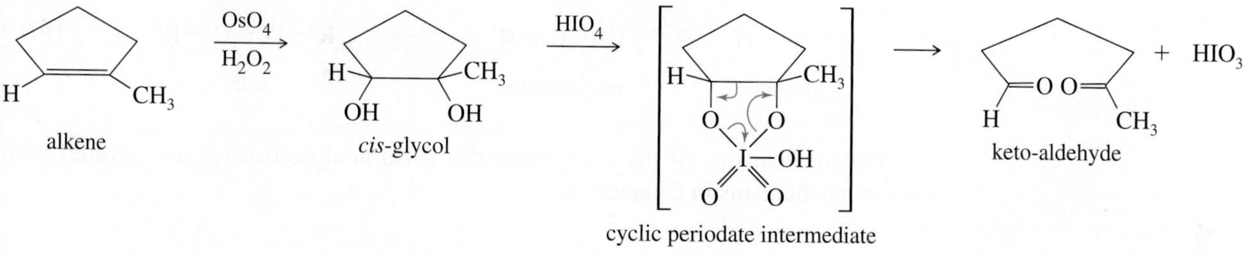

alkene $\xrightarrow[H_2O_2]{OsO_4}$ *cis*-glycol $\xrightarrow{HIO_4}$ [cyclic periodate intermediate] $\longrightarrow$ keto-aldehyde + HIO_3

PROBLEM 11-30

Predict the products formed by periodic acid cleavage of the following diols.

(a) $CH_3CH(OH)CH(OH)CH_3$

(b) 1-(hydroxymethyl)cyclopentanol (CH_2OH, OH on the same ring carbon)

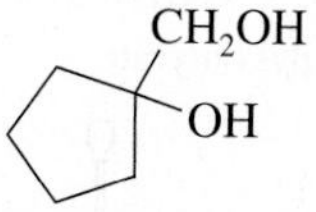

(c) Ph—C(OH)(CH$_3$)—CH(OH)CH$_2$CH$_3$

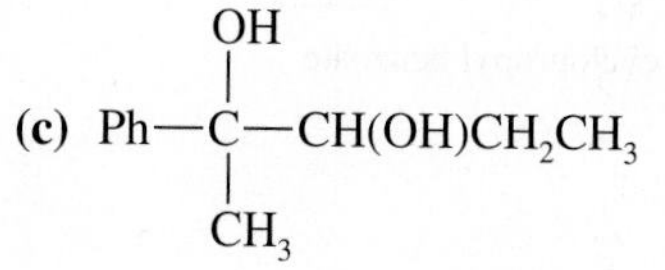

(d) bicyclic diol (OH, H; OH, H)

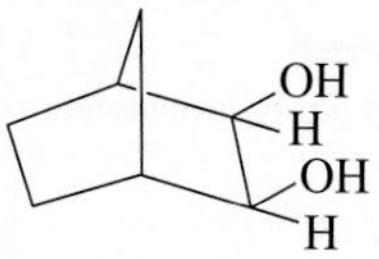

problem-solving Hint

Periodic acid cleaves a diol to give the same products as ozonolysis–reduction (O_3 followed by Me_2S) of the alkene.

11-12 Esterification of Alcohols

To an organic chemist, the term **ester** normally means an ester of a carboxylic acid, unless some other kind of ester is specified. Replacing the —OH group of a carboxylic acid with the —OR group of an alcohol gives a carboxylic ester. The following reaction, called the **Fischer esterification**, shows the relationship between the alcohol and the acid on the left and the ester and water on the right.

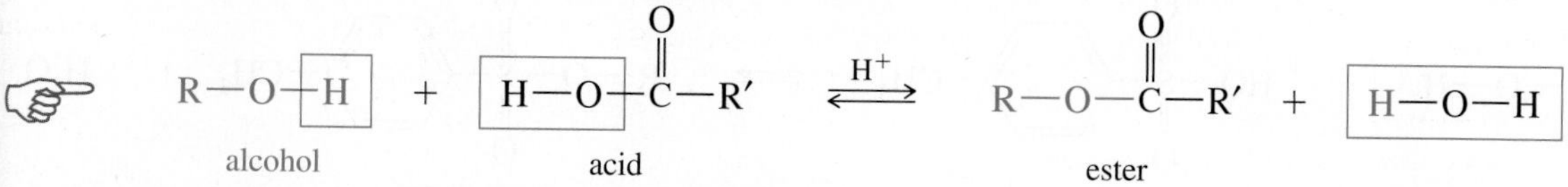

$$\underset{\text{alcohol}}{R{-}O{-}H} + \underset{\text{acid}}{H{-}O{-}\overset{O}{\overset{\|}{C}}{-}R'} \overset{H^+}{\rightleftharpoons} \underset{\text{ester}}{R{-}O{-}\overset{O}{\overset{\|}{C}}{-}R'} + H{-}O{-}H$$

For example, if we mix isopropyl alcohol with acetic acid and add a drop of sulfuric acid as a catalyst, the following equilibrium results.

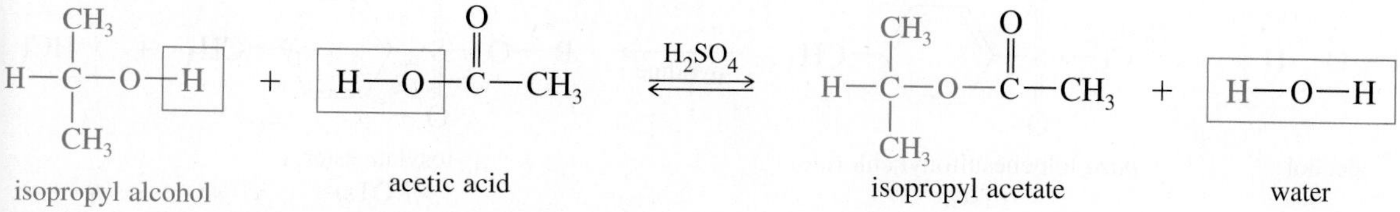

$$\underset{\text{isopropyl alcohol}}{(CH_3)_2CH{-}O{-}H} + \underset{\text{acetic acid}}{H{-}O{-}\overset{O}{\overset{\|}{C}}{-}CH_3} \overset{H_2SO_4}{\rightleftharpoons} \underset{\text{isopropyl acetate}}{(CH_3)_2CH{-}O{-}\overset{O}{\overset{\|}{C}}{-}CH_3} + \underset{\text{water}}{H{-}O{-}H}$$

The alcohol groups of unpleasant-tasting drugs are often converted to esters in order to mask the taste. In most cases, the ester has a less unpleasant taste than the free alcohol.

Because the Fischer esterification is an equilibrium (often with an unfavorable equilibrium constant), clever techniques are often required to achieve good yields of esters. For example, we can use a large excess of the alcohol or the acid. Adding a dehydrating agent removes water (one of the products), driving the reaction to the right. There is a more powerful way to form an ester, however, without having to deal with an unfavorable equilibrium. An alcohol reacts with an acid chloride in an exothermic reaction to give an ester.

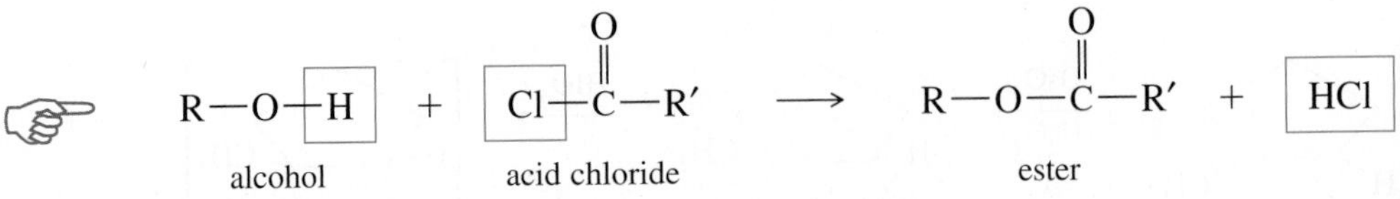

$$\underset{\text{alcohol}}{R{-}O{-}\boxed{H}} + \underset{\text{acid chloride}}{\boxed{Cl}{-}\overset{\overset{O}{\|}}{C}{-}R'} \longrightarrow \underset{\text{ester}}{R{-}O{-}\overset{\overset{O}{\|}}{C}{-}R'} + \boxed{HCl}$$

The mechanisms of these reactions that form acid derivatives are covered with similar mechanisms in Chapter 21.

PROBLEM 11-31

Show the alcohol and the acid chloride that combine to make the following esters.

problem-solving Hint

An ester is a composite of an acid plus an alcohol, with loss of water.

(a) $CH_3CH_2CH_2\overset{\overset{O}{\|}}{C}{-}OCH_2CH_2CH_3$
n-propyl butyrate

(b) $CH_3(CH_2)_3{-}O{-}\overset{\overset{O}{\|}}{C}{-}CH_2CH_3$
n-butyl propionate

(c) 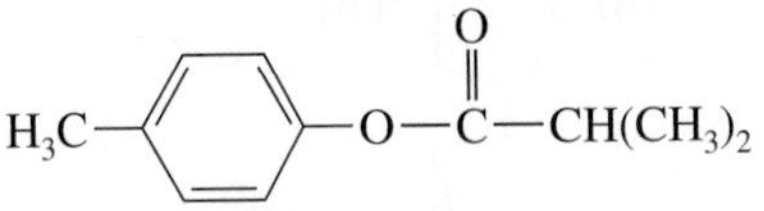 $H_3C{-}C_6H_4{-}O{-}\overset{\overset{O}{\|}}{C}{-}CH(CH_3)_2$
p-tolyl isobutyrate

(d) 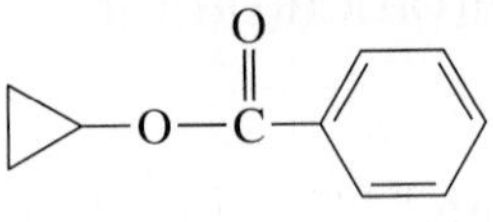 $C_3H_5{-}O{-}\overset{\overset{O}{\|}}{C}{-}C_6H_5$
cyclopropyl benzoate

11-13 Esters of Inorganic Acids

In addition to forming esters with carboxylic acids, alcohols form **inorganic esters** with inorganic acids such as nitric acid, sulfuric acid, and phosphoric acid. In each type of ester, the alkoxy (—OR) group of the alcohol replaces a hydroxyl group of the acid, with loss of water. We have already studied tosylate esters, composed of *para*-toluenesulfonic acid and alcohols (but made using tosyl chloride, Section 11-5). Tosylate esters are analogous to sulfate esters (Section 11-13A), which are composed of sulfuric acid and alcohols.

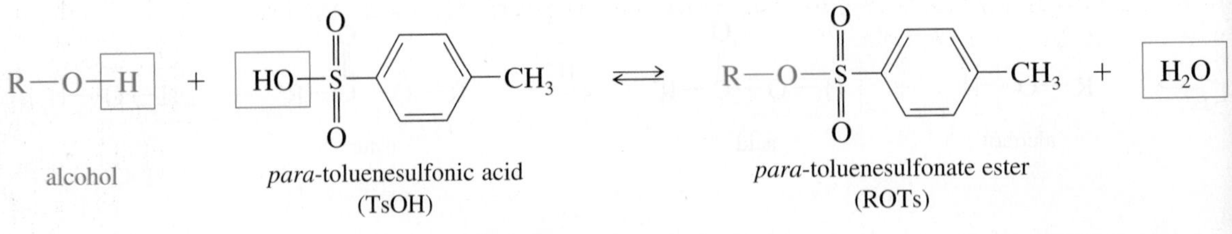

$$\underset{\text{alcohol}}{R{-}O{-}\boxed{H}} + \underset{\substack{\textit{para}\text{-toluenesulfonic acid}\\ \text{(TsOH)}}}{\boxed{HO}{-}SO_2{-}C_6H_4{-}CH_3} \rightleftarrows \underset{\substack{\textit{para}\text{-toluenesulfonate ester}\\ \text{(ROTs)}}}{R{-}O{-}SO_2{-}C_6H_4{-}CH_3} + \boxed{H_2O}$$

Made using tosyl chloride

$$\underset{\text{alcohol}}{R{-}O{-}\boxed{H}} + \underset{\substack{\textit{para}\text{-toluenesulfonyl chloride}\\ \text{(TsCl)}}}{\boxed{Cl}{-}SO_2{-}C_6H_4{-}CH_3} \xrightarrow{\text{pyridine}} \underset{\substack{\text{tosylate ester}\\ \text{(ROTs)}}}{R{-}O{-}SO_2{-}C_6H_4{-}CH_3} + \boxed{HCl}$$

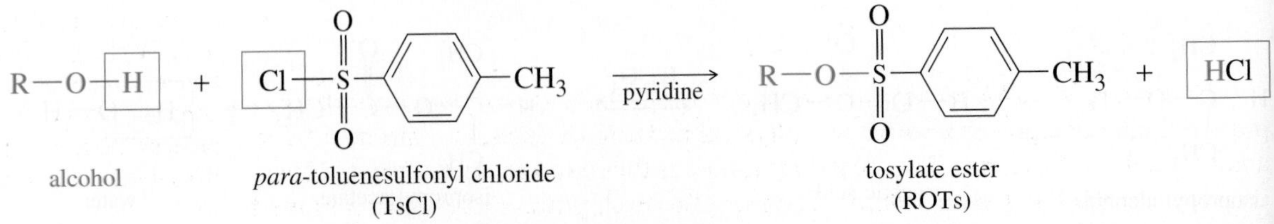

11-13A Sulfate Esters

A **sulfate ester** is like a sulfonate ester, except there is no alkyl group directly bonded to the sulfur atom. In an alkyl sulfate ester, alkoxy groups are bonded to sulfur through oxygen atoms. Using methanol as the alcohol,

$$\underset{\text{sulfuric acid}}{HO-S(=O)_2-OH} \underset{}{\overset{CH_3O-H}{\rightleftharpoons}} \underset{\text{methyl sulfate}}{CH_3-O-S(=O)_2-OH} + H_2O \overset{CH_3OH}{\rightleftharpoons} \underset{\text{dimethyl sulfate}}{CH_3-O-S(=O)_2-O-CH_3} + H_2O$$

Sulfate ions are excellent leaving groups. Like sulfonate esters, sulfate esters are good electrophiles. Nucleophiles react with sulfate esters to give alkylated products. For example, the reaction of dimethyl sulfate with ammonia gives a sulfate salt of methylamine, $CH_3NH_3^+\ CH_3OSO_3^-$.

$$\underset{\text{ammonia}}{H_3N:} + \underset{\text{dimethyl sulfate}}{CH_3-O-S(=O)_2-O-CH_3} \longrightarrow \underset{\text{methylammonium ion}}{H_3\overset{+}{N}-CH_3} \quad \underset{\text{methylsulfate ion}}{^{-}O-S(=O)_2-O-CH_3}$$

The body converts the hydroxyl groups of some drugs to their sulfate derivatives in order to produce water-soluble compounds that are readily excreted. The reaction is not as common as it might be because of limited availability of inorganic sulfate in the body.

PROBLEM 11-32

Use resonance forms of the conjugate bases to explain why methanesulfonic acid (CH_3SO_3H, $pK_a = -2.6$) is a much stronger acid than acetic acid (CH_3COOH, $pK_a = 4.8$).

11-13B Nitrate Esters

Nitrate esters are formed from alcohols and nitric acid.

$$\underset{\text{alcohol}}{R-O-H} + \underset{\text{nitric acid}}{H-O-\overset{+}{N}(=O)O^-} \longrightarrow \underset{\text{alkyl nitrate ester}}{R-O-\overset{+}{N}(=O)O^-} + H-O-H$$

The best-known nitrate ester is "nitroglycerine," whose systematic name is *glyceryl trinitrate*. Glyceryl trinitrate results from the reaction of glycerol (1,2,3-propanetriol) with three molecules of nitric acid.

$$\underset{\text{glycerol (glycerine)}}{\begin{matrix}CH_2-O-H\\ CH-O-H\\ CH_2-O-H\end{matrix}} + \underset{\text{nitric acid}}{3\ HO-NO_2} \longrightarrow \underset{\text{glyceryl trinitrate (nitroglycerine)}}{\begin{matrix}CH_2-O-NO_2\\ CH-O-NO_2\\ CH_2-O-NO_2\end{matrix}} + 3\ H_2O$$

Illustration of Alfred Nobel around 1860, operating the apparatus he used to make nitroglycerine. The temperature must be monitored and controlled carefully during this process; therefore, the operator's stool has only one leg to ensure that he stays awake.

First made in 1847, nitroglycerine was found to be a much more powerful explosive than black powder, which is a physical mixture of potassium nitrate, sulfur, and charcoal. In black powder, potassium nitrate is the oxidizer, and sulfur and charcoal provide the fuel to be oxidized. The rate of a black powder explosion is limited

Nitroglycerin is used to relieve angina, a condition where the heart is not receiving enough oxygen. Angina is characterized by severe pain in the chest, often triggered by stress or exercise. Workers with angina at the Nobel dynamite plant discovered this effect. They noticed that their symptoms improved when they went to work. In the mitochondria, nitroglycerin is metabolized to NO (nitric oxide), which regulates and controls many metabolic processes.

by how fast oxygen from the grains of heated potassium nitrate can diffuse to the grains of sulfur and charcoal. A black powder explosion does its work by the rapid increase in pressure resulting from the reaction. The explosion must be confined, as in a cannon or a firecracker, to be effective.

In nitroglycerine, the nitro groups are the oxidizer and the CH and CH_2 groups are the fuel to be oxidized. This intimate association of fuel and oxidizer allows the explosion to proceed at a much faster rate, forming a shock wave that propagates through the explosive and initiates the reaction. The explosive shock wave can shatter rock or other substances without the need for confinement. Because of its unprecedented explosive power, nitroglycerine was called a *high explosive*. Many other high explosives have been developed, including picric acid, TNT (trinitrotoluene), PETN (pentaerythritol tetranitrate), and RDX (research department explosive). Nitroglycerine and PETN are nitrate esters. Picric acid and TNT are nitrobenzene derivatives, not esters.

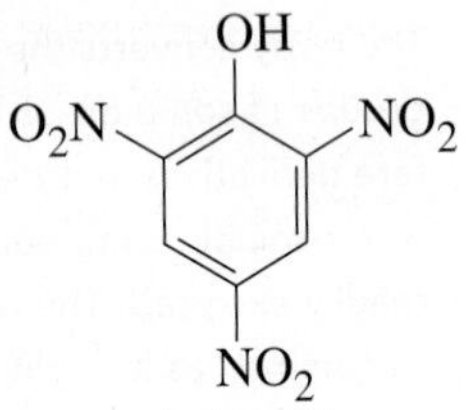

picric acid: OH, O_2N, NO_2, NO_2

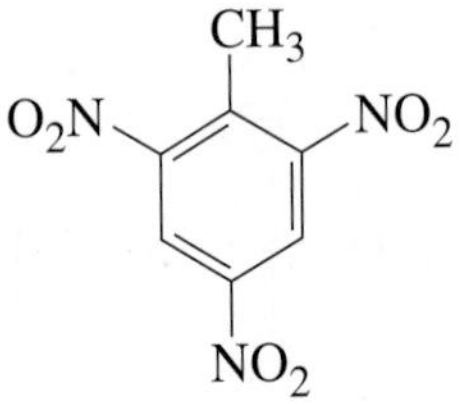

TNT: CH_3, O_2N, NO_2, NO_2

PETN: $C(CH_2ONO_2)_4$ — O_2NOCH_2—C—CH_2ONO_2, with CH_2ONO_2 above and below

RDX: NO_2, N, N, N, O_2N, NO_2

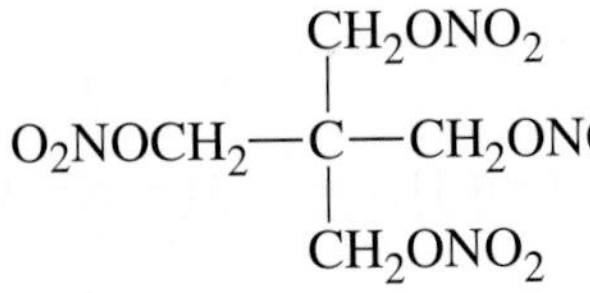

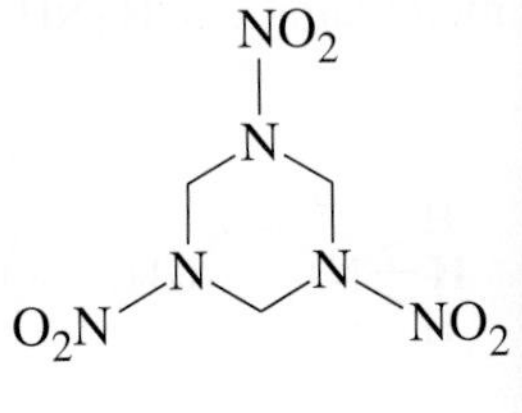

Pure nitroglycerine is hazardous to make, use, and transport. Alfred Nobel's family were experts at making and using nitroglycerine, yet his brother and several workers were killed by an explosion. In 1866, Nobel found that nitroglycerine soaks into diatomaceous earth to give a pasty mixture that can be molded into sticks that do not detonate so easily. He called the sticks *dynamite* and founded the firm Dynamit Nobel, which is still one of the world's leading ammunition and explosives manufacturers. The Nobel prizes are funded from an endowment that originated with Nobel's profits from the dynamite business.

11-13C Phosphate Esters

By controlling the formation of phosphate esters on key proteins, the body is able to regulate many cellular processes. Any disruption of these phosphorylation processes can result in numerous health problems, including cancer, diabetes, and obesity.

Alkyl phosphates are composed of 1 mole of phosphoric acid combined with 1, 2, or 3 moles of an alcohol. For example, methanol forms three **phosphate esters**.

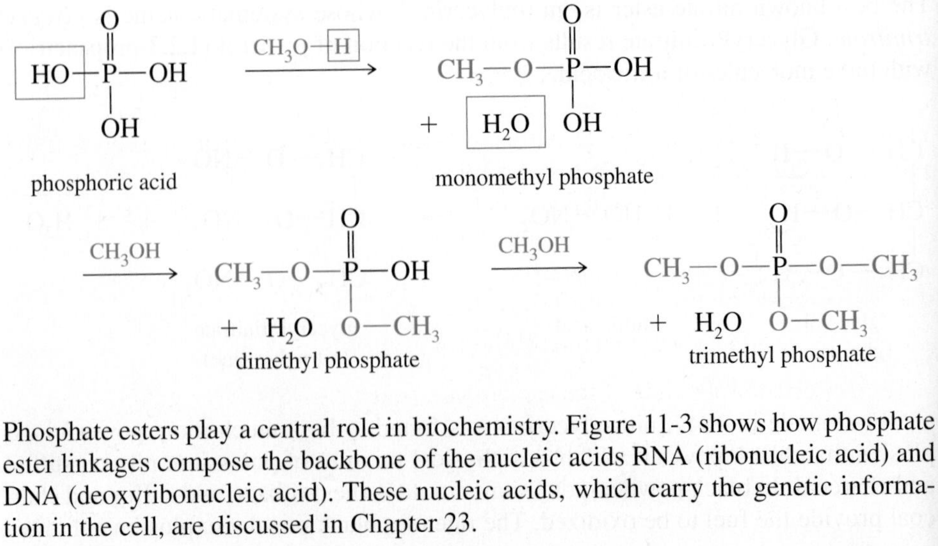

$$\underset{\text{phosphoric acid}}{\boxed{HO}-P(=O)(OH)-OH} \xrightarrow{CH_3O-\boxed{H}} \underset{\text{monomethyl phosphate}}{CH_3-O-P(=O)(OH)-OH} + \boxed{H_2O}$$

$$\xrightarrow{CH_3OH} \underset{\text{dimethyl phosphate}}{CH_3-O-P(=O)(O-CH_3)-OH} + H_2O \xrightarrow{CH_3OH} \underset{\text{trimethyl phosphate}}{CH_3-O-P(=O)(O-CH_3)-O-CH_3} + H_2O$$

Phosphate esters play a central role in biochemistry. Figure 11-3 shows how phosphate ester linkages compose the backbone of the nucleic acids RNA (ribonucleic acid) and DNA (deoxyribonucleic acid). These nucleic acids, which carry the genetic information in the cell, are discussed in Chapter 23.

phosphate ester linkage

■ **FIGURE 11-3**
Phosphate ester groups bond the individual nucleotides together in DNA. The "base" on each of the nucleotides corresponds to one of the four heterocyclic bases of DNA (see Section 23–20).

11-14 Reactions of Alkoxides

In Section 10-6B, we learned to remove the hydroxyl proton from an alcohol by reduction with an "active" metal such as sodium or potassium. This reaction generates a sodium or potassium salt of an **alkoxide ion** and hydrogen gas.

$$\text{R—}\ddot{\text{O}}\text{—H} + \text{Na} \longrightarrow \text{R—}\ddot{\text{O}}\text{:}^{-}\ {}^{+}\text{Na} + \tfrac{1}{2}\,\text{H}_2\uparrow$$

$$\text{R—}\ddot{\text{O}}\text{—H} + \text{K} \longrightarrow \text{R—}\ddot{\text{O}}\text{:}^{-}\ {}^{+}\text{K} + \tfrac{1}{2}\,\text{H}_2\uparrow$$

The reactivity of alcohols toward sodium and potassium decreases in the order: methyl $> 1° > 2° > 3°$. Sodium reacts quickly with primary alcohols and some secondary alcohols. Potassium is more reactive than sodium and is commonly used with tertiary alcohols and some secondary alcohols.

Some alcohols react sluggishly with both sodium and potassium. In these cases, a useful alternative is sodium hydride, usually in tetrahydrofuran solution. Sodium hydride reacts quickly to form the alkoxide, even with difficult compounds.

$$\underset{\text{alcohol}}{\text{R—}\ddot{\text{O}}\text{—H}} + \underset{\text{sodium hydride}}{\text{NaH}} \xrightarrow{\text{THF}} \underset{\text{sodium alkoxide}}{\text{R—}\ddot{\text{O}}\text{:}^{-}\ \text{Na}^{+}} + \underset{\text{hydrogen}}{\text{H}_2\uparrow}$$

Sodium metal reacts vigorously with simple primary alcohols such as ethanol.

The alkoxide ion is a strong nucleophile as well as a powerful base. Unlike the alcohol itself, the alkoxide ion reacts with primary alkyl halides and tosylates to form **ethers**. This general reaction, called the **Williamson ether synthesis**, is an S_N2 displacement. The alkyl halide (or tosylate) must be primary so that a back-side attack is not hindered. When the alkyl halide is not primary, elimination usually results.

KEY MECHANISM 11-6 The Williamson Ether Synthesis

This is the most important method for making ethers.

Step 1: Form the alkoxide of the alcohol having the more hindered group.

$$\text{R—}\ddot{\text{O}}\text{—H} + \text{Na (or NaH or K)} \longrightarrow \underset{\text{alkoxide ion}}{\text{R—}\ddot{\text{O}}\text{:}^{-}\ \text{Na}^{+}} + \tfrac{1}{2}\,\text{H}_2\uparrow$$

(Continued)

Step 2: The alkoxide displaces the leaving group of a good S_N2 substrate.

$$\underset{\text{alkoxide ion}}{R-\ddot{\underset{..}{O}}:^{-}\ {}^{+}Na} \qquad \underset{\text{primary halide or tosylate}}{R'-CH_2-X} \longrightarrow \underset{\text{ether}}{R-\ddot{\underset{..}{O}}-CH_2-R'} + NaX$$

EXAMPLE: Synthesis of cyclopentyl ethyl ether

Step 1: Form the alkoxide of the alcohol with the more hindered group.

$$\text{cyclopentyl–OH} + NaH \longrightarrow \text{cyclopentyl–}O^{-}\ Na^{+} + H_2\uparrow$$

Step 2: The alkoxide displaces the leaving group of a good S_N2 substrate.

$$\text{cyclopentyl–}O^{-}\ Na^{+} \quad H_3C-CH_2-Br \longrightarrow \text{cyclopentyl–}O-CH_2-CH_3 + Na^{+}\ Br^{-}$$

PROBLEM: Why is the cyclohexyl group chosen for the alkoxide and the ethyl group chosen for the halide? Why not use cyclohexyl bromide and sodium ethoxide to make cyclopentyl ethyl ether?

In the Williamson ether synthesis, the alkyl halide (or tosylate) must be a good S_N2 substrate (usually primary). In proposing a Williamson synthesis, we usually choose the less hindered alkyl group to be the halide (or tosylate) and the more hindered group to be the alkoxide ion.

PROBLEM 11-33

A good Williamson synthesis of ethyl methyl ether would be

$$\underset{\text{sodium ethoxide}}{CH_3CH_2-O^{-}\ {}^{+}Na} + \underset{\text{methyl iodide}}{CH_3I} \longrightarrow \underset{\text{ethyl methyl ether}}{CH_3CH_2-O-CH_3} + NaI$$

What is wrong with the following proposed synthesis of ethyl methyl ether? First, ethanol is treated with acid to protonate the hydroxyl group (making it a good leaving group), and then sodium methoxide is added to displace water.

$$CH_3CH_2-OH + H^{+} \longrightarrow CH_3CH_2-\overset{+}{O}H_2 \xrightarrow[\times]{NaOCH_3} CH_3CH_2-O-CH_3$$

(incorrect synthesis of ethyl methyl ether)

problem-solving Hint

When using the Williamson ether synthesis to make R—O—R′, choose the less hindered alkyl group to serve as the alkyl halide (R′—X), because it will make a better S_N2 substrate. Choose the more hindered alkyl group to form the alkoxide (R—O^{-}), because it is less sensitive to steric hindrance in the reaction.

$$R-O^{-} + R'-X \longrightarrow R-O-R'$$

PROBLEM 11-34

(a) Show how ethanol and cyclohexanol may be used to synthesize cyclohexyl ethyl ether (tosylation followed by the Williamson ether synthesis).

(b) Why can't we synthesize this product simply by mixing the two alcohols, adding some sulfuric acid, and heating?

PROBLEM 11-35

A student wanted to use the Williamson ether synthesis to make (*R*)-2-ethoxybutane. He remembered that the Williamson synthesis involves an S_N2 displacement, which takes place with inversion of configuration. He ordered a bottle of (*S*)-2-butanol for his chiral starting material. He also remembered that the S_N2 goes best on primary halides and tosylates, so he made ethyl tosylate and sodium (*S*)-2-butoxide. After warming these reagents together, he obtained an excellent yield of 2-ethoxybutane.

(a) What enantiomer of 2-ethoxybutane did he obtain? Explain how this enantiomer results from the S_N2 reaction of ethyl tosylate with sodium (*S*)-2-butoxide.
(b) What would have been the best synthesis of (*R*)-2-ethoxybutane?
(c) How can this student convert the rest of his bottle of (*S*)-2-butanol to (*R*)-2-ethoxybutane?

PROBLEM 11-36

The anions of phenols (phenoxide ions) may be used in the Williamson ether synthesis, especially with very reactive alkylating reagents such as dimethyl sulfate. Using phenol, dimethyl sulfate, and other necessary reagents, show how you would synthesize methyl phenyl ether.

PROBLEM-SOLVING STRATEGY

MULTISTEP SYNTHESIS

Chemists use organic syntheses both to make larger amounts of useful natural compounds and to invent totally new compounds in search of improved properties and biological effects. Solving synthesis problems also serves as one of the best methods for developing a firm command of organic chemistry. Planning a practical multistep synthesis requires a working knowledge of the applications and the limitations of a variety of organic reactions. We will often use synthesis problems for reviewing and reinforcing the reactions we have covered.

We use a systematic approach to solving multistep synthesis problems, working backward, in the "retrosynthetic" direction. We begin by studying the target molecule and considering what final reactions might be used to create it from simpler intermediate compounds. Most syntheses require comparison of two or more pathways and the intermediates involved. Eventually, this retrosynthetic analysis should lead back to starting materials that are readily available or meet the requirements defined in the problem.

We can now extend our systematic analysis to problems involving alcohols and Grignard reactions. As examples, we consider the syntheses of an acyclic diol and a disubstituted cyclohexane, concentrating on the crucial steps that assemble the carbon skeletons and generate the final functional groups.

SAMPLE PROBLEM

Our first problem is to synthesize 3-ethyl-2,3-pentanediol from compounds containing no more than three carbon atoms.

$$CH_3-CH(OH)-C(OH)(CH_2CH_3)-CH_2-CH_3$$

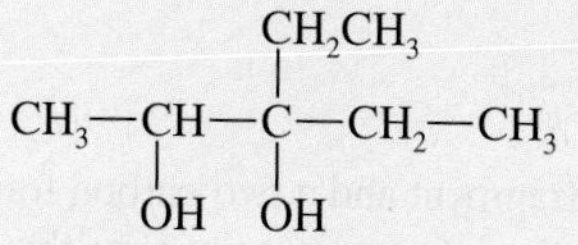

3-ethyl-2,3-pentanediol

1. **Review the functional groups and carbon skeleton of the target compound.**
The compound is a vicinal diol (glycol) containing seven carbon atoms. Glycols are commonly made by hydroxylation of alkenes, and this glycol would be made by hydroxylation of 3-ethyl-2-pentene, which effectively becomes the target compound.

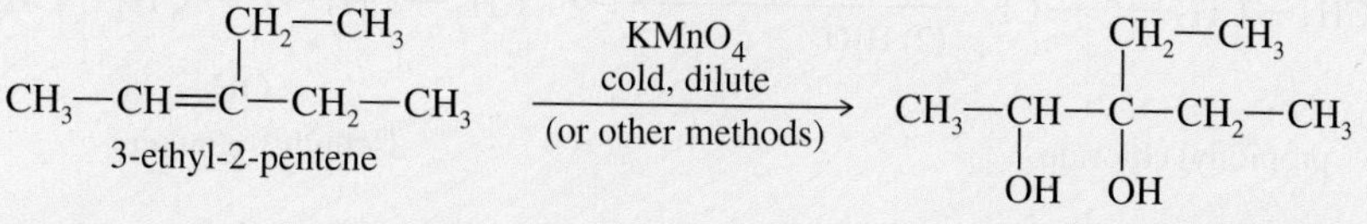

$$\underset{\text{3-ethyl-2-pentene}}{CH_3-CH=C(CH_2-CH_3)-CH_2-CH_3} \xrightarrow[\text{(or other methods)}]{KMnO_4\text{, cold, dilute}} \underset{\text{3-ethyl-2,3-pentanediol}}{CH_3-CH(OH)-C(OH)(CH_2-CH_3)-CH_2-CH_3}$$

2. **Review the functional groups and carbon skeletons of the starting materials (if specified), and see how their skeletons might fit together into the target compound.**
The limitation is that the starting materials must contain no more than three carbon atoms. To form a 7-carbon product requires at least three fragments, probably a 3-carbon fragment and two 2-carbon fragments. A functional group that can be converted to an alkene will be needed on either C2 or C3 of the chain, since 3-ethyl-2-pentene has a double bond between C2 and C3.

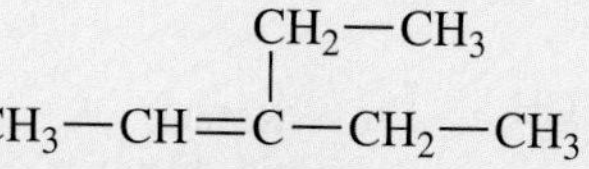

$$CH_3-CH=C(CH_2-CH_3)-CH_2-CH_3$$

3. **Compare methods for assembling the carbon skeleton of the target compound. Which ones provide a key intermediate with the correct carbon skeleton and functional groups correctly positioned for conversion to the functionality in the target molecule?**

(Continued)

At this point, the Grignard reaction is our most powerful method for assembling a carbon skeleton, and Grignards can be used to make primary, secondary, and tertiary alcohols (Section 10-9). The secondary alcohol 3-ethyl-2-pentanol has its functional group on C2, and the tertiary alcohol 3-ethyl-3-pentanol has it on C3. Either of these alcohols can be synthesized by an appropriate Grignard reaction, but 3-ethyl-2-pentanol may dehydrate to give a mixture of products. Because of its symmetry, 3-ethyl-3-pentanol dehydrates to give only the desired alkene, 3-ethyl-2-pentene. It also dehydrates more easily because it is a tertiary alcohol.

$$\underset{\text{3-ethyl-2-pentanol}}{CH_3-CH(OH)-CH(CH_2-CH_3)-CH_2-CH_3} \xrightarrow{H_2SO_4} \left\{ \underset{\substack{\text{(major)}\\ \text{3-ethyl-2-pentene}}}{CH_3-CH=C(CH_2-CH_3)-CH_2-CH_3} + \underset{\substack{\text{(minor)}\\ \text{3-ethyl-1-pentene}}}{CH_2=CH-CH(CH_2-CH_3)-CH_2-CH_3} \right\}$$

Preferred synthesis:

$$\underset{\text{3-ethyl-3-pentanol}}{CH_3-CH_2-C(OH)(CH_2-CH_3)-CH_2-CH_3} \xrightarrow{H_2SO_4} \underset{\substack{\text{(only product)}\\ \text{3-ethyl-2-pentene}}}{CH_3-CH=C(CH_2-CH_3)-CH_2-CH_3}$$

4. Working backward through as many steps as necessary, compare methods for synthesizing the reactants needed for assembly of the key intermediate. (This process may require writing several possible reaction sequences and evaluating them, keeping in mind the specified starting materials.)

The key intermediate, 3-ethyl-3-pentanol, is simply methanol substituted by three ethyl groups. The last step in its synthesis must add an ethyl group. Addition of ethyl magnesium bromide to 3-pentanone gives 3-ethyl-3-pentanol.

$$\underset{\text{3-pentanone}}{CH_3-CH_2-C(=O)-CH_2-CH_3} \xrightarrow[\text{(2) } H_3O^+]{\text{(1) } CH_3CH_2-MgBr} \underset{\text{3-ethyl-3-pentanol}}{CH_3-CH_2-C(OH)(CH_2-CH_3)-CH_2-CH_3}$$

The synthesis of 3-pentanone from a three-carbon fragment and a two-carbon fragment requires several steps (see Problem 11-37). Perhaps there is a better alternative, considering that the key intermediate has three ethyl groups on a carbinol carbon atom. Two similar alkyl groups can be added in one Grignard reaction with an acid chloride or an ester (Section 10-9D). Addition of 2 moles of ethyl magnesium bromide to a three-carbon acid chloride gives 3-ethyl-3-pentanol.

$$\underset{\text{propionyl chloride}}{CH_3-CH_2-C(=O)-Cl} \xrightarrow[\text{(2) } H_3O^+]{\text{(1) 2 } CH_3CH_2-MgBr} \underset{\text{3-ethyl-3-pentanol}}{CH_3-CH_2-C(OH)(CH_2-CH_3)-CH_2-CH_3}$$

5. Summarize the complete synthesis in the forward direction, including all steps and all reagents, and check it for errors and omissions.

$$\underset{\text{propionyl chloride}}{CH_3-CH_2-C(=O)-Cl} \xrightarrow[\text{(2) } H_3O^+]{\text{(1) 2 } CH_3CH_2-MgBr} \underset{\text{3-ethyl-3-pentanol}}{CH_3-CH_2-C(OH)(CH_2-CH_3)-CH_2-CH_3} \xrightarrow{H_2SO_4}$$

$$\underset{\text{3-ethyl-2-pentene}}{CH_3-CH=C(CH_2-CH_3)-CH_2-CH_3} \xrightarrow[\text{(cold, dilute)}]{KMnO_4} \underset{\text{3-ethyl-2,3-pentanediol}}{CH_3-CH(OH)-C(OH)(CH_2-CH_3)-CH_2-CH_3}$$

(Continued)

PROBLEM 11-37

To practice working through the early parts of a multistep synthesis, devise syntheses of
(a) 3-pentanone from alcohols containing no more than three carbon atoms.
(b) 3-ethyl-2-pentanone from compounds containing no more than three carbon atoms.

SAMPLE PROBLEM

As another example of the systematic approach to multistep synthesis, let's consider the synthesis of 1-bromo-2-methylcyclohexane from cyclohexanol.

1. **Review the functional groups and carbon skeleton of the target compound.**
The skeleton has seven carbon atoms: a cyclohexyl ring with a methyl group. It is an alkyl bromide, with the bromine atom on a ring carbon one atom removed from the methyl group.
2. **Review the functional groups and carbon skeletons of the starting materials (if specified), and see how their skeletons might fit together into the target compound.**
The starting compound has only six carbon atoms. So the methyl group must be added, presumably at the functional group. There are no restrictions on the methylating reagent, but it must provide a product with a functional group that can be converted to an adjacent halide.
3. **Compare methods for assembling the carbon skeleton of the target compound to determine which methods provide a key intermediate with the correct carbon skeleton and functional groups at the correct positions for being converted to the functionality in the target molecule.**
Once again, the best choice is a Grignard reaction, but there are two possible reactions that give the methylcyclohexane skeleton. A cyclohexyl Grignard reagent can add to formaldehyde, or a methyl Grignard reagent can add to cyclohexanone. (There are other possibilities, but none that are more direct.)

Cyclohexyl-MgBr + $H_2C{=}O$ $\xrightarrow{(1)\ \text{ether};\ (2)\ H_3O^+}$ cyclohexyl-CH_2OH (alcohol C) ← to be functionalized

CH_3MgBr + cyclohexanone $\xrightarrow{(1)\ \text{ether};\ (2)\ H_3O^+}$ 1-methylcyclohexanol (alcohol D) ← to be functionalized

Neither product has its alcohol functional group on the carbon atom that is functionalized in the target compound. Alcohol C needs its functional group moved two carbon atoms, but alcohol D needs it moved only one carbon atom. Converting alcohol D to an alkene functionalizes the correct carbon atom. Anti-Markovnikov addition of HBr converts the alkene to an alkyl halide with the bromine atom on the correct carbon atom.

alcohol D $\xrightarrow{H_2SO_4,\ \text{heat}}$ alkene $\xrightarrow{HBr,\ ROOR}$ target compound

4. **Working backward through as many steps as necessary, compare methods for synthesizing the reactants needed for assembly of the key intermediate.**
All that remains is to make cyclohexanone by oxidation of cyclohexanol.

cyclohexanol $\xrightarrow{Na_2Cr_2O_7,\ H_2SO_4}$ cyclohexanone

(*Continued*)

5. Summarize the complete synthesis in the forward direction, including all steps and all reagents, and check it for errors and omissions.

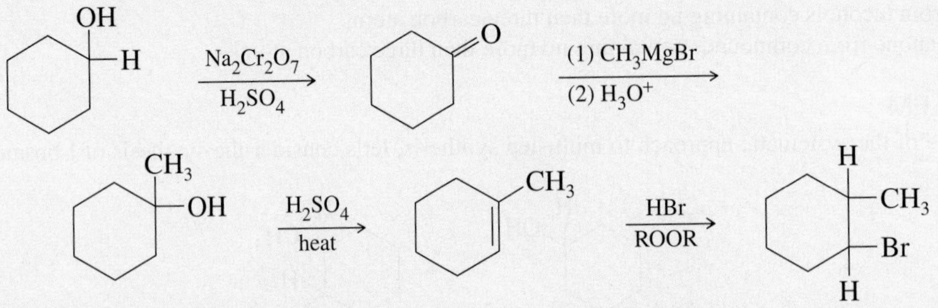

$$\text{cyclohexanol} \xrightarrow[H_2SO_4]{Na_2Cr_2O_7} \text{cyclohexanone} \xrightarrow[(2)\ H_3O^+]{(1)\ CH_3MgBr} \text{1-methylcyclohexanol} \xrightarrow[\text{heat}]{H_2SO_4} \text{1-methylcyclohexene} \xrightarrow[\text{ROOR}]{HBr} \text{trans-1-bromo-2-methylcyclohexane}$$

Problem 11-38 provides practice in multistep syntheses and using alcohols as intermediates.

PROBLEM 11-38

Develop syntheses for the following compounds. As starting materials, you may use cyclopentanol, alcohols containing no more than four carbon atoms, and any common reagents and solvents.

(a) *trans*-cyclopentane-1,2-diol **(b)** 1-chloro-1-ethylcyclopentane

(c) 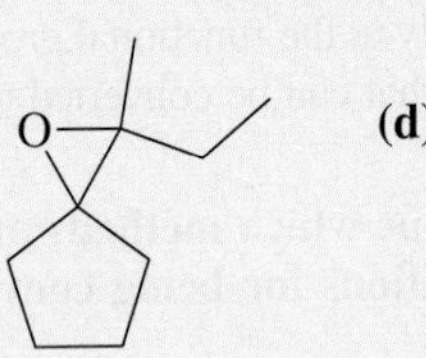 [epoxide: cyclopentylidene–O–C(CH₃)(CH₂CH₃)] **(d)** 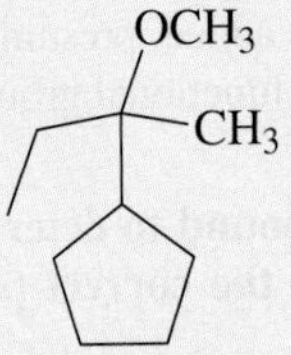 [cyclopentyl–C(OCH₃)(CH₃)(CH₂CH₃)] **(e)** 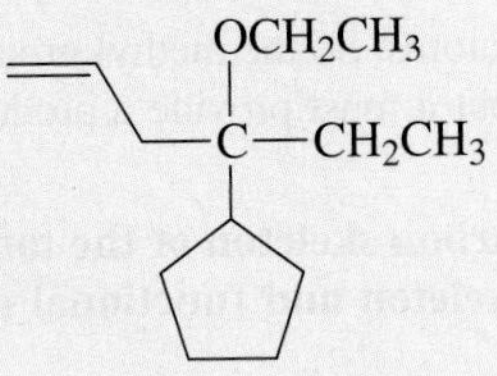 $CH_2{=}CH{-}C(OCH_2CH_3)(CH_2CH_3){-}$cyclopentyl **(f)** 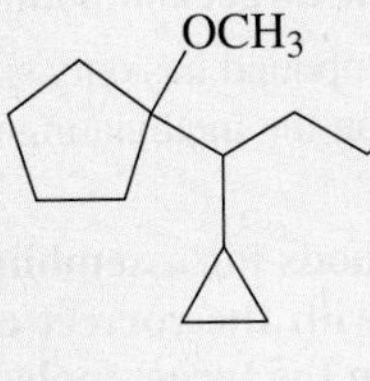 [1-methoxy-1-(1-cyclopropylbutyl)cyclopentane]

SUMMARY Reactions of Alcohols

1. Oxidation–reduction reactions

a. *Oxidation of secondary alcohols to ketones* (Section 11-2A)

$$R{-}CH(OH){-}R' \xrightarrow{Na_2Cr_2O_7,\ H_2SO_4} R{-}C(=O){-}R'$$

Example

$$\underset{\text{2-butanol}}{CH_3{-}CH(OH){-}CH_2CH_3} \xrightarrow{Na_2Cr_2O_7,\ H_2SO_4} \underset{\text{2-butanone}}{CH_3{-}C(=O){-}CH_2CH_3}$$

b. *Oxidation of primary alcohols to carboxylic acids* (Section 11-2B)

$$R{-}CH_2{-}OH \xrightarrow{Na_2Cr_2O_7,\ H_2SO_4} R{-}C(=O){-}OH$$

Example

$$\underset{\text{1-hexanol}}{CH_3(CH_2)_4{-}CH_2{-}OH} \xrightarrow{Na_2Cr_2O_7,\ H_2SO_4} \underset{\text{hexanoic acid}}{CH_3(CH_2)_4{-}C(=O){-}OH}$$

c. *Oxidation of primary alcohols to aldehydes* (Section 11-2B)

$$R{-}CH_2{-}OH \xrightarrow{PCC} R{-}C(=O){-}H$$

Example

$$\underset{\text{1-hexanol}}{CH_3(CH_2)_4{-}CH_2{-}OH} \xrightarrow{PCC} \underset{\text{hexanal}}{CH_3(CH_2)_4{-}C(=O){-}H}$$

(Continued)

d. *Reduction of alcohols to alkanes* (Section 11-6)

$$\text{R—OH} \xrightarrow[\text{(2) LiAlH}_4]{\text{(1) TsCl/pyridine}} \text{R—H}$$

Example

$$\text{cyclohexanol} \xrightarrow[\text{(2) LiAlH}_4]{\text{(1) TsCl/pyridine}} \text{cyclohexane}$$

cyclohexanol cyclohexane

2. Cleavage of the alcohol hydroxyl group —C⫶O—H

a. *Conversion of alcohols to alkyl halides* (Sections 11-7 through 11-9)

$$\text{R—OH} \xrightarrow{\text{HCl or SOCl}_2\text{/pyridine}} \text{R—Cl}$$

$$\text{R—OH} \xrightarrow{\text{HBr or PBr}_3} \text{R—Br}$$

$$\text{R—OH} \xrightarrow{\text{HI or P/I}_2} \text{R—I}$$

Examples

$$(CH_3)_3C\text{—OH} \xrightarrow{\text{HCl}} (CH_3)_3C\text{—Cl}$$

tert-butyl alcohol *tert*-butyl chloride

$$(CH_3)_2CH\text{—}CH_2OH \xrightarrow{\text{PBr}_3} (CH_3)_2CH\text{—}CH_2Br$$

isobutyl alcohol isobutyl bromide

$$CH_3(CH_2)_4\text{—}CH_2OH \xrightarrow{\text{P/I}_2} CH_3(CH_2)_4\text{—}CH_2I$$

1-hexanol 1-iodohexane

b. *Dehydration of alcohols to form alkenes* (Section 11-10A)

$$\text{H—C—C—OH} \underset{}{\overset{\text{H}_2\text{SO}_4 \text{ or H}_3\text{PO}_4}{\rightleftharpoons}} \text{C=C} + H_2O$$

Example

$$\text{cyclohexanol} \xrightarrow{\text{H}_2\text{SO}_4\text{, heat}} \text{cyclohexene} + H_2O$$

cyclohexanol cyclohexene

c. *Industrial dehydration of alcohols to form ethers* (Section 11-10B)

$$2\,\text{R—OH} \overset{\text{H}^+}{\rightleftharpoons} \text{R—O—R} + H_2O$$

Example

$$2\,CH_3CH_2OH \xrightarrow[140\,^\circ\text{C}]{\text{H}_2\text{SO}_4} CH_3CH_2\text{—O—}CH_2CH_3 + H_2O$$

ethanol diethyl ether

3. *Cleavage of the hydroxyl proton* —C—O⫶H

a. *Tosylation* (Section 11-5)

$$\text{R—OH} + \text{Cl—SO}_2\text{—C}_6\text{H}_4\text{—CH}_3 \xrightarrow{\text{pyridine}} \text{R—O—SO}_2\text{—C}_6\text{H}_4\text{—CH}_3 + \text{HCl}$$

alcohol tosyl chloride (TsCl) alkyl tosylate

(Continued)

Example

$$(CH_3)_2CH-OH \xrightarrow{TsCl/pyridine} (CH_3)_2CH-OTs$$

isopropyl alcohol → isopropyl tosylate

b. *Acylation to form esters* (Section 11-12)

$$R-OH \xrightarrow[\text{(acyl chloride)}]{R'-C(=O)-Cl} R-O-C(=O)-R' + HCl$$

ester

Example

$$\text{cyclohexanol} \xrightarrow[\text{(acetyl chloride)}]{CH_3-C(=O)-Cl} \text{cyclohexyl acetate } (C_6H_{11}-O-C(=O)-CH_3) + HCl$$

cyclohexanol → cyclohexyl acetate

c. *Deprotonation to form an alkoxide* (Section 11-14)

$$R-OH + Na\ (\text{or } K) \longrightarrow R-O^{-}\ {}^{+}Na + \tfrac{1}{2}H_2\uparrow$$

$$R-OH + NaH \longrightarrow R-O^{-}\ {}^{+}Na + H_2\uparrow$$

Example

$$CH_3-CH_2-OH + Na \longrightarrow Na^{+}\ {}^{-}O-CH_2-CH_3$$

ethanol → sodium ethoxide

d. *Williamson ether synthesis* (Sections 11-14 and 14-5)

$$R-O^{-} + R'X \longrightarrow R-O-R' + X^{-}$$

(R′ must be unhindered, usually primary)

Example

$$Na^{+}\ {}^{-}O-CH_2CH_3 + CH_3I \longrightarrow CH_3CH_2-O-CH_3 + NaI$$

sodium ethoxide + methyl iodide → ethyl methyl ether

11 Glossary

alcohol dehydrogenase (ADH) An enzyme used by living cells to catalyze the oxidation of ethyl alcohol to acetaldehyde. (p. 471)

aldehyde dehydrogenase (ALDH) An enzyme used by living cells to catalyze the oxidation of acetaldehyde to acetic acid. (p. 471)

alkoxide ion The anion formed by deprotonating an alcohol. (p. 497)

$$R-\ddot{\underset{..}{O}}-H + Na \longrightarrow R-\ddot{\underset{..}{O}}:^{-}\ {}^{+}Na + \tfrac{1}{2}H_2\uparrow$$

chromic acid reagent (H_2CrO_4) The solution formed by adding sodium or potassium dichromate (and a small amount of water) to concentrated sulfuric acid. (p. 466)

chromic acid test: When a primary or secondary alcohol is warmed with the chromic acid reagent, the orange color changes to green or blue. A nonoxidizable compound (such as a tertiary alcohol, a ketone, or an alkane) produces no color change. (p. 468)

Collins reagent ($CrO_3 \cdot 2$ pyridine) A complex of chromium trioxide with pyridine, used to oxidize primary alcohols selectively to aldehydes. (p. 469)

ester An acid derivative formed by the reaction of an acid with an alcohol with loss of water. The most common esters are carboxylic esters (or carboxylate esters), composed of carboxylic acids and alcohols. (p. 493)

inorganic esters Compounds derived from alcohols and inorganic acids with loss of water. (p. 494)
Examples are

$$\text{R—O—S(=O)_2—R} \quad \text{R—O—S(=O)_2—O—R} \quad \text{R—O—N}^+\text{(=O)O}^- \quad \text{R—O—P(=O)(O—R)—O—R}$$

sulfonate esters, sulfate esters, nitrate esters, phosphate esters

For comparison:

$$\text{R—O—C(=O)—R'}$$

carboxylate esters

Fischer esterification: The acid-catalyzed reaction of an alcohol with a carboxylic acid to form an ester. (p. 493)

$$\underset{\text{carboxylic acid}}{\text{R—C(=O)—OH}} + \underset{\text{alcohol}}{\text{H—O—R'}} \overset{H^+}{\rightleftharpoons} \underset{\text{carboxylic ester}}{\text{R—C(=O)—O—R'}} + H_2O$$

ether A compound containing an oxygen atom bonded to two alkyl or aryl groups. (p. 487)
glycol Synonymous with **diol**. The term "glycol" is most commonly applied to the 1,2-diols, also called **vicinal diols**. (p. 491)
Jones reagent A solution of dilute chromic acid dissolved in acetone, used for alcohol oxidations. (p. 469)
Lucas test A test used to determine whether an alcohol is primary, secondary, or tertiary. The test measures the rate of reaction with the **Lucas reagent**, $ZnCl_2$ in concentrated HCl. Tertiary alcohols react fast (seconds), secondary alcohols react more slowly (minutes), and primary alcohols react very slowly (hours). (p. 478)
nicotinamide adenine dinucleotide (NAD) A biological oxidizing/reducing reagent that operates in conjunction with enzymes such as alcohol dehydrogenase. (p. 471)
oxidation Loss of H_2; addition of O or O_2; addition of X_2 (halogens). Alternatively, an increase in the number of bonds to oxygen or halogens or a decrease in the number of bonds to hydrogen. (p. 464)
pinacol rearrangement Dehydration of a glycol in which one of the groups migrates to give a ketone. (p. 491)
pyridinium chlorochromate (PCC) A complex of chromium trioxide with pyridine and HCl. PCC oxidizes primary alcohols to aldehydes without over-oxidizing them to carboxylic acids. (p. 468)
reduction Addition of H_2 (or H^-); loss of O or O_2; loss of X_2 (halogens). Alternatively, a reduction in the number of bonds to oxygen or halogens or an increase in the number of bonds to hydrogen. (p. 464)
Swern oxidation A mild oxidation, using DMSO and oxalyl chloride, that can oxidize primary alcohols to aldehydes and secondary alcohols to ketones. (p. 469)
tosylate ester (R—OTs) An ester of an alcohol with *para*-toluenesulfonic acid. Like halide ions, the tosylate anion is an excellent leaving group. (p. 473)
Williamson ether synthesis The S_N2 reaction between an alkoxide ion and a primary alkyl halide or tosylate. The product is an ether. (p. 497)

$$\text{R—}\ddot{\underset{..}{O}}\text{:}^- \;\; \text{R'—X} \longrightarrow \text{R—}\ddot{\underset{..}{O}}\text{—R'} + X^-$$

Essential Problem-Solving Skills in Chapter 11

1. Identify whether oxidation or reduction is needed to interconvert alkanes, alcohols, aldehydes, ketones, and acids, and identify reagents that will accomplish the conversion.
2. Predict the products of the reactions of alcohols with
   (a) Oxidizing and reducing agents.
   (b) Carboxylic acids and acid chlorides.
   (c) Dehydrating reagents, especially H_2SO_4 and H_3PO_4.
   (d) Inorganic acids.
   (e) Sodium metal, potassium metal, and sodium hydride.

3. Predict the products of reactions of alkoxide ions.
4. Propose chemical tests to distinguish alcohols from the other types of compounds we have studied.
5. Use your knowledge of alcohol and diol reactions to propose mechanisms and products of similar reactions you have never seen before.
6. Show how to convert an alcohol to a related compound with a different functional group.
7. Predict the products of pinacol rearrangement and periodate cleavage of glycols.
8. Use retrosynthetic analysis to propose effective single-step and multistep syntheses of compounds using alcohols as intermediates (especially those using Grignard and organolithium reagents to assemble the carbon skeletons).

Study Problems

11-39 Briefly define each term, and give an example.

(a) oxidation **(b)** reduction **(c)** chromic acid oxidation
(d) PCC oxidation **(e)** ether **(f)** Williamson ether synthesis
(g) alkoxide ion **(h)** carboxylic ester **(i)** Fischer esterification
(j) tosylate ester **(k)** alkyl phosphate ester **(l)** alkyl nitrate ester
(m) Lucas test **(n)** pinacol rearrangement **(o)** Swern oxidation

11-40 In each case, show how you would synthesize the chloride, bromide, and iodide from the corresponding alcohol.

(a) 1-halobutane (halo = chloro, bromo, iodo) **(b)** halocyclopentane
(c) 1-halo-1-methylcyclohexane **(d)** 1-halo-2-methylcyclohexane

11-41 Predict the major products of the following reactions, including stereochemistry where appropriate.

(a) (*R*)-2-butanol + TsCl in pyridine **(b)** (*S*)-2-butyl tosylate + NaBr
(c) cyclooctanol + CrO_3/H_2SO_4 **(d)** cyclopentylmethanol + $CrO_3 \cdot$ pyridine $\cdot$ HCl
(e) cyclopentylmethanol + $Na_2Cr_2O_7/H_2SO_4$ **(f)** cyclopentanol + $HCl/ZnCl_2$
(g) *n*-butanol + HBr **(h)** cyclooctylmethanol + CH_3CH_2MgBr
(i) potassium *tert*-butoxide + methyl iodide **(j)** sodium methoxide + *tert*-butyl iodide
(k) cyclopentanol + H_2SO_4/heat **(l)** product from (k) + OsO_4/H_2O_2, then HIO_4
(m) sodium ethoxide + 1-bromobutane **(n)** sodium ethoxide + 2-methyl-2-bromobutane

11-42 Show how you would accomplish the following synthetic conversions.

(a) cyclohexane with OH, H → cyclohexane with OCH_2CH_3, H
(b) 2 benzene–CH_2Br → PhCH=CHPh
(c) cyclohexane with Br, H → cyclohexane with $C(=O)-CH_2CH_2CH_3$, H
(d) cyclohexane with CH_2OH, H → cyclohexane–$CH(OH)CH_2CH_3$

11-43 Predict the major products of dehydration catalyzed by sulfuric acid.

(a) 1-hexanol **(b)** 2-hexanol **(c)** 3-pentanol
(d) 1-methylcyclopentanol **(e)** cyclopentylmethanol **(f)** 2-methylcyclopentanol

11-44 Predict the esterification products of the following acid/alcohol pairs.

(a) $CH_3CH_2CH_2COOH + CH_3OH$ **(b)** $CH_3OH + HNO_3$ **(c)** $2\ CH_3CH_2OH + H_3PO_4$

(d) benzene–COOH + CH_3CH_2OH **(e)** benzene–OH + $CH_3-C(=O)-OH$

11-45 Show how you would make the methanesulfonate ester of cyclohexanol, beginning with cyclohexanol and an appropriate acid chloride.

cyclohexyl methanesulfonate:

11-46 Show how you would convert (*S*)-2-hexanol to
(a) (*S*)-2-chlorohexane **(b)** (*R*)-2-bromohexane **(c)** (*R*)-2-hexanol

11-47 When 1-cyclohexylethanol is treated with concentrated aqueous HBr, the major product is 1-bromo-1-ethylcyclohexane.

$\xrightarrow[H_2O]{HBr}$

(a) Propose a mechanism for this reaction.
(b) How would you convert 1-cyclohexylethanol to (1-bromoethyl)cyclohexane in good yield?

$\xrightarrow{?}$

11-48 Show how you would make each compound, beginning with an alcohol of your choice.

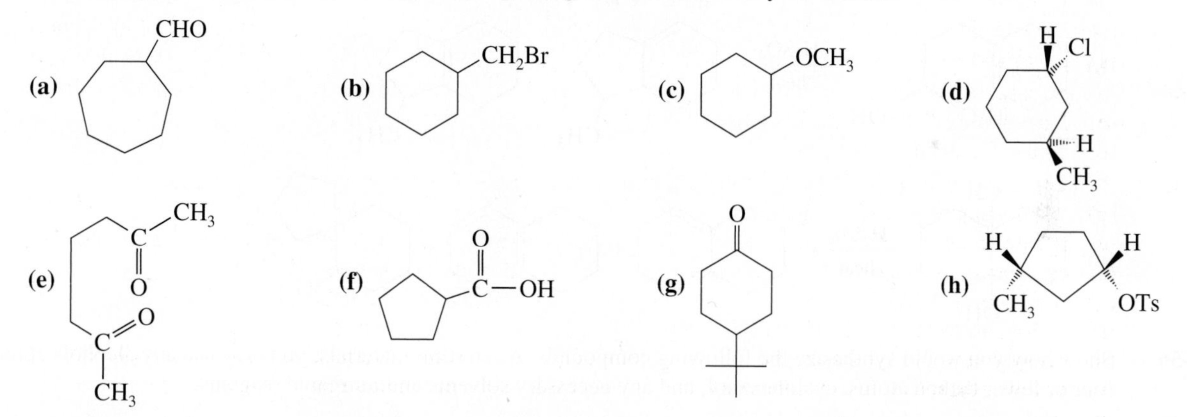

11-49 Predict the major products (including stereochemistry) when *cis*-3-methylcyclohexanol reacts with the following reagents.
(a) PBr_3 **(b)** $SOCl_2$ **(c)** Lucas reagent
(d) concentrated HBr **(e)** TsCl/pyridine, then NaBr

11-50 Show how you would use simple chemical tests to distinguish between the following pairs of compounds. In each case, describe what you would do and what you would observe.
(a) 1-butanol and 2-butanol **(b)** 2-butanol and 2-methyl-2-butanol
(c) cyclohexanol and cyclohexene **(d)** cyclohexanol and cyclohexanone
(e) cyclohexanone and 1-methylcyclohexanol

11-51 Write the important resonance structures of the following anions.

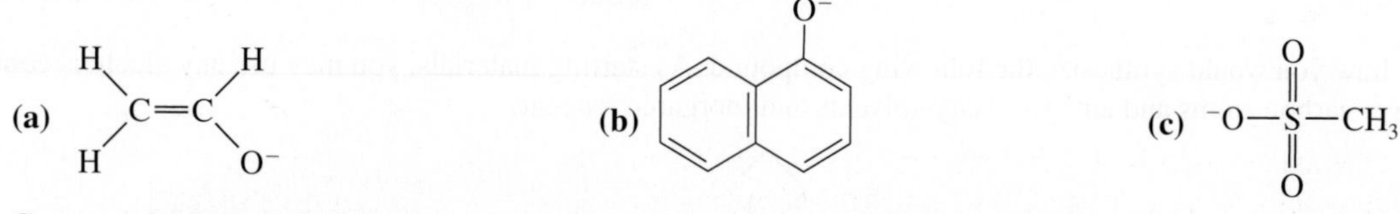

11-52 Compound **A** is an optically active alcohol. Treatment with chromic acid converts **A** into a ketone, **B**. In a separate reaction, **A** is treated with PBr_3, converting **A** into compound **C**. Compound **C** is purified, and then it is allowed to react with magnesium in ether to give a Grignard reagent, **D**. Compound **B** is added to the resulting solution of the Grignard reagent. After hydrolysis of the initial product (**E**), this solution is found to contain 3,4-dimethyl-3-hexanol. Propose structures for compounds **A**, **B**, **C**, **D**, and **E**.

A $\xrightarrow{PBr_3}$ **C** $\xrightarrow{\text{Mg, ether}}$ **D** (Grignard reagent)

A $\xrightarrow{Na_2Cr_2O_7,\ H_2SO_4}$ **B**

D + **B** $\longrightarrow$ **E** $\xrightarrow{H_3O^+}$ 3,4-dimethyl-3-hexanol

11-53 Give the structures of the intermediates and products **V** through **Z**.

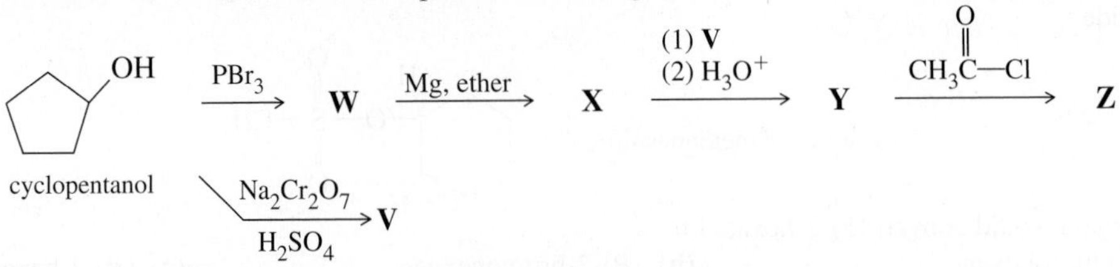

cyclopentanol $\xrightarrow{PBr_3}$ **W** $\xrightarrow{\text{Mg, ether}}$ **X** $\xrightarrow{(1)\ \mathbf{V}\quad (2)\ H_3O^+}$ **Y** $\xrightarrow{CH_3COCl}$ **Z**

cyclopentanol $\xrightarrow{Na_2Cr_2O_7,\ H_2SO_4}$ **V**

11-54 Under acid catalysis, tetrahydrofurfuryl alcohol reacts to give surprisingly good yields of dihydropyran. Propose a mechanism to explain this useful synthesis.

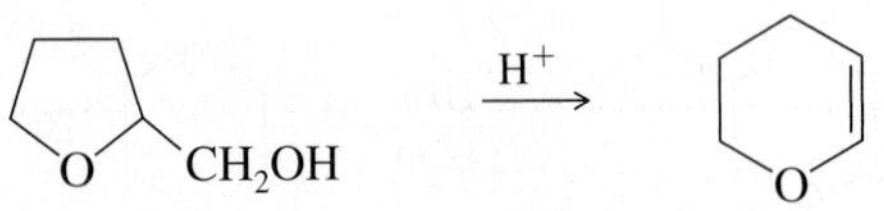

tetrahydrofurfuryl alcohol (O, CH_2OH) $\xrightarrow{H^+}$ dihydropyran

11-55 Propose mechanisms for the following reactions. In most cases, more products are formed than are shown here. You only need to explain the formation of the products shown, however.

(a) cyclohexyl–CH_2—OH $\xrightarrow{HCl,\ ZnCl_2}$ chlorocycloheptane (Cl) (a minor product)

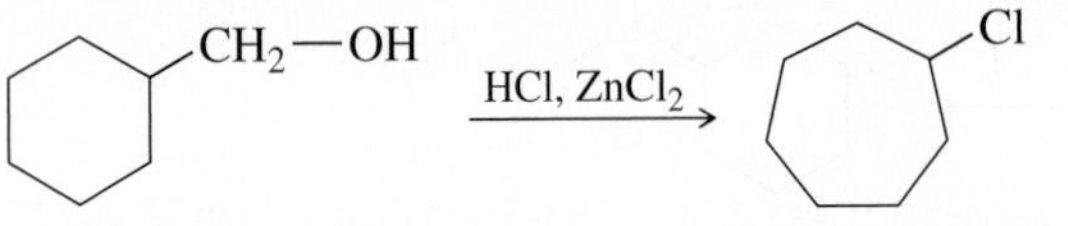

(b) (H_3C, OH) $\xrightarrow{H_2SO_4,\ \text{heat}}$ (CH_3) + (CH_3)

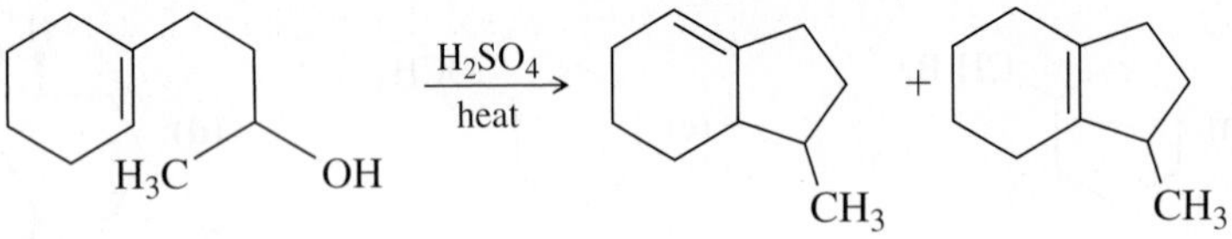

(c) (OH, OH) $\xrightarrow{H_2SO_4,\ \text{heat}}$ + + (O)

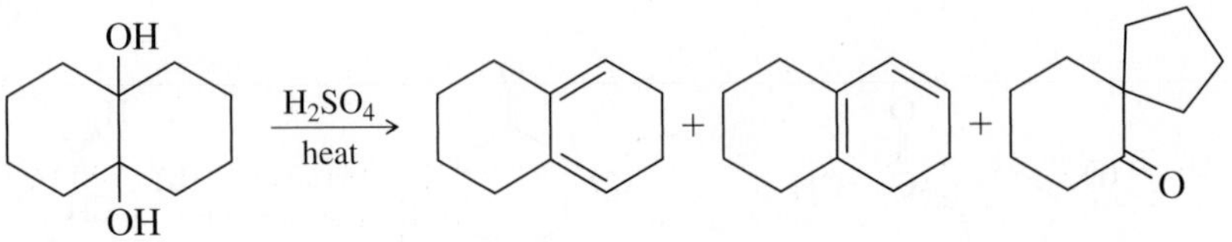

11-56 Show how you would synthesize the following compounds. As starting materials, you may use any alcohols containing four or fewer carbon atoms, cyclohexanol, and any necessary solvents and inorganic reagents.

(a) (CH_3, O) **(b)** (O) **(c)** cyclohexyl–C(OCH_3)(CH_3)(CH_2CH_3) **(d)** (OH)

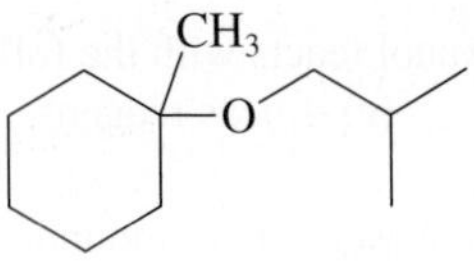

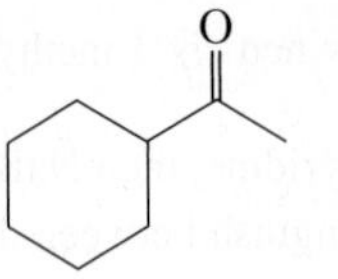

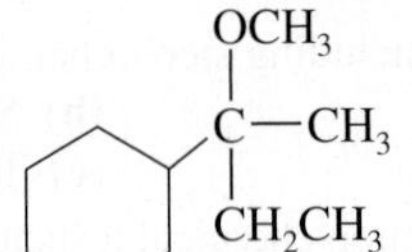

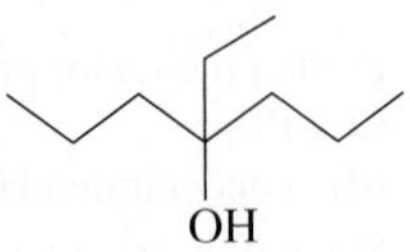

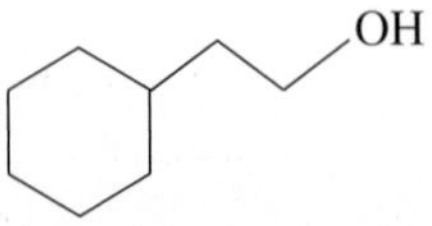

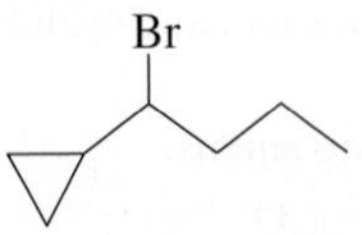

(e) (OH) **(f)** (Br) **(g)** CH_3, H, C, N≡C, CH_2CH_3 ***(h)** (—$CHOCH_2CH_3$, OH, OH)

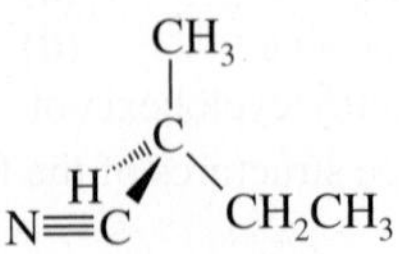

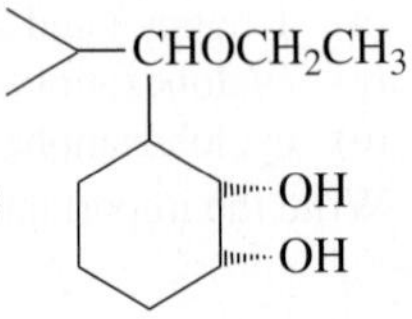

11-57 Show how you would synthesize the following compound. As starting materials, you may use any alcohols containing five or fewer carbon atoms and any necessary solvents and inorganic reagents.

(O)

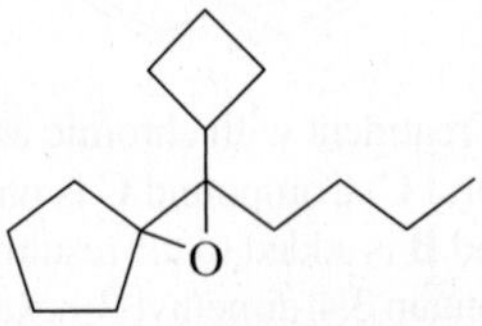

11-58 The following pseudo-syntheses (guaranteed not to work) exemplify a common conceptual error.

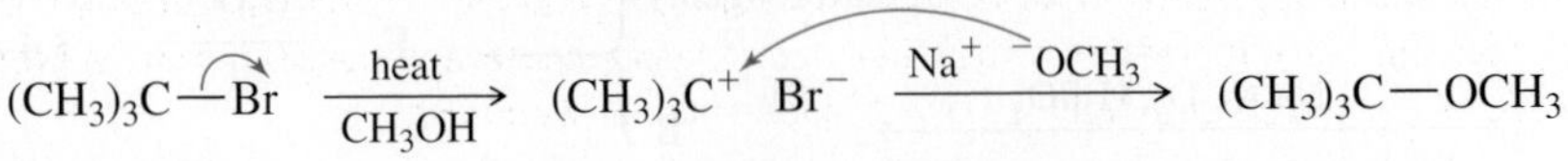

$(CH_3)_3C$—Br $\xrightarrow[CH_3OH]{\text{heat}}$ $(CH_3)_3C^+\ Br^-$ $\xrightarrow{Na^+\ ^-OCH_3}$ $(CH_3)_3C$—OCH_3

$$\text{CH}_3\text{CH}_2\text{CH}_2\text{CH}_2\text{OH} \xrightarrow{H_2SO_4} \text{CH}_3\text{CH}_2\text{CH}_2\text{CH}_2\overset{+}{O}H_2 \xrightarrow{Na^+\ ^-OCH_3} \text{CH}_3\text{CH}_2\text{CH}_2\text{CH}_2\text{OCH}_3 + H_2O$$

(a) What is the conceptual error implicit in these syntheses?
(b) Propose syntheses that are more likely to succeed.

11-59 Two unknowns, **X** and **Y**, both having the molecular formula C_4H_8O, give the following results with four chemical tests. Propose structures for **X** and **Y** consistent with this information.

	Bromine	Na Metal	Chromic Acid	Lucas Reagent
Compound **X**	decolorizes	bubbles	orange to green	no reaction
Compound **Y**	no reaction	no reaction	no reaction	no reaction

11-60 The Williamson ether synthesis involves the displacement of an alkyl halide or tosylate by an alkoxide ion. Would the synthesis shown be possible by making a tosylate and displacing it? If so, show the sequence of reactions. If not, explain why not and show an alternative synthesis that would be more likely to work.

OH → make the tosylate and displace? → OCH$_3$

***11-61** Chromic acid oxidation of an alcohol (Section 11-2A) occurs in two steps: formation of the chromate ester, followed by an elimination of H^+ and chromium. Which step do you expect to be rate-limiting? Careful kinetic studies have shown that Compound **A** undergoes chromic acid oxidation over 10 times as fast as Compound **B**. Explain this large difference in rates.

Compound A (CH$_3$, OH, H) —H_2CrO_4 (faster)→ ketone (CH$_3$, O, H) ←H_2CrO_4 (slower)— Compound B (CH$_3$, HO, H)

***11-62** Many alcohols undergo dehydration at 0 °C when treated with phosphorus oxychloride ($POCl_3$) in the mildly basic solvent pyridine. (Phosphorus oxychloride is the acid chloride of phosphoric acid, with chlorine atoms in place of the hydroxyl groups of phosphoric acid.)

(a) Propose a mechanism for the dehydration of cyclopentanol using $POCl_3$ and pyridine. The first half of the mechanism, formation of a dichlorophosphate ester, is similar to the first half of the mechanism of reaction of an alcohol with thionyl chloride. Like a tosylate, the dichlorophosphate group is a good leaving group. The second half of the mechanism might be either first order or second order; draw both alternatives for now.

(b) When *trans*-2-methylcyclopentanol undergoes dehydration using $POCl_3$ in pyridine, the major product is 3-methylcyclopentene, and not the Zaitsev product. What is the stereochemistry of the dehydration? What does this stereochemistry imply about the correct mechanism in part (a)? Explain your reasoning.

***11-63** Alcohols combine with ketones and aldehydes to form interesting derivatives, which we will discuss in Chapter 18. The following reactions show the hydrolysis of two such derivatives. Propose mechanisms for these reactions.

(a) 2-methoxytetrahydropyran (O, OCH$_3$) $\xrightarrow[H_2O]{H^+}$ HO–(CH$_2$)$_4$–CHO (HO, O, H) + CH_3OH

(b) bicyclic enol ether (O) $\xrightarrow[H_2O]{H^+}$ 2-(2-hydroxyethyl)cyclohexanone (O, OH)

***11-64** Unknown **Q** is determined to have a molecular formula of $C_6H_{12}O$. **Q** is not optically active, and passing it through a chiral column does not separate it into enantiomers. **Q** does not react with Br_2, nor with cold, dilute $KMnO_4$, nor does it take up H_2 under catalytic hydrogenation. Heating of **Q** with H_2SO_4 gives product **R**, of formula C_6H_{10}, which can be separated into enantiomers. Ozonolysis of a single enantiomer of **R** produces **S**, an acyclic, optically active ketoaldehyde of formula $C_6H_{10}O_2$. Propose structures for compounds **Q**, **R**, and **S**, and show how your structures would react appropriately to give these results.

***11-65** **(a)** The reaction of 2-butanol with concentrated aqueous HBr goes with partial racemization, giving more inversion than retention of configuration. Propose a mechanism that accounts for racemization with excess inversion.

(b) Under the same conditions, an optically active sample of *trans*-2-bromocyclopentanol reacts with concentrated aqueous HBr to give an optically inactive product, (racemic) *trans*-1,2-dibromocyclopentane. Propose a mechanism to show how this reaction goes with apparently complete retention of configuration, yet with racemization. (*Hint:* Draw out the mechanism of the reaction of cyclopentene with Br_2 in water to give the starting material, *trans*-2-bromocyclopentanol. Consider how parts of this mechanism might be involved in the reaction with HBr.)

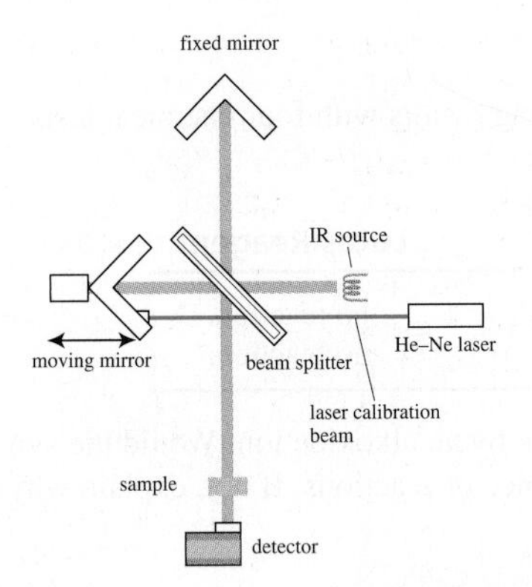

INFRARED SPECTROSCOPY AND MASS SPECTROMETRY

CHAPTER 12

12-1 Introduction

One of the most important tasks of organic chemistry is the determination of organic structures. When an interesting compound is isolated from a natural source, its structure must be completely determined before a synthesis can begin. Whenever we run a reaction, we must determine whether the product has the desired structure. The structure of an unwanted product must be known so the reaction conditions can be altered to favor the desired product.

In many cases, a compound can be identified by chemical means. We find the molecular formula by analyzing the elemental composition and determining the molecular weight. If the compound has been characterized before, we can compare its physical properties (melting point, boiling point, etc.) with the published values. Chemical tests can suggest the functional groups and narrow the range of possible structures before the physical properties are used to make an identification.

These procedures are insufficient, however, for complex compounds that have never been synthesized and characterized. They are also impractical with compounds that are difficult to obtain, because a relatively large sample is required to complete the elemental analysis and all the functional group tests. We need analytical techniques that work with tiny samples and that do not destroy the sample.

Spectroscopic techniques often meet these requirements. **Absorption spectroscopy** is the measurement of the amount of light absorbed by a compound as a function of the wavelength of light. In general, a spectrometer irradiates the sample with light, measures the amount of light transmitted as a function of wavelength and plots the results on a graph. Unlike chemical tests, most spectroscopic techniques are *nondestructive*; that is, the sample is not destroyed. Many different kinds of spectra can be measured with little or no loss of sample.

In this book, we cover four spectroscopic or related techniques that serve as powerful tools for structure determination in organic chemistry:

Infrared (IR) spectroscopy, covered in this chapter, observes the vibrations of bonds and provides evidence of the functional groups present.

Mass spectrometry (MS), also covered in this chapter, is not a *spectroscopic* technique, because it does not measure absorption or emission of light. A mass spectrometer bombards molecules with electrons and breaks the molecules into fragments. Analysis of the masses of the fragments gives the molecular weight, possibly the molecular formula, and clues to the structure and functional groups. Less than a milligram of sample is destroyed in this analysis.

Nuclear magnetic resonance (NMR) spectroscopy, covered in Chapter 13, observes the chemical environments of the hydrogen atoms (or the carbon

ANSWERS TO SELECTED PROBLEMS

These short answers are sometimes incomplete, but they should put you on the right track. Complete answers to all problems are found in the *Solutions Manual.*

CHAPTER 1

1.5. (a) $\overrightarrow{C-Cl}$; (b) $\overrightarrow{C-O}$; (c) $\overrightarrow{C-N}$; (d) $\overrightarrow{C-S}$; (e) $\overleftarrow{C-B}$; (f) $\overrightarrow{N-Cl}$; (g) $\overrightarrow{N-O}$; (h) $\overleftarrow{N-S}$; (i) $\overleftarrow{N-B}$; (j) $\overrightarrow{B-Cl}$; **1.6.** (a) +1 on O; (b) +1 on N, −1 on Cl; (c) +1 on N, −1 on Cl; (d) +1 on Na, −1 on O; (e) +1 on C; (f) −1 on C; (g) +1 on Na, −1 on B; (h) +1 on Na, −1 on B; (i) +1 on O, −1 on B; (j) +1 on N; (k) +1 on K, −1 on O; (l) +1 on O. **1.12.** (a) CH_2O, $C_3H_6O_3$; (b) $C_2H_5NO_2$, same; (c) C_2H_4ClNO, same; (d) C_2H_3Cl, $C_4H_6Cl_2$. **1.13.** (a) 0.209; (b) 13.875 **1.15.** (a) favors products; (b) favors reactants; (c) favors products; (d) favors products; (e) favors products; (f) favors products. **1.16.** There is no resonance stabilization of the positive charge when the other oxygen atom is protonated. **1.17.** (a) acetic acid, ethanol, methylamine; (b) ethoxide, methylamine, ethanol. **1.21.** (a) carbon; (b) oxygen; (c) phosphorus; (d) chlorine. **1.28.** The following are condensed structures that you should convert to Lewis structures. (a) $CH_3CH_2CH_2CH_3$ and $CH_3CH(CH_3)_2$; (c) $CH_3CH_2NH_2$ and CH_3NHCH_3; (e) $CH_2(CH_2OH)_2$ and $CH_3CHOHCH_2OH$ and $CH_3OCH_2OCH_3$ and others; (f) $CH_2{=}CHOH$ and CH_3CHO. **1.32.** (a) C_5H_5N; (b) C_4H_9N; (c) C_4H_9NO; (d) $C_4H_9NO_2$; (e) $C_{11}H_{21}NO$; (f) $C_9H_{18}O$; (g) $C_7H_8SO_3$; (h) $C_6H_6O_3$. **1.33.** Empirical formula C_3H_6O; molecular formula $C_6H_{12}O_2$. **1.36.** (a) different compounds; (b) resonance forms; (c) different compounds; (d) resonance forms; (e) different compounds; (f) resonance forms; (g) resonance forms; (h) different compounds; (i) resonance forms; (j) resonance forms. **1.39.** (b) The $=$NH nitrogen atom is the most basic. **1.41.** (a) second; (b) first; (c) second; (d) first; (e) first. **1.49.** (a) $CH_3CH_2O^-Li^+ + CH_4$; (b) Methane; CH_3Li is a very strong base. **1.53.** (a) $C_9H_{12}O$; (b) $C_{18}H_{24}O_2$.

CHAPTER 2

2.2. sp^3; Two lone pairs compress the bond angle to 104.5°. **2.4.** Methyl carbon; sp^3, about 109.5°. Nitrile carbon *sp*. 180°. Nitrile nitrogen *sp*, no bond angle. **2.6.** The central carbon is *sp*, with two unhybridized *p* orbitals at right angles. Each terminal $=CH_2$ group must be aligned with one of these *p* orbitals. **2.9.** $CH_3-CH{=}N-CH_3$ shows cis-trans isomerism about the C$=$N double bond, but $(CH_3)_2C{=}N-CH_3$ has two identical substituents on the C$=$N carbon atom, and there are no cis-trans isomers. **2.11.** (a) cis-trans isomers; (b) constitutional isomers; (c) constitutional isomers; (d) same compound; (e) same compound; (f) same compound; (g) not isomers; (h) constitutional isomers; (i) same compound; (j) constitutional isomers; (k) constitutional isomers. **2.13.** The N$-$F dipole moments oppose the dipole moment of the lone pair. **2.15.** *trans* has zero dipole moment because the bond dipole moments cancel. **2.18.** (a) $CH_3CH_2OCH_2CH_3$ (c) $CH_3CH_2NHCH_3$; (d) CH_3CH_2OH; (e) CH_3COCH_3. **2.19.** (a) alkane; (b) alkene; (c) alkyne; (d) cycloalkyne; (e) cycloalkane and alkene; (f) aromatic hydrocarbon and alkyne; (g) cycloalkene and alkene; (h) cycloalkane and alkane (i) aromatic hydrocarbon and cycloalkene. **2.20.** (a) aldehyde and alkene; (b) alcohol; (c) ketone; (d) ether and alkene; (e) carboxylic acid; (f) ether and alkene; (g) ketone and alkene; (h) aldehyde; (i) alcohol. **2.21.** (a) amide; (b) amine; (c) ester; (d) acid chloride and alkene; (e) ether; (f) nitrile; (g) carboxylic acid; (h) cyclic ester and alkene; (i) ketone, cyclic ether; (j) cyclic amine; (k) cyclic amide; (l) amide; (m) cyclic ester; (n) aldehyde, cyclic amine; (o) ketone, cyclic alkene. **2.25.** No stereoisomers. **2.26.** Cyclopropane has bond angles of 60°, compared with the 109.5° bond angle of an unstrained alkane. **2.29.** Formamide must have an sp^2-hybridized nitrogen atom because it is involved in pi-bonding in the other resonance form. **2.34.** (a), (e), and (f). **2.35.** (a) constitutional isomers; (b) constitutional isomers; (c) cis-trans isomers; (d) constitutional isomers; (e) cis-trans isomers; (f) same compound; (g) cis-trans isomers; (h) 1constitutional isomers. **2.36.** CO_2 is *sp*-hybridized and linear; the bond dipole moments cancel. The sulfur atom in SO_2 is sp^2-hybridized and bent; the bond dipole moments do not cancel. **2.38.** Both can form H-bonds with water, but only the alcohol can form H-bonds with itself. **2.40.** (a), (c), (h), and (l) can form hydrogen bonds in the pure state. These four plus (b), (d), (g), (i), (j), and (k) can form hydrogen bonds with water. **2.42.** (a) cyclic ether; (b) cyclic alkene, carboxylic acid; (c) alkene, aldehyde; (d) aromatic, ketone; (e) alkene, cyclic ester; (f) cyclic amide; (g) aromatic nitrile, ether; (h) amine, ester; (i) amine, alcohol, carboxylic acid.

CHAPTER 3

3.1. (a) $C_{28}H_{58}$; (b) $C_{44}H_{90}$; **3.2.** (a) 3-methylpentane; (b) 2-bromo-3-methylpentane; (c) 5-ethyl-2-methyl-4-propylheptane; (d) 4-isopropyl-2-methyldecane. **3.4.** (a) 2-methylbutane; (b) 2,2-dimethylpropane; (c) 3-ethyl-2-methylhexane; (d) 2,4-dimethylhexane; (e) 3-ethyl-2,2,4,5-tetramethylhexane; (f) 4-*t*-butyl-3-methylheptane. **3.8.** (a) $C_{12}H_{26}$; (b) $C_{15}H_{32}$. **3.9.** (a) hexane < octane < decane; (b) $(CH_3)_3C-C(CH_3)_3$ < $CH_3CH_2C(CH_3)_2CH_2CH_2CH_3$ < octane. **3.14.** (a) 1,1-dimethyl-3-(1-methylpropyl) cyclopentane or 3-*sec*-butyl-1,1-dimethylcyclopentane; (b) 3-cyclo-propyl-1,1-dimethylcyclohexane; (c) 4-cyclobutylnonane. **3.16.** (b), (c), and (d). **3.17.** (a) *cis*-1-methyl-3-propylcyclobutane; (b) *trans*-1-*t*-butyl-3-ethylcyclohexane; (c) *trans*-1,2-dimethylcyclopropane. **3.18.** Trans is more stable. In the cis isomer the methyl groups are nearly eclipsed. **3.28.** (a) *cis*-1,3-dimethylcyclohexane, (b) *cis*-1,4-dimethylcyclohexane; (c) *trans*-1,2-dimethylcyclohexane; (d) *cis*-1,3-dimethylcyclohexane; (e) *cis*-1,3-dimethylcyclohexane; (f) *trans*-1,4-dimethylcyclohexane. **3.30.** (a) bicyclo[3.1.0]hexane; (b) bicyclo[3.3.1] nonane; (c) bicyclo[2.2.2]octane; (d) bicyclo[3.1.1]heptane. **3.33.** (a) All except the third (isobutane) are *n*-butane. (b) Top left and bottom left are *cis*-2-butene. Top center and bottom center are 1-butene. Top right is *trans*-2-butene. Lower right is 2-methylpropene. (c) The first and second are *cis*-1,2-dimethylcyclopentane. The third and fourth are *trans*-1,2-dimethylcyclopentane. The fifth is *cis*-1,3-dimethylcyclopentane. **3.37.** (a) 3-ethyl-2,2,6-trimethylheptane; (b) 3-ethyl-2,6,7-trimethyloctane; (c) 3,7-diethyl-2,2,8-trimethyldecane; (d) 2-methyl-1,1-diethylcyclobutane; (e) bicyclo[4.1.0]heptane; (f) *cis*-1-ethyl-3-propylcyclopentane; (g) (1,1-diethylpropyl)cyclohexane; (h) *cis*-1-ethyl-4-isopropylcyclodecane. **3.39.** (a) should be 3-methylhexane; (b) 3-ethyl-2-methylhexane; (c) 2-chloro-3-methylhexane; (d) 2,2-dimethylbutane; (e) *sec*-butylcyclohexane or (1 methylpropyl) cyclohexane; (f) should be *cis* or *trans*-1,2-diethylcyclopentane. **3.40.** (a) octane; (b) nonane; (c) nonane. **3.45.** The trans isomer is more stable, because both of the bonds to the second cyclohexane ring are in equatorial positions.

CHAPTER 4

4.3. (a) One photon of light would be needed for every molecule of product formed (the quantum yield would be 1); (b) Methane does not absorb the visible light that initiates the reaction, and the quantum yield would be 1. **4.4.** (a) Hexane has three different kinds of hydrogen atoms, but cyclohexane has only one type. (b) Large excess of cyclohexane. **4.5.** (a) $K_{eq} = 2.3$; (b) $[CH_3Br] = [H_2S] = 0.40\,M$, $[CH_3SH] = [HBr] = 0.60\,M$. **4.8.** (a) positive; (b) negative; (c) not easy to predict.

4.10. (a) initiation +192 kJ/mole; propagation +67 kJ/mole and −101 kJ/mole; (b) overall −34 kJ/mole. **4.11.** (a) first order; (b) zeroth order; (c) first order overall. **4.13.** (a) zero, zero, zeroth order overall; (b) rate = k_r; (c) increase the surface area of the platinum catalyst. **4.14.** (b) +13 kJ/mole; (c) −4 kJ/mole. **4.15.** (c) +113 kJ/mole. **4.17.** (a) initiation +151 kJ/mole; propagation +138 kJ/mole and −83 kJ/mole; (b) overall +55 kJ/mole; (c) low rate and very unfavorable equilibrium constant. **4.18.** 1°:2° ratio of 6:2, product ratio of 75% 1° and 25% 2°. **4.22.** (a) The combustion of isooctane involves highly branched, more stable tertiary free radicals that react less explosively. (b) *t*-butyl alcohol forms relatively stable alkoxy radicals that react less explosively. **4.29.** Stability: (d) res 3° > (c) 3°> (b) 2°> (a) 1°. **4.30.** Stability: (d) res 3° > (c) 3°> (b) 2°> (a) 1°. **4.38.** rate = $k_r[H^+][(CH_3)_3C{-}OH]$; second order overall. **4.41.** $PhCH_2\cdot > CH_2{=}CHCH_2\cdot > (CH_3)_3C\cdot > (CH_3)_2CH\cdot > CH_3CH_2\cdot > CH_3\cdot$.

CHAPTER 5

5.1. chiral: corkscrew, desk, screw-cap bottle, rifle, knot, left-handed can opener. **5.2.** (b), (d), (e), and (f) are chiral. **5.3.** (a) chiral, one C*; (b) achiral, no C*; (c) chiral, one C*; (d) chiral, one C*; (e) achiral, no C*; (f) achiral, two C*; (g) chiral, one C*; (h) chiral, two C*; (i) chiral, two C*; **5.5.** (a) mirror, achiral; (b) mirror, achiral; (c) chiral, no mirror; (d) chiral, no mirror; (e) chiral, no mirror; (f) chiral, no mirror; (g) mirror, achiral; (h) mirror, achiral. **5.6.** (a) (*R*); (b) (*S*); (c) (*R*); (d) (*S*), (*S*); (e) (*R*), (*S*); (f) (*R*), (*S*); (g) (*R*), (*R*); (h) (*R*); (i) (*S*). **5.8.** +8.7°. **5.10.** Dilute the sample. If clockwise, will make less clockwise, and vice-versa. **5.12.** e.e. = 33.3%. Specific rotation = 33.3% of +13.5° = +4.5°. **5.15.** (a), (b), (e), and (f) are chiral. Only (e) has asymmetric carbons. **5.16.** (a) enantiomer, enantiomer, same; (b) same, enantiomer, enantiomer; (c) enantiomer, same, same. **5.18.** (a), (d), and (f) are chiral. The others have internal mirror planes. **5.19.** (from 5–17) (a) (*R*); (b) none; (c) none; (d) (2*R*), (3*R*); (e) (2*S*), (3*R*); (f) (2*R*), (3*R*); (new ones) (g) (*R*); (h) (*S*); (i) (*S*). **5.20.** (a) enantiomers; (b) diastereomers; (c) diastereomers; (d) constitutional isomers; (e) enantiomers; (f) diastereomers; (g) enantiomers; (h) same compound; (i) diastereomers. **5.23.** (a), (b), and (d) are pairs of diastereomers and could theoretically be separated by their physical properties. **5.30.** (a) same compound; (b) enantiomers; (c) enantiomers; (d) enantiomers; (e) diastereomers; (f) diastereomers; (g) enantiomers; (h) same compound. **5.34.** (b) (−)15.90°; (c) 7.95°/15.90° = 50%e.e. Composition is 75% (*R*) and 25% (*S*).

CHAPTER 6

6.1. (a) vinyl halide; (b) alkyl halide; (c) alkyl halide; (d) alkyl halide; (e) vinyl halide; (f) aryl halide. **6.5.** (a) ethyl chloride; (b) 1-bromopropane; (c) cyclopentene. **6.7.** Water is denser than hexane, so water forms the lower layer. Chloroform is denser than water, so chloroform forms the lower layer. Water and ethanol are miscible, so they form only one phase. **6.11.** (a) substitution; (b) elimination; (c) elimination, also a reduction. **6.13.** (a) 0.02 mol/L per second. **6.14.** (a) $(CH_3)_3COCH_2CH_3$; (b) $HC{\equiv}CCH_2CH_2CH_2CH_3$; (c) $(CH_3)_2CHCH_2NH_2$; (d) $CH_3CH_2CH_2C{\equiv}N$; (e) 1-iodopentane; (f) 1-fluoropentane. **6.16.** (a) $(CH_3CH_2)_2NH$, less hindered; (b) $(CH_3)_2S$, S more polarizable; (c) PH_3, P more polarizable; (d) CH_3S^-, neg. charged; (e) $(CH_3)_3N$, N less electronegative; (f) CH_3S^-, neg. charge, more polarizable; (g) $CH_3CH_2CH_2O^-$, less hindered; (h) I^-, more polarizable. **6.18.** methyl iodide > methyl chloride > ethyl chloride > isopropyl bromide ≫ neopentyl bromide, *t*-butyl iodide. **6.19.** (a) 2-methyl-1-iodopropane; (b) cyclohexyl bromide; (c) isopropyl bromide; (d) 2-chlorobutane; (e) 1-iodobutane. **6.23.** (a) 2-bromopropane; (b) 2-bromo-2-methylbutane; (c) allyl bromide; (d) 2-bromopropane; (e) 2-iodo-2-methylbutane; (f) 2-bromo-2-methylbutane.

6.27. (a) $(CH_3)_2C(OCOCH_3)CH_2CH_3$, first order; (b) 1-methoxy-2-methylpropane, second order; (c) 1-ethoxy-1-methylcyclohexane, first order; (d) methoxycyclohexane, first order; (e) ethoxycyclohexane, second order. **6.36.** 3-methyl-1-butene by E2 (minor); 2-methyl-2-butene by E2 (major); and 2-ethoxy-3-methylbutane (trace) by S_N2. **6.43.** (a) 2-bromo-2-methylpentane; (b) 1 chloro-1-methylcyclohexane; (c) 1,1-dichloro-3-fluorocycloheptane, (d) 4-(2-bromoethyl)-3-(fluoromethyl)-2-methylheptane; (e) 4,4-dichloro-5-cyclopropyl-1-iodoheptane; (f) *cis*-1,2-dichloro-1-methylcyclohexane. **6.44.** (a) 1-chlorobutane; (b) 1-iodobutane; (c) 4-chloro-2,2-dimethylpentane; (d) 1-bromo-2,2-dimethylpentane; (e) chloromethylcyclohexane; (f) 2-methyl-1-bromopropane. **6.45.** (a) *tert*-butyl chloride; (b) 2-chlorobutane; (c) bromocyclohexane; (d) iodocyclohexane; (e) $PhCHBrCH_3$ (f) 3-bromocyclohexene. **6.48.** (a) rate doubles; (b) rate multiplied by six; (c) rate increases. **6.55.** (a) (*R*)-2-cyanobutane (inversion); (b) (2*S*,3*R*)-3-methyl-2-pentanol (inversion); (c) racemic mixture of 3-ethoxy-2,3-dimethylpentanes (racemization). **6.56.** (a) diethyl ether; (b) $PhCH_2CH_2CN$; (c) $PhSCH_2CH_3$; (d) 1-dodecyne; (e) N-methylpyridinium iodide; (f) $(CH_3)_3CCH_2CH_2NH_2$; (g) tetrahydrofuran; (h) *cis*-4-methylcyclohexanol. **6.58.** (a) o.p. = e.e. = 15.58/15.90 = 98% (99%(*S*) and 1%(*R*); (b) The e.e. of (*S*) decreases twice as fast as radioactive iodide substitutes, thus gives the (*R*) enantiomer; implies the S_N2 mechanism. **6.64.** NBS provides low conc. Br_2 for free-radical bromination. Abstraction of one of the CH_2 hydrogens gives a resonance-stabilized free radical; product $PhCHBrCH_3$.

CHAPTER 7

7.4. (a) two; (b) one; (c) three; (d) four; (e) five. **7.5.** (a) 4-methyl-1-pentene; (b) 2-ethyl-1-hexene; (c) 1,4-pentadiene; (d) 1,2,4-pentatriene; (e) 2,5-dimethyl-1,3-cyclopentadiene; (f) 4-vinylcyclohexene; (g) allylbenzene or 3-phenylpropene; (h) *trans*-3,4-dimethylcyclopentene; (i) 7-methylene-1,3,5-cycloheptatriene; (j) (2*E*,4*Z*)-5,6-dimethylhepta-2,4-diene. **7.6.** (1) (a), (c), (d), and (f) show geometric isomerism. **7.7.** (a) 2,3-dimethyl-2-pentene; (b) 3-ethyl-1,4-hexadiene; (c) 1-methylcyclopentene; (d) give positions of double bonds; (e) specify cis or trans; (f) (*E*) or (*Z*), not *cis*. **7.9.** 2,3-dimethyl-2-butene is more stable by 6.0 kJ/mole. **7.11.** (a) stable; (b) unstable; (c) stable; (d) stable; (e) unstable (maybe stable cold); (f) stable; (g) unstable; (h) stable (i) unstable (maybe stable cold) **7.12.** (a) *cis*-1,2-dibromoethene; (b) *cis* (*trans* has zero dipole moment), (c) 1,2-dichlorocyclohexene. **7.17.** There is no hydrogen *trans* to the bromide leaving group. **7.23.** In the first example the bromines are axial; in the second, equatorial. **7.26.** (a) $\Delta G > 0$, disfavored. (b) $\Delta G < 0$, favored. **7.27.** (a) strong bases and nucleophiles; (b) strong acids and electrophiles; (c) free-radical chain reaction; (d) strong acids and electrophiles. **7.32.** (a) 2-ethyl-1-pentene; (b) 3-ethyl-2-pentene; (c) (3*E*,5*E*)-2,6-dimethyl-1,3,5-octatriene; (d) (*E*)-4-ethyl-3-heptene; (e) 1-cyclohexyl-1,3-cyclohexadiene; (f) (3*Z*,5*E*)-6-chloro-3-(chloromethyl)-1,3,5-octatriene. **7.36.** (b), (c), (e) and (f) show geometric isomerism. **7.38.** (a) cyclopentene; (b) 2-methyl-2-butene (major) and 2-methyl-1-butene (minor); (c) 1-methylcyclohexene (major) and methylenecyclohexane (minor); (d) 1-methylcyclopentene (major), methylenecyclopentane (minor), possibly 3-methylcyclopentene (minor). **7.42.** (a) a 1-halohexane; (b) a *tert*-butyl halide; (c) a 3-halopentane; (d) a halomethylcyclohexane; (e) a 4-halocyclohexane (preferably *cis*). **7.44.** (a) 2-pentene; (b) 1-methylcyclopentene; (c) 1-methylcyclohexene; (d) 2-methyl-2-butene (rearrangement). **7.56.** E1 with rearrangement by an alkyl shift. The Zaitsev product violates Bredt's rule.

CHAPTER 8

8.1. (a) 2-bromopentane; (b) 2-chloro-2-methylpropane; (c) 1-iodo-1-methylcyclohexane; (d) mixture of *cis* and *trans* 1-bromo-3-methyl- and 1-bromo-4-methylcyclohexane. **8.3.** (a) 1-bromo-2-methylcyclopentane; (b) 2-bromo-1-phenylpropane. **8.6.** (a) 1-methylcyclopentanol; (b) 2-phenyl-2-propanol; (c) 1-phenylcyclohexanol. **8.10.** (b) 1-propanol;

(d) 2-methyl-3-pentanol; (f) *trans*-2-methylcyclohexanol. **8.13.** (a) *trans*-2-methylcycloheptanol; (b) mostly 4,4-dimethyl-2-pentanol; (c) —OH *exo* on the less substituted carbon. **8.16.** (a) The carbocation can be attacked from either face. **8.22.** (a) Cl_2/H_2O; (b) KOH/heat, then Cl_2/H_2O; (c) H_2SO_4/heat, then Cl_2/H_2O. **8.28.** (a) CH_2I_2 + Zn(Cu); (b) CH_2Br_2, NaOH, H_2O, PTC; (c) dehydrate (H_2SO_4), then $CHCl_3$, NaOH/H_2O, PTC. **8.34.** (a) *cis*-cyclohexane-1,2-diol; (b) *trans*-cyclohexane-1,2-diol; (c) and (f) (*R,S*)-2,3-pentanediol (+enantiomer); (d) and (e) (*R,R*)-2,3-pentanediol (+enantiomer). **8.35.** (a) OsO_4/H_2O_2; (b) CH_3CO_3H/H_3O^+, (c) CH_3CO_3H/H_3O^+; (d) OsO_4/H_2O_2. **8.59.** (a) 1-methylcyclohexene, RCO_3H/H_3O^+; (b) cyclooctene, OsO_4/H_2O_2; (c) *trans*-cyclodecene, Br_2; (d) cyclohexene, Cl_2/H_2O. **8.62.** $CH_3(CH_2)_{12}CH{=}CH(CH_2)_7CH_3$, cis or trans unknown.

CHAPTER 9

9.3. decomposition to its elements, C and H_2. **9.4.** Treat the mixture with $NaNH_2$ to remove the 1-hexyne. **9.5.** (a) $Na^+ \, ^-C{\equiv}CH$ and NH_3; (b) $Li^+ \, ^-C{\equiv}CH$ and CH_4; (c) no reaction; (d) no reaction; (e) acetylene + $NaOCH_3$; (f) acetylene + NaOH; (g) no reaction; (h) no reaction; (i) NH_3 + $NaOCH_3$. **9.7.** (a) $NaNH_2$; butyl halide; (b) $NaNH_2$; propyl halide; $NaNH_2$; methyl halide. (c) $NaNH_2$; ethyl halide; repeat; (d) S_N2 on *sec*-butyl halide is unfavorable; (e) $NaNH_2$; isobutyl halide (low yield); $NaNH_2$; methyl halide; (f) $NaNH_2$ added for second substitution on 1,8-dibromooctane might attack the halide. **9.8.** (a) sodium acetylide + formaldehyde; (b) sodium acetylide + CH_3I, then $NaNH_2$, then $CH_3CH_2CH_2CHO$; (c) sodium acetylide + $PhCOCH_3$; (d) sodium acetylide + CH_3I, then $NaNH_2$, then $CH_3CH_2COCH_3$. **9.12.** (a) H_2, Lindlar; (b) Na, NH_3; (c) Add halogen, dehydrohalogenate to the alkyne, Na, NH_3; (d) $NaNH_2$, then EtBr, then H_2 with Lindlar. **9.18.** (a) Cl_2; (b) HBr, peroxides; (c) HBr, no peroxides; (d) excess Br_2; (e) reduce to 1-hexene, add HBr; (f) excess HBr. **9.20.** (a) The two ends of the triple bond are equivalent. (b) The two ends of the triple bond are not equivalent, yet not sufficiently different for good selectivity. **9.21.** (a) 2-hexanone; hexanal; (b) mixtures of 2-hexanone and 3-hexanone; (c) 3-hexanone for both; (d) cyclodecanone for both. **9.24.** (a) $CH_3C{\equiv}C(CH_2)_4C{\equiv}CCH_3$ **9.28.** (a) ethylmethylacetylene; (b) phenylacetylene; (c) *sec*-butyl-*n*-propylacetylene; (d) *sec*-butyl-*t*-butylacetylene. **9.38.** 1,3-cyclohexadiene with ($HC{\equiv}C{-}CH{=}CH{-}$) at the 1 position (cis or trans).

CHAPTER 10

10.1. (a) 2-phenyl-2-butanol; (b) (*E*)-5-bromohept-3-en-2-ol; (c) 4-methyl-3-cyclohexen-1-ol; (d) *trans*-2-methylcyclohexanol; (e) (*E*)-2chloro-3-methyl-2-penten-1-ol; (f) (2*R*,3*S*)-2-bromo-3-hexanol. **10.4.** (a) 8,8-dimethyl-2,7-nonanediol; (b) 1,8-octanediol; (c) *cis*-2-cyclohexene-1,4-diol; (d) 3-cyclopentyl-2,4-heptanediol; (e) *trans*-1,3-cyclobutanediol. **10.5.** (a) cyclohexanol; more compact; (b) 4-methylphenol; more compact, stronger H-bonds; (c) 3-ethyl-3-hexanol; more spherical; (d) cyclooctane-1,4-diol; more OH groups per carbon; (e) enantiomers; equal solubility. **10.7.** (a) methanol; less substituted; (b) 2-chloro-1-propanol; chlorine closer to the OH group; (c) 2,2-dichloroethanol; two chlorines to stabilize the alkoxide; (d) 2,2-difluoro-1-propanol; F is more electronegative than Cl, stabilizing the alkoxide. **10.9.** The anions of 2-nitrophenol and 4-nitrophenol (but not 3-nitrophenol) are stabilized by resonance with the nitro group. **10.10.** (a) The phenol (left) is deprotonated by sodium hydroxide; it dissolves. (b) In a separatory funnel, the alcohol (right) will go into an ether layer and the phenolic compound will go into an aqueous sodium hydroxide layer. **10.11.** (b), (f), (g), (h). **10.15.** (a) 3 ways: (i) CH_3CH_2MgBr + $PhCOCH_2CH_2CH_3$; (ii) PhMgBr + $CH_3CH_2COCH_2CH_2CH_3$; (iii) $CH_3CH_2CH_2MgBr$ + $PhCOCH_2CH_3$; (b) PhMgBr + PhCOPh. (c) EtMgBr + cyclopentanone; (d) c-C_5H_9MgBr + 2-pentanone **10.17.** (a) 2 PhMgBr + PhCOCl; (b) 2 CH_3CH_2MgBr + $(CH_3)_2CHCOCl$; (c) 2 *c*-HxMgBr + PhCOCl. **10.19.** (a) PhMgBr + ethylene oxide; (b) $(CH_3)_2CHCH_2MgBr$ + ethylene oxide; (c) 2-methylcyclohexylmagnesium bromide + ethylene oxide. **10.23.** (a) Grignard removes NH proton; (b) Grignard attacks ester; (c) Water will destroy Grignard; (d) Grignard removes OH proton. **10.26.** (a) heptanoic acid + $LiAlH_4$; or heptaldehyde + $NaBH_4$; (b) 2-heptanone + $NaBH_4$; (c) 2-methyl-3-hexanone + $NaBH_4$; (d) ketoester + $NaBH_4$. **10.34.** (a) 1-hexanol, larger surface area; (b) 2-hexanol, hydrogen-bonded; (c) 1,5-hexanediol, two OH groups; (d) 2-hexanol. **10.38.** (a) cyclohexylmethanol; (b) 2-cyclopentyl-2-pentanol; (c) 2-methyl-1-phenyl-1-propanol; (d) methane + 3-hydroxycyclohexanone; (e) cyclopentylmethanol; (f) triphenylmethanol; (g) $Ph_2C(OH)(CH_2)_4OH$ (h) 5-phenyl-5-nonanol; (i) reduction of just the ketone, but not the ester; (j) 3-(2-hydroxyethyl)cyclohexanol from reduction of ketone and ester; (k) the tertiary alcohol from Markovnikov orientation of addition of H—OH; (l) the secondary alcohol from anti-Markovnikov orientation of addition of H—OH; (m) (2*S*,3*S*)-2,3-hexanediol (+enantiomer); (n) (2*S*,3*R*)-2,3-hexanediol (+enantiomer); (o) 1,4-heptadiene. **10.39.** (a) EtMgBr; (b) Grignard with formaldehyde; (c) *c*-HxMgBr; (d) cyclohexylmagnesium bromide with ethylene oxide; (e) PhMgBr with formaldehyde; (f) 2 CH_3MgI; (g) cyclopentylmagnesium bromide.

CHAPTER 11

11.1. (a) oxidation, oxidation; (b) oxidation, oxidation, reduction, oxidation; (c) neither (C2 is oxidation, C3 reduction); (d) reduction; (e) neither; (f) oxidation; (g) neither; (h) neither; (i) oxidation; (j) oxidation then neither (k) reduction then oxidation, no net change; (l) oxidation. **11.6.** (a) PCC; (b) chromic acid; (c) chromic acid or Jones reagent; (d) oxidize, add Grignard; (f) dehydrate, hydroborate, oxidize (chromic acid or Jones reagent). **11.7.** An alcoholic has more alcohol dehydrogenase. More ethanol is needed to tie up this larger amount of enzyme. **11.8.** CH_3COCHO (pyruvaldehyde) and $CH_3COCOOH$ (pyruvic acid). **11.10.** Treat the tosylate with (a) bromide; (b) ammonia; (c) ethoxide; (d) cyanide. **11.14.** (a) chromic acid or Lucas reagent; (b) chromic acid or Lucas reagent; (c) Lucas reagent only; (d) Lucas reagent only; allyl alcohol forms a resonance-stabilized carbocation. (e) Lucas reagent only. **11.19.** (a) thionyl chloride (retention); (b) tosylate (retention), then S_N2 using chloride ion (inversion). **11.20.** resonance-delocalized cation, positive charge spread over two carbons. **11.22.** (a) 2-methyl-2-butene (+2-methyl-1-butene); (b) 2-pentene (+1-pentene); (c) 2-pentene (+1-pentene); (d) *c*-Hx=*C* $(CH_3)_2$(+1-isopropylcyclohexene); (e) 1-methylcyclohexene (+3-methylcyclohexene). **11.25.** Using R—OH and R′—OH will form R—O—R, R′—O—R′, and R—O—R′. **11.31.** (a) $CH_3CH_2CH_2COCl$ + 1-propanol; (b) CH_3CH_2COCl + 1-butanol; (c) $(CH_3)_2CHCOCl$ + *p*-methylphenol; (d) PhCOCl + cyclopropanol. **11.33.** An acidic solution (to protonate the alcohol) would protonate methoxide ion. **11.34.** (a) the alkoxide of cyclohexanol and an ethyl halide or tosylate; (b) dehydration of cyclohexanol. **11.42.** (a) Na, then ethyl bromide; (b) NaOH, then PCC to aldehyde; Grignard, then dehydrate; (c) Mg in ether, then $CH_3CH_2CH_2CHO$, then oxidize; (d) PCC, then EtMgBr. **11.45.** Use CH_3SO_2Cl. **11.46.** (a) thionyl chloride; (b) make tosylate, displace with bromide; (c) make tosylate, displace with hydroxide. **11.52.** Compound A is 2-butanol. **11.59.** **X** is 1-buten-4-ol; **Y** is tetrahydrofuran (5-membered cyclic ether).

CHAPTER 12

12.3. (a) alkene; (b) alkane; (c) terminal alkyne. **12.4.** (a) amine (secondary); (b) acid; (c) alcohol. **12.5.** (a) conjugated ketone; (b) ester; (c) primary amide. **12.6.** (a) 3070 C—H; 1642 C=C *alkene;* (b) 2712, 2814—CHO; 1691 carbonyl-*aldehyde*; (c) over-inflated C—H region —COOH; 1703 carbonyl (maybe conjugated); 1650 C=C (maybe conjugated)-*conjugated acid*; (d) 1742 ester (or strained ketone)-*ester.* **12.7.** (a) bromine (C_6H_5Br); (b) iodine (C_2H_5I); (c) chlorine

(C_4H_7Cl); (d) nitrogen ($C_7H_{17}N$). **12.8.** the isobutyl cation, $(CH_3)_2CHCH_2^+$ **12.11.** 126: loss of water; 111: allylic cleavage; 87: cleavage next to alcohol. **12.14.** (a) about 1660 and 1710; the carbonyl is much stronger; (b) about 1660 for both; the ether is much stronger; (c) about 1660 for both; the imine is much stronger; (d) about 1660 for both; the terminal alkene is stronger. **12.16.** (a) $CH_2{=}C(CH_3)COOH$; (b) $(CH_3)_2CHCOCH_3$; (c) $PhCH_2C{\equiv}N$; (d) $PhCH_2CH_2OH$. **12.17.** (a) 86, 71, 43; (b) 98, 69; (c) 84, 87, 45. **12.20** (a) 1-bromobutane. **12.23** (c) 1-octyne.

CHAPTER 13

13.1. (a) δ2.17; (b) 0.153 gauss; (c) δ2.17; (d) 130 Hz. **13.3.** (a) three; (b) two; (c) three; (d) two; (e) three; (f) five. **13.6.** (a) 2-methyl-3-butyn-2-ol; (b) *p*-dimethoxybenzene; (c) 1,2-dibromo-2-methylpropane. **13.10.** *trans* $CHCl{=}CHCN$. **13.11.** (a) 1-chloropropane; (b) methyl *p*-methylbenzoate, $CH_3C_6H_4COOCH_3$. **13.14.** (a) H^a, δ9.7 (doublet); H^b, δ6.6 (multiplet); H^c, δ7.4 (doublet); (b) J_{ab} = 8 Hz, J_{bc} = 18 Hz (approx). **13.18.** (a) Five; the two hydrogens on C3 are diastereotopic. (b) Six; all the CH_2 groups have diastereotopic hydrogens. (c) Six; three on the Ph, and the CH_2 hydrogens are diastereotopic. (d) Three; The hydrogens cis and trans to the Cl are diastereotopic. **13.21.** (a) butane-1,3-diol; (b) $H_2NCH_2CH_2OH$. **13.24.** (a) $(CH_3)_2CHCOOH$; (b) $PhCH_2CH_2CHO$; (c) $CH_3COCOCH_2CH_3$ (d) $CH_2{=}CHCH(OH)CH_3$; (e) $CH_3CH_2C(OH)(CH_3)CH(CH_3)_2$. **13.29.** (a) allyl alcohol, $H_2C{=}CHCH_2OH$. **13.30.** (a) 4-hydroxybutanoic acid lactone (cyclic ester). **13.31.** (a) cyclohexene. **13.32.** isobutyl bromide. **13.36.** (a) isopropyl alcohol. **13.38.** (a) $PhCH_2CH_2OCOCH_3$. **13.42.** 1,1,2-trichloropropane. **13.45.** **A** is 2-methyl-2-butene (Zaitsev product); **B** is 2-methyl-1-butene. **13.47.** $PhCH_2CN$.

CHAPTER 14

14.2. $(CH_3CH_2)_2O^{+}{-}AlCl_3^{-}$. **14.4.** (a) methoxyethene; methyl vinyl ether; (b) ethyl isopropyl ether; 2-ethoxypropane; (c) 2-chloroethyl methyl ether; 1-chloro-2-methoxyethane; (d) 2-ethoxy-2,3-dimethylpentane; (e) 1,1-dimethoxycyclopentane (f) *trans*-2-methoxycyclohexanol. (g) cyclopropyl methyl ether; methoxycyclopropane; **14.6.** (a) dihydropyran; (b) 2-chloro-1,4-dioxane; (c) 3-isopropylpyran; (d) *trans*-2,3-diethyloxirane or *trans*-3,4-epoxyhexane; (e) 3-bromo-2-ethoxyfuran; (f) 3-bromo-2,2-dimethyloxetane. **14.11.** Intermolecular dehydration of a mixture of methanol and ethanol would produce a mixture of diethyl ether, dimethyl ether, and ethyl methyl ether. **14.13.** Intermolecular dehydration might work for (a). Use the Williamson for (b). Alkoxymercuration is best for (c). **14.15.** (a) bromocyclohexane and ethyl bromide; (b) 1,5-diiodopentane; (c) phenol and methyl bromide; (e) phenol, ethyl bromide, and 1,4-dibromo-2-methylbutane. **14.22.** Epoxidiation of ethylene gives ethylene oxide, and catalytic hydration of ethylene gives ethanol. Acid-catalyzed opening of the epoxide in ethanol gives cellosolve. **14.26.** (a) $CH_3CH_2OCH_2CH_2O^- Na^+$; (b) $H_2NCH_2CH_2O^- Na^+$; (c) $Ph{-}SCH_2CH_2O^- Na^+$; (d) $PhNHCH_2CH_2OH$; (e) $N{\equiv}C{-}CH_2CH_2O^- Na^+$; (f) $N_3CH_2CH_2O^- Na^+$. **14.27.** (a) 2-methyl-1,2-propanediol, ^{18}O at the C2 hydroxyl group; (b) 2-methyl-1,2-propanediol, ^{18}O at the C1 hydroxyl group; (c), (d) same products, (2*S*,3*S*) and mixture. **14.34.** (a) The old ether had autoxidized to form peroxides. On distillation, the peroxides were heated and concentrated, and they detonated. (b) Discard the old ether or treat it to reduce the peroxides. **14.38.** (c) epoxide + PhMgBr; (d) epoxide + $NaOCH_3$ in methanol; (e) epoxide + methanol, H^+. **14.42.** Sodium then ethyl iodide gives retention of configuration. Tosylation gives retention, then the Williamson gives inversion. Second product (+)15.6°. **14.46.** $(CH_3OCH_2CH_2)_2O$ **14.47.** phenyloxirane.

CHAPTER 15

15.1. (a) 2,4-hexadiene < 1,3-hexadiene < 1,4-hexadiene < 1,5-hexadiene < 1,2-hexadiene < 1,3,5-hexatriene; (b) third < fifth < fourth < second < first. **15.8.** (a) **A** is 3,4-dibromo-1-butene; **B** is 1,4-dibromo-2-butene; (c) Hint: **A** is the kinetic product, **B** is the thermodynamic product; (d) Isomerization to an equilibrium mixture. 10% **A** and 90% **B**. **15.9.** (a) 1-(bromomethyl) cyclohexene and 2-bromo-1-methylenecyclohexane. **15.11.** (a) 3-bromocyclopentene; (c) $PhCH_2Br$ **15.12.** Both generate the same allylic carbanion. **15.13.** In this reaction, alkyllithiums or Grignard reagents can be used interchangeably. (a) allyl bromide + phenyllithium (b) isopropyllithium + 1-bromo-2-butene; (c) 1,4-dibromo-2-butene + two equivalents of propyllithium. **15.20.** (b) [4 + 2] cycloaddition of one butadiene with just one of the double bonds of another butadiene. **15.21.** 800. **15.22.** (a) 353 nm; (b) 313 nm; (c) 232 nm; (d) 273 nm; (e) 292 nm. **15.24.** (a) isolated; (b) conjugated; (c) cumulated; (d) conjugated; (e) conjugated; (f) cumulated and conjugated. **15.25.** (a) allylcyclohexane; (b) 3-chlorocyclopentene; (c) 3-bromo-2-methylpropene; (e) 4-bromo-2-buten-1-ol and 1-bromo-3-buten-2-ol; (f) 5,6-dibromo-1,3-hexadiene, 1,6-dibromo-2,4-hexadiene, and 3,6-dibromo-1, 4-hexadiene (minor); (g) 1-(methoxymethyl)-2-methylcyclopentene and 1-methoxy-1-methyl-2-methylenecyclopentane; (h) and (i) Diels–Alder adducts. **15.26.** (a) allyl bromide + isobutyl Grignard; (b) 1-bromo-3-methyl-2-butene + $CH_3CH_2C(CH_3)_2MgBr$; (c) cyclopentyl-MgBr + 1-bromo-2-pentene. **15.28.** (a) 19,000; (b) second structure. **15.32.** (a) The product isomerized, 1630 suggests conjugated; (b) 2-propyl-1,3-cyclohexadiene.

CHAPTER 16

16.2. (a) +31.8 kJ/mole; (b) −88.6 kJ/mole; (c) −112.0 kJ/mole. **16.5.** Two of the eight pi electrons are unpaired in two non-bonding orbitals, an unstable configuration. **16.7.** (a) nonaromatic (internal H's prevent planarity); (b) nonaromatic (one ring atom has no *p* orbital); (c) aromatic, [14]annulene; (d) aromatic (in the outer system). **16.8.** Azulene is aromatic, but the other two are antiaromatic. **16.10.** The cation (cyclopropenium ion) is aromatic; the anion is antiaromatic. **16.12.** (a) antiaromatic if planar; (b) aromatic if planar; (c) aromatic if planar; (d) antiaromatic if planar; (e) nonaromatic; (f) aromatic if planar. **16.14.** cyclopropenium fluoroborate. **16.19.** (a) aromatic; (b) aromatic; (c) nonaromatic; (d) aromatic; (e) aromatic; (f) nonaromatic; (g) aromatic. **16.24.** (a) fluorobenzene; (b) 4-phenyl-1-butyne; (c) 3-methyl-phenol or *m*-cresol; (d) *o*-nitrostyrene; (e) *p*-bromobenzoic acid; (f) isopropyl phenyl ether; (g) 3,4-dinitrophenol; (h) benzyl ethyl ether. **16.25.** 3-phenyl-2-propen-1-ol **16.28.** (a) *o*-dichlorobenzene; (b) *p*-nitroanisole; (c) 2,3-dibromobenzoic acid; (d) 2,7-dimethoxynaphthalene; (e) *m*-chlorobenzoic acid; (f) 2,4,6-trichlorophenol; (g) 2-*sec*-butylbenzaldehyde; (h) cyclopropenium fluoroborate. **16.30.** The second is deprotonated to an aromatic cyclopentadienyl anion. **16.31.** (d), (e) The fourth structure, with two three-membered rings, was considered the most likely and was called Ladenburg benzene. **16.37.** (a) three; (b) one; (c) *meta*-dibromobenzene. **16.38.** (a) α-chloroacetophenone; (b) 4-bromo-1-ethylbenzene. **16.45.** 2-isopropyl-5-methylphenol.

CHAPTER 17

17.4. The sigma complex for *p*-xylene has the + charge on two 2° carbons and one 3° carbon, compared with three 2° carbons in benzene. **17.10.** Bromine *adds* to the alkene but *substitutes* on the aryl ether, evolving gaseous HBr. **17.11.** Strong acid is used for nitration, and the amino group of aniline is protonated to a deactivating $-NH_3^+$ group. **17.13.** 1-Bromo-1-chlorocyclohexane; the intermediate cation is stabilized by a bromonium ion resonance form. **17.14.** (a) 2,4- and 2,6-

dinitrotoluene; (b) 3-chloro-4-nitrotoluene and 5-chloro-2-nitrotoluene; (c) 3- and 5-nitro-2-bromobenzoic acid; (d) 4-methoxy-3-nitrobenzoic acid; (e) 5-methyl-2-nitrophenol and 3-methyl-4-nitrophenol. **17.17.** (a) phenylcyclohexane; (b) *o*- and *p*-methylanisole, with overalkylation products; (c) 1-isopropyl-4-(1,1,2-trimethylpropyl)benzene. **17.18.** (a) phenylcyclohexane; (b) *tert*-butylbenzene; (c) *p*-di-*tert*-butylbenzene; (d) *o*- and *p*-isopropyl toluene. **17.19.** (a) *tert*-butylbenzene; (b) 2- and 4-*sec*-butyltoluene; (c) no reaction; (d) (1,1,2-trimethylpropyl)benzene. **17.20.** (a) *sec*-butylbenzene and others; (b) OK; (c) +disub, trisub; (d) No, deactivated; (e) OK. **17.22.** (a) $(CH_3)_2CHCH_2COCl$, benzene, $AlCl_3$; (b) $(CH_3)_3CCOCl$, benzene, $AlCl_3$; (c) PhCOCl, benzene, $AlCl_3$; (d) CO/HCl, $AlCl_3$/CuCl, anisole; (f) Clemmensen on (b); (g) $CH_3(CH_2)_2COCl$, benzene, $AlCl_3$ then Clemmensen. **17.23.** Fluoride leaves in a fast exothermic step; the C—F bond is only slightly weakened in the reactant-like transition state (Hammond postulate). **17.25.** (a) 2,4-dinitroanisole; (b) 2,4- and 3,5-dimethylphenol; (c) N-methyl-4-nitroaniline; (d) 2,4-dinitrophenylhydrazine. **17.29.** (a) (trichloromethyl) hexachlorocyclohexane; (c) *cis*- and *trans*-1,2- dimethylcyclohexane; (d) 1,4-dimethyl-1,4-cyclohexadiene. **17.30.** (a) benzoic acid; (b) terephthalic acid (benzene-1,4-dicarboxylic acid); (c) phthalic acid (benzene-1,2-dicarboxylic acid). **17.33.** 60% beta, 40% alpha; reactivity ratio = 1.9 to 1. **17.36.** (a) 1-bromo-1-phenylpropane. **17.38.** (a) HBr, then Grignard with ethylene oxide; (b) CH_3COCl and $AlCl_3$, then Clemmensen, Br_2 and light, then $^{-}OCH_3$; (c) nitrate, then Br_2 and light, then NaCN. **17.40.** (a) 3-ethoxytoluene; (b) *m*-tolyl acetate; (c) 2,4,6-tribromo-3-methylphenol; (d) 2,4,6-tribromo-3-(tribromomethyl)phenol; (e) 2-methyl-1,4-benzoquinone; (f) 2,4-di-*tert*-butyl-3-methyl-phenol. **17.50.** indanone **17.55.** The yellow species is the triphenylmethyl cation. **17.60.** kinetic control at 0°, thermodynamic control at 100°.

CHAPTER 18

18.1. (a) 5-hydroxy-3-hexanone; ethyl β-hydroxypropyl ketone; (b) 3-phenylbutanal: β-phenylbutyraldehyde; (c) *trans*-2-methoxycyclohexanecarbaldehyde; (d) 6,6-dimethyl-2,4-cyclohexadienone. **18.2.** (a) 2-phenylpropanal; (b) acetophenone. **18.3.** No γ-hydrogens. **18.5.** (a) <200, 280; (b) 230, 310; (c) 280, 360; (d) 270, 350. **18.9.** (a) 3-heptanone; (b) phenylacetonitrile; (c) benzyl cyclopentyl ketone. **18.11.** (a) benzyl alcohol; (b) benzaldehyde; (c) 1-hepten-3-one. (d) 3-butyl-1,4-pentadien-3-ol; **18.14.** $[(CH_3)_3P—R]^+$ could lose a proton from a CH_3. **18.17.** (a) Wittig of $PhCH_2Br$ + acetone; (b) Wittig of CH_3I + $PhCOCH_3$; (c) Wittig of $PhCH_2Br$ + PhCH=CHCHO; (d) Wittig of EtBr + cyclohexanone. **18.19.** second < fourth < first < third. **18.23.** *Z* and *E* isomers. **18.24.** (a) cyclohexanone and methylamine; (b) 2-butanone and ammonia; (c) acetaldehyde and aniline; (d) 6-amino-2-hexanone. **18.28.** (a) benzaldehyde and semicarbazide; (b) camphor and hydroxylamine; (c) tetralone and phenylhydrazine; (d) cyclohexanone and 2,4-DNP; (e) 4-(*o*-aminophenyl)-2-butanone. **18.31.** (a) tetralone and ethanol; (b) acetaldehyde and 2-propanol; (c) hexane-2, 4-dione and ethanediol; (d) tetralone and 1,3-propanediol; (e) 5-hydroxypentanal and cyclohexanol; (f) $(HOCH_2CH_2CH_2)_2CHCHO$. **18.35.** (a) 4-hydroxycyclohexanecarboxylic acid; (b) 4-oxocyclohexanecarboxylic acid; (c) 3-oxocyclohexanecarboxylic acid; (d) *cis*-3,4-dihydroxycyclohexanecarboxylic acid. **18.37.** (a) indane; (b) hexane; (c) ethylene ketal of 2-propylcyclohexanone; (d) propylcyclohexane. **18.42.** 240 nm and 300–320 nm. **18.43.** 2,5-hexanedione **18.44.** 1-phenyl-2-butanone (benzyl ethyl ketone). **18.47.** cyclobutanone **18.52.** (all H^+ cat.) (a) cyclobutanone and hydroxylamine; (b) benzaldehyde and cyclopentylamine; (c) benzylamine and cyclopentanone; (d) β-tetralone and ethylene glycol; (e) cyclohexylamine and acetone; (f) cyclopentanone and methanol. **18.57.** (a) $NaBD_4$, then H_2O; (b) $NaBD_4$, then D_2O; (c) $NaBH_4$, then D_2O. **18.60.** (a) $CH_3CH_2CH_2COCl$ and $AlCl_3$, then Clemmensen; (b) EtMgBr, then H_3O^+; (c) $Cl_2/FeCl_3$, then Dow process to phenol; NaOH, CH_3I, then Gatterman; (d) oxidize to the acid, $SOCl_2$, then $AlCl_3$. **18.64.** (a) 3-hexanone; (b) 2- and 3-hexanone; (c) 2-hexanone; (d) cyclodecanone; (e) 2- and 3-methylcyclodecanone. **18.66.** **A** is 2-heptanone. **18.72.** (b) The "THP ether" is an acetal, stable to base but hydrolyzed by acid. **18.73.** **A** is the ethylene ketal of 2-butanone; **B** is 2-butanone. **18.74.** *trans*-2-butenal (crotonaldehyde).

CHAPTER 19

19.1. Pyridine, 2-methylpyridine, pyrimidine, pyrrole, imidazole, indole, and purine are aromatic. **19.3.** (a) 2-pentanamine; (b) N-methyl-2-butanamine; (c) *m*-aminophenol; (d) 3-methylpyrrole; (e) *trans*-1,2-cyclopentanediamine; (f) *cis*-3-aminocyclohexanecarbaldehyde. **19.4.** (a) resolvable (chiral carbons); (b) not resolvable (N inverts); (c) symmetric; (d) not resolvable; proton on N is removable; (e) resolvable (chiral quat. salt). **19.6.** (a) aniline < ammonia < methylamine < NaOH; (b) *p*-nitroaniline < aniline < *p*-methylaniline; (c) pyrrole < aniline < pyridine < piperidine; (d) 3-nitropyrrole < pyrrole < imidazole. **19.7.** (a) secondary amine; (b) primary amine; (c) alcohol. **19.8.** isobutylamine **19.9.** (a) piperidine; (b) diethylmethylamine; (c) propanal; (d) 1-propanol. **19.16.** (a) benzylamine + excess CH_3I; (b) 1-bromopentane + excess NH_3; (c) benzyl bromide + excess NH_3. **19.17.** (a) $CH_3CONHCH_2CH_3$; (b) $PhCON(CH_3)_2$; (c) N-hexanoyl piperidine. **19.23.** (a) cyclohexanediazonium chloride (then cyclohexanol and cyclohexene); (b) N-nitroso-N-ethyl-2-hexanamine; (c) N-nitrosopiperidine; (d) benzenediazonium chloride. **19.25.** (a) diazotize, then HBF_4, heat; (b) diazotize, then CuCl; (c) protect (CH_3COCl), then 3 $CH_3I/AlCl_3$, H_3O^+, diazotize, H_3PO_2; (d) diazotize, then CuBr; (e) diazotize, then KI; (f) diazotize, then CuCN; (g) diazotize, then H_2SO_4, H_2O, heat; (h) diazotize, then couple with resorcinol. **19.26.** (a) CH_3NH_2, $Na(AcO)_3BH$; (b) PhCHO, $Na(AcO)_3BH$; (c) aniline/H^+, then $LiAlH_4$; (d) H_2NOH/H^+, then $LiAlH_4$; (e) H_2NOH/H^+ then $LiAlH_4$; (f) piperidine + cyclopentanone + $Na(AcO)_3BH$. **19.31.** (a) nitrate, reduce; (b) brominate, then nitrate and reduce; (c) nitrate, then brominate and reduce; (d) oxidize toluene, then nitrate and reduce. **19.33.** Hofmann rearrangement goes with retention of configuration. **19.38.** only (b), (d), (f), and (h). **19.40.** (a) 2-phenylethylamine; (b) 1,4-butanediamine; (c) *trans*-2-phenylcyclopropanamine. **19.53.** (a) triethylamine; (b) An acid converts it to a solid ammonium salt. (c) Rinse the clothes with diluted vinegar (acetic acid). **19.56.** **A** is 2-butanamine; **B** is diethylamine. **19.58.** 2,2-dimethyl-1-propanamine.

CHAPTER 20

20.2. (a) 2-iodo-3-methylpentanoic acid; α-iodo-β-methylvaleric acid; (b) (*Z*)-3,4-dimethyl-3-hexenoic acid; (c) 2,3-dinitrobenzoic acid; (d) *trans*-1,2-cyclohexanedicarboxylic acid; (e) 2-chlorobenzene-1,4-dicarboxylic acid; 2-chloroterephthalic acid; (f) 3-methylhexanedioic acid; β-methyladipic acid. **20.3.** (a) first, second, third; (b) third, second, first; (c) third, second, fourth, first. **20.7.** Broad acid OH centered around 3000; conjugated carbonyl about 1690; C=C about 1650. **20.8.** (a) propanoic acid; (b) —CHO proton triplet between $\delta 9$ and $\delta 10$. **20.11.** (a) $KMnO_4$ (b) $KMnO_4$; (c) PhMgBr + ethylene oxide, oxidize; (d) PBr_3, Grignard, CO_2; (e) conc. $KMnO_4$, heat; (f) KCN, then H_3O^+. **20.15.** (a) methanol and salicylic acid, H^+; methanol solvent, dehydrating agent; (b) methanol and formic acid, H^+, distill product as it forms; (c) ethanol and phenylacetic acid, H^+, ethanol solvent, dehydrating agent. **20.16.** (a) see Fischer esterification; (b) $C—^{18}O—CH_3$; (c) mass spectrometry. **20.19.** (a) phenylacetic acid and $LiAlH_4$; (b) phenylacetic acid and $LiAlH_4$, then PCC; (c) 3-oxocyclopentanecarboxylic acid + B_2H_6, then H_3O^+. **20.21.** (a) benzene + CH_3CH_2COCl, $AlCl_3$; or propionic acid + 2 PhLi, then H_3O^+; (b) Add 2 CH_3Li, then H_3O^+. **20.36.** (a) Grignard + CO_2; or KCN, then H_3O^+; (b) conc. $KMnO_4$, heat; (c) Ag^+; (d) $SOCl_2$, then $Li(t\text{-}BuO)_3AlH$; or $LiAlH_4$, then PCC; (e) CH_3OH, H^+; or CH_2N_2; (f) $LiAlH_4$ or B_2H_6; (g) $SOCl_2$, then excess CH_3NH_2.

20.38. diastereomers **20.40.** (a) 2-phenylpropanoic acid; (b) 2-methylpropenoic acid; (c) *trans*-2-hexenoic acid. **20.45.** (a) stockroom; heptaldehyde; students; heptanoic acid; (b) air oxidation; (c) prepare fresh samples immediately before using. **20.50.** phenoxyacetic acid

CHAPTER 21

21.2. No aldehyde C—H at 2700 and 2800; no acid O—H centered at 3000. **21.4.** (a) acid chloride C=O at 1810; (b) primary amide $H_2C{=}CHCONH_2$ at 1640, two N—H around 3300; (c) anhydride C=O double absorption at 1740 and 1810. **21.5.** (a) acrylamide, (b) 5-hydroxyhexanoic acid lactone. **21.8.** (a) ethanol, propionyl chloride; (b) phenol, 3-methylhexanoyl chloride; (c) benzyl alcohol, benzoyl chloride; (d) cyclopropanol, cyclohexanecarbonyl chloride; (e) *t*-butyl alcohol, acetyl chloride; (f) allyl alcohol, succinoyl chloride. **21.9.** (a) dimethylamine, acetyl chloride; (b) aniline, acetyl chloride; (c) ammonia, cyclohexanecarbonyl chloride; (d) piperidine, benzoyl chloride. **21.10.** (i) $PhCH_2OH$; (ii) Et_2NH. **21.25.** (a) 1-butanamine; (b) cyclohexylethylamine; (c) $(CH_2)_6NH$ (7-membered ring); (d) morpholine; (e) cyclohexylmethylpropylamine. **21.30.** (a) benzene + acetyl chloride; (b) benzene + benzoyl chloride; (c) benzene + butyryl chloride, then Clemmensen. **21.32.** (a) *n*-octyl alcohol, acetic formic anhydride (formyl chloride is unavailable); (b) *n*-octyl alcohol, acetic anhydride (cheap, easy to use); (c) phthalic anhydride, ammonia (anhydride forms monoamide); (d) succinic anhydride, methanol (annhydride forms monoester). **21.34.** (a) acetic anhydride; (b) methanol, H^+; (c) $LiAlH_4$, then protonate; (d) $PhNH_2$, warm. **21.37.** (a) $SOCl_2$, then $HN(CH_3)_2$, then $LiAlH_4$; (b) acetic anhydride, then $LiAlH_4$. **21.38.** (a) $SOCl_2$, then NH_3, then $POCl_3$; (b) $LiAlH_4$, make tosylate, NaCN; (c) Fe/HCl, diazotize, CuCN. **21.45.** (a) ethyl benzoate; (b) acetic benzoic anhydride; (c) PhCONHPh; (d) 4-methoxybenzophenone; (e) Ph_3COH; (f) benzaldehyde. **21.48.** (a) acetic formic anhydride; (b) $SOCl_2$, then CH_3COONa; (c) oxalyl chloride; (d) H^+ and heat to form anhydride, then one equivalent of $(CH_3)_2CHOH$; (e) oxidize aldehyde with Ag^+, then form lactone with H^+; (f) $NaBH_4$ to reduce aldehyde, then H^+ to form lactone. **21.51.** (after H^+) (a) HCOOH + PhOH; (b) $CH_3CH_2COOH + CH_3CH_2OH$; (c) 3-(*o*-hydroxyphenyl)-propanoic acid; (d) $(CH_2OH)_2$ + $(COOH)_2$ **21.55.** (a) Ph_3COH; (b) 3 EtMgBr + EtCOOEt, then H_3O^+. **21.58.** (a) diisopropyl carbonate; (b) $PhNHCOOCH_3$; (c) $(CH_3)_3COH$. **21.59.** A is hexanenitrile; B is hexanamide. **21.62.** Acetic anhydride; add water to hydrolyze it to dilute acetic acid. **21.64.** $CH_3CH_2OCOCH_2CN$ **21.65.** ethyl crotonate. **21.67.** δ-valerolactam

CHAPTER 22

22.8. (a) $PhC(NCH_3)CH_3$; (b) $CH_2{=}C(Ph)NMe_2$; (c) cyclohexanone phenyl imine; (d) piperidine enamine of cyclohexanone. **22.9.** (a) enamine + allyl bromide; (b) enamine + $PhCH_2Br$; (c) enamine + PhCOCl. **22.13.** (a), (b) cyclopentanecarboxylate and chloroform/iodoform; (c) $PhCOCBr_2CH_3$. **22.19.** (a) 3-hydroxy-2-methylpentanal; (b) 3-hydroxy-2,4-diphenylbutanal. **22.20.** retro-aldol, reverse of aldol condensation. **22.24.** (a) 2-ethyl-2- hexenal; (b) 1,3-diphenyl-2-buten-1-one; (c) 2-cyclohexylidenecyclohexanone. **22.26.** PhCH=CHCOCH=CHPh, "dibenzalacetone". **22.28.** (a) 2-methyl-3,3-diphenyl-2-propenal; (b) 4,4-dimethyl-1-phenyl-2-penten-1-one. **22.29.** benzaldehyde and acetaldehyde. **22.32.** (a) butanal and pentanal (no); (b) two $PhCOCH_2CH_3$ (yes); (c) acetone and PhCHO (yes); (d) 6-oxoheptanal (yes, but also attack by enolate of aldehyde); (e) nonane-2,8-dione (yes). **22.34.** (a) transesterification to a mixture of methyl and ethyl esters; (b) saponification. **22.35.** no second alpha proton to form the final enolate to drive the reaction to completion. **22.36.** (a) methyl 2-methyl-3-oxopentanoate; (b) ethyl 2,4-diphenyl-3-oxobutanoate. **22.37.** methyl 2-benzyl-5-phenyl-3-oxopentanoate **22.38.** (a) ethyl butyrate; (b) methyl phenylacetate; (c) ethyl 3-methylbutanoate, or common name: ethyl isovalerate. **22.42.** (a) PhCO—$CH(Ph)COOCH_3$; (b) poor choice, four products; (c) EtOCOCO—CH_2COOEt; (d) $EtOCOCH(CH_3)COOEt$. **22.43.** (a) PhCOOEt + CH_3CH_2COOEt; (b) $PhCH_2COOMe$ + MeOCOCOOMe; (c) $(EtO)_2C{=}O$ + $PhCH_2COOEt$; (d) $(CH_3)_3CCOOMe + CH_3(CH_2)_3COOMe$. **22.47.** Alkylate malonic ester with; (a) $PhCH_2Br$; (b) CH_3I twice; (c) $PhCH_2CH_2Br$; (d) $Br(CH_2)_4Br$ (twice). **22.49.** (a) 4-phenyl-2-butanone; (b) cyclobutyl methyl ketone; (c) cyclopentanone. **22.50.** Alkylate acetoacetic ester with; (a) $PhCH_2Br$; (b) $Br(CH_2)_4Br$ (twice); (c) $PhCH_2Br$, then $CH_2{=}CHCH_2Br$ **2.53.** Alkylate the enamine of cyclohexanone with MVK. **22.56.** (a) malonic ester anion + ethyl cinnamate; (b) acetoacetic ester anion + acrylonitrile, then H_3O^+ (c) enamine of cyclopentanone + acrylonitrile, then H_3O^+; (d) enamine of 2-methylcyclopentanone +$PhCOCH{=}CH_2$, then H_3O^+; (e) alkylate acetoacetic ester with CH_3I, then MVK, then H_3O^+; (f) cyclopentanone + $(CH_2{=}CH)_2CuLi$. **22.62.** (1) $g < b < f < a < e < c < d$; (2) a, c, d, e. **22.70.** Alkylate with: (a) $PhCH_2Br$; (b) CH_3CH_2Br, then (bromomethyl) cyclopentane; (c) $Br(CH_2)_5Br$, alkylate on each end to make a cyclohexane ring. **22.71.** Alkylate with: (a) CH_3CH_2Br, then $PhCH_2Br$; (b) $Br(CH_2)_4Br$; (c) MVK (hydrolysis, decarboxylation, then Aldol gives product). **22.75.** (a) Dieckmann of dimethyl adipate, alkylation by allyl bromide, hydrolysis and decarboxylation; (c) Robinson with $CH_3CH{=}CHCOCH_3$, then reduction; (d) form enamine or enolate, acylate with ClCOOEt, methylate with CH_3I, do aldol with benzaldehyde. **22.77.** (a) EtCOPh + MVK; (b) cyclohexanone and ethyl vinyl ketone; (c) cyclohexanone and $(CH_3)_2C{=}CHCOCH_3$.

CHAPTER 23

23.2. (a) two C*, two pairs of enantiomers; (b) one C*, one pair of enantiomers; (c) four C*, eight pairs of enantiomers; three C*, four pairs of enantiomers. **23.5.** (*R*) for D series, (*S*) for L series. **23.15.** 28% alpha, 72% beta. **23.19.** Galactitol is symmetrical (meso) and achiral. **23.20.** L-gulose has the same structure as D-glucose, but with the CHO and CH_2OH ends interchanged. **23.21.** (a) D-mannonic acid; (b) D-galactonic acid; (c) Br_2 does not oxidize ketoses. **23.22.** (a) D-mannaric acid; (b) D-galactaric acid. **23.23.** **A** is galactose; **B** is glucose. **23.24.** (a) non-reducing; (b) reducing; (c) reducing; (d) non-reducing; (e) reducing; (f) "sucrose" is nonreducing; should have "-oside" ending. **23.27.** glucose, benzaldehyde, and HCN (toxic). **23.38.** **A** = D-galactose; **B** = D-talose; **C** = D-lyxose; **D** = D-threose **23.39.** **E** = D-ribose; **F** = D-erythrose. **23.44.** reducing and mutarotating. **23.45.** reducing and mutarotating. **23.46.** Trehalose is α-D-glucopyranosyl-α-D-glucopyranoside. **23.47.** Melibiose is 6-O-(6-O-(α-D-galactopyranosyl)-D-glucopyranose. **23.58.** (a) D-ribose; (b) D-altrose; (c) L-erythrose; (d) L-galactose; (e) L-idose. **23.65.** (a) D-arabinose and D-lyxose; (b) D-threose; (c) **X** = D-galactose (d) No; the optically active hexose is degraded to an optically active pentose that is oxidized to an optically active aldaric acid; (e) D-threose gives an optically active aldaric acid. **23.66.** (a) D-tagatose is a ketohexose, the C4 epimer of D-fructose. (b) A pyranose with the anomeric carbon (C2) bonded to the oxygen atom of C6. **23.67.** D-altrose **23.71.** (a) no; (b) yes; (c) Only applies to double stranded DNA.

CHAPTER 24

24.6. As in pyrrole, the lone pair on the indole N is part of the aromatic sextet. One N in histidine is like that in pyridine, with the lone pair in an sp^2 hybrid orbital. **24.9.** Reductive amination of (a) $CH_3COCOOH$; (b) $(CH_3)_2CHCH_2COCOOH$; (c) $HOCH_2COCOOH$; (d) $H_2NCOCH_2CH_2COCOOH$. **24.10.** Start with (a) CH_3COOH; (b) $(CH_3)_2CHCH_2CH_2COOH$; (c) $HOOCCH_2CH_2CH_2COOH$. **24.11.** N-phthalimidomalonic ester and (a) $(CH_3)_2CHBr$; (b) $PhCH_2Br$; (c) $BrCH_2CH_2COO^-$; (d) $(CH_3)_2CHCH_2Br$. **24.15.** The free amino group of the deacylated L enantiomer should become protonated (and soluble) in dilute acid. **24.23.** (a) nucleophilic aromatic substitution; (b) Edman cleaves only the N-terminal amino acid, leaving the rest of the chain intact for further degradation. **24.25.** Cys-Tyr-Phe-Gln-Asn-Cys-Pro-Arg-Gly · NH_2. **24.27.** Add ethyl chloroformate, then Gly, ethyl chloroformate, then Leu. Deprotect using H_2 and Pd. **24.30.** Add TFA (CF_3COOH), then Boc-Gly and DCC, then TFA, then Boc-Leu and DCC, then HF. **24.34.** (a) Ruhemann's purple; (b) alanine; (c) $CH_3CONH(CH_2)_4CH(COOH)$ $NHCOCH_3$; (d) L-proline and N-acetyl-D-proline; (e) $CH_3CH_2CH(CH_3)$ $CH(NH_2)CN$; (f) isoleucine; (g) 2-bromo-4-methylpentanoic acid (after water workup); (h) 2-amino-4-methylpentanoic acid or leucine. **24.35.** (a) $NH_3/H_2/Pd$; (b) Br_2/PBr_3, H_2O, excess NH_3; (c) $NH_3/HCN/H_2O$, H_3O^+; (d) Gabriel-malonic ester synthesis. **24.37.** Convert the alcohol to a tosylate and displace with excess ammonia. **24.42.** aspartylphenylalanine methyl ester. **24.43.** Phe-Ala-Gly-Met-Ala. **24.46.** (a) C-terminal amide ($CONH_2$), or amide (Gln) of Glu; (b) The N-terminal Glu is a cyclic amide (a "pyroglutamyl" group) that effectively blocks the N-terminus. The C-terminal Pro is an amide; (c) cyclic pentapeptide. **24.49.** Ornithine is $H_2N(CH_2)_3CH(NH_2)COOH$, a homolog of lysine, with a similar IEP. **24.51.** Ala-Lys-Phe-Gln-Gly-Tyr-Arg-Ser-Leu-Ile.

CHAPTER 25

25.2. Hydrogenation of trilinolein (m.p. below −4 °C) gives tristearin (m.p. 72 °C). **25.9.** Estradiol is a phenol, soluble in aqueous sodium hydroxide. **25.13.** (1) sesquiterpene; (2) monoterpene; (3) monoterpene; (4) sesquiterpene. **25.15.** (a) a triglyceride (a fat); (b) an alkyl sulfate detergent; (c) a wax; (d) a sesquiterpene; (e) a prostaglandin; (f) a steroid. **25.17.** (a) H_2/Ni, $LiAlH_4$; (b) H_2/Ni; (c) stearic acid from (b), add $SOCl_2$, then l-octadecanol (a); (d) O_3, then $(CH_3)_2S$; (e) $KMnO_4$, then H^+; (f) Br_2/PBr_3, then H_2O. **25.19.** reduce ($LiAlH_4$), esterify with sulfuric acid. **25.21.** (a) Sodium stearate precipitates in dilute acid or Ca^{2+}; (b) Paraffin "wax" does not saponify; (c) Myristic acid shows acidic properties when treated with base; (d) Trolein decolorizes Br_2 in CCl_4. **25.28.** Petroselenic acid is *cis*-6-octadecenoic acid.

CHAPTER 26

26.1. The radical intermediates would not be benzylic if they added with the other orientation. **26.3.** The benzylic hydrogens are more likely to be abstracted. **26.4.** They all add to give the more highly substituted carbocation. **26.5.** (a) is possible; (b) is very good; (c) is terrible. **26.6.** The cation at the end of a chain abstracts hydride from a benzylic position in the middle of a chain. In isobutylene, a tertiary cation would have to abstract a hydride from a secondary position: unlikely. **26.15.** The third hydroxyl group of glycerol allows for profuse cross-linking of the chains (with a terephthalic acid linking two of these hydroxyl groups), giving a very rigid polyester. **26.19.** Glycerol allows profuse cross-linking, as in Problem 26-15. **26.23.** (a) a polyurethane; (b) condensation polymer; (c) $HO(CH_2)_3NH_2$ and CO_2. **26.24.** (a) a polyester; (b) condensation polymer; (c) dimethyl terephthalate and 1,4-butanediol; transesterification. **26.25.** (a) a polyurea; (b) condensation polymer; (c) $H_2N(CH_2)_9NH_2$ and CO_2. **26.26.** (a) polyether (addition polymer); (b) ethylene oxide; (c) base catalyst. **26.27.** (a) addition polymer; a synthetic rubber; (b) 2-chloro-1,3-butadiene ("chloroprene"). **26.28.** (a) $-CH_2-O-[CH_2-O]-$; (c) addition polymer. **26.31.** (b) and (c) No to both. Poly(vinyl acetate) is an addition polymer. The ester bonds are not in the main polymer chain; (d) Vinyl alcohol (the enol form of acetaldehyde) is not stable.

PHOTO CREDITS

page 1:	ABIOMED/Getty Images/Newscom
page 2 (1):	suebee65/iStockphoto
page 2 (2):	S. Solum/Getty Images, Inc./PhotoDisc
page 2 (3):	David T. Roberts/Nature's Images/Photo Researchers, Inc.
page 2 (4):	Dorling Kindersley
page 68:	Jerry Mason/Science Photo Library/Photo Researchers, Inc.
page 91:	AP Wide World Photos
page 93:	Alamo Area Council of Governments
page 94 (top):	Peter Jordan/Alamy
page 94 (bottom):	Ifm-Geomar Leibniz Institute of Marine Sciences located at Kiel (Germany).
page 95:	AP Wide World Photos
page 207 (top):	David Parker/Science Photo Library/Photo Researchers, Inc.
page 207 (bottom):	Roger Viollet/Getty Images, Inc/Liaison
page 219:	Corbis/Bettmann
page 311:	Kellogg Brown & Root Inc.
page 345:	Tom Bochsler/Pearson Education/PH College
page 350:	Parr Instrument Company
page 391:	John Blaustein/John Blaustein Photography
page 392:	Eric Lawton/Shutterstock
page 429:	AP Wide World Photos
page 455:	Marty Cordano/DRK Photo
page 469:	AP Wide World Photos
page 495:	Science Photo Library/Photo Researchers, Inc.
page 497:	Richard Megna/Fundamental Photographs, NYC
page 541:	Kratos Analytical Inc.
page 567:	Varian, Inc.
page 612 (left):	Simon Fraser/Science Photo Library/Photo Researchers, Inc.
page 612 (right):	Lunagraphix/Photo Researchers, Inc.
page 626:	Warren Anatomical Museum, Countway Library of Medicine, Harvard Medical School
page 655:	Jim Sugar Photography/Corbis/Bettmann
page 694:	NASA/JPL/University of Colorado
page 697:	Pavel Chelko/Shutterstock
page 708:	Stamp from the private collection of Professor C.M. Lang, photography by Gary J. Shulfer, University of Wisconsin, Stevens Point. "1966, Belgium (Scott #624)"; Scott Standard Postage Stamp Catalogue, Scott Pub. Co., Sidney, Ohio.
page 730:	Edmond Van Hoorick/Getty Images, Inc./PhotoDisc
page 795:	Thomas Eisner and Daniel Aneshansley/Thomas Eisner and Daniel Aneshansley, Cornell University.
page 841:	Thomas Eisner, Cornell University
page 854:	Richard Megna/Fundamental Photograph
page 884:	SuperStock, Inc.
page 956:	OSF/Fogden, M/Animals Animals/Earth Scenes
page 1019:	Richard Reid/Animals Animals/Earth Scenes
page 1023:	Ian Kimber
page 1024:	NASA/Langley Research Center
page 1027:	Ted Horowitz/Corbis/Stock Market
page 1032:	Lya Cattel/iStockphoto
page 1085:	Science Photo Library/Photo Researchers, Inc.
page 1134:	Andy Sacks/Getty Images Inc./Stone Allstock
page 1137:	Judy Davidson/Science Photo Library/Photo Researchers, Inc.
page 1138:	Institut Pasteur/CNRI/Phototake NYC
page 1145:	Dr. Gopal Murti/Phototake NYC
page 1189:	Chris Thomaidis/Getty Images Inc./Stone Allstock
page 1190:	James King-Holmes/OCMS/Science Photo Library/Photo Researchers, Inc.
page 1191:	Silver Burdett Ginn
page 1192 (top):	Michael Abbey/Photo Researchers, Inc.
page 1192 (bottom):	Ralph C. Eagle, Jr., M.D./Photo Researchers, Inc.
page 1201:	S. Solum/Getty Images, Inc./PhotoDisc
page 1211:	Martin Rotker/Phototake NYC
page 1213:	Charles Sheppard, University of Warwick
page 1222:	Oliver Meckes & Nicole Ottawa/Photo Researchers, Inc.
page 1231:	Thien Eu/Shutterstock
page 1232:	E.I. DuPont de Nemours & Co., Inc.
page 1233 (top):	Oliver Meckes & Nicole Ottawa/Photo Researchers, Inc.
page 1233 (bottom):	Courtesy of Dupont

INDEX

B

C

D

E

F

G

N

O

P

Q

R

S

Typical Values of Proton NMR Chemical Shifts

Type of Proton		Approximate δ
alkane (—CH_3)	methyl	0.9
alkane (—CH_2—)	methylene	1.3
alkane (—CH—)	methine	1.4
—C(=O)—CH_3	methyl ketone	2.1
—C≡C—H	acetylenic	2.5
R—CH_2—X	(X = halogen, —O—)	3–4
>C=C(H)< (H on C=C)	vinyl	5–6
>C=C(—CH_3)	allylic	1.7
Ph—H	aromatic	7.2
Ph—CH_3	benzylic	2.3
R—CHO	aldehyde	9–10
R—COOH	acid	10–12
R—OH	alcohol	variable, about 2–5
Ar—OH	phenol	variable, about 4–7
R—NH_2	amine	variable, about 1.5–4

These values are approximate, because all chemical shifts are affected by neighboring substituents. The numbers given here assume that alkyl groups are the only other substituents present. A more complete table of chemical shifts appears in Appendix 1.

Summary of Functional Group Nomenclature

Functional Group	Name as Main Group	Name as Substituent
Main groups in order of decreasing priority		
carboxylic acids	-oic acid	carboxy
esters	-oate	alkoxycarbonyl
amides	-amide	amido
nitriles	-nitrile	cyano
aldehydes	-al	formyl
ketones	-one	oxo
alcohols	-ol	hydroxy
amines	-amine	amino
alkenes	-ene	alkenyl
alkynes	-yne	alkynyl
alkanes	-ane	alkyl
ethers		alkoxy
halides		halo

Typical Values of IR Stretching Frequencies

Frequency (cm^{-1})	Functional Group		Comments
3300	alcohol	O—H	always broad
	amine, amide	N—H	may be broad, sharp, or broad with spikes
	alkyne	≡C—H	always sharp, usually strong
3000	alkane	—C—H	just below 3000 cm^{-1}
	alkene	=C—H	just above 3000 cm^{-1}
	acid	O—H	very broad 2500–3500 cm^{-1}
2200	alkyne	—C≡C—	just below 2200 cm^{-1}
	nitrile	—C≡N	just above 2200 cm^{-1}
1710 (very strong)	carbonyl	>C=O	ketones, acids about 1710 cm^{-1} aldehydes about 1725 cm^{-1} esters higher, about 1735 cm^{-1} conjugation lowers frequency amides lower, about 1650 cm^{-1}
1660	alkene	>C=C<	conjugation lowers frequency aromatic C=C about 1600 cm^{-1}
	imine	>C=N—	stronger than C=C
	amide	>C=O	stronger than C=C (see above)

Ethers, esters, and alcohols also show C—O stretching between 1000 and 1200 cm^{-1}.